THE FUNGI

VOLUME II
The Fungal Organism

Contributors to This Volume

CONSTANTINE J. ALEXOPOULOS

C. BOOTH
GILLIAN M. BUTLER
EDWARD C. CANTINO
ROWLAND H. DAVIS
STERLING EMERSON
KARL ESSER
JAMES H. GREGG
P. H. GREGORY
LILIAN E. HAWKER
C. T. INGOLD
J. L. JINKS

LEONARD MACHLIS
E. O. MORRIS
JOHN R. RAPER
ANTONIO H. ROMANO
J. A. ROPER
ALEXANDER H. SMITH
ALFRED S. SUSSMAN
W. A. TABER
KEISUKE TUBAKI
G. TURIAN
JULIO R. VILLANUEVA

THE FUNGI
An Advanced Treatise

Edited by

G. C. AINSWORTH
COMMONWEALTH MYCOLOGICAL INSTITUTE
KEW, SURREY, ENGLAND

ALFRED S. SUSSMAN
DEPARTMENT OF BOTANY
UNIVERSITY OF MICHIGAN
ANN ARBOR, MICHIGAN

VOLUME II
The Fungal Organism

1966

ACADEMIC PRESS   New York   San Francisco   London
A Subsidiary of Harcourt Brace Jovanovich, Publishers

COPYRIGHT © 1966, BY ACADEMIC PRESS, INC.
ALL RIGHTS RESERVED
NO PART OF THIS BOOK MAY BE REPRODUCED IN ANY FORM,
BY PHOTOSTAT, MICROFILM, OR ANY OTHER MEANS, WITHOUT
WRITTEN PERMISSION FROM THE PUBLISHERS.

ACADEMIC PRESS, INC.
111 Fifth Avenue, New York, New York 10003

United Kingdom Edition published by
ACADEMIC PRESS, INC. (LONDON) LTD.
24/28 Oval Road, London NW1

LIBRARY OF CONGRESS CATALOG CARD NUMBER: 65-15769

PRINTED IN THE UNITED STATES OF AMERICA

List of Contributors

Numbers in parentheses indicate the pages on which the authors' contributions begin.

Constantine J. Alexopoulos, *Department of Botany and the Cell Research Institute, University of Texas, Austin, Texas* (211)

C. Booth, *Commonwealth Mycological Institute, Kew, Surrey, England* (133)

Gillian M. Butler, *Department of Botany, University of Birmingham, Birmingham, England* (83)

Edward C. Cantino, *Department of Botany and Plant Pathology, Michigan State University, East Lansing, Michigan* (283)

Rowland H. Davis, *Department of Botany, University of Michigan, Ann Arbor, Michigan* (567)

Sterling Emerson, *Division of Biology, California Institute of Technology, Pasadena, California* (513)

Karl Esser, *Institut für Allegemeine Botanik, Ruhr-Universität, Bochum, Germany* (661)

James H. Gregg, *Department of Zoology, University of Florida, Gainesville, Florida* (235)

P. H. Gregory, *Rothamsted Experimental Station, Harpenden, Herts., England* (709)

Lilian E. Hawker, *Department of Botany, University of Bristol, Bristol, England* (435)

C. T. Ingold, *Birkbeck College, University of London, London, England* (679)

J. L. Jinks, *Department of Genetics, University of Birmingham, Birmingham, England* (619)

Leonard Machlis, *Department of Botany, University of California, Berkeley, California* (415)

E. O. Morris, *Department of Applied Microbiology and Biology, University of Strathclyde, Glasgow, Scotland* (63)

v

John R. Raper, *Biological Laboratories, Harvard University, Cambridge, Massachusetts* (473)

Antonio H. Romano, *Department of Biological Sciences and Graduate Division of Microbiology, University of Cincinnati, Cincinnati, Ohio* (181)

J. A. Roper, *Department of Genetics, The University, Sheffield, England* (589)

Alexander H. Smith, *University Herbarium and Department of Botany, University of Michigan, Ann Arbor, Michigan* (151)

Alfred S. Sussman, *Department of Botany, University of Michigan, Ann Arbor, Michigan* (733)

W. A. Taber, *Department of Biology, Texas A & M University, College Station, Texas* (387)

Keisuke Tubaki, *Institute for Fermentation, Osaka, Japan* (113)

G. Turian, *Institut de Botanique générale, Laboratoire de Microbiologie, Université de Genève, Geneva, Switzerland* (339)

Julio R. Villanueva, *Instituto de Biología Celular, Consejo Superior de Investigaciones Científicas, Madrid, Spain* (3)

Preface

The object of this work is to summarize what is known about fungi as fungi. In the first volume an attempt was made to summarize events at the cellular level. In the present volume the fungal organism is treated.

The first chapter, on the fungal protoplast, may seem somewhat out of character, but as protoplasts are self-contained units an account of them provides an appropriate transition from the cell to the complete organism. Furthermore, some fungi, like slime molds, lack a cell wall for much of their existence and may, therefore, be functionally akin to protoplasts.

This transition is followed by accounts of vegetative and sporulating structures of increasing complexity and representative examples of morphogenesis, and by reviews of sexuality and life cycles and the mechanisms of inheritance.

Finally, there are chapters on spore discharge, dispersal, and germination which prepare the way for a consideration, in the third volume, of the relationship of individual fungi and fungal populations to their environments and of the various approaches to the taxonomy of fungi.

G. C. AINSWORTH
Commonwealth Mycological Institute, Kew, Surrey, England

A. S. SUSSMAN
University of Michigan, Ann Arbor, Michigan

July, 1966

Contents

List of Contributors — v

Preface — vii

THE PROTOPLAST

1. Protoplasts of Fungi
Julio R. Villanueva

I. Lysis of the Fungal Cell	3
II. Preparation of Protoplasts	15
III. Morphology and Structure	20
IV. Protoplasts from Spores	33
V. Properties of Protoplasts	36
VI. Composition of Protoplasts	39
VII. Physiology and Biochemistry of Protoplasts	43
VIII. Conjugation between Protoplasts	49
IX. Reversion of Protoplasts	50
References	57

CELL AGGREGATES

2. Aggregation of Unicells: Yeasts
E. O. Morris

I. Introduction	63
II. Sexual Aggregation	65
III. Asexual Conjugation	66
IV. Aggregation in Liquid Media	69
V. Aggregation on Solid Media	76
References	80

THE MULTICELLULAR CONDITION

3. Vegetative Structures
Gillian M. Butler

I. Introduction	83
II. Colonies	84
III. Special Multihyphal Structures	93

IV. Fungal Tissues	108
References	109

4. Sporulating Structures in Fungi Imperfecti

Keisuke Tubaki

I. Introduction	113
II. Types of Spore Production	116
III. Types of Sporophores	126
References	128

5. Fruit Bodies in Ascomycetes

C. Booth

I. The Ascocarp	133
II. Plectomycetes	135
III. Pyrenomycetes	137
IV. Discomycetes	146
References	149

6. The Hyphal Structure of the Basidiocarp

Alexander H. Smith

I. Introduction	151
II. Origin of the Basidiocarp	152
III. The Mitic System	154
IV. Features of the Hyphal Wall	155
V. Chemical Tests and Chemical Features	158
VI. Cell Shape	162
VII. The Subhymenium	163
VIII. Hyphal Branching	164
IX. Clamp Connections	166
X. Hyphal Tip Differentiation	167
References	176

MECHANISMS OF MORPHOGENESIS

7. Dimorphism

Antonio H. Romano

I. Introduction	181
II. Temperature-Dependent Dimorphism	182
III. Temperature- and Nutrition-Dependent Dimorphism	185
IV. Nutrition-Dependent Dimorphism	188

V. The Relationship of Dimorphism to Pathogenicity	201
VI. Concluding Remarks	205
References	206

8. Morphogenesis in the Myxomycetes

Constantine J. Alexopoulos

I. Introduction	211
II. Spore Germination	211
III. Myxamoebae and Swarm Cells	213
IV. The Plasmodium	217
V. Sporulation	222
References	229
Notes Added in Proof	234

9. Organization and Synthesis in the Cellular Slime Molds

James H. Gregg

I. Introduction	235
II. Nutrition and Pattern of Development	236
III. Components of Aggregation	239
IV. Cellular Heterogeneity and Pseudoplasmodium Formation	242
V. Cell Adhesion and Morphogenesis	255
VI. Metabolism and Synthesis during Development	260
VII. General Conclusions	271
References	272

10. Morphogenesis in Aquatic Fungi

Edward C. Cantino

I. Introduction	283
II. Mechanisms of Morphogenesis at the Phylogenetic Level	284
III. Mechanisms of Morphogenesis at the Ontogenetic Level	297
IV. General Conclusions	329
References	330

11. Morphogenesis in Ascomycetes

G. Turian

I. Introduction	339
II. Morphogenetic Phases	340
III. Conclusions	368
Addendum	368
References	369

12. Morphogenesis in Basidiomycetes
W. A. Taber

I.	Introduction	387
II.	Morphogenetic Entities	388
III.	Morphogenetic Factors	403
IV.	Mechanical and Mathematical Analysis of Fruit Body	406
	References	408

PHYSIOLOGY OF REPRODUCTION

13. Sex Hormones in Fungi
Leonard Machlis

I.	Introduction	415
II.	Saprolegniales	415
III.	Chytridiales	420
IV.	Mucorales	420
V.	Blastocladiales	426
VI.	Ascomycetes	427
VII.	Basidiomycetes	430
VIII.	Summary	430
	References	431

14. Environmental Influences on Reproduction
Lilian E. Hawker

I.	Introduction	435
II.	Effects of External Factors	437
III.	Possible Mechanisms of Translation of External Stimuli into Visible Change of Phase	463
	References	465

REPRODUCTION AND INHERITANCE

15. Life Cycles, Basic Patterns of Sexuality, and Sexual Mechanisms
John R. Raper

I.	Introduction	473
II.	Life Cycles	474
III.	Basic Patterns of Sexuality	480
IV.	Sexual Mechanisms	496
V.	Correlations of Life Cycles, Sexuality, and Sexual Mechanisms	501
VI.	Summary	503
	References	504

16. Mechanisms of Inheritance

1. MENDELIAN

Sterling Emerson

I.	Introduction	513
II.	The Basic Mechanism of Mendelian Inheritance	514
III.	Nonreciprocal Recombination	530
IV.	Hypothetical Models of Recombination	535
V.	Possibility of Episomic Inheritance in Fungi	545
VI.	Genetic Characteristics of Selected Fungi	549
	References	559

17. Mechanisms of Inheritance

2. HETEROKARYOSIS

Rowland H. Davis

I.	Introduction	567
II.	The Study of Heterokaryons	568
III.	Dominance in Heterokaryons	572
IV.	Genetics of Heterokaryon Formation	573
V.	Nuclear Ratios and Growth of Heterokaryons	578
VI.	Heterokaryosis as a Mechanism of Natural Variation	584
	References	586

18. Mechanisms of Inheritance

3. THE PARASEXUAL CYCLE

J. A. Roper

I.	Introduction	589
II.	The Parasexual Cycle, and Its Individual Steps, in *Aspergillus nidulans*	590
III.	The Parasexual Cycle in Fungi Other Than *Aspergillus nidulans*	607
IV.	Applications and Implications of the Parasexual Cycle	609
V.	Conclusions	613
	References	614

19. Mechanisms of Inheritance

4. EXTRANUCLEAR INHERITANCE

J. L. Jinks

I.	Introduction	619
II.	Properties of Extrachromosomal Variants	619

xiv Contents

III. The Nature of the Extrachromosomal System	639
IV. The Role of Extrachromosomal Variation	652
V. General Remarks	657
References	657

20. Incompatibility

Karl Esser

I. Definitions	661
II. Introduction	662
III. Incompatibility Systems	662
IV. Incompatibility and Evolution	674
References	675

DISSEMINATION

21. Spore Release

C. T. Ingold

I. Introduction	679
II. Active Discharge	679
III. Passive Spore Liberation	699
IV. Liberation of Spores by Animals	702
References	705

22. Dispersal

P. H. Gregory

I. Introduction	709
II. Modes of Dispersal	710
III. Results of Wind-Dispersal Processes	723
IV. Conclusions	728
References	729

23. Dormancy and Spore Germination

Alfred S. Sussman

I. Introduction	733
II. Terminology of Dormancy and Germination	734
III. Means of Activation	735
IV. Mechanisms of Dormancy	739
V. Criteria of Germination	745
VI. Changes during Germination	746
VII. Stages in the Germination Process	757
VIII. Role of Spores in Nature	758
References	760

Author Index	765
Subject Index	787
Index to Fungi, Lichens, and Actinomycetes	793

Contents of Volume I
The Fungal Cell

INTRODUCTION

Historical Introduction to Mycology
G. C. AINSWORTH

Fungal Structure and Organization
C. J. HICKMAN

CELL COMPONENTS

The Cell Wall
JEROME M. ARONSON

Flagella
A. P. KOLE

The Ultrastructure of Fungal Cells
ROYALL T. MOORE

Somatic Nuclei and Forms of Mitosis in Fungi
C. F. ROBINOW AND A. BAKERSPIGEL

Nuclear Behavior during Meiosis
LINDSAY S. OLIVE

Chemical Constituents of the Fungal Cell
1. *Elemental Constituents and Their Roles*
VIRGIL GREENE LILLY

Chemical Constituents of the Fungal Cell
2. *Special Chemical Products*
JOHN HOWARD BIRKINSHAW

Carbohydrate Metabolism
1. *Glycolysis*
HAROLD J. BLUMENTHAL

Carbohydrate Metabolism
2. *Tricarboxylic Acid Cycle*
D. J. NIEDERPRUEM

Carbohydrate Metabolism
3. *Terminal Oxidation and Electron Transport*
ARISTID LINDENMAYER

Utilization of Inorganic Nitrogen Compounds and Amino Acids by Fungi
D. J. D. NICHOLAS

Integration of Cellular Metabolism
MARKO ZALOKAR

NUTRITION AND GROWTH OF CELLS

Uptake and Translocation
1. *Uptake*
ASER ROTHSTEIN

Uptake and Translocation
2. *Translocation*
E. P. HILL

The Chemical Environment for Fungal Growth
1. *Media, Macro- and Micronutrients*
VIRGIL GREENE LILLY

The Chemical Environment for Fungal Growth
2. *Carbon Sources*
D. PERLMAN

The Chemical Environment for Fungal Growth
3. *Vitamins and Other Organic Growth Factors*
NILS FRIES

The Chemical Environment for Fungal Growth
4. *Chemical Inhibition*
R. J. W. BYRDE

The Physical Environment for Fungal Growth
1. *Temperature*
B. J. DEVERALL

The Physical Environment for Fungal Growth
2. *Hydrostatic Pressure*
RICHARD Y. MORITA

The Physical Environment for Fungal Growth
3. *Light*
ROBERT M. PAGE

The Physical Environment for Fungal Growth
4. *Effects of Radiation*
S. POMPER

Contents of Volume I

Kinetics of Fungal Growth
G. R. MANDELS

The Mechanism of Cellular Extension and Branching
N. F. ROBERTSON

Growth Rhythms
STEPHEN JEREBZOFF

Special Growth Techniques (Synchrony, Chemostasis)
ALLAN CAMPBELL

GENE ACTION

Gene Action
D. G. CATCHESIDE

Author Index—Subject Index—Index to Fungi, Lichens, and Actinomycetes

THE FUNGI
VOLUME II
The Fungal Organism

The Protoplast

CHAPTER 1

Protoplasts of Fungi

JULIO R. VILLANUEVA

Instituto de Biología Celular
Consejo Superior de Investigaciones Científicas
Madrid, Spain

I. LYSIS OF THE FUNGAL CELL

A fungal cell may be considered to consist of two main parts: the outer firm cell wall, of varying thickness and constitution, and the inner protoplasm. The protoplasm is enveloped in a cell membrane or plasmalemma and contains the various cell organelles. In some cells the cytoplasm varies in consistency, and the viscosity may change under certain conditions. The mycelium may consist of a single multinucleate cell (a coenocyte) in which there are no transverse septa or it may be multicellular and composed of uni-, bi-, or multinucleate cells.

It has long been known that lysozyme can exert some lytic action on bacteria but that it has no effect on fungi. However, the finding by Giaja (1922) that the digestive juice of the snail *Helix pomatia* attacks the cell walls of fungal cells enabled Eddy and Williamson (1957) to prepare and study osmotically sensitive bodies which can be considered protoplasts.

The literature on the degradation of fungal walls, both by snail and microbial enzyme preparations, as well as on the formation of protoplasts is already large. Fortunately, many advances in studies on protoplasts of yeast and related organisms are included in the report of a recent symposium held at Jena. In this review a general outline is followed by a description of more recent advances.

A. The Terms Protoplast and "Protoplast"

It is difficult to define accurately what is intended by the term protoplast in fungi. Protoplast has been used for more than twelve years for bacterial cells deprived of their cell wall, and its use and full meaning might well be extended to fungi. Many features of protoplast structure are still obscure. For the present, our working criteria for the absence of a wall are osmotic fragility and loss of rigidity resulting in a spherical form. Immunological methods have not yet been developed for these structures, and phages and their receptors have not been described in fungi. It is obvious that the criteria fail to distinguish between the total absence of a wall and its functional impairment. Wall-less protoplasts have been prepared from a number of fungi. It remains to be proved, however, that the osmotically fragile structures so obtained are completely deprived of their walls, for the possibility cannot be excluded that some degraded wall material surrounds the protoplasm, even though the cells have become osmotically fragile. Thus it might be advisable not to use the term protoplast indiscriminately for osmotically fragile cells of fungi. In using enzymes or other methods for the isolation of fungal protoplasts, it seems important that the term protoplast should be used only when it has been established that the entire cell wall structure has been removed from the cells. It would be advisable to use "protoplast," or spheroplast, for fungal material in which we are not sure that the cell wall is completely absent.

B. Are the Fungal Protoplasts True Protoplasts?

The large bodies found in the stabilized medium after snail or microbial enzyme action on living cells show a rather complex organization. In most cases, sections of previously fixed protoplasts showed a thin outer membrane closely adhering to the cytoplasmic ground material. Chemical and immunological studies on released protoplasts are lacking although electron microscopical observations indicate that the cell wall structure is completely missing in protoplasts of some species, e.g., *Candida utilis* (Villanueva et al., 1966) and *Polystictus versicolor* (Strunk, 1964). The fact that the thin cytoplasmic membrane closely adheres to the cytoplasmic ground material makes it highly improbable that it represents remnants of a degraded cell wall. Sentandreu and Villanueva (1965a) have reported that the cell wall of *C. utilis* is composed of three layers and can easily be differentiated from the cytoplasmic membrane. Investigations of the nature of protoplasts of *C. utilis* by chemical analysis have shown that typical wall constituents such as glucans and mannans are not found in the osmotic spherical bodies (Sentandreu, 1965). Garcia Mendoza and Villanueva (1965) have also demonstrated complete absence of typical wall components by chemical analysis of isolated cytoplasmic membrane preparations obtained by osmotic lysis and differential centrifugation.

Some workers consider the fact that no distinct membrane is seen after lysis of the protoplasts an important point to prove the existence of naked protoplasts. Observations of bursting cells after osmotic shock which left no envelope were made on two species of filamentous fungi, *Neurospora crassa* (Bachmann and Bonner, 1959) and *P. versicolor* (Strunk, 1966b). This has not been so in *Fusarium culmorum* protoplasts, where, occasionally, thin membranes are observed after lysis (Rodriguez Aguirre *et al.*, 1964). Fusion of neighboring protoplasts, observed in the course of microcinematographic analysis, also argues for true protoplasts (Girbardt and Strunk, 1965).

Osmotically fragile structures have been obtained from certain filamentous fungi by dissolving the wall of living hyphae or spore cells with snail or microbial enzymes, after which electron microscopic studies have been made. It has been established, at least for hyphal protoplasts of *P. versicolor* (Strunk, 1966b) and spore protoplasts of *N. crassa* (Weiss, 1963), that treatment removes the entire cell wall. As pointed out above, wall-less protoplasts have been prepared from *F. culmorum* mycelium (Rodriguez Aguirre *et al.*, 1964). It remains to be proved that these osmotically fragile structures are deprived of their cell walls.

Bachmann and Bonner (1959) point out that the empty wall can be seen after emergence of *N. crassa* spherical structures, so they may represent naked protoplasts. Several workers (Holter and Ottolenghi, 1960; Svihla *et al.*, 1961; Garcia Mendoza and Villanueva, 1964a; Rost and Venner, 1965) have described protoplast formation in a number of yeasts by the action of lytic enzymes. The phenomenon of the release of osmotic spherical bodies is similar to that described in filamentous fungi in that a partly degraded wall is left behind.

Conjugation (fusion) of protoplasts has not yet been reported in any fungus. The retention of mating capacity points to the specificity of some wall (protein-polysaccharide) component (Brock, 1961) of the residual elements surrounding the cytoplasmic membrane of the protoplast. In view of the inability to show phage receptors in fungal cell walls, it might be profitable to study protoplasts obtained by different methods for mating specificity.

C. *The Nature of the Cell Wall*

Little is known of the chemical constituents or structural organization of the walls of filamentous fungi (cf. Chapter 3, Vol. I), although much more is known about similar structures in yeasts (Phaff, 1963; Nickerson, 1963; Villanueva, 1965). Evidence has been presented that there are quantitative chemical differences between cell walls from a variety of fungal species. Some fractionation of the walls of various species of fungi has been achieved. A number of studies of the composition of the cell wall have been qualitative in nature and very few data concerning quantitative analysis are available (Johnston, 1965). Similarly, little is known of the quantitative variations in wall composition that may occur in closely related species. Chitin (Mitchell and Alexander, 1963) and glucans (Horikoshi and Koffler, 1963) have been detected in the cell walls of certain yeasts and fungi. Potgieter and Alexander (1965) reported that the chief polysaccharides of *N. crassa* hyphal walls are chitin and a glucan susceptible to the action of a β-1,3-glucanase which converted it to free glucose. Crook and Johnston (1962) examined the composition of the cell walls of 16 species of fungi and detected the presence of six neutral sugars, but no polyols or uronic acids. With the exception of the presence of γ-aminobutyric acid and hydroxyproline which were found in a few species of Phycomycetes and Ascomycetes, all the other amino acids detected (16 in total) were those typical of protein hydrolyzates. On the basis of the range of components, it was suggested that the walls of fungi are of a protein carbohydrate nature. Other studies (Kessler and Nickerson, 1959; Korn and Northcote, 1960; Novaes and Villanueva, 1963) have analyzed components of yeast cell walls. There has been much discussion about the presence of amino sugars and their derivatives in fungal cell walls (Frey, 1950; Kreger, 1954). It is possible that the glucosamine in the cell wall is not necessary in chitin (Korn and Northcote, 1960).

Recently several papers have been concerned with the chemistry of the cell wall in filamentous species. Johnston (1965) made a complete study of the cell wall of *Aspergillus niger*, which consists chiefly of neutral carbohydrate (glucose, galactose, mannose, and arabinose) amounting to 73–83%, and hexosamine (9–13%) in the form of glucosamine and galactosamine, with small proportions of lipid (2–7%), protein (0.5–2, 5%), and phosphorus (0.1%). A chemical cell wall fractionation produced a component consisting largely of glucose and having properties similar to those of the polysaccharide nigeran, an α-glucan.

In understanding lysis, it is necessary to know which structures in the wall must be solubilized. Obviously these are molecules that owe their insolubility either to their polymeric or fatty nature. The major components are the glucans (β-1,3- and β-1,6-linked, and α-1,3- and α-1,4-linked), mannans (α-linked), chitin (β-linked N-acetylglucosamine), and protein. Fatty materials are also present.

Complicating the structure further are the binding forces between some of the components, as in the protein–mannan complexes. Then, too, there is a layering effect, whereby the inner components resist enzyme attack only because of their position. The fact that chitinase does not act on the cell wall is most often due to the fact that the chitin is covered by a layer of glucan.

D. The Lysis of Cell Walls

Although the cell wall is rigid and is formed of dynamic cellular constituents, it is nevertheless, subject to the action of various hydrolytic enzymes. Little is known of the mechanism of the microbiological digestion of fungus mycelium although it has been assumed that most microorganisms possess a battery of enzymes capable of acting on complex insoluble carbohydrates, proteins, and fats and converting them into soluble substances, which later are used as sources of energy. Enzymatic attack upon cell wall components may result from the action of two systems, first from the action of enzymes released by other cells or organisms, and second from the action of autolytic systems originated in their own protoplasm. Both systems play an important role in the dissolution of fungal cell walls. In nature cell wall lysis may be associated with several kinds of biological behavior or interactions among organisms. Lysis of rigid walls is a part of the process of spore release and of germination in bacteria and in fungi. Invasion and destruction of organisms by parasites depend on lysis of hosts walls or other constituents by the invader. Autolytic processes involve a team of enzymes able to degrade cell walls. Although great efforts have been made to characterize some of the wall-lysing enzymes, results are not yet satisfactory. Among the more representative lytic enzymes may be mentioned α- and β-glucanases, proteases and peptidases, cellulases, lipases, chitinases, hexosaminidases (lysozyme and lysozyme-like enzymes), glucuronidases, glucosaminidases, and cellobiases.

The complexity of the cell wall requires that several enzymes be used for its degradation. Mitchell and Alexander (1963) described the lysis of *Fusarium oxysporum* mycelium by *Bacillus cereus* and suggested that the phenomenon may be associated with chitinase and laminarinase activity. The possession of chitinase by all the lytic bacteria is noteworthy. However, experiments with chitinase alone or in combination with β-1,3-glucanase, proteases, and cellulases did not bring about a destruction of *Fusarium* cell walls. Fatty materials may contribute to this resistance. Nevertheless, Furuya and Ikeda (1960) reported the enhancement of lysis of *Aspergillus flavus* by *B. circulans* by the addition of chitinase, and the demonstration of chitin in the walls of many filamentous fungi suggests a functional role for this enzyme. Horikoshi *et al.* (1961) have presented evidence for laminarin, a β-1,3-glucan, in *Penicillium chrysogenum* cell walls, and glucans are also present in various species of *Fusarium*, suggesting an important role of the glucanases in the digestion of fungal wall structures. However, it is clear that other factors in addition to those enzymes are required for digestion.

E. Fungi Susceptible and Resistant to Lysis

It is well known that some fungi are susceptible and others are resistant to lysis. Similarly, cell wall preparations of *Streptomyces* species were lysed by lysozyme, whereas *Nocardia* species were resistant (Romano and Sohler, 1956). The striking differences in the carbohydrate composition of the cell walls of these two genera may explain the differences in susceptibility to lysozyme. Similar studies with fungi are lacking.

Skujins *et al.* (1965) have begun a study of the degradation of fungal hyphae of species most susceptible to enzymatic attack. They have shown that a *Streptomyces* chitinase and β-1,3-glucanase are involved in lysis and in dissolution of *Fusarium solani* and *Aspergillus oryzae* hyphal walls. Because of the resistance to lysis of other fungi, i.e., *Neurospora crassa* and *Rhizoctonia* [*Corticium*] *solani,* known to contain chitin and laminarin, it has been suggested that these organisms contain other cellular constituents concerned in susceptibility or resistance to enzymatic lysis. The cell walls of various fungi are known to contain in addition to chitin and laminarin a number of polysaccharides, lipids, and proteins (Bartnicki-Garcia and Nickerson, 1962; Russell *et al.*, 1964; Crook and Johnston, 1962), but it is not yet possible to say which of these substances is responsible for the resistance to lysis.

The cell wall hydrolyzing system of *Cytophaga* (Bacon *et al.*, 1965) was found to be effective on yeast cell walls, including autoclaved ones. The resistance of some living yeast cells which do not lose their walls when incubated with the lytic enzyme, or thiol compounds, was explained by the presence of a third network resistant to lysis. As chitinase is present in *C. johnsonii* it is difficult to believe that this third structure is chitinous.

In our laboratory it was recently found that the cell walls of *Fusarium* hyphae are resistant to lysis by a strepzyme preparation (produced by *Micromonospora AS*) which is very active on conidial walls. However, when the mycelium was exposed to a short incubation with pancreatic lipase, prior to exposure to the strepzyme preparation, the cell wall was digested, with liberation of protoplasts. Apparently the presence of lipid had interfered with lysis of the mycelium. Resistance to lysis is always related to the chemical composition of the cell walls although a physical layering effect may be present (Garcia Acha *et al.*, 1966).

F. Sensitivity of Fungal Cell Walls to Enzymatic Degradation

The observations of Weibull (1956) that lysozyme converted *Bacillus megaterium* to protoplasts in hypertonic sucrose solution indicated that a complex polymer provides the rigidity for the bacterial cell. There is no single lytic enzyme equivalent to lysozyme for fungi.

1. Protoplasts of Fungi

The digestion of the wall does not proceed uniformly around the cell, and the walls of old cells are poorly attacked. The composition of the medium markedly affects the composition of the walls, at least for yeasts (Dunwell *et al.*, 1961). Yeasts that grow in the complete absence of vitamins are more resistant to cell wall digestion (Rost and Venner, 1965). Because of the heterogeneity of the wall, the complex enzyme system of the lytic actinomycetes may either digest certain components of the wall (with liberation of protoplasts), or all components, including the protoplasts themselves. Conditions of growth promote either the former or the latter mode of action of the enzyme system, but on prolonged incubation both effects are observed.

Changes in the turbidity of isolated cell walls on incubation with the lytic enzymes have been considered one of the most sensitive methods for detecting the presence of specific substrates. Such a method avoids many of the complications encountered with intact cells. Dissolution of isolated yeast or mold cell walls by lytic enzymes has been accomplished with only a few organisms.

Differences in the cell walls of sensitive and resistant fungi have been poorly characterized. As for the action of lysozyme, it may be that sensitivity cannot be predicted by qualitative analysis of cell wall composition. For instance, there is no single amino acid, amino sugar, or sugar component that seems to confer lysozyme sensitivity on a particular organism (Salton, 1957). The kind of linkage of some of the constituents of the wall as well as the number of the linked units may be important factors in determining sensitivity or resistance.

G. Production of Fungal Cell Wall Lytic Enzymes by Microorganisms

Microorganisms produce a variety of extracellular and endocellular enzymes. Some of these have been isolated, concentrated, and purified. Some species of *Bacillus* and actinomycetes are remarkable for their production of enzymes able to dissolve cell walls of fungi. Among these enzymes are lysozyme, proteases, keratinase, chitinase, polysaccharidases, cellulases, and lipases.

A survey of the lytic activities of actinomycetes on fungal cell walls was made by Gascon and Villanueva (1963). Strains of *Streptomyces* were most active. *Nocardia, Corynebacterium,* and *Mycobacterium* showed no activity whereas *Actinomyces* and *Micromonospora* strains showed good activity. *Micromonospora* strains form as much lytic enzyme as do the lytic *Streptomyces* (Gascón *et al.*, 1965a). These organisms can be used to study not only the nature of the lytic enzymes, but also the chemical composition of the different structures which compose the fungal cells (Phaff, 1966).

There is some reason to believe that lysis is due to the combined action of two or more enzymes. Zones produced on agar plates of cell wall by different lytic actinomycetes were sometimes observed to overlap and to contain less opacity. This finding suggests that some organisms produced enzymes that initiate partial disintegration of the fungal walls, and that this action was complemented by that of enzymes that lysed other components of the walls (Gascón and Villanueva, 1963). Similar results were reported when fungal mycelium instead of isolated cell walls was used (Carter and Lockwood, 1957).

Yeast cell walls are disrupted by lytic enzymes produced by *Streptomyces albidoflavus* (Tabata *et al.,* 1965) and *Streptomyces GM* (Garcia Mendoza and Villanueva, 1962). Cell wall preparations from *Aspergillus oryzae* were dissolved by a lytic enzyme from *Bacillus circulans* and by chitinase from *Streptomyces* sp. (Horikoshi and Ida, 1959). Rodriguez Aguirre *et al.* (1964) and Lloyd *et al.* (1965) described *Streptomyces* spp. which have the ability to dissolve cell walls of a large number of fungal species. Few attempts have been made to study the enzyme systems of the lytic organisms in detail (Reynolds, 1954).

There are few examples in the literature describing the lytic action of one fungus on another. *Verticillium hemileiae* produces a lytic enzyme able to digest cell walls of various fungi (Leal and Villanueva, 1962), but unable to lyse a number of bacteria tested. Satomura *et al.* (1960) studied an active glucanase from *Sclerotinia libertiana* which on addition of lipase dissolved fungal cells.

Extensive efforts have been made in our laboratory to obtain protoplasts from those species of fungi which are known to have cellulose in their cell walls (e.g., *Pythium* and *Phytophthora*). Commercial preparations of cellulase, hemicellulase, etc., and crude preparations from *Trichoderma viride* were used. Since *T. viride* has been reported to grow inside mycelium of *Pythium* and *Phytophthora,* it was expected that *Trichoderma* which also is known to produce cellulase, would be useful for this purpose. Marked alterations were detected in the mycelium of these fungi, but cytoplasmic membranes and internal contents were also affected, possibly by proteolytic, but not by lipolytic, enzymes (Nicolas, 1965). Similar studies were made with *Verticillium hemileiae* lytic preparations (Garcia Acha *et al.,* 1965).

H. *The Use of Lytic Enzymes for Studies of Cell Wall Structure*

Lysozyme has been useful for investigating cell wall structure in bacteria and actinomycetes. The extensive biochemical information obtained in recent years in this field has stimulated similar studies with other enzymes. The lysis of the purified cell wall preparations results in the release of a complex mixture of dialyzable and nondialyzable compounds which can be identified by biochemical techniques. However, because of the complexity of the breakdown products resulting from enzyme action, the nature of the specific linkage responsible for lysis may not be easy to determine.

The study of fungal cell wall structures has been carried out much like the study described for bacteria (Perkins, 1963). Using enzymes from the snail *Helix pomatia,* Millbank and Macrae (1964) and Anderson (1966) obtained several enzyme fractions on Sephadex columns. One of these released both mannose and glucose from yeast walls, the others released glucose only. All three components produced in addition what was assumed to be a short-chain polysaccharide. No hexosamine was detected. These results suggest that with the snail enzyme preparation, protoplasts are formed only when both the mannan and glucan of the cell wall are degraded. These results suggested that the mannan–protein complex overlies the glucan. The glucan of resistant strains is degraded only when the inside of the wall is accessible.

The fungilytic properties of strepzyme from *Micromonospora chalcea* are attributable to a variety of enzymes or enzymatic systems, each showing a very high degree of specificity. That glucose is the main component released during yeast cell wall degradation by this system suggests strong glucanase activity (Novaes *et al.* 1966). Mannose was also detected, but in much smaller proportions. A number of amino acids are also present in the dialyzable products of cell wall digestion, suggesting an important function of proteolytic enzymes (Garcia Ochoa, 1965).

Bacon *et al.* (1965) have shown dissolution of yeast cell walls by means of filtrates of *Cytophaga johnsonii,* an organism described by Salton (1955) as able to clear agar plates of cell walls. The enzymes present in the filtrates were able to liberate glucose from the yeast cell walls; although some oligosaccharide was also present, no free mannose could be detected. The action of the myxobacterial culture, when combined with thiol compounds (Davies and Elvin, 1964), gave rise to interesting results. It seems that two structural systems exist, either of which, when intact, will preserve the integrity of the yeast cell wall. One is the glucan formed by glucosidic linkages that can be destroyed by the myxobacterial enzymes; the other is composed of mannan–protein complexes associated through disulfide linkages (Nickerson and Falcone, 1956) which can be broken by thiol compounds or by autoclaving. Only when both systems are degraded does the cell wall dissolve. The presence of a third network was suggested to explain the resistance of living yeast cells, but its existence is dubious.

Although chitin has been described as a fungal cell wall constituent and glucans have been shown to play an important role in yeast wall structure, the existence of such glucans in the mycelium-forming organisms and the significance of glucanases to wall dissolution and fungal lysis have not been appreciated until now. The wall structure of *Aspergillus oryzae* has also been studied by means of two lytic preparations, one obtained from the growth medium of *B. circulans* and the other, the chitinase, produced by a *Streptomyces* as suggested by Reynolds (1954). After incubation of isolated cell walls of *A. oryzae* with these lytic preparations, complete dissolution was observed with the release of hexosamine and hexose. Surprisingly, it was concluded that the cell wall was constituted of chitin coated by a melibiose polymer which could be lysed by the *Bacillus* enzyme (Horikoshi and Ida, 1959).

I. Analysis of Cell Wall Enzymatic Degradation Products

Partial chemical degradation has long been used in structural studies of fungal walls. The limitations of these drastic methods are obvious. It was evident that the characterization of the fungal wall-degrading enzymes, and the products formed by the action of specific enzymes, would throw light on the problem of cell wall structures. The use of snail enzymes to digest the cell wall of *Saccharomyces cerevisiae* (Millbank and Macrae, 1964; Anderson, 1966) simplified the identification and further characterization of the digestion products. Similar studies were carried out in our laboratory using cell wall preparations of *Candida utilis* and the lytic strepzyme of *Micromonospora chalcea* (Gascón et al., 1965a).

Cell walls of *S. cerevisiae* and *C. utilis* are completely degraded to soluble products on digestion with partially purified fractions of snail or microbial enzymes, and components may be separated on the basis of diffusibility through dialysis tubing into dialyzable and nondialyzable fractions. An investigation of the dialyzable fractions showed the presence of glucose, and lesser amounts of mannose, hexosamine, and a series of amino acids (Garcia Ochoa, 1965; Novaes et al., 1966).

Investigations by Skujins et al. (1965) using a combination of a *Streptomyces* chitinase and β-1,3-glucanase have shown nearly complete dissolution of hyphal walls of *Aspergillus oryzae* and *Fusarium solani*. The individual enzymes did not effect solubilization of the cell walls. The main mycelial wall components were found to be chitin and β-1,3-glucan, and no cellulose was detected. Digestion of *F. solani* walls liberated 14% glucose, 47% *N*-acetylhexosamine, and 6% of an insoluble residue which upon acid hydrolysis yielded galactose, mannose, and uronic acid but no glucose. The same group (Potgieter and Alexander, 1965) described the degradation of *Neurospora crassa* cell walls by chitinase and glucanase without microscopic alterations of the morphological characteristics of the walls. On the basis of the action of these lytic enzymes, it was suggested that various other cellular constituents are responsible for resistance to enzymatic lysis. There is no doubt that in future investigations, the addition of lipases, various polysaccharidases and proteases will be very useful in elucidating wall structure (Satomura *et al.*, 1960).

Horikoshi and Sakaguchi (1958) described a strain of *Bacillus circulans* which showed lytic activity toward walls of various molds and yeasts. Digestion of *Aspergillus oryzae* walls with the lytic preparation released only hexose polymers, although the hyphal walls have about 40% of a hexosamine polymer.

Tanaka succeeded in separating two glucanases (β-1,3 and β-1,6) from *B. circulans* (Phaff, 1963). Treatment of isolated bakers' yeast walls with either of the glucanases caused lysis. Release of laminaribiose and gentiobiose together with higher homologs upon treatment with β-1, 3- and β-1,6-glucanases, respectively, was shown chromatographically. In both cases, small proportions of unknown oligosaccharides were also formed. The same workers recently described the enzymatic hydrolysis of yeast cell walls using lytic systems from *B. circulans* and a species of *Streptomyces* (Tanaka and Phaff, 1965). The crude enzymes of the bacterium hydrolyzed only β-1,3- and β-1,6-glucans, to a mixture of gentiobiose and glucose. The authors demonstrate the usefulness of the enzymatic techniques for comparative studies of the cell wall composition of different fungi.

J. Mechanism of Lysis in Fungi

Lysis by strepzymes has been studied mainly with *Fusarium culmorum*, although *Trichothecium roseum, Aspergillus nidulans,* and a few other microorganisms have also been used. The lytic action must be explained as a complex system of reactions by distinct enzymes. The biosynthesis of these enzymes is influenced by the composition of the medium and by other cultural conditions. They can be separated from each other by adsorption chromatography. The demonstration that the microbial preparations contain several lytic agents, each with its characteristic range of activity, has made the elucidation of the mechanism of fungilysis by actinomycetes and bacteria even more complicated than had at first appeared.

K. Lysis of Fungal Cells by Natural Soil

Soil organic matter includes living organisms and their remains which are resistant to chemical and enzymatic decomposition. A knowledge of the action of enzymes on fungal mycelium may perhaps give an idea of the composition of this resistant fraction. The investigations of Waksman (1959) and collaborators have been largely responsible for our knowledge of many of the microbial activities in the soil. After proof of the existence of vegetative fungus mycelium in the soil there followed data on the lytic mechanisms that affect living populations. The study of activities of an organism in pure culture under the artificial conditions of the laboratory, cannot be expected to present a true picture of the natural metabolic performance of organisms.

Living and dead mycelia of a large number of plant pathogenic fungi were completely destroyed when agar cultures were covered with field soil (Lockwood, 1960). A natural toxicity to fungi exists in most soils, as suggested by the nonspecific inhibition of germination and by the lysis of fungal germ tubes and mycelium (Lockwood, 1959; Park, 1957).

Lysis of microbial cells in the soil involves a variety of reactions most of them considered to be enzymatic. Autolysis and bacteriolysis are known to occur not only in bacteria and actinomycetes, but also in fungi. Sensitivity to phages, however, is known only in the first two groups, although some workers claim its presence in some fungi (Lindegren and Bang, 1961).

Although some species of *Bacillus* and *Pseudomonas* (Mitchell and Alexander, 1963), can digest walls of living cells in manures and soils, actinomycetes are the most active. The first observations on the lytic effect of actinomycetes were made by Gasperini (1890). Welsch (1962) and his collaborators have published a number of papers on the lytic preparations from a species of *Streptomyces* along with other workers (McCarty, 1952; Borodulina, 1935).

Antibiotics are produced by many soil organisms, mainly *Streptomyces* species, and it might be claimed that lytic action of these isolates was also due to the excretion of these substances in the soil. This may be true in part but, as suggested by a number of workers (Salton, 1955; Carter and Lockwood, 1957), actinomycetes lyse both living and dead mycelium and isolated cell walls (Gascón and Villanueva, 1963b; Gascón *et al.*, 1965a), whereas antibiotics lyse only living mycelium. Thus, lysis of dead mycelium in soil must be due to the action of cell wall-decomposing enzymes (Lockwood, 1960).

The effect of autolysis on the composition of mold mycelium and the nature of the products liberated have been investigated (Arima *et al.*, 1965). As pointed out by Foster (1949), less is known about autolysis in fungi as compared to bacteria.

Mitchell and Alexander (1963) isolated from soil a number of bacteria capable of lysing *Fusarium oxysporum*. Living and dead *Fusarium* mycelium as well as cell wall preparations were digested by *Bacillus cereus*.

Examination of the breakdown by enzymatic action of a sample of mycelium of *Penicillium griseofulvum* has been made by Smithies (1953).

It is now well known that proteases, cellulases, and chitinases are common in microorganisms and invertebrates of the soil, and it is likely that these bring about dispersion of the greater part of fungal mycelium.

II. PREPARATION OF PROTOPLASTS

There are a number of methods for obtaining fungal protoplasts:

1. By a controlled autolytic process such as that described in *Saccharomyces cerevisiae* by Necas (1956).

2. By direct digestion of the rigid cell wall structure by means of enzymes present in the digestive juice of snails (Eddy and Williamson, 1957; Bachmann and Bonner, 1959; Rodriguez Aguirre and Villanueva, 1962).

3. By a process similar to the snail enzyme process, but using microbial enzyme preparations (Garcia Mendoza and Villanueva, 1962; Rodriguez Aguirre *et al.*, 1964).

4. By the use of commercial enzyme preparations, either isolated or combined with other hydrolytic enzymes (Emerson and Emerson, 1958; Garcia Acha *et al.*, 1966).

5. By metabolic disturbance in the presence of sorbose or other sugars which causes inhibition of cell-wall formation (Hamilton and Calvet, 1964).

6. By cultivation of the fungi on thickened serum as described by Meinecke (1960). The effectiveness of this technique is rather doubtful.

In addition, mechanical pressure on intact cells has produced plasma droplets, some containing the nucleus, which under same conditions might give rise to new regenerated cells (Necas, 1956).

A. The Importance of the Physiological Age and of Cultural Conditions

A number of workers have emphasized the importance of young cells (in the phase of active growth) in the conversion to protoplasts (Eddy and Williamson, 1957; Holter and Ottolenghi, 1960; Garcia Mendoza and Villanueva, 1962; Rost and Venner, 1965). Although the use of young cultures is important, cultural conditions and the strain used strongly affect sensitivity. Holter and Ottolenghi (1960) have reported that substituting melibiose for glucose in the culture medium made the cell walls sensitive. According to Svihla *et al.* (1961) this can be explained by the building of a different type of polysaccharide in the wall. A similar phenomenon was found in *Candida utilis* when grown in the presence of some sulfur-containing amino acids. Under these conditions, cells contain a high concentration of S-adenosylmethionine, which apparently does not contribute to the cell wall structure of the yeast, yet makes the cells more susceptible to the snail enzyme. Yeasts grown in the presence of a chemically defined medium plus vitamins are more susceptible to enzymatic attack than those grown in the complete absence of the growth factors (Rost and Venner, 1965). Apparently, all these facts might easily be explained by the finding of Dunwell et al. (1961) that growth conditions strongly affect the polysaccharide composition of fungal walls.

Preparation of protoplast suspensions of *Fusarium culmorum* free of remaining hyphal filaments can partially be achieved by filtration of the whole suspension through sintered glass filters to remove most of the mycelium. Microscopic examination of the filtrate revealed a high concentration (10^8 per milliliter) of the structures designated as mycelial protoplasts. The few hyphal remnants, which could also be observed, could be removed completely by low speed (500–1000 g) centrifugation. A purified preparation of protoplasts was obtained in this way, but recovery was generally about 50%.

B. The Use of Snail Enzymes

The digestive tract of *Helix pomatia* contains many digestive enzymes, including lipases, more than twenty different carbohydrases, and proteinases (Holden and Tracey, 1950; Myers and Northcote, 1958). The large number of carbohydrases may explain its usefulness for digesting fungal cell walls while the lipase and protease are probably important by contributing to the breakdown of lipoprotein structures in the cell envelopes. Earlier work suggested degradation of the cell walls (Giaja, 1922). Eddy (1958a) was first to report that enzymes present in the snail preparation were able to produce protoplasts from *Saccharomyces cerevisiae*.

Although some attempts at fractionation of the lytic enzymes present in crude preparations of the snail enzyme complex have been made (Millbank and Macrae, 1964; Anderson, 1966), these are still in the preliminary stages.

C. The Use of Microbial Lytic Enzymes

Microbial enzymes have been reported to liberate protoplasts from bacteria (McQuillen, 1960), yeast (Garcia Mendoza and Villanueva, 1962; Phaff, 1966), filamentous fungi (Rodriguez Aguirre et al., 1964), and higher plant cells (Cocking, 1960, 1965).

Garcia Mendoza and Villanueva (1962) described *Streptomyces* GM which was able to produce enzymes lytic toward a number of yeast species with the formation of protoplasts. Gascón et al. (1965b) have reported that *Micromonospora chalcea* grown in a variety of complex media, synthesizes a complex lytic system, able to release protoplasts from a number of fungi. These enzymes are released into the growth medium during exponential growth. The numerous problems concerned with optimal growth conditions have been studied with a view to obtaining consistent and maximal yields of the lytic material (Gascón et al., 1965a). From these studies it is not certain how many enzymes are involved in the lytic activities, and clarification of this point must await fractionation of the proteins liberated into the growth medium. The initial studies of the lysis of fungal cell walls demonstrated that the lytic enzyme present in filtrates of *M. chalcea* dissolved these walls and released soluble sugars, amino sugars, and amino acids (Novaes and Villanueva, 1965; Novaes et al., 1966). The difficulty in separating small amounts of proteolytic (or other interfering) enzymes from partially purified preparations of the lytic enzyme may limit its use to experiments where those concomitant activities are unimportant.

Furuya and Ikeda (1960) isolated a strain of *Streptomyces* that attacked heat-treated bakers' yeast, isolated cell walls, and in some conditions produced protoplasts. The protoplast-forming ability was thought to be due to a combined action of a polysaccharidase and other enzymes. Yeast protoplasts were also prepared from *Saccharomyces cerevisiae* using enzymes from *Streptomyces albidoflavus* (Tabata et al., 1965).

Spherical protoplast-like structures can be liberated from hyphae of *Fusarium culmorum* by the action of an enzyme preparation obtained from the cell-free supernatant of the growth medium of *Streptomyces RA* (Rodriguez Aguirre et al., 1964). Protoplasts can also be obtained from *Mucor sphaerosporus, Cladosporium* sp., *Gliocladium roseum, Diplocladium* sp., *Trichothecium roseum, Penicillium italicum, Aspergillus nidulans, Alternaria* sp., and *Verticillium*. However striking differences were found between the different species in rate and frequency of protoplast formation. No protoplast release was observed in *Helminthosporium* sp., *Polystictus versicolor*, and *Rhizopus microsporus*.

Crude *B. circulans* lytic enzyme had no detectable activity on suspensions of intact cells of various yeasts (Phaff, 1963). However, it completely dissolved cell wall preparations made from the same yeasts, and this action was associated with the release of simple sugars and amino sugars. The failure of this enzyme to digest intact cells and to form protoplasts, although it is active on cell wall preparations, is reminiscent of the properties of other lytic enzymes produced by various organisms.

Myrothecium verrucaria cellulase was successfully employed by Cocking (1960, 1963) for the isolation of protoplasts from roots. Unlike the cell walls of fungi and bacteria, higher plant cell walls are mainly cellulose so high concentrations of cellulase alone are more effective. Similar studies in our laboratory, using *Trichoderma viride* cellulase for the formation of protoplasts from mycelial cells of species of *Pythium* and *Phytophthora* reported to contain cellulose in their cell walls, have failed. Great distortions in the cell walls were observed, with even more marked alterations in the cytoplasmic contents. The latter were sometimes liberated, but no formation of protoplasts was detected. It is possible that the cellulases were contaminated by other enzymes which, once the cellulases digest the cell wall, will penetrate and alter the plasmalemma and internal contents.

D. Comparison of the Action of Snail and Microbial Enzymes

Garcia Acha and Villanueva (1963b) describe differences in the mode of action of strepzyme and snail enzyme preparations on fungal spores. The microbial enzyme produced protoplasts from *Trichothecium roseum* spores completely free of cell walls whereas *Helix pomatia* enzyme gave rise to osmotically sensitive forms contaminated with remnants of the wall. However, studies on digestion of intact cells of *C. utilis* did not show marked differences in the mode of action of the enzyme systems from *H. pomatia* and *Micromonospora AS*. The only differences in the course of lysis are the consistency of the remaining cell walls and time differences. The cell walls after the action of the snail enzyme (observed under the phase contrast microscope) are much more opaque and rigid. Those resulting from strepzyme digestion are thinner and more delicate. The strepzyme preparation appears to be much more active on a weight basis (Garcia Mendoza and Villanueva, 1964).

A number of crude enzyme preparations known to be rich in certain carbohydrases—*Micromonospora AS* and *H. pomatia*, *Trichoderma viride* and *Streptomyces* sp. (cellulase), *Rhizopus arrhizus* (β-1,3-glucanase) and *Serratia marcescens*, *Aspergillus fumigatus*, *Penicillium ochrochloron*, and *P. lilaceum* (chitinases)—were tested in our laboratory for their ability to lyse living and dead cells of *C. utilis*. Action on living cells was limited to relatively few preparations, and there was only one (*R. arrhizus*) showing activity at an acid pH. At a neutral or slightly alkaline pH, the *Micromonospora* enzyme consistently was most active (including the snail enzyme), the other preparations varying greatly. Dead cells were much more susceptible to lysis than living cells. Combinations of lytic enzymes show a synergistic action, and these are apparent not only on living cells, but also on dead cells and on isolated cell walls.

E. The Use of Other Enzymes

There have been reports referring to the preparation of protoplasts of various fungi, e.g., *N. crassa* and yeasts, by using a variety of commercial enzyme preparations. Emerson and Emerson (1958) first reported production of protoplast-like structures from all tested strains of *N. crassa* which carried the osmotic mutant gene (*os*) by treatment with a commercial hemicellulase preparation or crude snail hepatic juice. Hyphae were digested with 0.5–3% (w/v) hemicellulase in a medium containing sucrose, rhamnose, or sorbose and the standard salt mixture. Protoplasts were more readily maintained at the higher concentrations of sugars and enzyme. The spherical forms lysed in distilled water to leave a delicate membrane.

Eddy (1958a) studied the lysis of walls of *Saccharomyces cerevisiae* by proteolytic enzymes such as papain, trypsin, and an enzyme preparation from malt. Although walls are digested, he demonstrated that complete degradation occurred only with the snail enzyme. Satomura *et al.* (1960) obtained complete digestion of intact yeast walls by a combination of glucanase, lipase, and phospholipase. Recently Garcia Acha and her colleagues succeeded in obtaining protoplasts from *Fusarium culmorum* mycelium by a combination of pancreatic lipase and strepzyme M. This last preparation alone did not form protoplasts (Garcia Acha *et al.*, 1966).

F. Formation of Protoplasts by Inhibition of Cell Wall Synthesis

The specific inhibition of cell wall synthesis without affecting the synthesis of the cytoplasmic membrane and other internal structures has been used for preparation of protoplasts of bacteria (McQuillen, 1960). Similar attempts made by addition of antibiotics or by metabolic disturbance of fungi have been only partially successful. Hamilton and Calvet have shown (1964), that when sorbose (5–20%) was added to growth media, the osmotic mutant M 16 of *N. crassa* produced small colonies composed almost entirely of protoplasts. The preliminary report of de Terra and Tatum (1961) showed that hyphae of *Neurospora* become bulgy when grown in 4% sorbose medium. Results with glucose, sucrose, and fructose, which served as osmotic stabilizers and carbon sources, were similar to those with sorbose plus 2% sucrose, when considered on a molar basis. The protoplasts met all the criteria suggested by Bachmann and Bonner (1959) and the effect of the sugars may well be selective cell wall inhibition "by extracellular loss of necessary substrates or enzymes, although an alternative explanation would be the extracellular movement and activation of an autolytic enzyme." However, Robertson (1965) has suggested that the sorbose molecule might be preventing the normal building of dextrose units into the fungal wall at the apex of the cell.

G. *Attempts to Obtain Protoplasts by Means of Antibiotics*

Attempts have been made to prepare protoplasts of fungi by means of antibiotics and various fungicides. Antibiotics like griseofulvin are known to act on immature fungal cell walls in a small region of the hyphae around the tip (Dekker, 1963; Bent and Moore, 1966). This agent is primarily active on fungi containing chitin (Brian, 1960). Thus, griseofulvin and related compounds might interfere with fungal wall formation in similar way to that of penicillin on sensitive bacteria, specifically preventing the synthesis of cell wall material while allowing other components of the cell to develop normally. Although no protoplasts were detected, alterations of the permeability of the fungus were apparent (Kinsky, 1961). A variety of antifungal antibiotics tested on active growing cells of yeasts also failed to produce osmotically fragile protoplasts (Shockman and Lampen, 1962). It was concluded that these antifungal antibiotics act mainly on the protoplast, and indeed most of the antifungal agents produced marked inhibition of growth.

III. MORPHOLOGY AND STRUCTURE

A. *Release of Protoplasts*

Under specified conditions protoplasts can be observed emerging. As described by Bachmann and Bonner (1959) the formation of mycelial protoplasts converts the coenocytic mycelium of fungi into units which can be handled quantitatively by the techniques used for unicellular microorganisms. The different stages in the formation of yeast protoplasts with strepzyme have been described (Garcia Mendoza and Villanueva, 1964). Although the various stages of the conversion process are not synchronous in a yeast population it was possible to map in detail the sequence of events in some isolated cells after the addition of lytic enzyme to the medium. The cells underwent an apparent swelling, and the cell wall seemed to be digested rather than to break under these circumstances. Release of protoplasts in *Candida utilis* cells seemed to occur chiefly at the equatorial zone of the cell and only rarely at the polar ends (Fig. 1 A, B). As a rule, the entire contents of one cell are extruded at one time to form one free protoplast. During the last stages of protoplast release and once they have been extruded, the cell walls more or less rapidly, depending on the concentration of the lytic enzyme present, are completely dissolved, leaving a suspension of protoplasts free of debris.

The liberation of protoplasts in *Oospora suaveolens,* as described by Gascón et al. (1965b) can be summarized as follows: The protoplast retracts from one pole of the cell at an early stage, and later is extruded through a hole developed at the other pole (Fig. 1C). After emergence, the empty cells retain their original size and shape. Later they disappear by digestion with strepzyme. Occasionally it was the central part of an elongated cell which swelled and there the protoplast began to emerge through pores in the cell walls. Sometimes during protoplast liberation in *O. suaveolens* the protoplasm of one cell can divide into two parts, one remaining inside the cell wall and the other, usually the one at the end, giving rise to a protoplast (Fig. 1D). Sometimes when the protoplast was released from the cell wall some kind of filamentous structure remained behind. Strunk (1966) has described similar structures. She showed phase contrast micrographs in which one protoplast is linked to another, or to the contents remaining in the hyphae of *Polystictus versicolor,* by a thread of cytoplasm (Fig. 2). This filament not only keeps the protoplasts linked, but serves to originate some kind of attraction between the connected protoplasts, which later come together and fuse.

Liberation of protoplasts from the mycelium of *Fusarium culmorum* follows the attack on the cell wall, with the production of a budlike structure in the hyphae. A few minutes later the protoplast can be seen to emerge through an aperture and to attain a spherical shape (Fig. 3). Forces tending to make the protoplast assume a spherical shape apparently help in the extrusion of the body. Protoplasts of various sizes (4–15 μ in diameter) can often be seen. Sometimes the protoplasts swell (or grow) and eventually the spheres rupture, leaving either ghosts or clusters of granules. The various ways in which protoplasts may be released in this fungus are diagrammed in Fig. 1 E, F.

Substances usually used for stabilization of protoplasts affect their formation. Protoplast liberation by the action of the lytic enzyme of *Streptomyces RA* (Rodriguez Aguirre et al., 1964) on mycelium of *F. culmorum* takes place very quickly (in less than 60 minutes) when fructose, sorbose, sucrose, rhamnose, mannitol, NaCl, or KCl (at $0.8\,M$) are employed as stabilizers. On the other hand when the stabilizer used is xylose, sucrose, or maltose the process of protoplast release starts only after 3 hours' incubation. After extrusion of protoplasts, the empty cell walls remain, and these appear to be resistant to enzymatic digestion.

Protoplast release has also been described in *Neurospora crassa* after treatment with either commercial enzyme (Emerson and Emerson, 1958) or snail preparation (Bachmann and Bonner, 1959). One or several pores are formed in the hyphal walls, either at the sides or ends of the cells, and spherical bodies emerge. Although extrusion of all the contents of

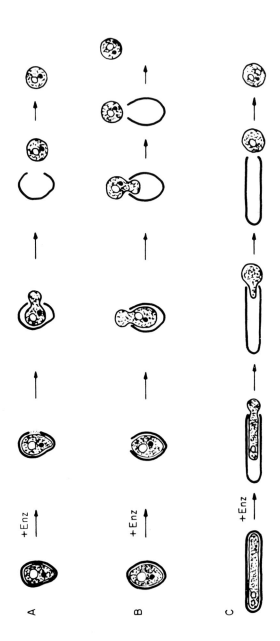

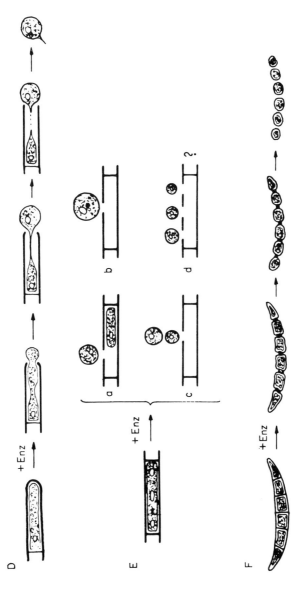

Fig. 1. Patterns of protoplast release in various types of fungi: A and B, *Candida utilis*; C and D, *Oospora suaveolens* and *Polystictus versicolor*; E, *Fusarium culmorum*; F, *F. culmorum* conidia. Explanation in text.

the compartment between septa may take place, occasionally some cytoplasmic material remains behind. The protoplasts and internal contents of hyphae of *Penicillium glaucum* are connected through pores (Meinecke, 1960). From the micrographs shown it seems that some kind of

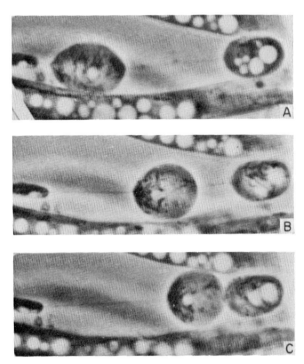

FIG. 2. Release of *Polystictus versicolor* protoplasts from a hyphal tip. All protoplasts are joined by a thread of cytoplasm. Interval between Figs. A and C, 6 minutes. Magnification: × 2000. Courtesy of Dr. C. Strunk.

vesicle is formed, similar to those obtained in the presence of amino acids, and substances which interfere with normal cell wall synthesis.

Electron microscopic studies of the process of protoplast release are almost lacking. Strunk (1964) has reported the direct connection of the emerging protoplast with the mother hypha, and her findings fit well with light microscope observations.

Microcinematographic studies made by Girbardt's group at Jena suggest that enormous masses of cytoplasmic materials are extruded from the hyphae, giving rise to extremely large protoplasts. In the film, protoplasts of various sizes fuse and produce even larger, more or less spherical, osmotically sensitive bodies. Sometimes several protoplasts were linked together by fine cytoplasmic threads. If the linked protoplasts correspond to two consecutive cells separated by a septum, the possibility exists that these threads were equivalent to plant plasmodesmata, but this does not seem to be the case.

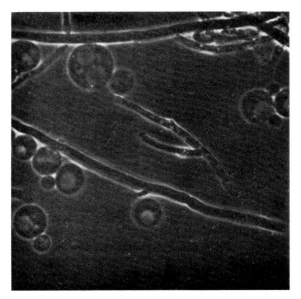

FIG. 3. Mycelial protoplasts of *Fusarium culmorum*. Note the variation in size of the spherical bodies. Magnification: × 7000.

B. *The Site of Enzyme Action and Protoplast Liberation*

Holter and Ottolenghi (1960) and Svihla *et al.* (1961) using snail enzyme reported the emergence of protoplasts through a hole in the cell wall of the yeast cells. Details observed by phase contrast microscopy of the different stages in protoplast formation by microbial enzyme digestion have been described (Garcia Mendoza and Villanueva, 1964). More recently an electron microscope study was described of sections of fungal cells made during the conversion of *Candida utilis* cells to spherical protoplasts (Villanueva *et al.*, 1966). Samples for electron microscopy were taken at various intervals from the beginning of the process until most of the transiently formed protoplast bodies had been converted into "ghosts." It was shown that digestion of the cell wall occurred preferentially at the growing areas of the wall, i.e., at the equatorial zone (Fig. 4) and at budding zones of the cell. This phenomenon was also observed in other fungal species, such as *Schizosaccharomyces pombe*, in which the growing

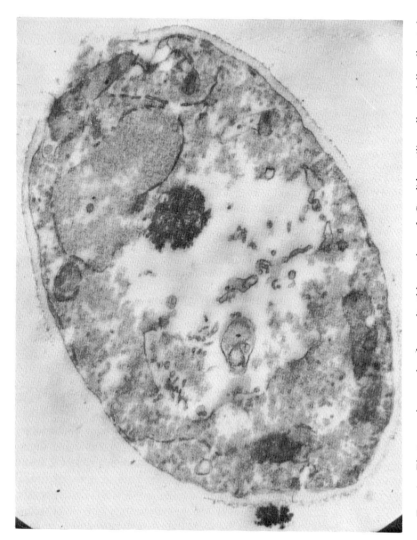

FIG. 4. Electron micrograph of an ultrathin section of *Candida utilis* cell partially digested with strepzyme. Note the preferential digestion of the equatorial zone. Magnification: × 20,000.

areas are at one end of the cell (Fig. 5). In yeast, complete digestion of the cell wall does not seem to take place.

Protoplasts from *Polystictus versicolor* may be obtained by the action of the *Helix pomatia* enzyme. Release of protoplasts is first observed at

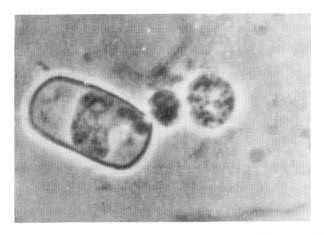

FIG. 5. Protoplast liberation in *Schizosaccharomyces pombe* by strepzyme. Note the liberation of two protoplasts. Magnification: × 7000.

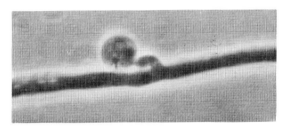

FIG. 6. A protoplast of *Polystictus versicolor* originating from a clamp. Magnification: × 6000. Courtesy of Dr. C. Strunk.

the tips of growing hyphae (Fig. 2) and clamps (Fig. 6), i.e., at the point where the cell is growing and the cell wall is thinnest (Strunk, 1966). The growing point at the tip of the hyphae (Strunk, 1963) is possibly the exact site of the action of lytic enzyme. In *Oospora suaveolens* (Gascón et al., 1965b) too, the cells seem to be attacked most readily at the tip where active growth is taking place.

Microscopic observations on living mycelium of *Fusarium culmorum* exposed to strepzyme did not show the site of protoplast release so clearly. Although protoplasts were seen to emerge through hyphal tips, liberation of spherical bodies takes place also at parts of the hyphae between septa. The first visible indication of digestion is the production of a budlike structure. Upon further observation this turns out to be the spot where the protoplast will be released (Rodriguez Aguirre et al., 1964).

C. Number of Protoplasts per Cell

As suggested by McQuillen (1960) for bacterial cells, the number of protoplasts which are extruded from a cell compartment depends on how "cell" is defined. In yeast cells, generally one spherical protoplast emerges from each unicellular compartment. Sometimes more than one protoplast can be seen to emerge. Thus in *Candida utilis* and *Saccharomyces cerevisiae*, when no budding occurs, one protoplast per cell is usually observed, whereas in *Schizosaccharomyces pombe* more than one protoplast may be produced (Fig. 5). Budding may cause the formation of one or more protoplasts (Rost and Venner, 1965). The contents of one cell, on squeezing out through the hole in the cell wall, may split and yield more than one protoplast (Holter and Ottolenghi, 1960).

Definition of the number of protoplasts per cell in hyphae of filamentous fungi is becoming complicated. Often the entire contents of a hyphal compartment emerge as a single, large protoplast. On other occasions, the contents are extruded intermittently through one or several pores, giving rise to a number of protoplasts from one compartment. Sometimes, a considerable amount of the cytoplasmic contents of a compartment remains inside of the walls. In *Oospora suaveolens* (Gascón et al., 1965b) the cytoplasmic contents may be liberated as one large protoplast, but more often they are extruded in two portions.

It is difficult to determine the significance of the released spherical structures. The easiest explanation, valid possibly only for *Oospora suaveolens* or *Schizosaccharomyces*, is that two cells were already formed even if they did not appear as such. O'Hern and Heway (1956) reported that cell division in *Coccidioides immitis* begins with the division of the cytoplasm by a cytoplasmic membrane. At a later stage, the septal wall is laid down, the membrane splits, and wall material is laid down between the two resulting membranes. The septa could be formed as a latter stage of division. While this theory may explain the mechanism of protoplast release in some types of cells, it is not valid for filamentous fungi, such as *Fusarium culmorum* and *Neurospora crassa*.

Cytological studies are needed to determine the distribution of nuclei into protoplasts when more than one spherical body is produced from one hyphal compartment. Has each of the protoplasts one or more nuclei? Some of the bodies could be without a nucleus: Are such protoplasts able to survive and regenerate? The demonstration that each free protoplast contains a full set of cytoplasmic elements, lacking only its cell wall, and represents a complete cell still awaits further investigations. As has been described for plant protoplasts (Cocking, 1963), those cytoplasmic structures released during lytic action might represent preformed organized protoplasmic units of the fungal cell equivalent in character to the subprotoplasts reported by the British worker. However, in contrast with Cocking's report, it has not been possible to identify individual protoplasmic units in the fungal cell compartment before protoplast release, or later in the large protoplasts.

The explanation of the variability of the number of protoplasts needs some understanding of the contents of that portion of hyphae between two consecutive septa. In contrast with phycomycetes, the hyphae of the ascomycetes, basidiomycetes, and fungi imperfecti are regularly septate, but each septum contains a minute central pore through which the continuity of the protoplasm can be maintained (Hickman, 1965). That is, the hyphae are not divided into a series of independent cells, but are typically coenocytic. Dissolution of the rigid cell wall under stabilized conditions may liberate portions of the protoplasm with no defined volumes. Under these conditions there is no reason to expect the release of bodies of the same size since, unless the whole content of a compartment is extruded as an entity, the number of protoplasts can fluctuate between wide limits. Furthermore, unless the internal contents of the protoplasm are divided into regional compartments, each one enveloped by a membrane of the endoplasmic reticulum, there is no clear explanation of how the cytoplasmic membrane can produce the numerous spheres which can be released from the hyphal compartment.

D. *Phase-Contrast Microscopy*

The conversion of fungal cells to protoplast bodies is usually followed by phase contrast microscopy. Almost all the cells became spherical although occasionally some abnormal elliptical or elongated forms can be observed. In a large protoplast, streaming can easily be observed. Protoplasts show great variability in diameter. Sometimes, those formed from hyphae and especially those released from tips, are somewhat larger in diameter. However, as has already been described, fusion among mycelial protoplasts occurs. The larger bodies often seen in *Fusarium culmorum* protoplasts, which are called "giant" protoplasts may, by comparison with Strunk's observations made on films of phase contrast preparations (Strunk, 1966), originate by fusion of various smaller bodies, though the possibility of protoplast swelling cannot be ignored (Rodriguez Aguirre *et al.*, 1964). Incubation conditions may affect the size of the bodies. Structures can be seen corresponding to vacuoles (varying in numbers and sizes), lipid globules and glycogen granules, vesicles and membranes, nuclei, and sometimes long filaments which may correspond to mitochondria (Strunk, 1966). Vacuolation inside the protoplasts varies from protoplast to protoplast. Apical cells are normally without vacuoles, but at a distance from the apex, vacuoles are more abundant (Robertson, 1965) and older cells seem to have more vacuoles than younger ones. The appearance of vacuoles is influenced not only by the age of the cells, but also by the strain and by the solution (hypertonic or hypotonic) in which the organism is growing. It is possible on this basis to explain the great variation in the protoplasts produced from hyphae (see Robertson, Chapter 26 in Volume I).

Better resolution of internal structure is always found in protoplasts than in intact cells. Internal structures in filamentous fungi are better observed in mycelium protoplasts than in those derived from spores, in which the density of the cytoplasm seems to be higher. By phase contrast the spherical bodies show a variety of internal structures with granular elements, vesicles, and vacuoles. Vegetative cells of *Oospora suaveolens* often have protoplasts with a large vacuole, on occasion occupying all the internal space of the body (Gascón *et al.*, 1965b). On prolonged incubation many of the cells may enlarge and produce a large vacuole. Sometimes an internal structure that might be the nucleus may be seen. In other protoplasts, not must detail can be seen because of the small size of the structures involved.

When incubation is continued, hyphal protoplasts often enlarge and lyse, and the cell contents disperse into the medium as diffuse granular material. The vacuoles may remain more or less intact as isolated units, or protected by some granular material surrounding the outer surface of the vesicle. In some fungi, after protoplast lysis, there remains a visible "ghost" in which no recognizable particles are observed.

Protoplasts appear to be markedly affected by the nature of the substance used for stabilization. On prolonged incubation there is a tendency for the spherical and turgid protoplasts to become contracted and crenated. During this process the refractile vacuole(s) seem to disappear.

E. *Electron Microscopy: Fine Structure of Protoplasts*

Electron microscope studies of protoplasts are few. Osmium tetroxide- or potassium permanganate-fixed protoplasts often resemble very electron dense spherical bodies possibly lacking the cell wall, though in the micrographs it is difficult to be completely certain of the total absence of that rigid and characteristic structure. Ultrathin sections of protoplasts of *C. utilis* (Fig. 7A) fixed in potassium permanganate, stained in uranyl acetate, and embedded in methacrylate showed no important changes in the internal structures of the cells (Villanueva et al., 1966).

Strunk (1964), using protoplasts of *Polystictus versicolor,* has succeeded in fixing protoplasts and obtaining electron micrographs (Fig. 7B) which

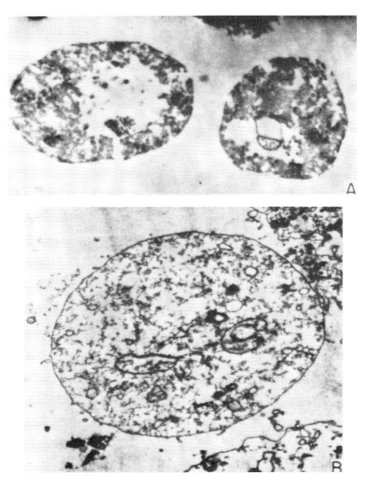

FIG. 7. Electron micrographs of sections of protoplasts (A) from *Candida utilis* (× 26,000) and (B) from *Polystictus versicolor* (× 16,500).

show a well-preserved membrane, in some places with double structure, and a multiplicity of internal structures not basically different from the internal organization of hyphae. No remnants of the cell wall on the surface of these protoplasts are observed. Invaginations of the plasmalemma and connection with endoplasmic reticular membranes were not observed.

The complex structures that consist of a few large bodies enclosing smaller elongated elements and of empty vesicles corresponding to the nucleoplasm were not found. The granules or small bodies are morphologically and structurally well defined. The endoplasmic reticulum was almost undetectable, and the coarse granularity of the cytoplasm was probably due to the presence of free ribosomes. Some of these ribosomes seem to adhere to the vesicular (mitochondrial) membranes.

F. Fixation of Protoplasts

Fungal protoplasts are osmotically sensitive and must be stabilized by sugars or salt solutions. Addition of chemicals to such suspensions during fixation may lead to the sudden disappearance of some of the cytoplasmic contents, or to complete disintegration. This phenomenon was observed by Lee (1960) and Thornsson and Weibull (1958) with bacterial protoplasts. Protoplasts are very fragile and cannot be dried without disruption. This difficulty can be avoided by means of careful fixation of the osmotically sensitive bodies. Fungal protoplasts are spherical when observed under the phase contrast microscope and this form can be preserved even after fixation. The ellipsoidal shape of the protoplasts often seen in the ultrathin sections may be the result of deformations during the embedding or sectioning procedures.

Studies on the plasma membrane of cells by correlation of physicochemical experiments and electron microscopical observations has often been difficult because membranes are very easily distorted when the cells are exposed to drastic procedures of fixation. A number of fixatives are suitable including osmium tetroxide (1% in distilled water or in an appropriate buffer), potassium permanganate (2%) and a mixture of osmium tetroxide and permanganate, as well as glutaraldehyde (5% w/v) or formalin (10% w/v) as suggested by Weiss (1963).

No fixation method was found which consistently stabilized the osmotically fragile forms, and simultaneously preserved their fine structure well. Very often the use of one fixative shows structures not detected with another. Fixation in buffered osmium tetroxide solution or potassium permanganate frequently caused a disintegration of osmotically fragile forms, even when the osmotic pressure of the medium was maintained at a high level. Bacterial protoplasts are apparently markedly stabilized by the addition of $0.01\ M$ $MgCl_2$ or serum albumin (Thornsson and Weibull, 1958). Yeast protoplasts have also been protected from disintegration by the addition of a highly charged, nonpermeating, macromolecule to the fixation fluid. Carrageenin, a sulfated polysaccharide, apparently yields good results in this respect (Elbers, 1961). Internal structures in protoplasts of *Polystictus versicolor* were well preserved by the use of osmium and buffered sucrose solution although the plasmalemma often disappeared (Strunk, 1964). On some occasions protoplasts of *C. utilis* were well preserved by fixation with $KMnO_4$ (Villanueva et al., 1966). Glutaraldehyde and formaldehyde were employed in fixation of conidial protoplasts of *Neurospora crassa* (Weiss, 1963). These fixatives, when compared with $KMnO_4$, increased complexity of the internal structures of the protoplasts. $KMnO_4$ apparently removes ribosomes but permits better observation of other cell components. Aldehyde-fixed protoplasts contained components not seen in $KMnO_4$-fixed organisms. Fixation by heating before or after digestion of the cell wall by the system has also been used for structural studies in microorganisms. This method, however, produces great alterations in the cytoplasm by coagulation and retraction of the internal contents.

IV. PROTOPLASTS FROM SPORES

In nature spores are more resistant than vegetative forms. The reason for the resistance of fully mature spores to various influences is not known, although it can probably be attributed in part to differences in wall composition. A number of studies on the lytic action of natural soil have shown that the important survival organs of plant pathogens are resistant spores or sclerotia, rather than vegetative mycelium (Lockwood, 1960). Resistant forms survive in soil for long periods. Due to the resistance of spores, it seems desirable to bring together some of the work on their lysis.

A. Lysis of Fungal Spores

The digestion of cell walls of vegetative cells of fungi by lytic enzymes has been reported by a number of workers, but the digestion of the spore wall has only rarely been studied in detail. The fate of germinated spores or fungal mycelia when added to soil has been reported (Lockwood, 1960; Stevenson, 1956; Chinn, 1959). Soil lysis appears to be associated with the presence of lytic microorganisms. Lysis of promycelia of *Ustilago zeae* [*U. maydis*] and *Sphacelotheca sorghi* is due to a lethal factor (Laskaris, 1941; Gattani, 1952). Several organisms associated with uredospores lyse germ tubes (Garcia Acha et al., 1965) of rust fungi, and the lytic agent is enzymatic. Direct attack by a species of *Verticillium* on spores and hyphae of *Hemileia vastatrix* was shown by Leal and Villanueva (1962). The mold developed luxuriantly when the rust spores provided the only carbon and nitrogen source, total disintegration being the last step of the lytic process. Johnston and Mortimer (1959) using snail enzymes were able to show release of yeast spore tetrads. Haskins and Spencer (1962) following the instructions of the previous workers described the liberation of ascospores from mature inoperculate asci by the use of the same type of enzymes.

B. Spore "Protoplasts"

Osmotically fragile structures may be obtained from certain fungal spores by dissolving the wall of living cells with snail and microbial enzymes. It has been established that, at least for *Neurospora crassa,* these treatments remove the entire wall (Weiss, 1963). Provided that the osmotic

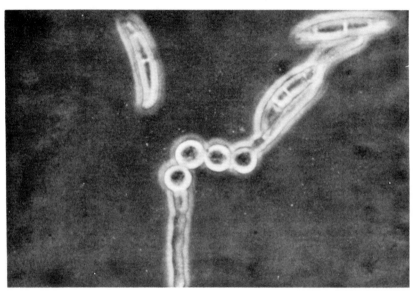

FIG. 8. *Fusarium culmorum* conidia and their "protoplasts." Magnification: × 7000.

pressure of the surrounding medium is maintained at a high level by means of suitable solutes, the wall-less protoplasts so obtained are rather stable. Bachmann and Bonner (1959) were first to describe liberation of protoplast from fungal spores using *Helix pomatia* enzymes. Free protoplasts were obtained when conidia of *N. crassa* were incubated with the snail preparation. Sometimes the protoplasts were extruded through one pore in the side wall, although frequently the protoplasts do not emerge from the conidia but remain as spherical bodies in the attacked walls which nearly disappear. Weiss (1963) also described the preparation of conidial protoplasts of *N. crassa* and studied them by electron microscopy. During preliminary structural studies of the conidia of *Fusarium culmorum,* it was observed that incubation of suspensions of the wall with the strepzymes yielded soluble material containing most of the typical components of the whole wall. Further reports from our laboratory have described the formation of protoplast-like structures from spores (Garcia Acha and Villanueva, 1963a,b; Garcia Acha *et al.*, 1963, 1964) of various molds by exposure to microbial lytic preparations. These systems apparently attack either partially or completely the outer layers of the spores, which

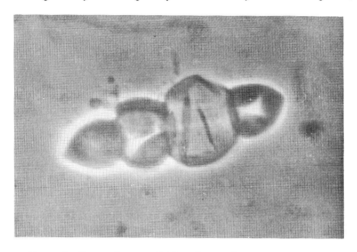

FIG. 9. "Protoplast" membranes of *Fusarium culmorum* conidia. **Magnification**: × 7000.

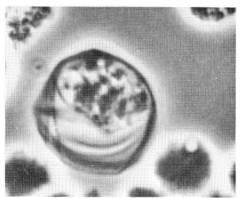

FIG. 10. Membranes of mycelial protoplasts of *Fusarium culmorum*. Magnification: × 8000 from Rodriguez Aguirre *et al.* (1964).

leads to formation of "protoplasts." The osmotically sensitive bodies do not emerge from the conidia, but remain as spherical bodies within weakened walls that virtually disappear. Later the individual cells making up a conidium are released, giving rise to isolated spherical "protoplasts" (Figs. 1F and 8). It has been suggested that it might be interesting to see the amount of wall attack that the conidial cell will tolerate without impairment of its capacity to grow and divide.

Spore protoplasts should prove useful for investigators interested in morphological, biochemical, and genetic studies. However, conidia do not represent the most appropriate material for obtaining suspensions of free protoplasts because of the difficulty of being sure that the protoplasts are wall-less. Protoplasts prepared from conidia are much more stable than those from young hyphae. Some (but not always all) of these "protoplasts" lysed after addition of distilled water to the stabilized suspension. Microscopic observation of this lytic phenomenon has shown a tenuous membrane of about the same size as the protoplast remaining after the explosive dispersion of the cell contents (Fig. 9). These membranes or "ghosts" have also been observed after lysis of mycelial protoplasts but seem to be more delicate structures (Fig. 10).

V. PROPERTIES OF PROTOPLASTS

A. Stabilizing Media

Due to the lack of external protection, protoplasts will immediately lyse during the process of release from the mother cell unless the osmotic concentration is adjusted. A number of substances have been used for stabilization. Eddy and Williamson (1957) in their historic work used rhamnose and later mannitol (Eddy and Williamson, 1959). The latter has been used extensively although an important limitation is its low solubility (0.8–1.0 M). Sorbitol, dulcitol, and even sucrose have been used. Most of these carbohydrates were previously found to stabilize bacterial protoplasts. McQuillen (1960) suggested that the solute ought not be able to penetrate the osmotic barrier of the protoplast at an appreciable rate in order to protect from lysis. Maltose and fructose have more rarely been used although they seem to be very effective in *Neurospora* protoplasts (Bachmann and Bonner, 1959). Xylose, on the other hand, was, apparently, completely ineffective and may even interfere with protoplast formation (Bachmann and Bonner, 1959). Sorbose (5–10%), used by Emerson and Emerson (1958), seems to be metabolized with great difficulty by fungi and bacteria, and its use is highly recommended when long incubations are required. Antibacterial antibiotics, sometimes used to suppress contaminants, may interfere with the experiment.

A number of common salts have also been studied in stabilization experiments; some were found to be very useful. KCl, at about 0.6–0.8 M, was employed for stabilization of protoplasts of yeasts (Holter and Ottolenghi, 1960; Svihla *et al.*, 1961; Shockman and Lampen, 1962) and filamentous fungi.

NaCl might be used for the same purposes, although it may affect some metabolic systems. These two salts conferred some stability on *Candida utilis* protoplasts but less than that given by mannitol (Gascón *et al.,* 1965b). These salts were found to interfere with the lytic activity of the strepzyme (Gascón *et al.,* 1965a). Magnesium sulfate at 0.8–1.0 M was the most effective in yielding a stable protoplast suspension, and the formation of protoplasts proceeded more rapidly in its presence than with any other salt tested (Gascón and Villanueva, 1965). With magnesium sulfate, it is also unusual to see any microbial contaminants; it was also used as stabilizer by Rost and Venner (1965) with *S. cerevisiae* and *S. fragilis* protoplasts. Phosphate buffer was found to produce strong inhibition of the lytic action of strepzyme M on intact cells at 0.1–0.05 M.

S. cerevisiae protoplasts are relatively stable in 0.3–1.0 M NaCl. Addition of bivalent cations to the above solution seems to increase the stability of protoplasts (Tabata *et al.,* 1965).

Stability of protoplasts is affected not only by the kind of stabilizer used, but also by the species (and even the strain) of the fungus. Eddy and Williamson (1957) report stabilizing *Saccharomyces* protoplasts for a few hours only, but, working with *Candida,* Svihla *et al.* (1961) found that the spherical bodies could be stored for days. Many protoplasts persist for over a week at 25°C. Bachmann and Bonner (1959) reported that *Neurospora* protoplasts retained their morphological integrity for days when stored at room temperature. *Fusarium* protoplasts seem to be very stable when kept at 2°C, and many persist for over 10 days at room temperature (Rodriguez Aguirre *et al.,* 1964). The lower limit of concentration of the stabilizers used satisfactorily for these protoplasts was 0.2 M.

Stability of the protoplasts is markedly affected by the reaction of the suspending medium. The range between pH 4.0 and 8.0 is satisfactory for producing fungal protoplasts, but the optimum pH for stability is 6–8.

B. *Osmotic Sensitivity of Protoplasts*

Intact fungal cells are assumed to have an osmotic barrier permeable to small molecules, which adheres to the wall and surrounds the protoplasm. This osmotic barrier probably corresponds to the cytoplasmic membrane. The free protoplasts of fungi like those of most bacteria are sensitive to osmotic shock and lyse immediately when placed in distilled water.

Svihla *et al.* (1961) have determined the optimum conditions for osmotic stability, by measuring the release of radioactivity from labeled spheroplasts placed in various concentrations of KCl. Higher stability of the spheres was found with KCl concentrations of 0.5–1.0 M. Low concentrations of the solute produced bursting of the protoplasts with release of the labeled cytoplasmic compounds. High solute concentrations gave rise to crenate structures, a phenomenon often observed when samples were suddenly transferred from a low concentration to much higher concentration of the stabilizer.

Ottolenghi and Lillehoj (1966) have recently reported fascinating results in relation to osmotic properties of yeast protoplasts. The minimum concentration for stability of *Saccharomyces* protoplasts, especially in the presence of growth medium, is about $0.6\,M$ KCl or $1\,M$ sorbitol. With lower concentrations the protoplasts tend to swell and burst. Furthermore, it was noticed that if intact cells were harvested, washed, and placed in $1\,M$ sorbitol, the cells shrank and the cell wall separated from the protoplasm. If growth medium is added to the cells, they swell again and become normal. However, if cells now adapted to $1\,M$ sorbitol are put into $2\,M$ sorbitol, they will again shrink, but in growth medium they will swell again. This can be repeated with $3\,M$ sorbitol. Using KCl, one can do the same thing. By $0.5\,M$ steps one can easily get up to $2\,M$ KCl. It is interesting to find that cells adapted in this way will grow in the media they have adapted to and will form protoplasts, stable in the tonicity to which the cells have become adapted. Protoplasts from cells grown in $1\,M$ sorbitol are stable in $1\,M$ sorbitol, those from $2\,M$ or $3\,M$ sorbitol are stable in $2\,M$ or $3\,M$ sorbitol. But those from $2\,M$ or $3\,M$ will burst in $1\,M$ sorbitol. In fact, if whole cells taken from 2 or $3\,M$ sorbitol are placed in water, many will burst. Another conclusion of this work was that cells grown in different osmotic pressures behave differently not only in respect to growth (increase in the osmotic pressure caused a decrease in the growth rate) but also in other physiological activities, i.e., respiratory activity of the cells is also affected by the high osmolarity of the medium.

Osmotic bursting can be used as a mild procedure for the preparation of protoplasmic components. Intact mitochondria have been successfully prepared by osmotic shock of yeast protoplasts (Duell *et al.*, 1964). However on some occasions the recovery of cell fractions has been difficult due to the instability of components arising as a result of the osmotic changes. The possibility of finding an agent able to induce bursting, as has been shown in plant protoplasts with 3-indolylacetic acid (Cocking, 1961, 1965), without changing the osmotic environment, seems promising.

A number of surface active agents and related substances known to disrupt cytoplasmic membranes were tested against protoplasts of fungi. Sodium dodecyl sulfate (0.05%) causes great alterations of the osmotic barrier of protoplasts followed by lysis (Rost and Venner, 1965). Digitonin, acting on *Fusarium* and *Aspergillus* protoplasts, causes immediate lysis (Rodriguez Aguirre, 1965). Nystatin and other polyene antibiotics, which bind to the sterols of fungal membranes, produce membrane damage and cell lysis (Lampen et al., 1962; Kinsky, 1963).

C. Resistance to Physical Factors

Protoplasts of fungi have been studied for their sensitivity to a number of physical factors such as centrifugation, shaking, sonic vibration, ultraviolet light irradiation. Being deprived of the protective wall, they are more susceptible to such forces. They may be centrifuged gently and washed, provided they are maintained in appropriate stabilizing solutions. However the extent of cell damage is proportional to the force employed and is affected by the organism used. Centrifugation at 10,000 g for 10 minutes produced a considerable amount of cell breakage of protoplasts of *C. utilis* (Svihla et al., 1961). By contrast, damage to *Fusarium* protoplasts was very small even at 20,000 g for 15 minutes (Rodriguez Aguirre et al., 1964).

The protoplasts of most fungi (*Fusarium* and *Candida* species among others) appear to be very sensitive to sonic vibration. An exposure of 1–2 minutes produced total breakage of the osmotic spheres (Svihla et al., 1961; Rodriguez Aguirre et al., 1964).

Irradiation with 6×10^4 erg/mm^2 of ultraviolet energy at 250–270 mµ, causes marked alterations of the cytoplasmic membrane and slow release of internal contents (Svihla et al., 1961). This method might be useful for preparation of vacuoles which remain intact or of other intracellular constituents. More extensive irradiation causes destruction of the cytoplasmic elements.

VI. COMPOSITION OF PROTOPLASTS

A. Chemical Composition of Protoplasts

With few exceptions, protoplasts of *F. culmorum* show practically the same qualitative chemical composition as the intact hyphae. Galactose, glucose and mannose are present in the normal mycelium in the ratio 2:8:1. In the protoplasts those substances are present but in different proportions, galactose being predominant, with almost none of the other sugars (López-Belmonte, 1965). The total amino sugar and polysaccharide content of the protoplasts was reduced by 50 and 80%, respectively, as compared with normal cells. The lipid and protein components were relatively little affected by the loss of the cell wall. Other cell components have not been determined.

B. Action of Enzymes on Protoplasts

Proteolytic enzymes and lipases have been found in our laboratory to affect strongly various constituents of the *Fusarium* protoplasts. No detailed study of isolated enzymes has yet been made. The effect of some of these enzymes might serve to explain the destructive action of various lytic enzyme preparations used for the formation of protoplasts.

C. Isolation of Subcellular Fragments of Protoplasts

In connection with the isolation of subcellular fragments, Zalokar (1965) writes: "The problem of breaking fungal cells gently was probably the chief reason for the lag in the use of fungi in modern studies of the function of cell organelles." Fortunately this problem is now approaching a solution. Subcellular components of protoplasts can be obtained by breakage of the enveloping membrane by osmotic stock. The residual structure, though leaving little to be seen by phase microscopy, should be fractionated for various biosynthetic capacities and for the various subcellular components. Cytoplasmic membranes have been isolated by differential centrifugation, as a "ghost" fraction from the lysates. Mitochondria have been obtained and used for phosphorylation studies, and attempts at isolation of nuclei and vacuoles have been made.

1. Cytoplasmic Membranes

Isolation of membranes from *Candida utilis* protoplasts has presented many difficulties due to the problem of stabilization. The membrane is very sensitive to physicochemical changes in the environment and usually exhibits rather weak contrast in the phase contrast microscope. Membranes vary in size between narrow limits comparable to the variation in size of the protoplasts. The electron micrographs showed very delicate "ghosts" in which no organized structure was observed (Fig. 11). Magnesium and lithium ions seem important to preserve this material. The membranes contain three major components (Table I): protein, lipid, and carbohydrate (Garcia Mendoza and Villanueva, 1965). It is important to remember here

TABLE I
CHEMICAL ANALYSIS OF PROTOPLAST MEMBRANES AND CELL WALLS OF *Candida utilis*[a]

Constituent	Cell walls (%)[a]	Cytoplasmic membranes (%)[a]
Carbohydrates	76.0	5.0
Hexosamine	1.0	0
Protein	7.5	37.5
Lipids	4.0	40.0
Ribonucleic acid	0	1.0
Total N	1.4	5.3
Total P	0.15	0.7

[a] Values are stated as percentage dry weight of walls and membranes.

that the chemical composition of membranes will vary depending on the extent of purification to which these structures have been subjected.

Another analysis of protoplast membranes (Boulton and Eddy, 1962; Boulton, 1965) shows: protein 40%, lipid 40%, hexose 4%, ribonucleic acid 5%, deoxyribonucleic acid 0.8%. The membranes represent 15% of the protein of the protoplast.

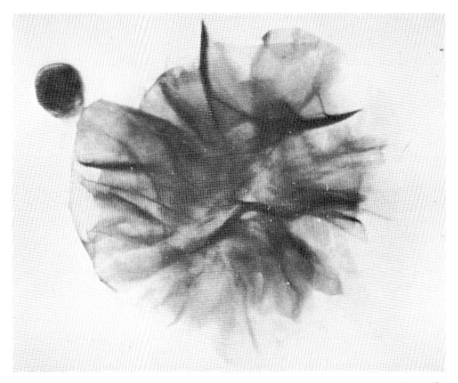

FIG. 11. Electron micrograph of cytoplasmic membranes of *Candida utilis* protoplasts. Magnification: × 36,000.

Phase contrast microscopic observations have shown that protoplasts from *F. culmorum* mycelium swell on aging and lyse. By the addition of certain chemicals, lysis is prevented or retarded for some time. The ghosts that are obtained when protoplasts of *F. culmorum* are shocked osmotically consist of a membrane which encloses some granular and vesicular structures (Fig. 10). The diffuse appearance of this structure made it difficult to estimate the thickness of the ghost membrane. Observations made in sections of intact cells give a value of about 70 Å. A double envelope in the membrane of the protoplast could not be seen.

Attempts to prepare purified membranes by osmotic lysis of protoplasts of *N. crassa* have been generally unsuccessful (Kinsky, 1962a), although the existence of a cell membrane in *Neurospora* has been demonstrated by electron microscopic studies (Shatkin and Tatum, 1959). Recent studies have suggested that the permeability changes which polyene antifungal antibiotics induce in mycelial mats and protoplasts of *Neurospora* may be a consequence of antibiotic binding to the cell membrane (a sterol might be required for this binding).

Although major attention to antibiotics has centered on interference with cell wall synthesis, several of these agents are believed to affect primarily the cell membrane, and hence permeability, e.g., nystatin (Marini *et al.*, 1961), and β-propiolactone (Gale, 1955).

2. Mitochondria

The work of Heyman-Blanchet *et al.* (1959) and of Duell *et al.* (1964) have shown that functionally intact mitochondria can be obtained in good yields by careful osmotic disruption of protoplasts. The protoplasts were prepared by digestion of the cell walls of *Saccharomyces cerevisiae* with snail enzyme in the presence of 2-mercaptoethylamine plus 0.63 M sorbitol as stabilizer. Lysis of the protoplasts was accomplished with 0.25 M sucrose containing 0.25 M potassium phosphate (pH 6.8) and 0.001 M ethylenediaminetetraacetic acid. The cell debris was removed by centrifugation at 1000 g for 10 minutes at 0°C. The resulting supernatant was centrifuged at 5000 g for 20 minutes at 0°C. The pellet containing the mitochondria was washed repeatedly with 20% sucrose. The normal yield was 20–25 mg of mitochondrial protein per gram of cells.

Heick and Stewart (1965) have used a pressure cell to disrupt protoplasts of *Lipomyces lipofer*. They obtained a particulate fraction sedimenting at 17,000 g in saline, consisting of a relatively homogeneous active preparation of mitochondria. The structure of the isolated mitochondria resembles that in whole protoplasts or of intact cells.

The usefulness of these mild methods are remarkable mainly when compared with the vigorous mechanical procedures needed to disintegrate the rigid cell wall (Utter *et al.*, 1958).

Centrifugation of broken protoplasts of *N. crassa* conidia produced mitochondria that were used for biochemical studies (Weiss, 1963). These mitochondria were found to be very similar to those found in hyphae.

3. Nuclei

Necas (1961) studied the division of the nuclei of naked yeast protoplasts and suggested that these bodies are appropriate material for investigations of the nucleus. This author showed that the protoplast can suffer marked flattening without impairing vitality. Under these conditions the whole process of nuclear division can be studied in the phase microscope by microcinematography. It seems that in growing protoplasts, the nucleus divides by simple constriction, without the appearance of structures typical of mitosis, and the disappearance of the nuclear membrane. The same phenomenon has been described in vegetative hyphae (Robinow, 1957). Preparations of nuclei from protoplasts have not yet been described, although some attempts have been made (Eddy, 1958b).

4. Vacuoles

The spherical osmotically sensitive bodies of *Candida utilis,* when exposed to irradiation with ultraviolet light, suffer the breakage of cytoplasmic membranes, and the vacuoles and their intact membranes move through the cytoplasm to become free (Svihla *et al.,* 1961). These spherical structures are relatively stable in $0.6\ M$ KCl plus $0.04\ M$ phosphate and have remained intact for more than 28 hours. Emerson and Emerson (1958) have observed a similar effect with *N. crassa* protoplasts, the discharged vacuoles increasing in diameter without bursting. Membranes of liberated vacuoles show remarkable elasticity when pressed with a glass needle. These interesting findings suggest an appropriate way for the preparation of vacuoles.

VII. PHYSIOLOGY AND BIOCHEMISTRY OF PROTOPLASTS

The extensive literature on bacterial protoplasts, excellently reviewed by McQuillen (1960) and Martin (1963), should stimulate progress in the physiology and biochemistry of fungal protoplasts. So far, protoplasts of fungi (mostly yeast) have proved to be of great value for metabolic studies, mainly those related to sugar transport. Little work has been done on the ability of fungal protoplasts to synthesize constitutive and inducible enzymes, but there is no doubt that protoplasts can make proteins, lipids, nucleic acids and various other compounds as rapidly as can intact living cells.

A. Growth of Protoplasts

Eddy and Williamson (1957, 1959) first described the growth and formation of abnormal forms in yeast protoplasts. When yeast protoplasts are placed in an adequate growth medium, under stabilized conditions, the spherical bodies grow, increasing in DNA and RNA, but do not divide (Tabata *et al.,* 1965). The type of substance used for stabilization of the protoplast may influence growth. Sodium chloride interfered with increase of cellular material, while growth took place in KCl, mannitol, sorbitol, or

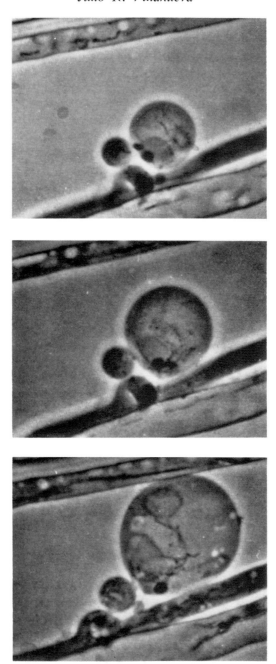

FIG. 12. Growth of *Polystictus versicolor* protoplasts. Interval between the first and last, 17 minutes. Sometimes fusion of protoplasts is observed. Note the direct connection between two protoplasts. Courtesy of Dr. C. Strunk.

rhamnose. Protoplasts of *S. carlsbergensis* begin to show growth when suspended in a medium containing glucose, yeast extract and 0.6 M KCl. The spherical shape of the protoplast changes, the total volume of the cell increases manyfold, and a variety of forms are assumed (Holter and Ottolenghi, 1960; Rost and Venner, 1965). Although regeneration to form new cell walls and normal cells has been demonstrated (Gascón *et al.,* 1965b; Necas, 1956, 1962), some cells died.

Growth of yeast protoplasts was followed during antibiotic inhibition experiments by Shockman and Lampen (1962). In media containing 10^7 protoplasts per milliliter, growth started after 1 hour and large abnormal masses, very similar to those described by other workers, appeared (Eddy and Williamson, 1959). Vigorous shaking gave rise to marked disruption of the cells and halted growth. The vitamins required for growth were exactly the same as those needed by intact cells. Growth was measured by turbidity changes using the 660 mµ filter in the Klett photometer, but the method was only qualitative because of the large aberrant structures present. Growth also was determined from the increase in total nitrogen. Using the aforementioned inoculum, cell nitrogen increased four- to eightfold in 1 day. Increases of twelve- to twentyfold were observed when a smaller inoculum was employed (2×10^6 per milliliter). The effect of various stabilizers on growth was studied, and it was found that replacement of 0.6 M KCl by 0.8 M mannitol or 1.0 M sorbitol did not alter protoplast growth. However, although initial enlargement of the protoplasts occurred when the stabilizer was 0.6 M NaCl, growth stopped after several hours.

The ability to grow of protoplasts obtained from filamentous fungi also has been observed (Bachmann and Bonner, 1959; Emerson and Emerson, 1958). However, growth of hyphal protoplasts soon results in regeneration with the ultimate formation of normal mycelium. No growth was ever observed in conidial protoplasts of *F. culmorum*. Instead the first result of incubation in the growth medium is the formation of the germ tube, and this is followed by the development of more or less normal hyphae.

Growth of protoplasts has been observed as the consequence of the incorporation (or fusion) of several cytoplasmic units (Fig. 12). This phenomenon has been reported for *Polystictus versicolor* by microcinematography (Strunk, 1966). We have also seen a similar phenomenon in *Fusarium* protoplasts (López-Belmonte *et al.,* 1966). Protoplast fusion in *F. culmorum* usually occurs between two bodies which seem to be connected by a thin filament. The frequency of the fusion was very low and the spherical forms produced in this process have not been seen to develop further.

B. Spore Formation

Eddy and Williamson (1959) were the first to describe conditions which induce protoplasts of *S. carlsbergensis* to form spores from which normal cells may arise on germination. The finding of these resistant structures was considered for some time to provide an intermediate stage in protoplast regeneration reported by Necas (1956), who found regenerated yeast cells to differ both among themselves and from the parent strain. This finding was considered by Eddy and Williamson support for the possibility that regenerated cells originate from different spore segregants.

Spores were obtained from protoplasts of *S. carlsbergensis* (Holter and Ottolenghi, 1960) when incubated in glucose-yeast extract containing 0.6 *M* KCl. Formation of spores started 14 hours after incubation in a starvation medium containing sorbitol and phosphate. After 3 days the spores were mature and present in large numbers, including 1–7 spores per cell. The fully formed spores are resistant to hypotonic conditions but will burst during the early stages of formation. Similar studies carried out with *Schizosaccharomyces pombe* of opposite mating types failed. Spore formation in this organism took place only if the yeast cells were allowed to form zygotes before the cell walls were digested with the snail enzyme.

C. Respiration of Protoplasts

Yeast protoplasts prepared from *S. cerevisiae* using lytic enzymes of *Streptomyces albidoflavus* have recently been used for respiration studies (Tabata et al., 1965). When the digestion of the cell wall was carried out in a balanced solution, no remarkable change in respiratory or fermentative activities was detected. The results suggest that the resistance of yeast cell walls to the penetration of dissolved oxygen does not affect the respiration rate of intact cells. The rate of change of oxygen consumption was also found to follow the same pattern in normal cells and protoplasts of *S. carlsbergensis* (Holter and Ottolenghi, 1960). Respiratory activity as well as growth are affected by the high osmolarity of the suspension medium (Ottolenghi and Lillehoj, 1966), but there is no great difference between protoplasts and intact cells grown in KCl or in sorbitol. Protoplasts and intact mycelium of *F. culmorum* were found to have fairly similar respiratory activities (Garcia Acha and López-Belmonte, 1966). Lysis of the protoplasts resulted in partial loss of activity. Marini et al. (1961) have used protoplasts of *S. cerevisiae* for studies of respiration during investigations of mode of action of nystatin.

D. Permeability of Protoplasts

A number of observations indicate that the permeability of fungal protoplasts is probably not too different from those of intact cells (Holter and Ottolenghi, 1960). When intact cells of *Saccharomyces* are impermeable to some sugars, such as sucrose and melibiose, their protoplasts retain this property. Succinate, which does not increase the oxygen uptake of intact yeast, is just as ineffective in protoplasts. It is assumed that the cell membrane acts as a barrier through which sucrose, melibiose and other substances are not free to pass. The efficiency of the membranes as a barrier depends presumably on the fungus. Heredia *et al.* (1963) studied the entry of glucose, fructose, and mannose in *S. cerevisiae* protoplasts and found that penetration may be catalyzed by a constitutive transport system common to the three sugars. The efficiency of such transport is much higher than penetration by simple diffusion (Cirillo, 1966).

Nystatin produces an alteration of cellular permeability with subsequent leakage of internal constituents. Yeast protoplasts have proved useful for the investigation of this phenomenon (Marini *et al.*, 1961).

Necas (1958) and Schlenk and Dainko (1966) investigated the penetration of ribonuclease into living yeast cells by comparing the action of ribonuclease on intact living yeast cells with that on protoplasts. While ribonuclease does not penetrate into intact cells, naked protoplasts are partially permeable to it although penetration is very slow. The stage of formation of the protoplasts may affect the penetration of the enzyme.

E. The Use of Protoplasts to Study Localization of Enzymes

Friis and Ottolenghi (1959) using protoplasts of a hybrid *Saccharomyces,* containing a single R_2 gene for invertase, showed that sucrose-adapted cells, released more than 74% of their invertase activity. Sutton and Lampen (1962) using *S. cerevisiae* proved that the isolated cell walls contain large amounts of β-fructosidase and that the protoplasts failed to ferment sucrose while still fermenting glucose. These workers found that protoplasts synthesized invertase but the enzyme was released to the surrounding medium (Islam and Lampen, 1962) and the secreted enzyme is very similar to that obtained by disruption of intact cells. On the other hand, Burger *et al.* (1961) believe that β-fructofuranosidase is in a soluble form *in vivo* and is located in a compartment outside the cell membrane.

Metzenberg (1963), using *Neurospora crassa* conidia, presented evidence that invertase is outside the cell membrane, but that most of it is interior to another barrier, probably the cell wall. Further studies (Metzenberg, 1964) have shown that the invertase can exist in two active forms "light" and "heavy." Protoplasts of *Neurospora,* like yeast protoplasts, secrete invertase. Trevithick and Metzenberg (1964) showed that the enzyme which predominates inside the protoplasts, and the form secreted by them, is the heavy form. More recently Sentandreu *et al.* (1966) have confirmed some of the previous results working with *Candida utilis* protoplasts.

Melibiase also appears to be associated with the cell wall. Friis and Ottolenghi (1959) demonstrated complete lack of melibiose-fermenting ability in protoplasts of *Saccharomyces cerevisiae,* although melibiase could be detected in intact cells.

The localization of some phosphatases has been studied in yeast cells after removal of the wall by the use of lytic enzymes. Yeast protoplasts are capable of synthesizing acid phosphatase, and, in the absence of the cell wall, this newly formed phosphatase is released into the medium (McLellan and Lampen, 1963). In contrast to *Escherichia coli* phosphatases, this alkaline phosphatase is internal. Tonino and Steyn-Parvé (1963) studied localization of phosphatases in *S. carlsbergensis* either by breaking intact cells or by osmotic shock of protoplasts. Acid phosphatase is located in the wall of the yeast cell, although situated in two different areas of that structure.

F. Protein (and Enzyme) Synthesis

During studies on protein synthesis by yeast, De Kloet *et al.* (1961) found that protein synthesis by protoplasts of *S. carlsbergensis* was strongly inhibited by ribonuclease (as previously reported in bacteria). The cause of that inhibition can be attributed in a great part to the marked inhibition of respiration. Amino acid uptake was found to be inhibited by 75%, and glycolysis by 50%. Amino acid incorporation by naked protoplasts is strongly inhibited after RNase treatment. Adaptive enzyme synthesis was likewise inhibited by preincubation of the protoplasts with RNase. Cell-free systems capable of incorporating amino acids into protein have proved more difficult to obtain from yeast than from bacteria or mammalian tissues (Cooper and Millin, 1964). In further studies part of the observed inhibition of protein synthesis was attributed to the action of ribonuclease on the yeast cell membrane (De Kloet *et al.,* 1962). Moreover a nucleopeptide-containing preparation was obtained from naked protoplasts which acted as a repressor of induced enzyme synthesis (van Dam *et al.,* 1964). Studies made with fluorescent proteins in *S. carlsbergensis* protoplasts suggested that the protoplasts are not capable of taking up extracellular proteins (Holter and Ottolenghi, 1960).

G. Studies on Mode of Action of Antibiotics

The growth of fungi is very sensitive to a number of antibiotics such as nystatin, amphotericin B, griseofulvin, filipin, Actidione, pimaricin, viridin. Direct evidence for an interaction between polyene antibiotics and membranes has been provided from studies with protoplasts and isolated membrane fractions (Kinsky, 1962a,b; Lampen *et al.,* 1962). This interaction appears to involve sterols of the membrane. A comparative study of three polyenes using fungal protoplasts (Cirillo *et al.,* 1964) suggests that the effects are related to the degree of physical damage to the cell membrane. Filipin destroys the structural integrity of the membrane of protoplasts whereas nystatin is less effective in this respect. The fungal wall does not protect against the polyene antibiotics (Shockman and Lampen, 1962).

The conclusion has been reached that all the polyene antibiotics have an identical mode of action since all induce atrophy in the mycelium of *Neurospora* and shrinkage of the protoplasts (Kinsky, 1962a). In the case of filipin, protoplast shrinkage was rapidly followed by swelling and lysis. It was suggested that the antibiotic causes extensive cell membrane damage. The absence of any polyene binding by bacterial protoplasts indicates that the selective toxicity of these agents is probably due to the existence of a unique binding component in the membranes of sensitive fungi.

VIII. CONJUGATION BETWEEN PROTOPLASTS

In the course of the more than eight years since protoplasts of yeast and filamentous fungi have been described, only a few studies were made on their artificial hybridization. Holter and Ottolenghi (1960) failed to obtain conjugation and spore formation by mixing protoplasts from two haploid strains of opposite mating types.

Various organisms, chiefly *Hansenula wingei,* have been used during recent years in studies of the physiology of the conjugation process, or cell fusion (Brock, 1961). Apparently the process takes place by a softening of the cell wall followed by formation of a conjugation tube, dissolution of the cross walls, and formation of a new bud at the region of contact of the two mating types. Electron microscopic studies of this process have recently been published (Conti and Brock, 1965). Some organisms are able to conjugate not only by the mating of vegetative cells, but by fusion of a vegetative cell and an ascospore, or by the fusion of two types of ascospores (Suminae and Dukmo, 1963). It remains to be seen whether protoplasts from such cells are able to conjugate.

Protoplasts of *Polystictus versicolor* (Strunk, 1966) and of *Fusarium culmorum* (Lopez-Belmonte *et al.,* 1966) fuse under appropriate conditions. Two or more of these protoplasts coalesce to form a larger sphere. It is not known whether this is a true conjugation process.

A possible explanation of the inability to obtain conjugation in *Saccharomyces* protoplasts is the finding by Brock (1959) that a protein of one strain and a wall polysaccharide of the opposite strain are needed for mating. The two mating (and at the same time, agglutination) components are complementary and are probably held together by hydrogen bonds. If either or both specific complementary mating components are to be found in the cell walls, mating reactions should not be expected between two opposite types of wall-less protoplasts.

IX. REVERSION OF PROTOPLASTS

A. *The Phenomenon of Regeneration in Fungal Protoplasts*

Naked protoplasts of fungi on incubation under appropriate conditions are capable of forming new normal cells. The spherical forms preserve most of the synthetic abilities of the normal cells from which they are derived, including the ability to make a new cell wall, with the characteristic structural and functional properties. Since the regeneration process in most fungal protoplasts takes place very slowly, it is possible to follow the individual stages of the biosynthesis of the new wall. Chemical and electron microscopic studies provided some basis for the understanding of the biosynthetic process.

1. *In Yeast Cells*

Necas (1956) first demonstrated a method of preparing stable protoplasts of *Saccharomyces cerevisiae* and described their reversion to normal cells. The formation of new wall material has been reported also by Eddy and Williamson (1959), and some excellent physiological and cytological studies by Necas (1965).

Eddy and Williamson (1959) incubated protoplasts of *S. carlsbergensis* in a series of nutrient media supplemented with an appropriate stabilizer. Observation of the bodies under the microscope revealed a sequence of striking changes in morphology. They were easily burst by dilution, and the membranes could be recovered by centrifugation. The chemical analysis of these structures showed a marked deficiency in amino acids, most of the nitrogen being accounted for as N-acetylglucosamine. The abnormal walls were thought to represent part of the cell wall in which protein was practically absent. These workers were unable to produce normal cells from the regenerated naked protoplasts. This was in marked contrast to Necas' (1956) results (i.e., 100% regeneration). He found direct development of yeast cells from protoplast-like bodies obtained from autolyzing cells. The total dissolution of walls by the autolytic systems, and the microscopic appearance of the structures resulting from digestion of intact cells, make it probable that true protoplasts were formed (Necas, 1965).

Chemical, immunological, and morphological analyses of regenerating protoplasts are needed to determine whether there is a gradual recovery of the ability to synthesize walls. As in bacteria (McQuillen, 1960), there is always the possibility that a small proportion of yeast cells (although bursting on dilution) retain remnants of wall material after lytic enzyme action. These may be the ones which subsequently regenerate, and it might be suggested that reversion can occur only when a trace of original wall material is still present.

Necas (1965) and Villanueva *et al.* (1966) have claimed, from electron micrographs, the total absence of cell wall remnants attached to the cytoplasmic membrane of the protoplasts. A number of cytoplasmic membranes obtained under controlled lysis of fungal protoplasts (Garcia Mendoza and Villanueva, 1964) showed very clean almost transparent preparations (Fig. 11). However, in our experience it is difficult to ascertain by electron microscopy when fungal protoplasts still possess some islets of polysaccharide-protein fragments, adhering to their protoplast membranes, from which the resynthesis of a rigid wall structure could start. Alternatively, the possibility cannot be excluded that regeneration occurs through an intermediate stage (Eddy and Williamson, 1959) with the formation of spores. Necas (1955) has described the regeneration of cells from "plasmatic elements" which grow in irregular vacuolated formations and divide to form a microscopically visible colony. When fully developed, they usually contain a number of nuclei. When reinoculated into fresh media, this abnormal colony continues to grow. Some of these plasmatic elements split off a number of tiny droplets which can reproduce by budding. The new cells formed by budding look very little like yeasts, but in later generations cells arise which correspond to the yeast cell in size and form, and which can easily be isolated. There is great variability in morphological and biochemical properties of the regenerated cells (Necas, 1956). These observations show that cell fragments can regenerate new cells even among ascomycetes. Regeneration studies with plasma droplets of other fungi have not been reported.

Holter and Ottolenghi (1960) and Takada and Yamamoto (1960) using protoplasts of yeast have confirmed the findings of Necas on regeneration. The Danish workers, however, observed regeneration of normal cells from protoplasts only in extremely rare cases. Recent reports by Necas (1962, 1965) suggest that physical factors determine the extent of regeneration of yeast protoplasts. Complete regeneration of spherical bodies takes place when cells are cultivated in the presence of gelatin (15–40%), and occasionally regeneration occurs on solid medium containing 2–5% agar. Regeneration depends not on the gelatin concentration, but on the degree of viscosity of the gel. The rate of regeneration depends on the gelatin concentration at a given temperature. Impurities in the gelatin were not involved, since hydrolyzed gelatin does not induce the process. On the basis of these results the author claims that the low rate of regeneration found in previous experiments (Necas, 1956; Holter and Ottolenghi, 1960) was due to inappropriate conditions of the regenerating media. In our laboratory, regeneration of new cells has been detected in protoplasts of *Candida*

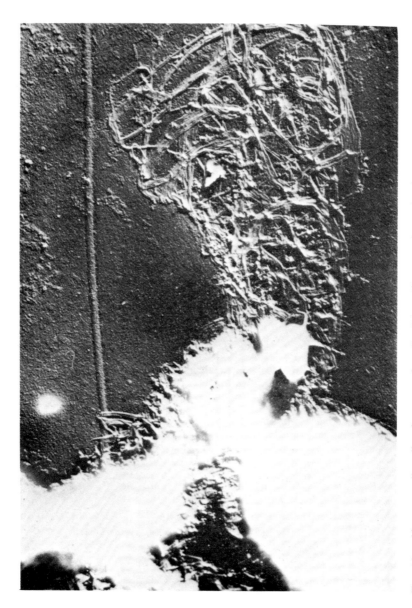

FIG. 13. Aberrant cell walls of regenerating *Candida utilis* protoplasts showing formation of glucan fibers. Shadowed electron micrograph. Magnification: × 29,600.

utilis, a yeast which does not form spores. Regeneration was obtained in liquid medium with 1 M MgSO$_4$ as stabilizer in the complete absence of gelatin or equivalent substance (Elorza, 1966). The complete process of regeneration was followed by phase contrast and electron microscopy. Formation of glucan fibers during the first stages of cell wall formation as described by Necas (1965) has been found (Fig. 13), the cementing substance (possibly the mannan complex) appearing at a later stage.

2. *In Filamentous Fungi*

Regeneration of protoplasts has also been described in filamentous fungi. Once protoplasts have been transferred to a growth medium with the stabilizer, they revert to typical mycelial growth. The type of growth and regeneration found vary with the osmotic strength of the medium and the cultural conditions under which they develop. Emerson and Emerson (1958) first

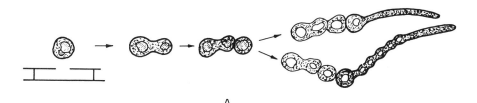

A

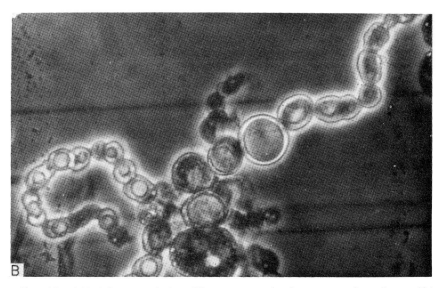

FIG. 14. (A) Diagram of the different stages in the regeneration of mycelial protoplasts of *Fusarium culmorum*. (B) Phase contrast micrograph of regenerating *Fusarium* protoplasts. Magnification: × 8000.

described regeneration from *Neurospora* protoplasts with the formation of hyphae, or a considerable amount of parenchymatous tissue. Using individual protoplasts of *N. crassa* on solid defined medium, Bachmann and Bonner (1959) found great variation in the process of regeneration.

Protoplasts derived from hyphae of *Fusarium culmorum* have been incubated in a growth medium, and regeneration has been followed microscopically (Fig. 15). Best regeneration takes place in a medium containing sorbose (10%), sucrose (2%), and mineral salts. The addition of agar (0.2%) seems to affect markedly the regenerative ability of the spherical structures. After 4 hours the majority begin to increase in volume and form a vacuole and a protuberance (bud). As incubation continues the proportion of buds increases (Fig. 14 A, B). These are still osmotically sensitive

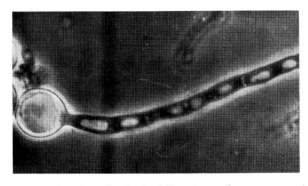

FIG. 15. Regeneration (germination) of *Fusarium culmorum* protoplasts. Magnification: × 7000.

and on dilution burst to leave some kind of ghost. The buds ultimately become germ tubes capable of normal growth, forming hyphae with septa. Production of conidia was also observed in the regenerated forms. On continued incubation most of the original spheres die. In most cases, normal hyphae were formed through production of convoluted figures similar to those reported in *Neurospora* by Bachmann and Bonner (1959).

Attempts have been made to see whether protoplasts of *F. culmorum* will revert to mycelial form on solid media. Washed protoplasts were inoculated on semisolid gelatin media (10–30%) containing various supplements. Upon incubation some individual spheres increased in size and produced a kind of pseudomycelium, and at a later stage normal hyphae.

Strunk (1966) has studied the regeneration process of *Polystictus versicolor* protoplasts. Sometimes the protoplasts were seen to revert directly to normal hyphae with rapid formation of a clamp.

B. Regeneration of Spore "Protoplasts"

Regeneration of conidial "protoplasts" from *Fusarium culmorum* has been investigated in our laboratory. During regeneration a highly refractile layer, similar to that described in *Neurospora* protoplasts, appears around the "protoplasts." The germ tube arises directly from the "protoplasts" and is not sensitive to osmotic shock. Occasionally there forms a pseudomycelium similar to that described in the regeneration of mycelial protoplasts.

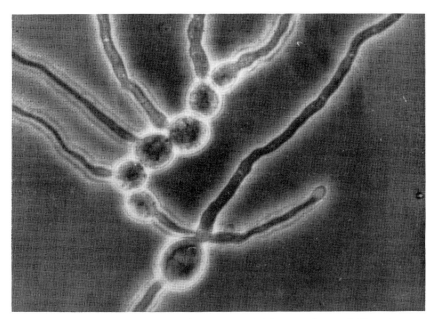

FIG. 16. Regeneration (germination) of conidial protoplasts of *Fusarium culmorum*. Magnification: × 7000.

In general, conditions required for regenerations are the same as those needed for the germination of intact spores. When the "protoplasts" were washed with the stabilizing solution and plated in an appropriate medium it was found that nearly 100% were able to regenerate and to give rise to the formation of normal mycelium (Figs. 14 and 16). These results are in contrast with those for mycelial protoplasts, where regeneration takes place to a lesser degree (50–75%).

Bachmann and Bonner (1959) followed the regenerative process in *N. crassa* "protoplasts" in moist chambers and found that although some of the "protoplasts" give rise to normal hyphae some spherical forms produce convoluted figures which may or may not form normal hyphae.

C. The Synthesis of the Cell Wall Materials

Electron microscopic studies on sections of *Polystictus versicolor* protoplasts placed in regeneration conditions have shown a number of vesicles on the membrane and traces of dense structures (Fig. 17). The appearance of the outer layers of regenerating protoplasts clearly differs from that of

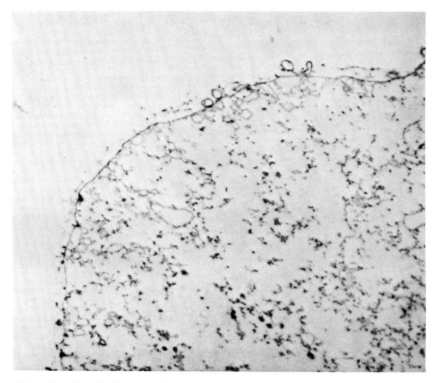

FIG. 17. Detail of an ultrathin section of a regenerating protoplast of *Polystictus versicolor*. Note the vesicles on the surface and the traces of dense newly formed particles. Magnification: × 16,500. Courtesy of Dr. C. Strunk.

recently formed naked protoplasts (Fig. 7). These vesicles are probably responsible for wall synthesis, perhaps as carriers of enzymes or precursors (Strunk, 1966). Vesicles very similar to those detected outside of the cytoplasmic membrane were also observed in the inner part of the cytoplasm surrounding the plasmalemma. It is possible that these vesicles are formed in the Golgi apparatus, which has been suggested to have a secretory role in the formation of yeast wall macromolecules (Northcote, 1963a,b). That clusters of particles on the cytoplasmic membranes are involved in production of the glucan fibrils of the wall of yeast cells has been suggested by Moor and Mühlethaler (1963) as the result of electron microscopic studies of freeze-etched yeast cells. A similar theory has been proposed for the secretion of invertase through the membrane to the outside medium (Lampen, 1965). The excretion of the vesicles (containing wall components or the appropriate enzymes) might be effected by reverse pinocytosis as suggested for invertase.

Algranati *et al.* (1963), using a particulate fraction obtained by centrifugation of a protoplast lysate of *Saccharomyces carlsbergensis,* showed that the cell membrane was the site of synthesis of yeast mannan. That chitin synthetase activity takes place in a particulate fraction that might be localized in particles derived from the cell membrane is suggested by Kinsky (1962a).

ACKNOWLEDGMENTS

It is a pleasure to acknowledge the assistance of my collaborators in kindly providing for this review information that would otherwise have been unavailable. The author is grateful to Dr. Christian Strunk of the Institute for Microbiology, Jena, for information and permission to quote unpublished results. He also wishes to thank Dr. E. T. Reese of the U.S. Quartermaster Corps Research Laboratories, for linguistic improvements of the manuscript and for much helpful discussion.

Much of this research was supported by a grant from the Ministerio de Educacion Nacional of Spain.

REFERENCES

Agar, H. D., and H. C. Douglas. (1957). *J. Bacteriol.* 73:365-375.
Algranati, I. D., H. Carminatti, and E. Cabid. (1963). *Biochem. Biophys. Res. Commun.* 12:504-509.
Anderson, F. B. (1966). *In* "Symposium über Hefe-Protoplasten Jena 1965" (R. Müller, ed.). Akademie Verlag, Berlin.
Arima, K., T. Uozumi, and M. Takahashi. (1965). *Agr. Biol. Chem.* 29:1033-1041.
Bachmann, B. J., and D. M. Bonner. (1959). *J. Bacteriol.* 78:550-556.
Bacon, J. S. D., B. D. Milne, I. F. Taylor, and D. M. Webley. (1965). *Biochem. J.* 95:28c.
Bartnicki-Garcia, S., and W. J. Nickerson. (1962). *Biochim. Biophys. Acta* 58:102-119.
Baumann-Grace, J. B., and J. Tomcsik. (1957). *J. Gen. Microbiol.* 17:227-237.
Bent, K. J., and R. H. Moore. (1966). *In* "Biochemical Studies of Antimicrobial Drugs" (B. A. Newton and P. E. Reynolds, eds.), p. 102. Cambridge Univ. Press, London and New York.
Borodulina, U. C. (1935). *Mikrobiologiya* 4:561-586.
Boulton, A. A. (1965). *Exptl. Cell Res.* 37:343.
Boulton, A. A., and A. A. Eddy. (1962). *Biochem. J.* 82:16 P.
Brenner, S., F. A. Dark, P. Gerhardt, M. H. Jeynes, O. Kandler, E. Kellenberger, E. Klieneberger-Nobel, K. McQuillen, M. Rubio-Huertos, M. R. J. Salton, R. E. Strange, J. Tomcsik, and C. Weibull. (1958). *Nature* 181:1713.
Brian, P. W. (1960). *Brit. Mycol. Soc. Trans.* 43:1-13.

Brock, T. D. (1959). *J. Bacteriol.* **78**:59-68.
Brock, T. D. (1961). *J. Gen. Microbiol.* **26**:487-497.
Burger, M., E. L. Bacon, and S. S. Bacon. (1961). *Biochem. J.* **78**:504-511.
Carter, H. P., and J. L. Lockwood. (1957). *Phytopathology* **47**:151-154.
Chinn, S. H. F. (1959). *Can. J. Botany* **31**:718-724.
Cirillo, V. P. (1966). *In* "Symposium über Hefe-Protoplasten Jena 1965" (R. Müller, ed.). Akademie Verlag, Berlin.
Cirillo, V. P., M. Harsch, and J. O. Lampen. (1964). *J. Gen. Microbiol.* **35**:249-259.
Cocking, E. C. (1960). *Nature* **187**:927-929.
Cocking, E. C. (1961). *Nature* **191**:780-782.
Cocking, E. C. (1963). *J. Exptl. Botany* **14**:504-511.
Cocking, E. C. (1965). *In* "Viewpoints in Biology" (J. D. Carthy and C. L. Duddington, eds.), Vol. 4, p. 170. Butterworths, London.
Conti, S. F., and T. D. Brock. (1965). *J. Bacteriol.* **90**:524-533.
Cooper, A. H., and D. J. Millin. (1964). *Biochem. J.* **92**:61 P.
Crook, E. M., and I. R. Johnston. (1962). *Biochem. J.* **83**:325-331.
Davies, R., and P. A. Elvin. (1964). *Biochem. J.* **93**:8 P.
Dekker, J. (1963). *Ann. Rev. Microbiol.* **17**:243-262.
De Kloet, S. R., R. K. A. van Wermeskerken, and V. V. Koningsberger. (1961). *Biochim. Biophys. Acta* **47**:138-148.
De Kloet, S. R., G. J. W. van Dam, and V. V. Koningsberger. (1962). *Biochim. Biophys. Acta* **55**:683-689.
de Terra, N., and E. L. Tatum. (1961). *Science* **134**:1066-1068.
Duell, E. A., S. Inoue, and M. F. Utter. (1964). *J. Bacteriol.* **88**:1762-1773.
Dunwell, J. L., F. Almad, and A. N. Rose. (1961). *Biochim. Biophys. Acta* **51**:604-607.
Eddy, A. A. (1958a). *Proc. Roy. Soc.* **B149**:425-440.
Eddy, A. A. (1958b). *Biochem. J.* **69**:47 P.
Eddy, A. A., and D. H. Williamson. (1957). *Nature* **179**:1252-1253.
Eddy, A. A., and D. H. Williamson. (1959). *Nature* **183**:1101-1104.
Elbers, P. F. (1961). *Nature* **191**:1022-1023.
Elorza, M. V. (1966). Enzimas líticos del *Streptomyces MR*. Obtención y reversión de protoplastos de levaduras. Ph.D. Thesis, Univ. of Madrid.
Emerson, S., and M. R. Emerson. (1958). *Proc. Natl. Acad. Sci. U.S.* **44**:668-671.
Fitz-James, P. C. (1960). *J. Biophys. Biochem. Cytol.* **8**:507-512.
Foster, J. W. (1949). "Chemical Activities of Fungi," 648 pp. Academic Press, New York.
Frey, R. (1950). *Ber. Schweiz. Botan. Ges.* **60**:199-206.
Friis, J., and P. Ottolenghi. (1959). *Compt. Rend. Trav. Lav. Carlsberg* **31**:259-271.
Furuya, A., and Y. Ikeda. (1960). *J. Gen. Appl. Microbiol. (Tokyo)* **6**:40-47.
Gale, G. R. (1955). *J. Infect. Diseases* **96**:250-255.
Garcia Acha, I., and F. López-Belmonte. (1966). Unpublished observations.
Garcia Acha, I., and J. R. Villanueva. (1963a). *Can. J. Microbiol.* **9**:139-141.
Garcia Acha, I., and J. R. Villanueva. (1963b). *Nature* **200**:1231.
Garcia Acha, I., M. J. Rodriguez Aguirre, and J. R. Villanueva. (1963). *Microbiol. Espan.* **16**:141-148.
Garcia Acha, I., M. J. Rodriguez Aguirre, and J. R. Villanueva. (1964). *Can. J. Microbiol.* **10**:99-101.
Garcia Acha, I., J. A. Leal, and J. R. Villanueva. (1965). *Phytopathology* **55**:40-42.

Garcia Acha, I., M. J. Rodriguez Aguirre, F. López-Belmonte, and J. R. Villanueva. (1966). *Nature* **209**:95-96.
Garcia Mendoza, C., and J. R. Villanueva. (1962). *Nature* **195**:1326-1327.
Garcia Mendoza, C., and J. R. Villanueva. (1964a). *Nature* **202**:1241-1242.
Garcia Mendoza, C., and J. R. Villanueva. (1964b). *Can. J. Microbiol.* **9**:900-902.
Garcia Mendoza, C., and J. R. Villanueva. (1965). *Proc. 2nd Meeting Federation European Biochem. Soc., Vienna, 1965* p. 122.
Garcia Ochoa, A. (1965). Degradación de paredes celulares de levaduras por enzimas líticos. Ph.D. thesis, University of Madrid.
Gascón, S., and J. R. Villanueva. (1963a). *Can. J. Microbiol.* **9**:651-652.
Gascón, S., and J. R. Villanueva. (1963b). *Nature* **198**:911-912.
Gascón, S., and J. R. Villanueva. (1965). *Nature* **205**:822-823.
Gascón, S., A. G. Ochoa, M. Novaes, and J. R. Villanueva. (1965a). *Arch. Mikrobiol.* **51**:156-167.
Gascón, S., A. G. Ochoa, and J. R. Villanueva. (1965b). *Can. J. Microbiol.* **11**:573-580.
Gasperini, G. (1890). *Ann. Microgr.* **2**:449-474.
Gattani, M. L. (1952). *Phytopathology* **42**:70-71.
Giaja, J. (1922). *Comt. Rend. Soc. Biol.* **86**:708-713.
Girbardt, M., and Ch. Strunk. (1965). Personal communication.
Hamilton, J. G., and J. Calvet. (1964). *J. Bacteriol.* **88**:1084-1086.
Haskins, R. H., and J. F. T. Spencer. (1962). *Can. J. Microbiol.* **8**:279-281.
Heick, H. M. C., and H. B. Stewart. (1965). *Can. J. Biochem.* **43**:561-571.
Heredia, C., G. de la Fuente, and A. Sols. (1963). Atti delle VII Giornate Biochimiche Latine. S. Margherita Ligure (Génova), p. 86.
Heyman-Blanchet, T., F. Zajdela, and P. Chaix. (1959). *Biochim. Biophys. Acta* **36**:569-570.
Hickman, C. J. (1965). *In* "The Fungi" (G. C. Ainsworth and A. S. Sussman, eds.), Vol. I, Chapter 2. Academic Press, New York.
Holden, M., and M. V. Tracey. (1950). *Biochem. J.* **47**:407-414.
Holter, H., and P. Ottolenghi. (1960). *Comt. Rend. Trav. Lab. Carlsberg* **31**:409-422.
Horikoshi, K., and S. Ida. (1959). *Nature* **183**:186-187.
Horikoshi, K., and H. Koffler. (1963). *Biochim. Biophys. Acta* **73**:268-275.
Horikoshi, K., H. Koffler, and H. R Garner. (1961). *Bacteriol. Proc.* p. 95.
Horikoshi, K., and K. Sakaguchi. (1958). *J. Gen. Appl. Microbiol. (Tokyo)* **4**:1-11.
Islam, M. F., and J. O. Lampen. (1962). *Biochim. Biophys. Acta* **58**:294-302.
Johnston, J. R. (1965). *Biochem. J.* **96**:651-658.
Johnston, J. R., and R. K. Mortimer. (1959). *J. Bacteriol.* **78**:282-292.
Kessler, G., and W. J. Nickerson. (1959). *J. Biol. Chem.* **234**:2281-2285.
Kinsky, S. C. (1961). *J. Bacteriol.* **86**:889-897.
Kinsky, S. C. (1962a). *J. Bacteriol.* **83**:351-358.
Kinsky, S. C. (1962b). *Proc. Natl. Acad. Sci. U.S.* **48**:1049-1056.
Kinsky, S. C. (1963). *Arch. Biochem. Biophys.* **102**:180-188.
Korn, E. D., and D. H. Northcote. (1960). *Biochem. J.* **75**:12-17.
Kreger, D. R. (1954). *Biochim. Biophys. Acta* **13**:1-9.
Lampen, J. O. (1965). *In* "The Function and Structure of Microorganisms" (M. Pollock and M. H. Richmond, eds.), Chapter 6. Cambridge Univ. Press, London and New York.
Lampen, J. O., P. M. Arnow, Z. Borowska, and A. I. Laskin. (1962). *J. Bacteriol.* **84**:1152-1160.

Laskaris, T. (1941). *Phytopathology* 31:254-263.
Leal, J. A., and J. R. Villanueva. (1962). *Science* 136:715-716.
Lee, S. (1960). *Exptl. Cell Res.* 21:252-262.
Lindegren, C. C., and Y. N. Bang. (1961). *Antonie van Leeuwenhoek, J. Microbiol. Serol.* 27:1-18.
Lloyd, A. G., R. L. Neveroske, and J. L. Lockwood. (1965). *Phytopathology* 55:871-875.
Lockwood, J. L. (1959). *Phytopathology* 49:327-331.
Lockwood, J. L. (1960). *Phytopathology* 50:787-789.
López-Belmonte, F. (1965). Unpublished observations.
López-Belmonte, F., I. Garcia Acha, and J. R. Villanueva. (1966). Observations on the protoplasts of *Fusarium culmorum* and on their fusion. *J. Gen. Microbiol.* 44:222-229.
McCarty, M. (1952). *J. Exptl. Med.* 96:555-558.
McLellan, W. L., Jr., and J. O. Lampen. (1963). *Biochim. Biophys. Acta* 67:324-326.
McQuillen, K. (1960). In "The Bacteria" (I. C. Gunsalus and R. Y. Stanier, eds.), Vol. 1, p. 249. Academic Press, New York.
Malamy, M., and B. L. Horecker. (1961). *Biochem. Biophys. Res. Commun.* 5:104-111.
Marini, F., P. M. Arnow, and J. O. Lampen. (1961). *J. Gen. Microbiol.* 24:51-62.
Martin, H. H. (1963). *J. Theoret. Biol.* 5:1-34.
Masschelein, C. A. (1959). *Rev. Ferment. Ind. Aliment.* 14:59-69.
Meinecke, G. (1960). *Nature* 188:426.
Metzenberg, R. L. (1963). *Arch. Biochem. Biophys.* 100:503-509.
Metzenberg, R. L. (1964). *Biochim. Biophys. Acta* 77:455-465.
Millbank, J. W., and R. M. Macrae. (1964). *Nature* 201:1347.
Mitchell, R., and M. Alexander. (1963). *Can. J. Microbiol.* 9:169-177.
Moor, H., and K. Mühlethaler. (1963). *J. Cell Biol.* 17:609-628.
Myers, F. L., and D. H. Northcote. (1958). *J. Exptl. Biol.* 35:639-648.
Necas, O. (1955). *Folia Biol.* (Prague) 1:220-229.
Necas, O. (1956). *Nature* 177:898.
Necas, O. (1958). *Exptl. Cell Res.* 14:216-219.
Necas, O. (1961). *Folia Biol.* (Prague) 7:202-205.
Necas, O. (1962). *Folia Biol.* (Prague) 8:256-262.
Necas, O. (1965). *Folia Biol.* (Prague) 11:97-102.
Nickerson, W. J. (1963). *Bacteriol. Rev.* 27:305-324.
Nickerson, W. J., and G. Falcone. (1956). *Science* 124:722.
Nicolas, G. (1965). Aspectos fisiologicos de algunos hongos hiperparásitos. Ph.D. thesis, University of Madrid.
Northcote, D. H. (1955). *Biochem. J.* 58:353-358.
Northcote, D. H. (1963a). *Proc. Symp. Chem. Biochem. Fungi Yeast, Dublin, 1962* p. 669. Butterworth, London and Washington, D.C.
Northcote, D. H. (1963b). *Symp. Soc. Exptl. Biol.* 17:157.
Novaes, M., and J. R. Villanueva. (1963). *Biochim. Biophys. Acta* 78:797-799.
Novaes, M., and J. R. Villanueva. (1965). *Proc. 2nd Meeting Federation European Biochem. Soc., Vienna, 1965* p. 122.
Novaes, M., S. Gascón, A. G. Ochoa, and J. R. Villanueva. (1966). *Biochim. Biophys. Acta* 115:486-488.
O'Hern, E. M., and B. S. A. Heway. (1956). *J. Bacteriol.* 72:632-645.

Ottolenghi, P., and E. B. Lillehoj. (1966). *In* "Symposium über Hefe-Protoplasten Jena 1965" (R. Müller, ed.). Akademie Verlag, Berlin.
Park, D. (1957). *Brit. Mycol. Soc. Trans.* **40**:283-291.
Park, J. T. (1952). *J. Biol. Chem.* **194**:877-884.
Perkins, H. R. (1963). *Bacteriol. Rev.* **27**:18-55.
Phaff, H. J. (1963). *Ann. Rev. Microbiol.* **17**:15-30.
Phaff, H. J. (1966). *In* "Symposium über Hefe-Protoplasten Jena 1965" (R. Müller, ed.). Akademie Verlag, Berlin.
Potgieter, H. J., and M. Alexander. (1965). *Can. J. Microbiol.* **11**:122-125.
Reynolds, D. M. (1954). *J. Gen. Microbiol.* **11**:150-159.
Robertson, N. F. (1965). *Brit. Mycol. Soc. Trans.* **48**:1-8.
Robinow, C. F. (1957). *Can. J. Microbiol.* **3**:771-789.
Rodriguez Aguirre, M. J. (1965). Unpublished observations.
Rodriguez Aguirre, M. J., and J. R. Villanueva. (1962). *Nature* **196**:693-694.
Rodriguez Aguirre, M. J., I. Garcia Acha, and J. R. Villanueva. (1964). *Antonie van Leeuwenhoek, J. Microbiol. Serol.* **30**:33-44.
Romano, A. H., and A. Sohler. (1956). *J. Bacteriol.* **72**:865-868.
Rost, H., and H. Venner. (1965). *Arch. Mikrobiol.* **51**:122-129.
Russell, D. W., R. J. Sturgeon, and V. Ward. (1964). *J. Gen. Microbiol.* **36**:289-296.
Salton, M. R. J. (1955). *J. Gen. Microbiol.* **12**:25-30.
Salton, M. R. J. (1957). *Bacteriol. Rev.* **21**:82-99.
Salton, M. R. J., and R. W. Horne. (1951). *Biochim. Biophys. Acta* **7**:177-197.
Satomura, Y., M. Ono, and J. Fujumoto. (1960). *Bull. Agr. Chem. Soc. Japan* **24**:317-321.
Schlenk, F., and J. L. Dainko. (1966). *J. Bacteriol.* **89**:428-436.
Sentandreu, R. (1965). Contribución al estudio de la levadura *C. utilis* por medio de enzimas líticos. Ph.D. Thesis, University of Madrid.
Sentandreu, R., and J. R. Villanueva. (1965). *Arch. Mikrobiol.* **50**:103-110.
Sentandreu, R., F. López-Belmonte, and J. R. Villanueva. (1966). *Proc. 2nd Meeting European Federation Biochem. Soc., Vienna, 1965,* p. 28.
Shatkin, A. J., and E. L. Tatum. (1959). *J. Biophys. Biochem. Cytol.* **6**:423-426.
Shockman, G. D., and J. O. Lampen. (1962). *J. Bacteriol.* **84**:508-512.
Skujins, J. J., H. J. Potgieter, and M. Alexander. (1965). *Arch. Biochem. Biophys.* **111**:358-364.
Smithies, W. R. (1953). *Biochem. J.* **55**:345-350.
Stevenson, J. L. (1956). *J. Gen. Microbiol.* **15**:372-380.
Strunk, Ch. (1963). *Z. Allgem. Mikrobiol.* **3**:265-274.
Strunk, Ch. (1964). *Proc. 3rd Reg. Conf. (Eur.), Electron Microscopy, Prague, 1964* p. 143. Czechoslovak Academy of Sciences, Prague.
Strunk, Ch. (1966). *In* "Symposium über Hefe-Protoplasten Jena 1965" (R. Müller, ed.). Akademie Verlag, Berlin.
Strunk, Ch. (1966). Personal communication.
Suminae, K., and H. Dukmo. (1963). *J. Gen. Microbiol.* **9**:243-248.
Sutton, D. D., and J. O. Lampen. (1962). *Biochim. Biophys. Acta* **56**:303-312.
Svihla, G., F. Schlenk, and J. L. Dainko. (1961). *J. Bacteriol.* **82**:808-814.
Tabata, S., T. Imai, and G. Termi. (1965). *J. Ferment. Technol.* **43**:221-227.
Takada, M., and B. T. Yamamoto. (1960). *J. Inst. Polytech., Osaka City Univ.* **D11**:33-37.
Tanaka, H., and H. J. Phaff. (1965). *J. Bacteriol.* **89**:1570-1580.
Thornsson, K. G., and C. Weibull. (1958). *J. Ultrastruct. Res.* **1**:412-417.

Tonino, G. J. M., and E. P. Steyn-Parvé. (1963). *Biochim. Biophys. Acta* 67:453-469.
Trevithick, J. R., and R. L. Metzenberg. (1964). *Biochem. Biophys. Res. Commun.* 16:319-325.
Utter, M. F., D. B. Keech, and P. M. Nossal. (1958). *Biochem. J.* 68:431-440.
van Dam, G. J. W., J. H. Slavenburg, and V. V. Koningsberger. (1964). *Biochem. J.* 92:48 P.
Villanueva, J. R. (1966). *In* "Symposium über Hefe-Protoplasten Jena 1965" (R. Müller, ed.). Akademie Verlag, Berlin.
Villanueva, J. R., R. Sentandreu, and C. Garcia Mendoza. (1966). *In* "Symposium über Hefe-Protoplasten Jena 1965" (R. Müller, ed.). Akademie Verlag, Berlin.
Vitols, E. R., R. J. North, and A. W. Linnane. (1961). *J. Biophys. Biochem. Cytol.* 9:689-699.
Waksman, S. A. (1959). "The Actinomycetes," Vol. 1, p. 168. Bailliére, London.
Weibull, C. (1956). *In* "Bacterial Anatomy" (E. T. C. Spooner and B. A. D. Stocker, eds.), p. 111. Cambridge Univ. Press, London and New York.
Weiss, B. (1963). *J. Gen. Microbiol.* 39:85-94.
Welsch, M. (1962). *J. Gen. Physiol.* 45:115-128.
Zalokar, M. (1965). *In* "The Fungi" (G. C. Ainsworth and A. S. Sussman, eds.), Vol. I, Chapter 14. Academic Press, New York.

Cell Aggregates

CHAPTER 2

Aggregation of Unicells: Yeasts

E. O. MORRIS

Department of Applied Microbiology and Biology
University of Strathclyde
Glasgow, Scotland

I. INTRODUCTION

Yeasts are fungi to which reference is made often as though these organisms comprise a well-defined group; that this is not so is clearly indicated by Lodder and Kreger-van Rij (1952) and Lodder et al. (1958). Even those microorganisms that are accepted generally as yeasts form a heterogeneous group. Some are asporogenous, hence should be regarded as belonging to the Fungi Imperfecti. The majority of the sporogenous strains show a clear relationship to the Ascomycetes; the others are now regarded as having an affinity to the Basidiomycetes, e.g., *Sporobolomyces* and *Bulleria*. The exact taxonomic position of *Endomyces* is not yet clear. Consideration of these facts indicates the difficulties of making generalizations as to the types of mechanisms of aggregation in yeasts. The problem is complicated further since most of the published literature deals only with strains of industrial and medical importance.

The common concept of yeasts is that of discrete round to ovoid cells which reproduce by budding (Fig. 1a). This is an oversimplification since it will be seen later (Section IV, A) that even such important yeasts as the industrial strains of *Saccharomyces* do not always exist as discrete cells. Some yeasts reproduce by fission (Fig. 1b), as is indicated by the generic name *Schizosaccharomyces*. Vegetative reproductive forms, intermediate between budding and fission, are found in the sporulating genus *Saccharomycodes* and in the asporogenous genus *Pityrosporum*. Besides these simple forms of yeasts, more or less organized cell aggregates are also found in some strains. *Trichosporon* may show a primitive type of mycelium or pseudomycelium in which reproduction by budding and fission may occur at the same time; cells of the former type may be regarded as arthrospores (Fig. 1c). True mycelium may be produced by some strains of *Candida* (Fig. 1d), while many other strains of yeasts, such as *Pichia*, produce pseudomycelium (Fig. 1e). Other than the elongated cells of pseudomycelium, round to ovoid cells are found associated with the former. Some arise terminally on the elongated cells, these are known as blastospores; others arise pleurally and may be called blastoconidia. The poten-

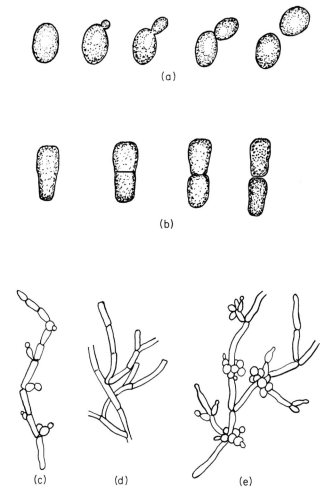

FIG. 1. Various forms of vegetative reproduction in yeasts. (a) Reproduction by budding, *Saccharomyces* sp. (b) Reproduction by fission, *Schizosaccharomyces* sp. (c) Arthrospores and blastospores, *Trichosporon* sp. (d) Mycelium, *Candida* sp. (e) Pseudomycelium and blastospores, *Candida* sp.

tial significance of these structures as taxonomic features has been discussed by Langeron and Talice (1932) and Langeron and Guerra (1938). Although the development of these structures indicate that they are spores or conidia there is little real evidence that they function in this capacity.

II. SEXUAL AGGREGATION

Some yeasts are able to reproduce sexually, and the formation of the zygote may be regarded as a special form of aggregation. There are at least five mechanisms whereby a zygote may be formed; these are discussed in some detail by Lodder and Kreger-van Rij (1952) and Ingram (1955). Briefly, the different types of conjugation are: (1) the fusion of two haploid cells with an ascus arising directly within the zygote; (2) the fusion of two haploid cells, or haploid spores, to give rise to a diploid generation of cells within which asci may develop; (3) the fusion of the contents of a bud with that of the mother cell, both being haploid, and an ascus developing within the mother cell; (4) conjugation occurs as in 3, but an ascus arises outside of the mother cell or bud; (5), two haploid cells push out germ or conjugation tubes, the latter make contact, the tips fuse, and eventually an ascus forms in one of the cells. An interesting type of conjugation has been reported for *Hansenula wingei* (Brock, 1959, 1961) in which the cells make contact; each then pushes out a short conjugation tube and a bud appears rapidly at the point of contact of the conjugation tubes. This bud may or may not remain in contact with the parent cells, and the bud may produce further buds which become detached. Herman (1961) suggests that this type of conjugation results in the production of a heterokaryotic generation.

Conjugation in yeasts may be isogamous or heterogamous. Attempts are being made to understand how the mating types of heterogamous yeasts attract each other. Brock (1959) working with *Hansenula wingei* indicates that the composition of the cell walls may differ in the two types. One type may contain a proteinlike substance, the other a polysaccharide, and the binding of the two types is by H bonds. Further, he conjectures that the specificity of the mating types may be explained on the basis of analogy with serological principles. A somewhat different view is expressed by Levi (1956), who studied conjugation in *Saccharomyces cerevisiae*. He states that only the "minus" strain produces conjugation tubes on solid medium, whereas such a mating response is shown by both types in liquid medium. He notes also that if "minus" strains are placed on sites previously occupied by "plus" strains on solid medium, mating response is stimulated; from this it is inferred that the mating response is initiated by a hormonelike substance. This is a field of study that should be explored.

III. ASEXUAL CONJUGATION

It has been stated that yeasts may produce either pseudomycelium or true mycelium. The latter may be difficult at times to differentiate from the former because of the difficulty in observing cross walls or septa, but it has been found that, on occasion, this problem may be resolved by making use of the staining techniques used to demonstrate cell walls of bacteria (Robinow, 1942; Hale, 1953).

Another difficulty is that of defining pseudomycelium. Probably the clearest definition is that proposed by Lodder and Kreger-van Rij (1952), ". . . filaments consisting of elongated cells which have arisen by budding. These may be branched."

One reason why it is important to identify the filamentous form of a yeast is that taxonomists treat this criterion as a valuable diagnostic feature. However, it should be borne in mind that other experienced workers are aware that it is unwise to rely indiscriminately on this feature. This is because the examination of a large number of strains of particular species often reveals a wide range of ability to produce this character, both in species which, according to the authentic description, do or do not produce pseudomycelium. Furthermore, it frequently happens that a culture will or will not reveal a filamentous form, depending on the conditions under which it is cultivated.

Only a limited amount of work has been directed toward elucidating the mechanisms which control the change from budding forms to filamentous forms and to the reversion of this process. This is regrettable since such information will lead to a better understanding of cell differentiation in general.

Experience in handling slide cultures has shown that aerobic or anaerobic conditions can assist the formation of pseudomycelia, depending on the particular strain being studied and the other environmental factors operating at any time. However, most reports indicate that anaerobic or partially anaerobic conditions are most favorable for this purpose (Talice, 1930; Revalier and Seydal, 1932; Wickerham and Rettger, 1939; Diddens and Lodder, 1942). Filamentous growth can be stimulated also by the use of media deficient in nutrients. This can be demonstrated easily by growing a suitable yeast on a nutrient-deficient medium: filamentous growth will eventually occur. The addition of nutrients to the medium will then result in the filamentous forms giving way to reproduction by budding. So far as nutrients are concerned, it seems that the less readily assimilated sources of carbon increase the incidence of pseudomycelia (Nickerson and Mankowski, 1953).

Pseudomycelia often develop more readily when the cultures are grown at a temperature appreciably below that required for optimal growth (Hansen, 1886; Levine and Ordal, 1946). It is known also that media on which yeasts have been grown previously will, if reinoculated, enhance the production of pseudomycelia (Connell and Skinner, 1953). It has not been established for certain whether this latter phenomenon is the result of depletion of nutrients or the release of metabolic products, or both. The serum of various animals, when incorporated into the medium, stimulates pseudomycelium formation in *Candida albicans* (Lamedica, 1959). It would be interesting to know whether such serum media will exert a similar influence on other species of yeasts.

The addition of specific chemicals to the medium may enhance the production of pseudomycelia (Bauch, 1941, 1943a,b); camphor is particularly active in this respect. It is well known also that penicillin will inhibit cell division in bacteria, hence, it is not surprising to find that the antibiotic stimulates the formation of filamentous forms in yeasts, a characteristic which may be regarded as growth wthout associated cell division. Certain metal complexes are active in this respect also and those of cobalt and boron are particularly active (Nickerson and van Rij, 1949).

It has been mentioned that the filamentous forms can revert to the budding forms under certain environmental conditions, e.g., the addition of readily assimilated nutrients to the nutrient-deficient growth medium. This reversion process has been studied by Nickerson and his co-workers. During their earlier work it was shown that media rich in sulfhydryl compounds, such as cysteine, glutathione, and sodium thioglycolate, cause reversion of the filamentous forms of *Candida albicans* to the budding form (Nickerson, 1951). Later Nickerson *et al.* (1956) reported that similar results are obtained by incorporating in the growth medium either potassium tellurite or sodium selenite. Under such conditions both a normal strain and a mutant which exists predominantly in the filamentous form reverted. A selenite-resistant strain of *C. albicans* was isolated from the filamentous mutant. This new mutant existed in the budding form both in the presence and the absence of selenite. This observation was interesting inasmuch as the filamentous parental strain was nonpathogenic whereas the mutant was pathogenic; such an observation agrees with the generally accepted opinion that pathogenic strains are usually nonfilamentous.

The behavior of *C. albicans* in the presence of tellurite and selenite is not altogether surprising bearing in mind the similar properties of tellurium, selenium, and sulfur. In a series of reports, attempts have been made to explain the action of sulfhydryl groups and tellurium and selenium compounds (Falcone and Nickerson, 1956, 1957; Nickerson and Falcone, 1956; Nickerson *et al.,* 1956). It is claimed that the cell walls contain a mannan–protein complex of high sulfur content and that the mitochondria of the cells contain a reductase capable of reducing the sulfhydryl bonds; further the filamentous mutant is deficient in the protein-sulfhydryl reductase. From a consideration of these observations, it is deduced that cell division (budding forms) results from an increased plasticity of the cell wall due to a shift to the left of the equilibrium of the SH $\rightleftharpoons$ SS reaction. To explain the action of tellurite and selenite it is postulated that these can be incorporated into the mannan-protein complex of the cell wall as reduced tellurhydryl and selenhydryl complexes. Hence, in the case of the filamentous mutant, which is deficient in the protein-sulfhydryl reductase, the stability of the -TeH and -SeH complexes offsets the enzyme deficiency. This concept was used also to explain the observation that the filamentous mutant grew in the budding form in the presence of medium deficient in sulfur compounds. Thus, it was suggested that because less sulfur was included in the cell wall, the limited supply of protein-sulfhydryl reductase in the mutant permits the provision of a relatively greater proportion of reduced sulfhydryl groups, and so the plasticity of the cell wall is increased and consequently the budding-phase predominates.

Other sulfur compounds have been found to bring about reversion from the filamentous to the budding state; particularly active is (2-aminoethyl) thiourea dihydrogen bromide (AET) (Szilvinyi, 1960). The high activity of AET, the fact that radiation induces the formation of pseudomycelium, and the fact that the animal enzyme cathepsin affords protection against radiation damage, suggests that such protection may be associated with the formation of mixed disulfides, which in the case of AET is probably connected with its conversion to N-guanidylcysteamine (Hagen and Koch, 1957; Hagen and Blumenthal, 1956; Koch and Schwartz, 1957). Such speculation can be carried further to suggest that the use of suitable yeasts may be of value in providing a convenient and rapid means of studying some of the effects of irradiation.

Although some attention has been paid to the understanding of the mechanisms involved in the formation of the elongated cells of pseudomycelia, no attention has been directed toward increasing our understanding of the mechanisms involved in the formation or function of the other structures associated with the filamentous cells, i.e., the blastospores and blastoconidia.

IV. AGGREGATION IN LIQUID MEDIA

A. Growth Characteristics

In liquid media, under ideal cultural conditions, yeasts reproduce in an orderly manner, so that the mother cell reaches maximum volume before a bud is formed and the generation time of the cells of the same age is of the same order (Lindegren and Haddad, 1954). Even though various strains of yeast may have different generation times (Townsend and Lindegren, 1953), from these facts it may be expected that the course of vegetative reproduction can be ascertained reliably; however, this is not always

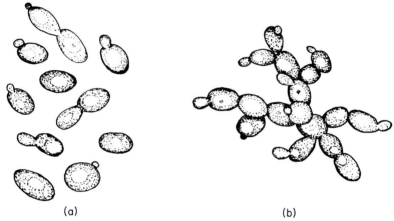

FIG. 2. Cells from liquid cultures of different strains of *Saccharomyces cerevisiae*. (a) Cells separate immediately after the daughter cell has fully developed. (b) Cells do not separate after the daughter cell has developed: microcolony.

the case. Even under ideal environmental conditions, the morphological characteristics of the cells can give rise to false estimates of cell numbers, depending on the method used to obtain such estimates. This problem can be illustrated by considering *Saccharomyces cerevisiae,* which can exist as discrete cells (Fig. 2a), or as microcolonies (Fig. 2b). The latter type arises because the intimate association of the mother and daughter cells continues for several generations (Morris and Hough, 1956).

The rather tedious method of carrying out direct cell counts under the microscope gives estimates which are reliable within the recognized limits of such procedures; such methods do not of course distinguish between total and viable cell numbers, but the use of a suitable dye permits viable counts to be made. Total nitrogen and dry-weight estimations are reasonably reliable, but inaccuracies arise because these methods depend on the assumption that all cells contain the same amount of cellular material, and clearly this does not hold true in the case of actively budding cells. Similar objections are applicable to estimates made directly by electronic devices such as the Coulter counter, which depends on cell volume. This is due to the fact that microcolonies contain cells of different sizes, hence the estimate of cell number for each colony will be based on the average cell volume. Plate counts on solid medium may yield inaccurate results because the reliability of the technique depends on the assumption that each colony arises from a single cell. In the case of dispersed yeasts, the plate count cannot allow for budding cells, and the presence of microcolonies is an obvious source of error.

Unshaken cultures of yeast, in liquid medium, will multiply regularly and rapidly during the initial stages of exponential growth, and such cellular activity will soon result in a depletion of oxygen in the medium. Under such conditions some yeasts will produce a pellicle at the air-liquid interface, e.g., *Pichia*. Pellicles are used often as a taxonomic feature. Three main types of pellicle are recognized: (1) a thick membranous type which is composed almost entirely of pseudomycelium; (2) a thin lusterless, wrinkled type which develops often soon after active growth commences; (3) a very thin, even film that usually starts as a ring around the junction of the medium and the containing vessel. It is emphasized that the placing of yeasts into these groups is subjective and that intermediate types of pellicles are not uncommonly found. Not all cells in the culture may be found in the pellicle; depending on the type of yeasts and the age of the culture, some cells may be dispersed throughout the medium or form a deposit at the bottom of the vessel. This may be taken to indicate that not all cells are in the same state, but little attention has been paid to clarifying this point. In Section IV, B it is shown that various single cell clones, derived originally from a single cell clone, may show different characteristics as a result of unequal distribution of cytoplasmic characters. The possibilities are that the differences between cells in a liquid medium may be either an expression of cytoplasmic inheritance or due to the selection of mutant strains. This may be important when considering the stability of subcultures arising from a master culture. The chances of selective subculturing can be reduced by thoroughly mixing the master culture before making the subculture.

Almost all cultures of yeast in liquid culture will produce, sooner or later, loose aggregates of cells in the form of a ring at the liquid-glass interface. In some cases a thin film of cells will creep up the side of the vessel above the medium. Since, at such sites, nutrition is limited and the supply of oxygen is plentiful, it is not surprising that spores may be plentiful. For maintenance of a stable culture, such sporulation should be kept to a minimum in order to avoid the possible consequences of segregation of characters.

B. Flocculence

It is well known that aggregation (agglutination) of bacteria occurs when these organisms are brought in contact with specific antibodies. Because of the importance of these antibody-antigen reactions, a considerable volume of literature has accumulated on this topic, but relatively little work has been concerned with this phenomenon in yeasts.

Bacteria will, on occasions, aggregate spontaneously (autoagglutination), but relatively little is known concerning the mechanisms of this reaction. The converse is true in the case of yeasts, particularly in the case of *Saccharomyces cerevisiae* and related species. This is because autoagglutination, or flocculence, is a very important factor in some fermentation industries where maladjustment of the degree of flocculence can give rise to considerable trouble.

It is important to appreciate that not all industrial strains of yeasts have the same ability to flocculate, with the consequence that one of the basic problems in some industries is that of selecting a yeast which, under the conditions employed, will flocculate at the desired stage of the process. In order to understand the problem, the course of events in brewing fermentation is outlined. A suspension of yeast is inoculated into a malt-wort, where cellular reproduction takes place; conditions at this stage are aerobic. Eventually more anaerobic conditions prevail, cellular reproduction ceases, and alcohol fermentation commences; it is at this stage that the cells of suitable brewing yeasts usually begin to show some tendency to flocculate (Eddy, 1955a; Gilliland, 1957). Depending on the type of brewing process, the cells will then predominantly rise to the surface to form a "head" (top yeasts) or sink to the bottom of the vessel to form a sludge (bottom yeasts). This is the stage when the characteristics of flocculence, if present, can be readily observed. Usually such characteristics can be demonstrated after approximately 72 hours from the time of inoculation.

It was believed originally that aggregation of the cells to form a "head" was an expression of the same phenomenon as aggregation of cells to form "flocs"; recently evidence has been presented to indicate that this is not the case. Eddy (1958a) showed that top yeasts are capable of forming a film of cells at the air-liquid interface when they have been washed and suspended in a solution of calcium chloride, whereas bottom yeasts do not form such films. Further, since both top yeasts and bottom yeasts include flocculent and nonflocculent strains, it can be inferred that "head" formation is a character distinct from flocculence.

Because of the possibility of confusing other characteristics with true flocculence, the latter has been defined as a reversible aggregation of cells to form discrete groups (Curtis and Wenham, 1958). The reversible nature of the aggregation is revealed by the ability of certain carbohydrates to disperse the cells of true flocs (Burns, 1937; Lindquist, 1953; Eddy, 1955a; Gilliland, 1957).

Attempts to understand the nature of flocculation began with the work of Kusserow (1885) and Lange (1907) following the observation of the phenomenon by Pasteur (1876). Even at the present time the problem has not been elucidated fully. It seems now that much of the work in this field of study has been concerned with factors which accentuate the phenomenon rather than with the fundamental factors which initiate the ability of yeasts to form aggregates. The early reports on this topic have been reviewed by Jansen (1958). During the last one and a half decades much relevant information has become available as a result of studies in quite diverse fields, studies which may be divided into three groups: those concerned with the effect of environment on flocculation; those concerned with genetics; and those on the nature and structure of the cell wall.

Arising from the observation that yeasts were nonflocculent when soft waters were used for brewing, but were flocculent when lime was added to the water, it was postulated that salts may influence flocculence (Seyffert, 1896). Calcium salts in particular were claimed to be active, as is evident from the reports of Hayduck and Schuckling (1908) and Schönfeld and Krumhaar (1918). As is so often the case when this problem is considered, a contrary opinion was expressed: thus Maufang (1912) claimed that magnesium was highly active and calcium of no consequence. Conclusive confirmation that calcium salts permit the appearance of flocculence was put forward by Burns (1937), who incidentally developed the first practicable method of assessing the degree of flocculence.

More recently the role of ions in general has been studied; because many of these studies have been carried out under clearly defined conditions, greater reliance can be placed on the results published. Now it is quite clear that many ions inhibit or enhance flocculation. The presence in the medium of such cations as calcium and magnesium is considered to be essential before flocculence can be revealed (Jansen and Mendlik, 1951), and the positive effect of zinc, cadmium, and ferrous ions has been reported also (Lindquist, 1953). Eddy (1955a) studied the action of cations in considerable detail and concluded that many have the ability to enhance flocculation but that there is a marked difference in response by the different strains of yeast, particularly with respect to the action of calcium. Eddy clearly showed the complexity of the problem when it was found that some yeasts flocculate in the presence of calcium ions alone whereas others will flocculate only in the presence of calcium ions and ethyl alcohol. The action of lanthanum and thorium ions is not definite, Eddy (1955a) being unable to confirm the opinion of Jansen and Mendlik (1951) that these ions enhance the expression of flocculence. Such differences of opinion are not easily explained unless they arise as a result of different experimental conditions or are again an expression of strain differences among yeasts.

Very much less attention has been paid to the action of anions, but there is evidence that carbonate, phosphate, and fluoride ions may inhibit flocculence (Lindquist, 1953). The same worker also observed that boron anions, under particular environmental conditions will inhibit flocculence, thus giving some support to the early report that boric acid has a similar effect (Laer, 1905).

It has already been indicated that the action of electrolytes was one of the first factors studied. At about the same time there were reports that carbohydrates had the ability to inhibit flocculence (Lindner, 1901), and such inhibitory action was observed by subsequent workers (Burns, 1937; Gilliland, 1951; Lindquist, 1953; Eddy, 1955a,b). During the investigations concerning the effect of carbohydrate it was revealed that not all yeasts behave similarly; e.g., in order to disperse flocs of different strains of yeasts, a fairly wide range of critical sugar concentrations is required. Further, it is evident that reproducing yeasts are nonflocculent but, when reproduction ceases, the *ability* to flocculate develops although this may not be obvious because the sugar in the culture medium will inhibit the *expression* of this characteristic. As the concentration of the sugar is reduced, as a result of fermentation, flocculence is expressed when the sugar concentration reaches a level critical for that particular strain of yeast.

Many reports concerning flocculence indicate that the pH at which various tests are made is a critical factor; also this observation suggests one of the reasons why the charge carried by the cells was considered to be a possible contributing factor. There is considerable difference of opinion as to the nature of the charge carried by the cells and its function in relation to flocculence. The technical problems involved in making measurements of the surface charge carried by cells may account for some of the discrepancies. Geys (1922) claims that normally yeasts carry a positive charge which becomes negative during fermentation and finally reverts to positive. This view is at variance with those of other workers who have reported that washed cells normally have a negative surface charge (Winslow and Flason, 1926; Moldavskaya, 1933; Silbereisen, 1938; St. Johnston, 1949; Wiles, 1951; Jansen and Mendlik, 1951; Eddy and Rudin, 1958a). As a result of these studies of surface charge density and electrophoretic mobility, it appears that changes of charge on the surface of the cells may occur, but the role of such changes in bringing about flocculence is probably insignificant.

It has been claimed that yeasts can adsorb components from the medium in which they are grown, and the possibility that the adsorbed material may change the surface charges was investigated by Jansen and Mendlik (1953). It was found that the adsorbed organic substances may or may not increase the negative charge. If the negative charge is increased, there is a reduction in the ability of the yeast to flocculate and, further, it was found that if the surface charge of coated yeasts is neutralized by the addition of certain cations, flocculence is restored. The conditions used in such investigations were quite drastic and artificial, and Jansen (1958) expressed doubt whether these results are significant. There is evidence that the charge on the cell surface may be due, at least in part, to the presence of a mannan–phosphate–protein complex (Eddy and Rudin, 1958a,b; Eddy, 1958b).

All the evidence presented so far has concerned various factors that may contribute to the expression of flocculence, but, with the possible exception of the latter reports, little evidence has been provided to indicate the agent or agents responsible for the potential ability to flocculate. The possibility that adsorbed organic matter on the cell surface is related to the ability to flocculate has been studied by Kodo (1954), who isolated from six-row barley a polysaccharide-like compound "treberine" which he claims brings about flocculence. Humic acid-like compounds from malt wort have been claimed to have an effect similar to that of treberine (Kijima, 1954; Kodo and Kijima, 1953, 1960). Eddy (1956) contradicted these findings by showing that the yeasts used by the latter were flocculent in the absence of a humic acid-like substance. Hence it can be concluded that these adsorbed organic substances are yet again external factors that permit the expression of flocculence in cells which have the ability to flocculate already developed.

It is surprising to find that after 1951 many workers continued to seek external factors alone as the cause of flocculence because Gilliland (1951) and Thorne (1951) independently showed that flocculence is an inherent character of the yeast cell itself, an opinion later expressed by Eddy (1956). It was shown that flocculence is under the control of genes, and that hybridization of flocculent and nonflocculent strains results in the segregation of this character, the flocculent character being dominant. Thorne claims that at least three gene pairs are involved. There is other indirect evidence to support the complex nature of the phenomenon, such as that of Eddy and Rudin (1958c), who showed that when two relatively nonflocculent yeasts are mixed together the mixture may be strongly flocculent. Somewhat similar findings have been reported by Curtis and Wenham (1958). Recently, Chester (1963) reported that cultures arising from a single cell, and in which no sporulation has been observed, give rise to strains possessing different degrees of flocculence. It is suggested that this degree of variability does not arise as a result of gene mutation, but rather that flocculence is controlled, at least in part, by inheritable cytoplasmic elements and that the unequal distribution of such elements during the formation of the daughter cells results in the production of new variants. A similar explanation has been offered in the case of the high incidence of "petite" colonies (see Section V).

Another approach to solving this problem is to identify differences in the cell walls of flocculent and nonflocculent yeasts. Attention has been concentrated on the cell wall because it is known that the separated cell walls of sufficiently mature cells, which have been disintegrated, retain the flocculence characteristic of the intact cell (Eddy and Rudin, 1958c; Eddy, 1958c; Maaschelein and Jeunehomme, 1958). Because young cells are nonflocculent, the latter workers compared the amino acids in the walls of cells of different ages. It was found that serine and threonine were more abundant in the older cell walls. From these results and other studies they postulated that an important factor in flocculence is the presence probably of a mannan complex on the cell surface. Changes in this complex, or the localization of specific amino acids on it, influence the ability to flocculate. The probability that a mannan complex is involved has been proposed by Eddy and Rudin (1958a,b,c) and Eddy (1958b,c). From a study of the cell walls of cultures starved of phosphate, it was concluded that phosphate groups were responsible for a considerable amount of the charge on the cell surface. Further, the treatment of the cells with papain provided valuable and interesting information, from which the following conclusions can be drawn: (1) The phosphate ions are bound to a mannan–protein complex; (2) The removal of the mannan complex by the enzyme papain coincides with the loss of flocculence.

The results of investigations concerning the mechanisms of flocculence may be summarized as follows: (1) Flocculence is an inheritable characteristic involving the interplay of genes and possibly cytoplasmic elements. (2) The inheritable character finds expression in the cell wall, and variation in a phosphate–mannan–protein complex may determine the degree of flocculence. (3) The charge on the cell surface, and interference with this charge by adsorbed material, may play a minor role in the expression of flocculence. (4) The flocculation of the cells in liquid media is dependent on pH and temperature. (5) The expression of flocculence is a variable character depending on the environment in which the cells are grown or suspended. Some metal cations and organic substances enhance the expression of flocculence, whereas some anions and carbohydrates inhibit it.

Many industrial cultures of yeasts are not homogeneous inasmuch as strain differences can be detected by a study of cellular and colonial morphology (see Sections III and V) and a study of the flocculence characteristics of clones selected from such cultures. Furthermore, since yeasts have the potential, on reproduction, to give rise to new strains (Chester, 1963), it is important that tests be available which indicate such changes before they are manifested in an industrial process.

Gilliland (1951) recognized four classes of yeast based on flocculation tests and brewing characteristics. For estimation of the proportion of these different types in an industrial culture, a sample of yeast is spread on solidified malt-wort medium in such a manner as to produce well-separated discrete colonies. Fifty of the colonies are selected at random and each transferred to a separate vessel containing malt wort. After a standardized procedure of incubation, the cultures are assessed and the number belonging to each type is recorded as a percentage of the number of cultures examined. Hough (1957) surveyed a number of industrial cultures, both from different breweries and from the same brewery at different times, and he found many more types of yeasts than did Gilliland. Hough found that the population varied from time to time as judged by morphological studies and assessment of the flocculence characteristics. This is a time-consuming exercise, as Hough realized; he later (1960) made use of the characteristics of microcolonies as the sole means of distinguishing between various strains. It is reported that there is close correlation between results obtained by the two procedures, but this close correlation is perhaps a little surprising.

V. AGGREGATION ON SOLID MEDIA

The introduction of solid media was a significant step forward in the study of microorganisms because it afforded a means of obtaining pure cultures easily. Further, it was realized that the morphology of colonies on solid media could be a useful tool in helping to identify particular organisms. The latter criterion has proved to be less valuable in identifying yeasts than it has in the case of bacteria. This is because strains of the same species of yeast may reveal greater differences in colonial morphology than may be observed between different species or even genera (Fig. 3a,b). However, it can be shown that the colonial features of any strain is reasonably constant when the yeast is grown on the same medium under the same environmental conditions.

In general media with gelatin as the solidifying matrix tend to enhance the distinctive features of colonial morphology to a greater extent than does agar, which, in turn, is better than silica gel. Again, it is usual to find that media containing plant extracts and infusions, such as malt wort, corn-steep liquor, and fruit and vegetable infusions, induce greater colony

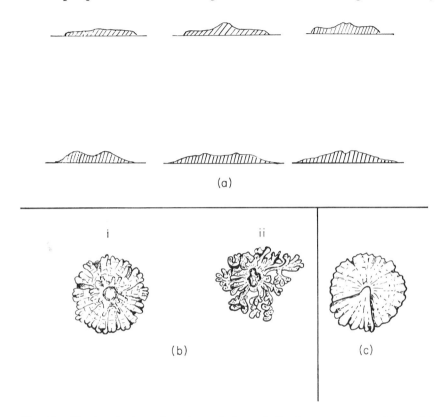

FIG. 3. Giant colonies of various strains of *Saccharomyces cerevisiae*. (a) Transverse sections through various types of colony. (bi) Colonies of a dispersed-cell strain which produces relatively few pseudomycelia. (bii) Colony of a strain which produces both microcolonies and pseudomycelium. (c) Colony showing a mutant segment.

differentiation than do apparently complete media based on nutrients from animal sources, or defined synthetic media. In the latter case, it has been shown that deficiency of particular vitamins can influence the morphology of colonies of certain yeasts, if these yeasts have a requirement for that particular vitamin. (Weinfurtner *et al.*, 1960; Eschenbecker, 1960). Even when the same undefined medium is used care must be taken in its preparation; e.g., it can be shown that malt-wort gelatin is quite sensitive to heat treatment and any prolonged heating reduces the chances of distinguishing between yeasts by their colonial characteristics.

The morphology of colonies can, of course, be used to assist in the identification of yeasts. For instance, most strains of *Pichia* and *Candida* can easily be distinguished from, say, *Saccharomyces* or *Cryptococcus*. Pigmented strains of *Rhodotorula* can usually be distinguished from *Candida pulcherrima* by the diffusion of the pigment from the colony into the medium in the case of the last-mentioned yeast. Various strains of *S. cerevisiae* can be distinguished by their "giant" colony characteristics (Hall, 1954a,b). There is evidence that sometimes differences in the features of "giant" colonies can be correlated with differences in other characteristics such as flocculence and fermentation activity. Similar correlation with microcolony morphology and other activities is noted in Section IV, B.

Three types of "giant" colony of *S. carlsbergensis* grown on malt-wort media have been described by Eschenbecker (1960), who reported that these yeasts, when grown on a defined medium, gave rise to colonies that were indistinguishable one from the other. When these yeasts were grown on defined media deficient in biotin, inositol, or thiamine again the yeasts gave rise to three distinctive types of colony. The distinctive colonies were found in each case to have a requirement for the vitamin that was lacking in the medium. It is not clear whether the types of colonies on malt wort correspond to the distinctive colonies on the media deficient in vitamins.

In general, it is found that colonial strain differences can best be demonstrated by studying "giant" colonies and, in the case of *S. cerevisiae,* good results can be obtained by incubating cultures on malt-wort gelatin for 3–6 weeks at 20°C. In order to reduce the chance of contamination in such cultures subjected to prolonged incubation, diphenyl may be incorporated into the medium (Hall, 1954a). However, it should be mentioned that diphenyl may interfere with the results, since Eschenbecker (1960) claims that this compound hastens the onset of cell autolysis. In general, the greater the tendency for yeasts to produce pseudomycelia, or to grow as microcolonies in broth cultures, the greater is the chance that rough types of "giant" colony will develop. (Fig. 3b).

Gross morphological features of colonies may be used for other purposes also. When haploid and diploid strains of yeasts are evenly dispersed on solid media, the resulting colonies of the haploid strain are usually appreciably smaller than the diploid ones. Of course, this criterion is useful in sorting out the two strains, but care should be taken not to mistake the small haploid colonies for "petite" colonies, which are not uncommonly found in cultures of *S. cerevisiae*. These "petite" colonies were first described by Ephrussi *et al.* (1949) and have been shown to be stable forms of the yeast which are deficient in respiratory enzymes (Ephrussi *et al.,*

1955; Sherman, 1959; Yotsuzanagi, 1959). Less stable forms of "petite" colonies have been described in *Candida albicans* (Bianchi, 1961), and these do not appear to be respiratory-deficient mutants but, rather, the size of the colony appears to be related to changes in purine metabolism.

The gross appearance of "giant" colonies reveals, on occasions, the presence of mutants arising in colonies from clones. Such mutants may appear as distinctive segments of the colony which are clearly distinguishable from the main body of the colony (Fig. 3c).

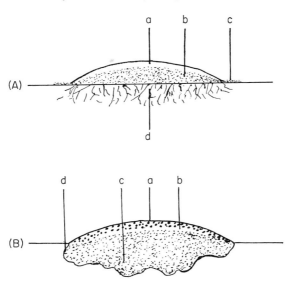

FIG. 4. Transverse sections through giant colonies. (A) On agar medium (after Lindegren and Hamilton, 1944): *a*, Zone of autolyzed cells containing asci. *b*, Apparently healthy cells. *c*, Thin spreading edge of colony. *d*, Pseudomycelium penetrating into the agar. (B) On gelatin medium: *a*, Zone of resting cells; asci may be present. *b*, Zone of autolyzed cells. *c*, Apparently healthy cells; some may be budding. *d*, Most advanced edge of colony, may be gelatin.

The microanatomy of "giant" colonies has been studied by Lindegren and Hamilton (1944) and Morris and Hough (1956). These reports are based on observations made of sections prepared from colonies on agar and gelatin media, respectively. This difference and, possibly, differences in the yeasts studied, may account for the lack of complete agreement in the results. The major differences between colonies grown on agar and on gelatin appear to be found in the outer layer of cells and in the form of penetration of the cells into the solid matrix of the media. On agar media the outer layer of cells autolyzes and asci are to be found in this layer, whereas on gelatin media the asci are formed in the outer layer of cells which appear to be in the resting stage (Fig. 4). On gelatin, a zone of autolysis eventually develops immediately below the zone of resting cells. Lindegren and Hamilton (1944) found that, on agar, pseudomycelium-like structures are pushed out of the colony into the matrix; it is the present author's experience that not all yeasts show this characteristic; e.g., some strains of *Debaryomyces kloeckeri* do not penetrate into agar even after 6 weeks, whereas infiltration is observed on gelatin medium. All strains of *S. cerevisiae* on malt-wort gelatin will infiltrate into the matrix of the medium, so much so that the leading edge of the colonies may be beneath the surface of the medium. Often this extensive infiltration can be observed after 4-6 days of incubation at 20°C. Infiltration of the gelatin takes place whether or not the strain produces pseudomycelium. In the case of those strains which do not produce pseudomycelium, it is difficult to believe that penetration into the medium is the result of mechanical pressure; hence it seems reasonable to suppose that the cells produce amounts of proteinase sufficient to cause localized softening of the medium in the immediate neighborhood of the cells with the consequence that the cells can settle into the matrix. Often no macroscopic liquefaction of the matrix is observed after 6-8 weeks' growth of the colonies. It is probable that the products of this localized proteolysis diffuse into the colony and are used by the cells; such a hypothesis is supported by the fact that usually there is a relatively large number of cells, which appear to be actively budding, situated in the deeper lower regions of the colony.

REFERENCES

Bauch, R. (1941). *Naturwissenschaften* **29**:503.
Bauch, R. (1943a). *Arch. Mikrobol.* **13**:352.
Bauch, R. (1943b). *Ber. Deut. Botan. Ges.* **60**:42.
Bianchi, D. E. (1961). *Am. J. Botany* **48**:499.
Brock, T. D. (1959). *Science* **129**:960.
Brock, T. D. (1961). *J. Gen. Microbiol.* **26**:487.
Burns, J. A. (1937). *J. Inst. Brewing* **43**:31.
Chester, V. E. (1963). *Proc. Roy. Soc.* **B157**:223.
Connell, C. H., and S. E. Skinner. (1953). *Mycopathol. Mycol. Appl.* **6**:65.
Curtis, N. S., and S. Wenham. (1958). *J. Inst. Brewing* **64**:368.
Diddens, H. A., and J. Lodder. (1942). "Die Hefesammlang Des Centraal-Bureau Voor Schmmelcultures," Part II, North-Holland Publ., Amsterdam.
Eddy, A. A. (1955a). *J. Inst. Brewing* **61**:307.
Eddy, A. A. (1955b). *J. Inst. Brewing* **61**:313.
Eddy, A. A. (1955c). *J. Inst. Brewing* **61**:318.
Eddy, A. A. (1956). *J. Inst. Brewing* **62**:320.
Eddy, A. A. (1958a). *J. Inst. Brewing* **64**:143.
Eddy A. A. (1958b). *Proc. Roy. Soc.* **B149**:425.
Eddy, A. A. (1958c). *J. Inst. Brewing* **64**:368.
Eddy, A. A., and A. D. Rudin. (1958a). *J. Inst. Brewing* **64**:139.

Eddy, A. A., and A. D. Rudin. (1958b). *Proc. Roy. Soc.* **B148**:419.
Eddy, A. A., and A. D. Rudin. (1958c). *J. Inst. Brewing* **64**:19.
Ephrussi, B., H. Hottinguer, and A. M. Chimènes. (1949). *Ann. Inst. Pasteur.* **76**:351.
Ephrussi, B., H. Hottinguer, and H. Roman. (1955). *Proc. Natl. Acad. Sci. U.S.* **41**:1065.
Eschenbecker, F. (1960). *Brauer Mälzer* **13**:16.
Falcone, G., and W. J. Nickerson. (1956). *Science* **124**:277.
Falcone, G., and W. J. Nickerson. (1957). *Giorn. Microbiol.* **4**:105.
Geys, K. (1922). *Z. Ges. Brauw.* **45**:51.
Gilliland, R. B. (1951). *Proc. European Brewery Conv. Congr., Brighton, 1950* p. 35. Elsevier, Amsterdam.
Gilliland, R. B. (1957). *Wallerstein Lab. Commun.* **20**:41.
Hagen, U., and H. J. Blumenthal. (1956). *Z. Naturforsch.* **11b**:607.
Hagen, U., and R. Koch. (1957). *Z. Naturforsch.* **12b**:240.
Hale, G. W. F. (1953). *Lab. Pract.* **2**:114.
Hall, J. F. (1954a). *J. Inst. Brewing* **60**:482.
Hall, J. F. (1954b). *J. Inst. Brewing* **60**:486.
Hansen, E. C. (1886). *Medd. Carlsberg Lab.* **1**:168.
Hayduck, F., and K. Schuckling. (1908). *Wochschr. Brau.* **25**:241.
Herman, A. (1961). "Some Aspects of Genetics of Actidione Resistance by the Yeast *Hansenula wingei*." Thesis. Western Reserve University, Cleveland, Ohio (cited by T. D. Brock).
Hough, J. S. (1957). *J. Inst. Brewing* **63**:483.
Hough, J. S. (1960). *J. Inst. Brewing* **66**:475.
Ingram, M. (1955). "An Introduction to the Biology of Yeasts," p. 180. Pitman, New York.
Jansen, H. F. (1958). *In* "The Chemistry and Biology of Yeasts," (A. H. Cook, ed.), p. 635. Academic Press, New York.
Jansen, H. F., and E. Mendlik. (1951). *Proc. European Brewery Conv. Congr., Brighton, 1950* p. 59. Elsevier, Amsterdam.
Jansen, H. F., and F. Mendlik. (1953). *Proc. European Brewery Conv. Congr., Nice, 1952* p. 163. Elsevier, Amsterdam.
Kijima M. (1954). *J. Inst. Brewing* **60**:223.
Koch, R., and M. N. Schwartz. (1957). *Arzneimittel-Forsch.* **7**:76.
Kodo, S. (1954). *Brauerei* **8**:345.
Kodo, S., and M. Kijima. (1953). *J. Agr. Chem. Soc. Japan* **27**:809.
Kodo, S., and M. Kijima. (1960). *Rept. Res. Lab. Kirin Brewery Co., Ltd.* **3**:25 and 33.
Kusserow, R. (1885). *Brennerei-Ztg.* **14**. Cited by H. E. Jansen, *in* "The Chemistry and Biology of Yeasts" (A. H. Cook, ed.), p. 636. Academic Press, New York, 1958.
Laer, H. (1905). *Bull. Soc. Chim. Belges* **19**:31.
Lamedica, G. M. (1959). *Boll. Ist. Sieroterap. Milan.* **38**:255.
Lange, H. (1907). *Wochschr. Brau.* **24**:445.
Langeron, N., and P. Guerra. (1938). *Ann. Parasitol. Humaine Comparee* **16**:36.
Langeron, N., and R. V. Talice. (1932). *Ann. Parasitol. Humaine Comparee* **10**:1.
Levi, J. D. (1956). *Nature* **177**:753.
Levine, S., and Z. J. Ordal. (1946). *J. Bacteriol.* **52**:687.
Lindegren, C. C., and S. A. Haddad. (1954). *Genetica* **28**:45.
Lindegren, C. C., and E. Hamilton. (1944). *Botan. Gaz.* **105**:304.

Lindner, P. (1901). *Jahrb. Versuchs-Lehranst. Brauerei* **4**:309.
Lindquist, W. (1953). *J. Inst. Brewing* **59**:59.
Lodder, J., and N. J. W. Kreger-van Rij. (1952). "The Yeasts: A Taxonomic Study," pp. 1, 10, and 40. North-Holland Pub., Amsterdam.
Lodder, J., W. C. Slooff, and N. J. W. Kreger-van Rij. (1958). *In* "The Chemistry and Biology of Yeasts." (A. H. Cook, ed.), p. 1. Academic Press, New York.
Maaschelein, C. A., and C. Jeunehomme. (1958). *J. Inst. Brewing* **64**:368.
Maufang, E. (1912). *Wochschr. Brau.* **29**:721.
Moldavskaya, E. A. (1933). *Biochem. Z.* **257**:480.
Morris, E. O., and J. S. Hough. (1956). *J. Inst. Brewing* **62**:34.
Nickerson, W. J. (1951). *Trans. N.Y. Acad. Sci.* **13**:140.
Nickerson, W. J., and G. Falcone. (1956). *Science* **124**:272.
Nickerson, W. J., and N. J. W. van Rij. (1949). *Biochim. Biophys. Acta* **3**:461.
Nickerson, W. J., and Z. Mankowski. (1953). *Am. J. Botany* **40**:584.
Nickerson, W. J., W. A. Taber, and G. Falcone. (1956). *Can. J. Microbiol.* **2**:575.
Pasteur, L. (1876). "Etudes sur la bières," p. 196. Gauthier-Villars, Paris.
Revalier E., and S. Seydal. (1932). *Ann. Parasitol. Humaine Comparee* **10**:463.
Robinow, C. F. (1942). *Proc. Roy. Soc.* **B138**:299.
St. Johnston, J. H. (1949). *Proc. European Brewery Conv. Congr., Lucerne, 1948* p. 62. Elsevier, Amsterdam.
Schönfeld, E., and H. Krumhaar. (1918). *Wochschr. Brau.* **35**:302.
Seyffert, H. (1896). *Z. Ges. Brau.* **19**:318.
Sherman, F. (1959). *J. Cellular Comp. Physiol.* **54**:29.
Silbereisen, K. (1938). *Wochschr. Brau.* **55**:153.
Szilvinyi, A. (1960). *Naturwissenschaften* **47**:140.
Talice, R. V. (1930). *Ann. Parasitol. Humaine Comparee* **8**:396.
Thorne, R. S. W. (1951). *Proc. European Brewery Conv. Congr., Brighton, 1950* p. 21. Elsevier, Amsterdam.
Townsend, G. F., and C. C. Lindegren. (1953). *Cytologia (Toyko)* **18**:183.
Weinfurtner, F., F. Eschenbecker, and W. Borges. (1960). *Arch. Mikrobiol.* **37**:193.
Wickerham, L. J., and L. J. Rettger. (1939). *J. Trop. Med. Hyg.* **42**:174, 187, and 204.
Wiles, H. E. (1951). *Proc. European Brewery Conv. Congr., Brighton, 1950* p. 84. Elsevier, Amsterdam.
Winslow, C. E. A., and E. H. Flason. (1926). *J. Gen. Physiol.* **8**:195.
Yotsuzanagi, Y. (1959). *Compt. Rend.* **248**:274.

The Multicellular Condition

CHAPTER 3

Vegetative Structures

GILLIAN M. BUTLER

Department of Botany
University of Birmingham
Birmingham, England

I. INTRODUCTION

The thalli of the great majority of fungi are constructed from filamentous hyphae. At the hyphal apex, extension in length is potentially unlimited while increase in width is strictly limited. Sooner or later, behind the apex, branch hyphal apices are initiated and cross septa may be formed. Both hyphal apices and older segments of hyphae may be capable of differentiation. Growth and differentiation of individual hyphae take place with varying degrees of coordination with adjacent hyphae, thus forming more or less organized multihyphal aggregates. This section explores the special capacities and limitations of the hyphal method of construction that are revealed in the structure of vegetative aggregates.

In nature fungal vegetative structures are often cryptic and were not well understood before the advent of pure culture techniques. Mostly toward the end of the eighteenth century the more obvious sterile fungal structures occurring in nature were given generic names (de Bary, 1887). However, as early as 1837 Trog pointed out the connection between the mycelium and fungal fruiting structures (Hein, 1930), and since then the majority of special sterile structures have been recognized as vegetative stages of a wide range of ascomycetes and basidiomycetes. Some of the old generic names have since been used as descriptive terms for vegetative categories, e.g., sclerotium, ozonium, xylostroma, rhizomorph. Early investigations culminated in a comprehensive account by de Bary (1887), who delimited four categories encompassing all the previously described sterile structures i.e., filamentous mycelia, membranous mycelia, strands, and sclerotia. De Bary's categories were of necessity based on very little information, and it is significant that for sclerotia, about which most was known, his concept was more precise, including morphological, anatomical, and functional features. Thus he distinguished true sclerotia from sclerotioid structures similar in function but morphologically distinct. He also recognized that individual categories did not necessarily occur in all species within a circle of affinity.

Bommer (1896) contributed greatly to our information about strands and sclerotia and attempted to construct a natural classification based on anatomy and presumed function. Haberlandt's anatomicophysiological criteria of classification were carried to their logical conclusion in the fungi by Lohwag (1941). Here de Bary's categories fall roughly within the absorption system (mycelia), the conduction system (strands), and the storage system (sclerotia). More recent studies, which will be considered later, have revealed heterogeneity, particularly in patterns of organization, within de Bary's categories. Nevertheless it is convenient at present to retain groups similar to those of de Bary. The three groups, colonies, strands, and sclerotia, are based on both structural and behavioral characters. They are purely descriptive and are not intended to imply real morphological entities.

II. COLONIES

The term colony is used in a particular sense in describing the unspecialized vegetative parts of all fungi that possess hyphae. Although hyphae remain attached at their point of initiation, individual hyphal apices for the most part grow separately and only fortuitously in contact with one another. The colony thus consists of hyphae with matrix or air between, and the term refers equally to a thallus derived from a single spore and to the structure derived from a group of individuals.

In nature, colony structure is complicated by the uneven restraints imposed by the environment. In special cases where external restraints are relatively uniform, e.g., "fairy rings," or a pathogen in a leaf, colonies occur which are comparable in appearance to those seen in single-organism culture. Also, concentrations of available nutrients in culture are usually higher than those in nature. Two sorts of culture system can be distinguished which result in somewhat different colony structures. First, growth may take place in association with an air/substrate interface, with some of the hyphae in and on the substrate and others in the air above, e.g., at the surface of a liquid or solid medium, or on a permeable membrane over a medium. Second, growth may occur entirely within a homogeneous medium, e.g., submerged liquid culture, or within an agar medium. Although features of colonies are used in taxonomic diagnoses (e.g., Raper and

Thom, 1949; Nobles, 1948), and although it is a common experience of mycologists to recognize the hyphal growth habit of a much used culture, there is a singular lack of information about the hyphal basis of colony structure.

A. Surface Colonies

1. Margin

In the familiar petri dish culture, when a fungal colony is growing from a point inoculum, growth into the air and into the medium is soon restricted but growth along or close to the air/substrate interface continues, usually to the edge of the dish. The more or less circular colony increases in diameter by apical extension of marginal outwardly directed juvenile hyphae. W. Brown (1923) first drew attention to dynamic features affecting colony growth form. Three successive phases of marginal extension may be recognized: an overall lag phase of increasing extension rate, a linear phase of constant extension rate and, finally, a staling phase of diminishing extension rate. The meager data available suggest that each phase is associated with a characteristic behavior of the marginal hyphae.

a. Linear Phase. Probably the majority of descriptions of petri dish cultures refer to the linear phase since this phase often occupies most of the growth period. During this phase, submerged, surface, and aerial marginal hyphae are most frequently morphologically similar, but their relative abundance varies considerably. In some instances sparse aerial marginal growth is followed by a phase of aerial consolidation whereas in others the margin itself has dense aerial mycelium. Marginal hyphae are fairly wide, thin-walled, full of protoplasm and, with their apices at more or less the same level, giving a smooth outline to the colony (Plomley, 1959; Zalokar, 1959). Leading hyphae are usually oriented radially (Ryan *et al.,* 1943), but varying degrees of consistent angular displacement occur, resulting in a spiral growth form in some fungi under conditions that are not at present clear (Ritchie, 1960).

It seems likely that individual hyphal tips most commonly persist in the margin. Branching typically occurs behind the parent hyphal tip, and only rarely do parent tips stop growing or are they overtaken by hyphae from within the colony (Butler, 1961). Dichotomous branching in which the main apex stops growing at the initiation of two apical branches is unusual but is characteristic of *Allomyces* (R. Emerson, 1955). Sympodial growth, in which parent hyphal tips are successively overtaken by branches, occurs consistently in some fungi, e.g., a mutant of *Ascobolus immersus* (Chevaugeon, 1959). Most frequently, however, branching is monopodial and leading hyphal tips have at least the same chance of survival in the margin as their most progressive branches.

Primary branches develop singly in acropetal succession some distance behind the parent hyphal tips. Rarely, pairs or whorls of branches may be initiated simultaneously (Langeron, 1945). These branches tend to grow away from other hyphae and into the spaces between the leading hyphae and are most frequently subordinate in growth rate and diameter to their parents (Butler, 1961; Grover, 1961; Park, 1961). Sooner or later heterogeneity develops among these branches. Usually more branches are initiated than subsequently are incorporated in the margin and it seems that

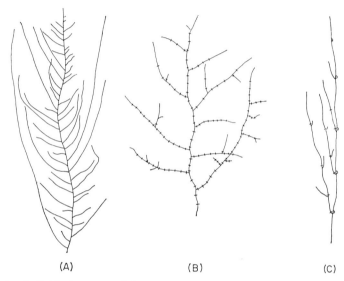

FIG. 1. Individual monopodial branching systems of marginal hyphae of *Absidia* sp. (A), *Sordaria fimicola* (B), and *Coprinus disseminatus* (C) on 0.2% malt agar. Only primary branches are shown in (A). ‑+‑, Septum; ‑•‑, clamp connection. Magnification: (A) and (C), × 25; (B) × 50.

some branches lag behind while others are progressive and form new leaders. In *Absidia* a small proportion of the primary branches are distinguishable as potential leaders by their greater length quite soon after initiation (Fig. 1). Although some of these potential leaders may later lag behind, new ones do not subsequently arise from previously suppressed branches (Table I). During the linear phase density of the margin often appears unchanged, but this impression requires substantiation.

It is evident that the characteristic appearance of the colony margin of a particular isolate is based on special branching potentialities, the frequency and position of branch initials, their angle of insertion, their angle of growth and their subsequent fate (Fig. 1). Buller (1931) contrasted the wide angle of branching of haploid *Coprinus lagopus* marginal hyphae with the consistently more acute angle in the dikaryon. Septa are formed in the terminal cells of marginal hyphae in ascomycetes and basidiomycetes. In many basidiomycetes, the capacity to form branch initials appears to be particularly associated with the region just behind developing septa or clamp connections (Grover, 1961; Butler, 1961) whereas in ascomycetes septa and branch initials seem to occur independently, e.g., *Sordaria fimicola* (Grover, 1961). Morphological mutants are potentially of great interest in understanding branching patterns (Shatkin and Tatum, 1961). Furthermore profound marginal growth form modifications often accompany changes in the environment. Clearly these involve changes in

TABLE I
BEHAVIOR OF PRIMARY BRANCH HYPHAE IN *Absidia* sp.

Primary branches numbered in basipetal succession behind the main tip	Mean number of potential leaders among the ten primary branches[a]
1–10	Not assessed
11–20	1.4
21–30	0.9
31–40	1.0

[a] Data from 12 main hyphae growing on 0.2% malt agar, colony diameter 5.0 cm.

the relative rates of leader extension, branch initiation and branch extension (Grover, 1961; Larpent, 1962). These three rates remain correlated during some changes in the nutrients or inhibitors contained in the medium but vary independently during other changes (Larpent, 1963).

b. *Lag Phase.* The morphological lag phase covers all stages of development from spore germination to the establishment of a smooth margin of radially arranged hyphae. By this time the colony may be quite large, e.g., 6–10 mm in diameter in *Chaetomium globosum* (Plomley, 1959). It seems likely that the morphological and overall physiological lag periods are completed simultaneously. Branching begins while the germ tubes are growing exponentially (Smith, 1924), and the most obvious difference from an established colony is in the direction of growth of the branches. Thus in *Cunninghamella elegans* one or a few germ tubes grow out from the spore and sooner or later start to branch in acropetal succession. The first branches usually extend at a wide angle to the parent, and from among these early hyphal tips are formed the principal radial spokes of the young colony. Further monopodial branching and subbranching continues, the branches growing away from their parents toward open spaces until they begin to meet between the spokes. The direction of branch growth near the colony edge becomes progressively more radial as the spaces between the spokes become filled in and a smooth circular colony margin is set up

(Tarn, 1963). Formation of aerial mycelium may be delayed until quite late in colony development.

c. Staling Phase. W. Brown (1923) described morphological features associated with marginal staling, i.e., with the decrease in extension rate of the colony margin. The margin is frequently wavy to deeply lobed and the balance between aerial and submerged mycelium may be disturbed with either a piling up of aerial mycelium at the margin or submerged mycelium exceeding aerial growth. Changes in hyphal orientation and branching patterns occur but, in general, the hyphal basis of the staled margin appears not to have been investigated.

2. *Changes behind the Margin*

a. Types of Change. Extension growth at right angles to the substrate surface is soon curtailed, but a variety of further developments occur, often having very striking consequences for the macroscopic appearance of the colony. Cytological changes occur in hyphal parts which were laid down in the margin (Zalokar, 1959). Most prominent among these is the development of vacuoles, but in *Neurospora crassa* Zalokar also demonstrated changes in other cytoplasmic constituents, e.g., mitochondria, glycogen, and fat granules, and in enzyme activity, with increasing age of a hyphal part (cf. Chapter 14, Volume I). Local or general changes in the hyphal wall, e.g., pigmentation, thickening, increase in surface area with consequent changes in size and shape of the hyphal lumen, formation of additional septa, and plugging of septal pores, are all fairly common changes in hyphal segments behind the margin (Nobles, 1948; Zalokar, 1959; Flentje *et al.,* 1963). At a later stage, autolysis with disorganization of the protoplast and dissolution of the wall occurs in many fungi, particularly stylosporic species (Park, 1961).

Growth of new hyphae occurs within the margin; this is evident in Brown's profile of a nonstaling *Fusarium* colony (W. Brown, 1923). During growth of very small colonies of *Chaetomium globosum* Plomley (1959) showed that hyphal density (total hyphal length/unit area) increased exponentially with age close to the margin, but the rate of increase rapidly declined until a maximum saturation density was reached. This decline began at about the same density in colonies of different size, and hyphal saturation extended outward as the colony enlarged. Vegetative hyphae initiated within the colony, both as branches of primary branches and as later branches from main hyphae, differ from marginal hyphae. Plomley (1959) reported that hyphae formed within the colony were progressively narrower as branching proceeded. Later formed branches also grow more slowly than primary branches (Butler, 1961) and their course is often meandering (Park, 1961). It is also interesting that hyphal anastomoses do not occur among juvenile marginal hyphae (in spite of frequent close proximity), but are common in older parts of colonies in basidiomycetes, ascomycetes and many fungi imperfecti (Buller, 1933). Later-formed vegetative hyphae may subsequently undergo similar cytological changes to their parent hyphae. The internal buckling characteristic of some colonies, e.g., *Penicillium* spp., is reported to be due to continued growth within the colony (Raper and Thom, 1949), but its precise mechanism needs elucidating. Specialized structures, usually formed by the growth and differentiation of branch hyphae behind the margin, are a prominent feature of many colonies. There is here a striking contrast in behavior between aerial and submerged hyphae. The majority of special hyphal ends (sporangiophores, conidiophores, stolons, setae, etc.) and multihyphal structures (fruit bodies, sclerotia, coremia, strands) are typically formed in the aerial mycelium. A few, e.g., rhizoids in some phycomycetes and rhizomorphs of *Armillaria mellea* and *Sphaerostilbe repens,* are more characteristic of submerged growth.

A final feature contributing to colony appearance is extracellular products of metabolism. Crystals may be deposited in the medium, and water-soluble substances which accumulate in the medium are sometimes brightly colored (Raper and Thom, 1949; Nobles, 1948).

b. Distribution of Changes. Not only pathways of hyphal development but also their relative timing is important for colony structure. The time of onset and duration of any particular growth feature varies but, in the simplest situation, during the linear phase, and where plenty of space is available for extension, each change proceeds centrifugally and behind the margin. Since surface colonies are not perfect planes vertical heterogeneity occurs. The pathways of development of aerial and submerged hyphae are different and among the aerial mycelium conidiophores, for example, may be formed superficially after growth has ceased at lower levels in the aerial mass. Yanagita and Kogané (1962, 1963) divide sporulating colonies of *Aspergillus niger* and *Penicillium urticae* into four concentric growth zones and show that these differ in morphology, cytochemistry, and metabolic activity. The distribution of special structures does not always appear to follow this centrifugal pattern. In many fungi with relatively massive fruit bodies the resources of very considerable areas of mycelium may be used in producing one such body (Buller, 1931). In some cultures distribution seems more related to the shape of the container, and in others it is patchy. In staling cultures some of these usually nonmarginal changes proceed right up to the margin. More special forms of colony heterogeneity are those in which a particular growth feature occurs intermittently, for example, forming successive rings of sporulation alternating with vegetative growth. Such rhythmic growth is sometimes a response to an intermittent external stimulus while in others it is apparently endogenous (Chapter 27, Volume I). These essentially concentric patterns of distribution contrast with the sectors of different structure formed as a result of segregation of inherited particles during marginal growth.

3. Corporate Colonies

Where growth proceeds at an air/substrate interface from more than one propagule the pattern of colony development depends on the relative proximity of these propagules. Neglecting special incompatibility effects each propagule tends to form an individual colony until it reaches the sphere of influence of an adjacent colony. In many instances the outermost hyphae intermingle and form a joint margin for any further colony extension over unoccupied medium. In this further extension colonies from one or many inoculum units are thus virtually identical, but protoplasmic continuity must be reduced in colonies from multiple inocula in phycomycetes, where vegetative hyphal fusions are lacking. Within the area of inoculation, after individual colonies become continguous, pathways of hyphal development are much as behind the margin in colonies from single inocula (Park, 1961). With a relatively heavy seeding the whole behaves as a structure of even age developing and differentiating more or less uniformly. In ascomycetes, basidiomycetes, and many fungi imperfecti vegetative hyphal fusions emphasize physiological unity. Nuclei can apparently move through such reticulate colonies (Snider and Raper, 1958), and the hyphae may combine in providing nutrients for a single fruit body (Buller, 1931).

In other instances marginal staling occurs in the individual colonies before the hyphae of adjacent colonies meet, and a permanent gap may remain between the individuals (W. Brown, 1923). Lesser growth form abnormalities of marginal hyphae may also occur before colonies meet in situations where an isolated colony would be growing linearly (Park, 1961).

B. Submerged Colonies

The behavior of submerged colonies contrasts with that of surface colonies in several ways. A single fungal propagule submerged in nutrient agar or liquid tends to form a spherical colony with the older hyphal parts completely surrounded by a margin of outwardly directed juvenile hyphal tips. Much of our information about submerged colonies is derived from industrial fermentation processes in which growth is proceeding from an inoculum of many individual units. Under these conditions true colonies are not always formed and, as with corporate surface colonies, varying degrees of interference occur between developing individuals. Dimorphism can be induced in a considerable number of fungi in liquid culture

(Cochrane, 1958; Pirt and Callow, 1959), the growth form of the unit of construction varying from branching filaments to budding cells. In *Penicillium chrysogenum,* a change from long thin hyphae with few branches through intermediate forms to short, much branched, swollen and often distorted hyphae can be induced by intense agitation, particularly at relatively high pH values (Dion *et al.,* 1954; Pirt and Callow, 1959). Where growth is hyphal, the appearance of submerged agitated cultures varies with the inoculum load and the nutrient status of the medium (Camici *et al.,* 1952). With a large inoculum a more or less dense homogeneous suspension of relatively short sparsely branching filaments develops. At lower inoculum loads, and particularly in nutrient-rich media, discrete spherical or subspherical colonies (pellets) are formed and the surrounding liquid is virtually clear. In one medium, pellet diameter after a given growth period is inversely related to inoculum load.

Phases of growth somewhat comparable with those on solid media may be distinguished in batchwise cultures of both the filamentous and pellet types (Chapter 25, Volume I). These phases, of increasing, constant, and decreasing growth rate, are based on dry weight and mass physiological characters, but must ultimately be related to growth at the hyphal level. Borrow *et al.* (1964) discuss the relative merits of exponential and cube root models for the phase of constant growth rate. For the situation in their cultures, where growth is filamentous, they consider that the exponential model, implying that every unit of mycelium increases in weight at a constant rate, is more appropriate. Completion of the exponential phase occurs at the same time as marked metabolic changes. However they indicate that the cube root model may be more appropriate for cultures of the pellet type. This latter model has been related to the morphology of pellet cultures (S. Emerson, 1950; Machlis, 1957). There is an initial overall lag phase of increasing growth rate during which the pellets are organized both by individual propagules growing and branching and by individuals becoming associated in clumps. Association of pellets to form compound structures at later stages of growth is unusual (Burkholder and Sinnott, 1945; Clark, 1962). A circumference of outwardly directed hyphae is soon completed around each pellet and there ensues a period in which the cube root of dry weight increases linearly with time. This is in agreement with the supposition that growth during this phase is at the surface and that the spheres have constant density. As the medium becomes spent the growth rate falls off.

Burkholder and Sinnott (1945) showed that pellets developed in submerged agitated cultures of a wide range of fungi and that the surface features of pellets differed. In the absence of information one can speculate that such surface features are a consequence of branching behavior of the marginal hyphae. Sections of pellets reveal radiating branching hyphae with interhyphal spaces filled with medium. In the early stages of linear growth the hyphae are homogeneous and fairly loosely packed, but later zones may be distinguished which, as in surface cultures, cut across the direction of hyphal growth (Burkholder and Sinnott, 1945; Clark, 1962). In general a rind of more closely packed branched and interwoven hyphae with dense granular contents is formed surrounding a less dense intermediate zone and a central core of highly vacuolated and later autolyzed hyphal segments. In *Aspergillus niger* the time of onset and intensity of autolysis in the center is associated with rind development, the latter varying with cultural conditions (Clark, 1962). Internal changes within colonies are virtually restricted to modifications of preexisting hyphal segments. Most submerged colonies remain entirely vegetative, and this is consistent with the finding that most differentiated structures are characteristic of aerial mycelium in surface cultures. However, submerged sporulation can be induced in some fungi (Morton, 1961).

A significant feature of submerged batchwise agitated cultures is that development of a culture proceeds as a whole, similar modification of most of the growing hyphae occurring in all individuals in the culture at the same time. This applies both where growth is filamentous, e.g., changes in hyphal growth form (Duckworth and Harris, 1949), changes in hyphal growth form and cell constituents (Borrow et al., 1961), and also where growth is in the form of pellets, e.g., rind formation (Clark, 1962) and sporulation (Hadley and Harrold, 1958). However, both Duckworth and Harris and Borrow et al. report the occurrence of some hyphal segments which differ morphologically from the majority.

C. Factors in Colony Development

This survey of colony structure demonstrates that the behavior of a hypha is related to its position in the colony as a whole as much as to its hyphal lineage. The implications of this have been expressed by Ryan et al. (1943) for one particular growth feature of surface colonies, viz. margin regimentation. In order to explain their observations they postulated the production of an extracellular branching inhibitor in the margin and an inverse relationship between branch frequency and parent growth rate. This has not been substantiated, and Plomley (1959) reports that the rate of leader extension in *Chaetomium globosum* is not affected by the space available for branching. However, other evidence of extracellular effects has accumulated. Some of the differences between liquid and agar cultures are consistent with rapid mixing of extracellular factors in liquid medium by stirring, compared with slow spread by diffusion through agar. Physical conditions and nutrient supplies in the medium are clearly altered by hyphal activities. Thus, anaerobic conditions, which influence hyphal growth form, often prevail within colonies while the surface is under aerobic conditions (Foster, 1949). Also, Borrow et al. (1961) relate changes in cell shape and contents to the time of exhaustion of one or more specific nutrients from the medium in fermentations of *Gibberella fujikuroi*.

There is evidence that morphogenetically active factors are produced by colonies and accumulate in the medium. Thus Hadley and Harrold (1958) provide clear evidence that an extracellular thermolabile factor produced during vegetative growth is involved in the induction of submerged sporulation in *Penicillium notatum*. On agar media such factors are reported to affect a wide variety of growth features: spore germination, hyphal growth form, hyphal differentiation, hyphal lysis (Park, 1961); spore germination (Carlile and Sellin, 1963); hyphal orientation (Stadler, 1952); hyphal growth rate and growth form (Butler, 1963). During the staling phase, activity ("staling") is evident beyond the colony margin and, during the linear phase, there is a gradient of increasing activity from the margin inward to a peak of activity over young mycelium. Robinson and Park (1965) have made considerable progress in determining the biological activity of a factor which is produced by *Fusarium oxysporum,* is labile in the presence of the producer fungus, and causes vacuolation and cessation of extension growth of hyphal tips. However, as yet none of these elusive factors has been characterized.

Other aspects of colony development, e.g., internal interactions and development of heterogeneity between adjacent hyphae, have been little explored. Plomley (1959) stresses the significance of a functional rather than morphological growth unit consisting of a free-growing hyphal tip associated with a growing mass of constant size in a constant environment. As the hypha extends it leaves behind segments in which branch growth is independent. Larpent (1965) has observed in young colonies that there is a characteristic pattern of changes in branch development as parental extension rate increases. He suggests that this may be explained in terms of changes in the relative ability of different apices within a branching system to compete for nutrient supplies.

III. SPECIAL MULTIHYPHAL STRUCTURES

Particularly in the ascomycetes and basidiomycetes, but also in fungi imperfecti, multihyphal structures are formed that appear to involve a degree of coordination between the constituent hyphae greater than that in a colony. This coordination may be manifested in several ways, by interhyphal contact to form a solid tissue, by differentiation with neighboring hyphae, by formation of a structure with a definite boundary, by a period of existence as a more or less discrete structure. Not all these features may be apparent in one structure and, particularly in culture, there occur a variety of ill-defined hyphal associations which are nevertheless fungus- and medium-specific, e.g., sclerotic patches in *Hypholoma fasciculare* and *Armillaria mellea*. Coordination is very evident in multihyphal reproductive structures, including stromata of ascomycetes and fungi imperfecti. The majority of sterile phases fall within the two categories that have significant functions in the life of the organisms, strands and sclerotia. One example of an exceptional and distinct structure is the infection cushion of *Helicobasidium purpureum* (Hering, 1962).

A. Strands

1. Concept and Occurrence

Strands are linear hyphal aggregates with the capacity to extend unidirectionally. They sometimes contain differentiated hyphae and may be any thickness from a few hyphae to several millimeters. The category includes all the structures variously described as mycelial strands and rhizomorphs (de Bary, 1887; Garrett, 1960). These arise from vegetative mycelium in a corpus of colonized material or from a sclerotium and are potentially capable of unlimited extension, usually over the surface of, or away from, a nutrient substrate, e.g., in soil, sand, litter or under fallen logs. Ultimately such strands either form vegetative mycelium in a new substrate or give rise to reproductive structures. They are particularly characteristic of fungi forming massive fruit bodies or colonizing relatively massive, often woody substrates. Although the majority are formed by basidiomycetes, strands of comparable elaboration are formed by a few ascomycetes and fungi imperfecti, e.g., *Sphaerostilbe repens, Phymatotrichum omnivorum*. In the Phycomycetes true strands have not been reported.

This category corresponds to Langeron's broad group of *synnemata* (Langeron, 1945, p. 79) and its precise limits are difficult to define. Some aggregates have a limited length or soon form reproductive structures. Thus funicular mycelium is a consistent cultural character of some fungi, e.g., species of *Paecilomyces* (A. H. S. Brown and Smith, 1957). In spore-bearing synnemata growth may be determinate with terminal spores, e.g., Stilbaceae, or indeterminate with lateral formation of conidia, e.g., *Isaria cretacea* (Taber and Vining, 1959) and *Penicillium isariiforme* (Carlile et al., 1962). Furthermore, there may be a comparable period of vegetative extension during the development of sexual reproductive structures, e.g., stroma of *Xylaria hypoxylon,* stipe of *Polyporus brumalis*.

Much of our information is based on naturally occurring strands where considerable caution is necessary in interpreting developmental relations

3. Vegetative Structures

and degree of maturity. Many of these structures can, however, be induced to form in culture (Garrett, 1960).

2. Methods of Unidirectional Extension

The variations in pattern of development occurring in the few species that have been investigated can be divided into two reasonably distinct

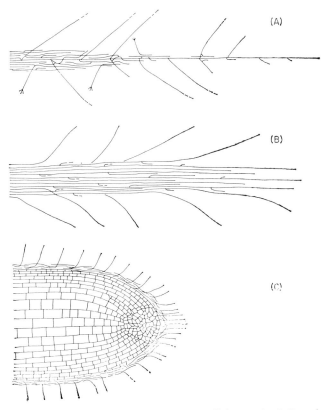

FIG. 2. Diagrams of extending regions of mycelial strand of *Serpula lacrimans* (A), rhizomorph of *Phallus impudicus* (B); and rhizomorph of *Armillaria mellea* (C). (C) After de Bary (1887).

groups (Garrett, 1960): (a) Gradual build-up around a pre-existing mycelial framework—*mycelial strand;* (b) Concerted apical extension of a number of associated hyphae—*rhizomorph*. These contrasting patterns have significant consequences for the relation between strands and mycelium (Fig. 2).

a. Mycelial Strands (see also Chapter 12, II, B). Mycelial strand development has been summarized by Garrett (1960) and further details for

Agaricus bisporus have been described more recently (Mathew, 1961). Strand formation is preceded by growth of free aerial mycelium in which individual hyphae and their branches tend to grow away from one another. Later special "following" hyphae develop with the characteristic quality of growing either backward or forward alongside preexisting "adopted" hyphae of the aerial mycelium. Initiation of "following" hyphae varies in different fungi. In *Helicobasidium purpureum* many arise from the food base some time after growth of the leading hyphae while a few are accumulated at other points along the length of the "adopted" hyphae or arise by branching of "following" hyphae. In *Merulius lacrymans* [*Serpula lacrimans*] (Butler, 1958) and *Phymatotrichum omnivorum* "following" hyphae are initiated as narrow "tendril" hyphae at a particular and late stage in the hierarchy of branch development from main leading hyphae. Such tendril hyphae adopt adjacent main hyphae (often their parent hyphae) and continue to grow and branch to form further "tendril" hyphae.

Longitudinal strands are thus formed by a combination of growth of already existing "following" hyphae with the continued initiation of new "following" hyphae in acropetal succession along younger parts of "adopted" hyphae. Since in all instances "following" hyphae are not initiated in the mycelial margin and do not grow faster than leading hyphae, strand development consistently lags behind marginal extension of the colony, each strand tapering to the single "adopted" hypha in the mycelial margin (Fig. 2A). Increase in strand thickness by further growth of "following" hyphae can continue after adjacent free mycelial growth has ceased and seems potentially unlimited in *S. lacrimans* and *Agaricus campestris*. Alternatively, strand thickness may be limited by poor development of "following" hyphae (*H. purpureum*), or by differentiation of the strand surface (*P. omnivorum*). Strand branching also reflects the characteristics of "following" and "adopted" hyphae. Where an "adopted" hypha has formed a free branch or crosses the path of another hypha, the "following" hyphae may grow along either. Thus the nature of the preceding mycelium is an important factor in strand orientation and, depending upon conditions of growth, strands may branch dendritically or a reticulum may be formed.

b. Rhizomorphs (see also Chapter 12, II, C). Rhizomorphs, like spore-bearing synnemata (Langeron, 1945), are initiated as local centers of associated growth, often behind the mycelial margin. After initiation they extend unidirectionally as autonomous structures growing separately from and faster than unassociated mycelium (Garrett, 1953; Snider, 1959). Initiation of synnemata in *Hirsutella gigantea* (Loughheed, 1963) as discrete areas of hyphal proliferation in the aerial mycelium which later

3. Vegetative Structures

develop an organized growing point is to some extent comparable with development in *Armillaria mellea*. Here rhizomorph apices are initiated at the surface of a microsclerotium in the medium (Brefeld, 1877). On the other hand, rhizomorphs in *Phallus impudicus* seem to arise by association between aerial leader hyphae of equal status (Butler, 1963). Whereas rhizomorphs of *P. impudicus* and *Marasmius androsaceus* (Macdonald, 1949) and spore-bearing synnemata grow in the air, those of *A. mellea* and *Sphaerostilbe repens* (Goos, 1962) extend within agar media.

In all instances, increase in length is limited to a short apical region. In the most famous rhizomorph, that of *A. mellea,* the apex is highly organized (de Bary, 1887) (Fig. 2C). The growing point is surrounded by an outwardly directed layer of filamentous hyphae with gelatinous membranes. Hyphal construction of the growing point is concealed by lack of intercellular spaces and by short cell length. Cell multiplication occurs here, and behind this is a short region (ca. 1 mm) of elongation and increase in width in which the longitudinal rows of hyphal segments are apparent, with large cells in the central medulla and smaller cells in the surrounding cortex. Here both increase in cell size and intercalary cell division play significant parts.

Although some subapical inflation occurs, for example, in the stipe of *Polyporus brumalis* (Plunkett, 1961), the organization of *A. mellea* seems to be distinct from the bundle of parallel apically extending hyphae occurring at the tips of other aggregates, e.g., *Isaria cretacea* (Taber and Vining, 1959) and *M. androsaceus* (Macdonald, 1949). Thus in *Phallus impudicus* (Butler, 1963; Fig. 2B) the apex is like a paint brush, consisting of a loose array of forwardly directed unbranched hyphae with their individual apices at different levels. The hyphae here are readily teased apart, but about 1 mm behind the leading tips they are much more resistant to teasing. The hyphae are more closely packed, often in contact with one another, anastomoses occur, and small hyphal branches are developing. This column is surrounded by a sparse fringe of hyphae directed obliquely forward. Perhaps associated with their lower level of structural integrity, rhizomorph apices of *P. impudicus* tend to break down into unassociated mycelium much more readily than those of *A. mellea*.

So far as is known increase in thickness behind the apex is small. Branching occurs apically by dichotomous or palmate division in *A. mellea* and *P. impudicus,* or lateral branches arise endogenously as new centers of growth in mature parts of rhizomorphs (*A. mellea, M. androsaceus*).

Thus, there is considerable heterogeneity in strand growth, and Garrett (1960) has suggested that different and probably intermediate patterns will be found as further fungi are investigated. It is interesting that in both types, although hyphal proximity is universal, other features enhancing hyphal association, notably surface contact, twining, and hyphal anastomoses, do not necessarily occur in the earliest stages of strand development.

3. Structure

In mycelial strands the "adopted" hypha is often wider than the "following" hyphae. Apart from this size difference, hyphae contributing to extension of both mycelial strands and rhizomorphs are usually all similar, having indeterminate growth, thin walls, dense protoplasmic contents, and septa ("structural" hyphae of Falck, 1912). In older parts of strands changes may involve growth of new structural branches and, sooner or later, differentiation by modification of segments of these structural hyphae or by growth of specialized hyphal branches. Strand structure has previously been reviewed by Bommer (1896) and Lohwag (1941). The processes leading to strand differentiation are not well understood and it seems likely that some of the discrepancies between different accounts of the same fungus are due to differences in degree of maturity of the material studied.

a. Hyphal Differentiation. This is sometimes absent, particularly in fungi forming thinner strands, e.g., *Helicobasidium purpureum* (Valder, 1958). Among the diverse array of fungi with differentiated strands, although the detailed structure and patterns of hyphal development are specific for individual fungi, two general forms of hyphal differentiation can be distinguished. Some hyphae differentiate by wall thickening, often with pigmentation, but with little or no wall extension. Concomitant with wall thickening, the cell lumen is reduced and protoplasmic contents may disappear. In some instances these can be seen to arise from structural hyphae as special branches which remain unbranched and have limited growth, e.g., fiber hyphae of *Serpula lacrimans* (Falck, 1912) (Fig. 3D). In others intercalary segments develop thickened walls, e.g., *Armillaria mellea* (Fig. 3C).

The second type of differentiation is characterized by increase in width of intercalary hyphal segments. Internal accumulation of clear homogeneous contents or crystalloid deposits is a very common feature of such wide hyphae. Lohwag (1941) provides evidence that these contents are storage materials, often proteins. Rather less commonly, local or general wall thickening occurs or the cross walls between such elements disappear so that continuous tubes are formed, e.g., *S. lacrimans* (Falck, 1912). All these wide hyphae are sometimes called "vascular" or "conducting" hyphae (Lohwag, 1941) (Fig. 3D) but there seems no experimental evidence that they are more efficient channels of conduction than ordinary hyphae. Some

3. Vegetative Structures

of wide, thin-walled hyphae with abundant septa which grows out from the margin of the medulla.

4. Types of Strand

Virtually the only structural feature common to all strands is their linear aggregation. Strands differ greatly in method of initiation, method of extension, and pattern of differentiation. Falck (1912) distinguished between "syrrotia," which arise by later transformation of mycelium and contain crowded elongated elements, including "vascular" and "fiber" hyphae as in *Serpula lacrimans,* and rhizomorphs, which have an apical growing point and lack vascular hyphae and, instead, at some stage have an internal hollow space, e.g., *Armillaria mellea.* His developmental criteria correspond to Garrett's distinction between mycelial strands and rhizomorphs. However, with our present information, there is not a consistent correlation between method of extension and pattern of differentiation. For example, *Phymatotrichum omnivorum* develops as a mycelial strand but differentiates more like *A. mellea,* whereas *Phallus impudicus* extends apically but after differentiation contains densely packed elongated elements.

Strands occur in a considerable taxonomic diversity of fungi, and much of their structure is related to their taxonomic position. Strands of closely related species are similar in general plan and type of differentiation but differ in the degree of differentiation, e.g., *Merulius* spp. (Harmsen, 1954) and Lycoperdaceae (Swartz, 1933). In *Ramularia* the dimitic construction of the strand, as well as of the fruit body, is taxonomically significant (Corner and Thind, 1961), and in *Marasmius androsaceus* rhizomorphs and fruit body stipes are indistinguishable in structure and tropic sensitivity over a considerable period of development (Macdonald, 1949).

Functionally, strands appear to occupy a similar position in all fungi, as a multihyphal link between nutrient supplies and massive fruit bodies or massive substrates to be colonized. Garrett (1960) provides evidence that aggregation per se is significant in giving an adequate inoculum potential for substrate colonization (or, by extrapolation, energy for fruit body production). Whether hyphal differentiation is important for functional efficiency, whether for conduction, storage, or protection, remains an open question.

B. Sclerotia

1. Concept and Occurrence

Sclerotia are firm aggregations of vegetative hyphae with determinate growth. They contain reserve materials and after maturity are capable of independent persistence for a considerable period of time. On germination they form either mycelia or reproductive structures at the expense of the reserve materials. Tode's genus *Sclerotium* is retained for sclerotium-forming sterile mycelia, and sclerotia also occur sporadically in a wide diversity of higher fungi. They are particularly characteristic of certain taxa, e.g., *Sclerotinia, Claviceps,* and *Typhula.*

There have been various attempts to give the concept a more precise morphological significance but, while this is appropriate within a close circle of affinity, more broadly it invariably excludes some of the structures generally accepted as sclerotia. They are very variable in form, often rounded, and may be any size from a few cells to more than 10 cm across. There is often a clearly defined dark-colored and sometimes hard outer rind enclosing a medulla of densely packed hyphae lacking consistent orientation. Some of the smallest structures, consisting of a few cells without a rind and medulla, are sometimes described as "bulbils" or "microsclerotia." The sclerotium may also enclose tissue of the substratum but is usually separated from the substratum after maturity. However, the degree of separation depends on the nature of the substratum as well as on the activity of the fungus. The areas of colonized wood enclosed by sclerotic fungal tissue formed by some wood-destroying fungi have been compared with sclerotia (Campbell and Munson, 1936), but their physiological significance is at present uncertain. Leakey (1964) discusses the propriety of including the structures formed by *Dactuliophora* as sclerotia. Each of these is borne on a multihyphal cuplike sclerotiophore on the surface of the mycelial mass. The sclerotiophore fractures to liberate a multicellular structure, the sclerotium, which appears to be functionally analogous with a multicellular conidium. Parts of multihyphal reproductive structures may persist as an independent vegetative phase for some time and, therefore, are sclerotia, e.g., some stromata and pseudorhizae. In the ascomycetes, the distinction between sclerotial and nonsclerotial stromata is not sharp (see Chapter 5), and only those with a clearly separate vegetative sclerotial phase will be considered further in this section.

2. Development

Since the pioneer studies of Brefeld (1877) and de Bary (1887) little attention had been paid to morphological features of sclerotium development until the work of Townsend and Willetts (1954).

a. Initiation. The majority of sclerotia arise as discrete initials among the vegetative mycelium, and Townsend and Willetts distinguished between two main types (Fig. 4). In the *"terminal"* type the initial is formed by condensed terminal growth and branching of an individual hyphal tip, e.g., *Botrytis allii, B. cinerea,* and *Sclerotium cepivorum* (Townsend and Willetts, 1954), *Pyronema domesticum* (Moore, 1962), and *Coprinus stercorarius* (Brefeld, 1877). Initials from adjacent hyphae sometimes develop together to form a single sclerotium, e.g., *C. stercorarius*. Alternatively, in the *"strand"* type, intercalary segments of one or more hyphae develop by the formation of additional septa and the production of numerous side branches or budlike outgrowths, e.g., *Sclerotinia gladioli* (Townsend and Willetts, 1954), *Aspergillus alliaceus* (Rudolph, 1962), and *Verticillium dahliae* (Isaac, 1949). The number of hyphal segments contributing to one sclerotium is variable within one species, e.g., *S. gladioli,* and Townsend and Willetts suggest that this variation is dependent on the degree of proximity of initials on separate hyphae. Whether there is a tendency for

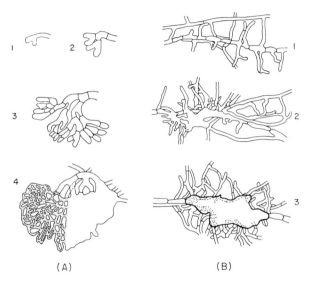

FIG. 4. Sclerotium development. (A) Stages in development of *Botrytis allii* ("terminal" type). Magnification: × 225. (B) Stages in development of *Sclerotinia gladioli* ("strand" type). Magnification: × 225. After Townsend and Willetts (1954).

sclerotium initials of separate hyphae to develop close together in clumps has not been ascertained. However, in *Sclerotium rolfsii* and *Phymatotrichum omnivorum* sclerotia consistently develop from intercalary segments of the associated hyphae in a strand.

These two types seem reasonably distinct for most of the species so far investigated but may well require modification as more becomes known. Hotson (1917) describes both terminal and intercalary development of bulbils in one species of *Papulospora*. *Rhizoctonia solani* [*Corticium solani*] stands somewhat by itself (Townsend and Willetts, 1954) in that sclerotia are initiated by intercalary septation and development of one or a few specialized branches from adjacent hyphae.

b. *Increase in Size.* Initiation is followed by a phase of increase in size, usually by hyphal tip growth. The growing hyphae branch at short intervals and are often wide with short cells. In an extreme example, *C. solani*, these short, much-branched cells appear almost yeastlike. The developing mass is loose, with actively growing tips within, as well as at, its surface. In some sclerotia there is a general outward direction of growth, at least of the surface hyphae, e.g., *Coprinus stercorarius,* and *Botrytis,* where the terminal initials branch dichotomously. Very frequently, however, the hyphae seem randomly orientated, coiling and interweaving throughout the mass, e.g., *Typhula* (Corner, 1950) and *Pyronema domesticum.* Even in these early stages intercalary inflation may play a part in increase in size. In *Phymatotrichum omnivorum* the very young enlarging initial appears to consist of closely packed short-celled elements and the hyphal processes involved in enlargement are not clear. Intervening host or substrate tissue is sometimes incorporated into the sclerotium as it increases in size, e.g., *Botrytis* (Noviello and Korf, 1961).

c. *Maturation.* Sclerotia are characteristically structures of limited growth, and maturation is marked by surface delimitation and internal consolidation and is often associated with the excretion of liquid droplets (de Bary, 1887). Most frequently the structure is delimited by the formation of a rind of coalesced hyphal segments which develop thickened, agglutinated, and dark-colored walls. Internal consolidation may involve some infilling by hyphal tip growth in the early stages but appears to consist mostly of intercalary expansion and septation associated with hyphal anastomoses. Rather later, reserve materials accumulate either as wall thickening or in the cell lumina. The mature structure of the sclerotium can to some extent be related to the proportion and relative timing of the various growth and differentiation processes. Thus, Townsend and Willetts distinguished between groups on the basis of the temporal relation between rind development and attainment of maximum size. Firstly, in *C. solani* no rind develops and cell size and wall thickening are uniform throughout. The peripheral region is loose, surrounding a more densely packed central area. Then, in a number of species (*Botrytis* spp., *Sclerotinia sclerotiorum,* and *Pyronema domesticum*) rind development occurs relatively late and terminates the phases of increase in size by growth and internal expansion. Thus, in *P. domesticum* a phase of hyphal branching, coiling, and bulging is followed by one of septation and cell expansion which ceases as the rind is differentiated. De Bary (1887) describes the centrifugal spread of differentiation in *S. sclerotiorum.* Thirdly, the rind may develop relatively earlier and become stretched as internal expansion continues, e.g., *Typhula, S. gladioli* and *Sclerotium rolfsii.* Among the few species so far investigated there seems to be a correlation between terminal development and late rinding and between strand development and early rinding (Townsend and Willetts, 1954). It remains to be seen how far this will hold as details for other species become established.

Rind formation does not necessarily take place at the outer surface of the developing initial. Thus, in *Typhula* (Remsberg, 1940), *S. rolfsii, S. sclerotiorum,* and *P. domesticum* the rind is covered by an outer undifferentiated hyphal weft. A striking property of the rind is that rind excision from a mature sclerotium, as in *Sclerotinia* and *C. stercorarius,* results in regeneration of a differentiated rind. On the other hand, no regeneration occurs in *Typhula.* In *Botrytis cinerea* rind is poorly developed on the side in contact with a solid surface but soon differentiates on exposure to the air.

d. Other Patterns of Development. In *Claviceps purpurea* (de Bary, 1887) the sclerotium replaces preexisting mycelium in the host ovary, starting at the base of the mycelium-filled ovary and extending acropetally. The hyphae become densely interwoven and closely septate, with thick walls and oil drops in the cell lumina. The structure appears to increase in length by intercalary growth and the outermost hyphae form a violet-brown rind.

In *Cordyceps* the infected host behaves as a resting stage enclosed not by a fungal rind, but by the host cuticle. It is possible that other sclerotia may develop by conversion of an extensive preexisting vegetative mycelium rather than by growth from a localized initial. The large sclerotia of some polypores are enclosed by a fungal rind but incorporate host roots (*Polyporus umbellatus*) or stones and soil (*P. tuberaster*) (Bommer, 1896). Their development is not known, but the zone lines enclosing vegetative mycelium of *Polyporus squamosus* and other fungi in colonized wood are morphologically similar to a rind (Campbell and Munson, 1936) and suggest the possibility of sclerotium development by transformation and rinding of vegetative mycelium. In this context the mechanism of delimitation of the stroma in agar cultures of *Lambertella copticola* is interesting (Tewari, 1963). Patches of hyphae at the surface of the aerial mass over the agar medium produce abundant short, stubby primary, secondary, and tertiary branches, which then differentiate to form the rind. The patches are at first small (up to 10 mm) but eventually coalesce to cover an extensive area.

3. Range of Variation in Mature Structure

The basic pattern of differentiation is into concentric zones, but there is a considerable range of structural detail (de Bary, 1887; Lohwag, 1941) (Fig. 5). A rind is absent in *Corticium solani* and in most bulbils, e.g., *Papulospora* (Hotson, 1917). The bulbil consists of an aggregation of isodiametric cells with slightly thickened brown walls or, in some instances, an outer layer of empty cells encloses central cells with dense contents. Gordee and Porter (1961) claim that the microsclerotia of *Verticillium alboatrum* contain an interspersed mixture of thick- and thin-walled cells.

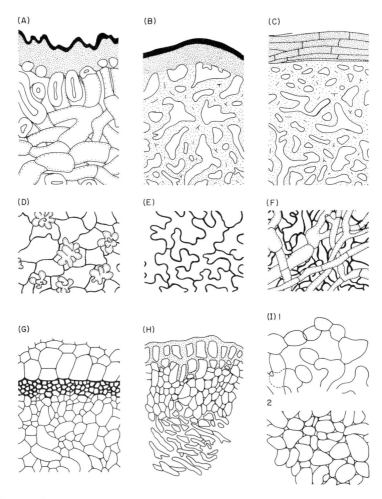

FIG. 5. Structure of mature sclerotium. Sections of peripheral regions of *Typhula intermedia*. (A) *T. phacorrhiza*. (B) and *T. gyrans*. (C) Magnification: × 350 Surface views of *T. intermedia*. (D) *T. phacorrhiza*. (E) and *T. gyrans*. (F) Magnification: × 225. After Remsberg (1940). Sections of peripheral regions of *Coprinus stercorarius*. (G) (after Brefeld 1877), *Botrytis cinerea*. (H) and *Corticium solani*. (I; *1*, peripheral hyphae; *2*, central region). After Townsend and Willetts (1954). Magnification: × 350.

Isaac (1949) distinguishes consolidated microsclerotia from looser "mycelial knots," consisting of intertwined hyphae.

A great many sclerotia have a rind and medulla, each of which is either entirely homogeneous or is subdivided into further concentric layers. Individual layers contain homogeneous elements. In *Aspergillus alliaceus* (Rudolph, 1962), *Pyronema domesticum* (Moore, 1962), and *Claviceps purpurea* (de Bary, 1887), only two layers, rind and medulla, are present whereas in *Coprinus stercorarius* the medulla of thin-walled, closely packed hyphae with short cells is enclosed by a double rind—an inner region of four to five layers of small cells with brown thick walls and an outer region of three or more layers of large, irregular, black-walled cells (Brefeld, 1877). Multiple zonation occurs in some species of *Sclerotinia* (Townsend and Willetts, 1954; de Bary, 1887) and of *Typhula* (Corner, 1950). The range of variation within one group of closely related species is instructive for the relation between zones. In *Typhula* the dark-colored rind consists either of a thick deposit ("cuticle") on the outer walls of the peripheral hyphal cells or of layers of thick-walled hyphae ("epidermis"), which may or may not be agglutinated and are wound round the medulla. The outermost cells have specific lumen shapes and patterns of wall thickening. The internal hyphae are thick-walled and show varying degrees of agglutination, always reaching a maximum toward the outside. Sometimes the hyphal wall boundaries remain distinct but, in others, the walls are completely fused and the lumina appear to be embedded in a continuous matrix. In all species with an epidermis, and in some others, the whole internal tissue is agglutinated and there is no distinct cortex. In the remaining species the medulla contains loose hyphae and the surrounding agglutinated region is one to many cells thick. Thus, in *Typhula,* there are two distinct types of rind and the detail of internal zonation is a specific character. In *Sclerotinia,* an additional variable is the presence and frequency of host inclusions (Noviello and Korf, 1961).

A final group of sclerotia have a rind and medulla but the latter contains intermingled heterogeneous elements. This construction is particularly characteristic of the massive sclerotia now known to belong to polypores and related forms, e.g., *Polyporus tuberaster* (stone fungus, Canadian tuckahoe), *P. mylittae* (blackfellow's bread), *P. umbellatus, P. sacer, P. rhinoceros, Poria cocos,* and *Lentinus* spp. (*Pachyma,* tuckahoe, Indian bread). Their structure was described in detail by Bommer (1896) and subsequently reviewed by Lohwag (1941). These sclerotia vary in many features, e.g., shape and extramatrical inclusions, but in all the medulla contains distinct hyphae (thin-walled and narrow thick-walled hyphae) interspersed with grossly distorted very thick-walled structures whose hyphal nature is difficult to discern ("coralloid hyphae" and "light refractive bodies"; Lohwag, 1941).

4. *True Sclerotia and Sclerotioid Structures*

In the broad sense, sclerotia are united functionally as persistent resting stages but reveal considerable developmental and structural diversity. They also differ in their behavior on germination. Renewed activity usually occurs at localized but random points in the medulla, but in one instance, *Coprinus stercorarius,* germination occurs from the rind (Brefeld, 1877). In some bulbils all the cells are capable of germination, but Gordee and Porter (1961) report germination only from the thin-walled cells in *Verticillium alboatrum*. Many germinate to form an external reproductive structure, e.g., *Claviceps, Typhula, Sclerotinia,* and *Polyporus,* but others may form internal reproductive structures, e.g., *Aspergillus alliaceus* (Rudolph, 1962) and the pycnosclerotia of *Guignardia bidwellii* (Caltrider, 1961). Yet others form mycelium on germination, e.g., *Sclerotium, Phymatotrichum omnivorum, Corticium solani* and bulbils. Moreover, some of those whose germination is mycelial or uncertain seem clearly related to reproductive phases of the same or allied species. Thus, *Sclerotium cepivorum* sclerotia are very similar to those of *Botrytis* spp., and in *Neurospora sitophila* the sterile sclerotia look like perithecia. Pseudorhizae of the Agaricales, e.g., *Collybia fusipes,* and the Ascomycetes, e.g., *Sarcoscypha protracta,* have some of the structural and functional properties of sclerotia. Buller (1934) has shown that these are formed by intercalary growth of part of the fruit body.

It is not possible to separate categories of sclerotia on the basis of structure alone, but de Bary (1887) and Lohwag (1941) prefer to restrict true sclerotia to those that germinate forming external reproductive structures or that are clearly related to such forms. They separate the remainder into a variety of categories of sclerotioid structure, e.g., resting mycelia, bulbils, sclerotioid reproductive structures, and pseudorhizae.

IV. FUNGAL TISSUES

There is evidence, particularly among sclerotia, that development involves not only hyphal tip growth, which can in some instances approach yeastlike budding, but also modification of intercalary segments, including cell enlargement and formation of additional cross walls. In fungal aggregations the resultant tissue, plectenchyma, after differentiation may retain its hyphal character (prosenchyma) or may appear not to be hyphal (pseudoparenchyma). However, the derivation of the latter during development may be diverse, e.g., extension as short-celled hyphae, later formation of additional septa or hyphal distortion and wall agglutination. Appreciation of such ontogenetic diversity is a feature of more recent studies, including that on fungal gel tissue (Moore, 1965).

Although colonies consist of hyphae that are only intermittently in contact with one another, they have definable structure suggesting some degree of coordination as well as internal organization. Growth and specialization of hyphae occurs together in zones and also as individual elements. However, these features are much more evident in strands and sclerotia. The sporadic occurrence and structural and ontogenetic diversity of both strands and sclerotia suggest that each category includes a number of analogous aggregations. Their detailed patterns of hyphal differentiation must be considered with regard to the taxonomic position of the individual fungi.

REFERENCES

Bommer, C. (1896). Sclérotes et cordons mycéliens. *Mem. Acad. Roy. Sci. Belg.* **54**:1–116.

Borrow, A., E. G. Jefferys, R. H. J. Kessell, E. C. Lloyd, P. B. Lloyd, and I. S. Nixon. (1961). The metabolism of *Gibberella fujikuroi* in stirred culture. *Can. J. Microbiol.* **7**:227–276.

Borrow, A., S. Brown, E. G. Jeffreys, R. H. J. Kessel, E. C. Lloyd, P. B. Lloyd, A. Rothwell, B. Rothwell, and J. C. Swait. (1964). The kinetics of metabolism of *Gibberella fujikuroi* in stirred culture. *Can. J. Microbiol.* **10**:407–444.

Brefeld, O. (1877). "Botanische Untersuchungen über Schimmelpilze," Vol. III. Felix, Leipzig.

Brown, A. H. S., and G. Smith. (1957). The genus *Paecilomyces* Bainier and its perfect stage *Byssochlamys* Westling. *Brit. Mycol. Soc. Trans.* **40**:17–89.

Brown, W. (1923). Experiments on the growth of fungi on culture media. *Ann. Botany (London)* **37**:105–129.

Buller, A. H. R. (1924). "Researches on Fungi," Vol. III, 611 pp. Longmans, Green, New York.

Buller, A. H. R. (1931). "Researches on Fungi," Vol. IV, 329 pp. Longmans, Green, New York.

Buller, A. H. R. (1933). "Researches on Fungi," Vol. V, 416 pp. Longmans, Green, New York.

Buller, A. H. R. (1934). "Researches on Fungi," Vol. VI, 513 pp. Longmans, Green, New York.

Burkholder, P. R., and E. W. Sinnott. (1945). Morphogenesis of fungus colonies in submerged, shaken cultures. *Am. J. Botany* **32**:424–431.

Butler, G. M. (1958). The development and behaviour of mycelial strands in *Merulius lacrymans* (Wulf.) Fr. II. Hyphal behaviour during strand formation. *Ann. Botany (London)* [N.S.] **22**:219-236.

Butler, G. M. (1961). Growth of hyphal branching systems in *Coprinus disseminatus*. *Ann. Botany (London)* [N.S.] **25**:341–352.

Butler, G. M. (1963). Unpublished data.

Caltrider, P. G. (1961). Growth and sporulation in *Guignardia bidwellii*. *Phytopathology* **51**:860–863.

Camici, L., G. Sermonti, and E. B. Chain. (1952). Observations on *Penicillium chrysogenum* in submerged culture. I. Mycelial growth and autolysis. *Bull. World Health Organ.* 6:265–276.

Campbell, A. H., and R. G. Munson. (1936). Zone lines in plant tissues III. The black lines formed by *Polyporus squamosus* (Huds.) Fr. *Ann. Appl. Biol.* 23:453–464.

Carlile, M. J., and M. A. Sellin. (1963). An endogenous inhibition of spore germination in fungi. *Brit. Mycol. Soc. Trans.* 46:15–18.

Carlile, M. J., J. S. W. Dickens, E. M. Mordue and M. A. A. Schipper. (1962). The development of coremia II. *Penicillium isariiforme*. *Brit. Mycol. Soc. Trans.* 45:457–461.

Chevaugeon, J. (1959). La zonation du thalle, phénomène périodique autonome chez l'*Ascobolus immersus*. *Compt. Rend.* 248:1381–1384.

Clark, D. S. (1962). Submerged citric acid fermentation of ferrocyanide-treated beet molasses: Morphology of pellets of *Aspergillus niger*. *Can. J. Microbiol.* 8:133–136.

Cochrane, V. W. (1958). "Physiology of Fungi," 524 pp. Wiley, New York.

Corner, E. J. H. (1950). "A Monograph of *Clavaria* and Allied Genera," 740 pp. Oxford Univ. Press, London and New York.

Corner, E. J. H., and K. S. Thind. (1961). Dimitic species of *Ramaria* (Clavariaceae). *Brit. Mycol. Soc. Trans.* 44:233–238.

de Bary, A. (1887). "Comparative Morphology and Biology of the Fungi, Mycetozoa and Bacteria," 525 pp. Oxford Univ. Press (Clarendon), London and New York.

Dion, W. M., A. Carilli, G. Sermonti, and E. B. Chain. (1954). The effect of mechanical agitation on the morphology of *Penicillium chrysogenum* Thom in stirred fermenters. *Rend. Ist. Super. Sanita* 17:187–205.

Duckworth, R. B., and G. C. M. Harris. (1949). The morphology of *Penicillium chrysogenum* in submerged fermentations. *Brit. Mycol. Soc. Trans.* 32:224–235.

Emerson, R. (1955). *In* "Aspects of Synthesis and Order in Growth" (D. Rudnick, ed.), pp. 171–208. Princeton Univ. Press, Princeton, New Jersey.

Emerson, S. (1950). The growth phase in *Neurospora* corresponding to the logarithmic phase in unicellular organisms. *J. Bacteriol.* 60:221–223.

Falck, R. (1912). Die *Merulius* Fäule des Bauholzes. *Hausschwammforsch.* 6:1–405.

Flentje, N. T., H. M. Stratton, and E. J. Hawn. (1963). Nuclear distribution and behaviour throughout the life cycles of *Thatanephorus, Waitea* and *Ceratobasidium* spp. *Australian J. Biol. Sci.* 16:450–467.

Foster, J. W. (1949). "Chemical Activities of Fungi," 648 pp. Academic Press, New York.

Garrett, S. D. (1953). Rhizomorph behaviour in *Armillaria mellea* (Vahl) Quél. I. Factors controlling rhizomorph initiation by *A. mellea* in pure culture. *Ann. Botany (London)* [N.S.] 17:63–79.

Garrett, S. D. (1960). *In* "Plant Pathology" (J. G. Horsfall and A. E. Dimond, eds.), Vol. 3, pp. 23–56. Academic Press, New York.

Goos, R. D. (1962). The occurrence of *Sphaerostilbe repens* in Central American soils. *Am. J. Botany* 49:19–23.

Gordee, R. S., and C. L. Porter. (1961). Structure, germination and physiology of microsclerotia of *Verticillium alboatrum*. *Mycologia* 53:171–182.

Grover, S. (1961). An experimental study on the growth of fungal colonies in relation to hyphal behaviour. Ph.D. Thesis, University of London.

3. Vegetative Structures

Hadley, G., and C. E. Harrold. (1958). The sporulation of *Penicillium notatum* Westling in submerged liquid culture. II. The initial sporulation phase. *J. Exptl. Botany* 9:418–425.

Harmsen, L. (1954). De danske *Merulius*—arter. *Botan. Tidsskr.* 50:146–162.

Hein, I. (1930). Studies on the mycelium of *Psalliota campestris*. *Am. J. Botany* 17:197–211.

Hering, T. F. (1962). Infection cushions of *Helicobasidium purpureum* Pat. *Brit. Mycol. Soc. Trans.* 45:46–54.

Hotson, J. W. (1917). Notes on bulbiferous fungi with a key to described species. *Botan. Gaz.* 64:265–284.

Isaac, I. (1949). A comparative study of pathogenic isolates of *Verticillium*. *Brit. Mycol. Soc. Trans.* 32:137–157.

Lander, C. A. (1933). The morphology of the developing fruiting body of *Lycoperdon gemmatum*. *Am. J. Botany* 20:204–215.

Langeron, M. (1945). "Précis de mycologie," 674 pp. Masson, Paris.

Larpent, J. P. (1962). La notion de dominance apicale chez *Rhizoctonia solani* Kühn. *Compt. Rend.* 254:1137–1139.

Larpent, J. P. (1963). Croissance et ramification dans le mycélium jeune du *Saprolegnia monoica* Pringsheim. *88ᵉ Congr. Soc. Savantes, Clermont-Ferrand* pp. 399–405.

Larpent, J. P. (1965). Relation entre vitesse de croissance et ramification du mycélium jeune de quelques champignons. *Compt. Rend.* 260:265–267.

Leakey, C. L. A. (1964). *Dactuliophora*, a new genus of Mycelia Sterilia from tropical Africa. *Brit. Mycol. Soc. Trans.* 47:341–350.

Lohwag, H. (1941). "Anatomie der Asco- und Basidiomyceten," 529 pp. Bornträger, Berlin (Microfilm of translation by W. B. Cooke and H. Q. Middendorf).

Loughheed, T. C. (1963). Studies on the morphology of synnemata of *Hirsutella gigantea* Petch. *Can. J. Botany* 41:947–952.

Macdonald, J. A. (1949). The heather rhizomorph fungus *Marasmius androsaceus* Fr. *Proc. Roy. Soc. Edinburgh* B63:230–241.

Machlis, L. (1957). Factors affecting the lag phase of growth of the filamentous fungus *Allomyces macrogynus*. *Am. J. Botany* 44:113–119.

Mathew, K. T. (1961). Morphogenesis of mycelial strands in the cultivated mushroom, *Agaricus bisporus*. *Brit. Mycol. Soc. Trans.* 44:285–290.

Moore, E. J. (1962). The ontogeny of the sclerotia of *Pyronema domesticum*. *Mycologia* 54:312–316.

Moore, E. J. (1965). Fungal gel tissue ontogenesis. *Am. J. Botany* 52:389–395.

Morton, A. G. (1961). The induction of sporulation in mould fungi. *Proc. Roy. Soc.* B153:548–569.

Nobles, M. K. (1948). Studies in forest pathology 6. Identification of cultures of wood rotting fungi. *Can. J. Res.* C26:281–431.

Noviello, C., and R. P. Korf. (1961). A simple technique for investigating stromatal formation in the Sclerotiniaceae. *Mycologia* 53:237–243.

Park, D. (1961). Morphogenesis, fungistasis and cultural staling in *Fusarium oxysporum* Snyder and Hansen. *Brit. Mycol. Soc. Trans.* 44:377–390.

Pirt, S. J., and D. S. Callow. (1959). Continuous-flow culture of the filamentous mould *Penicillium chrysogenum* and the control of its morphology. *Nature* 184:307–310.

Plomley, N. J. B. (1959). Formation of the colony in the fungus *Chaetomium*. *Australian J. Biol. Sci.* 12:53–64.

Plunkett, B. E. (1961). The change of tropism in *Polyporus brumalis* stipes and the effect of directional stimuli on pileus differentiation. *Ann. Botany (London)* [N.S.] 25:206–223.
Raper, K. B., and C. Thom. (1949). "A Manual of the Penicillia," 875 pp. Williams & Wilkins, Baltimore, Maryland.
Remsberg, R. E. (1940). Studies in the genus *Typhula*. *Mycologia* 32:52–96.
Ritchie, D. (1960). Spiral growth of fungus colonies. *Growth* 24:390–400.
Robinson, P. M., and D. Park. (1965). The production and quantitative estimation of a fungal morphogen. *Brit. Mycol. Soc. Trans.* 48:561–571.
Rogers, C. H., and G. M. Watkins. (1938). Strand formation in *Phymatotrichum omnivorum*. *Am. J. Botany* 25:244–246.
Rudolph, E. D. (1962). The effect of some physiological and environmental factors on sclerotial Aspergilli. *Am. J. Botany* 49:71–78.
Ryan, F. J., G. W. Beadle, and E. L. Tatum. (1943). The tube method of measuring the growth rate of *Neurospora*. *Am. J. Botany* 30:784–799.
Shatkin, A. J., and E. L. Tatum. (1961). The relationship of *m*-inositol to morphology in *Neurospora crassa*. *Am. J. Botany* 48:760–771.
Smith, J. H. (1924). On the early growth rate of the individual fungus hypha. *New Phytologist* 23:65–78.
Snider, P. J. (1959). Stages of development in rhizomorphic thalli of *Armillaria mellea*. *Mycologia* 51:693–707.
Snider, P. J., and Raper, J. R. (1958). Nuclear migration in the basidiomycete *Schizophyllum commune*. *Am. J. Botany* 45:538–546.
Stadler, D. R. (1952). Chemotropism in *Rhizopus nigricans:* The staling reaction. *J. Cellular Comp. Physiol.* 39:449–474.
Swartz, D. (1933). Some developmental characters of species of Lycoperdaceae. *Am. J. Botany* 20:440–465.
Taber, W. A., and L. C. Vining. (1959). Studies on *Isaria cretacea*. Nutritional and morphological characteristics of two strains and morphogenesis of the synnema. *Can. J. Microbiol.* 5:513–535.
Tarn, T. R. (1963). Unpublished B.Sc. project, University of Birmingham.
Tewari, V. P. (1963). Morphology and physiology of a new species of *Lambertella* on *Coptis trifolia*. *Mycologia* 55:595–607.
Townsend, B. B. (1954). Morphology and development of fungal rhizomorphs. *Brit. Mycol. Soc. Trans.* 37:222–233.
Townsend, B. B. and H. J. Willetts. (1954). The development of sclerotia of certain fungi. *Brit. Mycol. Soc. Trans.* 37:213–221.
Valder, P. G. (1958). The biology of *Helicobasidium purpureum* Pat. *Brit. Mycol. Soc. Trans.* 41:283–308.
Yanagita, T., and F. Koganė. (1962). Growth and cytochemical differentiation of mold colonies. *J. Gen. Appl. Microbiol.* 8:201–213.
Yanagita, T., and F. Koganė. (1963). Cellular differentiation of growing mold colonies with special reference to phosphorus metabolism. *J. Gen. Appl. Microbiol.* 9:313–330.
Zalokar, M. (1959). Growth and differentiation of *Neurospora* hyphae. *Am. J. Botany* 46:602–610.

CHAPTER 4

Sporulating Structures in Fungi Imperfecti

Keisuke Tubaki

*Institute for Fermentation
Osaka, Japan*

I. INTRODUCTION

In microfungi spores may be produced directly on the hyphae or, more usually, on specialized branches (sporophores). Spores produced without a previous nuclear fusion followed by meiosis and not produced in a sporangium, have commonly been lumped together as "conidia," but on critical examination imperfect fungi show many different kinds of sporulation.

Sporulating structures were first used as a taxonomic criterion by Saccardo in the "Sylloge Fungorum." Saccardo divided spores into many types based on morphological characteristics such as shape, septation, and color (Table I). He was, however, not concerned with the method of conidial production, and it was Vuillemin (1910, 1911, 1912) who stimulated interest in spore development rather than the characteristics of the spores themselves. He drew attention to the difficulties involved in classifying different kinds of spores of imperfect fungi under the single term conidium and recognized two basic spore types: the thallospore and the conidium verum. Vuillemin's proposals were reviewed in detail and clarified by Mason (1933), who introduced additional categories, and Langeron and Vanbreuseghem (1952), following Vuillemin and Mason, used *thallospore* to include arthrospore, blastospore, chlamydospore, dictyospore, and aleuriospore, and *conidiospore* (conidium verum) to include radulaspore, terminus spore and phialospore (meristem spore) (Fig. 1). Moreau (1952, 1953) was the first to extend Vuillemin's ideas on conidial ontogeny

TABLE I
SACCARDO'S SPORE GROUPS[a]

Spores		Saccardo's group names	
		Color of spores and/or mycelium	
Morphology	Designation	Hyaline or pale	Dark
One-celled (0-septate) (Fig. 1 A,B,E)	Amerospore	Hyalosporae	Phaeosporae
Two-celled (1-septate)	Didymospore	Hyalodidymae	Phaeodidymae
Two or more cross septa (Fig. 1F, left)	Phragmospore	Hyalophragmiae	Phaeophragmiae
Muriform (i.e., having both cross and longitudinal septa) (Fig. 1C)	Dictyospore	Hyalodictyae	Phaeodictyae
Threadlike	Scolecospore	—	—
Spirally coiled	Helicospore	—	—
Star-shaped	Staurospore	—	—

[a] Smith (1954, 1962).

from hyphomycetes to other imperfect fungi. In "formes de propagation," he discussed several types of diaspore, and aleuriospore production was recognized in *Discosia, Pestalotia,* and *Siridium.* A year later, Hughes (1953a) advanced criteria for differentiating spore development in hyphomycetes. He divided the various methods of spore production, on the

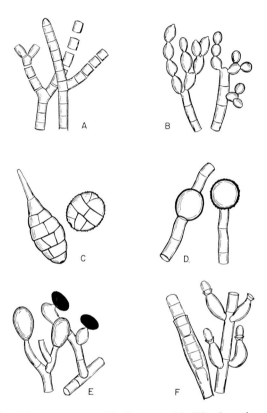

FIG. 1. Vuillemin's spore groups. Thallospores (A–D): A, arthrospores; B, blastospores; C, dictyospores; D, terminal (right) and intercalary (left) chlamydospores. Conidiospores (E and F): E, aleuriospores; F, phialospores.

basis of spore and sporophore ontogeny, into the following eight types: Section Ia, blastospores produced in chains; Section Ib, blastospores: the botryose solitary blastospore as in *Botrytis* and the botryose blastospore as in *Gonatobotryum* or *Nematogonium* in which the spores are in chains; Section II, the terminus spore, as in *Ramularia* or *Heterosporium,* and the botryose terminus spore, as in *Arthrobotrys*; Section III, chlamydospores, solitary, as in *Bactridium,* or successively produced on annellophores, as in *Scopulariopsis*; Section IV, phialospores, in basipetal succession, as in *Phialophora*, or on polyphialides as in *Catenularia*; Section V, meristem arthrospores produced in true basipetal chains due to the meristematic growth of the sporophore, as in *Erysiphe* and coleomyctes; Section VI, porospores, as in *Helminthosporium*; Section VII, arthrospores, as in *Geotrichum*; Section VIII, spores on basauxic conidiophores. Goos (1956) discussed Hughes' scheme and listed and redefined the spore terms, and Tubaki (1958) somewhat amplified Hughes' scheme by dividing each of sections III, IV, and VII into two or three subsections and recognized a new section, IX, for *Trichothecium*-type spores. Subramanian (1962) believed that several more categories were needed to classify the Indian and other tropical fungi. He therefore proposed the following six morphological categories of the spores based on their method of formation: (1) the blastospore, (2) the gangliospore, (3) the phialospore, (4) the porospore, (5) the arthrospore, and (6) the meristem arthrospore. He also foresaw a seventh category, the spiculospore, which is formed at the tip of a pointed structure, as in *Hirsutella* and *Akanthomyces*. Tubaki (1963), extending his previous work, discussed spore and sporophore ontogeny, and proposed six divisions in Hypomycetes. He defined the foregoing spore types and proposed three new ones: *terminoradulaspore*, as in *Beauveria*; *meristem aleuriospore*, as in *Trichothecium*; and *pleuroradulaspore*, as in *Aureobasidium*. In addition, he recognized that the method by which a conidium functions as a growing point should be taken as a differential character. These different types of spore will now be considered individually and in greater detail.

II. TYPES OF SPORE PRODUCTION

A. *Blastospore Type*

The term blastospore has been used loosely. In general, blastospores are spores which originate as buds or blown-out hyphal tips, and develop in acropetal chains (Fig. 1B). Typical blastospore formation is shown by *Cladosporium, Bispora*, and *Septonema*. In these fungi, the first spore develops as a blown-out sporophore apex and then acts as the growing point and buds off a second blastospore. This development was fully discussed in *Cladosporium* by De Vries (1952): although he rejected the term, blastospore is used for the spore by many authors. In *Cladosporium*, the blastospores are produced in chains from a parent cell on an elongated hyphal system, and may be one-, two- or several-celled. When such spores are one-celled, the generic name *Hormodendrum* has been applied. Hughes (1953a) divided the blastospores into four types: (a) *blastospores* which arise as globular buds or blown-out ends and are in acropetal chains; (b) *solitary blastospores*; (c) *botryose solitary blastospores* which occur in botryose clusters, not in chains; and (d) *botryose blastospores* for catenulate blastospores in botryose clusters.

In the earlier stage of blastospore production in *Cladosporium*, a papilla arises from the apex of the sporophore, increasing in size to form a globose cell which becomes the young blastospore. De Vries observed a short and narrow disjunctor as an only connection between blastospore and sporophores. These are also found between spores. Chains of blastospores may branch when two or more spores bud from one spore. The basal blastospore in spore chains is often designated as a sterigma from the viewpoint of gross morphology, not of spore ontogeny. Plasmodesmata connect the two adjacent protoplasts of the blastospores in *C. sphaerospermum*, and in *C. herbarum* the dark episporium was observed to be drawn away from the hyaline endosporium, the endosporium then appearing to be completely homogeneous (De Vries, 1952).

In the case of blastospores formed in acropetal chains, Mason (1937) presumed that organic connection is not severed at the base and the first-formed spore (at the base of a chain) acts as part of the thallus and transmits nutriment to the later formed spores. Electron microscopically minute pores in the plasmoderma of the spores of *C. herbarum* can be observed (Fig. 2) (Minoura, 1964). This characteristic of blastospores is clearly different from those of other spore types, and blastospore production is not, though it is often considered to be, the same as basipetal sporulation. *Cladosarum olivaceum* provides an interesting example. Yuill and Yuill (1938) showed *C. olivaceum* to have a gross morphology similar to *Aspergillus niger*, but the secondary sterigmata do not give rise to chains of phialospores. Instead, they produce septate branching outgrowths of irregular form, and so the secondary sterigmata have resumed the function of primary sterigmata and repeat the process of producing chains of cells each resembling a sterigma. Thom and Raper (1945) noted in this development that the nuclear procedure of ordinary sterigmata of *A. niger* is reversed; the resting nucleus remains in the sterigma while the active one moves into the newly forming cell, and the active, multiplying nucleus is always in the youngest cell. If true, this nuclear behavior is exactly that of blastospore formation, and a relationship between the blastospore and phialospore may be established.

Blastospore formation of a curious kind was reported by Petersen (1962, 1963) in *Tricellula* and *Volucrispora*. In *T. inaequalis*, a bud arises from the apical cell of the conidiophore and a second cell is budded from its apex; when the second bud is nearly mature, a third cell buds from the first one to one side of the second; thus, the three-celled conidium develops. The apical and lateral cells are connected to the basal cell by narrow protoplasmic isthmuses or constrictions, but eventually separate from it by deposition of wall material. Similar connections between the cells of the spore also occur in *Volucrispora*. Such features were also described by Van Beverwijk (1954) and Haskins (1958).

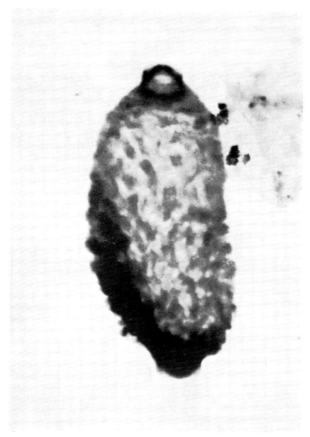

FIG. 2. Pore of the spore of *Cladosporium herbarum*. From Minoura (1964).

B. *Radulaspore Type*

The term radulaspore was originally suggested by Mason (1933) for spores borne on the little pegs which originate from the surface of the hypha, and he considered the radulaspore to be the most primitive type of conidium verum. Goos (1956) recognized the radulaspores as small conidia, borne side by side upon small denticles which cover the surface of the sporophore tips, or which may be produced upon intercalary swellings. Cooke (1962) described the radulaspore as one produced on a minute spicule projecting from the hyphal wall, with usually more than one spicule on each cell and arranged irregularly along its length. These spores are usually not produced in chains, though several spores may be initiated at one point, giving the appearance of clusters of blastospores. Such spicules are morphologically similar to the sterigmata of basidia as recalled by Viala and Boyer (1891) and were recognized typically in *Aureobasidium pullulans* by Cooke (1959, 1962). The conidia of this species were designated slimy radulaspores by Mason (1937).

Mason also coined the term terminus spores, for spores which terminate the growth of the sporophores. Further growth can take place only by the formation of a new growing point below the apex, and it is accordingly always lateral. Hughes (1953a) used the term botryose terminus spores for those which develop in clusters as in *Arthrobotrys*. A similar process was described and discussed intensively in *Sphaerospora minuta* by Cain and Haskins (1958). Tubaki (1963) divided radulaspores into *terminoradulaspores* and *pleuroradulaspores*: the former may result from increasing the length of the sporophores and the latter may develop on intercalary or terminal swellings of the sporophore. The *sympodioconidia* of Kendrick (1962) may correspond to the second type.

In the wide sense, both radulaspores and terminus spores, are similar to each other, and Goos (1956) treated both types as radulaspores.

Depending on the orientation of the spicules, Cooke (1962) differentiated five types: (1) irregular, as in *Botrytis* or *Sporotrichum*; (2) very regular but scattered, as in *Ramularia*; (3) very regular with rather long spaces between the spores giving a zigzag appearance, as in *Tritirachium*; (4) the spaces between spores short, as in *Beauveria*; (5) the scars all on one side of the branch and close together, as in *Costantiella*. The *Ramularia* type was also discussed by Mangenot (1952, 1953) in *R. urticae* and *R. alospora*, and developmental stages of other radulaspores were described in *Beauveria*, *Rhinocladiella*, and *Haplaria*. Mangenot figured the developmental stage of sporulation in *Margarinomyces heteromorpha* var. *robusta* in which radulaspore-like structures developed. Detailed observations of radulaspore formation were made by Jacques (1941) for *Heterosporium*. After the first-formed spore assumes a more or less lateral position and the newly formed, geniculate branch has lengthened, a second spore is produced at its tip. The branch then swells beneath the spore, another branch arises from it, and so on. This developmental study showed that the spores are always more or less pedicellate and, depending on the location of the plane of abscission, the resultant scars are of greater or lesser prominence. The degree of prolongation of the branch between the neighboring two scars is variable, as described by Meredith in *Pyridularia musae*. From Jacques' study, it appeared that the spore primordium, a hyaline papilla when young, soon increases in size and assumes an ovate shape while remaining in open connection through the pedicel with the sporophore. As it increases in size and length, a rough epispore begins to form on the proximal end. When the short, delicate pedicel breaks at the time of dehiscence, the rupture occurring somewhere near its middle, part remains attached to the spore and part to the sporophore. The two portions appear as small warts or disks at their respective positions. After maturation of the primary radulaspore, a small papilla often arises at its apical end, especially in old cultures, and thereby a chain of two spores develops. The formation of the radulaspore and blastospore may thus be linked.

C. Aleuriospore Type

Aleuriospore (Fig. 1E) was coined by Vuillemin (1911) and also defined by Grigorakis (1936), Ingold (1942), Mason (1933), Langeron and Vanbreuseghem (1952), Hughes (1953a), Ranzoni (1953), Goos (1956), Nilsson (1958, 1962), Petersen (1962, 1963), Subramanian (1962), and Tubaki (1958, 1963). The term, in meaning and definition, is not clearly differentiated from chlamydospore, and Goos (1956) revised and emended the concept and defined an aleuriospore as a spore formed as the blown-out end of a hyphal tip or as a lateral protrusion, which is then cut off by a septum. Aleuriospores resemble conidiospores in position, form, and dimensions, and each is inserted on a surface equal in diameter to the hypha which bears it. Goos also defined chlamydospores [which may be terminal or lateral (Fig. ID), single or in chains] as being formed by rounding up of mycelial units, coupled with a thickening of the cytoplasm and wall, so that the mature spore is generally spherical and of larger diameter than the hypha which bears it. Tubaki (1963) added to the above characterization that an aleuriospore usually has a flattened base encircled by a minute frill.

In Section III of Hughes' system, the first-formed spore is a *terminal aleuriospore* (*sensu* Vuillemin), but as succeeding aleuriospores develop by proliferation of the sporophore through the scar left by the previous spore (as in *Scopulariopsis brevicaulis*) the sporophore increases in length and becomes annellated. Such a sporophore was termed an *annellophore* by Hughes (1951a, 1953a).

Solitary aleuriospores are found in *Allescheriella, Bactridium, Chrysosporium, Nigrospora,* and *Trichocladium,* and typical examples of the successive aleuriospores are characteristic of *Annellephora, Leptographium, Scopulariopsis, Sporidesmium,* and *Stysanus*. Annellation is frequently not easy to detect, so careful examination is necessary. Phase contrast microscopy is fairly effective. Smith (1962) mentioned that successive aleuriospore formation from annellophores is fairly common among hyphomycetes, and a number of so-called phialides have proved to be annellate when critically examined.

Ingold (1956) reported that in *Trichothecium roseum* the first formed spore is morphologically distinct from those formed later, and the development was illustrated and discussed. He suggested that the conidiophore of this fungus may represent a modification of Hughes' Section III where the level at which each successive spore is cut off remains the same. Tubaki (1958), in emendation of his previous work in which this type was included into his Section IX, has termed such spores as *meristem aleuriospores*. Tubaki (1963) divided Hughes' Section III into three subsections: A, producing typical annellophores; B, producing solitary aleuriospores; C, forming separating cells between sporophore and spore. Typical examples of Subsection C are *Anguillospora, Culicidospora, Microsporum,* and *Tetrachaetum,* in all of which separating cells develop just before maturation of the spores and break down to liberate them (Ingold, 1942; Tubaki, 1958; Petersen, 1962, 1963). The aleuriospore type is fairly common in freshwater microfungi. Ingold and Cox (1957) noted that the development of the 5-radiate aleuriospores of the aquatic *Tripospermum mytri* and *Campylospora chaetocladia* was essentially the same. Somewhat modified annellation is shown by *Deightoniella* and *Endophragmia* (Ellis, 1961). Hughes (1952), Ellis (1957a), and Meredith (1961) discussed the spore formation of these fungi in which the sporophores elongate by successive subglobose or elbowed apical proliferations and the bi- or multicelled aleuriospores are formed singly as blown-out ends at the apex of the sporophores and each proliferation. This was also described by Wardlaw (1932). Such proliferation of the sporophore, however, is not restricted to fungi which form aleuriospores, but appears in blastospore-forming fungi such as *Lacellinopsis* (Ellis, 1957b). The scar left by the solitary aleuriospore is usually not distinct except for the circular scar of *Hansfordiella,* in which old scars are pushed to one side and lie flat against the side of the sporophore (Deighton, 1960; Hughes, 1951b; Subramanian, 1957b).

Subramanian coined the term gangliospore for spores which developed by the transformation of the swollen tip of a hypha into a spore, as typical of *Bactridium.*

Among many authors who have described other aleuriospore formations are Mangenot (1952), on *Trichosporium,* and Hudson (1961), on dictyospores of *Oncopodium.*

D. Phialospore Type

This type, which has been discussed by Vuillemin (1911), Mason (1933), Hughes (1953a), Goos (1956), Tubaki (1958, 1963), and

Subramanian (1962), may be defined as spores abstricted in basipetal succession from the mouths of phialides (which may or may not possess an evident collarette) and grouped into false heads or forming chains (Fig. 1F). Phialospores are Vuillemin's *conidia vera*. Hughes (1953a) coined *radula phialospores* for the spores that are produced on the surface of the ascospores and are homologous with phialospores as suggested by Mason (1933).

It is still a question whether all phialospores from phialides are endogenous or not. True endogenous production of phialospores occurs in *Chalara, Endosporostilbe, Sporoschima,* and *Thielaviopsis*. In these fungi, phialospores are laid down within the stalked tube from the apex backward; finally the thinner-walled apical cap of the phialide is torn off, presumably by pressure from within (Hughes, 1953a). Brierley (1915) first showed endospore production within the cannon-shaped sporophore of *Thielaviopsis basicola*. By contrast, in *Phialophora* (Hughes, 1953a) the first-formed phialospore is laid down within the unbroken extension of the phialide and is endogenous while the succeeding phialospores are not precisely endogenous even though they may be sunk, to a greater or lesser degree, within the open collarette. In phialospore production, the rim of the wall at the open end of the phialide is continued outward in the form of a flaring collar which forms a bottomless cap. This collarette varies considerably in different species; it is large and flaring in some and very small and indistinct in others. Pethybridge and Lafferty (1917) made a detailed study of the mechanism of spore formation in *Fusarium* and described the collaration. Cain (1952) noted the nature of the collarette of *Phialophora* and discussed whether or not it was formed by the accumulation and drying of the slimy material of the phialospore.

An addition to the above types are the biphialide and polyphialide. Biphialide production according to Van Beyma (1940) includes forms that have double tops, surrounded by a small single collar, and two spores can be produced at the same time. It is typical of *Bisporomyces* and *Gonytrichum* (Swart, 1959). Biphialides were later described by Mangenot (1952, 1953) for *Bisporomyces lignicola* and *Cacumisporium tenebrosum*. Polyphialide was applied by Hughes (1953a) to phialides which produce more than one open end from each of which a basipetal succession of phialospores is produced, as in *Catenularia cuneiformis*. The fertile hypha or conidiophores of *Zygosporium* in side view is strikingly similar to a billhook for which the term *falx* was proposed by Mason (1941), and the sporophore borne on slightly differentiated hypha was designated a *falciphore*. The falx of *Zygosporium* is apparently designed to shoot off the conidia from the phialide (Mason, 1941).

Phialospores are usually massed in a false head or in chains, but Hughes described a peculiar spore chain in *Fusariella* in which each four-celled phialospore is attached to the second cell from the apex of the phialospore below it, as a result of the lateral and curved growth of that spore during development (Hughes, 1949).

FIG. 3. A section showing a conidium seemingly in a fairly ripened state with formation of a distinct spore coat. It is, however, still linked by a short stem to a unmatured secondary conidium. From Tanaka and Yanagita (1963).

Recently, electron microscopic observations of phialospore development have been published by Tanaka and Yanagita (1963), who described the fine structure of the spore-bearing apparatus of *Aspergillus niger* seen in ultrathin sections (Fig. 3). In the earlier stage of sporulation, when the narrow neck is closed to form a rudimentary conidium, it contains a nucleus, mitochondria, and other cytoplasmic organelles; by this time the secondary thickening of the cell wall between the conidium and sterigma has already taken place as shown in Fig. 3. The method of sporulation in *Penicillium* was discussed by Gueguen (1898/1899), Thom (1944), Scaramella (1928), and Raper and Thom (1949). Raper and Thom recorded a case in which the conidia seemed to be found within the sterigma tube as described by Gueguen and as illustrated by Scaramella for *P. digitatum*.

E. Porospore Type

Porospore was proposed by Hughes (1953a) for spores which are thick walled, solitary or in whorls, and developed through minute, single, or numerous pores in the sporophore wall, a definition emended by Subramanian (1962). These spores are formed in acropetal chains through minute or lateral pores and are usually rounded at the base and even in contour except for a basal pore corresponding in position to its point of attachment to the sporophore. The apex of the sporophore is rounded and the outer and inner walls come to an end abruptly, thus delimiting a more or less cylindrical pore. Hughes illustrated and described examples of porospore formation in *Exosporium, Helminthosporium, Spondylocladium, Stemphylium, Curvularia, Alternaria, Dendryphion,* and *Dendryphiopsis*. In the production of successive porospores sometimes seen in *Curvularia, Exosporium,* or *Helminthosporium,* the inner wall of the sporophore busts through the outer wall just below the septum and displaces the pore left by the apical porospore.

Porospore formation was described by Ellis (1960) in *Corynespora* in which multicelled, long porospores formed singly through a pore at the apex of the sporophore.

F. Arthrospore Type

Arthrospore is another of Vuillemin's terms. In general, arthrospores are recognized by being formed by the septation and breaking up of simple or branched hyphae (Fig. 1A). Both exogenous and endogenous processes are involved. In the former case, e.g., in *Geotrichum candidum,* transverse septa are laid down in hyphae. The outer wall and the protoplasm of the hyphae may break down by the formation of transverse septa at nearly the same time. This was the only known method of arthrospore development until Hughes (1953a) recognized the endogenous formation of the arthrospores of *Coremiella ulmariae*. In this type, transverse septa are laid down in the hyphae and neighboring or alternate cells develop a thinner wall. The intermediate cells lose their contents entirely, and the thin lateral walls then break to free the arthrospores. The arthrospore has thus developed within the outer wall of the original hypha and has a minute frill at both ends. Caretta (1960) also examined the *endogenous* formation of arthrospores in *Coprotrichum purpurascens* which differed from the exogenous formation by plasma condensation of arthrospores in short and discontinuous sectors of the mother hyphae.

Formation of arthrospores in *Oidiodendron* was described by Robak (1932), Hughes (1953a), and Barron (1961, 1962). Barron (1962) noted the endogenous formation of arthrospores in detail: fertile hyphae become septate from the apex backward toward the point of origin of the branches, and thick walls are laid down with the original hyphal walls. Another type of arthrospore formation is found in *Oidiodendron truncatum*. In this species, as the arthrospores mature, they seem to draw apart slightly and the clear area appears as a gelatinous plug between the spores; the plug diminishes, and finally all that remains is a narrow connective between adjacent spores, like the beads on a string. Barron discussed the relationships between *Oidiodendron* and *Coremiella,* in which endogenous arthrospore formation was noted by Hughes (1953a). Subramanian (1958) described the endogenous arthrospore production in *Bahusakala olivaceo-nigra* in which individual spores are enclosed within the cell wall of the segmented fungus hypha.

Meristem arthrospore was proposed by Hughes (1953a) for arthrospores produced basipetally in chains due to the meristematic growth of the conidiophores, as typically in *Sirodesmium, Hysterium,* and *Erysiphe*. In these fungi, the conidiophore merges imperceptibly with the chain of conidial initials, which exhibit a gradual maturation toward the distal end of the chain. This is because the conidiophore is meristematic at its upper end so that a basipetal chain of conidial initials develops and the mycelial cell and the stipe cell show no clear change.

G. *Other Sporulating Structures*

A special sporulating type was found by Hughes (1953a) in *Arthrinium, Dictyoarthrinium, Papularia,* and *Spegazzinia*. No term was suggested for these spores, but *basauxic conidiophore* was proposed for the sporophore because of their basal elongation. A similar but different type of the sporulation was reported by Subramanian (1957a) in *Sadasivania girisa* which produces chains of sporogenous cells acropetally from the fertile part of the conidiophore stipe, from which conidia are produced singly at one to four points of each sporogenous cell. These conidia seem to be of the radulaspore type, but the aggregation of conidia around the conidiophores resembles *Arthrinium*. The characteristics of isthmospores of *Spegazzina* (*Isthmospora*) were described in detail by Hughes (1953a). The isthmospore is an asexual spore composed of four or more thick-walled cells separated by thin walled cells. The conidiophores arise from conidiophore-mother cells and bear the single terminal conidium prior to elongation.

Sporogenous cells is a loosely used term commonly applied to cells producing, bearing, or supporting spores. However, the function of these cells varies with the species. In conidiophores of *Deightoniella indica* the apical cell of a torulose chain is a sporogenous cell which bears acrogenously a single conidium (Subramanian, 1958). This feature resembles that of *Torula herbarum*, in which conidia are considered by Hughes (1953a) to be a kind of porospore. Sporogenous cells of similar function were described in *Dwayabeeja sundara* and *Pseudotorula heterospora* by Subramanian (1958) and in *Lacellina* (Ellis, 1957b; Subramanian, 1952) and *Lacellinopsis* (Ellis, 1957b; Subramanian, 1953).

A peculiar spore appendage (membraneous appendage) is shown by conidia of *Anthasthoopa, Diplophospora, Koorchalomella, Lomachashaska, Neottiospora, Sakireeta, Samukuta,* and *Starkeyomyces,* among others. These appendages are unusual in being evanescent and soluble in lactophenol, but they can be clearly demonstrated in aqueous methylene blue. Desmazières (1843), then Grove (1935), described the appendages of *Neottiospora* in which each spore has an apical tuft of little mucoid setae, which readily disappear. Subramanian and Ramakrishnan (1953, 1957) agreed that the appendage is formed in *N. carinum* as follows: During the development of the spore (pycnidiospore), the outer wall splits transversely along a line just below the middle of the spore because of elongation of the spore body. The spore then becomes detached from the conidiophore, and the upper portion of the outer wall which has split is now seen as a cap enclosing the spore for more than half its length. This thin cap later gets everted and then appears as a hyaline, inverted hollow cone with very thin walls. In conclusion, they considered that the spore appendage is mucoid and evanescent and formed of the broken outermost membrane of the spore wall.

III. TYPES OF SPOROPHORES

Sporophores may be produced singly and at random by the somatic hyphae or be grouped in various types of asexual fruiting bodies. The simplest form of aggregation is seen when a group sporophores is joined at the base and part way up toward the tip to form a *synnema* (plural synnemata).

Coremium is frequently used as the equivalent of synnema, but for looser fascicles not necessarially fused at the base. Slightly more complex is the sporodochium, a mass of sporophores which arise together from the surface of a cushionlike structure which is, in effect a type of coremium in which the sporophores are too short to form a stalk.

Simple or branched sporophores may line a hollow flask-shaped fruit body, the *pycnidium,* of which the wall is pseudoparenchymatous (Fig. 4). Kempton (1919) found that there are three kinds of pycnidial development, simple-, composed-, and symphogenous. The *acervulus* is a mass of

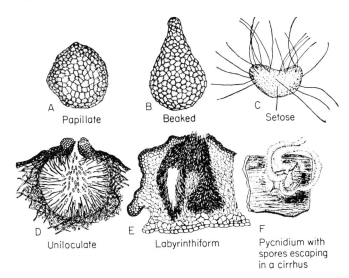

Fig. 4. Various types of pycnidia: (A) *Zythia fragariae;* (B) *Dendrophoma obscurans;* (C) *Chaetomella atra;* (D) *Diplodia zeae;* (E) *Fusicoccum viticolum;* (F) *Endothia parasitica,* pycnidial state. From Alexopoulos (1962), Fig. 138.

hyphae grouped to form an open bed of short sporophores closely packed together. It varies from discoid and saucer-shaped to a thick and pulvinate layer or cushion. Often, long, stiff, and dark bristlelike structures, the *setae,* develop intermixed with the sporophores. Some authors do not consider such structures as part of the acervulus when they are formed underneath the cuticle or epidermis of the host plant and eventually become erumpent, but Alexopoulos (1962) does not agree because a fungal structure should be viewed in terms of its total morphology. Frequently, an acervulus appears as a sporodochium in culture.

Mason (1937) said that one fungus stroma may be both a "sporodochium" and "pycnidium," and these two words are applied to the fungus stroma: the first signifies that the stroma is producing conidia internally and the second that the stroma is producing conidia on its exposed face. He also considered that these organs, sporodochia, pycnidia, and acervuli, imply a transition from imprisoned conidiophores to free conidiophores. A sporodochium may not be developed under culture by genera which typically produce such a structure in nature (Goos, 1956).

REFERENCES

Alexopoulos, C. J. (1962). "Introductory Mycology," 613 pp. Wiley, New York.
Barron, G. L. (1961). *Monocillium humicola* sp. nov. and *Paecilomyces variabilis* sp. nov. from soil. *Can. J. Botany* 39:1573-1578.
Barron, G. L. (1962). New species and new records of *Oidiodendron*. *Can. J. Botany* 40:589-607.
Brierley, W. B. (1915). The endoconidia of *Thielavia basicola* Zopf. *Ann. Botany (London)* 29:483-493.
Cain, R. F. (1952). Studies of Fungi Imperfecti. I. *Phialophora*. *Can. J. Botany* 30:338-343.
Cain, R. F., and N. A. Haskins. (1958). Studies of soil fungi. II. A new species of *Sphaerospora* with a *Botrytis*-like stage. *Can. J. Botany* 34:360-376.
Caretta, G. (1960). Caratteristische ed affinità del genere *Coprotrichum*. *Atti Ist. Botan. Univ. Pavia, Ser. V* 17:283-292.
Cooke, W. B. (1959). An ecological life history of *Aureobasidium pullulans* (de Bary) Arnaud. *Mycopathol. Mycol. Appl.* 12:1-45.
Cooke, W. B. (1962). A taxonomic study in the "Black Yeasts." *Mycopathol. Mycol. Appl.* 17:1-43.
Deighton, F. C. (1960). African fungi. I. *Mycol. Papers* 78:1-43.
Desmazières, J. B. H. J. (1843). Dixième notice sur quelques plantes crytogames nouvelles qui ont été publiées en nature, dans les Fascicules XIV-XVII des Plantes Cryptogames de France. I. *Ann. Sci. Nat.: Botan. Biol. Vegetale* [2] 6:242-247.
De Vries, G. A. (1952). Contribution to the knowledge of the genus *Cladosporium* Link ex Fr. Thesis, Vitgeverji and Drukkerij, Baarn, Holland.
Ellis, M. B. (1957a). Some species of *Deightiniella*. *Mycol. Papers* 66:1-12.
Ellis, M. B. (1957b). *Hyalobasidion, Lacellinopsis* and *Lacellina*. *Mycol. Papers* 67:1-15.
Ellis, M. B. (1960). Dematiaceous Hyphomycetes. I. *Mycol. Papers* 76:1-36.
Ellis, M. B. (1961). Dematiaceous Hyphomycetes. II. *Mycol. Papers* 82:1-55.
Goos, R. D. (1956). Classification of the Fungi Imperfecti. *Proc. Iowa Acad. Sci.* 63:311-320.
Grigorakis, L. (1936). L'aleurie, sa forme et sa définition. *Rev. Mycol.* [N.S.] 1:37-39.
Grove, W. B. (1935). "British Stem- and Leaf-Fungi," Vol. 1, 488 pp. Cambridge Univ. Press, London and New York.
Gueguen, F. (1898/1899). Recherches sur les organisms mycéliens des solutions pharmaceutiques. Études biologiques sur la *Penicillium glaucum*. *Soc. Mycol. France Bull. Trimest.* 14:201-255; 15:15-35.
Haskins, R. H. (1958). Hyphomycetous fungi: *Volucrispora aurantiaca* n.gen., n.sp.; with the genus *Tricellula* emended. *Can. J. Microbiol.* 4:273-285.
Hudson, H. J. (1961). *Oncopodium panici* sp. nov., a hyphomycete from Jamaica. *Brit. Mycol. Soc. Trans.* 44:406-408.
Hughes, S. J. (1949). Studies in microfungi. I. The genus *Fusariella* Sacc. *Mycol. Papers* 28:1-11.

Hughes, S. J. (1951a). *Annellophora* nom. nov. (=*Chaetotrichum* Syd. non Rabenh.). *Brit. Mycol. Soc. Trans.* 34:544-550.
Hughes, S. J. (1951b). Studies in microfungi. XII. *Beltrania, Ceratocladium, Diplorhinotrichum,* and *Hansfordiella* (gen. nov.). *Mycol. Papers* 47:1-15.
Hughes, S. J. (1952). Fungi from the Gold Coast. I. *Mycol. Papers* 48:1-91.
Hughes, S. J. (1953a). Conidiophores, conidia and classification. *Can. J. Botany* 31:577-659.
Hughes, S. J. (1953b). Some foliicolous hyphomycetes. *Can. J. Botany* 31:560-576.
Ingold, C. T. (1942). Aquatic Hyphomycetes of decaying alder leaves. *Brit. Mycol. Soc. Trans.* 25:339-417.
Ingold, C. T. (1956). The conidial apparatus of *Trichothecium roseum*. *Brit. Mycol. Soc. Trans.* 39:460-464.
Ingold, C. T., and V. J. Cox. (1957). On *Tripospermum* and *Campylospora*. *Brit. Mycol. Soc. Trans.* 40:317-321.
Jacques, J. E. (1941). Studies in the genus *Heterosporium*. *Contrib. Inst. Botan. Univ. Montreal* 39:7.
Kempton, F. E. (1919). Origin and development of the pycnidium. *Botan. Gaz.* 68:233-261.
Kendrick, W. B. (1962). The *Leptographium* complex and *Verticicladiella* Hughes. *Can. J. Botany* 40:771-797.
Langeron, M., and R. Vanbreuseghem. (1952). "Précis de mycologie," 703 pp. Masson, Paris.
Mangenot, M. F. (1952). "Recherches méthodiques sur les champignons de certains bois en décomposition," 116 pp. Thèse Fac. Sci. Nancy.
Mangenot, M. F. (1953). Sur quelques Hyphales dématiées lignicoles. *Rev. Mycol.* [N.S] 18:132-148.
Mason, E. W. (1933). Annotated account of fungi received at the Imperial Mycological Institute, List. II, fasc. 2:1-67. Commonwealth Mycol. Inst.
Mason, E. W. (1937). Annotated account of fungi received at the Imperial Mycological Institute, List. II, fasc. 3:Gen. Pt., 68-99. Commonwealth Mycol. Inst.
Mason, E. W. (1941). Annotated account of fungi received at the Imperial Mycological Institute, List. II, fasc. 3:Spec. Pt., 101-144. Commonwealth Mycol. Inst.
Meredith, D. S. (1961). Fruit-spot of Jamaica bananas caused by *Deightoniella torulosa* (Syd.) Ellis III. Spore formation, liberation and dispersal. *Brit. Mycol. Soc. Trans.* 44:391-405.
Minoura, K. (1964). Taxonomical studies on the Cladosporia. *J. Ferment. Technol.* 42:723-738.
Moreau, F. (1952). "Les champignons," Vol. I, 940 pp. Lechevalier, Paris.
Moreau, F. (1953). "Les champignons," Vol. II, 835 pp. Lechevalier, Paris.
Nilsson, S. (1958). On some Swedish freshwater Hyphomycetes. *Svensk Botan. Tidskr.* 52:291-318.
Nilsson, S. (1962). Second note on Swedish freshwater Hyphomycetes. *Svensk Botan. Tidskr.* 115:73-86.
Petersen, R. H. (1962). Aquatic Hyphomycetes from North America I. Aleuriosporae (Part I) and key to the genera. *Mycologia* 54:117-151.
Petersen, R. H. (1963). Aquatic Hyphomycetes from North America II. Aleuriosporae (Part II) and Blastosporae. *Mycologia* 55:18-29.
Pethybridge, G. H., and H. A. Lafferty. (1917). Further observations on the cause of the common dry rot of the potato tuber in the British Isles. *Sci. Proc. Roy. Dublin Soc.* [N.S.] 21:193-222.

Ranzoni, F. V. (1953). The aquatic hyphomycetes of California. *Farlowia* 4:353-398.
Raper, K. B., and C. Thom. (1949). "A Manual of the Penicillia," 875 pp. Williams & Wilkins, Baltimore, Maryland.
Robak, H. (1932). Investigations regarding fungi on Norwegian ground woodpulp and fungal infections at wood pulp mills. *Nyt. Mag. for Naturvidenskaberne* 71: 185-330.
Scaramella, P. (1928). Ricerche preliminari sul modo di formazione dei conidi nil *Penicillium digitatum. Nuova Giorn. Botan. Ital.* [N.S.] 34:1078-1084.
Smith, G. (1954). "An Introduction to Industrial Mycology," 378 pp. Arnold, London.
Smith, G. (1962). The morphological approach to the taxonomy of microfungi. *In* "Microbial Classification" (G. C. Ainsworth and P. H. A. Sneath, eds.), pp. 111-118. Cambridge Univ. Press, London and New York.
Subramanian, C. V. (1952). Fungi Imperfecti from Madras II, III. *Proc. Indian Acad. Sci.* **B36**:160-168 and 223-228.
Subramanian, C. V. (1953). Fungi Imperfecti from Madras IV. *Proc. Indian Acad. Sci.* **B37**:96-105.
Subramanian, C. V. (1957a). Two new genera, *Dwayaloma* and *Sadasivania*. *J. Indian Botan. Soc.* 36:61-67.
Subramanian, C. V. (1957b). Additions to the genus *Hansfordiella*. *Proc. Indian Acad. Sci.* **B45**:282-287.
Subramanian, C. V. (1958). Hyphomycetes V. *J. Indian Botan. Soc.* 37:47-64.
Subramanian, C. V. (1962). A classification of the Hyphomycetes. *Current Sci. (India)* 31:409-411.
Subramanian, C. V., and K. Ramakrishnan. (1953). On the nature of the spore-appendages in *Neottiospora* Desm. *Proc. Indian Acad. Sci.* **B37**:228-231.
Subramanian, C. V., and K. Ramakrishnan. (1957). *Neottiospora* Desm. and two new genera, *Samukuta* and *Sakireeta*. *J. Indian Botan. Soc.* 36:68-86.
Swart, H. J. (1959). A comparative study of the genera *Gonytrichum* and *Bisporomyces*. *Antonie van Leeuwenhoek, J. Microbiol. Serol.* 25:439-444.
Tanaka, K., and T. Yanagita. (1963). Electron microscopy on ultrathin sections of *Aspergillus niger* II. Fine structure of conidia-bearing apparatus. *J. Gen. Appl. Microbiol.* 9:189-202.
Thom, C. (1944). Molds in the cheese industry. *J. N. Y. Botan. Garden* 45:105-113.
Thom, C., and K. B. Raper. (1945). "A Manual of the Aspergilli," 373 pp. Williams & Wilkins, Baltimore, Maryland.
Tubaki, K. (1958). Studies on the Japanese Hyphomycetes V. Leaf and stem group with a discussion of the classification of Hyphomycetes and their perfect stages. *J. Hattori Botan. Lab.* 31:142-244.
Tubaki, K. (1963). Taxonomic study of Hyphomycetes. *Ann. Rept. Inst. Ferment., Osaka* 1:25-52.
Van Beverwijk, A. L. (1954). Three new fungi: *Helicoon pluriseptatum* n.sp., *Papulaspora pulmonaria* n.sp., and *Tricellula inaequalis* n.gen., n.sp. *Antonie van Leeuwenhoek, J. Microbiol. Serol.* 20:1-16.
Van Beyma, T. K. (1940). Beschreibung einiger neuer Pilzarten aus dem C.B.S. Baarn. *Antonie van Leeuwenhoek, J. Microbiol. Serol.* 6:263-290.
Van Beyma, T. K. (1943). Beschreibung der im C.B.S. vorhandenen Arten der Gattung *Phialophora* Thaxter und *Margarinomyces* Laxa, nebst Schüssel zu ihrer Bestimmung. *Antonie van Leeuwenhoek, J. Microbiol. Serol.* 9:51-76.
Viala, P., and G. Boyer. (1891). Une nouvelle maladie des raisins (*Aureobasidium vitis* sp. nov.). *Rev. Gen. Botan.* 111:369-371.

Vuillemin, P. (1910). Les conidiophores. *Bull. Soc. Sci. Nancy* **11**:129-172.
Vuillemin, P. (1911). Les aleuriospores. *Bull. Soc. Sci. Nancy* **12**:151-175.
Vuillemin, P. (1912). "Les champignons, essai de classification," 425 pp. Doin, Paris.
Wardlaw, C. W. (1932). Banana diseases. 4. Note on black-tip disease in Trinidad. *Helminthosporium torulosum* (Syd.) comb. nov. Ashby. *Trop. Agr. (Trinidad)* **9**:3-6.
Yuill, E., and J. L. Yuill. (1938). *Cladosarum olivaceum,* a new hyphomycete. *Brit. Mycol. Soc. Trans.* **22**:194-200.

CHAPTER 5

Fruit Bodies in Ascomycetes

C. BOOTH

*Commonwealth Mycological Institute
Kew, Surrey, England*

The Laboulbeniales, a very specialized order of ascomycetes, is not included in this highly condensed review, in which emphasis is given to the type of development and the basic structures found in ascocarps. This development often bears little relationship to the gross morphological characters of the fructification which are, however, still widely used as the basis of ascomycete classification.

I. THE ASCOCARP

The fruit bodies or sexual fructifications of ascomycetes are structures containing asci surrounded by, or enclosed within, protective tissue. Ascocarps are, roughly, of three types which in the past have characterized the Plectomycetes, Pyrenomycetes, and Discomycetes, respectively. Typically, the first of these taxa has a closed, globose ascocarp, the second an obpyriform or flask-shaped ascocarp perforated at the apex by a pore, and the third an open, saucer-shaped ascocarp.

The differentiation of these three groups has led to the traditional approach to the study of ascomycetes, an approach which unfortunately obscures the true structural relationships within the group as a whole.

Ascomycetes are, by definition, fungi which possess an ascus, a sac-like structure containing ascospores. In this organ fusion of the two haploid nuclei (karyogamy) occurs followed by meiosis, and the ascospores are produced freely within protoplasm as separate units. Thus, the presence of an ascus is an indication of the sexual processes occurring during the formation of the fructifications. These sexual processes are not readily observed when they occur within a preformed protective stromatic tissue;

and although the asci are preceded by the development of an ascogonium, this may not possess any specialized morphological characters.

The simplest ascomycetes (Hemiascomycetes) include the yeasts, which are characterized by nuclear fusion leading directly to the formation of an ascus. Thus, no specialized structures are associated with the asci and no ascocarp is formed.

Ascomycetes forming specialized fructifications comprise the Euascomycetes. This large section, which shows great diversity, is characterized by the ascogonium producing ascogenous hyphae from which the asci develop. These tissues develop under sexual stimulation and differ from the surrounding vegetative tissues. Although the system of "hyphal analysis"

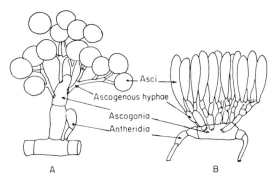

FIG. 1. Hypothetical gametophytes. (A) Plectomycetes. (B) Pyrenomycetes and Discomycetes.

introduced by Corner (1932) for basidiomycetes is not applicable in the same sense to the ascomycetes, one can in most fruit bodies differentiate two, and in more highly developed groups three, hyphal systems whose origins can be summarized as follows: (1) tissues derived from the ascogonium; (2) vegetative protective tissue developed from the surrounding mycelium; (3) secondary protective tissue formed under stimulus from the ascogonium.

The tissue derived from the ascogonium consists of the ascogenous hyphae and the asci. The ascogonium, which may or may not be fertilized by an antheridium, gives rise to the ascogenous hyphae which ultimately produce the asci (Fig. 1). The ascogenous hyphae are generally broader than the associated vegetative hyphae and have thinner walls, and dense easily stained contents. Typically they grow out radially to form a plate or hollow disk in the lower part of the fruit body, but in the more primitive groups they ramify throughout the central tissue of the ascocarp. Species with a plate of ascogenous hyphae are characterized by cylindrical or

5. Fruit Bodies in Ascomycetes

clavate asci produced as a palisade, and this condition is typical of the Pyrenomycetes and Discomycetes.

II. PLECTOMYCETES

In early classifications the Tuberales [Section IV, C] were included in the Plectomycetes, a class now typified by ascogenous hyphae that ramify throughout the central tissues and by globose asci produced at all levels within the fructifications. It includes the Gymnascales, Eurotiales, Onygenales, and Microascales. In the first two orders fructifications develop after the sexual organs are produced and serve only to protect the asco-

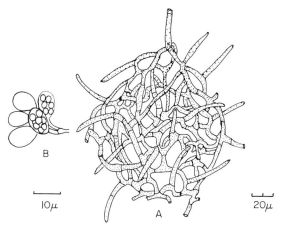

FIG. 2. (A) The peripheral protective hyphae of the ascocarp of *Gymnoascus*. (B) Asci.

genous hyphae and asci. That globose asci are scattered throughout the central matrix is considered to be a primitive character by Benjamin (1956) and Gäumann (1952), and many earlier authors, who thought that formation of a distinct peridium around the ascocarp, as found in the Eurotiales, was the next step in evolution toward the higher ascomycetes. However, Bessey (1950) and Cain (1956) consider the Gymnascales to have evolved from the Eurotiales, a view depending on what are considered to be the ancestors of the higher ascomycetes.

A. *The Gymnascales*

The Gymnascales differ from the Eurotiales in not having a definite peridial wall, the ascocarp being formed by modified hyphae which surround and enmesh the ascogenous hyphae and asci (Fig. 2). Usually only two types of hyphae are recognizable—those of vegetative origin and those developing directly from the ascogonium.

In *Gymnoascus reesii* Kuehn (1956) found that the sexual organs may develop side by side on the same hyphae or from different hyphae. The protective hyphae develop after the formation of the sexual organs from the surrounding vegetative mycelium and form a loose globose mass of hyphae around the ascogonium. The peridial hyphae of the fructification then become thick walled and undergo multiple branching to form spiny appendages. However, Kuehn and Orr (1959) described the protective hyphae of the peridium in *Arachniotus flavoluteus* as arising from the base of the ascogonium which makes these structures analogous to the perithecial wall of higher groups. The type of modification which these outer peridial hyphae undergo is the chief basis of separation of the various genera in the Gymnascales. Little modification is shown by *Amauroascus,* although in *A. aureus* some peridial hyphae do undergo a weak spiral coiling. Extreme modifications are found in *Eidamella deflexa,* which has bramblelike spines, and *Ctenomyces reflexa,* which has curved comblike appendages.

B. The Eurotiales

The ascocarps of the Eurotiales have a distinct peridium formed of pseudoparenchyma. Because undue emphasis has been placed on the asexual or conidial fructifications, species such as *Penicillium wortmannii* and *P. luteum* have been placed in the Eurotiales although their sexual fructifications resemble those of the Gymnascales (Emmons, 1935). The possible development of the true parenchymatous peridium can be traced through *P. spiculisporum* and *P. egyptiacum* where the peridial layer is a pseudotissue formed from several layers of interlacing hyphae, to the well-developed pseudoparenchymatous peridium found in *Thielavia* and *Pseudeurotium.* The ascocarps are generally symmetrical and smooth walled, and in most species no mechanism is apparent for spore discharge. It is frequently stated that the spores are not liberated until the ascocarp wall disintegrates, but observation suggests that in some species the wall is ruptured by the pressure of the mucilage formed by the disintegration of the asci and ascogenous hyphae. The ascocarps of *Cephalotheca* have distinct lines of dehiscence which appear as sutures visible in the wall of the mature ascocarp (Fig. 3).

The Onygenales, usually allied to the Eurotiales, have somewhat specialized ascocarps. These are much larger, stalked fructifications with the fertile region at the top. This consists of an inner tissue through which the ascogenous hyphae ramify and a well-developed peridial layer. *Onygena equina,* which grows on discarded hooves and horns, is a cosmopolitan member of this family and has ascocarps about 1 cm high, but in the related *Dendrosphaera eberhardtii* they may be 26 cm high. Species with the most highly developed ascocarps in this series belong to the order Microascales (Luttrell, 1951). Here the cleistocarpic or closed fructification is superseded by an ascocarp possessing an ostiole, a preformed canal for the liberation of the ascospores. The fructifications are typically beaked, and the ascospores are extruded from the ostiole in a cirrus of mucilage formed by disintegration of the asci and ascogenous hyphae.

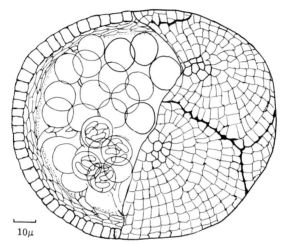

FIG. 3. The ascocarp of *Cephalotheca savoryi* (Eurotiales) showing the wall sutures.

III. PYRENOMYCETES

In progressing from the Plectascales to species with a more highly organized fructification, two major lines of development are apparent. These two lines show a difference in origin of the protective tissue immediately adjacent to the asci, but they are most readily separated on the structure of the ascus wall. Nannfeldt (1932) defined the first series as having a double-walled ascus and referred to it as the Ascoloculares, and the second series, the Ascohymeniales, as possessing a single-walled ascus. Luttrell (1951) introduced the term Bitunicatae for what was roughly the Ascoloculares, and Unitunicatae for the Ascohymeniales.

Chadefaud (1942) says all asci have two walls, an inner thick and an outer thin wall, regardless of the separation into unitunicate and bitunicate series. This view appears to be correct, but the characteristic development of the ascus in the bitunicate series, as related to the method of spore liberation, defines a coherent group of major taxonomic importance. Its significance is fully explained by Luttrell (1951) and is utilized by von Arx and Müller (1954) as a basic character in their classification. In the three major groups of the early classifications Plectomycetes, Pyrenomycetes, and Discomycetes, the orders were based on the gross morphological structure of the fructification. Thus, the Microthyriales had a flattened, inverted saucer-shaped ascocarp called a *thyriothecium,* the Hysteriales an ascocarp opening by a long slit, a *hysterothecium,* and the Sphaeriales a flask-shaped ascocarp generally referred to as a *perithecium* which may or may not be embedded in a stroma. The term perithecium was, however, confused as no clear understanding or definition existed and many species with asci formed within a vegetative stroma were included.

Developmental studies have enabled an analysis to be made of the origin of the hyphae and tissues which make up the various fructifications found in the major groups. Thus the vegetative stroma which surrounds the locule in the Bitunicatae forms the sole protective tissue in the more primitive species. But in the Pleosporales the interascal tissue has a different time sequence in its development. Another feature that has become apparent is that each line of development shows similar superficial morphological modifications to their habitat. Thus, within a single order ascocarps are found modified as cleistothecia, hysterothecia, thyriothecia, or even apothecia. These apparently parallel lines of development in response to habitat have in the past resulted in unrelated species being placed in the same family and even in the same genus.

A. The Bitunicatae

The development of the ascus type referred to as the bitunicate ascus must be regarded as a major step in the evolution of the Ascomycetes, and the ascocarps possessing this type of ascus can be grouped into three sections: Myriangiales, Dothideales, and Pleosporales.

The ascocarps of the Myriangiales show the closest relationship to the true Plectascales. The members of this somewhat anomalous order, usually placed in the stem of the bitunicate series, have bitunicate asci developing in monascus locules in a large vegetative stroma. Miller (1938) demonstrated in *Myriangium duriaei* that whereas the basal stroma was of vegetative origin the upper fertile part developed in response to the presence of the ascogonium. In this respect it is analogous to the interascal tissue of the Eurotiales and in fact may represent a transitional stage between this order and the rest of the Bitunicatae.

The majority of the species in the Bitunicatae belong to the Dothideales or the Pleosporales, and the ascocarp is basically a vegetatively produced stroma. Both produce asci within the stroma but in the Dothideales the locule is formed by the crushing or disintegration of the vegetative pseudoparenchyma cells above the ascogonium by the developing ascogenous hyphae and asci. In the Pleosporales the locule is preformed during the development of the stroma.

In the ascocarp of the Dothideales (Fig. 4) the ascogonium arises below the surface of the stroma. Initially the inner cells of the stroma are delicate and thin walled, and in the region above the ascogonium the cells remain thin walled and ultimately are ruptured by the development of the ascogenous hyphae and asci. The compact, radially produced ascogenous hyphae are a feature of the Dothideales and result in the asci being formed in a tight fascicle. If the stroma is superficial the outer cells usually become

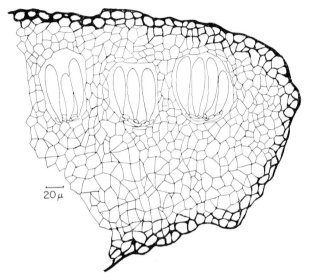

FIG. 4. Section of ascocarp of *Dothidea sambuci* (Dothideales) with asci borne in stromatic locules.

thick walled or their lumen is occluded with a tannin-like deposit. This forms a protective crust which generally undergoes irregular disintegration before the ascospores are released. The lack of this disintegration above the locule results in a cleistocarpic fructification as found in *Preussia*, but this does not reflect any close relationship with the true Eurotiales.

The basis of the Dothideales fructification is therefore a vegetative stroma containing one or more ascogonia. These give rise to ascogenous hyphae and asci which break down the overlying cells by mechanical growth processes to form a locule. Although this is the simplest type of fructification found in higher ascomycetes, the variety of shapes and forms the various members assume is just as varied as in any other group.

This simplest form of uniloculate stroma develops immersed in the host tissue in *Pringsheimia,* and is superficial in *Balladyna* although in the evolutionary scale these probably represent a reduction from the multiloculate stroma of *Dothidea sambuci* (Fig. 5), which can be derived from the Myriangiales through forms such as *Atichia glomerulosa. Dothiora* differs from *Dothidea* in showing a tendency for the locules to merge into a common hymenium. In *Bagnisiella mirabilis* this tendency is carried further and the overlying tissue of the stroma is much thinner, a trend that ultimately results in the formation of an apothecium as found in the discomycetes *Buellia disciformis,* a lichenized species, and *Patellaria atrata*. By a process of reduction in the thickness of the vegetative stroma the thyro-

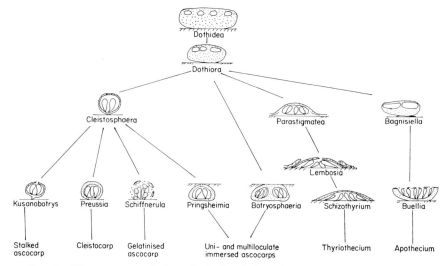

FIG. 5. The range and hypothetical relationships of the ascocarps of the Dothideales.

thecium-type of ascocarp is formed, as in the superficial *Schizothyrium perexiguum* or the subcuticular *Lembosia* species. A somewhat modified form is found in *Myriostigmella guatteriae,* where a series of thin disk-shaped fertile regions are linked by a vegetative thallus-like stroma.

From the superficial uniloculate *Balladyna,* two or three trends in ascocarp modifications are apparent. One is toward a stalked fructification terminating in species such as *Kusanobotrys bambusae.* Another most interesting modification is found in *Englerula macarangae* and *Schiffnerula pulchra.* In these species the whole inner tissue of the fructification undergoes gelatinization at maturity, with the uptake of moisture, which swells and bursts the outer wall leaving the asci embedded in a mass of mucilage. The cleistocarpic ascocarps of *Preussia* are another modification of this simple uniloculate fructification.

5. Fruit Bodies in Ascomycetes

The Pleosporales resemble the Dothideales in having the asci formed in locules within a stroma, but differ in having the locular tissue modified before ascus formation and in having a lysigenously formed ostiole through which the ascospores are discharged (Fig. 6).

The ascocarps of *Melanomma pulvis-pyrius* (Chesters, 1938) have the tissue occupying the region of the locule modified as filaments of cells which separate from each other laterally as the surrounding stroma enlarges so

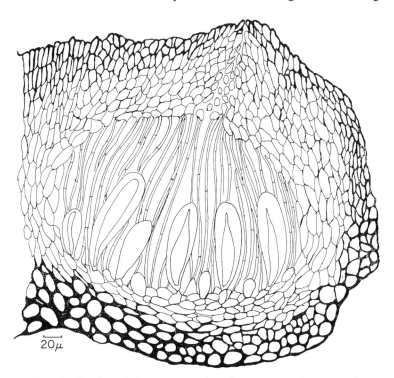

FIG. 6. Section of the ascocarp of *Otthia spireae* (Pleosporales).

as to form parallel filaments. These are known as *pseudoparaphyses* and are attached at both the apex and base.

In the ascocarps of *Myiocopron smilacis* and *Ellisiodothis inquinans* (Luttrell, 1944) a lysigenously formed cavity appears before the asci are produced and strands of tissue grow down from the apex of the locule to fuse with the tissue at the base. While the variety of forms assumed by the Pleosporales is similar in range to those of the Dothideales, the basic ascocarp type of the order appears to be the uniloculate stroma as found in *Wettsteinina gigaspora,* a species intermediate between the Dothideales and the Pleosporales. These ascocarps have no prior development of the locule as in the Pleosporales but possess a well-developed ostiole. *Pleospora, Leptosphaeria,* and *Ophiobolus* are three very large genera with uniloculate immersed fructifications. Some species have a poorly developed stromatic part of the fructification. In others, especially where the ascospores are retained in the ascocarp during a long period of dormancy, such as *Leptosphaeria acuta* and *L. doliolum,* the vegetative outer tissues are well developed and form a thick protective wall. Often the outer tissues of the host have decayed before the ascospores are released and the fructification appears superficial. The genera *Teichospora, Melanomma,* and *Thyridaria* are uniloculate superficial species on dead wood which have a thick carbonaceous outer wall. As stated by Wehmeyer (1961) the details of the ascostroma which is primarily a vegetative structure are not of great importance in classification and vary greatly in relation to habitat. However, many genera have been erected on superficial characters of the ascostroma. *Scleroplea* is a sclerotioid form of *Pleospora* whereas *Teichospora* is a thick walled superficial lignicolous form. The ascocarps of *Pleosphaeria* are similar but develop setae. In *Cucurbitaria* the ascocarps are confluent and attached to a basal stroma. *Fenestella* is also closely allied but somewhat unusual in having a secondary stromatic development around the ascostroma. This links with *Pleospora infernalis,* where a similar development of secondary stroma occurs.

Arnaudiella and *Stomiopeltis* are Pleosporales (Müller and von Arx, 1962) with an ascocarp forming a thyriothecium. The origin of these reduced multiloculate ascocarps can be considered as the end result of the trend developing in *Trichodothis,* where they occur in a thin superficial multiloculate stroma.

Although not strictly parallel, the Lophiostomaceae with their massive ostiolar slit is analogous to the Hysteriales. Another somewhat unusual feature is found in the ascocarps of *Lasiobotrys lonicerae,* where a massive vegetative stroma produces around the periphery a series of secondary stromatic buds in which the locules and asci are produced.

B. The Unitunicatae

The second major series of ascomycetes, the Unitunicatae (or Ascohymeniales) reaches its highest form of development in those species which produce either an apothecium or perithecium. The predominant factor in their development is the protective wall, immediately adjacent to the asci and paraphyses, developed as a response to the presence of the ascogonium and usually from the stalk cells of this organ. All the tissues within, known as the centrum or, in older literature, the nucleus, are also derived from the ascogonial components.

Chaetomium is one of the more primitive members of the series in which the development of the perithecium has been studied. Whiteside (1961) demonstrated that after fertilization of the ascogonium in *Chaetomium globosum* and *C. brasiliense* certain cells of the hyphae from which the ascogonium arose begin to produce the perithecial wall. These hyphae form a tissue which grows around the developing ascogenous hyphae to form a typical oval to globose locule. *Chaetomium* species have stalked asci with the oval spore-bearing part formed at different heights within the perithecium. The asci soon disintegrate and the locule becomes filled with ascospores.

Not all the Unitunicatae with enclosed ascocarps have a true perithecial stroma. The Coryneliales and Coronophorales are two orders with unitunicate asci which have the asci formed in an ascostroma. In *Caliciopsis pinea* which produces cankers on conifers, McCormack (1936) and Funk (1963) described the development of the ascogenous stroma. The asci are borne in a lysigenously formed cavity which may be enlarged by the swelling of the ascogenous hyphae and asci and, by continuation of the lysigenous action, a definite canal is formed through the apical beak of the stroma. No paraphyses or pseudoparaphyses are present.

The Coryneliales in general have ovate asci with long thin stalks. As the ascospores mature the stalk disintegrates and the spore-bearing part of the ascus is forced out of the ostiole by the developing asci beneath. Because of the stromatic ascocarp the Coryneliales have been placed in the Dothideales but they have obviously no close relationship with the group and most probably represent a distinct line of development from the Plectomycetes through genera such as *Lophotrichus*.

The Erysiphales include the powdery mildews, which have black cleistocarpic perithecia. Those attacking cultivated plants are often of serious economic importance. The common name comes from their conidial state, which gives the host a powdery appearance, but they also frequently produce dark spherical perithecia. These are particularly common in temperate regions, where the perithecia may serve as the resting bodies by which the fungus survives between successive crops. They do not possess an ostiole, and before the asci develop they are filled with large, thin-walled pseudoparenchyma cells. The asci are large in relation to the size of the perithecium and form in the center. In *Podosphaera* and *Sphaerotheca* only one ascus is usually found, but several occur in *Erysiphe* and most other genera of the family. A large family with somewhat similar ascocarps is the Meliolaceae. The members are predominantly tropical leaf parasites and are often included as a family of the Erysiphales because of the pseudoparenchymatic tissue filling the perithecium before the formation of the asci. However, as the ascospores are forcibly discharged through an apical pore, the family is better placed in the Sphaeriales.

The remainder of the Unitunicatae form a more or less related series linked with the Plectomycetes through genera such as *Chaetomium, Chaetomidium* to *Microascus,* and *Pseudeurotium.* Many of the so-called pyrenomycetes belong here and are placed in the Sphaeriales. In this large order the ascocarps range from single perithecia, which may initially be filled with pseudoparenchyma, to single or aggregate stromatic forms with one or numerous immersed perithecia in a common stroma which have true paraphyses between the developing asci (Fig. 7).

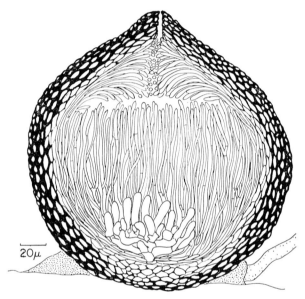

FIG. 7. Section of perithecial stroma of *Chaetosphaeria innumera* (Sphaeriales).

The Diaporthaceae are characterized by having immersed perithecia with a locule filled with pseudoparenchyma before the asci develop and also by highly refractive hyaline rings at the apex of the ascus. This pseudoparenchymatous centrum is also found in *Chaetomium fimeti* (Whiteside, 1962). In some members of the Diaporthaceae the stalk of the ascus deliquesces so that the asci are freed within the perithecium. The immersed perithecia may be vertical, obliquely inclined, or horizontal to the surface of the host, but in the latter types the long neck curves to come out vertically in relation to the substrate. In genera such as *Savulescua* the perithecia grow in groups with the necks inclining together, the whole being surrounded by a stroma. Throughout the Diaporthaceae the stroma generally is formed partly of true fungal stroma ("ectostroma") and partly of fungal and host tissue ("entostroma"), the extent of the latter within the host being frequently marked by a dark line.

The Xylariaceae and the Hypocreaceae are two families with a similar range of variations regarding the structure of the fructification. The former have a black, usually carbonaceous stroma surrounding the perithecium, and the latter a soft usually brightly colored stroma.

The Xylariaceae also have paraphyses formed within the perithecial cavity. These filaments of tissue grow from the base of the cavity to form a palisade which serves to support the developing asci. In the Hypocreaceae, a somewhat intermediate condition exists between the Diaporthaceae and the Xylariaceae. In *Neuronectria peziza,* Hanlin (1963) demonstrated that within the developing ascocarp an apical meristem exists which produces a compact pseudoparenchymatous tissue which gradually grows downward to fill the cavity of the developing perithecium. A similar development exists in *Nectria mammoidea* except that the apical meristem produces strands of paraphyses-like tissue which grow down into the cavity, a condition analogous to that found in the Pleosporales. In the solitary immersed perithecia found in *Hypocopra* and *Hyponectria* the stromatic part of the locule is not well developed, its supporting role being taken by the surrounding substrate. Many immersed species however, do have a strongly developed carbonaceous wall, as in *Anthostoma,* and this is further developed to form a clypeus in species of *Anthostomella*. Superficial perithecia which are scattered or grouped on the surface of the substrate are common in the Hypocreaceae *Nectria, Gibberella,* and *Calonectria* and in the Xylariaceae in genera such as *Bombardia, Sordaria, Gelasinospora,* all of which have the perithecium surrounded by a relatively soft stroma. On the other hand, *Rosellinia,* which occurs in similar although often drier situations, has a heavy carbonaceous stromatic layer. Superficial effuse multiperithecial stromata are found in both families. In *Hypocrea* and *Polystigma* they are soft and colorful, generally red, yellow, or cream, whereas those of *Hypoxylon* and *Bombardia* are black and carbonaceous. In *Daldinia* the stroma is large and hemispherical and the perithecia are confined to the outer layer. The stroma is unusual in being formed of concentric zones. Nothing analogous to this occurs in the Hypocreaceae, although many of the *Hypocrella* spp. have hemispherical stromata. Other examples of parallel development are to be found in the large clavate stromata with the outer layer of immersed perithecia in *Xylosphaera* (*Xylaria*) of the Xylariaceae and *Cordyceps* in the Hypocreaceae. Some of the latter may be quite dark in color, but they are not to be confused with *Xylosphaera* sp. as no carbonization of the outer crust occurs. The Sphaeriales do not appear to have any members producing thyriothecia, but *Rehmiodothis* does show a tendency toward the scutate type of fructification.

The ascocarps of the Diatrypaceae are very similar to those of the Xylariaceae. Munk (1957), in fact, included the Diatrypaceae as a tribe of the Xylariaceae, emphasizing the tendency within the group toward smaller asci and smaller light-colored allantoid ascospores. The development of this trend can be traced through *Lopadostoma* of the Xylariaceae to *Quaternaria, Diatrype,* and finally *Peroneutypa* of the Diatrypaceae.

The importance of the ascus structure within the various sections of the Xylariaceae, Diaporthaceae, and Diatrypaceae has been emphasized by Chadefaud (Chadefaud and Emberger, 1960).

The asci of the Diaporthaceae have a chitinous nonamyloid ring at the apex. *Cryptospora longispora* possesses a thin amyloid ring at the base of the large nonamyloid ring and most Xylariaceae have a well-marked amyloid ring. In *Hypoxylon multiforme* and *H. serpens* the typical ring is present, but in the closely related *Hypoxylon cohaerens* it is absent. In the Diatrypaceae the amyloid ring is reduced and is seldom more than a perforated disk.

IV. DISCOMYCETES

In passing from the perithecial to the apothecial type of ascocarp, the Phacidiales show how one type may have arisen from the other. The ascocarps of this order are generally produced within the substratum, and the hymenium forms within a fungal stroma, the upper part of which later ruptures to expose the asci. *Lophophacidium* shows an intermediate type of structure between the Phacidiales and the Hemiphacidiaceae of the Helotiales in that the overlying tissue is rudimentary and the ascocarp resembles the true apothecium.

The apothecial development of many discomycetes has been studied and is exemplified in the work of Moore (1963) on the apothecium of *Pyronema domesticum*. In this species clusters of ascogonia and antheridia originate from single aerial hyphae which enlarge and branch with a regular dichotomy. Nuclear fusion between an antheridium and the trychogyne of an ascogonium is believed to occur. From the ascogonium ascogenous hyphae develop as buds which branch on elongation to form the characteristic short thick hyphae. Croziers form as the ascogenous hyphae approach the hymenial layer. Before the development of the ascogenous hyphae, anchoring hyphae attaching the developing fructification to the substrate form as a halo around the cluster of ascogonia. Paraphyses develop as protrusions from the stalk cells supporting the ascogonia. Hairs and, later, chains of pseudoparenchyma cells grow from neighboring cells to the paraphyses.

These form part of the hypothecium and the excipulum, which are analogous in part to the perithecial wall (Fig. 8).

Corner (1929) defined three types of development found in species with apothecia: (1) angiocarpic development, in which the tissues of the excipulum initially grow over and protect the developing hymenial layer, as in *Ascobolus stercorarius;* (2) gymnocarpic development, in which the hymenium is exposed throughout its development, as in *Pyronema domesticum;* (3) hemiangiocarpic development, an intermediate condition in which the hymenium is partially covered, as in *Cheilymenia stercorea* and *Ascophanus granuliformis.* However, Corner did not attribute any great significance to these types of development and stated that both types could be found in the genus *Ascobolus.*

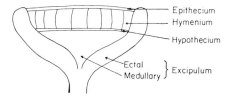

Fig. 8. Standardized longitudinal section through an apothecium showing arrangement of tissues.

The forms and shapes assumed by the ascocarp of discomycetes are quite diverse. Ignoring the hypogeal species for the moment, the ascocarp is bell-shaped in *Verpa conica,* saddlelike in *Helvella crispa,* tongue-shaped in *Geoglossum,* and brainlike in *Gyromitra esculenta.* However, the majority are typical apothecia and cup- or saucer-shaped as in *Sarcoscypha* and *Peziza* and, in addition, may be stalked as in *Chlorociboria aeruginascens* and *Sclerotinia tuberosa.*

Korf (1958) redefined the terminology relating to the types of tissue found in the excipulum. He recognized two distinct types; the first, short-celled, in which the individual hyphae are not recognizable; and the second, with long cells in which the component hyphae are visible. The short-celled tissue he subdivided into three types as follows: (1) cells globose with intercellular spaces—*textura globosa;* (2) cells polyhedral by mutual pressure, no intercellular spaces—*textura angularis;* (3) cells rectangular in section—*textura prismatica.* The long-celled tissue he divided into four subgroups: Hyphae running in all directions: (a) hyphal walls not united, usually with distinct interhyphal spaces—*textura intricata;* (b) hyphal walls united, with distinct interhyphal spaces—*textura epidermoidea.* Hyphae more or less parallel: (c) hyphae with strongly thickened walls, cohering—*textura oblita;* (d) hyphae without thickened walls, not cohering— *textura porrecta.*

As in the Pyrenomycetes, the Discomycetes are divided into two major groups, in this case, based on the apical structure of the asci. In the first group, the Inoperculatae, the asci open at the tip by a slit or irregular tear to release the ascospores, whereas in the second, the Operculatae, the asci possess a small lid at the apex and this is thrown back as the ascospores are released.

A. The Inoperculatae

The Ostropales is an order intermediate in some of its characteristics between the Discomycetes and Pyrenomycetes. Miller (1949) noted the similarity of the asci of many Ostropales with those of the Clavicipitaceae. Both have long cylindrical asci with an excessive thickening of the wall at the apex to such an extent that the lumen of the ascus is almost occluded and only a narrow canal is left for the discharge of the ascospores.

Superficially the apothecia of the Ostropales show a wide range of form. They are superficial and circular in *Apostemidium guernisaci* and stalked in *Vibrissea truncorum*. In *Acrospermum compressum* they are clavate with a cylindrical stalk and laterally compressed in the upper fertile part. *Stictis stellata* has apothecia immersed in the tissues of the host, and in *Schizoxylon berkeleyanum,* another species with initially immersed apothecia, the paraphyses branch at the tip to form a matted epithecial layer above the asci. A type of fructification that is very close to the hysterothecium is found in *Ostropa barbara,* which also has the apothecium initially immersed.

The second major order of the inoperculate series is the Helotiales, probably the most heterogeneous order of ascomycetes.

The structure of the apothecium is of major importance in the separation of the various families. The Dermateaceae have the tissues of the excipulum composed of subglobose cells, *textura globosa,* whereas in the Hyaloscyphaceae they are composed of soft prismatic cells, *textura angularis,* and in the Helotiaceae of elongated cells or of strands of parallel hyphae, *textura porrecta* to *textura intricata*. The apothecia are cup-shaped and sessile in *Orbilia curvatispora,* subsessile in *O. luteorubella,* and stalked in *Gloeotinia temulenta*. The family Hyaloscyphaceae is characterized by hairs on the margin or outer surface of the apothecium, and the Sclerotiniaceae by a sclerotium or stromatized patch of host tissue below the apothecia.

Roesleria pallida is an anomalous species with the apothecium forming a mazaedium. It resembles *Onygena equina* of the Eurotiales, and the asci soon disintegrate leaving a loose mass of ascospores held together by hyphal threads in the cup-shaped head.

The family Geoglossaceae has long-stalked, usually clavate, ascocarps which correspond morphologically to those of *Morchella* and *Helvella* in the Pezizales.

B. The Operculatae

All members of the Pezizales are characterized by having asci which dehisce by an apical lid, the operculum. The diversity of external characters of the Pezizales is as wide as that described for the Helotiales, with sessile to stalked, smooth to hairy apothecia. *Morchella esculenta* has a fructification typical of the morels. These are clavate with a thick stalk, the fertile part forming a pileus covered with a honeycomb arrangement of ridges separated by pits that are lined by the hymenial layer. *Helvella crispa*, a false morel, has a saddle-shaped pileus bearing the hymenial layer on the upper surface.

C. The Tuberales

The Tuberales is an exceptional order comprising the truffles, which have hypogean ascocarps that remain closed after maturation of the ascospores. The order shows extreme adaptation to habitat, but it is believed to have developed from the Pezizales (Gäumann, 1952). The extensive retrogressive evolution is reflected in the structure of the ascus, which may be globose or oval, a marked contrast to the Discomycetes in general and reminiscent of the Eurotiales.

REFERENCES

Benjamin, R. K. (1956). A new genus of the Gymnascales with a review of the other genera. *Aliso* 3:301-328.

Bessey, E. A. (1950). "Morphology and Taxonomy of Fungi," 791 pp. Blakiston, Philadelphia, Pennsylvania.

Cain, R. F. (1956). Studies of coprophilous ascomycetes. II. *Can. J. Botany* 34:675-687.

Chadefaud, M. (1942). Etudes d'Asques. II. *Rev. Mycol.* [N.S.] 7:57-88.

Chadefaud, M., and L. Emberger. (1960). "Les végétaux non vasculaires," Vol. I, 1018 pp. Masson, Paris.

Chesters, C. G. C. (1938). Studies on British pyrenomycetes. II. *Brit. Mycol. Soc. Trans.* 22:116-150.

Corner, E. J. H. (1929). Studies in the morphology of discomycetes. II. *Brit. Mycol. Soc. Trans.* 14:275-291.

Corner, E. J. H. (1932). A Fomes with two systems of hyphae. *Brit. Mycol. Soc. Trans.* 17:51-81.

Emmons, C. W. (1935). The ascocarps in species of *Penicillium*. *Mycologia* 27:128-150.

Funk, A. (1963). Studies in the genus *Caliciopsis*. *Can. J. Botany* 41:503-543.

Gäumann, E. A. (1952). "The Fungi" (English transl. by F. L. Wynd), 420 pp. Hafner, New York.

Hanlin, R. T. (1963). Morphology of *Neuronectria peziza*. *Am. J. Botany* 50:56-66.

Korf, R. P. (1958). Japanese Discomycetes, 1-8. *Sci. Rept. Yokohama Natl. Univ.*, Sect. II 7:1-35.

Kuehn, H. H. (1956). Observations on Gymnoascaceae. *Mycologia* 48:805-820.

Kuehn, H. H., and G. F. Orr. (1959). Observations on Gymnoascaceae. VI. *Mycologia* 51:864-870.

Luttrell, E. S. (1944). The morphology of *Myiocopron smilacis*. *Am. J. Botany* 31: 640-649.

Luttrell, E. S. (1951). Taxonomy of the Pyrenomycetes. *Missouri, Univ., Studies* 24: 1-120.

McCormack, H. W. (1936). The morphology and development of *Caliciopsis pinea*. *Mycologia* 28:188-196.

Miller, J. H. (1938). Studies in the developments of two *Myriangium* species and the systematic position of the order Myriangiales. *Mycologia* 30:158-181.

Miller, J. H. (1949). A revision of the classification of the ascomycetes with special emphasis on the pyrenomycetes. *Mycologia* 41:99-127.

Moore, E. J. (1963). Ontogeny of the apothecia of *Pyronema domesticum*. *Am. J. Botany* 50:37-144.

Müller, E., and J. A. von Arx. (1962). Die Gattungen der didymosporen Pyrenomyceten. *Beitr. Kryptogamenflora Schweiz* 2:1-922.

Munk, A. (1957). Danish Pyrenomycetes. *Dansk. Botan. Arkiv* 17:1-491.

Nannfeldt, J. A. (1932). Studien über die Morphologie and Systematik der Nicht Lichenisierten. Inoperculaten Discomyceten. *Nova Acta Regiae Soc. Sci. Upsaliensis* [4] 8:1-368.

von Arx, J. A., and E. Müller. (1954). Die Gattungen der amerosporen Pyrenomycetes. *Beitr. Kryptogamenflora Schweiz* 2:1-434.

Wehmeyer, L. E. (1961). "A World Monograph of the Genus Pleospora and Its Segregates'," 451 pp. Univ. of Michigan Press, Ann Arbor, Michigan.

Whiteside, W. C. (1961). Morphological studies in the Chaetomiaceae. I. *Mycologia* 53:512-523.

Whiteside, W. C. (1962). Morphological studies in the Chaetomiaceae. II. *Mycologia* 54:152-159.

CHAPTER 6

The Hyphal Structure of the Basidiocarp

ALEXANDER H. SMITH

*University Herbarium and Department of Botany
University of Michigan
Ann Arbor, Michigan*

I. INTRODUCTION

To understand the structure of the basidiocarp in relation to the hyphal systems or tissues which comprise it, we must first consider briefly the details of the individual hyphae of the vegetative mycelium. Although each species to some extent may be said to have individual features peculiar to its mycelium, it is obvious that for higher fungi generally, the secondary mycelium, from which basidiocarps typically originate, is very similar for most basidiomycetes. However, if we examine the hyphae of a pure culture we are likely to find them to be tubular (equal in diameter throughout their length). The length of the individual cells will vary greatly with the species and within the same mycelium depending on the area from which the sample is taken, or its age. The amount and type of branching also will vary similarly. Nutritional and other environmental and genetic factors effect changes in the morphology of the mycelial pad of a pure culture on an agar plate. Many of the hyphal changes which produce the differences in appearance of the mycelial pad are of the same type as those found in the hyphae of the fruiting, i.e., the development of pigment in the cells (*Mycena subcaerulea* and *Lyophyllum palustre* (Smith, 1932), shortened inflated cells (*Lyophyllum palustre*), different patterns in submerged and aerial hyphae (*Mycena* sp. The point to keep in mind is that the modifications found in the hyphae of the basidiocarp, though more elaborate than those of the vegetative hyphae, are essentially similar basically, as one would expect. That the fungus is a very adaptable organism in either its vegetative or reproductive stage must be remembered when developing a terminology to cover all aspects of the present subject.

II. ORIGIN OF THE BASIDIOCARP

In this chapter we are concerned with the morphological changes that take place when the stimulus for reproduction becomes manifest regardless of what hyphal changes have previously occurred during the vegetative stage. In most higher fungi one of the first evidences of basidiocarp production is stimulation of branching in local areas to produce knots of hyphae, often with short almost isodiametric cells. However, great variation from species to species is found from very loose cottony balls of hyphae 35 mm in extent (*Rhizopogon pseudoaffinis*: Smith and Zeller, 1966), to very compact knots. The basidiocarp in some cases may even be derived from a single cell in a knot (Reijenders, 1963). In some very unspecialized basidiocarps developing on wood, the fruiting initial may cover a considerable area and exhibit indeterminate growth. For most of the higher basidiomycetes it is a hopeless task to attempt to use the manner of origin of a basidiocarp for purposes of identification, but it may be important in helping to understand the taxomonic position of a species. This information is indeed difficult to obtain from material collected in nature. However, Corner (1950) gives an account of the origin of the basidiocarp in certain species where he was reasonably certain of the identity of the naturally occurring primordia. In *Clavariadelphus pistillaris,* a fluffy patch of mycelium is the first indication of basidiocarp differentiation. The hyphae of the rudimentary basidiocarp are differentiated from those of the mycelium by their smooth, rather than incrusted, walls. According to Corner, because of their incrusted walls, the mycelial hyphae of this species can be identified at all stages in the development of the basidiocarp. That this degree of difference between vegetative mycelium and hyphae of the basidiocarp may occur is of great interest to our analysis because it points the way to an understanding of the features considered significant in modern taxonomic mycology. In addition, it also indicates that these features may be characteristic of a particular hyphal system within the vegetative mycelium. This observation by Corner shows the need for caution in interpreting the fibrils and hairs at the base of a basidiocarp as being part of the basidiocarp itself. It is clear that to understand hyphal differentiation in the vegetative state of *C. pistillaris* we need to start with pure cultures and observe at what stage in the formation of the mycelial pad the incrusted hyphae appear, for it is unlikely that they are present from the inception of the dikaryon. The pattern of hyphal differentiation in each family varies to some extent with the species, but it is

6. The Hyphal Structure of the Basidiocarp

important to compare the patterns at a given stage in the overall development of the basidiocarp. Our classification of these fungi can never be complete from even a simple morphological basis until the development and hyphal systems of the basidiocarp are known for each species.

The development of *Rhizopogon pseudoaffinis* illustrates this well. The basidiocarp initial is a loose wad of mycelium originating in the soil in response to a localized stimulus to branch. In the interior of this cottony wad further localized branching soon develops, the branches being only 2–3 cells long with the apical cells soon becoming clavate and arranged in a palisade which, by continued development of the branching system, soon forms a palisade completely lining a hollow space (the locule, which at first is slitlike). Some of the terminal cells of the palisade then produce basidiospores. All this happens long before the peridial hyphae have become matted down to form a true tissue (the peridium). At this stage none of the hyphal walls show any sign of gelatinization and the whole basidiocarp (it can be called that since it is producing spores at this stage) is soft and fluffy. Also, at this stage, there has been no development of pigment and no inter- or intracellular deposits of amorphous material.

By studying a series of basidiocarps from the same fairy ring it was found that, as the number of locules increased, the surrounding fluffy hyphae forming the protective covering (the peridium) became matted down into a layer forming a tissue, and that at this stage as one cuts a basidiocarp in half considerable drag is noted on the razor, indicating a more cartilaginous consistency of the tramal plates. Under the microscope it is noted that the hyphae of the tramal plates, although of the same size and shape as in the truly soft specimens, now have a different index of refraction for transmitted light, a difference which almost always indicates some degree of gelatinization of the walls; in other words, a chemical change has taken place in the hyphae of the tramal plates. If the hyphae of the tramal plates are now compared to those of the peridium it will be noted that the peridial hyphae are not as refractive (not gelatinous). However, pigments dissolved in the cell sap or incrusted on the walls may be found in at least some of the peridial hyphae, or pigment may be deposited between the hyphae as colored amorphous material. Spores are produced from the hymenium while the above changes proceed. An attempt to describe the hyphal systems of a mature *Rhizopogon* basidiocarp will involve some difficulty because of the inadequacy of the word "mature" to meet this situation. In many *Rhizopogon* species the hymenial elements are all thin-walled and hyaline during the early stages of sporulation; as the basidiocarps age, however, the walls of the hymenial elements become thick enough almost to fill the lumen and, in a number of species (Smith and Zeller, 1966), the walls of subhymenial cells and even of some of the tramal-plate hyphae thicken. At this stage one might insist that the basidiocarp is past maturity, but this is true for the oldest (centrally located) locules only. Those near the peridium may still have thin-walled hymenial elements and still produce basidiospores. Obviously, by the time the gleba liquefies the basidiocarp is old, but liquefaction does not always occur in nature as a regular feature of aging. It is not uncommon for the basidiocarps to dry *in situ* and to decay later, presumably when the weather turns both wet and warm.

In other words, changes in the size and shape of hyphae, as well as in chemical composition, are continuous from the time the basidiocarp first forms until decay sets in. Maturity, therefore, must be defined in relation to the genus or family of fungi under consideration. Perhaps the most acceptable definition would be that stage represented by the peak of spore dispersal, or the elevating of the spore mass for immediate dispersal.

III. THE MITIC SYSTEM

Although the hyphal structure of the basidiocarp was known early, it was Corner (1932) who focused attention on it as a major means of understanding the identity and relationships of the higher fungi. Much information had accumulated before Corner's work, but the emphasis was different. For instance, in the early work, such as that of Fayod (1889) and Patouillard (1900) many hyphal features were used in descriptions. Some students of the Agaricales were interested mainly in the development of the basidiocarp: e.g., Atkinson (1906), Sawyer (1917), Walker (1919), and Kühner (1926) used hyphal and tissue characters where they appeared most definitive. Such systems as the laticiferous system, the tissue structure of the Russulaceae (designated as heteromerous), and the arrangement of the hyphae in the trama of the hymenophore in such genera as *Amanita, Hygrophorus, Volvariella,* and others were all well known before Corner published his first paper. Corner's contribution lies chiefly in his system of hyphal types in basidiocarps where there is little special differentiation into tissue systems. His approach has become known as the *mitic* system, in which a basidiocarp with only one kind of hypha is termed monomitic; if two types are present, dimitic; three kinds, trimitic and, if the hyphal cells inflate, physalomitic. However, this system is not very applicable to the Agaricales. Its greatest value was psychological in that it finally brought mycologists face to face with the real problem, namely, the degree to which the hyphae of the basidiocarp become specialized to further the processes of spore production and dispersal, directly or indirectly. Looked at in this light it seems ineffectual to set up

6. The Hyphal Structure of the Basidiocarp

special terms for generalized situations when they can be properly evaluated only by careful attention to detail. In other words, two species, one "monomitic" and another "dimitic" might be more closely related than two "monomitic" species. True, a terminology is convenient for general reference, but the mycologist should not let it obscure his vision to the point of failing to describe the hyphae in detail. Such terms as parallel, divergent, convergent, etc., for hymenophoral trama deal only with a hyphal pattern, not the hyphae in detail, and even this may differ from genus to genus for a single category such as divergent, and the manner of origin for such a single category may differ as well. Such terms as generative hyphae, fundamental hyphae, and ground hyphae applied across the board, as it were, fail to express adequately for scientific purposes what the investigator sees under his microscope for individual species, and are best used for general orientation of the reader.

Our concern with the hyphal structure of the basidiocarp is primarily for the purpose of identifying taxa and ascertaining their natural relationships. We are not limited in our search to one set of characters—morphological, anatomical chemical, etc.—but rather to the sum of all. We are concerned with the manner in which the hyphae are arranged in the basidiocarp, and the various modifications that they or their individual cells undergo. In the mitic system Talbot (1954) describes monomitic as applying to a system composed of generative hyphae. A dimitic system is said to be composed of generative and skeletal hyphae, and a trimitic system of generative, skeletal, and binding hyphae. He describes generative hyphae as being thin-walled, branched, septate, and narrow (1.5–10 μ), and either hyaline or colored. Binding hyphae are said to be aseptate and thick-walled. The definitions of skeletal hyphae are confusing but the term should apply to the main hyphal system specialized to maintain the shape of the basidiocarp. Unfortunately, this has not always been done.

IV. FEATURES OF THE HYPHAL WALL

I have described the primitive or undifferentiated hypha [Fig. 1 (*1*)] as a cylindrical thin-walled colorless tube lacking adhering material such as debris or incrustations. Starting from this, some of the modifications a hyphal wall may show are: (a) incrustations [Fig. 1 (*9*)] that may be remains of an early primary wall adhering in patches or zones; (b) deposition on the wall of excreted metabolic products, a feature likely to be influenced by nutrition; (c) the formation of distinctive pigments, possibly of aid in preventing moisture loss; (d) chemical changes taking place in the wall itself [Fig. 1 (*12*)].

By the time one has studied thousands of species so many different patterns are found that detailed classifications of them become of little

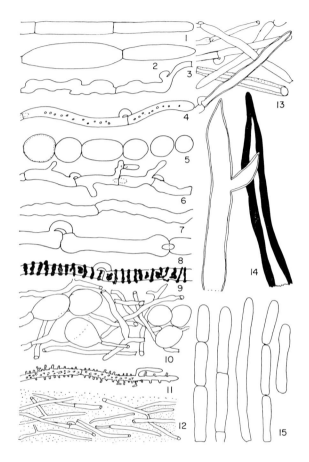

FIG. 1. Differentiation in hyphae and hyphal cells of hymenomycetes. (*1*) Tubular (undifferentiated) hypha from *Pluteus cervinus* (*sensu lato*). (*2*) Slightly inflated hyphal cells, and (*3*) oleiferous hyphae from *Cantharellus floccosus*. (*4*) Tubular hyphae with clamps (*Sistotrema,* Smith 71299). (*5*) Sphaerocysts from cutis of *Cystoderma* (Smith 70903). (*6*) Hypha of subcutis showing short branches (*Cystoderma,* Smith 70903). (*7*) Flexuous hypha from *Polyporus glomeratus*. (*8*) Context hypha of *Gymnopilus spectabilis* showing tibiiform cell (enlargement at septum) (Thiers 4048). (*9*) Encrusted hypha *Pholiota lubrica* (Smith 46383). (*10*) Sphaerocysts and binding hyphae making the heteromerous context of *Russula aeruginea* (Sm 21905). (*11*) Hyphae with rodlike wall protrusions. *Mycena iodiolens* (Sm 32487). (*12*) Gelatinous hyphae from cutis of *Mycena vulgaris* (Sm 7935). (*13*) Hyphae from context of *Panus strigosus* showing varying degrees of wall thickening (Imshaug 3828). (*14*) Mycosclerids as "skeletals" in context of *Polyporus glomeratus*. Both thin- and thick-walled elements occur. (*15*) Hyphal cells from cutis of variants of stirps Scabrum in *Leccinum* (Boletaceae).

6. The Hyphal Structure of the Basidiocarp

help in adequately dealing with them as heritable features, which, in fact, is what they probably are for the most part.

A. Wall Thickenings

A varied pattern of wall thickenings exists from one group of fungi to another, or in a single species [Fig. 1 *(13)*]. A thin wall is generally regarded as not being measurable accurately with the light microscope, usually it is less than 0.5 µ thick. The wall may become thick by the deposition of an inner wall of solid material against the primary wall. It is usually laid down rather evenly throughout the cell. In some cases local thickenings may occur, such as are frequently noted in hyphal end cells known as cystidia (Section X, D). Local thickenings are known in some spores, e.g., *Galerina allospora* (Smith and Singer, 1964). In *Rhizopogon* and other hymenogastraceous genera the thickening of the wall in the basidium, basidiole or "brachybasidiole" appears at first to be an accumulation of mucilage which later hardens and may nearly obliterate the cell lumen. Such thickenings may occur in the terminal cell of the hyphal branch, or involve the entire hypha back to and including its connections to the tramal-plate hyphae. Thickened hyphal walls of one type or another both on mycelium and in basidiocarps have arisen in so many groups independently that this feature must be regarded as a rather routine response of basidiocarp-forming fungi to environmental stimuli.

B. Clamp Connections

From my own observations the presence or absence of clamp connections [Fig. 1 *(4)*] is an independent feature which, from circumstantial evidence, may or may not be genetically linked with hyphal wall thickenings. Artifacts may cause some confusion. I have noted on many occasions, in the course of collecting and studying species of *Rhizopogon,* the presence in the peridium, of thick-walled hyphae with clamps at the cross-walls, and these were not part of the basidiocarp—at least not connected to it.

To me it seems futile to define "skeletals" as thick-walled hyphae lacking clamps. All the matrical hyphae (ground hyphae) of a basidiocarp are skeletal hyphae in the sense that they are the framework of the fruiting structure. If they are weak and collapse readily the basidiocarp is soft and readily decays. If they are thick-walled and rigid, the basidiocarp is tough to woody in consistency. It seems to me that there is much virtue in descriptive terms which "mean what they say" and that the best possible foundation for the application of terms must be based on the function of the part being named. The term skeletal hyphae clearly implies that such hyphae form most of the framework of the basidiocarp and impart such rigidity to it as it possesses. The term "mycosclerid" proposed by Wright (1955) is perhaps a better term than "skeletal" for the thick-walled aseptate cell or hyphal systems so common in the polypores.

V. CHEMICAL TESTS AND CHEMICAL FEATURES

A. Gelification and Thickening

One chemical feature involves the gelification of the wall to form a viscous material which imparts a sticky or slimy feel to the surface of the structure involved. This material has a different index of refraction in transmitted light than nongelified walls. In the Agaricales species occur in which all degrees of gelification of the wall occur so that, at one extreme taxa are found in which the hyphae of the epicutis of the pileus are almost completely obliterated by this process (species of *Resupinatus, Mycena,* etc.). At the other and more common extreme are species in which the process does not occur at all, or is scarcely noticeable. Also, some cells may extrude gelatinous material without themselves gelatinizing.

The opposite trend, that of the laying down of an inner thicker wall which is more brittle (in many cases) than the original thin wall, is of very common occurrence. That these hyphae are brittle is deduced from the irregularly fractured ends of broken pieces in crushed mounts. The thickened wall, like the gelatinous one, probably aids in the preservation of the basidiocarp to allow spore discharge to be carried out at repeated intervals. Thus, perennial basidiocarps, for the most part, contain many thick-walled elements. The walls themselves are hyaline or colored various degrees of ochraceous to dark rusty brown, and one very common feature is that in KOH they change to a darker brown. This point comes up again under setae.

B. Iodine Reactions

Color reactions resulting from the application of certain chemicals to the basidiocarp are also important and are not necessarily limited to reactions with the wall. Of these, the iodine reactions are most important and will be treated first. The solution used to carry out these reactions is composed of chloral hydrate (3 parts), water (5 parts), both by weight, one or two crystals of KI, and iodine crystals to saturation. This solution, termed Melzer's solution, or slight modifications of it, is now universally used in the study of basidiomycetes and ascomycetes, with both spores and hyphal structures. It can be used as a mounting medium directly or as a stain that is washed out with a colorless solution of chloral hydrate. Sections should never be revived in a weak base first; or if this is done, the alkali must be carefully removed. It is best to mount directly in Melzer's solution. Several color distinctions may be obtained including, a gray, blue-gray, blue, or violet. Such a color change is termed *amyloid*. Although used mainly to show ornamentation on spores, this reagent has come into prominence in the general study of hyphal walls (Imler, 1950; Miller, 1964). Kühner (1926) used the term amyloid for stipe hyphae in *Mycena* which became dark wine-red to brownish red in this medium. This color change is now included under the term *dextrinoid* (Orton, 1960), and Singer's term pseudamyloid is an approximate equivalent. A yellow to orange or tawny orange reaction is termed inamyloid (nonamyloid). It can be seen that this category intergrades, to some extent, with dextrinoid, and this is indeed the case since an inamyloid reaction may darken to a weakly dextrinoid one if the mount is allowed to stand a few hours. Changes of this degree often occur in the boletes (Luridi), where in many species the spores are amyloid when fresh, but become nonamyloid to dextrinoid on drying out. In general, however, even for the spores of boletes, the pattern of color change and its intensity are very constant for a species and are now being given great emphasis in the recognition of taxa. The change noted in the boletes is in the opposite direction to the one found in most fungi, where the spores are likely to be nonamyloid at first and weakly amyloid after drying. Crushed mounts in Melzer's solution of dried hymenophoral tissue of many boletes gives a bluish to violet black reaction against a white background macroscopically, but no localized color change in hyphal or spore walls is noted microscopically. This reaction has been observed most frequently with fungi in which the fresh context or the tubes stain blue when injured, and it may be associated with the blue staining reaction, although it is true that some species not staining blue also show it. This reaction has been termed a "fleeting amyloid" reaction. Imler (1950) was apparently the first to discuss this subject as applied to boletes, but he also noted true amyloid reactions on the hyphae of some species (*Boletus calopus*). However, it is not only the wall that may react with iodine, but also the incrustations, interhyphal debris, or intracellular material. These, along with the globules which become blue in iodine, are discussed below.

Harrison (1964) noted amyloid particles along some hyphae in the stipitate Hydnaceae. These particles adhered to the wall (along it) much in the manner of iron filings aggregating along a magnet; he termed these "apparent amyloid" partly for the reason that some darken in KOH as well as Melzer's solution. As yet it has been impossible to be sure that one kind of granule gives both reactions. Smith (Smith and Zeller, 1966) found these granules to be a prominent feature in some species of *Rhizopogon* and interhyphal debris is amyloid in some species of *Chroogomphus* (Miller, 1964). Thiers and Smith (1966) have used amorphous material in the trichodermal hyphae of one of the *Boletus rubellus* complex as a means of recognizing a species. Heinemann (1942) used the amyloid content of cystidia for the same purpose in *Psathyrella*. Lange (1956) used the presence of large pigment balls (droplets) which are orange red in color as an aid in characterizing some species of *Rhizopogon*. Smith (1966) verified Lange's observations and also found a few species in which the pigment balls were violaceous to purplish in Melzer's solution. These pigment balls are apparently formed by the partial solubility in chloral hydrate of the amorphous material deposited between the hyphae which thereupon form a viscous mass globose to versiform in shape and 6–70 μ in diameter. Originally this material must have been in solution and then coagulated as the liquid evaporated.

In *Mycolevis* (Smith, 1966) a green reaction on the peridial wall was obtained with Melzer's solution. Under the microscope some blue pigment was noted in aggregations of hyphae, but most of the pigment appeared to be dissolved in the mounting medium.

C. Chemicals Other Than Iodine

The reaction of KOH (2.5–5%) in producing a brown discoloration in the hyphal wall has already been noted. This is a feature of the well-known "xanthochroic" line of the Basidiomycetes wherein mycologists have now placed more emphasis on the color of the hyphal walls than on the configuration of the hymenophore in analyzing relationships. It should be remembered that this same color reaction is also a feature of the hyphae of the cutis in many species of *Cortinarius* (Agaricales) as well as of their spores. Also, Smith (1963) described a species of *Martellia* (astrogastraceous line of the Gastromycetes) in which the tissues of the basidiocarp as well as the spore wall darken to rusty brown on aging or when the basidiocarp is bruised, and darken further when revived in KOH. One basidiocarp was found in nature half of which had white spores and half brown spores. It appears that whatever chemical gives this reaction with KOH it is quite common in hyphal and spore walls and, like other common metabolites, may not have much value in uniting species differing sharply in fundamental morphological features.

Another color reaction with KOH is that in the spores of many of the Strophariaceae (Agaricales) in which the spore when fresh has a distinct violaceous color as seen in water mounts under the microscope. This color changes to yellow-brown immediately upon the introduction of KOH. A number of color changes are produced by KOH in the fresh basidiocarp, including the yellow-brown which is evident in a number of *Rhizopogon* species. In many species of *Agaricus* (Agaricales) a lemon-yellow color is produced. In many species of *Rhizopogon,* and in members of the Can-

6. The Hyphal Structure of the Basidiocarp

tharellales (*Polyozellus multiplex*) a color change to olive is produced and is very characteristic; it is demonstrable both in fresh and dried material. However, KOH may also give a red reaction, as in many species of *Rhizopogon* and *Cortinarius*. Also in *Cortinarius,* KOH may give a red reaction with intercellular deposits of amorphous pigment (*C. sanguineus,* etc.) and in others may produce a change to purplish in the granules in the basidium (*C. orichalceus* group). When fresh, *C. semisanguineus* gives an inky violet color upon application of KOH.

In some species of *Rhizopogon* in sections of the fresh peridium, some sharply defined areas or zones stain green and others stain red upon application of KOH, a reaction that is constant for the species. Most of the KOH reactions—to brown, yellow, red, or green—can be demonstrated on dried as well as fresh material. For obvious reasons they are regarded as being more important taxonomically than reactions shown only by fresh specimens.

Such salts as ferric chloride, or ferric or ferrous sulfate (10% aqueous), will frequently give a green to olive color to the fresh context or cutis of a basidiocarp. In some species of *Russula* a reddish discoloration is induced. Ethanol (70%) will also cause certain color changes, and since this chemical is frequently used for a solvent for reagents it is important to test it separately. An interesting reaction is obtained with ethanol followed by a drop of ferric or ferrous sulfate (or vice versa). Usually this merely speeds up the reaction with the iron salt or makes the reaction more intense, but in some species it causes a change from olive to blue. This test should be made before reporting a species as reacting negatively to iron salts. For instance, some species of *Rhizopogon,* which at first appeared to be negative, were positive with this combination. Ethanol alone has been found to cause a pinkish to reddish cinnamon color in some species of *Rhizopogon*. Ammonium hydroxide also is used on fresh specimens, especially on boletes where pinkish, violaceous, or fuscous colors are sometimes produced, or in the cutis of *Phylloporus,* where green colors are produced.

Other well-known reactions include the Shaffer reaction, used mostly for species of *Agaricus,* and the sulfovanillin reaction for species of *Russula*. In the former, a streak of nitric acid is applied to the cap with a streak of aniline oil crossing it. A red color at the intersection of the streaks is a positive reaction. The sulfovanillin reaction gives a dark color to the elements of the laticiferous system in most of the Russulaceae, as does sulfobenzaldehyde.

The above listing and discussion of color changes produced by application of chemicals is by no means complete, but it is sufficient to show the scope of their use with hyphae of basidiocarps and the empirical manner in which they are being used. It is obvious at a glance that all chemicals test for is the presence of certain compounds or classes of compounds (such as resins) in the tissues or regions of the basidiocarp. It follows that closely related fungi may differ in the presence or absence of a compound and, although the color reaction may be very distinct, the difference may be in a single gene or less in one of a multigenic complex. Hence, attempts to arrange a classification into families and genera on the basis of color reactions with chemicals, especially those based mainly on one reaction, are as weak as any other classification involving a single character. Chemical characters should be used in conjunction with all other features including the configuration of the hymenophore. Mycologists have been so desperate to find demonstrable features which correlate with the intangible differences they observe on fresh specimens that they have tended to fall into the error of overinterpreting color changes produced by chemicals before they know the chemistry involved. Levenberg (1961) has shown that the production of a certain compound (agaricine) in *Agaricus* follows a pattern consistent with the presumed relationships of the species as worked out on the basis of morphology and hyphal anatomy. This is the level we must attain in "chemotaxonomy" before we can say that the subject is on a firm foundation.

VI. CELL SHAPE

This is a most important feature and obviously must be used in relation to the part of the basidiocarp under consideration. If we refer again to our unspecialized hypha [Fig. 1 (1)], it is a long straight tube with a thin wall and is divided into cells by cross-walls (septa) that are a considerable distance apart. One of the first changes that may occur in a hypha is the formation of numerous septa to produce short, almost isodiametric cells. A tissue composed of this type often resembles parenchyma and is described as being pseudoparenchymatic. The cells in this type of tissue may inflate considerably, and some become keg-shaped to globose, the pattern depending on the species involved. In many fungi the hyphal cells enlarge next to the septa at either end, the remainder of the cell remaining tubular [Fig. 1 (8)], hence the shape of the cell is somewhat tibiiform. The walls of some hyphae may become undulated (flexuous) [Fig. 1 (7)], or develop bumps or short rodlike or wartlike projections, or spinelike processes may be produced [Fig. 1 (11)]. Since much of the rapid "growth" in size by basidiocarps of agaricales is associated with cell enlargement and accompanying changes in shape, it is important to study both mature and immature specimens to ascertain the pattern for each species. The hyphae of the laticiferous system [Fig. 1 (3)] are often misshapen. It is not uncommon for cells in a tissue such as the epicutis in some species of *Rhizopogon* (section Villosuli) to be versiform—meaning all sorts of odd shapes.

6. The Hyphal Structure of the Basidiocarp

Outline Summary of Cell Shape

1. Tubular: Increase in size due to increase in length and/or width
2. Inflated
   a. Barrel-shaped to globose
   b. Sausage-shaped—curved and enlarged evenly but narrow at septa
   c. Tibiiform: Inflated near septa but tubular between
3. Irregular: Wider in one part and tapered to tubular or nearly so at one end
4. Compound shapes
   a. Tubular with flexuous walls
   b. Inflated with various irregularities including short protuberances from the wall
   c. Versiform—odd shapes involving any combination of above types and often including irregular branching

A chemical (enzymatic) reaction is involved in the dissolution of the cross wall, especially in chains of globose cells [Fig. 1 (5)], to produce a powdery layer made up of individual cells (see *Lepiota* sect. Pruinosi, and *Cystoderma* in part). However, disarticulation of hyphae is not limited to chains of globose cells. In *Leccinum* (Boletaceae) there is a strong tendency of the hyphal cells of the pileus epicutis to disarticulate [Fig. 1 (15)]. These cells vary from subglobose to cylindrical. A pileus which at first appears fibrillose-streaked may by maturity appear glabrous if the cuticular hyphae show this feature. This distinction is difficult to make at times, especially if gelatinous hyphal walls are involved.

VII. THE SUBHYMENIUM

Since features of the subhymenium are now being used to group species into genera, some observations made on the subhymenium of *Rhizopogon* are pertinent. When spores first begin to form in some species this tissue consists of interwoven, much branched filamentous hyphae which give rise to the hymenial elements in the form of a trichodermal palisade. As the process of growth continues the subhymenial elements inflate to 4–5 times their original diameter and the layer appears as if it were composed of sphaerocysts and more or less continuous with the hymenial elements. Thus it seems like a layer of a completely different type. This argues for the use of caution in assigning great taxonomic emphasis to subhymenial features, especially at the generic level. These features are likely to be most useful in genera where the basidiocarp is little more than a layer of basidia and cystidia over the substratum. Those species in which numerous crops of basidia are produced during one season, or over several, show accompanying changes such as specialized types of subhymenia and deep hymenia caused by the growth of a new crop of basidia beyond the old ones which do not collapse completely.

VIII. HYPHAL BRANCHING

The patterns of hyphal branching are many and sometimes bizarre, but are usually constant for a given tissue, such as the hymenium, the cutis of the pileus or of the stipe. In the hymenium of some species the "candelabra effect" occurs in which a hypha as it approaches the hymenium branches dichotomously repeatedly with the apical cells forming the hymenial elements. A most troublesome type of branching to interpret is that when false clamps are formed. In this case the branch which was supposed to have formed the clamp does not fuse with the penultimate cell formed after cell division and is found dangling with a free tip, appearing much like any other short branch. In order to identify such a branch correctly, one must know the direction in which it grows: if away from the terminal cell it is a false clamp; if toward it the branch has nothing to do with clamp formation [Fig. 1 (6)]. In the latter type, which is much the commonest, the branch originates just below the distal septum of the mother cell and grows toward the outer edge of the culture, if growing on a petri dish. Such branches are usually long and finally become divided into tubular cells and rebranch in the same manner. In the context of a fleshy basidiocarp, in contrast to a culture of vegetative mycelium, the branching may be random to produce what is commonly termed an intricately interwoven arrangement. This complicates a determination of the direction of branch growth. In the context of most species, however, whether fleshy or woody in texture, there is a general direction of hyphal orientation from the stipe toward the margin of the pileus. This may also be noticed on the pileus cutis where, especially if it is fibrillose in texture, the fibrils are arranged approximately radially, i.e., the tips are directed toward the pileus margin.

One of the most important features of hyphal branching is that the branch from any given hypha does not necessarily become a cell with the same features as the parent cell. Oleiferous hyphae in many species become differentiated late in the development of the basidiocarp and may be only segments of a hypha. In sphaerocyst formation in *Russula* and *Lactarius* slender branches may give rise to a terminal sphaerocyst, but in other hyphae globose cells may arise by the formation of secondary septa and then cell inflation. Both types may occur in the same species. The walls of the sphaerocysts are typically thin but thick-walled ones are known (*Martellia*). In *Rhizopogon* such cells are scattered in the peridial context and do not form a tissue. In the Russulaceae they are a regular feature of the context of the pileus so that they are regarded as one of the components of a specialized tissue termed *heteromerous* [Fig. 1 (*10*)] in which groups of inflated cells are surrounded by filamentous hyphae. In *Rhizopogon* such cells aid in distinguishing species; in the Russulaceae their presence as a component of a specialized tissue is one of the basic features of the family.

In many species of the Polyporales, as well as in some of the Agaricales, reduced types of branching occur which produce rather weird structures at times. These most often are present on the hyphae of the pileus cutis, as in many species of *Mycena* (Smith, 1947) where all stages from true branches to short rodlike projections are found, often in a single pileus. Similarly branched cells may also occur on the gill edges or as pileo- or caulocystidia. In cells of the hymenium or gill edge the projections have at times been interpreted as being rudimentary or modified sterigmata. It is perfectly clear that in some species the cellular ornamentation has been derived from the sterigmata, but this is not the case with hyphae of the pileus cutis. These abortive branches serve to bind the hyphae of the cutis into a cohesive layer which protects the tissue beneath and are most logically regarded as a reduced type of branch. Clusters of cells along the gill edge with the same type of "branching" could easily serve as an air trap to protect against excessive water loss from the gill edge. Also, the production of sterigmata on the basidia may be interpreted as a pattern of branching in itself, so perhaps the question of the homologies of these atypical types of branching may not be particularly significant.

Certain hyphae of the basidiocarp may become differentiated into long tubes by the failure of septa to form or possibly by their dissolution as the hypha matures. Thus, septate and nonseptate hyphae may be found in a fruiting body of a single species, especially in the laticiferous system. In some hyphae, either septate or nonseptate, the wall becomes irregularly enlarged and narrowed and the cell content may be seen in revived material to be mostly of an amorphous, possibly resinous to oily, material. In fresh material the contents may or may not be homogeneous and have more of a tendency to absorb dyes such as cresyl blue than other matrical hyphae. These are the elements of the laticiferous system. If such hyphae actually contain a latex when the basidiocarp is fresh they must be termed laticifers; otherwise they are referred to as oleiferous hyphae. Singer (1963) has tried to distinguish between the two types on morphological bases, but in my estimation, without success. The hyphae of the laticiferous system have also been referred to as vascular hyphae, but this term creates the false impression, as Donk (1964) has so appropriately pointed out, that they are special conducting hyphae. They appear to function more as repositories of metabolic products—probably wastes. The tips of the hyphae of this system often project into the hymenium and form cystidia of various shapes and sizes, and possibly some waste materials and moisture are removed by evaporation from these organs. Indeed, this appears to be the function of most cystidia which occur in the hymenium. The elements of the laticiferous system vary in size from one cell long to hyphae that can be traced for long distances in the context of stipe pileus and hymenophore. They may arise so early in the formation of the basidiocarp that it is difficult to determine just when they first appear. Certain chemical "reactions" are characteristic of these elements as, for example, in the Russulaceae where many species show a dark reaction in sulfobenzaldehyde or sulfovanillin.

IX. CLAMP CONNECTIONS

The presence or absence of these structures at the septa of the hyphae of the secondary mycelium, whether they belong to the vegetative stage or the basidiocarp, has been used by all taxonomists of the modern era as a character of importance, but again, rather empirically and without an understanding of the basis of the observation. For instance, the "skeletal" has been defined as a thick-walled hypha lacking clamps and cross walls. This would seem to imply that hyphae without septa but with clamps are known, but this violates the definition of a clamp connection. At the present time the presence or absence of clamp connections at the septa of hyphae is not to be regarded as linked regularly with either thick-walled or thin-walled as a character.

There are a few species in which whorls of clamps are known to occur at each septum but this is very unusual. It is now known that there are large groups (e.g., the astrogastraceous line of the Gastromycetes) which lack them. In *Rhizopogon* (Smith and Zeller, 1966) clamps are present on the hyphae of the basidiocarp in fewer than five of 137 species. In the Boletaceae they are absent on the hyphae of the basidiocarps in the larger genera such as *Boletus,* but present in the more "primitive" (?) groups including a few species of *Suillus.* It is in this group that Pantidou (1961) found clamps on the mycelium of some species in which the hyphae of the basidiocarp lacked them. Miller (1964) clearly demonstrated in *Chroogomphus* (Gomphidiaceae) that clamps occurred on the mycelium found in nature, but not on the hyphae of the basidiocarp, an observation made possible by the amyloid reaction of the hyphae, a rare feature in basidiomycetes which are mycorrhiza formers. In the type subgenus of *Pluteus* (Volvariaceae), species with and without clamps on the hyphae of the basidiocarp occur with equal frequency (Smith 1956-66). In *Cortinarius* they are regularly present except in less than a dozen of over 700 species known to me. These examples are limited to those I have personally verified, but others are given in the literature. As can be seen, large groups of fungi vary in the proportion of clamped species from none or few to about half to nearly 100%. A study of the mycelia of "clampless" species is needed to determine to what degree they are clamped, if at all. Moreover, a quantitative study of the proportion of septa on which clamps occur in basidiocarps of a given species is needed as well as whether clampless and clamped "species" show any mating compatibility when single spores are paired. Until these questions have been answered it seems prudent not to use the presence or absence of clamps on the hyphae of the basidiocarp as an important feature of genera or higher categories. In *Galerina* (Kühner, 1935; Smith and Singer, 1964) it was used as a section and subgeneric category, respectively, but recent observations by Bass (1965), and my own recent experience, indicate that it would probably have been wiser to have placed certain clampless species alongside some having clamps but which resemble them in most of their other features. At present I regard the presence of absence of these structures as not being necessarily linked with any of the routine anatomical features of the hyphae, such as width of cells, thickness of wall, presence of incrustations, etc. It would be interesting to get nuclear details of the hyphal cells bounded by clampless septa in species where clamps were present with some frequency. Originally (Bensaude, 1918; Kniep, 1918) clamp connections were regarded as a device to allow the nuclei of a dikaryon to divide separately, and thus the idea that the clamp was a basic and primitive feature of the Basidiomycetes probably had its origin.

X. HYPHAL TIP DIFFERENTIATION

It is in the terminology of hyphal tips that mycologists are tending to lose themselves in a complicated terminology comparable to the branching pattern in "dichophyses." Those who love new terms have truly experienced a field day, but fortunately the work of Donk (1964) and others now points the way toward fewer and more meaningful terms. In this chapter I have tried to influence this trend even further.

A. *The Hymenium*

The hymenium is a palisade formed by the end cells of hyphae and their branches, but these have been so reduced and changed morphologically that the hyphal aspect of the layer (including the subhymenium) is usually rather obscure. The *basidia* (Section X, B) are the most important element since they are the cells in which the vital processes of karyogamy and meiosis occur, culminating in the production of spores. The next most important element functionally is the *basidiole* (Section X, C) (and brachybasidiole). Basidioles resemble young basidia in size and shape, hence they cannot be distinguished under the microscope. However, in some genera (*Coprinus,* and numerous hymenogastraceous species) the basidioles inflate markedly and form a distinct cellular pavement supporting the basidia as these produce their spores. When they inflate to twice or more the diameter of the young basidia, they should be termed brachybasidioles (Smith, 1966). The third category of end cells includes many kinds of *cystidia* (Section X, D). These occur haphazardly in the hymenium, depending on the species, and vary from abundant to absent. They differ from basidioles in that a typical hymenium can form without them. Also, it is assumed that their function is not that of support for the basidia. The last element, named *hyphoids* (Section X, D, 4), is in reality a kind of cystidium. Hyphoids are simple or branched filaments, sometimes very elaborately so, and are more numerous in the Aphyllophorales than in fleshy fungi. It is obvious that the function of the basidia is spore production, and that of the basidioles to support the basidia in the palisade, but it is not so clear what functions the cystidia (including hyphoids) serve. It is assumed that since metabolic products are deposited in many cystidia they are a type of excretory organ. Lentz (1954) has given a detailed account of the history of these bodies, and Watling (1966) has advanced the idea that they might aid in drawing water down from the pileus because of their ability to evaporate it readily, thereby tending to increase the humidity in the area where spores are forming. Hyphoids may be considered to be somewhat like air traps, also preserving a high relative humidity during the development of the basidia and possibly during spore formation. These seem to be reasonable explanations since most hyphal modifications in the basidiocarp appear to be adjustments to meet the problem of moisture loss. That different species have evolved different ways of meeting the problem explains the diversity in both form and content of these cells.

B. *The Basidium*

The morphology of the basidium is given great importance in the classification of the basidiomycetes. Morphology, however, reflects the pressures of the environment in selecting successful variants. Thus, those species with a gelified hymenium nearly always produce long sterigmata to ensure that the spores form in a position where, when shot off, they can be dispersed by air currents. The Tremellales characteristically show this adaptation. At the other extreme, in *Rhizopogon,* the basidium varies from cylindric to urn-shaped or clavate in a single basidiocarp, depending upon its position in the hymenium in relation to pressures from other cells. In the Aphyllophorales (Donk, 1964) basidial shape is more constant within a species and is used as a feature to separate a number of groups. The "tuning fork" type of *Dacrymyces* is well known, and the two-spored basidia of *Cerato-*

6. The Hyphal Structure of the Basidiocarp

basidium resemble them to a striking degree. *Tulasnella* features odd variations (Rogers, 1933), such as inflated deciduous sterigmata. In the Agaricales the basidium is a very constant structure. Normally it is merely narrowly to broadly clavate but varies to cylindrical or, when one-spored, sometimes fusoid (*Mycena*). It is a single cell cut off by a basal septum. In the Tremellales two walls vertical or oblique to the basal septum are laid down making the basidium 4-celled, each cell of which produces a sterigma and spore. Basidia developing septa in addition to the original basal one have in the past been classified as Heterobasidiomycetes, meaning a group of fungi with types of basidia other than those found in the "Homobasidiomycetes" of which the type found in the Agaricales is an example. Talbot (1954) refers to basidia with septa in addition to the basal one as phragmobasidiate. Rarely in the homobasidium a secondary transverse septum may form as the spores mature. A rather complex nomenclature has been developed for naming the parts of the heterobasidium at various stages in its development. The term probasidium in the Heterobasidiomycetes is applied to the young basidium before the longitudinal or oblique walls are formed. The metabasidium is the stage, as in the Tremellales, when the longitudinal septa have been laid down. The epibasidium is represented by the thick outgrowth terminated by a point (spicule), the latter representing the sterigma to some authors. Donk (1964) has made the most logical solution to the complicated situation which has resulted from trying to apply the above nomenclature to basidiomycetes in general. Donk defines the probasidium and metabasidium in relation to the nuclear phase involved. The probasidium is that stage in which nuclear fusion occurs. The metabasidium is the stage in which the fusion nucleus divides, and the other terms epibasidium and spicule may be regarded as the sterigmal apparatus. The features of the basidium furnish the basic taxonomic characters of the major groups of basidiomycetes.

C. Basidioles

Basidioles may be defined as basidia which have not yet produced spores or cells like them which will never produce spores. No morphological distinction can be made between them. They make up the body of the hymenium and act as support for the cells that are sporulating. When they do become differentiated from young basidia as in *Coprinus* (and hymenogastraceous fungi in part), they can be readily recognized at sight by their larger size. These enlarged cells have had various designations in the literature: pseudoparaphyses; coprinoid paraphyses; and, most recently by Donk, brachycystidia. In keeping with correlating the name of a structure with its function or supposed function, the term *brachybasidiole* is much more appropriate and has been proposed as a replacement for brachycystidia. In some species of *Marasmius* the basidioles are somewhat fusoid as are also the basidia. It is generally accepted that the basidioles are derived from unmodified basidia or that they represent sterile basidia. Both typically originate from elements of the subhymenium, but they can originate from tramal hyphae even in species with well-developed subhymenia, as I have observed on some occasions in *Suillus* species.

D. Cystidia

The definition of a cystidium suggested here is: "an element of the hymenium apparently functioning mainly to aid in the evaporation of moisture and other volatile substances or acting as an air trap and not being found in the hymenium or basidiocarp of every species." Typically cystidia are distinguishable morphologically from basidia and basidioles of all kinds. Vesiculate to clavate hymenial cystidia project beyond the basidia or are randomly situated. Rarely do they serve the secondary function of support, as in certain coprini, where they hold the young gills apart, thus allowing the spores to form. They undoubtedly serve other functions, such as operating as air traps. The mechanical function of cystidia generally has been greatly overemphasized even for coprini.

Cystidia have been variously classified: one terminology very useful in routine descriptive work is that of Buller (1922), who assigned terms indicative of their position on the basidiocarp. In the agarics, those cystidia occurring on the face of the hymenophore were termed *pleurocystidia* [Fig. 2 (*2–7* and *12–14, 20*)]; those on the gill edge, *cheilocystidia* [Fig. 2 (*11, 18–20*)]; those on the stipe, *caulocystidia* [Fig. 2 (*8, 16*)]; and those on the pileus, *pileocystidia* (sometimes erroneously spelled pilocystidia). Singer has grouped the pileocystidia and caulocystidia under the term dermatocystidia, but this leads to ambiguity in descriptive work since the two are different in many species. For example, those on the stipe tend to be longer or to show more variation in shape. Of course Buller's terms are applicable only to those species with highly developed basidiocarps and hymenophores. In those forms lacking a stipe or a pileus or both, and having a smooth hymenium, the best term to use is hymenial cystidia. This is necessary because, as we shall see, some species have internal cystidium-like cells now often referred to as endocystidia. Buller's system is applicable to the polypores, hydnums, and agarics. The term dermatocystidia is most appropriate for cystidia on the peridia of gastromycetes.

If the problem of classifying cystidia is approached from a different point of view, we find that many modern authors, such as Romagnesi (1944), and Singer (1963), have based a classification on morphological types and to some extent on presumed function. Actually both this and Buller's system

6. The Hyphal Structure of the Basidiocarp

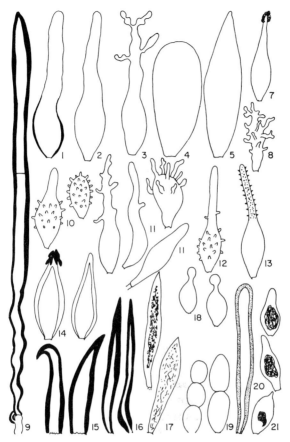

FIG. 2. Differentiated end cells of hyphae in hymenomycetes. (*1*) Cheilocystidium with basal wall thickening becoming brown in KOH; from *Galerina vittaeformis* var. *albescens* f. *tetraspora*. (*2*) Pleurocystidium of *Galerina umbrinipes* (a leptocystidium). (*3*) Pleurocystidium of *Galerina thujina* (a branched letocystidium). (*4*) Pleurocystidium in *Mycena pura* (a leptocystidium). (*5*) Pleurocystidium in *Mycena pelianthina* (a leptocystidium). (*7*) Pleurocystidium in *Mycena gypsea* (a leptocystidium with apical incrustation insoluble in KOH). (*8*) Caulocystidium of *Mycena corticola* showing development of branches. (*9*) Setiform cystidium (seta) from pileus of *Crinipellis zonata* showing thick-walled clamp at base and secondary wall lacking a clamp. (*10*) Cheilocystidia of *Mycena rosella*. (*11*) Cheilocystidia of *Mycena citrinomarginata*. (*12*) Pleurocystidium of *Mycena latifolia*. (*13*) Pleurocystidium of *Mycena borealis*. (*14*) Pleurocystidium (lamprocystidium) of *Psathyrella camptopoda*. (*15*) Colored lamprocystidia in *Polyporus tomentosus* var. *circinatus*. (*16*) Caulocystidia (setae) from *Collybia setulosa*. (*17*) Pseudocystidia in *Lactarius vellereus* (macrocystidia). (*18*) Cheilocystidia of *Conocybe tenera* sensu lato. (*19*) Cheilocystidia of *Agaricus augustus* (the end cell in the chain is technically the cystidium). (*20*) Pleurocystidium of *Chroogomphus vinicolor*. (*21*) Chrysocystidia (pleurocystidia) in *Naematoloma* (Strophariaceae).

can be used together to make descriptive work concise and to allow the user quickly to locate and identify the cells he sees under the microscope.

1. Leptocystidia

The common type found in most of the Agaricales and to a lesser extent in other groups is called a leptocystidium [Fig. 2 (4)]. It is presumed to be a modified basidium since it typically arises from the same area as the basidia. If this supposition is correct, then these cystidia must be regarded as being more highly specialized than basidioles because so many species lack them and, when present, they occur randomly. Leptocystidia are typically thin-walled and lack significant incrustations, although amorphous material often adheres to the exterior when the cell is fresh. This material usually dissolves in the mounting medium and so is not ordinarily observed (personal observations). These cystidia originate in the subhymenium or the adjacent tramal tissue, and vary in shape from fusoid-ventricose to clavate or clavate-mucronate or utriform (ventricose with a short neck and very broadly rounded to subcapitate apex). Their content is usually hyaline but is colored at times from pigment in the cell sap—as in a number of species of *Mycena* sect. Calodontes. One needless term introduced to the nomenclature of cystidia is cystidiole. The only justification for it is to regard it as a parallel term to basidiole, but this is not the way it is being used. Cystidiole should apply to the young cystidium as a cell which will form a cystidium, but in which the morphological differentiation has not yet taken place. Hence, in many cases, basidioles and cystidioles will not be distinguishable from each other. The tendency to regard small cystidia as cystidioles is unjustifiable inasmuch as size is one of the most variable features of leptocystidia. Neither does the fact that some cystidia fail to project beyond the hymenium have any bearing on their nomenclature. Lentz's (1954) definition of a cystidiole (p. 190) as being "a simple hymenial cell of approximately the same diameter as the basidium but remaining sterile and protruding beyond the hymenial surface" expresses no worthwhile distinction between leptocystidia and cystidioles.

Although most leptocystidia originate in the subhymenium at the level of the basidia, this position of origin is not rigidly fixed for all hymenomycetes. In *Suillus* (Boletaceae), Smith and Thiers (1964) have traced sporulating basidia back into the tramal area before finding a cross wall, so I do not regard the point of origin of cystidia to be of any more significance than that of basidia. Certainly there appears to be no good justification for applying different names to cystidia simply because the larger number come from the subhymenium as compared to the adjacent hymenophoral trama or vice versa.

2. Lamprocystidia

Lamprocystidia are a second recognizable type [Fig. 2 (*14*)]. They vary in shape from fusoid to bristlelike with pointed tips (setae) or to fusoid-ventricose (much like leptocystidia). Moreover the two intergrade, as in the *Pluteus salicinus* group. The walls may be evenly or irregularly thickened, or thickened only in a particular area such as the neck. They are often ornamented with crystalline or amorphous deposits not readily soluble in routine mounting media, but it seems prudent not to involve such deposits in the nomenclature of the cells. To be specific, the term metuloid appears superfluous. It must be recognized that incrustations, especially of calcium oxalate, are not per se a part of the cystidium but a product of the biochemistry of the species and hence best considered as a separate "chemical" feature. More to the point, it must be remembered that in such genera as *Psathyrella* and *Acanthocystis* not all the cystidia show such incrustations even on sections of a single gill so that ambiguity is at once apparent if one tries to apply separate names to nonincrusted and incrusted thick-walled cystidia.

The most acute problem in cystidial nomenclature involves lamprocystidia of the setiform type, i.e., setae as generally recognized by mycologists [Fig. 2 (*9*)], but not in the specialized sense of Lentz (1954). I believe that setae in the Hymenomycetes are simply lamprocystidia, typically with colored walls. The walls frequently deepen in color when treated with KOH. These cells may occur as pleurocystidia (*Marasmius cohaerans*), pileocystidia (*Psathyrella subatrata*), endocystidia (Xanthochroic series), and, undoubtedly, as caulocystidia in a number of agarics. In general, if the cystidium is ten times, or more, longer than it is wide in its widest place, and tapers to an acute apex, it meets the criteria set for a setiform lamprocystidium. I can see no justification for so much emphasis being placed on the color of the wall since in the Agaricales examples of such cells with almost all degrees of wall coloring are known, including species of *Psathyrella* and *Galerina* [Fig. 2 (*1*)] where the wall is colored only in the lower or basal portion of the cell. Nor is the color reaction with KOH of sufficient importance to justify restricting the term seta to only those thick-walled cystidia which show it. The KOH reaction is well known on spore and hyphal walls to students of brown-spored agarics. That larger groups of species which react positively in this test have arisen in some families than in others is to be expected. The definition of the term seta in Snell and Dick (1957) is a good one.

Lentz (1954, p. 191) defined a "false seta" as "a seta-like end of a skeletal hypha extending into or beyond the hymenium." If by this the author implies that the cross wall differentiates the hyphal end as a cell, there is no need for another term. If he is using the term skeletal hypha in the sense that it is not a hypha but a greatly elongated end cell from a hyphal branch back in the context which finally grows out to project from the hymenium, a better term might be mycosclerid (Wright, 1955) [Fig. 1 *(14)*]. This consideration becomes important in a discussion of the basidiocarp in many of the Aphyllophorales *sensu* Donk. Many of the "skeletals" described as thick-walled nonseptate hyphae are probably only mycoslerids since they are the end cells of hyphae or hyphal branches. The feature which makes these elements unrepresentative of setae is that they are not pointed at the apex and are reminiscent of hyphae in the way they are arranged in the context of the pileus and/or hymenophore. The criteria for distinguishing between a true hypha and a mycosclerid include the manner of origin, that is, whether they are end-cells or not. Another criterion is, if aseptate, is this condition derived instead of primary, i.e., were cross-walls originally present and then eliminated as the hypha matured? If so, the structure is a modified hypha, not a modified hyphal cell. This area of study is one of the most difficult in the Hymenomycetes, so it is not surprising that there are many problems still unresolved. Perhaps too much work has been done on preserved herbarium material (not always collected in the best condition) instead of by following the hyphal changes through the development of the basidiocarp. Corner has attempted more of the latter type of work than most investigators, but much still remains to be done.

Stellate setae are branched cells, the spines typically radiating, which are found in *Asterodon* as a classical example. Thus we find branching even in elements as specialized as thick-walled end cells.

3. *Gloeocystidia*

Gloeocystidia constitute a third major type of cystidium and one with an extremely varied history. Like the terms leptocystidia and lamprocystidia, gloeocystidia must be regarded as applying to a wide range of morphological subtypes. These cells are characterized by having oily to refractile contents, but almost any cystidium containing such material, even if coagulated, is called a gloeocystidium. Their outline is often quite irregular, and many different chemical compounds may be involved in the deposits within these cystidia although more remains to be known about them. Some gloeocystidia appear to be identical with leptocystidia except that their contents when fresh, although homogeneous, show a strong affinity for certain dyes, and when revived in KOH the contents often coagulate to form a highly refractile amorphous body often filling less than a third of the cell. Such cells are termed chrysocystidia [Fig. 2 *(21)*] by some authors. Frequently, especially in the Russulaceae, cystidia have an oily content when fresh and are terminal members of the laticiferous system [Fig. 2 *(17)*]. It is assumed that this origin is characteristic for the great majority of the gloeocystidia, but it is not very evident for those termed chrysocystidia. Filamentous hyphal ends embedded in the hymenium, but having oily contents, represent the simplest gloeocystidia and are called pseudocystidia [Fig. 2 (*17*)]. To be designated a gloeocystidium the end cell of the laticiferous element must project into or beyond the hymenium. Otherwise the structure is simply a laticiferous element, unless one elects to combine the terminology with that of Buller. In this case there could be endogloeocystidia, etc.

4. Hyphoids

The last type of hymenial element, the hyphoids meet my definition of cystidia and perhaps should be so classified, but there is some merit in giving them special consideration because of the strong likelihood that they function in a different manner. It seems most probable to me that they are air traps which help to contain the air around or over the developing basidia and thereby slow evaporation at the surface of the hymenium. Hyphoids are branched hyphal end cells, often so intricately branched that it is difficult to follow their ramifications. They are found more often in the Aphylophorales than in the Agaricales, probably because the hymenial surface of the former remains functional for a longer period of time. Types of hyphoids include: dendrophyses, cells with treelike branching; acanthophyses, cells with fine branches (bottlebrush-like); and dichophyses, cells which repeatedly branch dichotomously with the branches becoming smaller and smaller. Donk (1964), who proposed the term hyphoid, gives a good account of them. Dichophyses comprise much of the basidiocarp context in some species (Corner, 1948).

5. Summary of Cystidial Types and Their Nomenclature

  a. *Classification by Position*

   1. Pleurocystidia: on face of lamellae tubes or teeth
   2. Cheilocystidia: on gill edges, ends of teeth, and edges of dissepiments of tubes
   3. Pileocystidia: on the pileus
   4. Caulocystidia: on the stipe
   5. Dermatocystidia: on either pileus or stipe, or peridium of gastromycetes
   6. Endocystidia: in context of pileus, hymenophore, or stipe

  b. *Classification by Types*

   1. Leptocystidia: smooth, thin-walled, shape different from that of basidia

2. Lamprocystidia: thick-walled at least in some part, and with or without incrustations, walls colored to hyaline
   (a) Setiform lamprocystidia: awl-shaped, wall typically colored
   (b) Astrosetae: radially branched lamprocystidia
   (c) Mycosclerids: versiform endolamprocystidia, often hyphalike
3. Gloeocystidia: versiform cells distinguished by their contents, which either stain heavily, or are oily or amorphous and refractive
   (a) Chrysocystidia: like leptocystidia but with highly staining contents, refractive as revived in KOH
   (b) Pseudocystidia: Filamentous to fusoid elements with oily contents when fresh
4. Hyphoids: filamentous to cystidium-like cells characterized by peculiar systems of branching
   (a) Dendrophyses: having treelike branching
   (b) Acanthophyses: with bottlebrush-like projections
   (c) Dichophyses: dichotomously branched repeatedly

REFERENCES

Atkinson, G. F. (1906). The development of *Agaricus campestris*. *Botan. Gaz.* **42**: 113-121.

Bass, C. (1965). Personal communication.

Bensaude, M. (1918). Recherches sur le cycle évolutis et la sexualité chez Basidiomycétes. Thesis, Paris.

Buller, A. H. R. (1922). "Researches on Fungi," Vol. II, 491 pp. Longmans, Green, New York.

Corner, E. J. H. (1932). The fruitbody of *Polystictus xanthopus* Fr. *Ann. Botany (London)* **46**:71-111.

Corner, E. J. H. (1948). *Asterodon*, a clue to the morphology of fungus fruit bodies: with notes on *Asterostroma* and *Asterostromella*. *Brit. Mycol. Soc. Trans.* **31**:234-245.

Corner, E. J. H. (1950). "A Monograph of Clavaria and Allied Genera," 740 pp. Oxford Univ. Press, London and New York.

Donk, M. A. (1964). A conspectus of the families of Aphyllophorales. *Persoonia (Leiden)* **3**:199-324.

Fayod, V. (1889). Prodrome d'une histoire naturelle des Agaricinés. *Ann. Sci. Nat.: Botan. Biol. Vegetale* **7-9**:179-411.

Harrison, K. A. (1964). New or little known North American stipitate hydnums. *Can. J. Botany* **42**:1205-1233.

Heinemann, P. (1942). *Bull. Soc. Botan. Belg.* **74**:139-153.

Imler, L. (1950). Recherches sur les boletes. *Bull. Soc. Mycol. France* **66**:177-202.

Kniep, H. (1918). Über die Bedingungen der Schnallenbildung bei den Basidiomyceten. *Flora (Jena)* **111**:380-395.

Kühner, R. (1926). Contribution a l'étude des Hymenomycètes et spécialement des Agaricacés. *Botaniste* **17**:1-244.

Kühner, R. (1935). Le Genre Galera (Fr.) Quél. *Encyclopedie Mycol.* **7**:1-240.

Lange, M. (1956). Danish hypogeous macromycetes. *Dansk Botanisk Arkiv* **16**:1-84.

6. The Hyphal Structure of the Basidiocarp

Lentz, P. L. (1954). Modified hyphae of hymenomycetes. *Botan. Rev.* 20:1-199.

Levenberg, B. (1961). Structure and enzymatic cleavage of agaritine, a phenylhydrazide of L-glutamic acid isolated from Agaricaceae. *J. Am. Chem. Soc.* 83:503.

Miller, O. K. (1964). Monograph of Chroogomphus (Gomphidiaceae). *Mycologia* 56:526-549.

Orton, P. D. (1960). New check list of British agarics and boleti. Part II. Notes on genera and species in the list. *Brit. Mycol. Soc. Trans.* 43:159-439.

Pantidou, M. E. (1961). Culture studies of the Boletaceae: *Gyrodon merulioides* and four species of *Boletinus. Can. J. Botany* 39:1149-1162.

Patouillard, N. (1900). "Essai taxonomique sur les familles et les genres des Hyménomycètes," 184 pp. Lons-le Saunier.

Reijenders, A. F. M. (1963). "Les problèmes du développement des carpophores des Agaricales et de quelques groupes voisins," 412 pp. Junk, Den Haag.

Rogers, D. P. (1933). A taxonomic review of the Tulasnellaceae. *Ann. Mycol.* 31:181-203.

Romagnesi, H. (1944). La cystide chez les Agaricacées. *Rev. Mycol.* [N.S.] 9: Suppl., 4-21.

Sawyer, W. H., Jr. (1917). Development of some species of *Pholiota. Botan. Gaz.* 64:206-228.

Singer, R. (1963). "The Agaricales in Modern Taxonomy," 915 pp. Cramer, Weinheim.

Smith, A. H. (1947). "North American Species of Mycena," 507 pp. Univ. of Michigan Press, Ann Arbor, Michigan.

Smith, A. H. (1956-1966). Unpublished data.

Smith, A. H. (1963). New astrogastraceous fungi from the Pacific North West. *Mycologia* 55:421-441.

Smith, A. H. (1965). New and unusual basidiomycetes with comments on hyphal and spore wall reactions with Melzer's solution. *Mycopathol. Mycol. Appl.* 24:385-402.

Smith, A. H. (1966). New and noteworthier higher fungi from Michigan. *Mich. Botanist* 5:18-25.

Smith, A. H., and R. Singer. (1964). "A Monograph on the genus *Galerina*," 357 pp. Hafner, New York.

Smith, A. H., and H. D. Thiers. (1964). "A contribution toward a monograph of North American species of *Suillus*," 116 pp. Ann Arbor, Michigan. (Privately published.)

Smith, A. H., and S. M. Zeller. (1966). A preliminary account of the North American species of Rhizopogon. *Mem. N.Y. Botan. Garden* 14:1-176.

Snell, W. H., and E. A. Dick. (1957). "A Glossary of Mycology," 169 pp. Harvard Univ. Press, Cambridge, Massachusetts.

Talbot, P. H. B. (1954). Micromorphology of the lower hymenomycetes. *Bothalia* 6:249-299.

Thiers, H. D., and A. H. Smith. (1966). An unusual bolete of the *B. rubellus* complex. *Mich. Botanist* 5:118-119.

Walker, L. B. (1919). Development of *Pluteus admirabilis* and *Tubaria furfuracea. Botan. Gaz.* 68:1-21.

Watling, R. (1966). Personal communication.

Wright, J. E. (1955). Evaluation of specific characters in the genus Tulostoma Pers. *Papers Mich. Acad. Sci.* 50:79-87.

Mechanisms of Morphogenesis

CHAPTER 7

Dimorphism

ANTONIO H. ROMANO

*Department of Biological Sciences and
Graduate Division of Microbiology
University of Cincinnati
Cincinnati, Ohio*

I. INTRODUCTION

A number of fungi exhibit a phenotypic duality in cell form. Depending upon environmental conditions, they may develop either in the form of a mycelium composed of long, branching, septate or aseptate filaments, or in the form of spherical or ovoid yeast cells that reproduce principally by budding. In addition, a number of yeasts are capable of a filamentous mode of growth through the formation of a pseudomycelium, whereby frequently branched filaments arise by successive formation and elongation of buds. While many yeasts can form a rudimentary pseudomycelium, this tendency is especially marked in members of the genus *Candida*.

The term "dimorphism" generally has been used in reference to a group of fungi which cause systemic infections in man and animals; it has been defined by Ainsworth (1955) as "the condition in which there is a yeast-like parasitic phase and a mycelial saprophytic phase." The term will be used in a broader sense in this review, and will be used in reference to nonpathogens as well as pathogens, and without particular distinction between parasitic and saprophytic modes of existence. Dimorphism, in its broad sense, then, is defined as an environmentally controlled reversible interconversion of yeast and mycelial forms, and is denoted as $Y \rightleftharpoons M$.

Dimorphism has been equated with morphogenesis, and this review is included in a section bearing that title. This is entirely proper if morphogenesis is taken literally to mean origin of form. However, as Lockhart (1959) has emphasized, morphogenesis generally is taken to mean the development of differentiated metabolic patterns and structures. It should be pointed out that cellular differentiation and development of specialized structures does not take place in situations discussed here in the same sense that it does in slime molds and other fungi, discussed in subsequent chapters, and in higher plants and animals.

This phenomenon has been of great interest to the medical mycologist, since many dimorphic fungi are pathogenic. The significance of these organisms in medicine has thus given impetus to many studies of the phenomenon. However, dimorphism has interesting, and perhaps more fundamental implications to the general physiologist. Filamentation in yeasts has been interpreted as an uncoupling of cell division from growth without impairment of growth (Nickerson, 1948); the situation is entirely analogous to filamentation in bacteria, which can be induced by a variety of means (Webb, 1953). This fortuitous separation of the two processes allows an advantageous system for studying the two processes, particularly since the separation can be subjected to a considerable degree of experimental control in some organisms.

The organisms discussed here do not represent an exhaustive list of dimorphic fungi. Emphasis is placed on the elucidation of the physiological basis of dimorphism, and material has been selected with that objective. The reader is referred to other reviews by Ainsworth (1955, 1958) and Scherr and Weaver (1953).

II. TEMPERATURE-DEPENDENT DIMORPHISM

In the case of *Blastomyces dermatitidis,* the causative agent of North American blastomycosis, there is compelling evidence that temperature is the sole factor determining cellular form. In lesions, this organism occurs as budding yeast cells. When cultured *in vitro* and incubated at 37°C, yeastlike cells develop that are similar to those occurring *in vivo;* when cultured at 25°C, a mycelial phase develops (Fig. 1). That this dimorphism is entirely temperature dependent and independent of nutrition was shown by Levine and Ordal (1946). These workers were able to culture both the mycelial form and the yeast form on a minimal glucose-ammonium sulfate-mineral salts medium, showing that the nutritional requirements of both forms are the same. The mycelial to yeast conversion took place readily on this minimal medium when the incubation temperature was raised to 37°C. These findings were corroborated by Nickerson and Ed-

---

Fig. 1. *Blastomyces dermatitidis.* A. Budding yeastlike cells in pus from a subcutaneous abcess. B. Yeastlike cells from beef infusion glucose agar at 37°C. C. Filamentous stage with round and pyriform conidia from Sabouraud's glucose agar at room temperature. Magnification: × 700. From Conant *et al.* (1954).

7. Dimorphism

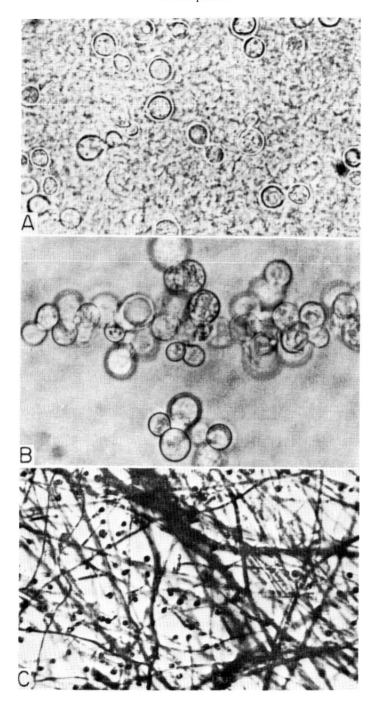

wards (1949), and by Salvin (1949a), who found that in both *B. dermatitidis* and *B.* [*Paracoccidioides*] *brasiliensis*, no amino acid, carbohydrate, or growth factor was essential for yeast growth or for mycelial to yeast conversion. This temperature-dependent interconversion of form has been termed by Nickerson and Edwards (1949) "thermal dimorphism."

Since yeast to mycelial conversion has been considered as an interruption of cell division without a concomitant interruption of growth, and such a conversion can be closely controlled in *Blastomyces* by varying only temperature, Nickerson and Edwards viewed this system as a favorable one in which to study the effect of temperature on cell division and to investigate physiological bases of morphogenesis. Accordingly, they studied the effect of temperature on oxygen uptake by mycelial and yeast forms of *B. dermatitidis*. Oxygen uptake was selected for study because of the abundance of data concerning the effect of temperature on this activity in other organisms. They found that the yeast form consumed 5–6 times as much oxygen as did the mycelial form; in addition, the yeast form oxidized exogenous acetate and glucose, whereas the mycelial form showed no exogenous respiration. They hypothesized that the greater energy potential exhibited by the Y form may be related to its invasiveness in host tissues.

The respiratory rate of the M form was proportional to temperature, and from the Arrhenius equation an activation energy of 13,250 calories per gram molecule was calculated for the process. An Arrhenius plot (log rate vs. $1/T$) showed deviation from linearity above 30°C, indicating enzyme inactivation above this point. When temperature was changed quickly upward or downward, there was an "overshoot phenomenon"; that is, there was a lag in the adjustment of the respiratory rate at the new temperature. These data were interpreted as follows: a sudden temperature change disrupts a steady state balance between a rate-limiting process ($\mu = 13,250$ cal/gm mole) and reversible enzyme inactivation. An analogous disruption in balance between enzymes competing for substrate for cell division, and enzymes concerned with growth, was considered as a possible explanation for differences in cellular form.

Taylor (1961) compared DNA, RNA, and protein content of yeast and mycelial cells. He found DNA content to be essentially the same in both phases. Protein was relatively low and constant in the M phase, and much higher in the Y phase, decreasing with age. There was a larger amount of RNA in the Y phase and greater fluctuation in concentration; there was an abrupt increase and decrease between the 3rd and 10th to 15th day of incubation. Amounts of RNA in the M phase remained relatively low and constant. On this basis, an involvement of RNA fluctuation in dimorphism was speculated. However, the greater amounts of RNA and protein in the Y phase developing at 37°C may be related to the increased energy potential and growth rate at this elevated temperature; the dependence of protein synthesis on RNA synthesis is now well known (Gale, 1962).

Taylor (1961) has expressed the view that variation in structure results from many metabolic processes within the cell rather than from the activity of one enzyme, such as the protein disulfide reductase of Nickerson and Falcone (Section IV, A). It would appear desirable to reinvestigate thermal dimorphism in the light of recent developments concerning the regulation of enzyme synthesis in microorganisms by temperature.

III. TEMPERATURE- AND NUTRITION-DEPENDENT DIMORPHISM

There is a group of fungi for which incubation at 37°C alone is not sufficient to maintain the yeast phase in culture or to bring about mycelial to yeast conversion; additional nutrients are required. Included in this group are *Sporotrichum* [*Sporothrix*] *schenckii, Histoplasma farciminosum,* and *H. capsulatum.*

In the case of *S. schenckii,* CO_2 appears to play an important role in conversion to the yeast form. Drouhet and Mariat (1952) were able to obtain the yeast form of this organism at 37°C on synthetic solid or liquid media containing an inorganic nitrogen source, if a mixture of 5% CO_2 in air was provided. Supplying N_2–air mixtures or air alone resulted in mycelial growth under these conditions. However, M → Y conversion could be obtained in agitated liquid media without addition of CO_2 if the nitrogen source was casein hydrolyzate or certain amino acids, alone or in combination. It is indicated that an increase in CO_2 tension from amino acid decarboxylation determines the M → Y conversion under these conditions.

Carbon dioxide is also required to convert and maintain *H. farciminosum* in the yeast phase. Bullen (1949) showed that when this organism was incubated in a variety of media at 37°C, growth was mycelial. Conversion to the yeast form was accomplished by incubation on blood agar at pH 7.4 in a McIntosh and Fildes jar in an atmosphere of 15–30% CO_2. The optimum CO_2 concentration was 15–20%. To show that the response was in fact due to CO_2, and not merely to decreased O_2 tension, the yeast phase was cultured on the same medium in jars containing 10–20% N_2 instead of CO_2. Soda lime was placed in the jars to absorb metabolic CO_2. The culture reverted to the mycelial phase under these conditions.

The situation with regard to *H. capsulatum* is much more complex. Although yeast to mycelial conversion takes place readily if the incubation temperature is lowered from 37°C to 25°C, conversion from the mycelial to the yeast phase *in vitro* is extremely difficult. Thus, the environmental factors governing this conversion, which takes place invariably in the mammalian host, are not well understood. Requirements of the yeast phase for good growth from small inocula are numerous, and there is a considerable degree of variation among strains. This has necessitated the use of numerous strains in all experiments in order that valid conclusions could be drawn. Experimentation is therefore laborious, and interpretation difficult.

Consistent conversion of mycelial to yeast phase has been accomplished at 37°C in a number of complex media. Conant (1941) found that M → Y conversion took place on blood agar slants sealed with paraffin. Campbell (1947) employed a cystine blood medium, and Kurung and Yegian (1954) described a congealed egg-potato flour medium which supported excellent M → Y conversion. Larsh *et al.* (1956) reported conversion of all 13 strains tested in a HeLa cell tissue culture.

Salvin (1949b) undertook studies with synthetic media in order to identify nutritional factors concerned with growth of each of the two phases and their interconversion. He found that the nutritional requirements of the two phases differed: biotin was required by yeastlike cells but, with one exception among six strains studied, had no effect on mycelial growth. While no single amino acid was necessary for the growth of either the yeast or mycelial phase, a sulfide or sulfhydryl group in a small organic molecule, preferably an amino acid, was essential for yeast growth. Even in a medium with 16 nonsulfur amino acids, maintained at 37°C, yeast cells always reverted to the mycelial phase. On the other hand, cystine or cysteine added as sole amino acids supported growth of the yeast phase. On comparing the relative activities of various sulfur-containing compounds in maintaining the yeast phase, it was found that cystine and cysteine were more effective than the tripeptide glutathione, and cystine was effective at a lower concentration than cysteine. Salvin attributed this latter observation to the greater amount of sulfur present per molecule in cystine.

Further studies employing synthetic media were carried out by Scherr (1957) and Pine and his colleagues (Pine, 1954, 1955, 1957; Pine and Peacock, 1958). Scherr (1957) found that no yeast phase growth took place with an inoculum of 10^5 cells/ml or less, regardless of conditions. He found that while, in general, 37°C was better than 25°C for the maintenance of the yeast form, it was possible to maintain the yeast form at lower temperatures (25°C better than 30°C) provided the cysteine concentration was high enough. It appeared, therefore, that the concentration of -SH groups or cysteine is more critical for yeast phase maintenance than 37°C temperature. It was emphasized, however, that while the Y phase could be *maintained* at lower temperature, it was never possible to carry out *conversion* of M to Y *in vitro* at temperatures lower than 37°C. He feels that Y growth, once initiated, could be propagated indefinitely if the -SH content or the oxidation-reduction potential were maintained at an optimum level. The fact that M → Y conversion could not be accomplished below 37°C was interpreted as an indication that the role of 37°C temperature is to maintain optimum conditions for enzymes directing the M → Y transition, and that metabolic pathways governing *maintenance* of Y are distinct from those governing M → Y *conversion*.

Pine (1954) developed a synthetic medium containing glucose, glutamic acid, aspartic acid, and cysteine, which supported good growth of the yeast phase. The fact that glutathione did not substitute for cysteine indicated that the cysteine requirement could not be ascribed entirely to a requirement for -SH. The essentiality of the -SH group for the yeast growth, however, was confirmed, since addition of substances reacting with -SH groups inhibited growth. It was concluded that the role of -SH groups was to initiate yeast growth, since after 4–6 hours of incubation under conditions of high aeration no significant amount of -SH groups could be detected in the medium.

The general requirement for large inocula may be explainable as (1) a requirement for CO_2, (2) a fatty acid requirement, (3) protection by dead cells against excess fatty acids (Pine, 1954). It was found that CO_2, oleic acid, and albumin, which could supply fatty acids or bind excess fatty acids, all stimulated growth.

The differential vitamin requirements of the mycelial phase at 25°C and the yeast phase at 37°C were confirmed by Pine (1957). The mycelial phase required no single added vitamin, whereas 8 of 11 yeast-phase strains required thiamine, one required biotin, and one required thioctic acid.

It was emphasized by Pine and Peacock (1958) that mere satisfaction of growth requirements of the yeast phase was not sufficient to bring about conversion of the mycelial phase to the yeast phase. In attempting to elucidate factors bringing about conversion, these workers found that citric acid stimulated M → Y conversion. Evidence was presented that this effect was due to selective inhibition of the M phase by metal chelation and stimulation of the Y phase by use of citrate as a substrate. Zinc was also found to stimulate conversion to the Y phase at 37°C.

Myers and Sherwood (1951) reported Y → M conversion in grass frogs (*Rana pipiens*) at 20–25°C. Pine and Peacock (1958) found that the yeast phase can infect frogs at 25°C and that conversion could occur in some strains at 30°C. These findings would indicate that the conversion may be temperature-independent under the proper conditions.

It is difficult to put forth a general scheme that would adequately explain the mechanism of M → Y conversion in *H. capsulatum*. Pine and Peacock (1958) view the situation as resolving itself into two factors (1) satisfaction of yeast phase requirements (2) inhibition of the mycelial phase without inhibition of conversion to the yeast phase. They have hypothesized that there are two different metabolic routes, one for each phase, which are competitive but not mutually exclusive. At 37°C, the mycelial phase is inhibited and the yeast phase more easily maintained; at 25°C, the mycelial phase is maintained more easily. The -SH requirement is probably involved, although it may be a secondary expression of a changed metabolism after conversion to the yeast phase. However, though the direct participation of the -SH group in conversion in *H. capsulatum* is yet to be demonstrated, it is interesting to speculate on this possibility on the basis of experiments with *Candida albicans* that are described in Section IV, A.

IV. NUTRITION-DEPENDENT DIMORPHISM

A. *Dimorphism in Candida*

Members of the genus *Candida* represent a group of anascosporogenous yeasts with a marked tendency toward filamentation. The most intensely studied species, *C. albicans,* is capable of causing a number of human and animal infections. While the other dimorphic fungi discussed in the previous sections occur almost exclusively in the yeast form in host tissues, *C. albicans* often occurs in systemic infections in the filamentous form. The relationship of cellular form to pathogenicity will be considered in Section V.

Earlier studies on the morphology, cultural characteristics, and dimorphism phenomenon in *Candida* have been reviewed by Skinner (1947). This organism is readily cultured on a variety of common media. On Sabouraud dextrose agar, the growth is almost entirely yeastlike both at room temperature and at 37°C; filaments may penetrate into the medium and may be observed at the periphery of a colony on prolonged incubation. Filamentation is more profuse on washed polysaccharide media low in free sugars such as corn meal agar or potato infusion broths. Under these conditions, chlamydospores characteristic of the species are formed at the ends of the filaments. These media have been used extensively, therefore, for diagnostic purposes.

The nutritional requirements of this yeast are comparatively simple. Burkholder (1943) found that a medium composed of glucose, $(NH_4)_2SO_4$, biotin, and inorganic salts supported maximal growth of several different strains.

Nickerson and Mankowski (1953) studied filament formation under well-defined nutritional conditions in order to elucidate nutritional factors controlling dimorphism. Using a basal medium containing $(NH_4)_2SO_4$, KH_2PO_4, biotin, and agar, the effect of carbon source on cell form was determined on slide cultures examined *in situ*. It was found that only budding yeast cells developed when glucose was used as the carbon source, even at widely differing carbon:nitrogen ratios. When a less readily utilized carbon source was used, such as purified soluble starch, glycogen, or dextrin, there was diminished growth and the appearance of extensive filamentation. This tendency toward filamentation was reversed by addition of 0.01 M cysteine to the polysaccharide media. No filamentous cells were observed in cultures receiving cysteine.

The results were interpreted as follows: the rapid metabolism of a readily utilizable carbon source such as glucose generates sufficient reducing power to maintain -SH groups required for optimum growth and cell division. Polysaccharides are not readily metabolized by *C. albicans,* hence there is insufficient reducing power generated to maintain adequate thiol groups for cell division. Cell division does not keep pace, even at the reduced growth rate, and cells elongate to form filaments. Under these conditions, cell division can be restored by addition of an exogenous source of -SH.

There are other lines of evidence supporting the contention that -SH groups are required to maintain the yeast shape in *Candida*. Nickerson and Van Rij (1949) found that cobalt-treated cells showed long mycelial fragments with no cross walls and wide spacings between blastospore clusters; the effect was reversed by 0.01 M cysteine. Waksman *et al.* (1953) found that fradicin, an antifungal antibiotic, induced filamentation in *C. albicans* in subinhibitory concentrations; both the filament-inducing effect and the inhibitory effect of the antibiotic could be abolished by cysteine. Winsten and Murray (1956) found that addition of cysteine to cultures of a filamentous strain of *C. albicans* enhanced yeast development and virulence in mice.

McClary (1952) also studied the factors affecting morphology in synthetic media. As to carbon source, he found that galactose gave heavy mycelial growth, and that maltose and sucrose were better than glucose, mannose, or fructose in this respect. On this basis, he disputed the importance of reducing sugars in cell division, since galactose, a reducing sugar, produced the most abundant mycelium. However, these findings can be interpreted as favoring Nickerson and Mankowski's views, since galactose is much less rapidly utilized than glucose, mannose, and fructose, and hence would be incapable of generating as much reducing power during metabolism.

Nickerson and co-workers carried out an extensive study on a permanently filamentous mutant designated as *C. albicans* 806 which was derived from a normal strain (*C. albicans* 582) by Mackinnon (1940). This mutant strain was viewed as having a genetic block in the cellular division mechanism; therefore, the nature of the biochemical lesion imposed by the mutation was sought. No significant difference between the parent strain and the divisionless mutant was found with respect to fermentation of sugars, vitamin requirement, endogenous respiration, or carbohydrate composition. Energy metabolism in the mutant was unimpaired, since growth on a number of media was only slightly less than that of the parent strain (Nickerson and Chung, 1954). The hypothesis that the biochemical lesion in the mutant was concerned with production or maintenance of -SH groups involved in cell division was supported by the finding that addition of cysteine to cultures of the mutant brought about the development of a high proportion of budding yeast cells in the population.

The most striking feature of the physiology of *C. albicans* 806 was its marked ability to accumulate and reduce tetrazolium dyes (Nickerson, 1954). The parent strain, growing as a budding yeast, accumulated the dye but did not reduce it; in older cultures, after available carbohydrate had been depleted, the filamentous cells which developed also were able to reduce tetrazolium dyes. Hence there was a "spillover" of metabolically generated reducing power in the mutant, and in the parent strain growing in the absence of cell division. This excess reducing power was diverted to dye reduction. The enzymatic locus at which the "uncoupling" of cell division took place was judged by Nickerson to be a metalloflavoprotein on the basis of the following evidence: (1) Brodie and Gots (1952), using a cell-free preparation from yeast, showed that the reduction of tetrazolium by coenzyme I is catalyzed by a flavoprotein system; neither coenzyme I-linked dehydrogenases nor coenzyme I alone could reduce tetrazolium. (2) Addition of low concentrations of sodium ethylenediaminetetraacetic acid (Na_2EDTA) to growing or resting cells of the normal yeast strain greatly stimulated tetrazolium reduction. Under these conditions, the normal strain behaved as the filamentous mutant. This indicated that dye reduction proceeded only after the removal of a metal from flavoprotein, or, possibly, the formation of a double chelate (flavoprotein–metal complexon). The metal involved was probably iron, since EDTA-metal chelates with stability constants lower than ferrous-EDTA were found to stimulate dye reduction, while ferrous-EDTA or more stable EDTA-metal chelates were without effect.

These facts led, therefore, to the postulation that this metalloflavoprotein locus is the site at which a reaction essential for cell division is coupled via an oxidation-reduction reaction to cellular metabolism. Uncoupling of cell division by genetic block in strain 806 is presumed to be due to an impairment of a dissociable metal chelate mechanism which normally couples a reaction essential to cell division to flavoprotein oxidation. The situation was diagrammed (Eq. 1).

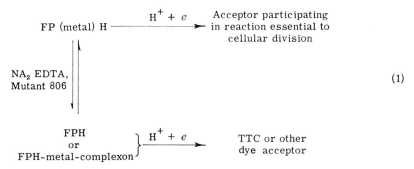

Ward and Nickerson (1958) compared the normal and filamentous strains with respect to respiratory physiology. Respiration was found to be qualitatively similar, and unique in that it is not mediated by cytochrome oxidase. In resting cells, respiration was found to be resistant to and stimulated by cyanide, carbon monoxide, and sodium azide. There was a quantitative difference, in that the filamentous mutant reduced oxygen more rapidly than the normal strain. Therefore, metabolically generated hydrogen, which spills over for nonspecific dye reduction in strain 806 is not at the expense of respiration or of growth. This is consistent with the concept that growth can proceed independently of cell division, as long as the energy required for growth can be supplied continuously by unimpaired respiration.

In the filamentous mutant, oxygen uptake was decreased by triphenyl tetrazolium chloride; hence the dye can compete with oxygen for reduction. In the normal strain, it does not. It appears that in the normal strain, metabolically generated hydrogen is strongly channeled to the cell division mechanism (presumably disulfide reduction); in the mutant strain, in the absence of such a mechanism, hydrogen can be used for reduction of oxygen or dyes.

The next important question to be answered concerns the nature of the specific hydrogen acceptor which normally participates in cell division. It is improbable that it is oxidized glutathione or cystine, since both glutathione reductase and cystine reductase were found to be operative in *C. albicans* 806 as well as the normal strain (Romano and Nickerson, 1954). Evidence has been presented by Nickerson and associates that the acceptor is a disulfide bond in a protein of the pseudokeratin type occurring in a glucomannan-protein complex which makes up the inner layer of the yeast cell wall. A specific enzyme has been described which catalyzes this reduction and has been identified as a cell division enzyme in yeast and has been termed "protein disulfide reductase." A discussion of the evidence leading to this conclusion is given below.

Falcone and Nickerson (1956) isolated purified cell walls of bakers' yeast by mechanical disruption of cells followed by differential centrifugation. From clean cell wall preparations, a major fraction (approximately 75%) was solubilized by extraction with 1 N NaOH. The solubilized material was dialyzed, redissolved in water, and purified by $(NH_4)_2SO_4$ precipitation. The isolated substance was found to be a glucomannan-protein complex containing 6.8% protein. The mannan was tightly bound to the protein, since the polysaccharide could not be precipitated as a copper complex. The protein portion was found to be of a pseudokeratin type containing 2.1% sulfur. Similar glucomannan-protein complexes were isolated also from *C. albicans* 582 and 806; more detailed data on the properties of these substances are given by Kessler and Nickerson (1959) and Nickerson *et al.* (1961).

Enzymatic reduction of the disulfide linkages in the cell wall protein was accomplished using a cell-free particulate preparation from yeast (Nickerson and Falcone, 1956a). When cell-free particulates were incubated together with a coenzyme concentrate, succinate, and ethanol as hydrogen donors, and with glucomannan protein in which sulfhydryl groups had been oxidized by ferricyanide, there was mercaptide formation, as determined spectrophotometrically by the reaction of mercaptides with *p*-chloromercuribenzoate. Control experiments with heated particulates showed no mercaptide formation.

On comparing the protein disulfide reductase activities of the normal and filamentous strains of *C. albicans,* it was found that mitochondrial particulates obtained from the normal strain showed strong activity on cell-wall protein, whereas preparations from the filamentous mutant showed only slight activity (Nickerson and Falcone, 1956b). The data are shown in Table I. It is seen that particulates from the normal strain had strong activity against cell-wall protein obtained from both the normal strain and the mutant. In contrast, particulates obtained from the mutant exhibited only slight activity against its own cell-wall protein and no activity against the cell-wall protein obtained from the normal strain. It was concluded that the enzymatic reduction of disulfide covalent bonds in the glucomannan-protein complex, a major structural component of the yeast cell wall, is the reaction essential for cell division in yeasts. The enzyme is presumed to be a flavoprotein which, when impaired by genetic block, channels metabolically generated hydrogen to oxygen or nonspecific dye reduction instead of to the normal protein-disulfide acceptor.

Normal operation of the enzyme is visualized to alter the fabric of the

TABLE I

Protein Disulfide Reductase Activity in Normal and Divisionless Strains of *Candida albicans*[a]

Reaction system	Mercaptide formation (optical density at 255 mµ)	
	Enzyme system from normal yeast	Enzyme system from divisionless mutant
Oxidized cell-wall protein from normal yeast	1.156 ⎫ 1.676	1.156 ⎫ 1.946
Mitochondrial particulates	0.520 ⎭	0.790 ⎭
Cell-wall protein + particulates[b]	3.800	1.880
Oxidized cell-wall protein from filamentous mutant	0.766 ⎫ 1.286	0.766 ⎫ 1.556
Mitochondrial particulates	0.520 ⎭	0.790 ⎭
Cell-wall protein + particulates[b]	1.920	1.730

[a] From Nickerson and Falcone (1956b).
[b] Values for controls using heated mitochondria were not greater than the sum of the constituents.

cell wall by rupturing disulfide bonds that form covalent links between molecules of the glucomannan-pseudokeratin complex (Falcone and Nickerson, 1959). This is diagrammed in Fig. 2. The rupture of the bonds causes a weakening of the cell wall, making plastic deformation possible. The en-

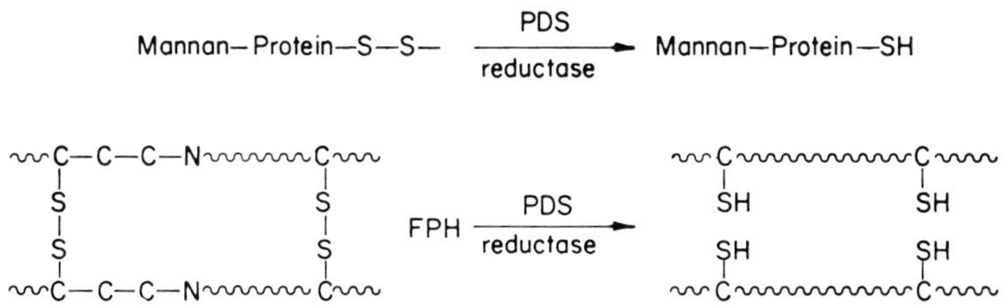

$$\text{Mannan–Protein–S–S–} \xrightarrow[\text{reductase}]{\text{PDS}} \text{Mannan–Protein–SH}$$

Fig. 2. Diagram of operation of protein disulfide (PDS) reductase on disulfide bonds that form covalent links between molecules of the glucomannan-pseudokeratin component of the cell wall. Preliminary evidence indicates that PDS may be a flavoprotein, and participation of the reduced form of the enzyme is indicated as FPH. From Falcone and Nickerson (1959).

suing events are purely physical consequences: the weakened spot fails to withstand the internal pressure of the cell and a naked protoplasmic mass is extruded in an explosive manner. This naked "protoplast," which represents the bud initial, is then covered with new wall substance, the synthesis of which begins at the base of the bud, using the preexisting cell wall fabric of the mother cell as a "primer."

The "explosive" nature of the appearance of the bud initial was confirmed by time-lapse photography, where it was shown that appearance of a well-developed bud initial from an intact mother cell took place within 30 seconds (Falcone and Nickerson, 1959). The wall of the bud then thickens gradually, and the wall of the parent cell at the budding site is rebuilt.

The fact that budding of a yeast cell usually begins at a "point" rather than on a broad area of the surface of the cell agrees well with the finding that the protein disulfide reductase is localized in particles. It is visualized that these particles are in a state of rapid motion in the cell and may bombard the cell wall. The selection of the site of budding is not random. Barton (1950) and Freifelder (1960) have observed an invariable sequence in the appearance of buds at specific sites on the surface of a *Saccharomyces cerevisiae* cell. The sequence was definite enough that the site of bud formation could be predicted on a given cell, provided it had not budded more than 3 or 4 times. Budding usually takes place at the point of maximum curvature of the cell, and development of the bud is consistently such that the long axis is perpendicular to a plane tangent to the surface of the mother cell (Nickerson, 1942). These observations were explained by Falcone and Nickerson (1959) by consideration of some principles of hydraulics: a fluid in motion, through inertial properties, exerts greatest force against the wall of its container in the region of maximal curvature of the container in a direction that is perpendicular to a plane tangent to the curved surface of the container. These considerations are consistent with the concept that in the yeast cell, particles containing the enzyme bombard the cell wall, causing point regions of weakness; the probability of a "blowout" occurring is greatest at the point of maximum curvature of the cell, so a bud is extruded at this site. Considerations of this sort may also explain the observation that multipolar budding occurs more often in yeast cells that are more spherical than ovoid. A spherical configuration would have no point of maximum curvature, hence, no preferential point of "blowout." Also, the spherical configuration may be due to a lesser degree of cell wall rigidity to begin with, and the appearance of sites of insufficient rigidity to withstand the internal pressure of the cell may become more probable.

Falcone and Nickerson (1959) use another mechanical model to support their "explosive extrusion" concept of yeast bud formation. Electron photomicrographs of isolated yeast cell walls reveal that the cell wall is made up of densely intermeshed microfibrils that are randomly oriented. However, at the bud scars, there is a very definite orientation of the microfibrils parallel to each other to form a cablelike pattern which encircles the bud scar. This is exactly the pattern that would be expected if the bonds holding the originally randomly oriented fibrils were weakened and a strong perpendicular force were applied. This orientation is identical to that shown in the deformation patterns formed in plastic that has been struck with liquid moving at high velocity in a direction perpendicular to the film.

This hypothesis on the mechanism of cell division in yeasts is an original and stimulating one, although it must be admitted that a great deal more experimental evidence is required to confirm its validity. Certainly there is a big step from the demonstration of an enzymatic activity *in vitro* to the assignment of an essential role *in vivo*. Other authors have offered evidence both in support of and in contradiction of this hypothesis.

Robson and Stockley (1962) have provided cytological evidence which supports Nickerson and Falcone's views on the involvement of -SH groups in the budding process in yeasts. A localization of the -SH groups was detected in the hyphal walls of *Eremothecium ashbyii* at the site of bud formation by using an autoradiographic technique whereby tritiated phenyl mercuric chloride was used to localize -SH groups. Experiments with *C. albicans* showed that -SH was localized in the walls of yeast cells, but not in walls of filamentous cells that developed on potato agar.

Also, the pattern of cell wall synthesis during the budding process followed by immunofluorescence is consistent with the notion that the cell wall of the bud is newly synthesized first at the base area, and then is added to the growing bud in a direction away from the base (Chung *et al.,* 1965).

On the other hand, the hypothesis of Nickerson and Falcone has been challenged by McClary and Bowers (1965). These authors examined budding yeast cells by dark field microscopy; they concluded that the apparent gaps which appeared in the cell wall were not due to the emergence of protoplast bud initials, but rather to changes in focus. Also, electron microscopy of thin sections of budding yeast cells that they examined showed that the wall extended around both the mother cell and the bud from the earliest appearance of the bud. Moreover, the bud retained both its structural integrity and essential constant degree of thickness throughout the budding process. They concluded, therefore, that neither rupture nor stretching of the wall occurs. A similar picture of the budding process based on electron microscopy has been described by Agar and Douglas (1955).

It can be argued, of course, that the failure to demonstrate naked buds by electron microscopy does not preclude their existence. Such a structure might not be preserved during fixation and sectioning. At any rate, a definitive answer to this question must await further data.

A more detailed discussion of the biochemistry and mechanics of cell division in yeast is to be found in a recent review by Nickerson (1963).

B. Dimorphism in Mucor

There is a marked tendency in a number of species of *Mucor* to develop as budding yeast cells under certain conditions of culture. It had been observed frequently in early studies on the alcoholic fermentation that when certain fungi were incubated in saccharine fluids that were more or less deprived of air, budding yeast forms appeared. While many fungi were observed to form aberrant spherical cells under these conditions, the tendency was greatest in *Mucor*. This phenomenon had been interpreted originally as a transmutation of species. However, later studies showed that the yeast forms developing from *Mucor* were independent of the common beer yeast (*Saccharomyces*), and the potentiality of *Mucor* to exhibit two distinct cellular forms was clearly recognized. The environmental factors controlling this dimorphism were not firmly established, however, and controversy existed as to whether the appearance of budding yeast cells was caused primarily by deprivation of oxygen or by accumulation of carbon dioxide during fermentation. The early literature on this subject has been reviewed by de Bary (1887), Foster (1949), and Bartnicki-Garcia and Nickerson (1962a).

The physiological control of dimorphism in *Mucor* has been studied comprehensively in recent years by Bartnicki-Garcia and Nickerson (1962a,b,c,d). These workers showed that in *M. rouxii,* and in all other species of *Mucor* studied, with the exception of a strain of *M. subtilissimus,* two environmental factors were necessary for yeastlike development: absence of oxygen and presence of carbon dioxide (Bartnicki-Garcia and Nickerson, 1962a). When grown in an anaerobic atmosphere under nitrogen, filamentous growth was obtained; when grown in an anaerobic atmosphere under carbon dioxide, spherical, budding, yeastlike cells were obtained. *M. subtilissimus* was an exception, forming yeastlike cells in an anaerobic atmosphere under nitrogen in the absence of carbon dioxide.

The capability of yeastlike development is not widespread among the Mucorales. A number of organisms of this order were cultured under air, nitrogen, and carbon dioxide. The tendency toward yeastlike development occurred only among species of *Mucor*. Species of *Rhizopus* tested grew under carbon dioxide but formed only filaments; other genera tested did not grow under a carbon dioxide atmosphere.

It is important to distinguish between yeastlike development and arthrospore formation; the latter is a normal consequence of filamentous growth in *Mucor*. Arthrospores are also spherical and are difficult to distinguish from yeastlike cells. The criterion to be applied, as emphasized by Bartnicki-Garcia and Nickerson (1962a), is that truly yeastlike cells of *Mucor* are only those cells which originate and multiply by budding.

It is probable that much of the confusion and disagreement in the earlier literature originates from the failure to distinguish between these two distinct forms of vegetative development.

Environmental factors causing yeastlike development were most extensively studied by the above workers in *M. rouxii*. In this organism, growth in air or under a nitrogen atmosphere resulted in a typically filamentous mycelium; development was entirely yeastlike under carbon dioxide (Fig. 3A and B). This dimorphism took place on solid medium as well as in liquid medium. On solid medium, colonial morphology was determined by the incubation conditions: aerobically, typical loose, fluffy, spreading colonies were obtained with extensive sporangiaphore formation; anaerobically, under nitrogen, a thin film of slowly growing, spreading, filamentous mycelium developed; anaerobically, under carbon dioxide, compact, opaque, convex colonies with an irregular surface and undulate border showing no tendency toward spreading were obtained. Colonies consisted entirely of yeastlike cells with multipolar buds. Further incubation of these plates in the air resulted in the formation of extensive filamentous growth.

Experiments with solid media were carried out to establish firmly that this dimorphism induced by CO_2 represents a phenotypic difference rather than a selection of different genotypes by varying environments. Spores derived from a single spore isolate of *M. rouxii* were plated out and incubated under CO_2 for 24 hours; all spores gave rise to identical microcolonies consisting exclusively of yeastlike cells. When subsequently exposed to air, all of 5000 such microcolonies examined developed extensive filamentous growth.

The effect of CO_2 concentration on the morphology of *M. rouxii* was determined by growing this organism in various atmospheres with adjusted partial pressures of CO_2. In N_2–CO_2 mixtures (anaerobic) a pCO_2 of 0.3 was sufficient to cause purely yeastlike development. In air–CO_2 mixtures (aerobic), a pCO_2 of 0.9 was required to induce distinctly yeastlike cells, although shorter mycelial fragments and arthrospores developed at lower CO_2 concentrations. Therefore, small amounts of oxygen can negate the effect of Co_2 in inducing yeastlike development.

The sequences of events which take place when spores of *M. rouxii* are allowed to germinate in different atmospheres are depicted in Fig. 3C, where, by interval photography, a spore germinating under air is compared with a spore germinating under CO_2. Under air, germination was fairly rapid; after 3 hours, the spore had swelled and the beginnings of a germ tube appeared shortly thereafter. A relatively large area of the surface of the spore bulged out in the formation of a single broad germ tube, which grew unidirectionally and was, therefore, polarized.

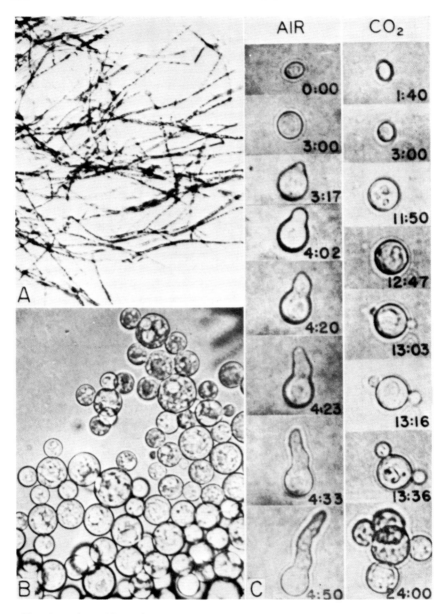

Fig. 3. Dimorphism of *Mucor rouxii*. A. Filamentous form grown under nitrogen (magnification: × 75). B. Yeastlike form grown under CO_2 (magnification: × 375). From Nickerson (1959). C. Germination of spores under air or CO_2; incubation time indicated in hr:min (magnification: × 900). From Bartnicki-Garcia and Nickerson (1962a).

7. Dimorphism

Under CO_2 the development of the spore was quite different and was relatively much slower. After the initial slow swelling, spherical buds were formed by extrusion of protoplasm through relatively small areas of the swollen spore wall. These buds did not appear until 13 hours after the spores were placed on the germinating medium. After their initial appearance the buds grew uniformly; therefore, it appears that there is no polarity of growth in this situation.

The development of yeastlike cells in *Mucor* appears to be metal-dependent (Bartnicki-Garcia and Nickerson, 1962b). Evidence for this lies in the demonstration that ethylenediaminetetraacetic acid (EDTA) and other chelating agents of the N-acetic acid type inhibit yeastlike development; concentrations of EDTA in the range of 2.7×10^{-5} M to 2.7×10^{-4} M caused a progressive inhibition of growth and an increasing tendency toward filamentation. In normally filamentous cultures (incubated in air or under N_2), *M. rouxii* showed a decrease in the number of arthrospores formed. In cultures incubated under CO_2, there was a shift from yeastlike development to filamentous development. *M. subtilissimus,* which exhibited yeastlike development under an N_2 atmosphere in the absence of CO_2, also shifted to a filamentous form of growth in the presence of EDTA.

The effects of the chelating agents on both *M. rouxii* and *M. subtilissimus* could be reversed by the addition of certain metal ions. Transition group metals (Fe^{++}, Mn^{++}, Cu^{++}, Zn^{++}, Al^{+++}, Co^{++}) were most effective in this respect.

It thus appears that yeastlike development in both *M. rouxii* and *M. subtilissimus* is dependent upon the metal-catalyzed formation of a metabolite inducing the yeast form. *M. rouxii* requires CO_2 to form this metabolite; *M. subtilissimus* does not. A model has been put forth by Bartnicki-Garcia and Nickerson (1962a) as a working hypothesis (Eq. 2),

$$CO_2 + W \xrightarrow{M.\ rouxii} X \xrightarrow{[metal]\ EDTA} Y \qquad (2)$$
$$V \xrightarrow{M.\ subtilissimus} \uparrow$$

where V, W, and X are metabolic precursors of Y. The action of Y was postulated by these workers to lead to an alteration in the chemical composition of the cell wall, since the rigid cell wall is the structure ultimately responsible for the shape of the cell.

A comparative study of the chemical composition and structure of purified cell walls of filamentous and yeastlike forms of *M. rouxii* was carried out by Bartnicki-Garcia and Nickerson (1962b) in order to explore morphogenetic implications. Filamentous and yeastlike cells were ruptured by mechanical means; the resulting cell wall fragments were then exhaustively washed and analyzed. Results of chemical determinations accounting for 93% of the total are shown in Table II. It is clear that cell walls of both filamentous and yeastlike cells are highly complex; the components contain most of the major protoplasmic constituents, including proteins, carbohydrates, lipids, purines-pyrimidines,

TABLE II
COMPOSITION OF CELL WALLS OF *Mucor rouxii*[a]

Components	Filaments (%)	Yeasts (%)
Readily extracted lipids	2.0	0.8
Bound lipids	5.8	4.9
Chitosan	32.7	27.9
Chitin	9.4	8.4
Unidentified 2-amino sugars	2.4	3.1
Fucose as $(C_6H_{10}O_4)_n$	3.8	3.2
Mannose as $(C_6H_{10}O_5)_n$	1.6	8.9
Galactose as $(C_6H_{10}O_5)_n$	1.6	1.1
Other carbohydrates	1.7	0.9
Protein	6.3	10.3
Purines and pyrimidines	0.6	1.3
Phosphate as $(H_2PO_3)_n$	23.3	22.1
Mg	1.0	—
Ca	1.0	—
Sum:	93.2	92.9

[a] From Bartnicki-Garcia and Nickerson (1962c).

and minerals. Differences between filamentous and yeastlike cell walls are principally quantitative rather than qualitative. The relatively higher amounts of protein and purines and pyrimidines in yeastlike cell walls are probably significant, but the most interesting feature is the much higher amount of mannose found in the yeastlike cell wall. Studies on the chemical composition of cell walls of other yeasts, such as *Saccharomyces cerevisiae* and *Candida albicans,* consistently have revealed mannan as a principal constituent (Northcote and Horne, 1952; Kessler and Nickerson, 1959; Nickerson et al., 1961). Even before the development of modern methods for isolation of purified cell walls, Garzuly-Janke (1940) found that mannan was present in most species of yeast but was undetectable in species of filamentous fungi examined. Moreover, a glucomannan–protein complex found in the cell wall of *C. albicans* and *S. cerevisiae* has been assigned a role in cell division (Section IV, A). It is tempting, therefore, to assign a major role to cell-wall mannan in the maintenance of the yeast shape.

Electron microscope examination of ultrathin sections of cells and isolated cell walls also revealed differences between filamentous and yeastlike cell walls (Bartnicki-Garcia and Nickerson, 1962b). Filamentous cells showed a compact envelope of uniform thickness (0.05–0.1 μ) consisting of a single layer of solidly packed microfibrils arranged parallel to the surface of the cell. Yeastlike cells showed a much thicker cell wall (0.5–1.0 μ) consisting of two distinct layers: an outer relatively thin, electron-dense layer with conspicuous microfibrillar structure, and a thick, more electron-transparent inner layer with a less distinct fibrillar appearance. It is difficult to interpret these differences in terms of cell shape at this time. It would be of interest to determine whether the outer layer of the yeastlike cell wall is the same as the single layer of the filamentous cell wall, and whether the inner layer occurring in the yeastlike cells represents an addition which may affect yeast shape. It would be hazardous to speculate too far, however, since, as Bartnicki-Garcia and Nickerson (1962c) have pointed out, these cells were necessarily grown under much different conditions, and gross differences may be due to mechanisms other than those immediately determining dimorphism.

Since the yeast shape in *Mucor rouxii* was induced by CO_2 in an anaerobic atmosphere, a biochemical explanation for the action of CO_2 was sought. Accordingly, the possibility that CO_2 might be fixed into a metabolite implicated in yeastlike development was explored by Bartnicki-Garcia and Nickerson (1962d). It was found that at the partial pressure of CO_2 inducing maximum yeastlike development ($pCO_2 = 0.3$), there was also maximum fixation of $C^{14}O_2$, and maximum malic enzyme activity. The major product of $C^{14}O_2$ fixation was found to be aspartic acid. These findings, though not completely conclusive, suggested the following relationships to the mechanism of dimorphism: the mannan–protein complex found in *Candida albicans* is notably rich in aspartic acid; the cell wall of the yeastlike form of *M. rouxii* contains increased amounts of mannan and protein. Hence, it was hypothesized that CO_2 fixation under anaerobic conditions may lead to increased formation of aspartic acid-containing mannan–protein complex. The validity of this hypothesis must await confirmation by further experiment.

V. THE RELATIONSHIP OF DIMORPHISM TO PATHOGENICITY

The generalization has been made that those fungi that are capable of causing infections of deep organs in man and higher animals are characterized by the capacity to develop in the yeast form, and the yeast form is that which is consistently found in infected tissues (Ainsworth, 1955, 1958; Scherr and Weaver, 1953; Rippon and Scherr, 1959). This is in contrast to the dermatophytes which cause superficial infections of the keratinized layers of the skin, and to fungi which cause plant infections. The dermatophytes are mycelial both in the infective stage and in culture, and do not have a yeast phase. Plant pathogenic fungi are principally filamentous; a few such as *Taphrina* and certain members of the Ustilaginales, have well-defined yeast phase, but it occurs only when growing as a saprophyte (Ainsworth, 1958).

This correlation between yeastlike development and ability to cause deep mycoses has invited speculation as to the relationship between yeastlike development and pathogenicity. Ainsworth (1958) has reasoned that since most of the systemic mycoses are exogenous, the potentiality to develop as a yeast may be an important factor in determining the ability of the fungi concerned to establish themselves as internal parasites of warm-blooded animals. He points out that the tissues may be looked upon as a relatively unfavorable environment for growth when host defense mechanisms are considered; most fungal pathogens of man and animals grow much more abundantly *in vitro* than *in vivo*. Therefore, it is possible to view the parasitic phase of the dimorphic fungi as the abnormal state, and yeastlike development may be a response to the less favorable conditions, just as is yeastlike development in *Mucor* under anaerobic conditions and high CO_2 tensions (Section IV, B). Ainsworth points out that *Candida albicans* is different in that it is well adapted to both a saprophytic and a parasitic existence in higher animals, and so much pseudomycelium may be produced in tissues that its yeastlike character may be obscured. At any rate, if the parasitic state is the abnormal state for the dimorphic fungi, the ability to assume the yeast form might have survival value in that it is the one which allows the greatest number of reproductive structures with the least synthesis of new protoplasm, as suggested by Baker et al. (1943).

Another aspect relating to the invasive mechanism of the yeast form of *Blastomyces dermatitidis* is to be recalled (Section II) from the work of Nickerson and Edwards (1949), who found that the yeast form consumed 5–6 times as much oxygen as the mycelial form; it was hypothesized that the greater energy potential exhibited by the yeast form may be related to its invasiveness in host tissues.

The concept that the ability of a fungus to invade deep tissues usually depends on the capacity of the organism to exist in or have the potential for yeastlike growth was strengthened by Rippon and Scherr (1959). They reasoned that if a dermatophyte, which does not normally invade deep tissues, could be induced to assume a morphological and physiological state more consistent with that of the dimorphic pathogenic fungi, the organism might show enhanced pathogenicity for deep organs. This was found to be the case; they were able to induce a morphological change simulating dimorphism whereby yeastlike "spherules" were formed in *Trichophyton rubrum, Microsporum audouinii,* and *Cladosporium mansonii* when cultured on gradient plates containing increasing concentrations of cysteine. These spherical cells so obtained had enhanced ability to invade and form lesions of the liver, kidney, and spleen when injected into mice. The prevalence of lesions of these deep organs was correlated with the position on the cysteine concentration gradient from which the cells had been isolated. A similar type of morphological alteration was achieved by incubating suspensions of the dermatophytes in dialysis bags within the peritoneal cavity of rabbits; these cells also exhibited enhanced invasion of the deep organs in experimental animals.

Scherr and Weaver (1953) have put forth the theory that since the yeast form of dimorphic fungi is best adapted to development in tissues, any agent that might bring about conversion to the mycelial form *in vivo* might be expected to arrest growth of the pathogen. This theory was tested by treating mice systemically infected with *C. albicans* with certain plant growth-promoting substances (auxins) which had been found to stimulate $Y \rightarrow M$ conversion *in vitro*. The results were negative, but the authors felt that the validity of this approach should not be discounted. It was pointed out that *C. albicans* may have been a poor choice for these studies, since this organism shows the concomitant existence of both forms is a culture grown at constant temperature; mycelial cultures contain yeast cells (blastospores) on the filaments. Moreover, while auxins may stimulate $Y \rightarrow M$ conversion *in vitro,* there is no assurance that they would do so *in vivo* because of difficulty of access, enzymatic transformation, and other possibilities.

While it seems clear that the yeast form is the invasive form in most of the dimorphic fungi, the situation with respect to *C. albicans* is controversial. As has been pointed out earlier, well developed pseudomycelia as well as budding yeast cells are observed commonly in tissues; the pseudomycelium itself characteristically has yeast cells attached (blastospores). Therefore it is difficult to make a decision as to the invasive form on the basis of microscopic examination alone.

Mackinnon (1940) reported that *C. albicans* 582 (normal strain) was highly virulent for experimental animals whereas the filamentous mutant (*C. albicans* 806) derived from it was avirulent. Nickerson *et al.* (1956) isolated a selenite-resistant variant from *C. albicans* 806 which had regained the capacity for yeast type growth, and concomitantly had regained virulence for mice. Eisman *et al.* (1953) isolated a number of colonial variants of *C. albicans* and found that yeast cells from smooth colony types were more virulent to mice than filamentous cells which occurred in a rough colonial strain. Winsten and Murray (1956) found that addition of cysteine to cultures of a filamentous strain enhanced both yeast development and virulence. All these data would implicate the yeast form as the virulent one.

On the other hand, there is evidence that the filamentous form is more invasive. Hill and Gebhardt (1956) found that yeast cells of *C. albicans*, when injected into a subcutaneous air pouch in mice, changed to elongated pseudomycelia within 60 minutes; at later times, considerable growth of filaments was observed. By contrast, nonpathogenic species of *Candida* did not do this. The filaments that were formed in the case of *C. albicans* were less readily phagocytosed than the yeast cells. It was postulated that filamentation *in vivo* is of significance to virulence and that the transformation favors survival of the fungus by mechanical interference with phagocytosis and by mechanical plugging of capillaries and arterioles.

Gresham and Whittle (1961) reported that isonicotinic acid hydrazide inhibits mycelial formation by *C. albicans* both *in vitro* and *in vivo*. Rabbits were not killed by *C. albicans* infection if a loading dose of INAH was given before injection, but protected animals showed small lesions. It was concluded that the mycelial form is invasive and that INAH confers a degree of protection by inhibiting mycelial formation.

Taschdjian *et al.* (1960) have attempted to reconcile these seemingly contradictory lines of evidence by making the tentative inference that the yeast phase plays an essential role in tissue penetration, but that the mycelial phase may evoke the tissue reactions which characterize clinical candidiasis. This would explain the lack of virulence of permanently filamentous variants cited above.

Heineman *et al.* (1961) have postulated that the inflammatory response of the host plays a role in dimorphism *in vivo*. In a postmortem study of a fatal case of human *C. albicans* endocarditis, they found that a vigorous cellular exudate found in kidney and brain abcesses was associated with marked suppression of mycelial growth and exclusive appearance of yeast forms. Lack of host response in the valvular region of the heart and in the infarcted renal papillae allowed uninhibited growth of mycelial elements with chlamydospores. It was concluded that protection of mycelia from inflammatory cells in a cardiac vegetation or a venous thrombus may be an essential stage in the initiation of systemic candidiasis. The observed ability of *C. albicans* to form chlamydospores *in vivo* and survive under conditions lethal to other members of this genus was put forth as a possible explanation of its greater pathogenicity.

Taschdjian and Kozinn (1961) suggested that *C. albicans* subsists saprophytically in human tissues under conditions that favor cell division;

invasion of host tissues is associated with at least partial inhibition of cell division, resulting in the presence of both mycelial and yeast cells. They pointed out that yeast morphology *in vivo* differs from that seen *in vitro*. In lesions, cells are ovoid, thin-walled, and have small vacuoles whereas in cultures, cells are more spherical, thick-walled, and have large vacuoles. They found that growth in serum resulted in mycelial cells; when grown in a serum dialyzate, typical tissue morphology was exhibited, which they denoted as TY/M, indicating the simultaneous presence of "tissue yeast" and mycelium. Development of the tissue morphology was inhibited by an unidentified nondialyzable serum component. Taschdjian and Kozinn tentatively concluded that conversion to tissue morphology was related to complete utilization of free amino acids and that some unidentified dialyzable serum component was essential for this purpose. Mycelial cells derived in serum or by inoculation into a subcutaneous air pouch by the technique of Hill and Gebhardt did not reduce triphenyl tetrazolium chloride. Therefore, it was implied that enzymatic pathways of cell division *in vivo* were different from those described for *in vitro* systems (Section IV, A).

It is clear that it would be difficult to make any generalizations concerning the physiological basis of dimorphism *in vivo* with any degree of confidence. Comparison of *in vitro* and *in vivo* experiments is fraught with pitfalls because of enormous differences in the complexities of the systems. Certainly, knowledge of virulence mechanisms in these organisms is rudimentary, and any conclusion to be drawn concerning dimorphism and pathogenicity must be speculative at this time.

VI. CONCLUDING REMARKS

Although the organisms discussed here present a diversified picture as to the physiological basis of dimorphism, there are similarities. There can be little doubt that oxidation-reduction potential and sulfhydryl compounds play a role in the determination of cell form; the evidence is suggestive in *Histoplasma capsulatum* and compelling in *Candida albicans*. It can even be speculated that the role of elevated temperature in determining the yeast shape in *Blastomyces* may be related to increased generation of reducing power.

The role of a thiol-disulfide equilibrium in morphogenetic processes in many organisms is suggested, for various -SH and -SS reagents have been shown to effect morphogenesis in such different materials as amphibian eggs, regenerating tadpoles, planarians, and the unicellular alga *Acetabularia mediterranea* (Brachet, 1961).

The concept of a specific cell-division enzyme put forth by Nickerson and Falcone is an exciting one, since it is the first and only such enzyme system described. The generality of the key role played by such an enzyme in dimorphic fungi remains to be established. However, the characterization and partial purification of a protein disulfide reductase from pea seeds by Hatch and Turner (1960) may indicate widespread occurrence of this enzyme.

The mechanism by which CO_2 induces yeastlike development in *Mucor rouxii, Sporothrix schenckii,* and *Histoplasma farciminosum* is obscure. It appears to be independent of the thiol–disulfide equilibrium. Elucidation of the mechanism awaits further investigation.

REFERENCES

Agar, H. D., and H. C. Douglas. (1955). Studies of budding and cell wall structure of yeast. *J. Bacteriol.* **70**:427-434.

Ainsworth, G. C. (1955). *In* "Mechanisms of Microbial Pathogenicity" (J. W. Howie and A. J. O'Hea, eds.), pp. 242-262. Cambridge Univ. Press, London and New York.

Ainsworth, G. C. (1958). *In* "The Chemistry and Biology of Yeasts" (A. H. Cook, ed.), pp. 587-602. Academic Press, New York.

Baker, E. E., E. M. Mrak, and C. E. Smith. (1943). The morphology, taxonomy, and distribution of *Coccidioides immitis,* Rixford and Gilchrist 1896. *Farlowia* **1**:199-244.

Bartnicki-Garcia, S., and W. J. Nickerson. (1962a). Induction of yeastlike development in *Mucor* by carbon dioxide. *J. Bacteriol.* **84**:829-840.

Bartnicki-Garcia, S., and W. J. Nickerson. (1962b). Nutrition, growth, and morphogenesis of *Mucor rouxii. J. Bacteriol.* **84**:841-858.

Bartnicki-Garcia, S., and W. J. Nickerson. (1962c). Isolation, composition, and structure of filamentous and yeast-like forms of *Mucor rouxii. Biochim. Biophys. Acta* **58**:102-119.

Bartnicki-Garcia, S., and W. J. Nickerson. (1962d). Assimilation of carbon dioxide and morphogenesis of *Mucor rouxii. Biochim. Biophys. Acta* **64**:548-551.

Barton, A. A. (1950). Some aspects of cell division in *Saccharomyces cerevisiae. J. Gen. Microbiol.* **4**:84-86.

Brachet, J. (1961). *In* "Growth in Living Systems" (M. X. Zarrow, ed.), pp. 241-275. Basic Books, New York.

Brodie, A. F., and J. S. Gots. (1952). The reduction of tetrazolium salts by an isolated bacterial flavoprotein. *Science* **116**:588-589.

Bullen, J. J. (1949). The yeastlike form of *Cryptococcus farciminosus* (*Histoplasma farciminosum*). *J. Pathol. Bacteriol.* **61**:117-120.

Burkholder, P. R. (1943). Vitamin deficiencies in yeast. *Am. J. Botany* **30**:206-211.

Campbell, C. C. (1947). Reverting *Histoplasma capsulatum* to the yeast phase. *J. Bacteriol.* **54**:263-264.

Chung, K. L., R. Z. Hawirko, and P. K. Isaac. (1965). Cell wall replication in *Saccharomyces cerevisiae. Bacteriol. Proc.* p. 38.

Conant, N. F. (1941). A cultural study of the life-cycle of *Histoplasma capsulatum* Darling 1906. *J. Bacteriol.* **41**:563-580.

Conant, N. F., D. T. Smith, R. D. Baker, J. L. Callaway, and D. S. Martin. (1954). "Manual of Clinical Mycology," 2nd. ed., 456 pp. Saunders, Philadelphia, Pennsylvania.

de Bary, A. (1887). "Comparative Morphology and Biology of the Fungi, Mycetozoa, and Bacteria," 525 pp. Oxford Univ. Press (Clarendon), London and New York.

Drouhet, E., and F. Mariat. (1952). Étude des facteurs déterminant le développement de la phase levure de *Sporotrichum schenki*. *Ann. Inst. Pasteur* 83:506-514.

Eisman, P. C., S. G. Geftic, and R. L. Mayer. (1953). Virulence in mice of colonial variants of *Candida albicans*. *Proc. Soc. Exptl. Biol. Med.* 82:263-264.

Falcone, G., and W. J. Nickerson. (1956). Cell-wall mannan-protein of bakers' yeast. *Science* 124:272-273.

Falcone, G., and W. J. Nickerson. (1959). Biochemistry of morphogenesis. *Proc. 4th Interna. Congr. Biochem., Vienna, 1958* Vol. 6, pp. 65-70. Pergamon Press, Oxford.

Foster, J. W. (1949). "Chemical Activities of Fungi," 648 pp. Academic Press, New York.

Freifelder, D. (1960). Bud position in *Saccharomyces cerevisiae*. *J. Bacteriol.* 80:567-568.

Gale, E. F. (1962). *In* "The Bacteria" (I. C. Gunsalus and R. Y. Stanier, eds.), Vol. 3, pp. 471-576. Academic Press, New York.

Garzuly-Janke, R. (1940). Ueber das Vorkommen von Mannan bei Hyphen- und Sprosspilzen. *Zentr. Bakteriol., Parasitenk., Abt. II* 102:361-365.

Gresham, G. A., and C. H. Whittle. (1961). Studies on the invasive mycelial form of *Candida albicans*. *Sabouraudia* 1:30-33.

Hatch, M. D., and J. F. Turner. (1960). A protein disulphide reductase from pea seeds. *Biochem. J.* 76:556-562.

Heineman, H. S., E. J. Yunis, J. Siemienski, and A. I. Braude. (1961). Chlamydospores and dimorphism in *Candida albicans* endocarditis. Observations in a fatal superinfection during treatment of Staphylococcus endocarditis. *Arch. Internal Med.* 108:570-577.

Hill, D. W., and L. P. Gebhardt. (1956). Morphological transformation of *Candida albicans* in tissues of mice. *Proc. Soc. Exptl. Biol. Med.* 92:640-644.

Kessler, G., and W. J. Nickerson. (1959). Glucomannan–protein complexes from cell walls of yeast. *J. Biol. Chem.* 234:2281-2285.

Kurung, J. M., and D. Yegian. (1954). Medium for maintenance and conversion of *Histoplasma capsulatum* to yeastlike phase. *Am. J. Clin. Pathol.* 24:505-508.

Larsh, H. W., A. Hinton, and S. L. Silberg. (1956). Conversion and maintenance of *Histoplasma capsulatum* in tissue culture. *Proc. Soc. Exptl. Biol. Med.* 93:612-615.

Levine, S., and Z. J. Ordal. (1946). Factors influencing the morphology of *Blastomyces dermatitidis*. *J. Bacteriol.* 52:687-694.

Lockhart, W. R. (1959). Use of microorganisms for studies of growth and morphogenesis. *Bacteriol. Rev.* 23:8-17.

McClary, D. O. (1952). Factors affecting the morphology of *Candida albicans*. *Ann. Missouri Botan. Garden* 39:137-164.

McClary, D. O., and W. D. Bowers, Jr. (1965). The integrity of the cell wall during bud formation in yeasts. *Can. J. Microbiol.* 11:447-452.

Mackinnon, J. E. (1940). Dissociation in *Candida albicans*. *J. Infect. Diseases* 66:59-77.

Myers, W. F., and N. P. Sherwood. (1951). Experimental histoplasmosis in the grass frog, *Rana pipiens*. *Bacteriol. Proc.* pp. 114-115.

Nickerson, W. J. (1942). Mechanics of budding and of conjugation in yeasts. *J. Cellular Comp. Physiol.* 19:379-382.

Nickerson, W. J. (1948). Enzymatic control of cell division in microorganisms. *Nature* 162:241-245.
Nickerson, W. J. (1954). An enzymatic locus participating in cellular division of a yeast. *J. Gen. Physiol.* 37:483-494.
Nickerson, W. J. (1959). Transactions of the plenary sessions. *Proc. 4th Interna. Congr. Biochem., Vienna, 1958* Vol. 14, pp. 191-209. Pergamon Press, Oxford.
Nickerson, W. J. (1963). Symposium on biochemical bases of morphogenesis in fungi. IV. Molecular bases of form in yeasts. *Bacteriol. Rev.* 27:305-324.
Nickerson, W. J., and C. W. Chung. (1954). Genetic block in the cellular division mechanism of a morphological mutant of a yeast. *Am. J. Botany* 41:114-120.
Nickerson, W. J., and G. A. Edwards. (1949). Studies on the physiological bases of morphogenesis in fungi I. The respiratory metabolism of dimorphic pathogenic fungi. *J. Gen. Physiol.* 33:41-55.
Nickerson, W. J., and G. Falcone. (1956a). Enzymatic reduction of disulfide bonds in cell wall protein of bakers' yeast. *Science* 124:318-319.
Nickerson, W. J., and G. Falcone. (1956b). Identification of protein disulfide reductase as a cellular division enzyme in yeasts. *Science* 124:722-723.
Nickerson, W. J., and Z. Mankowski. (1953). Role of nutrition in the maintenance of the yeast-shape in *Candida*. *Am. J. Botany.* 40:584-592.
Nickerson, W. J., and N. J. W. Van Rij. (1949). The effect of sulfhydryl compounds, penicillin, and cobalt on the cell division mechanism of yeasts. *Biochim. Biophys. Acta* 3:461-475.
Nickerson, W. J., W. A. Taber, and G. Falcone. (1956). Physiological bases of morphogenesis in fungi. 5. Effect of selenite and tellurite on cellular division of yeastlike fungi. *Can. J. Microbiol.* 2:575-584.
Nickerson, W. J., G. Falcone, and G. Kessler. (1961). *In* "Macromolecular Complexes" (M. V. Edds, Jr., ed.), pp. 205-228. Ronald Press, New York.
Northcote, D. H., and R. W. Horne. (1952). The chemical composition and structure of the yeast cell wall. *Biochem. J.* 51:232-236.
Pine, L. (1954). Studies on the growth of *Histoplasma capsulatum*. I. Growth of the yeast phase in liquid media. *J. Bacteriol.* 68:671-679.
Pine, L. (1955). Studies on the growth of *Histoplasma capsulatum*. II. Growth of the yeast phase on agar media. *J. Bacteriol.* 70:375-381.
Pine, L. (1957). Studies on the growth of *Histoplasma capsulatum*. III. Effects of thiamin and other vitamins on the growth of the yeast and mycelial phases of *Histoplasma capsulatum*. *J. Bacteriol.* 74:239-245.
Pine, L., and C. L. Peacock. (1958). Studies on the growth of *Histoplasma capsulatum*. IV. Factors influencing conversion of the mycelial phase to the yeast phase. *J. Bacteriol.* 75:167-174.
Rippon, J. W., and G. H. Scherr. (1959). Induced dimorphism in dermatophytes. *Mycologia* 51:902-914.
Robson, J. E., and Stockley, H. M. (1962). Sulphydryl metabolism of fungi grown in submerged culture. *J. Gen. Microbiol.* 28:57-68.
Romano, A. H., and W. J. Nickerson. (1954). Cystine reductase of pea seeds and yeast. *J. Biol. Chem.* 208:409-416.
Salvin, S. B. (1949a). Phase-determining factors in *Blastomyces dermatitidis*. *Mycologia* 41:311-319.
Salvin, S. B. (1949b). Cysteine and related compounds in the growth of the yeastlike phase of *Histoplasma capsulatum*. *J. Infect. Diseases* 84:275-283.

Scherr, G. H. (1957). Studies on the dimorphism of *Histoplasma capsulatum*. I. The role of -SH groups and incubation temperatures. *Exptl. Cell Res.* **12**:92-107.

Scherr, G. H., and R. H. Weaver. (1953). The dimorphism phenomenon in yeasts. *Bacteriol. Rev.* **17**:51-92.

Skinner, C. E. (1947). The yeastlike fungi: *Candida* and *Brettanomyces*. *Bacteriol. Rev.* **11**:227-274.

Taschdjian, C. L., and P. J. Kozinn. (1961). Metabolic studies on the tissue phase of *Candida albicans*. *Sabouraudia* **1**:73-82.

Taschdjian, C. L., F. Reiss, and P. J. Kozinn. (1960). Experimental vaginal candidiasis in mice; its implications for superficial candidiasis in humans. *J. Invest. Dermatol.* **34**:89-94.

Taylor, J. J. (1961). Nucleic acids and dimorphism in *Blastomyces*. *Exptl. Cell Res.* **24**:155-158.

Waksman, S. A., A. H. Romano, H. Lechevalier, and F. Raubitschek. (1953). Antifungal antibiotics. *Bull. World Health Organ.* **6**:163-173.

Ward, J. M., and W. J. Nickerson. (1958). Respiratory metabolism of normal and divisionless strains of *Candida albicans*. *J. Gen. Physiol.* **41**:703-724.

Webb, M. (1953). Effects of magnesium on cellular division in bacteria. *Science* **118**:607-611.

Winsten, S., and T. J. Murray. (1956). Virulence enhancement of a filamentous strain of *Candida albicans* after growth on media containing cysteine. *J. Bacteriol.* **71**:738.

CHAPTER 8

Morphogenesis in the Myxomycetes

CONSTANTINE J. ALEXOPOULOS[1]

Department of Botany and Cell Research Institute
The University of Texas
Austin, Texas

I. INTRODUCTION

The Myxomycetes are funguslike organisms with a free-living, mobile, acellular, multinucleate, assimilative stage, the plasmodium, which becomes converted into one or more, often intricately constructed, sporophores that bear the spores. Upon germination each spore liberates one to four swarm cells or myxamoebae which divide repeatedly by binary fission and produce large populations of uninucleate, haploid, naked cells. Compatible cells then fuse in pairs. Plasmodia are formed either by the growth of individual zygotes, in which repeated nuclear divisions take place, or by the coalescence of zygotes successively or, perhaps, en masse.

II. SPORE GERMINATION

Three general types of spore germination have been observed in the Myxomycetes. One type, exemplified by *Fuligo septica* and other species in the order Physarales, consists of the gradual or sudden cracking of the spore coat forming a wedge-shaped opening through which the protoplast escapes. The second type, usually encountered in the members of the Stemonitales, is accomplished by the formation of a very small, irregular pore in the spore coat (Gilbert, 1929a,b; Koevenig, 1961a,b; Smart, 1937). In *Ceratiomyxa fruticulosa* (McManus, 1958), the spore coat seems to dissolve and disappear. However, the spores of *Ceratiomyxa* are

---

[1] I am grateful to the National Science Foundation for financial assistance through Grant GB 2738 while this chapter was being written.

probably homologous with the sporangia of the majority of myxomycetes (Gilbert, 1935), and the spore coat must then be regarded as the peridium. Nevertheless, these structures do function as spores and each, upon germination, liberates a naked protoplast. In spite of the above it must be noted that Smart (1937) has shown that environmental conditions govern to some extent the type of germination exhibited by a single species, and that Koevenig (1961b, 1964) changed the germination of *Physarum gyrosum* from the split to the pore type by adding cellulase to the germination medium.

Factors that favor spore germination have been investigated by several workers (Martin, 1940; Alexopoulos, 1963), but the most comprehensive study is that of Smart (1937), who found that temperature, pH, germination medium, wetting and drying, and mass-spore effect were the most significant (see Chapter 23). Age of spores also has been observed by several workers to affect the percentage and time of germination. However, both Smith (1929) and Elliott (1949), who recorded the age of the spores with which they worked, stated that the spores of some myxomycetes are capable of germinating even after prolonged periods of storage (see chapter on "Resistance and Longevity of Fungi" by A. S. Sussman in Volume III). The oldest specimen that Elliott used in his studies had been collected 61 years before he germinated the spores. The time required for germination varies with the species. Freshly collected spores of *Fuligo septica*, for example, often will germinate in 15–20 minutes in distilled water at room temperature (22°–25° C). Spores of other species, such as many cribrarias or trichias, may require 1 week, or even 2 weeks, for germination.

An important criticism of spore germination experiments heretofore performed is that no attention has been paid to the sporangium from which the spores were collected. In studies of the germination of single spores obtained from individual sporangia of *Didymium iridis* produced in artificial culture, Collins (1961) showed that germination varies from 0 to 100% depending on the sporangium selected. Although the numbers of spores used were much too small for definite conclusions to be reached, these observations suggest that the sporangium is an important factor and may very well explain the discrepancy in results reported for the same species by different authors (Alexopoulos, 1963).

Whether hydrostatic pressure, created by water absorption and swelling of the protoplast, or enzymatic action, or both, is responsible for the actual germination of the spore has not been established. It would appear that the hydrostasis plays a greater part in type 1 germination and the enzymatic action in types 2 and 3, but it is probable that both are partially involved in all three types of germination. Koevenig's (1961b, 1964) results with

Physarum gyrosum indicate that cellulase may be a factor in spore germination.

III. MYXAMOEBAE AND SWARM CELLS

A. Development

When a spore germinates it liberates one to four naked cells. These may be myxamoebae or swarm cells. A swarm cell is a flagellated myxamoeba. The two stages are interconvertible, a relatively dry environment (absence of free water) usually favoring a myxamoebal condition, and the presence of free water often inducing the formation of flagella. Nevertheless, it must not be considered that the change from myxamoeba to swarm cell, and vice versa, may be induced in all species by supplying or withholding water. Ross (1957b) has proposed three general types of life cycle which he has called *briefly flagellate, flagellate,* and *completely flagellate.* All species do not strictly conform to the types of life cycle proposed by Ross, but the categories he has defined are useful in a general way. In the first of these the amoebal stage predominates. Once the flagellates are converted to myxamoebae, reversion to the flagellate condition usually does not occur. In the second type the flagellate condition predominates but interconversion between flagellate and amoeboid stages does take place. It appears that, in this case, the environment more or less governs the formation of flagella at any time during the naked, haploid stage. In the third type the amoeboid stage is absent or greatly restricted.

What stimulus initiates the formation of flagella is not known. It appears that the presence of water alone may be sufficient to evoke their development (Kerr, 1960). Research in progress by Aldrich in our laboratory indicates that in *Didymium iridis* the basal bodies are present not only in the swarm cells, but also in the resting spores. It has been demonstrated that optimum conditions for the development of flagella in *D. nigripes* are provided by a medium with a pH of 9.1 containing 0.05 M NaHCO$_3$, and that streptomycin at concentrations no greater than 100 µg/ml inhibits flagellum formation both in this species and in *Physarella oblonga* (Kerr, 1960, 1965).

The old controversy concerning the number of flagella which a mature swarm cell carries need not be reviewed in detail here. The evidence for a biflagellate condition is abundant and the examination of thin sections with the electron microscope reveals a biflagellate condition in *Didymium iridis, Stemonitis nigrescens, Comatricha typhoides, Physarum flavicomum,* etc. (Aldrich, 1965). Aldrich has demonstrated also that the flagella of the species he has examined exhibit the 9 + 2 fibrillar arrangement, as might be expected.

B. Syngamy

Although the occurrence of apogamy in myxomycetes cannot be ruled out, every species that has been critically investigated initiates its plasmodial stage through syngamy and the formation of zygotes. The controversy concerning syngamy, and the place of karyogamy in the life cycle, is of long standing and is so important in understanding development in the Myxomycetes that it warrants detailed treatment here. Beginning with Cienkowski (1863) many investigators had observed fusing cells in several species. But it was after the work of Jahn (1911) that syngamy as we think of it today was accepted as the phase of the life cycle which initiates the diploid condition. At the same time, a number of workers—among them von Stosch (1935, 1937), Luyet (1950), and Gehenio and Luyet (1950) more recently—have insisted that at least some species are apogamic. Moewus (1943), in discussing this situation pointed out the necessity for careful and painstaking observations before apogamy can be claimed. Although it is impossible to prove a negative proposition, it is noteworthy that for every claim of apogamy there is at least one observation of syngamy in the same species. Of course, it is always possible that apogamic strains may develop in any species, but the evidence for syngamy as a prerequisite for plasmodium formation is overwhelming (Martin, 1940; Alexopoulos, 1963). The recent discovery of heterothallism in several species leaves no doubt about the necessity of syngamy for plasmodial formation in those species. Heterothallism now has been established as occurring in *Physarum polycephalum* (Dee, 1960, 1962), *P. flavicomum* (Henney, 1965; Aldrich, 1965), *P. pusillum* (Collins, 1962; Collins *et al.* 1965), *Fuligo septica* (Alexopoulos and Henney, 1965), *Didymium iridis* (Alexopoulos and Zabka, 1962; Collins, 1961; Mukherjee and Zabka, 1964), *Comatricha laxa* (Wollman, 1966).

Although the occurrence of syngamy in myxomycetes has been abundantly demonstrated, the method by which it occurs is still not entirely clear. In some species fusion of amoebae in pairs results in an amoeboid zygote (Jahn, 1911; Ross, 1957b); in others, fusion of swarm cells appears to be the rule (M. Wilson and Cadman, 1928; Abe, 1934; Howard, 1931; McManus, 1961b; Ross, 1957b; Kerr, 1961). In still other species some investigators report fusion of amoebae and others report fusion of swarm cells (Howard, 1931; Jahn, 1911; Koevenig, 1961a,b). Skupienski (1926, 1927) found that in *Didymium difforme* either swarm cells or myxamoebae may fuse. Kerr (1961) and Koevenig (1961a,b, 1964) reported the same situation in *D. iridis* and *Physarum gyrosum,* respectively. In the "briefly flagellate" type of life cycle, Ross (1957b) states that only

8. Morphogenesis in the Myxomycetes

amoebae fuse, whereas in the other two types plasmogamy is said to occur through fusion of swarm cells. It is probable, however, that several species may employ either method, depending on the environment. McManus (1961a) and Benedict (1962) have given evidence which may indicate that in *Stemonitis fusca* syngamy occurs between a myxamoeba and a swarm cell. This is in contradiction to Ross' (1957b) finding that pairs of swarm cells fused in this species.

There is another question with regard to plasmogamy that has not been resolved satisfactorily. Although it is usually stated that only two cells are involved in syngamy, there have been persistent reports of multiple fusion of cells at this stage of the life cycle. From Cienkowski to the present time, workers have often reported fusion of three or more swarm cells in various species of myxomycetes. Skupienski (1927) and Cadman (1931–1932) observed this in *Didymium,* as did M. Wilson and Cadman (1928) and Koevenig (1961b, 1964) in *Reticularia,* Gilbert (1935) in *Ceratiomyxa,* Koevenig (1961b, 1964) in *Physarum,* etc. Wollman (1966) most recently stresses the frequency of the clumping of swarm cells in her cultures of several species of *Comatricha.* Without claiming that multiple fusion occurs, she does point out that in her cultures the clumps of swarm cells are characteristically formed at the time of plasmodium formation. However, she noted such clumping even in clonal cultures of the heterothallic *C. laxa,* an observation that may indicate that the clumping reaction is independent of sexual fusions, as cells within a clone of a heterothallic strain are sexually incompatible. Ross (1957b) in his study of syngamy in many species did not report multiple fusion and appears to be satisfied that only two gametic cells fuse to form a zygote.

Most workers who have investigated the nuclear cycle of myxomycetes are convinced that karyogamy follows plasmogamy and results in a uninucleate, diploid cell, the zygote. In recent years, Ross (1957b) concluded that this is the situation in the 19 species he investigated. However, he based his conclusions on stained preparations. Koevenig (1961b) actually proved through phase cinephotomicrography that karyogamy follows plasmogamy in *Physarum gyrosum.* Howard (1931) and Guttes *et al.* (1961), working with *P. polycephalum,* also reported karyogamy in the fusion cell. However, Dee (1962) found the same amount of DNA in the nuclei of the amoebae and the plasmodia of this organism and suggested, as had Skupienski (1926, 1927) and Schünemann (1930) previously, that karyogamy may be considerably delayed. Dee pointed out, at the same time, that the accuracy of her densitometer was not great and that her measurements were subject to considerable experimental error. A definitive answer to this interesting question has recently been given by Therrien

(1965) for four species, three of which are heterothallic. Measuring the DNA in Feulgen-stained nuclei spectrophotometrically, Therrien found that the plasmodial nuclei have twice the amount of DNA present in the myxamoebae. In the heterothallic species the sum of the mean DNA in the two mating types almost exactly equaled the amount of DNA measured in the plasmodial nuclei (Fig. 1). In the homothallic species (*Didymium nigripes*) he found two sizes of amoeboid cells in his cultures, the nuclei

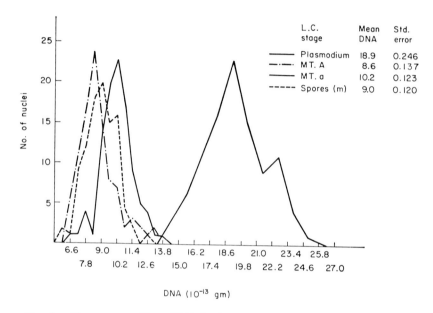

FIG. 1. *Physarum pusillum*. DNA in the nuclei of various stages of the life cycle (L.C.). Myxamoebae of mating type a contain more DNA than those of mating type A. Quantity of DNA in the nuclei of the mature spores (*m*) is intermediate between the amount in the nuclei of the myxamoebae of the two mating types. From Therrien (1965).

of the larger cells containing double the amount of DNA present in those of the smaller cells. He logically concluded that the large cells were zygotes. It is of considerable interest that the two mating types had different amounts of DNA in two of the three heterothallic species he investigated. In the third one, however, he found no measurable difference. Therrien's results leave no doubt that in *Didymium nigripes* karyogamy precedes plasmodium formation, and they support the view that this is also the case in the three other species he investigated (*D. iridis, Physarum flavicomum,* and *P. pusillum*).

IV. THE PLASMODIUM

A. Plasmodium Formation

Only about 10% of the known species have been cultured in the laboratory from spore to spore. The failure to grow many species is chiefly due to ignorance of the factors that induce plasmodium formation. Although usually there is little difficulty in germinating spores and growing large populations of myxamoebae or swarm cells, the conditions necessary for the continuation of the life cycle often cannot be provided.

Some species initiate plasmodia by the growth of the zygotes which undergo karyokinesis without cytokinesis. Several workers have demonstrated nuclear divisions in stained preparations of cells presumed to be zygotes, but since the cells had been fixed, could not prove that cytokinesis would not follow. Still others had demonstrated two simultaneous nuclear divisions in binucleate single cells but could not prove that these binucleate cells had not arisen by cytoplasmic fusion of two zygotes or myxamoebae. It remained for Koevenig (1961b) to furnish rigorous proof of the formation of a four-nucleated plasmodium in *Physarum gyrosum* from a uninucleate cell by filming the process with phase cinephotomicrography. Since he had also filmed nuclear division followed by cytokinesis in myxamoebae, the evidence that the plasmodium-forming cells were zygotes was conclusive.

According to Ross, in the "briefly flagellate" type of life cycle, plasmodia are formed by the aggregation and fusion of zygotes. In the center of such aggregations may be seen larger cells which are minute plasmodia. Whether these have been formed by the growth of single zygotes or by the fusion of two or more has not been determined. That zygotes do fuse with one another and with small plasmodia has been well established. Koevenig (1961a,b, 1964) observed the fusion of two zygotes and filmed the fusion of a zygote with a binucleate plasmodium. The two types of plasmodium formation, therefore, differ in that an aggregation stage precedes plasmodium formation in one type, whereas in the other, individual zygotes develop into plasmodia and only by chance do they fuse with other zygotes with which they come in contact. The stimulus which causes aggregation of zygotes in the "briefly flagellate" type of life cycle has not been determined.

B. Structure of Plasmodium

Three general types of myxomycete plasmodia, the phaneroplasmodium, the aphanoplasmodium, and the protoplasmodium have been described (Alexopoulos, 1960) (Fig. 2). The phaneroplasmodium, exemplified by

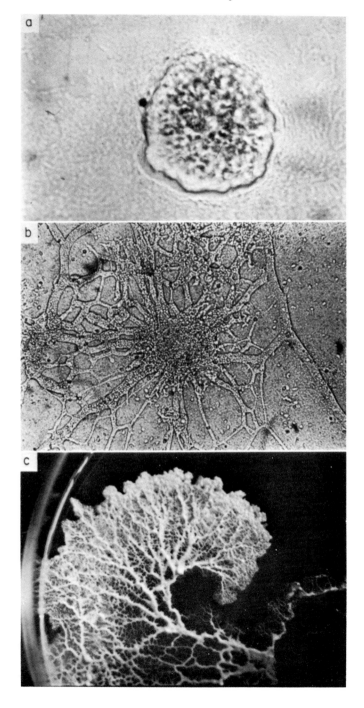

the well-known plasmodium of *Physarum polycephalum*, has been most studied. It is the plasmodium often seen in nature in its active state and the one which typifies—unfortunately to the exclusion of the other types— the assimilative stage of myxomycetes in the minds of most biologists. The phaneroplasmodium begins as a minute amoeboid structure which, at first, exhibits slow, irregular streaming. As it grows, its anterior end spreads out into a fan-shaped region and definite polarity is established. A system of channels now develops in the plasmodium and as it grows it differentiates into a network of veins, each with a thick, jellified region surrounding an inner fluid core which exhibits rhythmical, reversible streaming. Under optimum conditions of growth the fan becomes a fleshy sheet in which the protoplasm flows in well-defined channels. The protoplasm of the phaneroplasmodium is highly granular, rendering the plasmodium easily visible to the unaided eye when it reaches a size of about 0.5 mm. The phaneroplasmodium is characteristically associated with the order Physarales.

The aphanoplasmodium—associated with the Stemonitales—grows to a considerable size. Soon after it reaches about 100–200 μ in diameter, it begins to elongate and to produce long, hyphalike extensions in which reversible rhythmical streaming may be detected. As the plasmodium grows, the strands branch, but do not anastomose until later, so that for some time they end abruptly. Eventually, anastomosis takes place and a large meshed network is formed. In some species, at least, one or more advancing fans then develop. The younger strands of an aphanoplasmodium are not clearly differentiated into jellified and fluid protoplasm but are delimited by an extremely thin membrane which resembles a thin hyphal wall. Only when the major strands have attained considerable thickness can a nonstreaming region be detected. The large strands are often surrounded by small strands which originate from the former and appear to form a tubular net around them. The protoplasm in the strands of an aphanoplasmodium is much less granular than that in a phaneroplasmodium and renders the former difficult to see by reflected light. Aphanoplasmodia seem to prefer moist conditions and thrive throughout their existence under a layer of water. Many are so sensitive to dry conditions that they sclerotize as soon as they are deprived of a covering film of water.

The protoplasmodium appears to be a primitive type, which retains the juvenile characteristics of a phaneroplasmodium throughout its life.

FIG. 2. Major plasmodial types. (a) Protoplasmodium (*Echinostelium minutum*) (from Alexopoulos, 1962), (b) Aphanoplasmodium (*Comatricha nodulifera*), (c) Phaneroplasmodium (*Physarum gyrosum*) (from Doyle, 1964). Photographs by C. J. Alexopoulos. Magnification: (a) × 864; (b) × 288; (c) × 1.62.

It never grows to a large size, and in some species it divides before it reaches a diameter of 1 mm. Streaming in a protoplasmodium is irregular and slow; there are no veins or fans produced, but pseudopodia may be extended and withdrawn irregularly over the surface. A protoplasmodium, when it fruits, typically produces but a single minute sporangium. The method by which protoplasmodia form has not been determined. It is probable, but not certain, that they form by the growth of single zygotes. Protoplasmodia are characteristic of the small order Echinosteliales but are also produced by some species with minute sporocarps in some other orders.

A fourth type of plasmodium, intermediate in many respects between the aphano- and the phaneroplasmodium has been described briefly by Alexopoulos (1960) and more recently by McManus (1962). As more and more species are grown in artificial culture and their plasmodia are studied, more types will undoubtedly emerge. For example, *Licea biforis* appears to have a plasmodium intermediate between the phanero- and protoplasmodial types (Wollman, 1966). From our present knowledge, however, it seems that the three types discussed in the previous paragraphs are major centers from which other types may have been derived.

C. Physiology and Biochemistry of the Plasmodium

Much knowledge has accumulated concerning the biochemistry and physiology of the plasmodium of *Physarum polycephalum,* but not of the plasmodia of other species. It is outside the scope of this treatise to delve into the physiology of the plasmodium except when it relates to morphogenesis, but a short summary of our knowledge might be desirable here. The most significant discovery with regard to the motive force behind protoplasmic streaming in the plasmodium of *P. polycephalum* relates to at least two contractile proteins (myxomyosin and myosin B). Both undergo a reversible change in viscosity when allowed to react with ATP (Ts'O et al., 1956a,b, 1957a,b; Nakajima, 1964). Inasmuch as protoplasmic streaming is intricately linked with plasmodial migration, it is interesting to note here that potassium, which plays an important role in the migration of the plasmodium, (Anderson, 1962, 1964) appears also to be necessary for the response of myxomyosin to ATP.

Concerning the nutrition of the plasmodium, little is known beyond the requirements of *P. polycephalum.* Even so, these data are of considerable importance because this is the only plasmodium which has been grown, thus far, in axenic culture on a chemically defined medium. Such a medium contains inorganic salts, glucose, citric acid, various amino acids, and hematin (Daniel and Baldwin, 1964). Unfortunately, other species do not respond similarly to this medium (Ross, 1964).

8. Morphogenesis in the Myxomycetes

Plasmodial nuclei multiply by synchronous mitosis which is nearly absolute under rigidly controlled conditions (Guttes et al., 1961). When several microplasmodia with different mitotic rhythms are permitted to coalesce, a single rhythm is established within the whole plasmodial mass in about 6–7 hours, which represents about one-half of the interphase time. According to Nygaard et al. (1960), in the plasmodial nuclei synthesis of DNA occurs within a period of 1–2 hours following mitosis and then ceases. However, RNA synthesis continues at a more or less even rate throughout the mitotic cycle.

D. Sclerotization

Sclerotization in myxomycetes may be regarded as a rapid response to unfavorable conditions which keeps the organism alive until favorable conditions return. Among the conditions which induce sclerotial formation in *Physarum polycephalum* the following appear to be most important: gradual desiccation, low temperatures, high osmotic pressure, low pH, and sublethal doses of heavy metals (Jump, 1954). If the desiccation process is completed in less than 4 hours, the sclerotia formed will not be viable (Hodapp, 1942). Sclerotization in *P. polycephalum* begins with cessation of streaming and, under certain conditions, aggregation of plasmodial strands. Gelation of the whole structure follows and the nuclei are re-

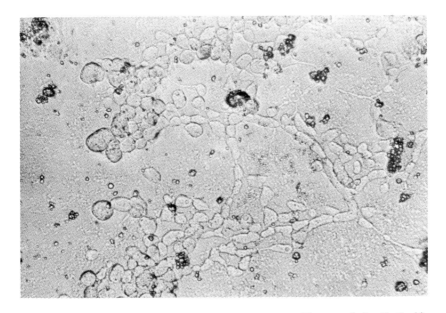

FIG. 3. Sclerotizing plasmodium of *Arcyria cinerea*. Photograph by C. J. Alexopoulos. Magnification: × 400.

distributed. Walls are now laid down which compartmentalize the plasmodium into a large number of macrocysts varying in size from 10 to 25 μ in diameter, each containing from 0 to 14 nuclei. Upon completion of macrocyst formation, the sclerotium hardens and the nuclei shrink to about one-half their original diameter. Such sclerotia remain viable for 1–3 years. Rehydration of the sclerotium reverses the process of sclerotization whereupon the sclerotium regains its plasticity, the nuclei enlarge to their normal size, the macrocysts merge, and streaming is resumed.

The process of sclerotization appears to be somewhat different in aphanoplasmodia. Instead of the strands aggregating, they segment and the entire plasmodium becomes converted into a large number of disconnected macrocysts distributed according to the pattern of the plasmodial network at the time of sclerotization (Alexopoulos, 1960; Wollman and Alexopoulos, 1964) (Fig. 3). Upon return to favorable conditions, the macrocysts merge and the plasmodial net is reconstituted. Although desiccation brings about rapid sclerotization of aphanoplasmodia, other unknown factors sometimes have the same effect, for aphanoplasmodia have been seen to sclerotize in culture under water. When this occurs, the macrocysts do not revert to the plasmodial stage under any known conditions.

Protoplasmodia encyst in the manner of amoebae under unfavorable conditions.

V. SPORULATION

A. Induction

Although many factors have been linked with sporulation by various authors, the conditions that actually trigger the process remain unknown. In nature, plasmodia often live between the bark and the wood of decaying logs, but their fruiting bodies are mostly formed on the surface of the bark or on the exposed wood where the bark has been stripped off. What causes the plasmodium to emerge before fruiting is not known.

In artificial culture, too, many species appear to be unpredictable in their fruiting habits. Notorious among these is *Fuligo septica,* a common and widespread myxomycete, which can be cultured easily from spores to the plasmodial stage. Eventually it fruits, but no one has been able to determine the conditions which bring about sporulation. In the most recent study on this species, Scholes (1962) reached the conclusion that the only factor, among those she studied, which appreciably influenced sporulation was age of the culture. It has been noted by a number of investigators that sporulation in axenic myxomycete cultures, if indeed it takes place at all, often is greatly delayed over that in synxenic cultures. However, Daniel and Rusch (1962a) have discovered factors which induce sporulation in *Physarum polycephalum,* in axenic culture. These authors distinguish between the growth medium in which the plasmodia have been growing and the sporulation medium to which, after they attain a certain age, they must be transferred in order to fruit. The sporulation medium must contain niacin, niacinamide, or tryptophan, although some other substances may be substituted (Daniel and Rusch, 1962b). The role niacin plays in the sporulation process is not known, but Daniel and Baldwin (1964) state that "it appears that niacin or a distal metabolite of niacin may induce anabolic pathways whose products are essential for sporulation."

Gray (1938, 1941, 1953) is usually credited with the discovery that light is required for sporulation of pigmented plasmodia. He found that the optimum wavelength for the sporulation of *P. polycephalum* is 436 mµ. Daniel and Rusch (1962a) confirmed Gray's work by showing that in axenic culture a minimum of 2 hours' exposure to light was an absolute requirement for sporulation and that the optimum wavelength lies between 350 and 500 mµ. The yellow plasmodium of *P. nudum* sporulates when irradiated with wavelengths between 330 and 560 mµ, but the higher range (417–560 mµ), at the optimum intensity, is more effective than the lower (330–400 mµ) (Rakoczy, 1963).

That the plasmodial pigments may be involved in the photochemical reaction is suggested by the fact that in acid the absorption peak of the yellow pigment suspected to be the photoreceptor in *P. polycephalum* is approximately 415–430 mµ (Daniel and Rusch, 1962a; Gray, 1953; Wolf, 1959). How light brings about sporulation is not known, but certain chemical reactions induced in the plasmodium by light have been reported. A "point of no return" past which the plasmodium of *P. polycephalum* "commits itself to sporulation" is reached after 18 hours of illumination at 25°C (Zeldin and Ward, 1963a,b). Although no morphological changes are evident at that time, acrylamide gel electrophoresis of illuminated plasmodial extracts revealed a 60% decrease in the activity of a specific α-amylase after the critical point, and a further decrease as morphological changes take place. Still and Ward (1963) showed that an enzyme, other than indole-3-acetic acid oxidase, was present in the plasmodium of *P. polycephalum* but was inactivated during a 20-hour period of illumination. Ward (1958) found a shift in oxidases from ascorbic acid to cytochrome oxidase as the organism proceeds from the plasmodial to the spore stage. In his own words: "Whereas there is approximately three times as much cytochrome oxidase activity in spores as in plasmodia, there is approximately six times as much ascorbic acid oxidase activity in the plasmodia as in the spores." Finally, on the basis of Ward and Havir's (1957) investigation of certain enzyme systems involved in melanin production during spore formation, Ward (1959) suggests "the possibility that sporulation can be triggered by the inactivation of -SH groups in the intact plasmodium."

B. Development of the Sporophore

Almost all that is known concerning sporophore development in myxomycetes is based on studies of the Physarales and the Stemonitales. Therefore the following brief discussion must be confined to these two orders with only the briefest reference to other groups.

1. The Physarales

When the plasmodium passes the "point of no return" in its biochemical progress toward sporulation, morphological changes begin to take place. The phaneroplasmodium, as exemplified by that of *Physarum polycephalum* and other members of the Physarales, flows into the already fleshy, spreading fans concentrating its protoplasm into a thick, continuous layer (Howard, 1931; Welden, 1955). In pure culture, the strands of *P. polycephalum* assume an undulating appearance (Guttes *et al.,* 1961). The plasmodium then becomes cleaved into a number of pulvinate masses or nodules which soon begin to elongate into pillars. No geotropic effect is evident, elongation being perpendicular to the surface of the substratum. Pigment and other granules are concentrated into the central axis of the pillars and, gradually, the sporangium becomes differentiated at the top of each pillar as an enlarged mass, the base of which appears to be constricted. This constriction is partly due to the shrinking of the material composing the stipe. This is composed of (1) a tough, irregular lamellate wall, (2) a foamlike cylinder of protoplasm, and (3) a central core of granular material responsible for the rigidity of the stipe (Howard, 1931; Welden, 1955). It is important to note, as Ross (1957a) has emphasized, that there is a continuous membrane on the outside of the sporangial initials and that the hypothallus, which is continuous with the stalk, is formed on the upper side of the plasmodium and is laid down on the substratum as the protoplasm moves upward on the inside. The sporangium at this stage is covered by a double-walled peridium and is filled with frothy protoplasm in which a vacuolar system is being organized.

2. The Stemonitales

Prior to fruiting, the aphanoplasmodium is flat and difficult to see. As it grows older and larger it forms definite fans at the advancing edges and, as fruiting approaches, the hitherto colorless and transparent protoplasm becomes opaque, and thickens and flows together, forming coralloid masses (Alexopoulos, 1959, 1960). As the sporangial primordia begin to form, the hypothallus is deposited directly on the substratum on the underside of the plasmodium (Ross, 1957a). The sporangial primordia, in the form of small pulvinate papillae, now deposit fibrous strands internally on the hypothallus on which they rest and the protoplast begins to move slowly up the stalk, continuously adding material to the tip of the stalk as it moves upward (De Bary, 1887; Jahn, 1931; Ross, 1957a, 1960; Goodwin, 1961). When the final height is reached, the protoplasm forms a sphere at the apex of the stalk but continues to deposit material internally, thus forming the columella in species in which this structure is present. The membrane which surrounds the protoplasmic sphere is now the thin, transparent peridium characteristic of the developing sporangia of *Comatricha* and *Lamproderma* (Goodwin, 1961; Ross, 1960). Thus, there is a fundamental difference in the origins of the hypothallus, stalk, and probably peridium, as exemplified by the few genera that have been studied, between the Stemonitales and the Physarales.

C. Capillitium Development

Inside the fructification of many myxomycetes there is, in addition to the spores, a system of threads forming the *capillitium*. These threads are free or united into an open or dense net. Although the capillitium often is thought to be formed by the deposition of waste products, such a view tends not to recognize that its structure is characteristic and constant for each species and that the capillitial system, by virtue of properties like hygroscopicity or elasticity, often plays an important role in the dispersal of the spores.

In the Physarales the capillitium is formed by the excretion of various products, including $CaCO_3$, into a network of vacuoles connected with invaginations originating at the peridial walls. This system transports material to the outside, but retains a sufficient amount to form the capillitial threads. In *Didymium iridis,* the sporangium expands and encloses the tip of the stalk. The protoplasm adjacent to the tip is cut off from the rest of the sporangium, disintegrates, and becomes deposited on the apex of the stalk, forming the columella (Welden, 1955). The nature of the capillitial threads remains unknown, but in *D. nigripes* they appear to be solid with a dense periphery and a less dense but solid, layered central core (Schuster, 1964).

In the Trichiales the capillitium is also formed as a result of a system of vacuoles (Strasburger, 1884; Harper and Dodge, 1914), but it appears that the material from which it forms is deposited by the protoplasm on the walls of the vacuolar network.

Whether in the Stemonitales the capillitium is deposited in or on a vacuolar system is not certain. Bisby (1914), who studied microtome sections of *Stemonitis fusca,* believed that the capillitium was formed by "the deposition of hollow threads by plasma membranes lining tubular capillary spaces." He described such capillary spaces as invaginations originating both from the peridial membrane and from the columella. Neither Ross (1957a, 1960) nor Goodwin (1961) found evidence of vacuolation or invagination in *Stemonitis, Lamproderma,* or *Comatricha*. These workers mounted whole sporangia at various stages of development in Hoyer's medium or squashed them in aceto-orcein. It is possible that the difference in technique was responsible for the different interpretation. In *Comatricha* and *Lamproderma,* when the full height of the fructification has been reached, the fibers which comprise the stipe and columella begin to bend out, and they continue to do so until the columella reaches its full length. The fibers now elongate and branches arise from them. Anastomosis takes place, and within a few hours the entire capillitial system has been formed. In *Stemonitis,* two capillitial systems are formed, one originating at the periphery of the sporangium and forming the surface net, and the other from the columella as described above. The two fuse when the branches from the columella reach the peripheral capillitium.

The structure of the fibers in the Stemonitales is not known. Ross speaks of tubules; Goodwin states that she found no evidence that capillitial threads are tubular and considers them to be solid. Only the electron microscope will resolve this question. Nor has the chemical composition of the capillitium been determined. Cihlar (1916) reported chitin in the capillitium of *S. fusca* and von Wettstein (1921) found cellulose in the membranes of *Comatricha* and *Stemonitis*. Goodwin identified cellulose but not chitin in the stalk and capillitium of the three species of *Comatricha* she studied. All these conclusions were based on microchemical tests. It remains for X-ray diffraction studies and chemical isolation to provide definitive answers to these interesting questions.

D. Spore Formation

At the completion of, or during, capillitium formation, nuclear division takes place in the sporangium (Howard, 1931; Ross, 1960). Whether one or two divisions occur at this point is a matter of dispute linked with the whole controversy as to where meiosis occurs in the life cycle of the Myxomycetes. The three principal views are: (1) that meiosis takes place just preceding spore delimitation; (2) that it occurs during spore maturation; and (3) that the first meiotic division occurs in the sporocarp just before spore formation and the second takes place later, probably in the spore before or during germination. The reader is referred to Martin (1940) and Alexopoulos (1963) for a detailed review of the literature concerning meiosis. All workers agree that in *Ceratiomyxa* meiosis takes place in the spores during germination, but there is great disagreement about the endosporous species. The most important contributions to this question in recent years are those of von Stosch (1935, 1937), C. Wilson

8. Morphogenesis in the Myxomycetes

and Ross (1955), Ross (1961), and Therrien (1965). C. Wilson and Ross, and subsequently Ross, using classical cytological methods, counted chromosomes and concluded that meiosis occurs, in all species they investigated, just before the spores are delimited in the fruiting body. Therrien reached the same conclusion for four species, on the basis of measurement of DNA content at different stages (Chapter 18). He found the spores to be typically uninucleate, and the amount of DNA in the nuclei of the mature spores to be half that in the nuclei of the plasmodium. Furthermore, in two species, he found the amount of DNA in very young spores just after cleavage to be about half that present in the nuclei of the mature spores. He concluded that the nuclei of the plasmodium pass 90% of their interphase time in the diploid 4c condition, that the nuclei in the postcleavage spores are in the haploid 1c condition, and that the mature spores are in the 2c condition and remain so until germination. The opposite view is held by von Stosch (1935, 1937) who, using classical cytological methods, reported that in species in which meiosis is a part of the life cycle it takes place in the spores and that one nucleus disintegrates after each division, leaving the spores uninucleate and haploid. Von Stosch insisted, however, that some isolates go through their life cycle apogamously.

Therrien's conclusions for the four species he investigated are in agreement with the general conclusions of Wilson and Ross and of Ross, referred to above. It is of further interest to note here that electron micrographs by Carroll and Dykstra (1966) seem to demonstrate clearly the occurrence of synaptinemal complexes in a developing sporangium of *Didymium iridis* (Fig. 4).

Mycologists have generally assumed that the Myxomycetes is a fairly homogenous group and that the nuclear cycle must, therefore, be the same in all endosporous species. Only further research employing various techniques and a large number of species will show whether this assumption is warranted. It is certainly possible that some of the endosporous species follow the nuclear cycle pattern of *Ceratiomyxa*, as Von Stosch's results indicate.

After meiosis, the protoplasm cleaves into uninucleate portions which are the young spores. In *D. nigripes* these already possess around their peripheries more or less evenly spaced projections with a granular consistency which become the spines of the mature spores. Two walls are now laid down, the inner wall giving a positive test for cellulose. The outer wall, of which the spines are a part, does not give a cellulose reaction, but may contain chitin (Schuster, 1964).

Thus, the developing spores in the few species that have been investigated are typically uninucleate. However, nuclear divisions have been reported in the spores of various species so that the mature, resting spores

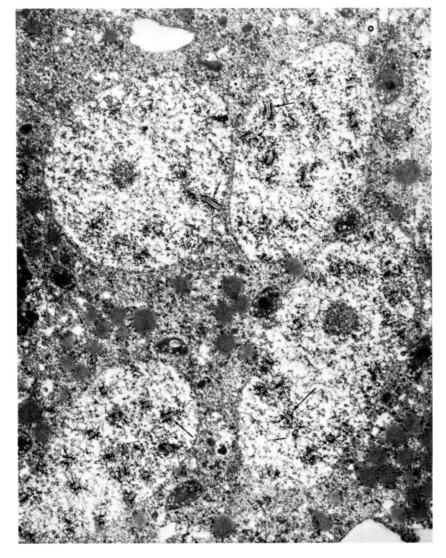

Fig. 4. *Didymium iridis*. Section through a sporangium at the time of sporulation showing synaptionemal complexes. From Caroll and Dykstra (1966). Magnification: × 11,799.

may contain 1–4 nuclei and give rise to 1–4 protoplasts upon germination. In a recent electron microscopic study of the spores of *Arcyria cinerea*, Carroll (1965) photographed a thin section of a spore which clearly shows 8 nuclei (Fig. 5). Whether this is the usual pattern for *A. cinerea*,

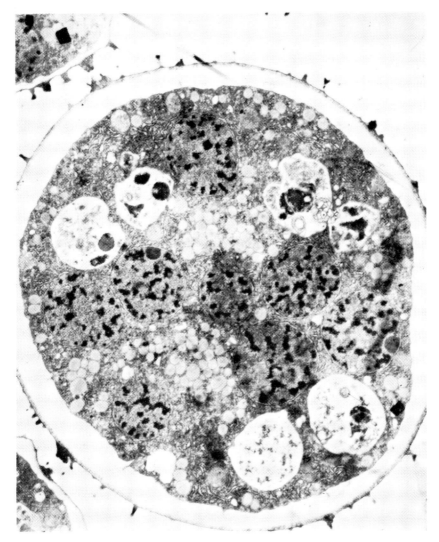

FIG. 5. *Arcyria cinerea.* Section through a mature spore showing 8 nuclei. Electron micrograph by G. Carroll. Magnification × 9,268.

or merely an unusual development with little general significance, remains to be seen.[2]

REFERENCES

Abe, S. (1934). On the syngamy of some Myxomycetes. *Sci. Rept. Tokyo Bunrika Daigaku* **B1**:193-202.

---

[2] For "Notes Added in Proof" see p. 234.

Aldrich, H. (1965). Unpublished data.

Alexopoulos, C. J. (1959). The laboratory cultivation of *Stemonitis*. *Am. J. Botany* **46**:140-142.

Alexopoulos, C. J. (1960). Gross morphology of the plasmodium and its possible significance in the relationships among the Myxomycetes. *Mycologia* **52**:1-20.

Alexopoulos, C. J. (1962). "Introductory Mycology," 2nd ed. Wiley, New York.

Alexopoulos, C. J. (1963). The Myxomycetes II. *Botan. Rev.* **29**:1-78.

Alexopoulos, C. J., and M. Henney. (1965). Unpublished data.

Alexopoulos, C. J., and G. G. Zabka. (1962). Production of hybrids between physiological races of the true slime mould *Didymium iridis*. *Nature* **193**:598-599.

Anderson, J. D. (1962). Potassium loss during galvanotaxis of slime molds. *J. Gen. Physiol.* **45**:567-574.

Anderson, J. D. (1964). Regional differences in ion concentration in migrating plasmodia. *In* "Primitive Motile Systems in Cell Biology" (R. D. Allen and N. Kamiya, eds.), pp. 125-136. Academic Press, New York.

Benedict, W. G. (1962). Haplophase activity in *Stemonitis fusca* Roth. *Can. J. Botany* **40**:71-76.

Bisby, G. R. (1914). Some observations on the formation of the capillitium and the development of *Physarella mirabilis* Peck and *Stemonitis fusca* Roth. *Am. J. Botany* **1**:274-288.

Cadman, E. (1931-1932). The life history and cytology of *Didymium nigripes* Fr. *Trans. Roy. Soc. Edinburgh* **57**:93-143.

Carroll, G. (1965). Unpublished data.

Carroll, G., and R. Dykstra. (1966). Synaptinemal complexes in *Didymium iridis*. *Mycologia* **58**:166-169.

Cienkowski, L. (1863). Zur Entwicklungsgeschichte de Myxomyceten. *Jahrb. Wiss. Botany* **3**:325-337.

Cihlar, C. (1916). Mikrokemijska istrazivan johitin ublinskim membranama. *Botan. Centr.* **131**:524 (in Goodwin, 1961).

Collins, O. R. (1961). Heterothallism and homothallism in two Myxomycetes. *Am. J. Botany* **48**:674-683.

Collins, O. R. (1962). Mating types in the slime mold *Physarum pusillum*. *Am. J. Botany* **49**:659 (abstract).

Collins, O. R., C. J. Alexopoulos, and M. Henney. (1965). Unpublished data.

Daniel, J. W., and H. H. Baldwin. (1964). Methods of culture for plasmodial Myxomycetes. *In* "Methods in Cell Physiology" (D. M. Prescott, ed.), Vol. 1, pp. 9-41. Academic Press, New York.

Daniel, J. W., and H. P. Rusch. (1962a). Method for inducing sporulation of pure cultures of the myxomycete *Physarum polycephalum*. *J. Bacteriol.* **83**:234-240.

Daniel, J. W., and H. P. Rusch. (1962b). Niacin requirement for sporulation of *Physarum polycephalum*. *J. Bacteriol.* **83**:1244-1250.

De Bary, A. (1887). "Comparative Morphology and Biology of the Fungi, Mycetozoa and Bacteria" (Transl. by H. E. F. Garnsey. Revised by I. B. Balfour), 525 pp. Oxford Univ. Press (Clarendon), London and New York.

Dee, J. (1960). A mating type system in an acellular slime-mould. *Nature* **185**:780-781.

Dee, J. (1962). Recombination in a myxomycete, *Physarum polycephalum* Schw. *Genet. Res.* **3**:11-23.

Doyle, W. T. (1964). "Nonvascular Plants: Form and Function." Wadsworth, Belmont, California.

Elliott, E. W. (1949). The swarm cells of Myxomycetes. *Mycologia* **41**:141-170.
Gehenio, P. M., and B. J. Luyet. (1950). Complete development of a mycetozoon from a single spore or a single myxamoeba. *Biodynamica* **7**:11-23.
Gilbert, H. C. (1929a). Factors influencing the germination of myxomycetous spores. *Am. J. Botany* **16**:280-286.
Gilbert, H. C. (1929b). Spore germination in the Myxomycetes: A comparative study of spore germination by families. *Am. J. Botany* **16**:421-432.
Gilbert, H. C. (1935). Critical events in the life history of *Ceratiomyxa*. *Am. J. Botany* **22**:52-74.
Goodwin, D. C. (1961). Morphogenesis of the sporangium of *Comatricha*. *Am. J. Botany* **48**:148-154.
Gray, W. D. (1938). The effect of light on the fruiting of Myxomycetes. *Am. J. Botany* **25**:511-522.
Gray, W. D. (1941). Some effects of heterochromatic ultra-violet radiation on myxomycete plasmodia. *Am. J. Botany* **28**:212-216.
Gray, W. D. (1953). Further studies on the fruiting of *Physarum polycephalum*. *Mycologia* **45**:817-824.
Guttes, E., S. Guttes, and H. P. Rusch. (1961). Morphological observations on growth and differentiation of *Physarum polycephalum* grown in pure culture. *Develop. Biol.* **3**:588-614.
Harper, R. A., and B. O. Dodge. (1914). The formation of the capillitium in certain Myxomycetes. *Ann. Botany (London)* **28**:1-18.
Henney, M. (1965). Unpublished data.
Hodapp, E. L. (1942). Some factors influencing sclerotization in Mycetozoa. *Biodynamica* **4**:33-46.
Howard, F. L. (1931). Life history of *P. polycephalum*. *Am. J. Botany* **18**:116-133.
Jahn, E. (1911). Myxomycetenstudien 8. Der Sexualakt. *Ber. Deut. Botan. Ges.* **29**:231-247.
Jahn, E. (1931). Myxomycetenstudien 13. Die Stielbildung bei den Sporangien der Gattung *Comatricha*. *Ber. Deut. Botan. Ges.* **49**:77-83.
Jump, J. A. (1954). Stduies on sclerotization in *Physarum polycephalum*. *Am. J. Botany* **41**:561-567.
Kerr, N. S. (1960). Flagella formation by myxamoebae of the true slime mold *Didymium nigripes*. *J. Protozool.* **7**:103-108.
Kerr, N. S. (1961). A study of plasmodium formation by the true slime mold *Didymium nigripes*. *Exptl. Cell Res.* **23**:603-611.
Kerr, N. S. (1965). Inhibition by streptomycin of flagella formation in a true slime mold. *J. Protozool.* **12**:276-278.
Koevenig, J. L. (1961a). Three educational films on Myxomycetes with a study of the life cycle of *Physarum gyrosum* Rost, 225 pp. Ph.D. Dissertation, University of Iowa, Iowa City.
Koevenig, J. L. (Technical Director). (1961b). Slime molds I. Life cycle, U-5518, 30 min. sd. color or B. & W. film. Bureau Aud.-Vis. Instr., Ext. Div., University of Iowa, Iowa City.
Koevenig, J. L. (1964). Studies on the life cycle of *Physarum gyrosum* and other Myxomycetes. *Mycologia* **56**:170-184.
Luyet, B. J. (1950). Evidence and lack of evidence of sexuality in Myxomycetes. *Proc. 7th Intern. Botan. Congr., Stockholm, 1950* p. 433.
McManus, S. M. A. (1958). In vivo studies of plasmogamy in *Ceratiomyxa*. *Bull. Torrey Botan. Club* **85**:28-37.

McManus, S. M. A. (1961a). Culture of *Stemonitis fusca* on glass. *Am. J. Botany* 48:582-588.
McManus, S. M. A. (1961b). Laboratory cultivation of *Clastoderma debaryanum*. *Am. J. Botany* 48:884-888.
McManus, S. M. A. (1962). Some observations on plasmodia of the Trichiales. *Mycologia* 54:78-90.
Martin, G. W. (1940). The Myxomycetes. *Botan. Rev.* 6:356-388.
Moewus, F. (1943). Zur Sexualität der niederen Organismen II. Myxomyceten und Phycomyceten. *Ergeb. Biol.* 19:82-142.
Mukherjee, K. S., and G. G. Zabka. (1964). Studies of multiple allelism in the myxomycete *Didymium iridis*. *Can. J. Botany* 42:1459-1466.
Nakajima, H. (1964). The mechanochemical system behind streaming in *Physarum*. *In* "Primitive Motile Systems in Cell Biology" (R. D. Allen and N. Kamiya, eds.), pp. 111-123. Academic Press, New York.
Nygaard, O. F., S. Guttes, and H. P. Rusch. (1960). Nucleic acid metabolism in a slime mold with synchronous mitosis. *Biochim. Biophys. Acta* 38:298-306.
Rakoczy, L. (1963). Influence of monochromatic light on the fructification of *Physarum nudum*. *Bull. Acad. Polon. Sci., Ser. Sci. Biol.* 11:559-562.
Ross, I. K. (1957a). Capillitial formation in the Stemonitaceae. *Mycologia* 49:809-819.
Ross, I. K. (1957b). Syngamy and plasmodium formation in the Myxogastres. *Am. J. Botany* 44:843-850.
Ross, I. K. (1960). Sporangial development in *Lamproderma arcyrionema*. *Mycologia* 52:621-627.
Ross, I. K. (1961). Further studies on meiosis in the Myxomycetes. *Am. J. Botany* 48:244-248.
Ross, I. K. (1964). Pure cultures of some Myxomycetes. *Bull. Torrey Botan. Club* 91:23-31.
Scholes, P. M. (1962). Some observations on the cultivation, fruiting, and germination of *Fuligo septica*. *J. Gen. Microbiol.* 29:137-148.
Schünemann, E. (1930). Untersuchungen über die Sexualität der Myxomyceten *Planta* 9:645-672.
Schuster, R. (1964). Electron microscope observations on spore formation in the true slime mold *Didymium nigripes*. *J. Protozool.* 11:207-216.
Skupienski, F. X. (1926). Sur de cycle èvolutif chez une espèce de myxomycète endosporée. *Compt. Rend.* 182:150-152.
Skupienski, F. X. (1927). Sur le cycle évolutif chez une espèce de myxomycète endosporée *Didymium difforme*. Étude cytologique. *Compt. Rend.* 184:1341-1344.
Smart, R. F. (1937). Influence of certain external factors on spore germination in the Myxomycetes. *Am. J. Botany* 24:145-159.
Smith, E. C. (1929). Longevity of myxomycete spores. *Mycologia* 21:321-323.
Still, C. C., and J. M. Ward. (1963). Photo-indole-3-acetic acid effects on morphogenesis in *Physarum polycephalum*. *Bacteriol. Proc.* p. 68 (abstract).
Strasburger, F. (1884). Zur Entwickelungsgeschichte der Sporangien von *Trichia fallax*. *Botan. Ztg.* 42:305-316 and 321-326.
Therrien, C. D. (1965). Microspectrophotometric analysis of nuclear deoxyribonucleic acid in some Myxomycetes. Ph.D. Dissertation, University of Texas, Austin.
Ts'O, P. O. P., J. T. Bonner, L. Eggman, and J. Vinograd. (1956a). Observations on an ATP-sensitive protein system from the plasmodia of a myxomycete. *J. Gen. Physiol.* 39:325-347.

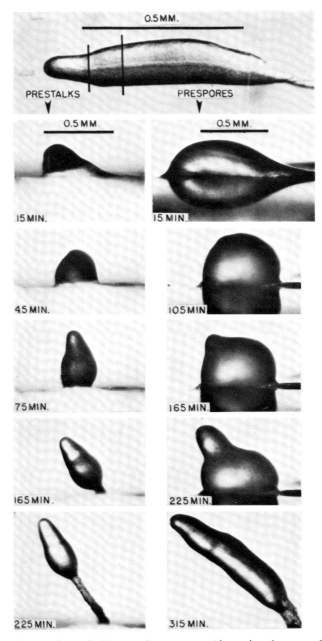

FIG. 12. Transection of *Dictyostelium mucoroides* migrating pseudoplasmodia and subsequent patterns of reorganization of prestalk and prespore isolates.

nation for the appearance of mitotic figures. Fragments examined at intervals following the operation showed no mitotic activity, and they concluded that regulation and differentiation do not depend on mitosis.

Although the exact mechanism regulating the proportions of cell types in a pseudoplasmodium remains obscure, it must depend upon the transfer

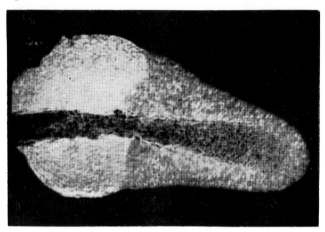

FIG. 13. An isolated *Dictyostelium mucoroides* cell mass composed of approximately equal proportions of prestalk and prespore cells. Following reorganization the isolate was stained with FAS. The prestalk cells did not stain cytoplasmically, apparently because of the presence of the prespore cells.

of information within the pseudoplasmodium (Bonner, 1957). Similar phenomena have been recognized in other systems. For example, an interacting system has been revealed in the green alga *Ulva mutabilis* Föyn (Lövlie, 1964) in which giant stem cells under certain conditions are capable of differentiating into blade cells. However, they are inhibited in

FIGS. 14–18. *Dictyostelium mucoroides.*

FIG. 14. Migrating pseudoplasmodium stained with normal fluorescent serum. Staining was negative in both cell types.

FIG. 15. Migrating pseudoplasmodium stained with *D. mucoroides* wild-type fluorescein-isothiocyanate labeled antiserum (FAS). Prestalk cells stained only on cell surfaces, but prespore cells were intensely stained cytoplasmically.

FIG. 16. An isolated prespore area following reorganization and staining with FAS. A margin of cytoplasmically unstained cells marks the differentiation of new prestalk cells.

FIG. 17. An isolated prestalk area from a migrating pseudoplasmodium following a period of reorganization. The isolate stained intensely with FAS in both prestalk and newly formed stalk cells.

FIG. 18. An MV migrating pseudoplasmodium stained with FAS. The prestalk area was not well defined and staining was irregular in intensity in the prespore area.

Figures 14–18 are reproduced from Gregg (1965).

14

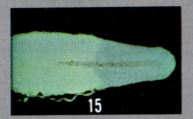
15

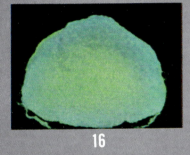
16

17

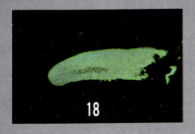
18

the attempt due to the presence of the blade cells. Also the synchronous nuclear divisions in the myxomycete *Physarum polycephalum* (Howard, 1932) and the regulation of size in *Amoeba proteus* must depend upon a coordinating mechanism (Prescott, 1955). At present the nature of the interactions between the cells of these various forms is unknown.

It is apparent, however, that either adjacent cell surfaces interact or materials are transferred across cell boundaries. Such interactions have been suggested by several investigators (Ennis and Sussman, 1958b; Filosa, 1962; M. Sussman, 1954; M. Sussman and Lee, 1955; R. R. Sussman and Sussman, 1953). Filosa (1962) determined that mutants ranging from aggregateless to fruitless forms, could be isolated from wild-type *D. mucoroides*. Kahn (1964b) and R. R. Sussman and Sussman (1953) produced a similar series of *Dictyostelium* mutants by ultraviolet irradiation. Mutant and wild-type cells were combined in various ways to determine the effect of cellular interaction on morphogenesis. When some mutants were combined with relatively small proportions of wild-type cells, the resulting fruiting bodies exhibited the wild-type phenotype (Filosa, 1962). In Kahn's experiments mixtures of an aggregateless mutant with the wild-type produced only wild-type upon plating out the spores. The conversion of these mutants to wild-type was attributed to either enzyme induction, epigenetic homeostasis, or cytoplasmic inheritance. If mutants are combined that are incapable of completing development alone, fruiting body formation occurs through synergistic action of the cells (M. Sussman and Lee, 1955). These authors attributed the ability of the mutants to complete morphogenesis to a mutual exchange of the necessary diffusible metabolites between adjacent cells. However, the cells in such preparations must be physically associated. When they interposed a thin agar membrane between wild-type myxamoebae and certain mutant types, the mutants were unable to complete morphogenesis.

During normal development of *Dictyostelium* or *Polysphondylium,* prestalk and prespore cells are associated. Possibly the differentiation of spore cells depends on an interaction with the prestalk cells. Gerisch (1961b), after studying the action of various chemical agents, concluded that differentiation of the two cell types does not depend on normal morphogenetic movements resulting in fruiting body formation. In Gerisch's experiments, stalk cell differentiation invariably occurred but was not necessarily accompanied by spore differentiation. Spore formation never occurred in the absence of stalk cell differentiation. Sonneborn et al. (1963) reported that a *D. discoideum* mutant, although capable of forming spores without fruiting body construction, synthesized both "spore" and "stalk" antigens. Thus, the possible biochemical effects of prestalk cells or cells producing stalk materials on spore differentiation have not been eliminated. It might be of interest to note, however, that a primitive slime mold, *Acytostelium leptosomum,* accomplishes spore differentiation and the construction of a noncellular cellulose stalk by secretory activity of the prespore cells alone (Raper and Quinlan, 1958). This does not contradict the possibility that more specialized slime molds accomplish differentiation by cellular interaction. How this association may affect the course of differentiation has yet to be assessed.

C. Distribution of Biochemical Properties

The two major cell types which occur in the pseudoplasmodium acquire characteristic biochemical properties. Physiological and biochemical heterogeneity accompany the differentiation of the cells. The following section is concerned with the variety and pattern of such heterogeneity in the pseudoplasmodium. Histological and histochemical techniques have yielded most of this information. Histochemical analyses revealed that the anterior prestalk area of *D. discoideum* has the greatest alkaline phosphatase (Bonner *et al.,* 1955; Krivanek, 1956) and 5'-nucleotidase activity (Krivanek and Krivanek, 1958). Considering the distribution of these enzymes there is a possibility that they are identical (Gezelius and Wright, 1965). The posterior, prespore area maintained high cytochrome oxidase and succinic dehydrogenase activity (Takeuchi, 1960). Nonstarch polysaccharides (Bonner *et al.,* 1955; Krivanek and Krivanek, 1958) are concentrated in this area which may partially account for the intense staining with fluorescent antisera (Takeuchi, 1963; Gregg, 1965).

A uniform distribution of amine oxidase, nonspecific dehydrogenases, lipase, acid polysaccharides, protein (Krivanek and Krivanek, 1958), and pentose nucleic acid occurs throughout the pseudoplasmodium (Bonner *et al.,* 1955).

In *Polysphondylium* a stalk is formed continuously as migration occurs. However, histological and histochemical observations disclosed that the remainder of the pseudoplasmodium is not separated into prestalk and prespore areas. The cells are apparently undifferentiated until those at the anterior tips form mature stalk cells followed by the differentiation of other cells into mature spores (Bonner *et al.,* 1955). Consequently, weak alkaline phosphatase activity and nonstarch polysaccharide staining are uniformly distributed in the undifferentiated cells.

During preculmination and just before culmination, the prestalk cells which are perpendicular to the stalk become particularly active in synthesis and secretion of PAS and acid polysaccharides (Bonner *et al.,* 1955; Krivanek and Krivanek, 1958) (Fig. 19). These cells are also high in alkaline phosphatase and contain relatively large quantities of RNA. Pre-

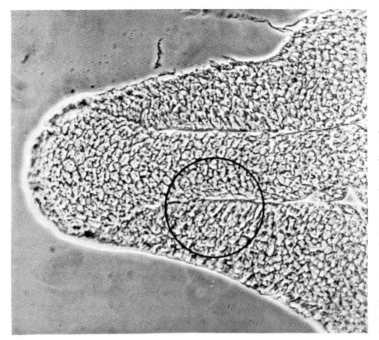
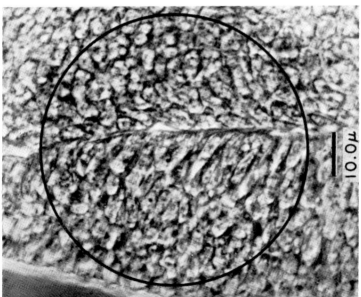

FIG. 19. Histological section of preculmination stage of *Dictyostelium discoideum* illustrating prestalk cells oriented perpendicularly to the stalk (phase microscopy).

stalk cells, just prior to becoming perpendicularly oriented, are high in 5'-nucleotidase activity (Krivanek and Krivanek, 1958). The activity of this enzyme may reflect the synthesis and consequent accumulation of RNA which appears when the cells become perpendicularly oriented.

In general during the culmination process in *D. discoideum* the prespores and prestalks retain the levels of substrates and enzymatic activities observed histochemically during migration.

Upon fruiting in *Dictyostelium* the mature stalk and spore cells show negligible alkaline phosphatase (Bonner *et al.*, 1955; Krivanek, 1956), amine oxidase, 5'-nucleotidase, and nonspecific dehydrogenase activity, as revealed by histochemical methods (Krivanek and Krivanek, 1958). On the other hand, Gezelius and Wright (1965) report that the maximum activity of alkaline phosphatase *in vitro* occurs in mature spores of *D. discoideum*. Lipase is high in activity in both spores and stalks while cytochrome oxidase activity was evident in only the spores (Krivanek and Krivanek, 1958). Polysaccharides, protein, and RNA were present in both spores and stalks although RNA had declined somewhat in the spores as compared to the stalks (Bonner *et al.*, 1955; Krivanek and Krivanek, 1958).

D. Summary

Slime mold myxamoebae are probably a homogeneous population. The appearance of acrasin secreting myxamoebae marks the beginning of functional heterogeneity in the cell population. Prestalk and prespore differentiation is initiated in the aggregate and is completed with the formation of a polarized migrating pseudoplasmodium. Although a wide range in size occurs in pseudoplasmodia the proportions of prestalk to prespore cells remain constant. The regulation of these proportions appears to depend upon an interaction between the cell types until an equilibrium is established. The evidence supporting cellular interactions is emphasized by the enhanced morphogenetic capacity of aggregateless strains combined with wild-type cells.

The prestalk and prespore cells are distinguishable by their particular biochemical entities and activities. This division of activities between the two cell types reflects the specialized tasks necessary in effecting the differentiation of the cells into mature stalks and spores. Apparently in *Dictyostelium* heterogeneity must be established prior to fruiting body construction when differentiation of the cells into stalks and spores occurs.

The heterogeneity observed in *Dictyostelium* does not occur in migrating pseudoplasmodia of *Polysphondylium*. This suggests that if a variety of biochemical changes are necessary to effect cell differentiation they must be accomplished in *Polysphondylium* immediately before stalk or spore formation.

V. CELL ADHESION AND MORPHOGENESIS

The cells of multicellular organisms tend to adhere. Otherwise unity of the organism would be lost and cellular interactions depending on the close association of the cells would be impossible. Cell adhesion appears to exist as a general phenomenon affecting a variety of cell types and functions. Wounds heal by the proliferation of cells which adhere through surface structures. Thus, the success of skin grafts depends on the adhesiveness between the host and the graft. Cell adhesion is responsible for the sorting out of dissociated vertebrate embryo cells into tissue-specific groups (Moscona, 1957) and for the reaggregation of sponge cells into species-specific aggregates (Spiegel, 1954a; H. V. Wilson, 1910). In addition Spiegel (1954b) provides evidence that selective cell adhesion may play a role in the development of amphibian embryos by assuring the association of tissues, such as mesoderm with endoderm and ectoderm. Fertilization is initiated by the interaction of specific substances present in eggs and sperm (Tyler, 1948) which affect adhesion between gametes. A decrease in adhesiveness relative to normal cells occurs in neoplastic squamous epithelial cells from carcinomas of the lip and cervix uteri (Coman, 1944). Thus, the possibility of invasiveness and metastasis is increased by the loss of mutual attraction.

How cells selectively associate and adhere is obscure, and several hypotheses have been advanced. Possibly cells adhere through forces similar to those existing in an antigen-antibody reaction (Tyler, 1947; Weiss, 1947). An intercellular cement, attached to each cell by specific bonds and divalent cations may effect adhesion in sponge cells (Humphreys, 1963).

In slime molds the myxamoebae change from an independent to a multicellular state by aggregation. The cells are in contact, and maintain close association throughout the morphogenetic process. A mechanism must exist which effects adhesion between the cells without restricting their morphogenetic movements. Thus, the slime molds present a system in which a normally nonadhesive stage is followed by an adhesive phase. The following evidence suggests that this change is accomplished by the acquisition of surface structures which appear at the onset of aggregation and persist until morphogenesis is completed.

A. Biological Criteria

From studies on several species of slime molds, Shaffer (1958) determined that vegetative myxamoebae adhere poorly if brought together. At aggregation, however, in the presence of acrasin the cells become strongly adhesive. The adhesive phenomenon, which Shaffer calls "integration," is considered important in aggregation and throughout morphogenesis. Gerisch (1964) observed that "integration" is accompanied by changes in the metachromatic granules in the aggregating cells. Consequently, he suggests these changes may be related to the ability of the cells to establish intercellular connections.

Electron microscopy has demonstrated that the plasma membranes of opposing cells of *D. discoideum* remain within approximately 200 Å of each other even though the movements of the cells result in convolution of the surface membranes (Mercer and Shaffer, 1960). This could probably occur only if adhesion existed between the cells.

It may be inferred from the experiments by Raper and Thom (1941) that cell adhesion occurs between the cells of developing slime molds. They combined myxamoebae of different species to determine the morphogenetic results. When *D. discoideum* and *D. purpureum* vegetative myxamoebae were mixed they formed fruiting bodies characteristic of their species. If the same two species were combined during the migrating stage, fruiting bodies composed of both species were formed. Regardless of the stage at which *D. discoideum* and *P. violaceum* cells were mixed, sorting out according to species invariably occurred so that communal fruiting bodies were not found.

Bonner and Adams (1958) examined the problem of cell mixtures in detail. They combined several species and strains of *Dictyostelium* in various combinations and then observed their responses. All strains of *Dictyostelium* responded to the same acrasin (Shaffer, 1953). It might be expected that acrasin action would produce a random distribution of cells of different species or strains forming a common fruiting body. Instead, depending on the particular mixture, the cells responded by sorting out completely to form separate fruiting bodies, a double fruiting body or a single mass containing spores grouped according to species. The fact that cells in these mixtures regrouped according to species or strains emphasizes the possibility that specific surface structures play a role in sorting out the cells. The varying degrees of morphogenetic compatibility observed in these species and strains of slime molds suggested that the cell surfaces may regulate this phenomenon (Bonner and Adams, 1958). However, they also considered the differential in rate of differentiation of these particular strains as a contributing factor in their results.

B. *Immunological Evidence*

Immunological techniques have been used to study the surfaces of the cells during development. Von Schuckmann (1925) and later Zaczynski (1951) demonstrated that antisera produced in rabbits to *Dictyostelium* myxamoebae caused agglutination of the cells. Gregg (1956, 1961), Sonneborn (1962), Takeuchi (1963), and Sonneborn *et al.* (1964), using various immunological techniques, found that new antigens or specific combining groups appear on the cell surfaces of strains of *Dictyostelium* and *Polysphondylium violaceum* during the transition from the vegetative myxamoebae to the migrating pseudoplasmodia.

The evidence suggests that the new antigens may play a role in the aggregation process. The species of *Dictyostelium* and *Polysphondylium* vegetative myxamoebae studied did not appear to have surface antigens in common as revealed by agglutination (Gregg, 1956) and fluorescent antibody techniques (Takeuchi, 1963). However, antigens in common appear as the time of aggregation is approached (Gregg, 1956) and as migrating pseudoplasmodia are formed (Takeuchi, 1963). Sonneborn (1962) and Sonneborn *et al.* (1964) contend that the "aggregation antigen" is functionally associated with aggregation because this process can be inhibited by antibodies to the antigen. Furthermore, immunological cross-specificity exists between "aggregation antigens" of *Dictyostelium.* Some species of *Dictyostelium* are capable of coaggregation. *Polysphondylium violaceum,* which will not form communal aggregates with *Dictyostelium,* showed little cross-specificity with *Dictyostelium* "aggregation antigen." Sonneborn (1962) and Sonneborn *et al.* (1964) reasoned that if "aggregation antigen" was somehow involved in aggregation, a series of aggregateless variants of *D. discoideum* might fail to develop this antigen. However, all but one of the aggregateless variants studied proved to synthesize "aggregation antigen" comparable to the wild type.

Gregg and Trygstad (1958) determined that defects in surface antigens existed in certain of the ultraviolet-induced aggregateless variants isolated by R. R. Sussman and Sussman (1953). Cells with such defects could not be agglutinated by wild-type antiserum and did not produce antiserum in rabbits capable of agglutinating wild-type cells. This failure might be attributed to the presence of aberrant surface antigens. Under these conditions cell adhesion would not be maintained and morphogenetic movements would be adversely affected.

Ennis (1957) determined that wild-type acrasin was produced by certain aggregateless variants. Consequently, in these instances developmental failure cannot be attributed to the absence of acrasin.

In addition to the adhesive and antigenic changes in cell surfaces on aggregation, another major change was observed upon differentiation into mature spores. In *D. discoideum* the adhesiveness of the spores and their ability to agglutinate in antisera were greatly reduced simultaneously (Gregg, 1960). The changes in these two characteristics were accompanied by large quantities of antigenic material appearing extracellularly around the spores, suggesting that adhesive material was loosely bound or eliminated from the cell surfaces at some phase of spore differentiation.

Raper (1956) observed that a single *D. polycephalum* pseudoplasmodium will produce several sorophores which maintain contact until culmination is three-fourths complete. At this point the sorophores diverge; this divergence results in the formation of separate fruiting bodies. Raper anticipated the existence of repellent substances which may account for this phenomenon. The repelling mechanism may be accompanied by a loss of adhesiveness in the mature spores which would tend to promote divergence of the fruiting bodies (Gregg, 1960).

C. Agents Inhibiting Adhesion

Among experiments designed to affect the cell surfaces of slime molds in order to determine the morphogenetic consequences are those of De Haan (1959) and Gerisch (1961b,c,d, 1962b). De Haan observed that aberrant loosely knit aggregates of *D. discoideum* myxamoebae and disaggregation of migrating pseudoplasmodia occurred in the presence of the chelating agent ethylenediaminetetraacetic acid (EDTA). He concluded that EDTA could inhibit normal intercellular adhesion. Gerisch (1961c) demonstrated that *Dictyostelium* cells prior to aggregation formed no groups, or groups of only a few cells, in the presence of EDTA. However, cells that were on the verge of aggregation were insensitive to the presence of EDTA and proceeded to aggregate. Gerisch (1961d) concluded that two forms of intercellular contacts existed during aggregation and migration. Thus, EDTA-insensitive bonds effect cell adhesion in the presence of EDTA. This emphasizes the importance of divalent ions, such as Ca^{++}, in cell adhesion processes, in addition to pointing out that an ion-independent mechanism may prevail during development of the cellular slime molds.

Whitfield (1964) conducted a study on the effect of proteolytic and other enzymes in disaggregating migrating pseudoplasmodia of *Dictyostelium* and *Polysphondylium*. Enzymes such as trypsin, pepsin, pancreatin, or cellulase were ineffective in dispersing the cells. Crystalline papain, however, was extremely active in disrupting the pseudoplasmodia. Considering the acid pH which was optimum for the splitting of peptides by papain, Whitfield suggests that intercellular adhesion may depend upon a polysaccharide in association with peptides instead of proteins. It is interesting to note in this connection the experiments of Gasic and Gasic (1962). In this instance neuramidase, which acts upon the mucopolysaccharide coating of cells, was injected intravenously into mice. When such mice were injected with ascites tumor cells a significant decrease in metastasis was observed as compared to animals not injected with the enzyme.

Gerisch (1961b) studied the effects of several chemicals on morphogenetic processes following aggregation. EDTA was found to cause aberrant fruiting structures although the cells differentiated into spores and stalks. Ethylurethan affected the cells in such a fashion that the spores in most of the fruiting bodies did not reach maturity. Furthermore, the positions of the two cell types in the fruiting body appeared to be inverted with respect to those of the normal fruiting body. Such inverted forms consisted of a stalk supporting a mature spore mass which was surrounded by stalk cells. Although cells of the stalk proper did not entirely differentiate into mature stalk cells, the cells which surrounded the spore mass were true stalk cells. Mercaptoethanol appeared to affect primarily the differentiation of the spores and, to a lesser degree, that of the stalk cells. This agent produced fruiting bodies which consisted of mature stalk cells and undifferentiated prespore cells. Gerisch (1962b) also noted that although mercaptoethanol tended to inhibit cell movement it had effects similar to EDTA on adhesion. Dinitrophenol inhibited cell movement but had little effect on cell adhesion.

Aggregation of *D. discoideum* myxamoebae can be inhibited by homologous antiaggregate serum absorbed by vegetative myxamoebae (Sonneborn, 1962; Sonneborn *et al.*, 1964). Such inhibition might occur through the blocking of surface antigens involved in morphogenetic movements.

D. Summary

There is no proof that the surface antigens involved in agglutination of myxamoebae by antisera are those involved in cell adhesion or other morphogenetic processes. However, the biological and immunological evidence indicates that during aggregation new surface antigens appear which promote adhesion between homologous cells and lead to the sorting out of cells of different strains or species. The normal complement of surface structures seems necessary because variants with aberrant cell surfaces fail to complete morphogenesis. Morphogenetic effects of chemical agents or specific antisera were considered to be caused by modifications or blockage of intercellular bonds. Consequently cell adhesion is regarded as necessary in promoting morphogenetic interactions, although nothing specifically is known of the dynamics of cell contacts and how they direct morphogenesis and differentiation. The loss of adhesion between mature spores of *D. discoideum* would be of selective advantage to the slime mold as spore dispersal would not be inhibited.

The adhesive material has yet to be identified although the evidence implicates substances like mucopolysaccharides.

VI. METABOLISM AND SYNTHESIS DURING DEVELOPMENT

The major growth phase of the slime molds ends with the initiation of aggregation resulting in a separation of the growth and morphogenetic phases of development. Since all food intake ceases at aggregation, endogenous substrates provide the only source of energy for the processes of morphogenesis. The cost in terms of dry weight loss during the growth and aggregation period was 26–40% of the initial weight of the vegetative myxamoebae (Liddel and Wright, 1961; White and Sussman, 1961). Loss during morphogenesis may range from 7 to 28% relative to the initial weight of the migrating pseudoplasmodium (Gregg and Bronsweig, 1956a; Liddel and Wright, 1961; White and Sussman, 1961). The extent to which this decrease in dry weight may be attributed solely to the loss of substrates by metabolism cannot be readily determined.

The discussion that follows concerns the metabolic and synthetic events which occur during the course of development. It is reasonable to assume that these physiological events reflect the demands of the slime molds during morphogenesis and cellular differentiation. An attempt is made to associate particular metabolic events with specific morphogenetic processes, although establishing causal relationships continues to be a major problem of developmental physiology.

A. *Respiratory Metabolism and Associated Enzymes*

Wright and Anderson (1958, 1959) determined that *D. discoideum* vegetative myxamoebae are facultative aerobes in that they will grow and undergo binary fission anaerobically. However, neither carbon dioxide nor acid production could be detected in vegetative myxamoebae, indicating a lack of glycolytic activity under anaerobic conditions (Takeuchi, 1960). Furthermore, all morphogenetic movements of *D. discoideum* are inhibited under anaerobic conditions or by metabolic inhibitors, such as KCN, which affect electron transport enzymes (Gregg, 1950; Takeuchi and Tazawa, 1955). Oxygen tension at a level sufficient to sustain aggregation did not allow migrating pseudoplasmodium formation (Takeuchi and Tazawa, 1955). Dinitrophenol, commonly believed to uncouple respiration from phosphorylation, was found to be highly inhibitory to aggregation (Hirschberg and Rusch, 1951; Takeuchi and Tazawa, 1955). Glycolytic system inhibitors, such as monoiodoacetic acid and sodium fluoride, except in high concentrations, did not suppress morphogenetic movements (Hirschberg and Rusch, 1950, 1951; Takeuchi and Tazawa, 1955). The insensitivity of *D. discoideum* to iodoacetic acid or sodium fluoride during morphogenesis may be attributed to a secondary metabolic pathway, the hexose monophosphate shunt (Wright and Bloom, 1961). Considering the effects of anaerobiosis and metabolic inhibitors, oxidative phosphorylations seem necessary for growth, morphogenetic movement, and cell differentiation.

Rates of oxygen consumption of *D. discoideum* during growth and morphogenetic stages were determined by Gregg (1950) and Liddel and Wright (1961). In Fig. 20 the results of these authors are compared.

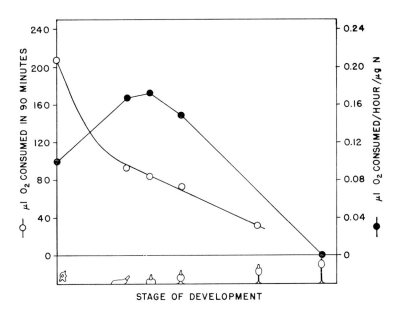

FIG. 20. Rate of oxygen consumption based on total N (derived from Gregg, 1950) and cell numbers (derived from Liddel and Wright, 1961).

There is disagreement concerning the change in rate of oxygen consumption during the transition from the vegetative myxamoebae to the migrating pseudoplasmodium. However, the fact that Liddel and Wright (1961) observed a decrease in rate may be attributed to a loss of cells during this period, through failure of synchronous aggregation or possibly lysis of the cells. They also attribute the decline in respiration during culmination to a "critical depletion of endogenous oxidizable substrates." However, development may be delayed by mechanically disrupting the migrating pseudoplasmodia. Despite the energy-consuming delay the cells are capable of continuing culmination. Furthermore, there is a close correlation between the rates of oxygen consumption and stalk formation during culmination (Gregg, 1950) (Fig. 21). This suggests that the decline in the rate of respiration may simply be due to a gradual loss of oxygen consuming cells as they differentiate into stalks and spores.

The increased rate of movement (Samuel, 1961) and oxygen tension requirements (Takeuchi and Tazawa, 1955) of the myxamoebae composing migrating pseudoplasmodia support the view that increased energy requirements parallel the morphogenetic stages.

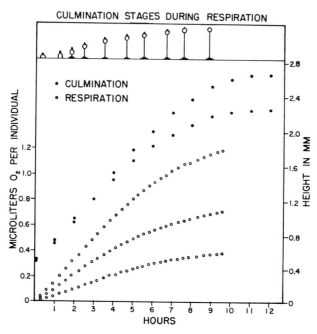

FIG. 21. Correlation between the rates of oxygen consumption and increase in height of individual *Dictyostelium discoideum* pseudoplasmodia during culmination. From Gregg (1950).

Bonner and Eldredge (1945) determined that the rate at which a *D. discoideum* pseudoplasmodium culminates to form a fruiting body depends on its size. They proved that a pseudoplasmodium twice the size of its neighbor would culminate at 30–35% greater rate. They related the delay in morphogenetic rate observed in a smaller pseudoplasmodium to the relatively greater adhesive force existing between the smaller prespore mass and its stalk. The oxygen consumption of pseudoplasmodia of various sizes proved to be identical per unit mass of tissue (Gregg, 1950). Thus, small pseudoplasmodia do not increase their rate of energy output to overcome the adhesive force that results in morphogenetic delay. However, the increased time required for the smaller slime molds to culminate results in a greater total energy expenditure per unit of morphogenetic work per unit mass of tissue. This interpretation was presented first by Tyler (1942) in explanation of similar morphogenetic and metabolic phenomena exhibited by dwarf sea urchin eggs.

During certain stages of development in *D. discoideum* several metabolic changes have been observed. Wright and Anderson (1958) investigated the biochemical mechanisms to which oxygen consumption and the metabolism of the major substrates might be attributed. They determined that malic and 6-phosphogluconic dehydrogenases increased in activity during the transition from the vegetative myxamoebae to the migrating pseudoplasmodia. Malic dehydrogenase (DPN-specific) declined in activity after the completion of culmination. Other enzymes, including isocitric dehydrogenase, glucose 6-phosphate dehydrogenase, glutamic dehydrogenase, and glutamic-pyruvic transminase, do not vary significantly in activity during development (Wright, 1960). Wright (1960, 1963) and Wright *et al.* (1964) suggest that the levels of endogenous substrates available at certain stages could result in enzyme inhibition or activation. Consequently metabolic pathways could be favored or inhibited, thereby determining the course of cell differentiation. As an example of this phenomenon Wright and Bard (1963) report that although glutamic acid oxidation *in vivo* increases during culmination it is due to a rise in the level of glutamic acid rather than to an increase in glutamic acid dehydrogenase. Thus, an increase in the substrate effected an increase in enzyme activity. Gezelius and Wright (1963) emphasize that *in vitro* experiments, such as analyses of alkaline phosphatase activity, do not necessarily reflect the activity of the enzyme *in vivo* as a result of the influence of substrate concentration.

Takeuchi (1960) studied the activities of succinic dehydrogenase and cytochrome oxidase quantitatively during the development of *D. mucoroides*. Succinic dehydrogenase activity began to rise during "interphase" and increased about fourfold at the time of formation of migrating pseudoplasmodia. Cytochrome oxidase activity was highest during the vegetative stage but dropped about 50% during "interphase" and remained at this level through aggregation and migration. Takeuchi attributed the decline in cytochrome oxidase activity to the possibility that it may not be the terminal oxidase in slime mold respiration.

B. Protein and Nucleoprotein Utilization

Protein breakdown was negligible in *D. discoideum* during transition from the vegetative myxamoebae to the migrating pseudoplasmodium (Gregg *at al.*, 1954), which may explain why antimetabolites were ineffective in inhibiting myxamoebae throughout the aggregation period (Hirschberg and Merson, 1955a,b; Kostellow, 1956). However, during the culmination process certain protein fractions decreased by approximately 50% relative to the initial amount in the migrating pseudoplasmodia. Separate analyses of the spores and stalks revealed that the greatest protein metabolism occurred in the prestalks during culmination (Gregg et al., 1954).

White and Sussman (1961) revealed that total protein decreased by approximately 72% during the course of development in wild-type *D. discoideum* as well as two aggregateless mutants and one fruitless mutant.

A variety of amino acids and antimetabolites was found to have inhibitory effects during culmination (Filosa, 1960; Hirschberg and Merson, 1955a,b). Kostellow (1956) determined that arginine affects the proportions of the fruiting body in that the spore mass is abnormally large relative to the stalk length. She attributes the effect of arginine to the high protein metabolism in the prestalk cells during culmination. Thus, the cells may synthesize abnormal proteins, resulting in an irregular structural organization. The permeability of *D. mucoroides* cells to *l*-arginine is relatively low, suggesting that the toxic effect of arginine may be directed at the cell surfaces (Faust and Filosa, 1959). Glucose did not prevent the morphogenetic effects of antimetabolites, consequently the interference was not due to the lack of an energy source (Kostellow, 1956). Although inhibitory effects were recorded for the action of ethionine on *D. discoideum,* Filosa (1960) observed that it did not affect *D. mucoroides.* Furthermore, ethionine promoted fruiting body formation in a *D. mucuroides* mutant which normally was arrested at culmination. Ethionine is known to inhibit the formation of disulfide bonds, an inhibition suggesting that the morphogenetic failure of the mutant may be associated with such linkages. Maintenance of cell division and prevention of abnormal filamentous forms of the yeast *Candida albicans* may depend upon an enzyme system which catalyzes the reduction of disulfide bonds to sulfhydryl groups (Nickerson and Mankowski, 1953; Nickerson and Romano, 1952; Romano and Nickerson, 1954).

Little is known concerning the synthesis of specific proteins during development. Solomon et al. (1964) have reported that additional acid and alkaline phosphatase and nonspecific esterase isozymes are synthesized during the morphogenetic stages. There is no indication, however, that the antimetabolites are affecting the synthesis of those particular enzymes. Protein synthesis during the preculmination stage was found to be inhibited by 2,4-dinitrophenol, emphasizing the necessity for normal metabolism in this process (Wright and Anderson, 1960).

Krivanek (1964) analyzed *D. discoideum* during development for RNA and DNA content. RNA increased about fourfold during the transition from vegetative myxamoebae to migrating pseudoplasmodia. During culmination the RNA decreased to the level observed in the vegetative myxamoebae. DNA content did not change during the entire developmental period. White and Sussman (1961) found, however, that RNA is metabolized throughout development in wild-type *D. discoideum* as well as in certain aggregateless and fruitless mutants of the same species.

The differences observed in RNA metabolism are difficult to explain. In view of the variety of syntheses known to begin following aggregation it should not be surprising that an increase in RNA content occurs simultaneously. It seems plausible that later the RNA content would decrease when vacuolated stalk and dormant spores have differentiated.

C. Carbohydrate and Lipid Syntheses

The formation of a fruiting body in the slime mold consists of the gradual conversion of certain cells into a basal disk and a slender stalk which must support a spore mass.

The myxamoebae and spores of *Dictyostelium* and *Acytostelium leptosomum* have double cell membranes or cell walls. The purified stalk substance of *A. leptosomum* and the outer stalk sheath of *Dictyostelium* appears to be cellulose (Gezelius, 1959). The cellulose sorophore sheath is synthesized during culmination and provides a supporting matrix surrounding the stalk (Gezelius and Ranby, 1957; Mühlethaler, 1956; Raper and Fennell, 1952). Krivanek (1956) provides evidence that alkaline phosphatase activity is intimately involved in the synthesis of the sheath. Therefore, carbohydrate appears to be a necessity in structural morphogenetic processes.

Clegg and Filosa (1961) report that the disaccharide trehalose constitutes 7% of the dry weight of *D. mucoroides* spores and serves as an energy source during germination.

Krichevsky and Wright (1961, 1963) consider glucose to be the primary energy source in maintaining the rate at which morphogenetic processes occur. Amino acids which provide an energy source enter the Krebs cycle primarily by conversion into glutamic acid which is subsequently oxidized (Brühmüller and Wright, 1963). Both glucose and histidine enhance the amino acid uptake by the cells. Consequently, protein synthesis is stimulated; this results in the increase observed in the rate of differentiation (Krichevsky and Wright, 1963).

Reserves of carbohydrates remain fairly constant (White and Sussman, 1961) or are increased during the transition from the vegetative myxamoebae to the mature sorocarp (Gregg and Bronsweig, 1956b). The latter authors suggest that protein metabolism, which is particularly high in the prestalk cells, provides intermediates from which carbohydrates may be synthesized. The deamination of glutamic acid and other amino acids may provide Krebs cycle intermediates later involved in carbohydrate synthesis (Krivanek and Krivanek, 1959). These authors also consider that transamination is involved in the conversion of protein to carbohydrate (Krivanek and Krivanek, 1965).

At the beginning of a series of studies on polysaccharides, White and Sussman (1961) fractionated *Dictyostelium* cells during development and showed that two polysaccharide components appeared at the onset of stalk construction. Certain mutant strains of *D. mucoroides,* known as glassy and curly, which form stalks also produce these polysaccharides. Aggregateless and fruitless *D. discoideum* mutants fail to produce either stalks or polysaccharides.

Subsequent research by White and Sussman (1963a,b) on *Dictyostelium* and *Polysphondylium* characterized further the polysaccharides which are synthesized during development. Three major components have been separated two of which are water-soluble glucose polymers and the third a water-soluble acid mucopolysaccharide(s). The mucopolysaccharide was antigenic and could be quantitatively estimated by complement fixation using antispore immune serum. It first appears during the transition of the aggregates into migrating pseudoplasmodia. It continues to be synthesized during culmination, finally comprising 1–2% of the dry weight of the fruiting body (Fig. 22). Acid mucopolysaccharides are composed of

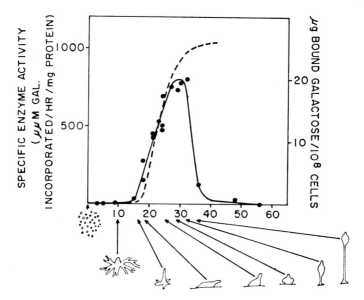

Fig. 22. Correlation between UDP-galactose transferase (solid line) and mucopolysaccharide synthesis (dashed line). Abscissa: time in hours after deposition of myxamoebae on nonnutrient agar. From M. Sussman and Osborn (1964).

galactose, galactosamine, and galacturonic acid. One of the important steps in the preparation of galactose for incorporation into mucopolysaccharide is indicated by the accompanying reaction sequence (Kleiner and Orten, 1962).

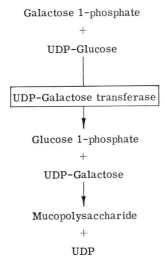

Additional reactions convert UDP-galactose into the other two mucopolysaccharide constituents galactosamine and galacturonic acid.

The activity of UDP-galactose polysaccharide transferase in cell free extracts of *D. discoideum* has been correlated with the synthesis of the polysaccharide (M. Sussman and Osborn, 1964) (Fig. 22). UDP-glucose synthetase also becomes active during the migration stage but declines in the mature sorocarps (Wright and Anderson, 1958). While UDP-glucose may be involved in polysaccharide synthesis, recent evidence suggests that it does not act as the glucosyl donor in cellulose formation in green plants (Aronson, 1965). UDP-galactose transferase commences activity at the time of migrating pseudoplasmodium formation and reaches a maximum just prior to the completion of mature sorocarps. Shortly after the completion of fruiting the enzyme begins to be excreted and consequently the activity declines steadily until it reaches negligible levels (M. Sussman and Lovgren, 1965). This apparently preferential release may be triggered by the synthesis of a protease which is discharged simultaneously with other enzymes no longer necessary in development (M. Sussman and Sussman, 1966).

The appearance and disappearance of UDP-galactose transferase depends upon the synthesis of RNA. Actinomycin D, which inhibits DNA-dependent RNA synthesis prevented the accumulation of the enzyme and, consequently, mucopolysaccharide synthesis. The relatively short actinomycin-sensitive period which begins during aggregation and persists into migration suggests that all messenger RNA synthesis for this enzyme is accomplished during this period (M. Sussman and Sussman, 1966). If Actidione, which inhibits protein synthesis, was added at the beginning of the actinomycin-sensitive period the synthesis of UDP-galactose transferase and its disappearance were prevented. The failure of the enzyme to disappear was considered to be associated with inhibition of protease synthesis (M. Sussman, 1965).

Mutant strains of *D. discoideum* which do not form stalks or spores neither synthesize mucopolysaccharide nor have transferase activity (White and Sussman, 1963b; M. Sussman and Osborn, 1964). Although the reason for the developmental failure is not apparent it could result from a mutation affecting the pathway of mucopolysaccharide synthesis. It is known that in *Salmonella* a mutation exists which prevents the synthesis of UDP-galactose 4-epimerase and, consequently, lipopolysaccharide synthesis in the cell walls (Nikaido, 1962).

The *D. discoideum* mutant, Fr-17, which forms stalks and spores which are arranged in an amorphous mass of cells, synthesized both transferase and polysaccharides. Differentiation and synthesis both occur at an accelerated rate in the mutant as compared to the wild type. This is considered to reflect disorder in the control mechanism initiating transferase synthesis rather than a gene mutation (Sonneborn *et al.*, 1963; White and Sussman, 1963b; M. Sussman and Osborn, 1964).

Davidoff and Korn (1962a), in an analysis of the lipids of *D. discoideum*, found that the fatty acid composition of the wild type and of an aggregateless mutant was identical. In a further series of investigations they have been concerned with the pathways through which the aggregateless mutant converts saturated fatty acids to unsaturated ones (Davidoff and Korn, 1962b, 1963a). The production of acetate from saturated fatty acids is used to form long-chain fatty acids, such as palmitate. Palmitate and stearate, both saturated fatty acids, are converted directly to unsaturated types. Although little is known about lipid metabolism in the slime molds, it is suggested that the short-chain fatty acids serve as a source of carbon and energy whereas the longer chains are synthesized into lipids (Davidoff and Korn, 1963b; Davidoff, 1964).

Some of the cellular slime molds are pigmented, the spore masses of *Dictyostelium purpureum* being purple while those of *D. discoideum* are yellow (Whittingham and Raper, 1956; Staples, 1964). The synthesis of these pigments may be inhibited by phenol and diphenylamine, respectively. Consequently, the yellow pigment has been identified as a carotenoid. However, the role of pigment synthesis in development is obscure.

The extent of protein (Gregg *et al.*, 1954), nucleoprotein (White and

Sussman, 1961), and lipid metabolism (Krivanek and Krivanek, 1958) which occurs, particularly in prestalk cells, suggests that these substrates are metabolized for energy and to provide the necessary intermediates for polysaccharide synthesis during stalk formation.

Protein, nucleoprotein metabolism, and the fatty acid composition of wild-type and mutant forms are not significantly different. However, in view of the correlation between defective polysaccharide synthesis and developmental abnormalities, White and Sussman (1961) contend that carbohydrate metabolism may be intimately linked with morphogenetic events.

D. Antigen Synthesis and Fate

One of the characteristics of a differentiated cell is its particular molecular specificity. The acquisition of such specificity depends on synthetic processes during development. Immunological techniques have provided a sensitive means of studying the ontogenetic changes in antigens or specific combining groups. The wealth of data available emphasizes that complements of antigens in a variety of organisms tend to change during the course of development. The objective of such studies is to causally relate specific antigens with particular morphological events. The reader is referred to reviews by Ebert (1952, 1958) and Tyler (1955) for comprehensive accounts of this general subject.

Immunoelectrophoretic evidence discloses that a total of 19 antigens or specific combining groups occur in *D. discoideum* during its life cycle. The numbers of antigens increase from 9 to 12 during the transition from vegetative myxamoebae to mature spores. Of these 12 antigens, however, only 4 have common specificity with the vegetative myxamoebae. This may be attributed to the alteration or destruction of certain antigens during the course of development (Gregg, 1961) (Table I). The evidence for

TABLE I
ANTIGEN CHANGES IN *Dictyostelium discoideum* DURING DEVELOPMENT DETERMINED BY IMMUNOELECTROPHORESIS

Antigen[a]	Antigens shared, synthesized, and destroyed
VA	1 2 3 4 5 6 7 8 9
MP	4 5 6 7 8 9 10 11 12 13
MS	6 7 8 9 10 11 14 15 16 17 18 19

[a] VA: vegetative myxamoebae; MP: migrating pseudoplasmodia; MS: mature spores.

these periodic antigenic changes is supported by studies with flourescent antisera on *Dictyostelium*. These observations reveal that cytoplasmic antigens are lost upon the differentiation of prestalk cells during pseudoplasmodium formation. Simultaneously new antigens appear in the prespore cells (Takeuchi, 1963; Gregg, 1965). The synthesis of a relatively large variety of antigens would be expected in view of the distribution of polyribosome sizes in *Polysphondylium pallidum* vegetative myxamoebae. These polysomes are composed of up to 20–30 ribosome clusters which is characteristic of certain mammalian cells engaged in the synthesis of many types of proteins (Phillips *et al.*, 1964).

Sonneborn (1962) and Sonneborn *et al.* (1964) determined immunologically in *D. discoideum* that four major antigens appear and persist during development. A "myxamoebae antigen" was detected in all stages of development except in the mature spores. An "aggregation antigen" appeared and increased in concentration between the stationary growth period and aggregation. The level of this antigen did not change significantly during the migration stage but appeared in the mature stalks in greater quantity than in the mature spores. "Stalk antigen" and "spore antigen" appeared at the migration stage, increased with the fruiting stage, and accumulated in stalks and spores. These two antigens did not appear in mutants of *D. discoideum* which were unable to form migrating pseudoplasmodia. The mutants capable of beginning the transition between the migrating pseudoplasmodia and the mature sorocarp contained detectable amounts of spore and stalk antigen. One mutant able to form mature spores without constructing sorocarps produced spore and stalk antigen quantitatively similar to the wild type. The *Dictyostelium mucoroides* mutant MV, which is characterized by producing small spore masses supported by short stalks, exhibits an aberrant staining pattern with fluorescent antisera (Gregg, 1965) (Fig. 15). Consequently, these morphological defects may be associated with a failure in synthesizing protein or polysaccharide antigens.

It appears from these investigations that antigen synthesis and change parallel morphogenesis and cell differentiation in the slime molds (Gregg, 1961; Sonneborn, 1962; Sonneborn *et al.*, 1964). However, the problem of attributing certain developmental processes to specific antigens has not been solved.

E. Summary

Oxidative phosphorylations provide the energy for growth and morphogenesis in certain slime molds, considering the inhibitory effects of anaerobiosis and certain enzyme poisons. Evidence from many sources suggests that the energy requirements increase during the morphogenetic phase of development. During this period differentiation of the stalk and spore cells is paralleled by increased activity of enzymes concerned with polysaccharide synthesis. Carbohydrate levels remain high, sustained possibly by a high rate of protein metabolism, particularly in the prestalk cells which must synthesize a cellulose sorophore sheath.

Immunological studies reveal the synthesis of new protein or polysaccharide antigens during development. The synthesis of mucopolysaccharide as a structural component of the fruiting body suggests that carbohydrate metabolism is causally involved in morphogenetic processes and cell differentiation. However, proteins appear to be closely involved in differentiation considering the morphogenetic defects caused by amino acids and antimetabolites. While Wright (1964) correctly points out that differentiation depends upon a multiplicity of reactions, it will continue to be of considerable interest to reveal the terminal events which effect form changes and cell transformations.

VII. GENERAL CONCLUSIONS

Although cellular slime molds could survive indefinitely as independent free-living vegetative myxamoebae or by encysting, normally they enter a more complex state of development by aggregating to form a multicellular organism. Aggregation occurs in response to a chemotactic substance, acrasin, which affects the rate of movement and orientation of the myxamoebae. Obviously, subsequent developmental progress is contingent upon a series of cellular interactions. Consequently, surface structures appear at aggregation which assure the intimate associations necessary to promote cellular interactions. In the process of forming a pseudoplasmodium two cell types, prestalk and prespore, differentiate and may be distinguished by their morphological and biochemical properties. The morphogenetic movements and subsequent transformation of these cells result in the formation of a mature sorocarp or fruiting body. A fruiting body is composed of a slender stalk which supports a mass of spore cells. A major event in culmination appears to be the synthesis of polysaccharide as a structural entity in the mature stalks and spores. The evidence suggests that the endogenous protein, nucleoprotein, and lipids may provide intermediates necessary in polysaccharide synthesis. The processes of growth and morphogenesis are sustained by aerobic metabolism. However, respiration declines to a negligible level following the completion of fruiting body construction.

Although a sequential synthesis and loss of antigens and enzymes occurs in the cells during morphogenesis, irreversible changes are not apparent prior to their final transformation into mature stalks and spores. Thus, prestalk and prespore cells can be induced experimentally to differentiate into the opposite cell type, emphasizing the lability of the genetic mechanism which must be responsible for their conversion. These phenomena suggest that cellular differentiation in the slime molds depends upon gradual and reversible processes rather than abrupt and final events.

ACKNOWLEDGMENTS

The author is indebted to Miss Kathleen Kelley and Mr. John Funk for research and clerical assistance during the preparation of this review.

REFERENCES

Allen, J. R., S. H. Hutner, E. Goldstone, J. J. Lee, and M. Sussman. (1963). Culture of the acrasian *Polysphondylium pallidum* WS-320 in defined media. *J. Protozool.* 10:Suppl., 13.

Aronson, J. M. (1965). In "The Fungi" (G. C. Ainsworth and A. S. Sussman, eds.), Vol. I, Chapter 3. Academic Press, New York.

Blaskovics, J. C., and K. B. Raper. (1957). Encystment stages of *Dictyostelium*. *Biol. Bull.* 113:58-88.

Bonner, J. T. (1944). A descriptive study of the development of the slime mold *Dictyostelium discoideum*. *Am. J. Botany* 31:175-182.

Bonner, J. T. (1947). Evidence for the formation of cell aggregates by chemotaxis in the development of the slime mold *Dictyostelium discoideum*. *J. Exptl. Zool.* 106:1-26.

Bonner, J. T. (1949). The demonstration of acrasin in the later stages of the development of the slime mold *Dictyostelium discoideum*. *J. Exptl. Zool.* 110:259-271.

Bonner, J. T. (1950). Observations on polarity in the slime mold *Dictyostelium discoideum*. *Biol. Bull.* 99:143-151.

Bonner, J. T. (1952). The pattern of differentiation in amoeboid slime molds. *Am. Naturalist* 86:79-89.

Bonner, J. T. (1957). A theory of the control of differentiation in the cellular slime molds. *Quart. Rev. Biol.* 32:232-246.

Bonner, J. T. (1959a). "The Cellular Slime Molds," 150 pp. Princeton Univ. Press, Princeton, New Jersey.

Bonner, J. T. (1959b). Differentiation of social amoebae. *Sci. Am.* 201:152-162.

Bonner, J. T. (1960). In "Developing Cell Systems and Their Control" (D. Rudnick, ed.), 18th Growth Symposium, pp. 3-20. Ronald Press, New York.

Bonner, J. T., and M. S. Adams. (1958). Cell mixtures of different species and strains of cellular slime molds. *J. Embryol. Exptl. Morphol.* 6:346-356.

Bonner, J. T., and M. R. Dodd. (1962a). Evidence for gas-induced orientation in the cellular slime molds. *Develop. Biol.* 5:344-361.

Bonner, J. T., and M. R. Dodd. (1962b). Aggregation territories in the cellular slime molds. *Biol. Bull.* 122:13-24.

Bonner, J. T., and D. Eldredge, Jr. (1945). A note on the rate of morphogenetic movement in the slime mold *Dictyostelium discoideum*. *Growth* 9:287-297.

Bonner, J. T., and E. B. Frascella. (1952). Mitotic activity in relation to differentiation in the slime mold *Dictyostelium discoideum*. *J. Exptl. Zool.* 121:561-571.

Bonner, J. T., and E. B. Frascella. (1953). Variation in cell size during the development of the slime mold *Dictyostelium discoideum*. *Biol. Bull.* 104:297-300.

Bonner, J. T., and M. E. Hoffman. (1963). Evidence for a substance responsible for the spacing pattern of aggregation and fruiting in the cellular slime molds. *J. Embryol. Exptl. Morphol.* 2:571-589.

Bonner, J. T., and M. J. Shaw. (1957). The role of humidity in the differentiation of the cellular slime molds. *J. Cellular Comp. Physiol.* 50:145-154.

Bonner, J. T., and F. E. Whitfield. (1965). The relation of sorocarp size to phototaxis in the cellular slime mold *Dictyostelium purpureum*. *Biol. Bull.* **128**:51-57.
Bonner, J. T., P. G. Koontz, Jr., and D. Paton. (1953). Size in relation to the rate of migration in the slime mold *Dictyostelium discoideum*. *Mycologia* **45**:235-240.
Bonner, J. T., A. D. Chiquoine, and M. Q. Kolderie. (1955). A histochemical study of differentiation in the cellular slime molds. *J. Exptl. Zool.* **130**:133-158.
Bonner, J. T., A. P. Kelso, and R. G. Gillmor. (1966). A new approach to the problem of aggregation in the cellular slime molds. *Biol. Bull.* **130**:28-42.
Bradley, S. G., and M. Sussman. (1952). Growth of amoeboid slime molds in one membered cultures. *Arch. Biochem. Biophys.* **39**:462-463.
Brühmüller, M., and B. Wright. (1963). Glutamate oxidation in the differentiating slime mold. II. Studies *in vitro*. *Biochim. Biophys. Acta* **71**:50-57.
Buller, A. H. R. (1900). Contributions to our knowledge of the physiology of the spermatozoa of ferns. *Ann. Botany (London)* **14**:543-582.
Clegg, J. S., and M. F. Filosa. (1961). Trehalose in the cellular slime mold *Dictyostelium mucoroides*. *Nature* **192**:1077-1078.
Coman, D. R. (1940). Additional observations on positive and negative chemotaxis: Experiments with a myxomycete. *A.M.A. Arch. Pathol.* **29**:220-228.
Coman, D. R. (1944). Decreased mutual adhesiveness, a property of cells from squamous cell carcinomas. *Cancer Res.* **4**:625-629.
Davidoff, F. (1964). The metabolism of 9(10)-hydroxystearic acid by the cellular slime mold, *Dictyostelium discoideum*. *Biochim. Biophys. Acta* **90**:414-416.
Davidoff, F., and E. D. Korn. (1962a). Lipids of *Dictyostelium discoideum*: Phospholipid composition and the presence of two new fatty acids: cis, cis-5, 11-octadecadienoic and cis, cis-5, 9-hexadecadienoic acids. *Biochem. Biophys. Res. Commun.* **9**:54-58.
Davidoff, F., and E. D. Korn. (1962b). Further studies on the biosynthesis of fatty acids in the cellular slime mold. *Biochem. Biophys. Res. Commun.* **9**:328-333.
Davidoff, F., and E. D. Korn. (1963a). Fatty acid and phospholipid composition of the cellular slime mold, *Dictyostelium discoideum*. The occurrence of previously undescribed fatty acids. *J. Biol. Chem.* **238**:3199-3209.
Davidoff, F., and E. D. Korn. (1963b). The biosynthesis of fatty acids in the cellular slime mold, *Dictyostelium discoideum*. *J. Biol. Chem.* **238**:3210-3215.
De Haan, R. L. (1959). The effects of the chelating agent ethylenediamine tetraacetic acid on cell adhesion in the slime mould *Dictyostelium discoideum*. *J. Embryol. Exptl. Morphol.* **7**:335-343.
Ebert, J. D. (1952). Appearance of tissue-specific proteins during development. *Ann. N.Y. Acad. Sci.* **55**:67-84.
Ebert, J. D. (1958). *In* "Embryonic Nutrition" (D. Rudnick, ed.), pp. 54-109. Univ. of Chicago Press, Chicago, Illinois.
Ennis, H. L. (1957). A comparative study of the aggregateless mutants of the cellular slime mold. Ph.D. thesis, Northwestern University.
Ennis, H. L., and M. Sussman. (1958a). The initiator cell for slime mold aggregation. *Proc. Natl. Acad. Sci. U.S.* **44**:401-411.
Ennis, H. L., and M. Sussman. (1958b). Synergistic morphogenesis by mixtures of *Dictyostelium discoideum* wild-type and aggregateless mutants. *J. Gen. Microbiol.* **18**:433-449.
Faust, R. G., and M. F. Filosa. (1959). Permeability studies on the amoebae of the slime mold, *Dictyostelium mucoroides*. *J. Cellular Comp. Physiol.* **54**:297-298.

Filosa, M. F. (1960). The effects of ethionine on the morphogenesis of cellular slime molds. *Anat. Record* **138**:348.
Filosa, M. F. (1962). Heterocytosis in cellular slime molds. *Am. Naturalist* **96**:79-91.
Francis, D. W. (1964). Some studies on phototaxis of *Dictyostelium*. *J. Cellular Comp. Physiol.* **64**:131-138.
Gasic, G., and T. Gasic. (1962). Removal of sialic acid from the cell coat in tumor cells and vascular endothelium, and its effects on metastasis. *Proc. Natl. Acad. Sci. U.S.* **48**:1172-1177.
Gerisch, G. (1961a). Zellfunktionen und Zellfunktionswechsel in der Entwicklung von *Dictyostelium discoideum*. II. Aggregation homogener Zellpopulationen und Zentrenbildung. *Develop. Biol.* **3**:685-724.
Gerisch, G. (1961b). Zellfunktionen und Zellfunktionswechsel in der Entwicklung von *Dictyostelium discoideum*. III. Getrennte Beeinflussung von Zelldifferenzierung und Morphogenese. *Arch. Entwicklungsmech. Organ.* **153**:158-167.
Gerisch, G. (1961c). Zellkontaktbildung vegetativer und aggregations-reifer Zellen von *Dictyostelium discoideum*. *Naturwissenschaften* **48**:436-437.
Gerisch, G. (1961d). Zellfunktionen und Zellfunktionswechsel in der Entwicklung von *Dictyostelium discoideum*. V. Stadienspezifische Zellkontaktbildung und ihre quantitative Erfassung. *Exptl. Cell Res.* **25**:535-554.
Gerisch, G. (1962a). Zellfunktionen und Zellfunktionswechsel in der Entwicklung von *Dictyostelium discoideum*. IV. Der Zeitplan der Entwicklung. *Arch. Entwicklungsmech. Organ.* **153**:603-620.
Gerisch, G. (1962b). Zellfunktionen und Zellfunktionswechsel in der Entwicklung von *Dictyostelium discoideum*. VI. Inhibitoren der Aggregation, ihr Einfluss auf Zellkontaktbildung und morphogenetische Bewegung. *Exptl. Cell Res.* **26**:462-484.
Gerisch, G. (1964). Die Bildung des Zellverbandes bei *Dictyostelium minutum*. I. Übersicht über die Aggregation und die Funktionswechsel der Zellen. *Arch. Entwicklungsmech. Organ.* **155**:342-357.
Gezelius, K. (1959). The ultrastructure of cells and cellulose membranes in Acrasiae. *Exptl. Cell Res.* **18**:425-453.
Gezelius, K. (1962). Growth of the cellular slime mold *Dictyostelium discoideum* on dead bacteria in liquid media. *Physiol. Plantarum* **15**:587-592.
Gezelius, K., and B. G. Ranby. (1957). Morphology and fine structure of the slime mold *Dictyostelium discoideum*. *Exptl. Cell Res.* **12**:265-289.
Gezelius, K., and B. E. Wright. (1963). Alkaline phosphatase and inorganic phosphate in *Dictyostelium discoideum*. *Bacteriol. Proc.* p. 48.
Gezelius, K., and B. E. Wright. (1965). Alkaline phosphatase in *Dictyostelium discoideum*. *J. Gen. Microbiol.* **38**:309-327.
Gregg, J. H. (1950). Oxygen utilization in relation to growth and morphogenesis of the slime mold *Dictyostelium discoideum*. *J. Exptl. Zool.* **114**:173-196.
Gregg, J. H. (1956). Serological investigations of cell adhesion in the slime molds, *Dictyostelium discoideum*, *Dictyostelium purpureum* and *Polysphondylium violaceum*. *J. Gen. Physiol.* **39**:813-820.
Gregg, J. H. (1960). Surface antigen dynamics in the slime mold, *Dictyostelium discoideum*. *Biol. Bull.* **118**:70-78.
Gregg, J. H. (1961). An immunoelectrophoretic study of the slime mold *Dictyostelium discoideum*. *Develop. Biol.* **3**:757-766.
Gregg, J. H. (1964). Developmental processes in cellular slime molds. *Physiol. Rev.* **44**:631-656.
Gregg, J. H. (1965). Regulation in the cellular slime molds. *Develop. Biol.* **12**:377-393.

Gregg, J. H., and R. D. Bronsweig. (1956a). Dry weight loss during culmination of the slime mold *Dictyostelium discoideum*. *J. Cellular Comp. Physiol.* **47**:483-487.

Gregg, J. H., and R. D. Bronsweig. (1956b). Biochemical events accompanying stalk formation in the slime mold *Dictyostelium discoideum*. *J. Cellular Comp. Physiol.* **48**:293-299.

Gregg, J. H., and C. W. Trygstad. (1958). Surface antigen defects contributing to developmental failure in aggregateless variants of the slime mold *Dictyostelium discoideum*. *Exptl. Cell Res.* **15**:358-369.

Gregg, J. H., A. L. Hackney, and J. O. Krivanek. (1954). Nitrogen metabolism of the slime mold *Dictyostelium discoideum* during growth and morphogenesis. *Biol. Bull.* **107**:226-235.

Grobstein, C. (1961). Passage of radioactivity into a membrane filter from spinal cord pre-incubated with tritiated amino acids or nucleosides. *Colloq. Intern. Cult. Organo-typique* **101**:169-182.

Grobstein, C. (1963). *In* "The Nature of Biological Diversity" (J. M. Allen, ed.), pp. 223-241. McGraw-Hill, New York.

Heftmann, E., B. E. Wright, and G. U. Liddel. (1960). The isolation of Δ^{22}-stigmasten-3β-ol from *Dictyostelium discoideum*. *Arch. Biochem. Biophys.* **91**:266-270.

Hirschberg, E., and G. Merson. (1955a). Inhibition of aggregation of *Dictyostelium discoideum* by a series of diaminopyrimidines and dihydrotriazines. *J. Protozool.* **2**:Suppl., 9.

Hirschberg, E., and G. Merson. (1955b). Effect of test compounds on the aggregation and culmination of the slime mold *Dictyostelium discoideum*. *Cancer Res.* Suppl. **3**:76-79.

Hirschberg, E., and H. P. Rusch. (1950). Effects of compounds of varied biochemical action on the aggregation of a slime mold, *Dictyostelium discoideum*. *J. Cellular Comp. Physiol.* **36**:105-114.

Hirschberg, E., and H. P. Rusch. (1951). Effect of 2,4-dinitrophenol on the differentiation of the slime mold *Dictyostelium discoideum*. *J. Cellular Comp. Physiol.* **37**:323-336.

Hohl, H. R., and K. B. Raper. (1963a). Nutrition of cellular slime molds. I. Growth on living and dead bacteria. *J. Bacteriol.* **85**:191-198.

Hohl, H. R., and K. B. Raper. (1963b). Nutrition of cellular slime molds. II. Growth of *Polysphondylium pallidum* in axenic culture. *J. Bacteriol.* **85**:199-206.

Hohl, H. R., and K. B. Raper. (1963c). Nutrition of cellular slime molds. III. Specific growth requirements of *Polysphondylium pallidum*. *J. Bacteriol.* **86**:1314-1320.

Hohl, H. R., and K. B. Raper. (1964). Control of sorocarp size in the cellular slime mold *Dictyostelium discoideum*. *Develop. Biol.* **9**:137-153.

Hostak, M. B., and K. B. Raper. (1960). The induction of cell aggregation in *Acytostelium* by alkaloids. *Bacteriol. Proc.* **14**:58-59.

Howard, F. L. (1932). Nuclear division in plasmodia of *Physarum*. *Ann. Botany (London)* **46**:461-477.

Huffman, D. M., and L. S. Olive. (1964). Engulfment and anastomosis in the cellular slime molds (Acrasiales). *Am. J. Botany* **51**:465-471.

Huffman, D. M., A. J. Kahn, and L. S. Olive. (1962). Anastomosis and cell fusions in *Dictyostelium*. *Proc. Natl. Acad. Sci. U.S.* **48**:1160-1164.

Humphreys, T. (1963). Chemical dissolution and *in vitro* reconstruction of sponge cell adhesions. 1. Isolation and functional demonstration of the components involved. *Develop. Biol.* **8**:27-47.

Johnson, D. F., B. E. Wright, and E. Heftmann. (1962). Biogenesis of Δ^{22}-stigmasten-3β-ol in *Dictyostelium discoideum*. *Arch. Biochem. Biophys.* **97**:232-235.

Kahn, A. J. (1964a). The influence of light on cell aggregation in *Polysphondylium pallidum*. *Biol. Bull.* **127**:85-96.

Kahn, A. J. (1964b). Some aspects of cell interaction in the development of the slime mold *Dictyostelium purpureum*. *Develop. Biol.* **9**:1-19.

Kleiner, I. S., and J. M. Orten. (1962). "Biochemistry," 6th ed., 867 pp. Mosby, St. Louis, Missouri.

Konijn, T. M., and K. B. Raper. (1961). Cell aggregation in *Dictyostelium discoideum*. *Develop. Biol.* **3**:725-756.

Konijn, T. M., and K. B. Raper. (1965). The influence of light on the time of cell aggregation in the *Dictyosteliaceae*. *Biol. Bull.* **128**:392-400.

Kostellow, A. B. (1956). Developmental responses of *Dictyostelium discoideum* to some amino acids and their analogues. Ph.D. thesis, Columbia University.

Krichevsky, M. I., and B. E. Wright. (1961). The effect of environmental factors on morphogenesis and protein synthesis in *Dictyostelium discoideum*. *Bacteriol. Proc.* p. 86.

Krichevsky, M. I., and B. E. Wright. (1963). Environmental control of the course of development in *Dictyostelium discoideum*. *J. Gen. Microbiol.* **32**:195-207.

Krivanek, J. O. (1956). Alkaline phosphatase activity in the developing slime mold, *Dictyostelium discoideum* Raper. *J. Exptl. Zool.* **133**:459-479.

Krivanek, J. O. (1964). Nucleic acids in the developing slime mold, *Dictyostelium discoideum*. *Assoc. S. E. Biologists' Bull.* **11**:49.

Krivanek, J. O., and R. C. Krivanek. (1958). The histochemical localization of certain biochemical intermediates and enzymes in the developing slime mold, *Dictyostelium discoideum* Raper. *J. Exptl. Zool.* **137**:89-115.

Krivanek, J. O., and R. C. Krivanek. (1959). Chromatographic analysis of amino acids in the developing slime mold, *Dictyostelium discoideum* Raper. *Biol. Bull.* **116**:265-271.

Krivanek, J. O., and R. C. Krivanek. (1965). Evidence for transaminase activity in the slime mold, *Dictyostelium discoideum* Raper. *Biol. Bull.* **129**:295-302.

Liddel, G. U., and B. E. Wright. (1961). The effect of glucose on respiration of the differentiating slime mold. *Develop. Biol.* **3**:265-276.

Lövlie, A. (1964). Genetic control of division rate and morphogenesis in *Ulva mutabilis* Föyn. *Compt. Rend. Trav. Lab. Carlsberg, Ser. Chim.* **34**:77-168.

McCutcheon, M. (1946). Chemotaxis in leucocytes. *Physiol. Rev.* **26**:319-336.

McKeehan, M. S. (1958). Induction of portions of the check lens without contact with the optic cup. *Anat. Record* **132**:297-305.

Markert, C. L. (1956). The ontogeny of divergent metabolic patterns in cells of identical genotype. *Cold Spring Harbor Symp. Quant. Biol.* **21**:339-348.

Mercer, E. H., and B. M. Shaffer. (1960). Electron microscopy of solitary and aggregated slime mold cells. *J. Biophys. Biochem. Cytol.* **7**:353-356.

Moscona, A. (1957). The development *in vitro* of chimeric aggregates of dissociated embryonic chick and mouse cells. *Proc. Natl. Acad. Sci. U.S.* **43**:184-194.

Mühlethaler, K. (1956). Electron microscopic study of the slime mold *Dictyostelium discoideum*. *Am. J. Botany* **43**:673-678.

Nickerson, W. J., and Z. Mankowski. (1953). Role of nutrition in the maintenance of the yeast-shape in *Candida*. *Am. J. Botany* **40**:584-592.

Nickerson, W. J., and A. H. Romano. (1952). Enzymatic reduction of cystine by co-enzyme I (DPNH). *Science* **115**:676-678.

Nikaido, H. (1962). Studies on the biosynthesis of cell-wall polysaccharide in mutant strains of *Salmonella*, I. *Proc. Natl. Acad. Sci. U.S.* **48**:1337-1341.

Olive, E. W. (1902). Monograph of the Acrasieae. *Proc. Boston Soc. Nat. Hist.* **30**:451-510.
Olive, L. G. (1962). The genus *Protostelium*. *Am. J. Botany* **49**:297-303.
Olive, L. S. (1963). The question of sexuality in cellular slime molds. *Bull. Torrey Botan. Club* **90**:144-153.
Olive, L. S., S. K. Dutta, and C. Stoiamovitch. (1961). Variation in the cellular slime mold *Acrasis rosea*. *J. Protozool.* **8**:467-472.
Pfeffer, W. (1884). Locomotorische Richtungsbewegungen durch chemische Reize. *Untersuch. Botan. Inst. Tubingen* **1**:364-482.
Pfutzner-Eckert, R. (1950). Entwicklungsphysiologische untersuchungen an *Dictyostelium mucoroides* Brefeld. *Arch. Entwicklungsmech. Organ.* **144**:381-409.
Phillips, W. D., A. Rich, and R. Sussman. (1964). The isolation and identification of polyribosomes from cellular slime molds. *Biochim. Biophys. Acta* **80**:508-510.
Prescott, D. M. (1955). Relations between cell growth and cell division. I. Reduced weight, cell volume, protein content, and nuclear volume of *Amoeba proteus* from division to division. *Exptl. Cell Res.* **9**:328-337.
Puck, T. T., and H. W. Fisher. (1956). Genetics of somatic mammalian cells. I. Demonstration of the existence of mutants with different growth requirements in a human cancer cell (HeLa). *J. Exptl. Med.* **104**:427-433.
Rafaeli, D. E. (1962). Studies on mixed morphological mutants of *Polysphondylium violaceum*. *Bull. Torrey Botan. Club* **89**:312-318.
Raper, K. B. (1935). *Dictyostelium discoideum*, a new species of slime mold from decaying forest leaves. *J. Agr. Res.* **50**:135-147.
Raper, K. B. (1937). Growth and development of *Dictyostelium discoideum* with different bacterial associates. *J. Agr. Res.* **55**:289-316.
Raper, K. B. (1939). Influence of cultural conditions upon the growth and development of *Dictyostelium discoideum*. *J. Agr. Res.* **58**:157-198.
Raper, K. B. (1940a). Pseudoplasmodium formation and organization in *Dictyostelium discoideum*. *J. Elisha Mitchell Sci. Soc.* **56**:241-282.
Raper, K. B. (1940b). The communal nature of the fruiting process in the Acrasieae. *Am. J. Botany* **27**:436-448.
Raper, K. B. (1941). Developmental patterns in simple slime molds. Third Growth Symposium. *Growth* **5**:41-76.
Raper, K. B. (1956). Factors affecting growth and differentiation in simple slime molds. *Mycologia* **48**:169-205.
Raper, K. B. (1960). Levels of cellular interaction in amoeboid populations. *Proc. Am. Phil. Soc.* **104**:579-604.
Raper, K. B., and D. I. Fennell. (1952). Stalk formation in *Dictyostelium*. *Bull. Torrey Botan. Club* **79**:25-51.
Raper, K. B., and M. S. Quinlan. (1958). *Acytostelium leptosomum*: A unique cellular slime mold with an acellular stalk. *J. Gen. Microbiol.* **18**:16-32.
Raper, K. B., and C. Thom. (1941). Interspecific mixtures in the Dictyosteliaceae. *Am. J. Botany* **28**:69-78.
Romano, A. H., and W. J. Nickerson. (1954). Cystine reductase of pea seeds and yeasts. *J. Biol. Chem.* **208**:409-416.
Rorke, J., and G. Rosenthal. (1959). Influences on the spatial arrangements of *Dictyostelium discoideum*. Senior thesis, Princeton University.
Ross, I. K. (1960). Studies on diploid strains of *Dictyostelium discoideum*. *Am. J. Botany* **47**:54-59.
Runyon, E. H. (1942). Aggregation of separate cells of *Dictyostelium* to form a multicellular body. *Collecting Net* **17**:88.

Samuel, E. W. (1961). Orientation and rate of locomotion of individual amoebae in the life cycle of the cellular slime mold *Dictyostelium mucoroides*. *Develop. Biol.* **3**:317-335.

Shaffer, B. M. (1953). Aggregation in cellular slime moulds: *in vitro* isolation of acrasin. *Nature* **171**:975.

Shaffer, B. M. (1956a). Properties of acrasin. *Science* **123**:1172-1173.

Shaffer, B. M. (1956b). Acrasin, the chemotactic agent in cellular slime moulds. *J. Exptl. Biol.* **33**:645-657.

Shaffer, B. M. (1957a). Aspects of aggregation in cellular slime moulds. 1. Orientation and chemotaxis. *Am. Naturalist* **91**:19-35.

Shaffer, B. M. (1957b). Properties of slime-mould amoebae of significance for aggregation. *Quart. J. Microscop. Sci.* **98**:377-392.

Shaffer, B. M. (1957c). Variability of behavior of aggregating cellular slime moulds. *Quart. J. Microscop. Sci.* **98**:393-405.

Shaffer, B. M. (1958). Integration in aggregating cellular slime moulds. *Quart. J. Microscop. Sci.* **99**:103-121.

Shaffer, B. M. (1961a). Differentiation in the lower fungi. Species differences in the aggregation of the Acrasieae. *In* "Recent Advances in Botany," pp. 294-298. Univ. of Toronto Press, Toronto, Canada.

Shaffer, B. M. (1961b). The cells founding aggregation centers in the slime mould *Polysphondylium violaceum*. *J. Exptl. Biol.* **38**:833-849.

Shaffer, B. M. (1962). The Acrasina. *Advan. Morphogenesis* **2**:109-182.

Shaffer, B. M. (1963a). Inhibition by existing aggregations of founder differentiation in the cellular slime mould *Polysphondylium violaceum*. *Exptl. Cell Res.* **31**:432-435.

Shaffer, B. M. (1963b). Behaviour of particles adhering to amoebae of the slime mould *Polysphondylium violaceum* and the fate of the cell surface during locomotion. *Exptl. Cell Res.* **32**:603-606.

Shaffer, B. M. (1964a). Attraction through air exerted by unaggregated cells on aggregates of the slime mould *Polysphondylium violaceum*. *J. Gen. Microbiol.* **36**:359-364.

Shaffer, B. M. (1964b). *In* "Primitive Motile Systems in Cell Biology" (R. D. Allen and N. Kamiya, eds.), pp. 387-405. Academic Press, New York.

Shaffer, B. M. (1965a). Cell movement within aggregates of the slime mould *Dictyostelium discoideum* revealed by surface markers. *J. Embryol. Exptl. Morphol.* **13**:97-117.

Shaffer, B. M. (1965b). Pseudopodia and intracytoplasmic displacements of the collective amoebae Dictyosteliidae. *Exptl. Cell Res.* **37**:12-25.

Shaffer, B. M. (1965c). Antistrophic pseudopodia of the collective amoeba *Polysphondylium violaceum*. *Exptl. Cell Res.* **37**:79-92.

Shaffer, B. M. (1965d). Mechanical control of the manufacture and resorption of cell surface in collective amoebae. *J. Theoret. Biol.* **8**:27-40.

Skupienski, F. X. (1920). "Recherches sur le cycle évolutif des certains Myxomycètes," 81 pp. Paris.

Slifkin, M. K., and J. T. Bonner. (1952). The effect of salts and organic solutes on the migration time of the slime mold *Dictyostelium discoideum*. *Biol. Bull.* **102**:273-277.

Slifkin, M. K., and H. S. Gutowsky. (1958). Infrared spectroscopy as a new method for assessing the nutritional requirements of the slime mold *Dictyostelium discoideum*. *J. Cellular Comp. Physiol.* **51**:249-257.

Solomon, E. P., E. M. Johnson, and J. H. Gregg. (1964). Multiple forms of enzymes in a cellular slime mold during morphogenesis. *Develop. Biol.* **9**:314-326.
Sonneborn, D. R. (1962). Immunological analyses of the development of the cellular slime mold, *Dictyostelium discoideum*. Ph.D. thesis, Brandeis University.
Sonneborn, D. R., G. J. White, and M. Sussman. (1963). A mutation affecting both rate and pattern of morphogenesis in *Dictyostelium discoideum*. *Develop. Biol.* **7**:79-93.
Sonneborn, D. R., M. Sussman, and L. Levine. (1964). Serological analyses of cellular slime-mold development. I. Changes in antigenic activity during cell aggregation. *J. Bacteriol.* **87**:1321-1329.
Spiegel, M. (1954a). The role of specific surface antigens in cell adhesion. Pt. I. The reaggregation of sponge cells. *Biol. Bull.* **107**:130-148.
Spiegel, M. (1954b). The role of specific surface antigens in cell adhesion. Pt. II. Studies on embryonic amphibian cells. *Biol. Bull.* **107**:149-155.
Staples, S. O. (1964). The formation and properties of a pigment in the cellular slime mold, *Dictyostelium discoideum*. Master's thesis, University of Florida.
Sussman, M. (1954). Synergistic and antagonistic interactions between morphogenetically deficient variants of the slime mold *Dictyostelium discoideum*. *J. Gen. Microbiol.* **10**:110-120.
Sussman, M. (1955). *In* "Biochemistry and Physiology of Protozoa" (S. Hutner and A. Lwoff, eds.), Vol. 2, pp. 201-223. Academic Press, New York.
Sussman, M. (1956a). On the relation between growth and morphogenesis in the slime mold *Dictyostelium discoideum*. *Biol. Bull.* **110**:91-95.
Sussman, M. (1956b). The biology of the cellular slime molds. *Ann. Rev. Microbiol.* **10**:21-50.
Sussman, M. (1961). *In* "Growth in Living Systems" (M. X. Zarrow, ed.), pp. 221-239. Basic Books, New York.
Sussman, M. (1963). Growth of the cellular slime mold *Polysphondylium pallidum* in a simple nutrient medium. *Science* **139**:338.
Sussman, M. (1965). Inhibition by Actidione of protein synthesis and UDP-gal polysaccharide transferase accumulation in *Dictyostelium discoideum*. *Biochem. Biophys. Res. Commun.* **18**:763-767.
Sussman, M., and S. G. Bradley. (1954). A protein growth factor of bacterial origin required by the cellular slime molds. *Arch. Biochem. Biophys.* **51**:428-435.
Sussman, M., and F. Lee. (1955). Interactions among variant and wild-type strains of cellular slime molds across thin agar membranes. *Proc. Natl. Acad. Sci. U.S.* **41**:70-78.
Sussman, M., and N. Lovgren. (1965). Preferential release of the enzyme UDP-galactose polysaccharide transferase during cellular differentiation in the slime mold, *Dictyostelium discoideum*. *Exptl. Cell Res.* **38**:97-105.
Sussman, M., and M. J. Osborn. (1964). UDP-galactose polysaccharide transferase in the cellular slime mold, *Dictyostelium discoideum*: Appearance and disappearance of activity during cell differentiation. *Proc. Natl. Acad. Sci. U.S.* **52**:81-87.
Sussman, M., and R. R. Sussman. (1956). *In* "Cellular Mechanisms in Differentiation and Growth" (D. Rudnick, ed.), 14th Growth Symposium, pp. 125-154. Princeton Univ. Press, Princeton, New Jersey.
Sussman, M., and R. R. Sussman. (1962). Ploidal inheritance in *Dictyostelium discoideum*: Stable haploid, stable diploid and metastable strains. *J. Gen. Microbiol.* **28**:417-429.

Sussman, M., and R. R. Sussman. (1965). The regulatory program for UDP-galactose polysaccharide transferase activity during slime mold cytodifferentiation: Requirement for specific synthesis of ribonucleic acid. *Biochim. Biophys. Acta* 108:463-473.

Sussman, M., F. Lee, and N. S. Kerr. (1956). Fractionation of acrasin, a specific chemotactic agent for slime mold aggregation. *Science* 123:1171-1172.

Sussman, R. R., and M. Sussman. (1953). Cellular differentiation in Dictyosteliaceae: Heritable modification of the developmental pattern. *Ann. N. Y. Acad. Sci.* 56:949-960.

Sussman, R. R., M. Sussman, and F. L. Fu. (1958). The chemotactic complex responsible for cellular slime mold aggregation. *Bacteriol. Proc.* p. 32.

Takeuchi, I. (1960). The correlation of cellular changes with succinic dehydrogenase and cytochrome oxidase activities in the development of the cellular slime molds. *Develop. Biol.* 2:343-366.

Takeuchi, I. (1963). Immunochemical and immunohistochemical studies on the development of the cellular slime mold *Dictyostelium mucoroides*. *Develop. Biol.* 8:1-26.

Takeuchi, I., and M. Tazawa. (1955). Studies on the morphogenesis of the slime mold, *Dictyostelium discoideum*. *Cytologia (Tokyo)* 20:157-165.

Tyler, A. (1942). Developmental processes and energetics. *Quart. Rev. Biol.* 17:197-212 and 339-353.

Tyler, A. (1947). An auto-antibody concept of cell structure, growth, and differentiation. *Growth* 10:Suppl., 7-19.

Tyler, A. (1948). Fertilization and immunity. *Physiol. Rev.* 28:180-219.

Tyler, A. (1955). In "Analysis of Development" (B. H. Willier, P. A. Weiss, and V. Hamburger, eds.), pp. 556-573. Saunders, Philadelphia, Pennsylvania.

Von Schuckmann, W. (1925). Zur Morphologie und Biologie von *Dictyostelium mucoroides* Brefeld. *Arch. Protistenk.* 51:495-529.

Weinkauff, A. M., and M. F. Filosa. (1965). Factors involved in the formation of macrocysts by the cellular slime mold, *Dictyostelium mucoroides*. *Can. J. Microbiol.* 11:385-387.

Weiss, P. (1947). The problem of specificity in growth and development. *Yale J. Biol. Med.* 19:235-278.

White, G. J., and M. Sussman. (1961). Metabolism of major cell components during slime mold morphogenesis. *Biochim. Biophys. Acta* 53:285-293.

White, G. J., and M. Sussman. (1963a). Polysaccharides involved in slime-mold development I. Water-soluble glucose polymer(s). *Biochim. Biophys. Acta* 74:173-178.

White, G. J., and M. Sussman. (1963b). Polysaccharides involved in slime-mold development II. Water-soluble acid mucopolysaccharide(s). *Biochim. Biophys. Acta* 74:179-187.

Whitfield, F. E. (1964). The use of proteolytic and other enzymes in the separation of slime mold grex. *Exptl. Cell Res.* 36:62-72.

Whittingham, W. F., and K. B. Raper. (1956). Inhibition of normal pigment synthesis in spores of *Dictyostelium purpureum*. *Am. J. Botany* 43:703-708.

Whittingham, W. F., and K. B. Raper. (1960). Nonviability of stalk cells in *Dictyostelium*. *Proc. Natl. Acad. Sci. U.S.* 46:642-649.

Wilde, C. E. (1961). Factors concerning the degree of cellular differentiation in organotypic and disaggregated tissue cultures. *Colloq. Intern. Cult. Organo-Typique* 101:183-198.

Wilson, C. M. (1952). Sexuality in Acrasiales. *Proc. Natl. Acad. Sci. U.S.* 38:659-662.

Wilson, C. M. (1953). Cytological study of the life cycle of *Dictyostelium*. *Am. J. Botany* **40**:714-718.
Wilson, C. M., and I. K. Ross. (1957). Further cytological studies in the Acrasiales. *Am. J. Botany* **44**:345-350.
Wilson, H. V. (1910). Development of sponges from dissociated tissue cells. *Bull. U.S. Bur. Fisheries* **30**:1-30.
Wright, B. E. (1958). Effect of steroids on aggregation in the slime mold *Dictyostelium discoideum*. *Bacteriol. Proc.* p. 115.
Wright, B. E. (1960). On enzyme-substrate relationships during biochemical differentiation. *Proc. Natl. Acad. Sci. U.S.* **46**:798-803.
Wright, B. E. (1963). Endogenous activity and sporulation in slime molds. *Ann. N. Y. Acad. Sci.* **102**:740-754.
Wright, B. E. (1964). *In* "Biochemistry and Physiology of Protozoa" (S. H. Hutner, ed.), Vol. 3, pp. 341-381. Academic Press, New York.
Wright, B. E., and M. L. Anderson. (1958). *In* "Chemical Basis of Development" (W. D. McElroy and B. Glass, eds.), pp. 296-313. Johns Hopkins Press, Baltimore, Maryland.
Wright, B. E., and M. L. Anderson. (1959). Biochemical differentiation in the slime mold. *Biochim. Biophys. Acta* **31**:310-322.
Wright, B. E., and M. L. Anderson. (1960). Protein and amino acid turnover during differentiation in the slime mold. II. Incorporation of (^{35}S) methionine into the amino acid pool and into protein. *Biochim. Biophys. Acta* **43**:67-78.
Wright, B. E., and S. Bard. (1963). Glutamate oxidation in the differentiating slime mold. I. Studies *in vivo*. *Biochim. Biophys. Acta* **71**:45-49.
Wright, B. E., and B. A. Bloom. (1961). *In vivo* evidence for metabolic shifts in the differentiating slime mold. *Biochim. Biophys. Acta* **48**:342-346.
Wright, B. E., M. Brühmüller, and C. Ward. (1964). Studies *in vivo* on hexose metabolism in *Dictyostelium discoideum*. *Develop. Biol.* **9**:287-297.
Zaczynski, E. J. (1951). The effect of antiserum on the growth and morphogenesis of the slime mold *Dictyostelium discoideum*. Master's thesis, Vanderbilt University.

CHAPTER 10

Morphogenesis in Aquatic Fungi

EDWARD C. CANTINO

Department of Botany and Plant Pathology
Michigan State University
East Lansing, Michigan

I. INTRODUCTION

In this chapter, we shall direct attention toward current concepts of morphogenetic mechanisms among aquatic Phycomycetes—an assemblage of unusually multifarious creatures which have come to be known as the "water molds" by an equally unusual breed of mycological Peeping Toms who cannot resist meddling in their various affairs. The dizzy pace with which this pastime has been pursued by those addicted to it becomes evident immediately upon glancing at Sparrow's monumental treatise, "Aquatic Phycomycetes" (1960). In it are documented the innumerable reports of past decades which have led to present facts and notions about the water fungi—the ideas about their oldness, their ancestry and descent, and their kinship with one another; observations of the way in which the motile zoospores navigate, and of the quarters in which they come to rest and nest; empirical tricks whereby these creatures have been ambushed and trapped on bits of snake skin and even fruits and twigs in wire cages, isolated from their natural societies, undraped of their protective camouflage of microorganismal slime, domesticated in the lab, and then rehabilitated to yield heretofore unheard of secrets about their courtships, fraternizations among impotent neuters, the stability of the more celibate water mold societies, and the like. Thus, although it is still proper to perform postmortems on pickled corpses, it has become quite fashionable—and certainly far more profitable—to herd these molds into the mycological arena where they can be made to go through their acts *ad infinitum* under conditions controlled by the spectator.

In order to achieve an appropriately manifold view of these motley molds, "morphogenesis" will be considered in the broadest sense; that is, in terms of the genesis of cellular and organismal architecture at any level of organization which can be detected and defined. Furthermore, attention will be devoted not only to the way in which cell differentiation operates during the life history of a single organism—i.e., ontogeny—but also to the way in which genesis of form may have operated over the span of many generations—i.e., phylogeny.

II. MECHANISMS OF MORPHOGENESIS AT THE PHYLOGENETIC LEVEL

A. Classic Morphological Foundations

Let us try to appraise, first, the racial history of aquatic Phycomycetes. Undoubtedly, like other living things, they evolved and differentiated into modern kinds of fungi through mutation and selection. By the same token, just as evolution has proceeded at divergent rates for other creatures, the pace at which water molds have gotten where they are today may have varied widely. In brief, broad generalizations about the evolution of plants and animals can probably be invoked for aquatic fungi. But how should we evaluate the details of fungal evolution? What kinds of yardsticks, and how many, should be used?

In the past, most mycologists supposed that morphological parameters made the best measuring devices. The mass and form of the total fungus was, after all, its most conspicuous feature and gave it identity. Indeed, even those who are grappling today with the overwhelming degree of tidiness in the complex machinery of living cells are aware (e.g., Racker, 1959) that the first degree of intracellular order is established by means of structure. Thus, there is good reason to employ morphological and structural criteria as a *terra firma* upon which to build evaluations of phylogeny in water fungi.

There is a second parameter, too, which ". . . aside from its recreational possibilities, has profound and far-reaching biological significance, . . ." (Raper, 1959), and which has long been recognized as a tool for analyses of evolution: namely, sex. In fact, Raper feels that it may provide a most critical key for explaining the origin and diversity of the fungi.

And so, from a fabric woven mainly of morphology but pieced and held together with fair supplies of sexuality, mycologists have tried for many years to reach conclusions about phylogenetic relationships among aquatic fungi. Early in this century, Atkinson's (1909) and Petersen's (1909) attempts culminated, so to speak, in Scherffel's (1925) suggestion that aquatic Phycomycetes had evolved along two major paths, each from a different kind of ancestor, which led to modern-day uniflagellate and biflagellate fungi. For some twenty years, these speculations fit the facts. But

10. *Morphogenesis in Aquatic Fungi*

Scherffel, like mycologists before him (and as many of us may be a decade hence) was handicapped by want of sufficient information. Now, with another score of years gone by, new organisms have been added to the fold, some old ones recast, and a few flung into obscurity by taxonomic annihilation. This, together with additional life histories and more extensive morphological criteria, has rendered today's version significantly different from Scherffel's simple scheme of two divergent lines leading to the uniflagellate "Chytridineen" and the biflagellate "Saprolegniineen-Peronosporineen." Two somewhat different slants have been placed upon this modern view (Fig. 1).

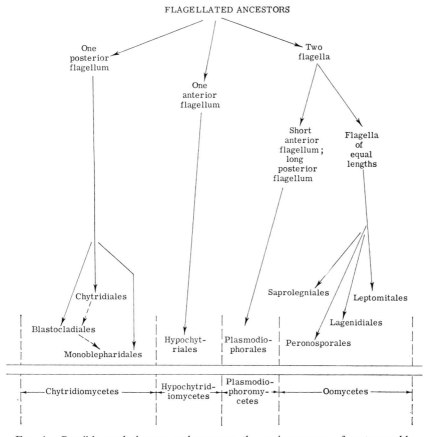

FIG. 1. Possible evolutionary paths among the major groups of water molds.

Alexopoulos (1962) thinks in terms of four groups coordinate in rank with one another (Fig. 1, bottom): the Chytridiomycetes, producing spores with a single posterior flagellum; the Hypochytridiomycetes, forming spores with a single anterior flagellum; the Oomycetes, which develop biflagellate spores; and the obligate endoparasites, the Plasmodiophoromycetes—also producing biflagellate but heterocont spores—which are set off as a separate class.

Sparrow, too (1960), sees four lines of descent (Fig. 1)—three major paths, with a dichotomy in one to yield a fourth—leading to nine orders of Phycomycetes. These presumptive evolutionary routes and relationships are based upon comparative life histories and morphology, with major emphasis upon the distinctive type of flagellation of the spores in each of the four main lines: the posterior, "whiplash" flagellum shared by the Chytridiales, Blastocladiales, and Monoblepharidales; the anterior "tinsel" flagellum with lateral threads in the Hypochytriales; and the paired flagella in the biflagellate series, including (a) the whiplash flagella of unequal lengths found in the Plasmodiophorales, and (b) the pair of whiplash and tinsel flagella, roughly equal in length, associated with the Saprolegniales, Leptomitales, Peronosporales (Pythiaceae), and the Lagenidiales.

A good case has also been made for sequential evolution linking the Chytridiales through some members of the Blastocladiales (Emerson, 1950; Crasemann, 1954) to the Monoblepharidales (Cantino, 1950, 1955; Cantino and Turian, 1959). In fact, the origin of a mutant with chytrid-like qualities from a blastocladiaceous progenitor has been demonstrated in the laboratory (Cantino and Hyatt, 1953b). But the biflagellate complex is a more tangled skein, and it is at just such a place that a critical—perhaps even a supercritical—approach is needed. To render judgment about evolutionary routes for the Saprolegniales, Peronosporales, Leptomitales, and Lagenidiales is very difficult on morphological grounds alone. Unmistakable affinities do exist among them, it is true. Also, with their parasitic tendency and adaptation to terrestrial habitats in mind, it is tempting to consider the Lagenidiales and Peronosporales as relatively advanced. But their points of origin along the line (Fig. 1) are certainly not resolvable on morphological grounds. The lack of fossil evidence for such fragile "boneless" creatures does not make the problem easier. Thus, it behooves all who are concerned with this matter to examine available data critically.

A quick glance at the reports about these molds might lead to the conclusion that an abundance of raw material—knowledge of morphology and sex—is available. Indeed, this lengthy literature has led to suggestions that aquatic Phycomycetes were derived from simple monad ancestors, from algae via loss of chlorophyll, from higher fungi by degeneration and adoption of parasitic habits, etc. But, a second glance at Sparrow's book will also show that most of them have not even been isolated in unifungal—let alone pure—culture. Thus, we simply do not know as yet just how static their morphology and sex really is, nor how distinctive it may be under natural conditions.

But even when degrees of morphological and sexual plasticity become established, the question of interpreting the data will remain. Recently, Grimstone (1959) reemphasized the dual nature of morphological resemblances among living things: those built on the same structural plan and phylogenetically related to common ancestors, and those found among organs of similar function regardless of phylogenetic ties. He stressed the need to make this distinction at all levels of organization, and cautioned that if two organisms of similar size occupy the same ecological niche, morphological resemblances would not be unexpected.

Aquatic Phycomycetes are world wide in distribution, and by and large they grow and propagate in bodies of water. The "buffering" capacities inherent therein probably ensure some degree of environmental uniformity and constancy. Thus, to distinguish between homologous and analogous structures among water fungi is a difficult and perilous task. For example, since the notion is widespread that the motile cells of water molds provide good morphological parameters for evaluations of phylogeny, let us pose two questions: (a) theoretically, to what extent should details about internal structure of the spore be employed? and (b) practically how much do we really know about these to begin with?

Consider, first, the question of internal cell morphology. Since all eukaryotic cells apparently contain mitochondria, is it not likely that such organelles arose independently in different groups of organisms in the course of evolution? Following Pantin (1951) (cf. Grimstone, 1959), should we not expect that different molds arrived independently at the same solutions to common problems when the number of possible answers was restricted in nature by the materials available? If we grant this to be true, then the mitochondria in their motile cells—organelles presumably dependent upon *relatively* few genes—evolved more often than the more complex spore itself. Thus, for purposes of phylogeny, similarities and dissimilarities in the spores' internal structures could be misleading, and they should be interpreted with caution.

But, notwithstanding eventual interpretations, what about the second question? What are the facts at our disposal to begin with? Both Waterhouse (1962) and Koch (1961) stress that if we are to use spore structure as a basis for interpretations, then we must learn much more about it than we know now; taxonomic speculations based thereon must be postponed until a later day. Ironically enough, the truth of this is nowhere better illustrated than in Koch's own paper. In a sketch of the spore of *Allomyces,* he depicts lipid granules in the cytoplasm, and a ring of mitochondria around the nuclear cap (clearly documented for the first time by Blondel and Turian, 1960), and says: "The mitoplanospore of *Allomyces macrogynous* ... diagrammed ... on the basis of personal observations, is representative of the Blastocladiales' motile cell which is rather well described in the literature." And yet, electron microscopy reveals (Cantino *et al.,* 1963) that in the spore of *Blastocladiella emersonii,* there is no ring of mitochondria; rather, *there is only one mitochondrion.* Furthermore, it lies not upon the cap, but eccentrically in the posterior end of the spore adjacent to the flagellum. Clearly, we are in no position to make generalizations about internal structure in the spore, even within a single family of the water fungi.

By the same token, generalizations about the chemistry and physiology of motile spores would be premature. For example, the spore of *B. emersonii* has been fingerprinted in some detail: its weight, the total N, soluble N, soluble protein N, and soluble nonprotein N, chitin, soluble polysaccharide, and lactic acid pools per cell, and its total content of glucosamine synthetase, glucose 6-phosphate dehydrogenase, glycine-alanine transaminase, isocitritase, and other enzyme activities have been established (Cantino, 1961; Cantino and Goldstein, 1961; Cantino and Lovett, 1960, 1964; Lovett and Cantino, 1960b; McCurdy and Cantino, 1960). Even its nuclear cap has been isolated and analyzed (Lovett, 1963). However, none of these has been recorded for any other spore of the water fungi. If we are to come to grips eventually with this question of the validity of using the motile spore as a basis for phylogeny, we shall have to learn much, much more about its chemistry and physics and about its structure and function from every possible point of view. Painstaking, time-consuming, definitive analyses will have to precede broad generalizations.

B. Recent Nutritional Substructures

In considering evolutionary mechanisms, there is no reason to restrict the point of view solely to morphology and life histories of aquatic fungi. Indeed, there has always been good reason *not* to do so. Even the experimental plant taxonomist, who must overcome greater hurdles than those confronting the mycologist, begins to see a panoramic view of the evolution of higher plants on the horizon. As Hiesey *et al.* (1962) point out, "The entire spectrum of expression of higher plant species, ranging from the multitudinous aspects they present ... in the wild to the detailed analysis of the functioning of their many component parts down to the cellular level, is now within reach. . . ."

Among aquatic fungi, non-"morphological" parameters such as disposition of chemical constituents within a thallus, overall synthetic capacities, etc., must also have evolved along with gross morphology, sexual competence and attributes, a tendency to parasitize a host, etc. The conclusion is inescapable that the aggregate morphology of a water mold results from the balance of many forces within it. The "master plan" (Mitchell, 1962) by which energy, metabolism, transport, and growth are integrated in the genesis of an organism's form is, as yet, far from comprehensible. While Mitchell's plea that we ". . . straighten our backs . . . and look carefully at the master plan . . ." is one to which we should all subscribe enthusiastically, the real question for us is: where is the vantage point from which the mycologist can start?

The capacity of a fungus to make certain molecular building blocks, and its inability to manufacture others, is certainly part of its master plan and constitutes a foothold. Let us see how firm a grip it gives us.

To begin with, there is a practical reason for considering nutrition: its effect upon the morphology of aquatic fungi has been recognized for decades. Klebs' classic, often quoted observations on the effect of environment upon the Saprolegniales, and subsequent studies of this sort by others, are summarized by Hawker (1957), Cochrane (1958), Sparrow (1960), etc. Recent years have reemphasized the import of environment in the genesis of form. Examples can be found among the saprophytic Blastocladiales (Cantino and Turian, 1959; Cantino, 1961; Cantino and Lovett, 1964; Horenstein and Cantino, 1962), where bicarbonate, light, and other factors affect morphology at different stages in ontogeny in precise, predictable fashion—even the morphology of the parasitic *Catenaria* apparently responds to changes in its environment (Gaertner, 1962); among the Chytridiales (Willoughby, 1962), where light (and perhaps vitamins) plays a role in the capacity of *Cladochytrium* to produce sporangia; and among the Saprolegniales, where stages in the formation of oogonia by *Saprolegnia* (Krause, 1960), *Achlya* (Barksdale, 1962), and *Aphanomyces* (Papavizas and Davey, 1960a) are affected, respectively, by temperature and light, by inorganic ions, total N, and sugars, and by the balance among amino acids, sugars, and the S source. But granting the utility of knowing how nutrition affects form, let us—for the moment—leave the latter out of it.

Presumably, the composition and organization of a water fungus in chemical and physical terms would be related to its synthetic capacity, but the data available (until recently: cf. reviews by Cantino, 1955; Cantino and Turian, 1959) have been limited in quantity and scope. It is true that more definitive information has begun to appear—structural details gotten by electron microscopy and diffraction (Aronson and Preston, 1960a,b; Blondel and Turian, 1960; Cantino et al., 1963), microchemical work (Fuller, 1960), studies of the enzymology and chemistry of the metabolic machinery in a cell at different stages in ontogeny (Cantino and Lovett,

1964), etc. But unfortunately, such work has involved so few water fungi that it would be premature to apply the results to phylogeny.

The second parameter is nutrition itself. An attempt to use this device was begun almost fifteen years ago (Cantino, 1950), and the approach has been updated and revised periodically (Cantino, 1955; Cantino and Turian, 1959). Now that another five years have gone by, the picture can be brought up to date. More than two decades ago, Lwoff (1944) postulated a scheme for physiological evolution among protozoa based upon his notion that increasing specialization in nutritional requirements is a concomitant of evolution. Thus, for example, an organism autotrophic for all vitamins and capable of reducing inorganic, highly oxidized N and S compounds would be relatively primitive. It already was evident in 1950 that the synthetic capacity of the water fungi was sufficiently diverse to warrant a trial application of this notion; it has become increasingly evident since then that the approach was justified. It appears as though physiological evolution among aquatic fungi has led to degeneration and heterotrophism, whereby progressive losses in the capacity for synthesis has rendered them more and more dependent upon the environment. The current view is depicted in Fig. 2. The data which underlie this evolutionary flow sheet have been summarized (Cantino, 1955; Cantino and Turian, 1959), and almost all nutritional reports after 1959 have fit the scheme.

Let us assume that a spore's flagellation, not its internal structure, is of some importance in delimiting major phylogenetic routes; i.e., that uniflagellate and biflagellate series have evolved separately. The losses in synthetic capacities associated with these two paths seem to differ quite significantly.

1. The Chytridiales-Blastocladiales-Monoblepharidales Complex

Nutritionally, the Chytridiales include the most primitive members of the uniflagellate series because apparently (a) all have retained the aboriginal capacity to use highly oxidized forms of inorganic S (i.e., sulfate) as sole S sources for growth; (b) likewise, some have retained the primitive capacity to synthesize all essential vitamins, although a few have lost the power to synthesize thiamine, and one cannot make biotin and nicotinamide; and (c) some have retained the capacity to use both oxidized and reduced forms of inorganic N (i.e., nitrate N and ammonia N), although a few can no longer utilize nitrate N. Since 1959, new chytrids have been isolated in pure culture. Once again, some of them, i.e., *Phlyctochytrium* (S. Goldstein, 1960a) and *Rhizophydium* (Gaertner, 1960), have retained the capacity to synthesize all essential vitamins and use sulfate S (and for *Phlyctochytrium*, both nitrate N and ammonia N) as sole sources of sulfur and nitrogen, respectively; two of them, *Cladochytrium* (Willoughly, 1962; S. Goldstein, 1960b) and *Nowokowskiella* (S. Goldstein, 1961), have lost the power to synthesize vitamin B_1 but have retained the capacity to use sulfate S as well as nitrate N and ammonia N; and yet others, i.e., *Rhizophydium* (S. Goldstein, 1960a) and *Chytriomyces* (Reisert and Fuller, 1962), have lost the capacity both to manufacture thiamine and to use nitrate N.

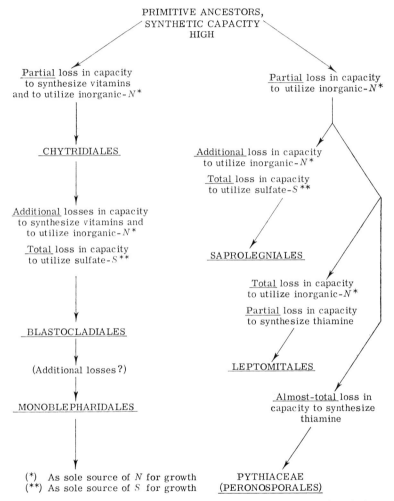

FIG. 2. Apparent evolutionary paths for losses in synthetic capacity of the saprophytic water molds.

The nutritional characteristics of the Blastocladiales are clearly more advanced than those of the Chytridiales. All of them have lost the capacity to use inorganic sulfate as a sole source of sulfur for growth and require reduced organic S (at least two, in fact, have specifically lost the power to synthesize methionine); all have lost the capacity to synthesize the pyrimidine moiety of thiamine—if not the complete—molecule, and some have suffered additional losses in the capacities for synthesis of biotin, p-aminobenzoate, and nicotinamide. Moreover, all have lost the capacity to grow on nitrate N, and one even on ammonia N. Thus, with respect to S, N, and vitamin nutrition, the Blastocladiales are more specialized and more dependent upon the environment than the Chytridiales. On this basis, the latter represent the more primitive, and the former the more advanced, members of the uniflagellate series.

As for the Monoblepharidales, no one has succeeded in establishing their nutritional requirements. An educated guess, however, may be in order: probably, they have suffered even more extensive losses in synthetic capacity than their supposed progenitors among the Blastocladiales. In fact, this may explain why they have not, as yet, been cultured in synthetic media (Cantino and Turian, 1959).

2. *The Saprolegniales-Peronosporales-Leptomitales-Lagenidiales Complex*

The Saprolegniales have lost the capacity to utilize sulfate and nitrate as sole sources of S and N, respectively, for growth. Practically all species, however, have retained the ability to use ammonia N, and to synthesize essential vitamins. Here, too, reports which have appeared since 1959 are in keeping with the scheme in Fig. 2. All the saprolegnias tested (Krause, 1960; Dayal, 1961a,b)—even a marine species (Vishniac, 1958)—as well as *Isoachlya* and *Achlya* (Dayal, 1961b) and *Aphanomyces* (Papavizas and Davey, 1960b; Haglund and King, 1962), have retained the capacity to synthesize the vitamins they need. On the other hand, they have lost the capacity to utilize sulfate S for growth. Furthermore, *Aphanomyces, Achlya, Isoachlya,* and *Saprolegnia* have lost the ability to use nitrate N but have retained the capacity to use ammonia N.

The Leptomitales, in contrast, have lost the capacity to use both ammonia N and nitrate N for growth, but they have retained the power to reduce sulfate for the biosynthesis of the S compounds they require. Finally, while some have remained autotrophic for vitamins, one (and perhaps two) can no longer manufacture thiamine.

The aquatic Peronosporales (i.e., the Pythiaceae), like the Leptomitales, have retained the capacity to satisfy their needs for S with sulfate. Like the Saprolegniales, on the other hand, practically all have retained the capacity to use ammonia N to satisfy growth requirements; apparently, some can also use nitrate N. But, unlike either the Saprolegniales or the Leptomitales, essentially all of them have become partially or completely heterotrophic for thiamine. Reports which have appeared after 1959 have brought about some shift in emphasis, but no real change in the scheme in Fig. 2. The capacity of the Pythiaceae to use sulfate S (Fothergill and Hide, 1962), and their inability to synthesize vitamin B_1 (Erwin and Katznelson, 1961), has been noted once again (however, Fothergill and Hide report one of the very few exceptions regarding vitamins). The partial loss in capacity of the Pythiaceae to utilize inorganic N now seems greater than originally visualized (Cantino, 1950, 1955). Davies (1959), Fleetwood-Walker (1954), and Erwin and Katznelson (1961) all report that neither ammonia N nor nitrate N is used as sole N source for growth. However, whether or not ammonia N supports growth may depend, in some cases, upon the exogenous carbohydrate supplied (Christie, 1959).

In conclusion, it is not implied that deep evolutionary significance should be attached to the difference between an organism which requires organic N and one which can use inorganic N (i.e., ammonia); a loss of capacity to synthesize any one of the multitude of amino acids, peptides, etc. would result in dependency upon a supply of organic N. But the living cell contains far fewer S compounds; thus, the power to reduce sulfate and to use it as the only sulfur source for growth should be more significant. It is supposed, therefore, that progressive losses in synthetic capacities of the biflagellate complex evolved along two independent paths (Fig. 2); one gave rise to the Saprolegniales, and the other, via a second, subsequent branching, to the Peronosporales and Leptomitales. From a nutritional point of view, therefore, the Leptomitales are more closely related to the Peronosporales than to the Saprolegniales.

C. Prospective Synoptic Footholds

For the present, the skeleton of any scheme for evolution of flagellated fungi must still be based upon structure and life cycles. Nutritional criteria can be employed as supplements for judging relationships well-founded on morphological grounds (as in the uniflagellate series), or for shifting emphasis in a new direction if other evidence is insufficient (as in the biflagellate series). But where should future efforts lead? That the ultimate aim is to achieve a quantitative understanding of evolution at all its levels of organization is self-evident—and so is the enormity of the task. Attention must be given to parasitic aquatic fungi, the sequence and turnover of water mold epidemics (Canter and Lund, 1951), interacting factors in the biology of lakes and mud puddles which could provide clues about the origin and maintenance of such relationships, etc. The ecological problem of populations (their number and what determines it) and the genetical problem of populations (their kinds, and what determines them) clearly overlap (Birch, 1960); for the water molds, too, we must learn how kind influences number, and vice versa. Conceivably, mycologists may even arise one day, to find a theory [perhaps akin to Slobodkin's (1961) for ecology] with which, along with an appropriate calculator, educated guesses will be made about the future evolutionary pathways of water fungi.

But along with this macrocosm about which we know so little, there is a microcosm equally deserving of attention. The metabolic machinery which governs synthesis and maintenance of morphological structure and sexual potency in water fungi had to evolve simultaneously. We must, therefore, learn much more about it, what it is made of, and how it operates. What does this imply? Ten years ago, we might have been gratified with a modest knowledge of the role of the Krebs cycle and the Embden-Meyerhof-Parnas (EMP) glycolytic pathway—perhaps even the hexose monophosphate shunt. But who, today, would be truly satisfied without some insight into the action of an upstrand operator sitting on a regulator operon about to send repressive agents off to war upon peaceful fellow operators on functional operons elsewhere in the cell? Our machine is infinitely more sophisticated, and many will want to know about the battery of relays, semiconductors, amplifiers, and other devices in the cell's milieu which mediate induction, repression, and gene control in general.

In this light, our nutritional approach is far from perfect and leaves much to be desired—indeed, it appears positively primitive! And yet, water-moldologists can only work with what they've got, and what they can expect to have in the foreseeable future. Besides, losses in capacity for synthesis must be related, in some measure at least, to the ecological capabilities of water fungi, on the one hand, and to the cogs in their metabolic wheels on the other. Somewhere in between lies a region of compromise wherein different approaches can be reconciled, and whereby it can be estimated how, by mutation and recombination, raw materials for evolution originated. Judging from comparative biology and contemporary thinking on the matter, selection probably operated via the routes in Fig. 3.

1. A Framework for Further Study

Undoubtedly, mutation was a major factor, but to what degree? Thus, is the mutation rate among water fungi about the same as in other living things? The sensitivity of enzymes and DNA in pneumococci to ionizing radiation is increased by oxygen (Hutchinson, 1960). If their niche in nature is relatively poor in oxygen, do the water molds, therefore, display low mutation rates? The opaqueness of water to certain radiations should provide additional "protection." Although evidence is meager and negative besides, the fact remains that spontaneous mutations among water molds appear to be exceedingly rare; even induced mutations are hard to come by. It may be fair to guess, therefore, that among the water fungi production of undirected genotypic plasticity (Fig. 3) via mutation occurred at rates below par.

10. Morphogenesis in Aquatic Fungi

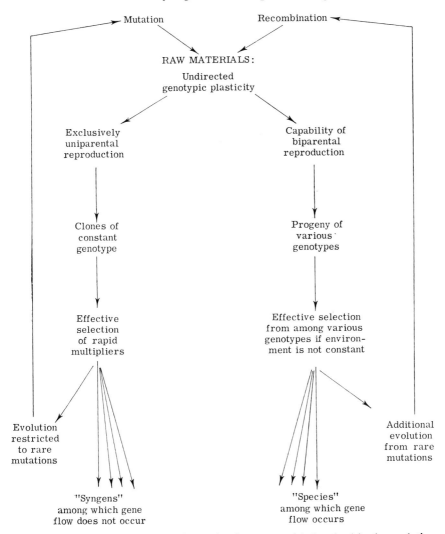

FIG. 3. The possible nature and genesis of raw materials involved in the evolution of water molds.

Recombination is the second major factor in evolution of most other living things. But among aquatic fungi, sex—at least, gesticulations *recognizable* as such—is all too often missing. Of course, for molds which do indulge, mycologists will have to grapple with the question ". . . is sexual versatility . . . the cause or the result of evolutionary diversity?" (Raper, 1959). But for those that don't, it doesn't really matter. Thus, a second source of undirected genotypic plasticity is, today, at least, lacking in the great majority of water molds.

Naturally, there is no question (Wright, 1956) that selection cannot operate without some raw material. Thus, future work will have to aim, first, toward gathering quantitative data about the origin of undirected genetic variability; and second, toward identifying the properties of the two paths (Fig. 3) which stem therefrom through the agency of uniparental and biparental reproduction.

Almost all aquatic Phycomycetes are homothallic and employ uniparental modes of reproduction. Apparently, they do not enjoy heterokaryosis as a "genetic balancing device" (Raper, 1959), and yield clones of constant genotype. Therefore, following Wright (1956), and ideas attributed by him to Haldane, effective selection of the most rapid multipliers in newly formed clones should ensue quickly. But thereafter, evolution would be restricted to rare mutations among them. Slight differences in longevity, survival under competition, fecundity, etc., would then be magnified and play a potent role. Thus, like other asexual creatures which have persisted in constant environments (Sonneborn, 1957), water fungi living in aquatic habitats buffered against rapid change presumably enjoy the same "advantages" and a sustained existence.

If the current view about common gene pools excludes asexual organisms from consideration, we are left (Fig. 3, bottom left) with water molds in anonymity. This kind of dilemma led Sonneborn to use the term "syngen" as a unit of evolution (vs. "species," the unit of identification). He distinguished syngens by lack of gene flow between them. Thus, their delimitation among asexual organisms must depend upon extensive comparative studies to provide bases for judgments about the probable complexity of their genetic makeup. This, perhaps, is one course to chart as we search for an understanding of evolutionary mechanisms among aquatic fungi. With reliable data about nutrition, the structure and function of their metabolic gear, their method of gene control, etc., the syngens of water molds can be characterized, and judgments made about degrees of discontinuity among them.

But having placed the emphasis upon the homothallic majority, we do not mean to slight the small minority capable of biparental reproduction (Fig. 3, right); some of the most venerable molds are found among them. However, as Raper (1959) points out, *Allomyces* is somewhat exceptional; not only does it have a $2N$ vegetative thallus, but—although homothallic—it also hybridizes with other members of its kind. And as for the achlyas, most of them are capable of sexual ambivalence and appear to constitute fungi in a state of sexual transition. Might this, too, stem in part from the "buffering" capacity of their aquatic environment? If effective selection could only have occurred in sharply changing settings, perhaps we should expect to find them in a state of flux. In any case, to evaluate evolutionary mechanisms for the very few fungi among which gene flow can occur (Fig. 3, right) may be more difficult than for those with single parents. Fortunately, we already know a good deal about them.

2. Synopsis

Extensive uniparental reproduction prevails among aquatic Phycomycetes. Cross-breeding is rare. If application of the words of Wright (1956) to this system is justified, we can conclude that it "is probably more significant as a means of insuring the appearance of adaptive genotypes, capable of taking advantage of any temporary bonanza . . . than of progressive evolution." Students of the water fungi have always regarded them fondly as the most primitive representatives of the true fungi. Perhaps we should add: and they have not gotten very far! If, by and large, they consist of groups in which irreversible evolutionary divergence has not yet occurred, intensive study of their syngens should provide definitive bases for judgments about the complexity of the genetic differences among aquatic Phycomycetes.

III. MECHANISMS OF MORPHOGENESIS AT THE ONTOGENETIC LEVEL

A. *Potential Utility of Aquatic Phycomycetes for Morphogenetic Studies*

This vast, ubiquitous assemblage of primitive fungi constitutes a grab bag of useful "guinea pigs" waiting to be exploited for experimental studies of cell differentiation. Unfortunately, few biologists have taken advantage of what they have to offer; even then, rarely have systematic attempts been made to develop and exploit them as vehicles for long-range studies. Furthermore, the intolerance of some molecular "biologists" for "descriptive" morphologists—and vice versa—has too often been painfully obvious in the past and needs no documentation. To jump with both feet into some highly special aspect of the biology of an aquatic fungus, paradoxically ignoring background knowledge of its life history and morphology, or alternatively, its chemistry and physics, is patently ludicrous. It is no wonder that knowledge of morphogenesis in water molds—indeed, in all the fungi—is spotty. Fortunately, there are some notable exceptions.

B. *Aquatic Phycomycetes Exclusive of the Blastocladiales*

1. *Saprolegniales*

The thallus of these creatures is a branched coenocytic mycelium with unlimited capacity for growth. The genesis of sexual and asexual structures thereon has been studied intensively and with ample rewards. It is instructive to see how our knowledge has evolved.

According to Waterhouse (1962), in the early 1820's F. P. Gruithuisen and C. G. Carus gave good descriptions of sporangia and of the emission and encystment of their spores. Later on, in the 1880's (Sparrow, 1960), M. Büsgen and M. M. Hartog wrote of the distinctive cytoplasmic changes which occur during the genesis of a sporangium and its spores. Finally, this led to knowledge of the sequence of events involved in spore formation; outward extension of cleavage planes to delimit spore initials and formation of discharge papillae, subsequent abrupt changes in "aspect" (degree of granulation) of the protoplast, and, last, relase of spores. Thus, an essential cornerstone was laid down early, and superstructures were built upon it later. The early 1900's saw development of now-classic Klebsian principles about the impact of environment on morphogenesis (Klebs, 1900; summarized in Coker, 1923; Sparrow, 1960). Mycelia well nourished in "rich" nutrients formed sporangia and discharged spores when transferred to a nutrient-poor environment such as water. Reduction (rather than severe depletion) of the food supply induced genesis of sex cells. From this point on, knowledge of morphogenesis in the Saprolegniales evolved along two paths of unequal length and different texture.

As ill-defined as Klebs' results may appear today to our sophisticated hindsight, we know astonishingly little more than he did about the genesis of sporangia. Aside from suggestions that metabolic products alter sporangial morphology (Salvin, 1942), and that aeration (Llanos and Lockwood, 1960) affects sporogenesis, there is little new. One cannot agree more wholeheartedly with Waterhouse (1962) that, as far as these sporangia are concerned, we are still in the dark ages.

But in sharp contrast, a bright beacon glows along the second road. After recognition that heterothallism (Couch, 1926), and staling products (Salvin, 1942), played a role in development, Raper (1951, 1952) uncovered a remarkably complicated hormonal control mechanism for the genesis of sex cells in *Achlya,* which is reviewed by Machlis in this volume. Raper showed that water-soluble substances sequentially initiated and coordinated sexual reproduction: (a) hormone A, produced by the female thallus, induces formation of male sex organs on the male thallus; (b) the latter then releases hormone B which initiates the formation of female sex organs on the female thallus; (c) the female now releases hormone C, which brings about delimitation of the male organ and, in fact, attracts it to itself; and finally (d) the male produces hormone D which delimits the female organ from the thallus. Emerson (1950) sums up the essence of this work thus: "Diffusion of the hormones across cellophane membranes was shown and the sequence of steps and the timing of each was ingeniously demonstrated by many types of experiments. Reciprocal matings between

A. ambisexualis and *A. bisexualis* revealed the nonspecificity of certain of the hormones and the specificity of others, the latter providing a precise explanation for the sexual incompatibility of these two species. It was shown that both hormone A and hormone B are stable at 100°C. . . . It was found that the number of antheridial hyphae produced was proportional to the concentration of hormone A applied and could be used as an accurate index of reaction intensity. Optimal conditions of temperature, hydrogen-ion concentration, and other factors were determined, and standard conditions for bioassay of hormone A were described. In 1942, Raper and Haagen-Smit . . . refined the method of assay still further and succeeded in obtaining, by a complex series of chemical fractionations, a preparation of hormone A 70,000 times more active than the starting material. Unfortunately, despite intensive effort, the substance was not isolated in a pure state, but many of its physical and chemical properties were established. Subsequently, Raper . . . discovered that the initial response of the male vegetative plant to the female vegetative plant depends upon a complex of interactions between two substances, A and A^2, produced by the female, and two substances, A^1 and an inhibitor, produced by the male."

Thanks to Raper, we already had ten years ago a tidy picture of an important mechanism of development involving 7 hormones, 4 secreted by the male and 3 by the female, which induced and regulated morphogenesis in one of the Saprolegniales. And yet, perhaps because Raper was a step ahead of the times—or maybe simply because the main obstacle for chemical identifications was the tremendous quantities of spent media containing the hormones which, so far as was then known, were ". . . of interest and importance only to other Achlyas" (Raper, 1951)—this outstanding work has not yet led to an interpretation of morphogenesis in chemical or metabolic terms. Undoubtedly, however, it will come with the recent flurry of renewed interest in the female gender of the Saprolegniales. Barksdale (1962) has defined the optimal balance between glucose and the quantities of C, P, K, S, Mg, and Ca necessary for formation of sex organs in *Achlya*. Krause (1960) outlined some five phases (i.e., induction, growth, differentiation, etc.) during genesis of oogonia in *Saprolegnia,* the first of these being sensitive (but the rest insensitive) to blue light. Vitamin nutrition did not appear to be involved. And finally, Papavizas and Davey (1960a) showed that various factors, particularly exogenous sugar:amino acid ratios and the kind of sulfur source, affected formation of oogonia in *Aphanomyces*. To what degree such studies will blend with what we know of the hormonal control of reproduction is a moot point. At this moment, a metabolic basis for morphogenesis in the Saprolegniales has not yet been suggested.

2. Leptomitales and Pythiaceae

Potentially, these organisms have as much to offer as the Saprolegniales, but experimental studies of their morphology—at least, the sort we have been discussing—have been almost wholly lacking. For *Apodachlya,* this seems to be particularly anomalous because the cytological foundations for sexual differentiation were available long ago. The simultaneous division of nuclei in the female organ, the outward migration and subsequent degeneration of all but one of them, and the fusion of the latter with a nucleus from the male—all was described by Kevorkian (1935) almost thirty years ago, but has not been exploited further. Bishop (1940) provided suggestive evidence for the role of hormones in sexual reproduction, but more than two decades have gone by and nothing much has been added. Even aspects of metabolism were explored (Schade and Thimann, 1940), but the work was not designed to bear upon questions of morphogenesis. Thus, experiments with the Leptomitales have been rare and spotty; in particular, they have not fertilized one another. At the moment, knowledge of the mechanism of morphogenesis in the Leptomitales (and the Pythiaceae, too) is almost nil.

3. Monoblepharidales and Chytridiales

The Monoblepharidales have not played a role in advancing our knowledge of morphogenesis; until recently (Perrott, 1958), they had not even been isolated in pure culture. But their relatives, the Chytridiales, have already left their mark and have much more to offer. Once again, this stems in part from the orderly fashion in which knowledge of them is evolving. An abundant background of descriptive morphology can be found in the 561 pages which Sparrow (1960) has devoted to them, and cytological research with them is well along.

Starting with early reports [see Sparrow (1960) for historical survey], such as Wagner's on *Polyphagus*—wherein, half a century ago, he had already discovered that during morphogenesis nuclear divisions were completed before cytokinesis was initiated—a cytological foundation began to accumulate. This is based on observations that cytoplasmic strands in *Cladochytrium* connect flagellum to nucleus and that a nuclear cap is attached thereto (Karling, 1937); the fact that in *Polychytrium* such caps contain coalesced granular material (Ajello, 1948), and that in *Asterophlyctis* (Antikajian, 1949) they are quickly lost following spore germination; findings that as a young chytrid germling grows, its single nucleus can enlarge in striking fashion—from twofold in *Endochytrium* and *Rhizophydium* (Hillegas, 1940; Hanson, 1945), to as much as fivefold in *Asterophlyctis* (Antikajian, 1949); discoveries that when nuclear division does begin in older thalli derived from germlings of *Cladochytrium* (Karling, 1937) and *Rhizophydium* (Hanson, 1945), crescent-shaped nucleoli persist during the apparently synchronous (Ajello, 1948) mitoses which ensue; and, finally, observations of a gradual reduction in size of nuclei with each successive division (Antikajian, 1949), thus regenerating the original nuclear dimension found in spores. Provided with such provocative focal points pregnant with possibilities for the future, along with evidence of mating type control in *Rhizophlyctis* (Couch, 1939), and the awareness that Klebsian principles are applicable to chytrids, too, an orderly continuation of studies in chytrid morphogenesis is inevitable. The increasing use of pure cultures for studies of nutrition (Section II, B), and work on the fine structure and composition of chytrid thalli (Aronson and Preston, 1960b; Fuller, 1960) has helped to set the stage. Effects of light and vitamins on the capacity of *Cladochytrium* to form sporangia (Willoughby, 1962), and the events involved in the differentiation of *Rhizidiomyces* (Fuller, 1962), will presumably be pursued further. Although metabolic bases for morphogenesis in the Chytridiales have not yet been studied, they are probably not too far off.

C. The Blastocladiales

1. Differentiation of Sexual Reproductive Cells

The self-fertile, hermaphroditic, 1 N mycelium of *Allomyces* forms paired sex organs (gametangia) from which male and female gametes are released and then attracted to one another by a hormonelike substance called "sirenin" (Machlis, 1958). The male organ is orange, while the female one is colorless (Fig. 4, top left). The nonfilamentous *Blastocladiella emersonii* also produces orange and colorless multinucleate cells—albeit only one kind or the other per plant (Fig. 4, top right). Although they do not lead to conventional gametic copulation, there is good reason to consider them, too, as nonfunctional sex organs (Cantino and Hyatt, 1953a). Because both fungi were maintained in culture and studied intensively for years by a small group of workers, knowledge of sexual differentiation in them evolved systematically and with increasing sophistication as new tools became available. The cross-fertilization (Cantino and Turian, 1959) which gradually ensued has led to promising notions about mechanisms of gametogenesis.

The literature on *Allomyces* dates back to the turn of the century, when Butler (1911) first described it, and Barrett (1912) isolated it in pure culture. However, it was 1929 before Kniep described its type of sex which was previously unknown in fungi, involving copulation of planogametes derived from paired sex organs—one, orange and terminal, and the other, colorless, subterminal, and attached to the mycelium. A year later, Kniep (1930) reported a second *Allomyces* in which arrangement of such pairs was reversed; the colorless cells were terminal, and orange ones subterminal. Once pure cultures had been obtained, along with a well-documented life history, and a solid background of descriptive morphology, there followed quickly a series of important reports (Fig. 4). Hatch (1935) made early observations of cytodifferentiation during the

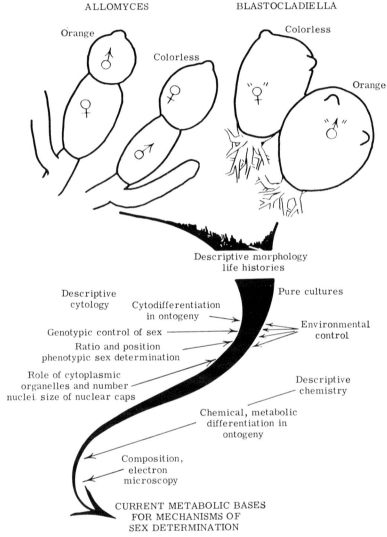

FIG. 4. Sexual differentiation in the Blastocladiales, and the evolution of current concepts about the mechanisms involved therein.

ontogeny of sex organs. Although these led him to postulate incorrectly the site of reduction division, stimuli for further work were provided, particularly by his thoughts on the possible role of mitochondria in differentiation. At about this time, Matthews (1937) described a new genus, *Blastocladiella*. Unlike *Allomyces,* it was not mycelial—rather, it displayed a determinate system of growth—but, like *Allomyces,* it could (as shown by Harder and Sörgel, 1938) form orange and colorless cells.

Emerson (1941) extensively surveyed life histories of *Allomyces,* described some departures therefrom, added new subgenera, and made crosses in an effort to learn about the genetic control of sex ratios and the position of gametangia relative to one another. The orange pigment in the male was identified as chiefly γ-carotene (Emerson and Fox, 1940). By mid-century, following the first detailed study (Emerson and Wilson, 1949; C. M. Wilson, 1952) of meiosis in any aquatic Phycomycete, it was established that the orange and colorless gametangia are haploid and that reduction division occurs elsewhere in the life history. Thus, differentiation of sex organs on the same hypha apparently does not result from segregation of sex chromosomes or genes; all nuclei originate by mitosis from a $1\,N$ nucleus in the spore from which the gametophyte is born. Such a situation is spoken of as *phenotypic* sex determination (in contrast to genotypic; Emerson, 1955). Finally, the work Emerson started in the late 1930's culminated in thorough documentation and discussion (Emerson and Wilson, 1954; Emerson, 1955) of the genetics, cytogenetics, and cytotaxonomy of the genus. Specifically, it was concluded that arrangements of gametangial pairs are ultimately controlled by the genotype, and that a wide range of hybrid forms is created by interspecific crossings in which the sex ratio appears to be controlled by a polygenic system.

At about this time, a new species of *Blastocladiella, B. emersonii,* was described in detail (Cantino, 1951; Cantino and Hyatt, 1953a). It, too, produces orange cells which are "phenotypically" determined. Thus, by the early 1950's it was clear (Fig. 4) that differentiation of sexually functional orange and colorless cells in *Allomyces,* and similar but apparently nonsexually functional ones in *Blastocladiella,* can be controlled and manipulated experimentally.

Since the immediate manifestation of sexual disjunction in *Allomyces* is the orange pigment in the male organ, it is no surprise that attention was swiftly turned toward it. Whiffen (1951) found that cycloheximide induces deposition of orange pigment in the $2\,N$ sporophytes of *Allomyces* with concomitant production of orange sex organs. Therefore, she suggested that cycloheximide may exert its effect by inducing chromosome reduction. Conversely, diphenylamine inhibits pigment formation and, when sex cells are thus rendered colorless, the decrease in γ-carotene is associated with an increase in δ-carotene and phytofluene (Turian, 1957a; Turian and Haxo, 1954). In *Blastocladiella,* too, the pigment in orange cells is predominantly γ-carotene (Cantino and Hyatt, 1953b), cycloheximide induces an extraordinary increase in its synthesis (i.e., up to a 40-fold increase) and in the incidence of orange cells in populations of the fungus (Cantino and Hyatt, 1953a). Moreover, diphenylamine depresses formation of carotenoids (Cantino and Horenstein, 1956b). Clearly, within obvious genetic lines of demarcation, differentiation of orange and colorless cells—that is, phenotypic sex determination—is profoundly subject to environmental control in both *Allomyces* and *Blastocladiella.*

Intensive work now began along different lines, and new techniques facilitated progress along the old ones. Electron microscopy revealed (Turian and Kellenberger, 1956) rings of mitochondria around the nuclear apparatus in gametes of *Allomyces,* and set the pace for studies of fine structure in the Blastocladiales. Also, new techniques for handling sexual generations of *Allomyces* were worked out. When gametophytes grow in liquid culture, the release of gametes is quickly followed by formation of $2N$ sporophytes from zygotes resulting from gametic copulation and/or from female gametes via parthenogenesis. Consequently, a mixed culture of $1N$ and $2N$ thalli ensues quickly. Turian (1955) overcame this difficulty by preventing gametic fusion with boric acid. This made it possible to propagate sexual generations in liquid media, and to study gametogenesis without contamination by the sporophyte. But most important was the fact that Emerson and Wilson (Emerson, 1955) had created interspecific hybrids, from parents with normal male:female ratios (i.e., unity), which bear less than one female organ for every thousand male organs and which are in effect, therefore, male strains. Their potential utility was exploited further, as we shall see.

With *Blastocladiella,* on the other hand, the fact that a thallus can produce *either* an orange cell *or* a colorless cell (but not both at once) permits certain direct observations of the wild type on solid media. For example, the ratio of orange:colorless cells in a population depends upon the age and nature of their parents (Cantino and Hyatt, 1953a). It is also of great interest that although most swarmers from an orange cell are not viable (their inability to retract flagella is believed to be the cause), a few of them do germinate and grow directly into new blastocladiellas. *Thus, in sharp contrast to Allomyces, the nonfunctional male "gametes" of B. emersonii are capable of ephebogenesis.* But here, too, further progress came with the isolation of mutant strains (Cantino, 1953; Cantino and Hyatt, 1953b) which, much like the male hybrids of *Allomyces,* produce orange cells exclusively. From this point on, studies of *Allomyces* and *Blastocladiella* diverged for a few years, but they complemented one another, gradually converged, and finally anastomosed to reinforce the fabric woven from earlier observations.

Comparisons of the orange mutant of *Blastocladiella* with the wild type (Cantino and Hyatt, 1953b,c) revealed that isocitric, succinic, malic, and α-ketoglutaric-dehydrogenases, fumarase, aconitase, and cytochrome oxidase activities are demonstrable in cell-free preparations of colorless cells. However, in orange cells fumarase and malic dehydrogenase are lower by 50% or more, and aconitase and α-ketoglutaric dehydrogenase are virtually missing. Thus, the mutant appears to be incapable of carrying out the two, successive oxidative decarboxylations in the Krebs cycle. This led to the notion that orange cells of *B. emersonii* possess an enzymatic lesion which prevents normal turnover of the tricarboxylic acid cycle, the consequent lack of reducing power leading via shunts to accumulation of the γ-carotene characteristic of an orange cell. At a different level of organization, a new, Nadi-positive, cytoplasmic "gamma" particle, possibly a lysosome, was discovered in *B. emersonii* (Cantino and Horenstein, 1954, 1956b; Cantino *et al.*, 1963). Such particles are less numerous in orange cells than colorless ones, and their number responds to treatments with diphenylamine and cycloheximide as does synthesis of carotene itself. Thus, it was thought that the metabolic lesion in an orange cell may result from—or at least be related to—this deficiency of "gamma" particles, and that the overall defect induces the genesis of an orange "sex" cell in *B. emersonii*.

With *Allomyces,* comparative studies were at first cytological and cytochemical rather than metabolic. Although $1 N$ and $2 N$ generations were shown (Machlis and Crasemann, 1956) to be similar in nutrition and growth rates [and recently, in glutamine synthetase and dehydrogenase activities (Klinkhammer, 1959)], sex determination was not the issue in this work. Starting with undifferentiated gametophytes, Turian (1957b, 1958) described the early phases of sexual differentiation. Since Hatch (1935) had suggested that differential distribution of mitochondria might be responsible for sexual disjunction, Turian explored this further. He found that not all "mitochondria"-like particles in the region undergoing sexual differentiation react strongly to the Nadi reagent; indeed, those that do are more numerous in the colorless female than in the orange male organ. This situation is in harmony with that in *Blastocladiella,* where a low content of Nadi-positive "gamma" particles is associated with orange cells and a higher content with colorless cells. Along with Foley's (1958) reaffirmation of the possibilities for cytoplasmic control of sex in *Allomyces,* this lends emphasis again to the apparent homology between orange and colorless "sporangia" of *Blastocladiella* and male and female gametangia of *Allomyces.*

In *Allomyces,* sex organs differ in two other important respects: the greater number of nuclei per unit volume of male protoplast, and the greater size of the nuclear cap per unit volume of female protoplast. Turian showed that although nuclei are randomly distributed in fertile, hyphal tips before septation, a *differentiated* male organ still contains about the same number of nuclei as the much larger (ca. fourfold) female organ. Thus, male nuclei appear to multiply 4 times as fast as female nuclei after a cross wall delimits these sexual territories. As for the nuclear cap, its basophilic properties result largely from its content of RNA (Turian, 1956; compare with *Blastocladiella:* Cantino et al., 1963; Lovett, 1963). But even before caps are formed, basophilic intensity in the protoplast of a young, female organ is already greater than in the male. This difference is detectable when the cytoplasm becomes granular. It becomes more pronounced when nuclear caps are finally organized, apparently by an aggregation of preexisting ribosomes (Blondel and Turian, 1960), around gametic nuclei at the cleavage stage. Furthermore, the increase in basophily of a female organ is independent of its position relative to the male (Turian, 1958). This led to the thought that a potential gradient for RNA synthesis exists long before it manifests itself visibly (and as shown later, chemically; Turian, 1961a), during maturation of the sex organs. The notion thus developed that the cytoplasm of a young male organ constitutes a zone of intense utilization of RNA, whereby it is converted to DNA needed for the increased rate of nuclear multiplication found therein. Conversely, the more sluggish nuclear reproduction in the female permits retention of this RNA and, therefore, formation of the larger nuclear caps so typical of the colorless sex organ. Some of these relationships were then quantified by chemical analyses.

Thymine induces increased numbers of male organs in *Allomyces* (Turian, 1958) and increases the DNA:RNA ratio in *Blastocladiella* (Turian and Cantino, 1959) and, as shown subsequently (Turian, 1961a), in *Allomyces* too. Subsequent analyses revealed (Turian, 1961c, 1962) that the DNA:RNA ratio in the orange male of *Allomyces* is one and one-half to two times greater than in a colorless female and that it can be traced back to an early stage in sexual morphogenesis when differential nuclear multiplication in the male first becomes detectable. It appears as though (a) the DNA:RNA ratio begins to fall in the female organ because of an increase in RNA synthesis which, as we have seen, is finally expressed in massive nuclear caps; and (b) the DNA:RNA ratio remains high in the male organ because net synthesis of DNA is maintained at a high level while net synthesis of RNA is lower, and this is finally expressed in relatively thin nuclear caps.

Finally, attempts were made to relate these nucleic acid transformations to metabolism. The *Allomyces* male displays less reducing power than the female (Chodat and Turian, 1955). Extracts of a male hybrid possess (Turian, 1960b) less succinic and α-ketoglutaric dehydrogenase but more lactic dehydrogenase activity than a female *Allomyces*. Krebs cycle inhibitors like malonate and arsenite (Turian, 1960a), as well as acetate, promote the genesis of orange male organs in hybrid females. This led to the observation (Turian, 1961b) that isocitritase and glycine-alanine transaminase activities are more abundant in males than in females and that the acetate induction of increased maleness actually brings on a simultaneous increase in isocitritase activity. The current notion, therefore, is that an orange male organ is characterized by a lesion in oxidative metabolism—presumably in the Krebs cycle—and that the glyoxylate cycle may provide an alternative route by which it carries on. Once these enzymes from *Allomyces* have been partially purified, their properties determined, and their activities *per cell* established during the genesis of male and female organs, mycologists may find themselves with the most well-defined metabolic basis for sexual differentiation in a water mold—perhaps in any fungus.

By way of summary, these investigations with *Blastocladiella* and *Allomyces* have complemented one another nicely although some major gaps, of course, remain. To begin with, extensive genetic work with *Allomyces* provides an important fabric in which the results of other studies of sexual disjunction can be interwoven. By contrast, in *B. emersonii,* wherein even the degree of ploidy is unknown, conventional genetic analysis cannot be done. Second, a lot is known about the progressive cytological changes which occur during transformations of undifferentiated hyphae into pairs of sex organs in *Allomyces;* in *Blastocladiella,* knowledge of this sort is almost nil. And third, although the number of nuclei per unit of protoplasm—and, therefore, the rate of nuclear reproduction—is known to be greater in orange cells than in colorless ones of both organisms, comparative analyses of DNA and RNA during nuclear multiplication in orange and colorless cells has been done only with *Allomyces.*

On the other hand, it is clear that in *Blastocladiella* (a) differential distribution of cytoplasmic "gamma" particles is correlated with the color of the "sex" organs, (b) electron microscopy reveals that gamma particles are *not* mitochondria (although they may be lysosomes), and (c) experimental alteration of the number of gamma particles per cell with chemicals is associated with a simultaneous change in color (i.e., in "sex") of the cell. In *Allomyces,* the relation between cytoplasmic particles and sex has not been manipulated, and the degree of possible plasticity is not known.

Finally, in both *Blastocladiella* and *Allomyces,* orange cells appear to display two main lesions, one in common and one different, in the tricarboxylic acid cycle. To what degree, and by what mechanism, these differences may be causally related to synthesis of carotene and the nucleic acid transformations characteristic of an orange male organ remains to be established.

2. Differentiation of Asexual Reproductive Cells

Almost all the Blastocladiales produce a well-defined, multinucleate cell—known as a "resting spore," a "resistant sporangium," or, when appropriate, a "meiosporangium"—which possesses a thick, brown, and usually pitted wall. We shall refer to it as the RS cell. Under appropriate conditions, its protoplast is converted into motile spores which are released and germinate to start a second generation. Among the saprophytic Blastocladiales which we shall discuss, thin-walled, colorless, unpitted multinucleate cells—called zoosporangia, or when appropriate, mitosporangia—are also formed. Their protoplasts, too, are converted into motile spores. In *Allomyces* and *Blastocladia,* both sporangial types can form on the same thallus; in *Blastocladiella,* only one or the other is produced. A good deal is known about the mechanism which underlies this dual capacity for morphogenesis, and we shall try to trace its history.

Morphological descriptions date back to Reinsch's (1878) discovery of the organism now known (Petersen, 1909) as *Blastocladia*. The brown, thick-walled, pitted cells borne on its thallus received further attention, notably from Thaxter (1896), von Minden (1916), Kanouse (1927), Blackwell (1937, 1940), and Lloyd (1938). With the discoveries of *Allomyces* (Butler, 1911) and *Blastocladiella* (Matthews, 1937), and the works which followed (Couch and Whiffen, 1942; other references cited in previous sections), the RS cell became diagnostic for all the Blastocladiales. By the early 1940's, its morphology and behavior were well known; they are nicely summarized by Sparrow (1960, p. 610): "The peculiar, often pitted, resting spores so characteristic of this order are unquestionably a device for tiding the plant over unfavorable environmental circumstances. Unlike other parts of the fungus they can withstand drying and freezing and probably high temperatures. Although found for the most part on the zoospore-bearing plant they are occasionally observed on the gametophyte, if it is formed. Their structure in practically all instances is identical. In the early stages of development they resemble in position and shape ordinary zoosporangia. The increasing density and darkening of the protoplasm and the thickening and pigmentation of the wall, however, together with the lack of formation of discharge papillae, soon distinguish them from developing zoosporangia. . . . At maturity the obpyriform, ovoid, clavate, beaked, or sometimes spherical resting spore is more or less closely enveloped by the thin wall of the container within which it lies. The outer wall of the spore is thick, of varying shades of brown, and usually perforated by innumerable minute inwardly directed cone-shaped pits or pores. The apices of these pores are in contact with a second, thinner, smooth colorless wall which surrounds the cytoplasm. The living contents, although considerably masked by the pigmented outer wall, are composed of numerous large fat globules imbedded in a finely granular matrix. The resting spores vary somewhat in shape in the different species, but they frequently have a narrow truncate base and, for the most part, are broadest slightly above the equatorial region. . . . Although the container or hyphal sheath may burst to liberate its resting spore, more commonly it persists around the resting spore and is shed with it. If persistent, upon germination the container bursts and the thick outer wall of the resting spore cracks open along a preformed line. Discharge papillae develop on the bulging, exposed, thin, inner wall and deliquesce to form pores through which the posteriorly uniflagellate planonts emerge. . . . In certain forms a somewhat prolonged discharge tube is produced. What type of plant is subsequently developed from these swarmers depends upon the particular organism involved."

Although these facts about the RS cell have been known for many years, the mechanism of its formation remained a mystery until about the middle of this century. Then, with a sudden burst of activity—and in little more than a decade—knowledge about the formation of these thick-walled cells was accumulated, along one path for *Allomyces* and another for *Blastocladia* and *Blastocladiella*. It is convenient to consider them separately.

a. *Allomyces*. On yeast–starch agar (Emerson, 1941), sporophytes of *Allomyces* produce RS cells without special treatment, and they mature (i.e., can produce spores) in 3–6 weeks. Notably through the efforts of Emerson (1950), Emerson and Wilson (1949), C. M. Wilson (1952), Rorem and Machlis (1957), and Machlis and Ossia (1953a,b), our understanding of RS development in *Allomyces* has made remarkable progress. Part of it is best summarized in Emerson's (1955, p. 196) own words: "When young resistant sporangia are first formed at the hyphal tips their protoplasm is evenly granular and similar to that of the vegetative hyphae. Within about 48 hours, however, aceto-orcein smears reveal many spherical, deeply staining bodies that have appeared quite suddenly and form a conspicuous part of the cytoplasm. They are one to several microns in diameter, and we have called them *chromospheres* because of their shape and staining properties. They persist in the resistant sporangia during the entire period of maturation, which lasts from one or two to many weeks depending upon the isolate concerned and the conditions of culture. Then, very suddenly, probably in less than 24 hours, all the chromospheres are disintegrated and disappear. Simultaneously the expanded diploid nuclei are revealed and prove to be in an advanced prophase of Meiosis I. If the RS are air-dried at this time they can remain viable for at least twenty years with meiosis arrested in prophase. . . . If, however, they are placed in water as soon as the chromospheres have disappeared, they will usually germinate." Finally, during this last stage, both meiotic divisions are completed. As Emerson (1955, p. 198) points out, ". . . shortly before the spores are being cleaved out, aceto-orcein smears again reveal momentarily spherical masses of deeply staining material in the cytoplasm. These have been called . . . post-meiotic chromospheres, to distinguish them from the pre-meiotic chromospheres that are found during the maturation period. They appear to coalesce and form the nuclear caps which are so conspicuous in the spores of the Blastocladiales. . . . The precision of their appearance and disappearance and the regularity of their association with meiosis and the motile stages of *Allomyces* mark them as distinctive cytochemical features with morphogenetic roles of undoubted significance."

Thus, disappearance of chromospheres, appearance of nuclei at prophase of meiosis I, and attainment of capacity to germinate occur simultaneously and signify RS maturation. Machlis and Ossia succeeded in reducing the maturation time in liquid media, and showed that (a) indoleacetic acid accelerates disappearance of chromospheres; (b) swelling of the protoplast, like germination itself, will not occur if chromospheres are still present; and (c) additional factors are also involved in the attainment of maturity. Further cytological work (Turian, 1957c) suggested that both pre- and postmeiotic chromospheres are rich in RNA; at the same time, Rorem and Machlis (1957) isolated premeiotic chromospheres and showed that they contain 12% RNA and 60% protein, but no DNA. Thus, it seems probable that premeiotic chromospheres are nucleoprotein organelles which, after meiosis, reappear as postmeiotic chromospheres and finally collect around the nuclei to become spore nuclear caps.

This notion has been greatly strengthened by Lovett's (1963) isolation of the nuclear caps themselves from *Blastocladiella*. The cap contains 60% protein and 40% RNA, and its amino acid composition is similar to that of ribosomal protein of other organisms. Over 95% of the particles in the cap have a sedimentation coefficient of 83 S (in 0.005 M Mg), contain 63% RNA and 37% protein, and are dissociable into 63 S and 41 S particles. Clearly, the nuclear cap appears to be a package of ribosomes. Further discussion is provided in Cantino *et al.* (1963), Cantino and Lovett (1964), and in Lovett (1963).

b. *Blastocladia.* The capacity of *Blastocladia* to produce RS cells has always been apparent to those who have collected it in nature. But in striking contrast to *Allomyces,* when it was isolated (Emerson and Cantino, 1948), in pure culture it promptly refused to produce them even though, in all other respects, it seemed to grow well. This dilemma was resolved when it was learned (Emerson and Cantino, 1948; Cantino, 1949) that (a) it requires very little oxygen for growth and is at least microaerophyllic, if not facultatively anaerobic. Moreover, it does, indeed, produce RS provided that it is grown under extraordinarily high CO_2 tensions (literally, a stream of tank CO_2) and at a suitable pH. A metabolic shift, involving the liberation of more succinate and less lactate, is associated with the shift in morphogenesis. Although knowledge of the nutrition of the genus has been extended since that time (Crasemann, 1957), the CO_2 effect on RS formation has not been pursued further. However, the slack was quickly picked up in its close relative, *B. emersonii*.

c. *Blastocladiella*. Under ordinary circumstances on solid media, over 99% of the spores of *B. emersonii* give rise, upon germination, to plants with a determinate system of growth (Fig. 5); the terminal sporangium is thin walled and not obviously pigmented. When such a first-generation ordinary colorless (OC) cell is mature, it proliferates further *in situ* by liberating a crop of first-generation spores from which a clone of second-generation cells is produced. If a viable OC cell is removed from this clone and placed in a fresh environment, it will repeat the process; this cycle can continue *ad infinitum*. However, if all cells are left in place, the second-generation clone now displays its totipotency (Cantino, 1951; Cantino and Hyatt, 1953a). Some cells develop into colorless, thin-walled OC types, others differentiate into thick-walled, brown, pitted, nonproliferating RS types, and a few produce orange types. Furthermore, some OC cells cease growth prematurely, while others reproduce via spores with varying degrees of viability; in this way, new clones of third-generation progeny are formed. Thus, when this heterogeneous mass of cells finally ceases to proliferate, it consists mainly of RS cells, an occasional orange cell, and some OC cells the growth of which is interrupted at different stages in their ontogeny.

This was our understanding of *B. emersonii* in the early 1950's. In the years which followed, these developmental paths were studied in detail, at first with multiple generation cultures, and later with synchronous single generations. Consequently, it is now known that any population of spores can give rise to *four* different phenotypes (Fig. 6) which are distinguishable from one another by various parameters, and whose proportions in the population depend upon environmental conditions. Synopses of the information available on these phenotypes were published recently (Cantino, 1961, 1965a; Cantino and Lovett, 1964; Cantino and Turian, 1959).

d. *The Spore of Blastocladiella emersonii*. The living, swimming spore of *B. emersonii* measures ca. 7×9 μ, weighs (dry) between 7.6 and 11.3×10^{-5} μg, contains ca. 1.3×10^{-6} μg of DNA and ca. 20×10^{-6} μg of RNA, propels itself with a single flagellum some 20 μ long, and displays an extraordinarily high (Q_{O_2}, ca. 100) endogenous respiration.

Recent studies of its fine structure reveal a distinctive internal architecture which—for the moment, at least—is unique among the fungi (see Fig. 11). A single nucleus, with nucleolus embedded therein, is separated by a double

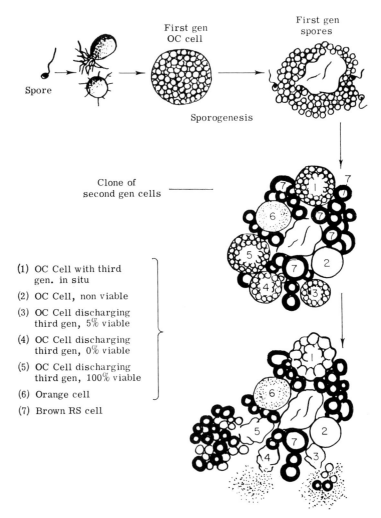

FIG. 5. Clonal development of *Blastocladiella emersonii* on solid media. Gen = generation.

membrane from its massive nuclear cap, an aggregate of 83 S ribosomal particles which accounts for 68% of the RNA in the spore. Numerous pores (100 mμ in diameter) in this membrane establish continuity between the nucleus and its cap. The flagellum has a classical internal structure, with

9 outer and 2 inner fibers, each a double structure, and is surrounded by a sheath continuous with the spore's outer membrane. The 2 central fibers terminate abruptly at the nucleus. The 9 outer fibers run through—and

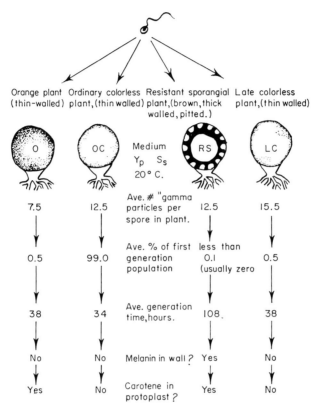

FIG. 6. The four developmental paths that can be taken by spores of *Blastocladiella emersonii*, and the gross parameters which distinguish them from one another. From Cantino (1961).

some are linked by a banded rootlet to—a mitochondrion, situated eccentrically in the posterior end of the spore and extending up along one side almost to the anterior end of the nuclear cap. This mitochondrion *is the only one in the spore* and occupies an extraordinarily large proportion of the cell's volume. Although it resembles mitochondria from other organisms, about a dozen lipid granules are attached to it peripherally in single layers and are separated from the cytoplasm by a double membrane of their own. The cytoplasm is devoid of endoplasmic reticulum, but contains randomly scattered organelles with single membranes which look like lysosomes and are undoubtedly the "gamma" particles seen earlier with the light microscope. This cellular architecture exists only in the spore, and is maintained only so long as the spore retains its flagellum (Cantino et al., 1963; Cantino and Horenstein, 1956b; Cantino and Hyatt, 1953a; Cantino and Lovett, 1964; Lovett, 1963; Lovett and Cantino, 1960b; McCurdy and Cantino, 1960; Turian and Cantino, 1959).

The spore can swim for many hours, particularly if it is placed in water and thus deprived of exogenous nutrients. This is not surprising, for it is supplied with a large amount of lipid, ca. 48 µg of soluble protein and ca. 50 µg of soluble polysaccharide per milligram dry weight. Because of its high glucose 6-phosphate- and 6-phosphogluconic dehydrogenase activities, and its high capacity for producing lactic acid ($0.25\ \mu M \times$ mg dry $wt^{-1} \times hr^{-1}$), it is thought that polysaccharide (apparently disposable via the first steps of the hexose monophosphate shunt) is the main source of energy. The intimate contact between the mitochondrion and flagellum may provide the device which transduces this chemical energy into flagellar motion (Cantino and Goldstein, 1961; Cantino and Lovett, 1960, 1964; Lovett and Cantino, 1960b).

Prior to germination, the spore stops swimming and retracts its flagellum. The process is irreversible and takes but a few moments. Simultaneously, the nucleus and its cap rotate about 270 degrees in one direction within the cell while the flagellum, in complementary fashion, curves in a wide arc in the opposite direction as it is being pulled in. The nuclear cap is then dispersed, and the spore sends out a germ tube which later gives rise to the rhizoidal system of the cell. Currently, little is known about the significance of this relation between the turning of the flagellum and rotation of the cap, the dispersal of the ribosomes in the cap, and the fate of the absorbed flagellum. Recent pictures obtained by Lovett (unpublished data, 1965) with the electron microscope, however, reveal that the retracted flagellum can be detected within the body of the spore after it has been withdrawn. The reader can be certain that these phenomena will be studied intensively in the future (Cantino, et al., 1963; Cantino and Lovett, 1964).

e. Genesis and Nature of the OC Cell. In liquid media which support vigorous growth, the spore sends out a germ tube (Fig. 7, top left), and its nucleus divides mitotically by a process in which the nuclear membrane remains intact. The germ tube develops into extensive, tapering, nonseptate rhizoids and, at the same time, the cell enlarges several hundredfold. Later, a cross wall is laid down (Fig. 7, bottom left) which delimits the thallus into a tiny, basal, rhizoid-bearing cell and an apical, multinucleate, fertile cell. Since the lower cell is devoid of protoplasm at maturity, development is from a uninucleate spore to a multinucleate but unicelled thallus. Finally, the terminal cell which contains all the protoplasm is partitioned into hundreds of uninucleate spores which are released through pores formed by the dissolution of several papillae. If these first-generation spores

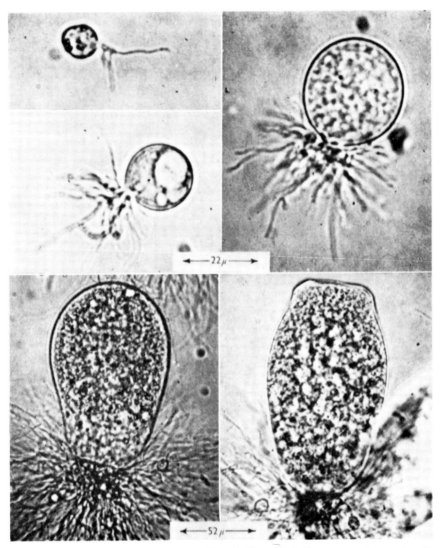

FIG. 7. The appearance of OC cells of *Blastocladiella emersonii* growing in synchronous, single-generation culture. From A. Goldstein and Cantino (1962).

are collected from many plants at once, an extremely heavy suspension can be obtained with which millions of *Blastocladiella* cells have been grown synchronously for a single generation and induced to differentiate into either OC or RS cells (A. Goldstein and Cantino, 1962; Lovett and Cantino, 1960b; McCurdy and Cantino, 1960; Turian and Cantino, 1960). Let us see what has been done with the OC cells.

Chemical analyses of growing OC cells reveal that changes, not detectable microscopically, occur. Starting with the germinating spore, its nuclear cap disintegrates, its DNA doubles, simultaneously its RNA decreases almost proportionately, and then the first nuclear division occurs. Thus, the disappearance of the RNA-containing nuclear cap is apparently associated with the synthesis of DNA necessary for the manufacture of the first daughter nucleus (Turian and Cantino, 1959). Then the cell begins its exponential phase of growth.

In vitro, crude cell-free extracts of OC cells can mediate (Cantino, 1965a): (a) conversion of fructose 1,6-diphosphate to phosphoglycerate via a DPN-specific, iodoacetate-sensitive triosephosphate dehydrogenase; (b) metabolism of phosphoglycerate through a slower, fluoride-sensitive step (between triosephosphate and pyruvate) to lactate via a strong DPN-specific lactic dehydrogenase; (c) a DPN-specific side reaction forming α-glycerophosphate; (d) formation of glucose 6-phosphate via a rate-limiting hexokinase, which can lead to glycerophosphate and lactate, or be metabolized by way of a TPN-specific glucose 6-phosphate dehydrogenase. *In vivo,* a growing OC cell can actually carry on a predominantly homolactic fermentation. A nonproliferating cell is capable of dissimilating glucose fermentatively, whereby no oxygen is consumed or CO_2 produced, and the only labeled nonnitrogenous acid formed from labeled glucose is lactic acid (Brown and Cantino, 1955; Cantino, 1951, 1965b; Cantino and Horenstein, 1956a).

Apparently, an OC cell also has the capacity to carry on the tricarboxylic acid cycle, judging from the facts that (a) intermediates of the cycle are metabolized *in vivo,* and almost all of them are detectable in the cell's soluble pool when previously labeled with C^{14}; and (b) extracts of an OC cell contain the activities of a CN-sensitive aconitase, TPN-specific isocitric dehydrogenase, DPN-dependent arsenite-sensitive α-ketoglutaric dehydrogenase, malonate-sensitive succinic dehydrogenase, fumarase, DPN-dependent oxalacetate-sensitive malic dehydrogenase, and a cyanide-sensitive cytochrome oxidase (Cantino, 1951, 1953; Cantino and Horenstein, 1956a; Cantino and Hyatt, 1953b,c).

What happens to these and other aspects of the cell's machinery in ontogeny? During exponential growth of the OC cell, its weight and its polysaccharide pool increase exponentially at identical rates; on the other hand, although its soluble protein pool also increases exponentially, the rate is only 78% of the above. Similarly, synthesis of a glucose 6-phosphate dehydrogenase also proceeds at the same rate as growth itself, whereas synthesis of isocitritase does not occur at all until half the cell's generation time has gone by. Thus, during its exponential growth, various components of the OC cell are synthesized at differential exponential rates and, therefore, the composition of the cell does not remain constant. Furthermore, differential

10. Morphogenesis in Aquatic Fungi

rates of synthesis during growth are themselves affected differentially by environmental factors (Cantino, 1961; Cantino and Lovett, 1964; A. Goldstein and Cantino, 1962; McCurdy and Cantino, 1960). The inherent plasticity of the OC cell's metabolic machinery, and its susceptibility to exogenous control, is revealed in striking fashion, as discussed below.

f. Effect of Light on the OC Cell. The early stages in ontogeny, down to the first nuclear division, are accelerated by white light (as compared to a dark-grown OC cell). Cytologically, the rate of nuclear reproduction is increased 30–40%; chemically, the ratio of DNA:total nucleic acid increases. Since exogenous thymine (but not uracil) substitutes for light, thymine synthesis may be a limiting barrier in the growth of *B. emersonii*. Light also alters glycine uptake by the cell, which is totally dependent upon the presence of exogenous CO_2 and/or bicarbonate. These effects, however, are not limited to the germling stage. For example, light causes older cells to consume more glycine-2-C^{14}, and, simultaneously, net synthesis of labeled DNA increases. These effects occur when nuclear divisions and DNA synthesis in the dark-grown cell have almost come to a complete halt, but may be induced to continue by illumination. Thus, prolongation of the cell's generation time is involved, which also requires exogenous bicarbonate. Furthermore, light causes an OC cell to fix $C^{14}O_2$ at twice the dark rate, a rate change which is accompanied by a twofold increase in the internal pool of labeled succinate. Such cells grow more rapidly in volume, with altered internal ratio of organic:inorganic P, and different quantities of inorganic P released into the medium, along with a decrease in the pool of free amino acids. Finally, a fully mature OC light-grown cell in synchronous culture contains 51% more dry weight, 28% more nucleic acid, 37% more protein, and 74% more polysaccharide than its dark-grown counterpart; simultaneously, even the composition of its protein pool is altered. It is not surprising, then, that patterns of enzyme synthesis are also different in light and dark grown cells, including those of glucose 6-phosphate and 6-phosphogluconic dehydrogenases, arginase, glutaminase, asparaginase, ornithine transcarbamylase, and undoubtedly others. For some of these effects, 100 foot-candles of white light is sufficient, the effective wavelengths lying between 400 and 500 mµ. Identification of the elusive light receptor has been a serious stumbling block, but there are indications (Cantino, 1965b) that it may be a protein-bound porphyrin; proof of this would remove a major hurdle in this work. But whatever the final result, the fact remains that *B. emersonii* is a water mold devoid of chlorophyll; its astonishing response to visible radiation is unique and represents, apparently, the only well-documented example of a nonchlorophyllous organism which, *provided CO_2 is available,* grows more rapidly in the light than in the dark (Cantino, 1959; Cantino and Horenstein, 1957, 1959; Cantino and Turian,

1961; Domnas and Cantino, 1965; Goldstein and Cantino, 1962; Turian and Cantino, 1959).

g. Effect of Bicarbonate on Development. The plasticity of *B. emersonii*'s metabolic machinery has been demonstrated in more detail in another way. It will be recalled (Fig. 6) that a population of spores may develop into four distinct kinds of cells. However, virtually all germlings—except the very few destined to become orange—form the thick-walled, brown, pitted RS cells if ca. $10^{-2}\,M$ bicarbonate is incorporated in the growth medium. In effect, over 99% of the spores, which ordinarily would have become OC cells, are induced to develop along a new path. The response is not due, per se, to shifts in pH or CO_2 partial pressure (Cantino, 1951, 1956; A. Goldstein and Cantino, unpublished data, 1963) because bicarbonate itself, at a suitable pH, is the principal agent involved. External conditions can be set up, however, such that bicarbonate alone does not suffice unless it is augmented with α-ketoglutarate, or an oxidative decarboxylation inhibitor (i.e., arsenite), or a keto-binding reagent (i.e., semicarbazide). In order to discuss the mechanism of this bicarbonate trigger mechanism, let us first see how mature RS and OC cells differ.

h. Nature of the RS Cell Produced in Response to Bicarbonate. The thick wall of an RS cell is impregnated with melanin and tyrosinase; an OC cell contains neither. The RS cell wall has about 4 times more chitin than the thin wall of an OC cell. An RS protoplast contains about 8×10^{-6} μg γ-carotene whereas an OC cell contains none. Microscopically, an RS protoplast has more lipid-like globules than an OC cell. Furthermore, in an RS cell (versus an OC cell), the free amino acid pool—the tyrosine content in particular—is smaller, and the composition of its soluble protein is markedly different, both quantitatively and qualitatively. Clearly, the bicarbonate trigger mechanism involves machinery for the *de novo* synthesis of melanin and carotene, increased synthesis of chitin and lipids, and a multitude of other events sooner or later associated with morphogenesis. It is no surprise, therefore, that physiological and enzymatic changes are also detectable. Endogenous respiration in an OC cell is about 200 times greater than in an RS cell. Almost all the enzyme activities of the Krebs cycle, easily demonstrable in an OC cell, are lost or greatly reduced in an RS cell, as is cytochrome oxidase. However, an RS cell retains a high level of isocitric dehydrogenase and, indeed, possesses *more* isocitritase and glycine-alanine transaminase activity than an OC cell (Cantino *et al.*, 1957; Cantino and Goldstein, 1962; Cantino and Horenstein, 1955, 1956a; Cantino and Hyatt, 1953b; McCurdy and Cantino, 1960).

The biochemical events in the bicarbonate trigger mechanism which appear to be responsible are summarized in Fig. 8. Bicarbonate induces multiple enzymatic lesions in the tricarboxylic acid cycle and, simultaneously, a directional shift in the operation of the isocitric dehydrogenase which remains—from oxidative decarboxylation of isocitrate to reductive carboxylation of α-ketoglutarate. Isocitrate is removed via isocitritase, and the glyoxylate is metabolized via glycine-alanine transaminase. With synchronized single-generation RS populations, per-cell data were obtained

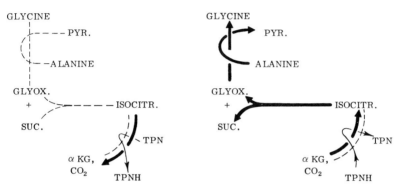

FIG. 8. The basic, bicarbonate-induced, presumably causal metabolic shift associated with the genesis of an RS cell. From Cantino (1961).

about the way in which these and other characteristics of the RS cell evolve during ontogeny.

i. Exponential Growth of the Young RS Cell. Precise data are available for the increase in weight, volume, chitin, lipid, polysaccharide, DNA, RNA, total N, soluble protein, enzyme activities (glucosamine synthetase, isocitric-, α-ketoglutaric-, and glucose 6-phosphate dehydrogenases, glycine-alanine transaminase, isocitritase, and others), etc., all on a per-cell basis. Furthermore, some enzymes were partially concentrated and characterized. The isocitritase was purified about 50-fold, and its reversibility, pH optimum (7.4), specificity for the D-isomer, requirement for -SH groups and Mg^{++} or Mn^{++}, its Michaelis constant ($4.8 \times 10^{-4} M$), activation energy (10,700 cal/mole), and Q_{10} (1.8) for the reaction established. The glycine-alanine transaminase, never heretofore purified from any other source, was concentrated 80-fold, and its reversibility, pH optimum (8.5), requirement for pyridoxal phosphate, high degree of stability, and specificity for alanine were determined. The glucosamine synthetase (glutamine–fructose 6-phosphate transamidase) was purified about 20-fold, and it, too, was characterized. Exponential synthesis of many of these enzymes and metabolites occurs during exponential growth of an RS cell, and the rates for a good number of them are different. Thus, like an OC cell, the RS cell simply does not maintain a constant composition during its exponential growth (Cantino and Lovett, 1964; Lovett and Cantino, 1960a,b; McCurdy and Cantino, 1960).

Microscopically, the young RS cell looks much like a young OC cell (compare Fig. 9, 24-hour cell with Fig. 7, top). Nonetheless, such cells have embarked upon different paths. It is here during exponential growth and long before morphological differentiation occurs, that control devices involved in morphogenesis are initiated. But not all occurrences are simultaneous: some are first detected in early exponential growth and cease long before it ends, others commence later and do not halt until growth has stopped, and some do not even begin until exponential growth has ceased (Fig. 10). Let us examine some of these devices.

A spore's endogenous oxygen consumption is inhibited by arsenite and malonate, and the effect of the latter is overcome by succinate. But once the organism begins development along the RS path (versus the OC path), its respiration drops precipitously, exogenous glucose is not consumed, its exponential growth rate is reduced by 46%, and exponential synthesis of its pool of polysaccharide (relative to dry weight) is doubled. At the enzyme level, spore germination is followed immediately by exponential synthesis of isocitritase. By the end of its exponential growth, oxygen consumption has been reduced to one-tenth the level of the spore. Simultaneously, the total isocitric dehydrogenase activity per cell rises 6500-fold, but the total activity of the α-ketoglutaric dehydrogenase increases only one-tenth as much. Thus, *the 10-fold reduction in oxygen consumption induced by bicarbonate appears to result from a corresponding 10-fold decrease in the rate at which α-ketoglutaric dehydrogenase is synthesized by the cell relative to its isocitric dehydrogenase. Simultaneously, the immediate, bicarbonate-induced exponential synthesis of isocitritase apparently provides relief for this partial lesion in the Krebs cycle by mediating removal of isocitrate along a new metabolic path* (Fig. 8). It is important to reemphasize that in the OC cell growing in the absence of the morphogenetic inducer, bicarbonate, the increase in total activity per cell of *both* isocitric- and α-ketoglutaric dehydrogenase is approximately the same so that the latter does not constitute a bottleneck; conversely, isocitritase is not produced by the OC cell, and what little there was in the spore to begin with is quickly diluted out. Thus, a bicarbonate-induced alteration of metabolic pathways *during exponential growth* appears to be a major focal point for the morphological differentiation which is to follow. The tricarboxylic acid cycle is disrupted, most of its enzymes ultimately disappear, the terminal

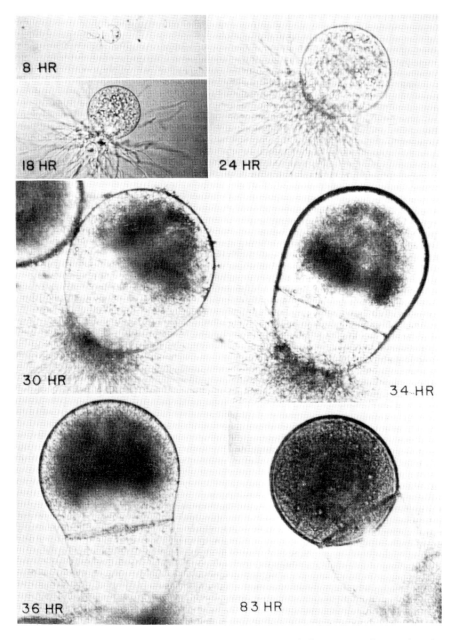

FIG. 9. The appearance of RS cells of *Blastocladiella emersonii* growing in synchronous, single generation culture. Magnification: the diameter of the spherical, 83-hour RS cell is 130 μ. From Lovett and Cantino (1960b).

cytochrome oxidase to which it was previously coupled is lost, and the flow of intermediates is shunted via isocitritase to succinate and glyoxylate, and the latter, via glycine-alanine transaminase, to glycine (Cantino, 1961; Cantino and Goldstein, 1961; Cantino and Lovett, 1960; Lovett and Cantino, 1961; McCurdy and Cantino, 1960).

The facts outlined above have been thoroughly documented. But the continued operation of this metabolic machine demands that the cell provide a supply route for generation of α-ketoglutarate to replace that being siphoned off through isocitritase, and for reduced TPN used up in the carboxylation of α-ketoglutarate. The precise mechanisms involved are not yet fully understood, but good presumptive evidence provides a probable answer to the second question. The rapid exponential synthesis of glucose 6-phosphate dehydrogenase which can generate the needed TPNH suggests that an important source of reducing power lies in the early stages of the hexose monophosphate shunt. The synthesis of polyphenol oxidase may do the same. Its appearance is associated with *de novo* deposition of melanin and with a sharp reduction in the cell's free pool of tyrosine. Electrons generated by polyphenol oxidase can be coupled to the reduction of TPN (but not DPN) instead of oxygen. Indeed, dialyzed preparations of the enzyme are relatively inactive unless provided with bicarbonate and α-ketoglutarate. Thus, a second major source of reducing power for carboxylation of α-ketoglutarate seems to lie on the path to melanogenesis (Cantino *et al.*, 1957; Cantino and Horenstein, 1955, 1959; Cantino and Lovett, 1964; Lovett and Cantino, 1960b).

j. Differentiation of the RS Cell. The next phase in development is the transition from exponential growth to the differentiation of a thick-walled, brown, pitted cell. Associated with this is a morphological "point of no return" before which RS formation can still be reversed. On certain solid media (Cantino, 1952), it is about 60% of the RS generation time. Removal of bicarbonate before this stage in ontogeny causes the fungus to reverse its developmental path and to mature into an OC cell, but beyond this time, the shift in morphology does not occur. In synchronized liquid cultures, this "point of no return" is reduced to 43% of the RS cell's 84-hour generation time. The biochemical bases which underlie the "point of no return" have been examined in some detail.

k. Reversibility of Differentiation before the "Point of No Return." Growth in the size of the cell stops when cross-wall formation is complete, and this, in turn, coincides with its irreversible commitment to RS formation (Fig. 9, 36-hour cell). Simultaneously, other events are detectable (Fig. 10): the cell's pool of amino acids and inorganic P drops; its Q_{O_2} declines even further; net synthesis of protein and DNA ceases; numerous enzymes decrease in activity. Conversely, synthesis of chitin, lipid, melanin, polysaccharide, and RNA continues without interruption for some time. Some of the earliest transformations are particularly significant. For example, both melanin and carotene appear in the young RS cell long before its morphological "point of no return." Since neither substance is normally produced by an OC cell, bicarbonate must induce two, new, biosynthetic pathways early in ontogeny. Furthermore, in addition to such all-or-none

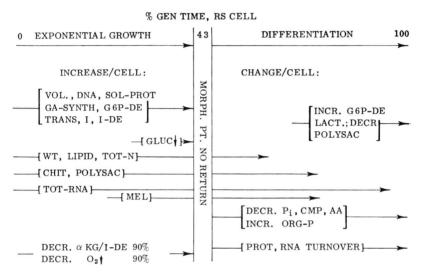

FIG. 10. The initiation and duration of the synthesis of cell components, metabolic products, etc., during exponential growth, the "point of no return," and differentiation of an RS cell. Explanation of symbols: *DNA*, deoxyribonucleic acid; *SOL-PROT*, soluble protein; *GA-SYNTH*, glucosamine synthetase; *G6P-DE*, glucose 6-phosphate dehydrogenase; *TRANS*, glycine-alanine transaminase; *I*, isocitritase; *I-DE*, isocitric dehydrogenase; *GLUC*, glucose; *WT*, dry weight; *TOT-N*, total nitrogen; *CHIT*, chitin; *POLYSAC*, soluble polysaccharide; *MEL*, melanin; *LACT*, lactic acid; P_i, orthophosphate; *CMP*, cytidylic acid; *AA*, amino acids; ORG-P, organic phosphorus; *DECR aKG/I-DE*, decrease in the ratio of α-ketoglutaric/isocitric dehydrogenase activities; *DECR.* O_2, decrease in O_2 consumption; *TOT-RNA*, total RNA.

effects, bicarbonate also causes quantitative changes in metabolism before the "point of no return," i.e.: (a) a 1.8-fold increase in the exponential rate of synthesis of polysaccharide, apparently due to a metabolic shift whereby the cell's capacity to dissimilate glucose to lactic acid is suppressed while its capacity to polymerize glucose to polysaccharide is expressed; (b) a quantitative change in composition of the cell's soluble protein pool; (c) a sharp increase in total isocitritase and isocitric dehydrogenase per cell, but simultaneously, a decrease in the α-ketoglutaric dehydrogenase and, as mentioned earlier, a 46% reduction in growth rate and about a 90% drop in respiration (Cantino, 1961, 1962; Cantino and Goldstein, 1961; Cantino and Lovett, 1960; Lovett and Cantino, 1960b, 1961; McCurdy and Cantino, 1960).

Clearly, bicarbonate exerts a full-toned effect early in the ontogeny of a growing thallus of *B. emersonii,* but in spite of this an inherent morphological plasticity is retained up to the "point of no return," when an OC cell is formed if the bicarbonate inducer is removed on time. When this is done, some of the internal changes described above are also reversed—but others are not. For example, total protein per cell does not change, but its composition does, for it is converted back to one more typical of an OC cell. Part of the cell's nucleic acid pool displays a similar reversal. Furthermore, the activities of two key systems, α-ketoglutaric and isocitric dehydrogenases, rise and fall, respectively, to levels characteristic of OC cells. The fact that these two, differential, enzyme alterations occur only when consummation of RS development is prevented by removal of bicarbonate is particularly noteworthy for it is directly in agreement with their presumed role in the bicarbonate trigger mechanism. But, it is also noteworthy that some of the properties characteristic of the young RS cell are not altered upon morphological reversal. For instance, neither the small amount of melanin nor the increased quantities of chitin found in the wall of the young RS cell are degraded during its "dedifferentiation." Indeed, whereas the quantitative relationship among some protein components reverses as pointed out above, others are not altered. Although the morphological "point of no return" is sharply defined, that for the metabolic machinery which underlies it is more obtuse, perhaps because each biochemical event probably has its own "point of no return." For this reason, an OC cell derived from a developing RS cell by morphological reversal *functions* like an OC cell but it need not be—and, in fact, is not—*entirely* identical to it in total structure and composition. This in no way negates the functional significance of morphological reversibility in *B. emersonii* because no change occurs in an RS cell, prior to its "point of no return," which (upon removal of inducer) prevents it from regaining the function of an OC cell. Whatever structural changes occur before this stage in ontogeny, they do not play a central, regulatory function in RS morphogenesis (Cantino, 1961; Cantino and Goldstein, 1962; Lovett and Cantino, 1961).

l. Functional Significance of Internal Changes during Morphogenetic Reversal. To establish that internal changes are responsible for a new developmental pathway, an obligatory connection between them must be demonstrable. This requires discrimination between causal and dependent factors in morphogenesis. In this connection, let us turn first to the bicarbonate-induced melanogenesis in the RS cell. Phenylthiourea can suppress synthesis of melanin but does not otherwise interfere with RS differentia-

10. Morphogenesis in Aquatic Fungi

tion. Since melanogenesis is depressed during morphological reversal, this metabolic path requires bicarbonate for its maintenance as well as its induction. Thus, melanin appears *de novo* as a result of RS differentiation, but it is not essential to it (Cantino, 1953).

Second, consider the significance of the tricarboxylic cycle. Extensive circumstantial evidence for its role in RS formation has been cited. More direct proof came with demonstrations that certain mutants which lost their capacity to form α-ketoglutaric dehydrogenase simultaneously lost their capacity to manufacture RS cells in response to bicarbonate (Cantino, 1953; Cantino and Hyatt, 1953b,c).

The data available today do not provide an unequivocal explanation for the rapid shift from a plastic system to one that is essentially unidirectional. If some pool or pathway which reaches a critical threshold level is responsible, it has not yet been identified. More likely, however, no single factor is responsible. Thus, "The underlying biochemical events, if each of them could be viewed and taken separately, would probably have their 'points of no return' dispersed over a much broader range of time and physiological age, each with its own degree of 'indispensableness,' and each, if rendered inoperative, contributing a certain degree of somatic 'hybridity' to the protoplast of the RS cell which finally is formed. Thus, *it would be a certain cumulative degree of this hybridity* which would constitute the biochemical point of no return that underlies the morphological point of no return" (Cantino and Goldstein, 1962).

m. RS Differentiation after the "Point of No Return." Once beyond its "point of no return," the cell is led inevitably to form the resistant sporangium so characteristic of the order. The only visible sign of activity is a gradual thickening, pitting, and darkening of the wall, but, inside the cell, a great deal is going on. For example (see Fig. 10), the thallus weighs 0.63 µg at the "point of no return" and increases to about 0.86 µg by 57% of its generation time and then drops slightly. The cell's lipid and total N also rise during this period—from about 100×10^{-3} and 42×10^{-3} µg per cell to 170×10^{-3} and 55×10^{-3} µg, respectively. Later, the lipid decreases again to 142×10^{-3} µg, while the total N simply levels off. But within the N pool, differential changes occur: soluble protein N per cell reaches about 15×10^{-3} µg at the "point of no return" and then levels off, while the total soluble N per cell decreases from 36×10^{-3} to ca. 24×10^{-3} µg (due in part to a sharp loss in the soluble pool of free amino acids). Chitin continues to rise even longer, from about 470×10^{-4} µg per cell at the "point of no return" to about 880×10^{-4} µg at 72% of the generation time, and the cell's melanin pool follows a similar pattern, rising about 5-fold. The pools of free nucleotides and bases also change. Cytidylic acid rises slightly, from 5.4×10^{-6} µmole per cell at the "point of no return" to about 5.7×10^{-6} μmole at 50% of the generation time; then it drops sharply to 0.5×10^{-6} μmole by the time the RS cell matures. Free adenine rises to 4×10^{-6} μmole per cell at 55% of the generation time and then decreases to about 1.0×10^{-6} μmole. Guanine, on the other hand, exhibits no pronounced change. Some of the most striking differential changes, however, occur in the cell's RNA pool (see below). Soluble polysaccharide rises slightly after the "point of no return" (12×10^{-2} μg per cell) to about 14×10^{-2} μg per cell at 58% of the generation time; then it decreases again to 8×10^{-2} μg at 70% of the generation time. Orthophosphate, too, drops rapidly, while soluble organic P increases (Cantino, 1961; Cantino and Goldstein, 1961, 1962; Lovett and Cantino, 1960b; McCurdy and Cantino, 1960).

As might be predicted from all this, physiological changes occur as well. For example, at the "point of no return" the cell ceases to use exogenous glucose. At this time, it consumes about 6.4×10^{-3} μl oxygen per hour, which rises slightly to 6.8×10^{-3} and then quickly drops again to less than 0.5×10^{-3} μl. Conversely, a young RS does not produce lactic acid until the "point of no return" is reached. Thereafter, it releases large amounts of it into the medium. Simultaneously, the internal lactate pool also increases, from 6×10^{-5} μmole per cell at the "point of no return" to about 9×10^{-5} μmole at maturity. Although enzyme activities usually either level off or decrease, glucose 6-phosphate dehydrogenase rises greatly, from 105×10^{-5} arbitrary units per cell at the "point of no return" to 155×10^{-5} units at RS maturity.

Thus, many of the events described above begin and end (Fig. 10) during the period in ontogeny when the cell, although committed, has not yet arrived. Considerable breakdown and resynthesis occurs during the critical interval following the "point of no return" and preceding actual formation of a mature RS cell (see discussion, Cantino and Lovett, 1964). With such turmoil in the cell, this is hardly the picture of a static system.

n. Final Internal Affairs; the RS Cell as a Spore Producer. Certain transformations occur in the RNA pool during RS maturation which relate to its ultimate fate—the production of spores. Net synthesis of RNA continues until the RS cell is nearly mature. Simultaneously, the nucleic acid pool is altered chemically. Between the "point of no return" and about 78% of generation time, total RNA per cell rises from 37×10^{-6} μmole (as total RNA nucleotides) to about 65×10^{-6} μmole. This RNA can be divided into two fractions, one NaCl soluble, and the other NaCl insoluble. Immediately after the "point of no return," NaCl-insoluble RNA begins to accumulate linearly up to about 78% of the generation time, increasing 20-fold from about 2×10^{-6} μmole per cell to about 42×10^{-6} μmole. During this same period, NaCl-soluble RNA (which includes essentially

10. Morphogenesis in Aquatic Fungi

all the RNA of a young RS cell which has not yet reached its "point of no return") decreases by almost one half—from 34×10^{-6} µmole/cell to about 20×10^{-6} µmole. When the transformation is complete, base ratios in the NaCl-soluble RNA which remains are the same as those in the newly formed NaCl-insoluble RNA; all four nucleotides are present in essentially equimolar quantities. And yet, before the "point of no return," the base ratio in NaCl-soluble RNA is not unity, but rather (CMP:AMP:UMP: GMP) 1.00:1.28:1.08:1.31. NaCl-insoluble RNA is about 65% of the total RNA in a mature RS cell. Moreover, the RNA in a spore nuclear cap is 69%. Many data point to the conclusion that NaCl-insoluble RNA is laid down during RS differentiation in the form of protein-bound organelles (perhaps similar to chromospheres of *Allomyces*) which are ultimately transformed into the nuclear caps of RS spores. Although these hypothetical organelles have not been detected microscopically, it is clear that they must exist—at least as molecular aggregates which sediment in fields as low as 15,000–20,000 g—and that a minimum of 35% (if not all) of their RNA is newly synthesized (Cantino, 1962; Cantino and Lovett, 1964; Lovett, 1963).

The end result (Fig. 11) is a thallus which bears a terminal, thick-walled, pitted, pigmented, dormant, resistant-sporangial cell borne upon a smaller, empty cell to which rootlike rhizoids are attached. Its fate now depends upon the environment in which it finds itself in nature, or in which it is placed in the laboratory. In a dry state, it remains dormant but viable for years. But if it is submerged in water, it liberates the motile spores (Fig. 11) each of which—with its single nuclear cap, single mitochondrion, and single nucleus—begins a new generation of *Blastocladiella emersonii*.

o. Blastocladiella britannica. This unicellular relative of *B. emersonii* was described as a new species only recently (Horenstein and Cantino, 1961, 1962, 1964). On solid media, certain strains produce cells which, as in *B. emersonii,* culminate in the formation of either a hyaline, thin-walled cell, or a thick-walled, brown, pitted, resistant sporangial cell. But in *B. britannica,* unlike *B. emersonii,* alternate morphogenetic pathways are not controlled by bicarbonate. Instead, white light is the environmental factor which affects differentiation. Thin-walled cells are formed in its presence, whereas RS cells are formed in its absence. A method was devised for growing synchronized, single generations of *B. britannica,* uniformly suspended in agitated media. Throughout ontogeny, it is almost a perfect sphere, and in cultures containing up to 10^5 cells per milliliter, the all-or-none effect of light and darkness is demonstrable. Precise quantitative data associated with these two developmental pathways are now available and set a groundwork for future studies of the biochemical basis for photomorphogenesis in *B. britannica*. Its exponential growth rates, its response to

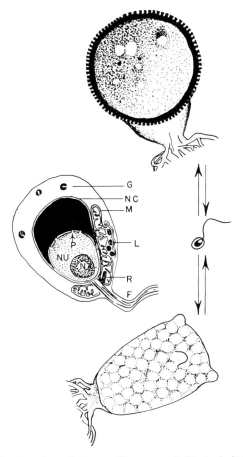

Fig. 11. The structure of the motile spore of *Blastocladiella emersonii*, and the two major developmental paths that it may take. Explanation of symbols: *G*, gamma particle; *NC*, nuclear cap with double membrane; *M*, mitochondrion; *L*, aggregate of lipid granules attached to *M* and bound by its own double membrane; *F*, flagellum; *R*, banded rootlet anchoring *F* to *M*; *N*, nucleolus; *NU*, nucleus with double membrane; *P*, pores in double membrane separating *NU* from *NC*.

various pH levels, the effect of population density upon size, generation times, and other growth parameters have been established. The exact "points of no return" in ontogeny for both developmental paths have been delimited and are very sharp indeed, being 65% and 53% of the generation times of the thin-walled cell and the RS cell, respectively. The available data (Horenstein and Cantino, 1964) point to a light-sensitive glucose-uptake capacity as being a critical—and possibly a causal—factor in the photomorphogenetic response of *B. britannica*.

IV. GENERAL CONCLUSIONS

For years, biologists have focused attention upon the nature of the processes which, via ontogeny and phylogeny, culminate in the manufacture of a living system. No single creature or group of organisms has provided sufficient evidence for establishing the exact mechanisms involved. In this chapter, emphasis has been placed upon the potential utility of aquatic fungi for studies of this sort, and what has been done with a few of them. In particular, conspicuous differences in metabolism exist among the undifferentiated, differentiating, and differentiated cells of *Blastocladiella emersonii,* and the evidence points sharply to a manifold induction and repression of enzyme synthesis as a partial basis for these changes. Furthermore, just as interactions between nucleus and cytoplasm can be approached most directly by studying synthetic capacities in a cell deprived of its nucleus (Keck, 1961), for which the alga *Acetabularia* is so well suited, so an equally direct approach would be to study a "living" nucleus deprived of its cytoplasm. The spore of *B. emersonii* comes pretty close to providing such a system (cf. Cantino and Lovett, 1964). And for investigations of the way in which visible light exerts control over growth, development, and differentiation (cf. review by Mohr, 1962), both *B. emersonii* and *B. britannica* give ample testimony of their utility.

In the last analysis, the intellectual profit to be gained from working with water fungi such as the Blastocladiales stems from the fact that they can be observed and manipulated under controlled conditions as *intact, living, growing, differentiating systems in operation.* We agree wholeheartedly with Steward (1961) that in the current eagerness to know more and more in detail about ever more refined parts and systems found in living things, perspective is badly needed. With *B. emersonii,* it *is* possible to do enzymology and descriptive biochemistry, to integrate these with cytology and descriptive morphology, and to shift out minutiae with concomitant clarification and magnification of the whole; with it and its relatives, it *is* possible to have the cake and to eat it too! It is apparent that the water molds have arrived as experimental guinea pigs, and that they can help those of us so inclined to reverse the trend whereby, if carried to its logical conclusion, "the modern doctrine of molecular biology would leave botany a branch of chemistry" (Steward, 1961).

ACKNOWLEDGMENTS

Unpublished studies of *Blastocladiella* referred to in this chapter were supported by research grants from the National Science Foundation and the National Institutes of Health. I am grateful to my students and colleagues, particularly Drs. Horenstein, Lovett, McCurdy, Turian, and Domnas, without whose skills and devoted participation in our research program, many of the things we now know about *Blastocladiella* would still be obscure if not unknown.

REFERENCES

Ajello, L. (1948). A cytological and nutritional study of *Polychytrium aggregatum*. I. Cytology. *Am. J. Botany* **35**:1-12.
Alexopoulos, C. J. (1962). "Introductory Mycology," 613 pp. Wiley, New York.
Antikajian, G. (1949). A developmental, morphological, and cytological study of *Asterophlyctis* with special reference to its sexuality, taxonomy, and relationships. *Am. J. Botany* **36**:245-262.
Aronson, J. M., and R. D. Preston. (1960a). The microfibrillar structure of the cell walls of the filamentous fungus, *Allomyces*. *J. Biophys. Biochem. Cytol.* **8**:247-256.
Aronson, J. M., and R. D. Preston. (1960b). An electron microscopic and X-ray analysis of the walls of selected lower Phycomycetes. *Proc. Roy. Soc.* **B152**:346-352.
Atkinson, G. F. (1909). Some problems in the evolution of the lower fungi. *Ann. Mycol., Berlin* **7**:441-472.
Barksdale, A. W. (1962). Effect of nutritional deficiency on growth and sexual reproduction of *Achlya ambisexualis*. *Am. J. Botany* **49**:633-638.
Barrett, J. T. (1912). The development of *Blastocladia strangulata*, n. sp. *Botan. Gaz.* **54**:353-371.
Birch, L. C. (1960). The genetic factor in population ecology. *Am. Naturalist* **94**:5-24.
Bishop, H. (1940). A study of sexuality in *Sapromyces reinschii*. *Mycologia* **32**:505-529.
Blackwell, E. M. (1937). Germination of the resistant spores of *Blastocladia pringsheimii*. *Nature* **140**:933.
Blackwell, E. M. (1940). A life cycle of *Blastocladia pringsheimii* Reinsch. *Brit. Mycol. Soc. Trans.* **24**:68-86.
Blondel, B., and G. Turian. (1960). Relation between basophilia and fine structure of cytoplasm in the fungus *Allomyces macrogynus* Em. *J. Biophys. Biochem. Cytol.* **7**:127-134.
Brown, D. H., and E. C. Cantino. (1955). The oxidation of malate by *Blastocladiella emersonii*. *Am. J. Botany* **42**:337-341.
Butler, E. J. (1911). On *Allomyces*, a new aquatic fungus. *Ann. Botany (London)* **25**:1023-1035.
Canter, H. M., and J. W. G. Lund. (1951). Studies on plankton parasites. III. Examples of the interaction between parasitism and other factors determining the growth of diatoms. *Ann. Botany (London)* [N.S.] **15**:359-371.
Cantino, E. C. (1949). The physiology of the aquatic Phycomycete *Blastocladia pringsheimii*, with emphasis on its nutrition and metabolism. *Am. J. Botany* **36**:95-112.
Cantino, E. C. (1950). Nutrition and phylogeny in the water molds. *Quart. Rev. Biol.* **25**:269-277.
Cantino, E. C. (1951). Metabolism and morphogenesis in a new *Blastocladiella*. *Antonie van Leeuwenhoek, J. Microbiol. Serol.* **17**:325-362.
Cantino, E. C. (1952). The biochemical nature of morphogenetic patterns in *Blastocladiella*. *Am. Naturalist* **86**:399-404.
Cantino, E. C. (1953). The role of metabolism and α-ketoglutarate oxidase in the growth and differentiation of the aquatic Phycomycete *Blastocladiella emersonii*. *Trans. N.Y. Acad. Sci.* **15**:159-163.
Cantino, E. C. (1955). Physiology and phylogeny in the water molds—a reevaluation. *Quart. Rev. Biol.* **30**:138-149.

Cantino, E. C. (1956). The relation between cellular metabolism and morphogenesis in *Blastocladiella*. *Mycologia* **48**:225-240.
Cantino, E. C. (1959). Light-stimulated development and phosphorus metabolism in the mold *Blastocladiella emersonii*. *Develop. Biol.* **1**:396-412.
Cantino, E. C. (1961). The relationship between biochemical and morphological differentiation in non-filamentous aquatic fungi. *Symp. Soc. Gen. Microbiol.* **11**:243-271.
Cantino, E. C. (1962). Transitional states of ribonucleic acid and morphogenesis in synchronous single generations of *Blastocladiella emersonii*. *Phytochemistry* **1**:107-124.
Cantino, E. C. (1965a). Relations of metabolism to cell development in plants. In "Handbuch der Pflanzenphysiologie" (A. Lang, ed.), Vol. 15, Part 1, pp. 213-233. Springer, Berlin.
Cantino, E. C. (1965b). Intracellular distribution of ^{14}C during sporogenesis in *Blastocladiella emersonii*. Effect of light on hemoprotein. *Arch. Mikrobiol.* **51**:42-59.
Cantino, E. C., and A. Goldstein. (1961). Bicarbonate-induced synthesis of polysaccharide during morphogenesis by synchronous, single-generations of *Blastocladiella emersonii*. *Arch. Mikrobiol.* **39**:43-52.
Cantino, E. C., and A. Goldstein. (1962). Protein changes during morphological differentiation and its reversal in synchronized single generations of *Blastocladiella emersonii*. *Am. J. Botany* **49**:642-646.
Cantino, E. C., and E. A. Horenstein. (1954). Cytoplasmic exchange without gametic copulation in the water mold *Blastocladiella emersonii*. *Am. Naturalist* **88**:142-154.
Cantino, E. C., and E. A. Horenstein. (1955). The role of ketoglutarate and polyphenol oxidase in the synthesis of melanin during morphogenesis in *Blastocladiella emersonii*. *Physiol. Plantarum* **8**:189-221.
Cantino, E. C., and E. A. Horenstein. (1956a). The stimulatory effect of light upon growth and CO_2 fixation in *Blastocladiella*. I. The S.K.I. cycle. *Mycologia* **48**:777-799.
Cantino, E. C., and E. A. Horenstein. (1956b). Gamma and the cytoplasmic control of differentiation in *Blastocladiella*. *Mycologia* **48**:443-446.
Cantino, E. C., and E. A. Horenstein. (1957). The stimulatory effect of light upon growth and CO_2 fixation in *Blastocladiella*. II. Mechanism at an organismal level of integration. *Mycologia* **49**:892-894.
Cantino, E. C., and E. A. Horenstein. (1959). The stimulatory effect of light upon growth and carbon dioxide fixation in *Blastocladiella*. III. Further studies, *in vivo* and *in vitro*. *Physiol. Plantarum* **12**:251-263.
Cantino, E. C., and M. T. Hyatt. (1953a). Phenotypic "sex" determination in the life history of a new species of *Blastocladiella*, *B. emersonii*. *Antonie van Leeuwenhoek, J. Microbiol. Serol.* **19**:25-70.
Cantino, E. C., and M. T. Hyatt. (1953b). Carotenoids and oxidative enzymes in the aquatic Phycomycetes *Blastocladiella* and *Rhizophlyctis*. *Am. J. Botany* **40**:688-694.
Cantino, E. C., and M. T. Hyatt. (1953c). Further evidence for the role of the tricarboxylic acid cycle in morphogenesis in *Blastocladiella emersonii*. *J. Bacteriol.* **66**:712-720.
Cantino, E. C., and J. S. Lovett. (1960). Respiration of *Blastocladiella* during bicarbonate-induced morphogenesis in synchronous culture. *Physiol. Plantarum* **13**:450-458.

Cantino, E. C., and J. S. Lovett. (1964). Non-filamentous aquatic fungi: Model systems for biochemical studies of morphological differentiation. In "Advances in Morphogenesis" (M. Abercrombie and J. Brachet, eds.), Vol. 3, pp. 33-93. Academic Press, New York.

Cantino, E. C., and G. Turian. (1959). Physiology and development of lower fungi (Phycomycetes). Ann. Rev. Microbiol. 13:97-124.

Cantino, E. C., and G. Turian. (1961). A role for glycine in light stimulated nucleic acid synthesis by Blastocladiella emersonii. Arch. Mikrobiol. 38:272-282.

Cantino, E. C., J. Lovett, and E. A. Horenstein. (1957). Chitin synthesis and nitrogen metabolism during differentiation in Blastocladiella emersonii. Am. J. Botany 44: 498-505.

Cantino, E. C., J. S. Lovett, L. V. Leak, and J. Lythgoe. (1963). The single mitochondrion, fine structure and germination of the spore of Blastocladiella emersonii. J. Gen. Microbiol. 31:393-404.

Chodat, F., and G. Turian. (1955). Nouveaux signes biochimiques de la différenciation sexuelle chez Allomyces. Ber. Schweiz. Botan. Ges. 65:519-524.

Christie, T. (1959). Nutritional studies of Phytophthora cactorum. II. Influence of pH of a culture medium on utilization of some nitrogen and carbon compounds. New Zealand J. Sci. 2:320-322.

Cochrane, V. W. (1958). "Physiology of Fungi," 524 pp. Wiley, New York.

Coker, W. C. (1923). "The Saprolegniaceae, With Notes on Other Water Molds," 201 pp. Univ. of North Carolina Press, Chapel Hill, North Carolina.

Couch, J. N. (1926). Heterothallism in Dictyuchus, a genus of the water moulds. Ann. Botany (London) 40:849-881.

Couch, J. N. (1939). Heterothallism in the Chytridiales. J. Elisha Mitchell Sci. Soc. 55:409-414.

Couch, J. N., and A. J. Whiffen. (1942). Observations on the genus Blastocladiella. Am. J. Botany 29:582-591.

Crasemann, J. M. (1954). The nutrition of Chytridium and Macrochytrium. Am. J. Botany 41:302-310.

Crasemann, J. M. (1957). Comparative nutrition of two species of Blastocladia. Am. J. Botany 44:218-224.

Davies, M. E. (1959). The nutrition of Phytophthora fragariae. Brit. Mycol. Soc. Trans. 42:193-200.

Dayal, R. (1961a). Sulphur requirements of some members of the family Saprolegniaceae. Proc. Natl. Acad. Sci., India B31:399-401.

Dayal, R. (1961b). Nitrogen requirements of some members of the family Saprolegniaceae. Proc. Natl. Acad. Sci., India B31:332-336.

Domnas, A., and E. C. Cantino. (1965). The fate of arginine prior to sporogenesis in synchronized ordinary colorless cells of Blastocladiella emersonii. Biochim. Biophys. Acta 97:300-309.

Emerson, R. (1941). An experimental study of the life cycles and taxonomy of Allomyces. Lloydia 4:77-144.

Emerson, R. (1950). Current trends of experimental research on the aquatic Phycomycetes. Ann. Rev. Microbiol. 4:169-200.

Emerson, R. (1955). The biology of water molds. In "Aspects of Synthesis and Order in Growth" (D. Rudnick, ed.), Vol. 13, pp. 171-208. Princeton Univ. Press, Princeton, New Jersey.

Emerson, R., and E. C. Cantino. (1948). The isolation, growth, and metabolism of Blastocladia in pure culture. Am. J. Botany 35:157-171.

Emerson, R., and D. L. Fox. (1940). α-Carotene in the sexual phase of the aquatic fungus *Allomyces*. *Proc. Roy. Soc.* **B128**:275-293.
Emerson, R., and C. M. Wilson. (1949). The significance of meiosis in *Allomyces*. *Science* **110**:86-88.
Emerson, R., and C. M. Wilson. (1954). Interspecific hybrids and the cytogenetics and cytotaxonomy of Euallomyces. *Mycologia* **46**:393-434.
Erwin, D. C., and H. Katznelson. (1961). Studies on the nutrition of *Phytophthora cryptogea*. *Can. J. Microbiol.* **7**:15-25.
Fleetwood-Walker, P. M. (1954). Physiology of Phycomycetes with particular reference to Phytophthora fragariae Hickman. Ph.D. Thesis, University of Birmingham.
Foley, J. M. (1958). The occurrence, characteristics and genetic behavior of albino gametophytes in *Allomyces*. *Am. J. Botany* **45**:639-648.
Fothergill, P. G., and D. Hide. (1962). Comparative nutritional studies of *Pythium* spp. *J. Gen. Microbiol.* **29**:325-334.
Fuller, M. S. (1960). Biochemical and microchemical study of the cell walls of *Rhizidiomyces* sp. *Am. J. Botany* **47**:838-842.
Fuller, M. S. (1962). Growth and development of the water mold *Rhizidiomyces* in pure culture. *Am. J. Botany* **49**:64-71.
Gaertner, A. (1960). Nutrition of *Rhizophydium patellarium*. *Arch. Mikrobiol.* **36**: 46-50.
Gaertner, A. (1962). *Catenaria anguillulae* Sorokin als Parasit in dem Embryonen von *Daphnia magna* Strauss nebst Beobachtungen zur Entwicklung, zur Morphologie und zum Substratverhalten des Pilzes. *Arch. Mikrobiol.* **43**:280-289.
Goldstein, A., and E. C. Cantino. (1962). Light-stimulated polysaccharide and protein synthesis by synchronized, single generations of *Blastocladiella emersonii*. *J. Gen. Microbiol.* **28**:689-699.
Goldstein, A., and E. C. Cantino. (1963). Unpublished data.
Goldstein, S. (1960a). Physiology of aquatic fungi. I. Nutrition of two monocentric chytrids. *J. Bacteriol.* **80**:701-707.
Goldstein, S. (1960b). Factors affecting the growth and pigmentation of *Cladochytrium replicatum*. *Mycologia* **52**:490-498.
Goldstein, S. (1961). Studies of two polycentric chytrids in pure culture. *Am. J. Botany* **48**:294-298.
Grimstone, A. V. (1959). Cytology, homology, and phylogeny—a note on "organic design." *Am. Naturalist* **93**:273-282.
Haglund, W. A., and T. H. King. (1962). Sulfur nutrition of *Aphanomyces euteiches*. *Phytopathology* **52**:315-317.
Hanson, A. M. (1945). A morphological, developmental, and cytological study of four saprophytic chytrids. II. *Rhizophydium coronum* Hanson. *Am. J. Botany* **32**: 479-487.
Harder, R. B., and G. Sörgel. (1938). Über einen neuen plano-isogamen Phycomyceten mit Generationswechsel und seine phylogenetische Bedeutung. *Nachr. Ges. Wiss. Gottingen, Math.-Physik. Kl., VI* [N.S.] **3**:119-127.
Hatch, W. R. (1935). Gametogenesis in *Allomyces arbuscula*. *Ann. Botany (London)* **49**:623-649.
Hawker, L. E. (1957). "The Physiology of Reproduction in Fungi," 128 pp. Cambridge Univ. Press, London and New York.
Hiesey, W. M., H. W. Milner, and M. A. Nobs. (1962). New vistas in experimental taxonomy. *Carnegie Inst. Wash. Year Book* **61**:311-312.

Hillegas, A. B. (1940). The cytology of *Endochytrium operculatum* (de Wildeman) Karling in relation to its development and organization. *Bull. Torrey Botan. Club* 67:1-32.

Horenstein, E. A., and E. C. Cantino. (1961). Morphogenesis in and the effect of light on *Blastocladiella britannica*, sp. nov. *Brit. Mycol. Soc. Trans.* 44:185-198.

Horenstein, E. A., and E. C. Cantino. (1962). Dark-induced morphogenesis in synchronized cultures of *Blastocladiella britannica*. *J. Bacteriol.* 84:37-45.

Horenstein, E. A., and E. C. Cantino. (1964). An effect of light on glucose uptake by the fungus *Blastocladiella britannica*. *J. Gen. Microbiol.* 37:59-65.

Hutchinson, F. (1960). Radiation inactivation of molecules in cells. *Am. Naturalist* 94:59-70.

Kanouse, B. B. (1927). A monographic study of special groups of the water molds. I. Blastocladiaceae. *Am. J. Botany* 14:287-306.

Karling, J. S. (1937). The cytology of the Chytridiales with special reference to *Cladochytrium replicatum*. *Mem. Torrey Botan. Club* 19:3-92.

Keck, K. (1961). Nuclear and cytoplasmic factors determining the species specificity of enzyme proteins in *Acetabularia*. *Ann. N.Y. Acad. Sci.* 94:741-752.

Kevorkian, A. G. (1935). Studies in the Leptomitaceae. II. Cytology of *Apodachlya brachynema* and *Sapromyces reinschii*. *Mycologia* 27:274-285.

Klebs, G. (1900). Zur physiologie der Fortpflanzung einiger Pilze. III. *Jahrb. Wiss. Botan.* 32:80-203.

Klinkhammer, F. (1959). Untersuchungen über Glutaminsynthease und Glutaminsäuredehydrogenase bei *Allomyces arbuscula*. *Arch. Mikrobiol.* 33:357-377.

Kniep, H. (1929). *Allomyces javanicus*, n. sp., ein anisogamer Phycomycet mit Planogameten. *Ber. Deut. Botan. Ges.* 47:199-212.

Kniep, H. (1930). Über den Generationswechsel von *Allomyces*. *Z. Botan.* 22:433-441.

Koch, W. J. (1961). Studies of the motile cells of chytrids. III. Major types. *Am. J. Botany* 48:786-788.

Krause, R. (1960). Untersuchungen über den Einfluss der Aussenfaktoren auf die Bildung der Oogonien bei *Saprolegnia ferax* (Gruith.) Thuret. *Arch. Mikrobiol.* 36:373-386.

Llanos, C. M., and J. L. Lockwood. (1960). Factors affecting zoospore production by *Aphanomyces euteiches*. *Phytopathology* 50:826-830.

Lloyd, D. (1938). A record of two years' continuous observations on *Blastocladia pringsheimii* Reinsch. *Brit. Mycol. Soc. Trans.* 21:152-166.

Lovett, J. S. (1963). Chemical and physical characterization of "nuclear caps" isolated from *Blastocladiella* zoospores. *J. Bacteriol.* 85:1235-1246.

Lovett, J. S. (1965). Unpublished data.

Lovett, J. S., and E. C. Cantino. (1960a). The relation between biochemical and morphological differentiation in *Blastocladiella emersonii*. I. Enzymatic synthesis of glucosamine-6-phosphate. *Am. J. Botany* 47:499-505.

Lovett, J. S., and E. C. Cantino. (1960b). The relation between biochemical and morphological differentiation in *Blastocladiella emersonii*. II. Nitrogen metabolism in synchronous cultures. *Am. J. Botany* 47:550-560.

Lovett, J. S., and E. C. Cantino. (1961). Reversible bicarbonate-induced enzyme activity and the point of no return during morphogenesis in *Blastocladiella*. *J. Gen. Microbiol.* 24:87-93.

Lwoff, A. (1944). "L'Évolution physiologique: Étude de pertes de fonctions chez les microorganismes," 308 pp. Hermann, Paris.

McCurdy, H. D., Jr., and E. C. Cantino. (1960). Isocitritase, glycine-alanine transaminase, and development in *Blastocladiella emersonii*. *Plant Physiol.* **35**:463-476.
Machlis, L. (1958). A study of Sirenin, the chemotactic sexual hormone from the water mold *Allomyces*. *Physiol. Plantarum* **11**:845-854.
Machlis, L., and J. M. Crasemann. (1956). Physiological variation between the generations and among the strains of water molds in the subgenus Euallomyces. *Am. J. Botany* **43**:601-611.
Machlis, L., and E. Ossia. (1953a). Maturation of the meiosporangia of Euallomyces. I. The effect of cultural conditions. *Am. J. Botany* **40**:358-365.
Machlis, L., and E. Ossia. (1953b). Maturation of the meiosporangia of Euallomyces. II. Preliminary observations on the effect of auxins. *Am. J. Botany* **40**:465-468.
Matthews, V. D. (1937). A new genus of the Blastocladiaceae. *J. Elisha Mitchell Sci. Soc.* **53**:191-195.
Mitchell, P. (1962). Metabolism, transport, and morphogenesis: Which drives which? *J. Gen. Microbiol.* **29**:25-37.
Mohr, H. (1962). Primary effects of light on growth. *Ann. Rev. Plant Physiol.* **13**:465-488.
Pantin, C. F. A. (1951). Organic design. *Advan. Sci.* **8**:138-150.
Papavizas, G. C., and C. B. Davey. (1960a). Some factors affecting sexual reproduction of *Aphanomyces euteiches*. *Am. J. Botany* **47**:884-889.
Papavizas, G. C., and C. B. Davey. (1960b). Some factors affecting growth of *Aphanomyces euteiches* in synthetic media. Am. J. Botany **47**:758-765.
Perrott, P. E. (1958). Isolation and pure culture of *Monoblepharis*. *Nature* **182**:1322-1324.
Petersen, H. E. (1909). Studier over Ferskvands-Phycomyceter. Bidrag til Kundskaben om de submerse Phykomyceters Biologi og Systematik, samt om deres Udbredelse i. Danmark. *Botan. Tidsskr.* **29**:345-440.
Racker, E. (1959). Multienzyme systems. *Am. Naturalist* **93**:237-244.
Raper, J. R. (1951). Sexual hormones in *Achlya*. *Am. Sci.* **39**:110-120.
Raper, J. R. (1952). Chemical regulation of sexual processes in the Thallophytes. *Botan. Rev.* **18**:447-545.
Raper, J. R. (1959). Sexual versatility and evolutionary processes in fungi. *Mycologia* **51**:107-124.
Reinsch, P. F. (1878). Beobachtungen über einige neue Saprolegnieae, über die Parasiten in Desmidienzellen und über die Stachelkugeln in Achlyaschläuchen. *Jahrb. Wiss. Botan.* **11**:283-311.
Reisert, P. S., and M. S. Fuller. (1962). Decomposition of chitin by *Chytriomyces* species. *Mycologia* **54**:647-657.
Rorem, E. S., and L. Machlis. (1957). The ribonucleoprotein nature of large particles in the meiosporangia of *Allomyces*. *J. Biophys. Biochem. Cytol.* **3**:879-888.
Salvin, S. B. (1942). Factors controlling sporangial type in *Thraustotheca primoachyla* and *Dictyuchus achlyoides*. *Am. J. Botany* **29**:97-104.
Schade, A. L., and K. V. Thimann. (1940). The metabolism of the water-mold *Leptomitus lacteus*. *Am. J. Botany* **27**:659-670.
Scherffel, A. (1925). Endophytische Phycomyceten-Parasiten der Bacillariaceen und einige neue Monadinen. Ein Beitrag zur Phylogenie der Oomyceten (Schröter). *Arch. Protistenk.* **52**:1-141.
Slobodkin, L. B. (1961). Preliminary ideas for a predictive theory of ecology. *Am. Naturalist* **95**:147-153.

Sonneborn, T. M. (1957). Breeding systems, reproductive methods, and species problems in protozoa. *In* "The Species Problem," pp. 155-324. Am. Assoc. Advance. Sci., Washington, D.C.

Sparrow, F. K., Jr. (1960). "Aquatic Phycomycetes," 1187 pp. Univ. of Michigan Press, Ann Arbor, Michigan.

Steward, F. C. (1961). Organization and integration: plant cell growth and nutrition. *In* "Growth in Living Systems" (M. X. Zarrow, ed.) pp. 453-490. Basic Books, New York.

Thaxter, R. (1896). New or peculiar aquatic fungi. 3. *Blastocladia*. *Botan. Gaz.* **21**:45-52.

Turian, G. (1955). Culture de la phase gamétophytique d'*Allomyces javanicus* en milieu synthétique liquide. *Compt. Rend.* **240**:1005-1007.

Turian, G. (1956). Le corps paranucléaire des gamètes géants d'*Allomyces javanicus* traité à l'acide borique. *Protoplasma* **47**:135-138.

Turian, G. (1957a). Recherches sur l'action anticaroténogène de la diphénylamine et ses conséquences sur la morphogenèse reproductive chez *Allomyces* et *Neurospora*. *Physiol. Plantarum* **10**:667-680.

Turian, G. (1957b). Recherches sur la morphogenèse sexuelle chez *Allomyces*. *Ber. Schweiz. Botan. Ges.* **67**:458-486.

Turian, G. (1957c). Détection cytochimique de l'acide ribonucléique dans les chromosphères pré- et post-méiotiques des sporanges de résistance d'*Allomyces*. *Experientia* **13**:315.

Turian, G. (1958). Recherches sur les bases cytochimiques et cytophysiologiques de la morphogenèse chez le champignon aquatique *Allomyces*. *Rev. Cytol. Biol. Vegetales* **19**:241-272.

Turian, G. (1960a). Indices d'un fonctionnement compensatoire du cycle glyoxylique lors de la différenciation mâle chez *Allomyces* et *Neurospora*. *Ber. Schweiz. Botan. Ges.* **70**:451-458.

Turian, G. (1960b). Déficiences du métabolisme oxydatif et différenciation sexuelle chez *Allomyces* et *Neurospora*. Activité d'une DPN-deshydrogénase lactique chez *Allomyces*. *Pathol. Microbiol.* **23**:687-699.

Turian, G. (1961a). Nucleic acids and sexual differentiation in *Allomyces*. *Nature* **190**:825.

Turian, G. (1961b). Cycle glyoxylique, transaminase alanine-glyoxylate et différenciation sexuelle chez *Allomyces* et *Neurospora*. *Pathol. Microbiol.* **24**:819-839.

Turian, G. (1961c). Differential rate of nuclear multiplication and nucleic acid biosynthetic balance in sexual differentiation of *Allomyces*. *Nucleus (Calcutta)* **4**:151-156.

Turian, G. (1962). Differential synthesis of nucleic acids in sexual differentiation of *Allomyces*. *Nature* **196**:493-494.

Turian, G., and E. C. Cantino. (1959). The stimulatory effect of light on nucleic acid synthesis in the mould *Blastocladiella emersonii*. *J. Gen. Microbiol.* **21**:721-735.

Turian, G., and E. C. Cantino. (1960). A study of mitosis in the mold *Blastocladiella* with a ribonuclease-aceto orcein staining technique. *Cytologia (Tokyo)* **25**:101-107.

Turian, G., and F. T. Haxo. (1954). Minor polyene components in the sexual phase of *Allomyces javanicus*. *Botan. Gaz.* **115**:254-260.

Turian, G., and E. Kellenberger. (1956). Ultrastructure du corps paranucléaire, des mitochondries et de la membrane nucléaire des gamètes d'*Allomyces macrogynus*. *Exptl. Cell Res.* **11**:417-422.

Vishniac, H. S. (1958). A new marine Phycomycete. *Mycologia* **50**:66-79.
von Minden, M. (1916). Beiträge zur Biologie und Systematik einheimischer submerser Phycomyceten (Falck). *Mykol. Untersuch. Ber.* **2**:146-255.
Waterhouse, G. M. (1962). The zoospore. *Brit. Mycol. Soc. Trans.* **45**:1-20.
Whiffen, A. J. (1951). The effect of cycloheximide on the sporophyte of *Allomyces arbuscula*. *Mycologia* **43**:635-644.
Willoughby, L. G. (1962). The fruiting behaviour and nutrition of *Cladochytrium replicatum* Karling. *Ann. Botany (London)* [N.S.] **26**:13-36.
Wilson, C. M. (1952). Meiosis in *Allomyces*. *Bull. Torrey Botan. Club* **79**:139-160.
Wright, S. (1956). Models of Selection. *Am. Naturalist* **90**:5-24.

CHAPTER 11

Morphogenesis in Ascomycetes

G. TURIAN

Institut de Botanique générale
Université de Genève
Geneva, Switzerland

I. INTRODUCTION

In considering as a morphogenetic process any developmental change in fungal form toward either greater complexity or simplification, we can distinguish two main phases. In the morphogenesis of ascomycetes these are:

1. An *initial,* simplificative morphogenesis corresponding to the vegetative phenomenon of spore germination. This phase is characterized by the morphological transition from the differentiated structure of the spore, through a short dedifferentiative stage associated with the resumption of the proliferative capacity, to the redifferentiated, simpler, growing structure of the germ tube or first vegetative hypha.

2. A *final,* elaborative morphogenesis corresponding to the reproductive phenomenon of spore formation or sporulation. This phase is initiated by the physiological transition from the vegetative to the reproductive state and expresses itself morphologically either by the direct differentiation of asexual spores (conidia, etc.) or the more complicated morphogenesis of sexual spores (ascospores), subsequent to the differentiation of sexual organs.

These two phases delimit the whole fungal life cycle defined as spore to spore development separated by a more or less prolonged period of mycelial growth. During this intermediate vegetative period, a few peculiar structures, such as oidia, chlamydospores, sclerotia, etc. may be formed under particular conditions. They can adequately be considered as formative manifestations of an *intermediate,* accessory phase of morphogenesis essentially concerned with vegetative reproduction.

The main morphological features of development in ascomycetes are common to all taxonomic groupings. Therefore, our conceptual frame for the successive phases and stages of their morphogenesis can apply to any ascomycetous fungus. By contrast with this morphological unity, the environmental and physiological factors influencing morphogenesis, or concerned in its realization, are very diverse, or so they appear to be in our present state of insufficient knowledge. In consequence, the best-known effects of these factors will have to be envisaged for each individual fungus, at each of its morphogenetic stages, because "there is apparently no one 'formula' known for sporulation" (Cochrane, 1958).

Until now, morphogenesis in ascomycetes has not been considered as a defined field, but only incidentally in relation to reproduction of fungi, with the main focus on the problem of initiation of sporulation (Hawker, 1950, 1957; Cochrane, 1958). The stepwise development of their reproductive structures has in the main been treated as a problem of morphology (Gäumann, 1949, 1964; Bessey, 1950; Alexopoulos, 1952, 1962; F. Moreau, 1952-1953; Chadefaud, 1960) and biochemical and physiological aspects are still inadequately known. Some of its primary genetic determinants have been unraveled in a few cases and can be ordered in a sequence corresponding to the main morphogenetic stages. Considering that the normal expression of these genetic potentialities depends on the environmental conditions and that morphological differentiation ultimately rests on the underlying respiratory and metabolic pathways, we will present successively genetic, environmental, and metabolic aspects for any morphogenetic stage when our present state of knowledge permits it. As this can be easily achieved with only a few ascomycetes, yeasts, penicillia, aspergilli, *Ophiostoma, Glomerella, Venturia, Podospora, Sordaria,* and especially *Neurospora* spp., we have centered our review on these "experimental ascomycetous molds."

II. MORPHOGENETIC PHASES

A. *Initial or Vegetative Morphogenesis: Spore Germination*

Fungal spores are differentiated, resting cells capable of initiating new growth by germination. The process of spore germination corresponds therefore to the dedifferentiation of a complex but relatively inactive structure and its redifferentiation into the simpler one of an actively growing hyphal tube (simplificative morphogenesis).

The emergence of the hyphal germ tube is the most obvious morphogenetic event of spore germination and, as such, is commonly used as its main criterion. However, it is already the last stage of a whole developmental sequence including: (1) an initiating physiological stage with several incipient, metabolic processes associated with the transition from the resting to the activated sporal condition in the pregermination period; (2) a first morphological stage, the swelling stage (Mandels and Darby, 1953;

Yanagita, 1957); (3) the stage of emergence of the germ tube, or sprouting.

The nature and complexity of the initial metabolic processes, under the control of hereditary factors, determine the minimal duration of the pregermination period. On such a specific time criterion, it is possible to distinguish two main categories of spores: (1) those which germinate soon after their transfer into a fresh medium, i.e., only after a short maturation period; they include the asexual spores and many ascospores; (2) those which germinate only after a pronounced period of dormancy (weeks or months), as exhibited particularly, but not exclusively, by ascospores of the coprophilic ascomycetes.

In each of these two categories, a few examples have been chosen to illustrate the existence of well-defined physiological and morphological stages during spore germination. Further information concerning the action of various factors, mainly environmental, on spore germination can be obtained in the reviews by Doran (1922), Gottlieb (1950, 1964) and Allen (1965) as well as chapters in Lilly and Barnett (1951), Cochrane (1958), and Sussman (1965) and Chapter 23 of this volume.

1. Spores without Dormant Stage

Even spores which have undergone maturation may not germinate immediately on transfer into a fresh medium (Jones, 1919; Burgert, 1934; Ryan, 1948). The so-called latent period is the last pregerminative stage. Its duration depends upon environmental factors, and its associated metabolic reactions are usually much more sensitive to temperature changes than those of the following morphological stages. Thus, it has been shown that low temperature delays the onset of germination by increasing the latent period in *Sclerotinia fructicola* (Wellman and McCallan, 1942) and in *Fusarium moniliforme* (Saccas, 1951). However, in *Uncinula necator* (Delp, 1954), both the latent period and, in addition, the rate of germination (emergence of germ tubes) are affected by low temperature. The latent period may also manifest a differential sensitivity toward toxicants (Tomkins, 1932).

The metabolic processes during the latent period are concerned with the progressive activation of the spores as a prerequisite physiological condition preceding the initiation of the morphological changes associated with the process of germination proper. Among the many changes that the complex enzymatic pattern of the spores undergoes (Gottlieb, 1950, 1964) is a noticeable activation of the hydrolytic enzymes (Mandels, 1956), especially the nonspecific phosphatases (Bhatnager and Krishnan, 1960b) and polyphosphate kinase (Nishi, 1960) in *Aspergillus niger*. The oxidative enzymes are also stimulated, as in germinating macroconidia of *Neurospora* (Owens, 1955), even though catalase is more active in ungerminated conidia of *A.*

niger (Bhatnagar and Krishnan, 1960a). As expected, respiration increases at germination, especially after a mild heat treatment of the spores (Bhatnagar and Krishnan, 1959). Furthermore, during their initial 2-hour germination period, the conidia of *A. niger* exhibit a loss of resistance to heat and germicides and a decrease in polyphosphate content (Yanagita and Yamagishi, 1958). In this fungus, *l*-alanine or *l*-proline are required as key substances for the initiation of spore germination (Yanagita, 1957; Takebe and Shimizu, 1959), as they are concerned with its primary biochemical event directed toward ribonucleic acid (RNA) synthesis, which precedes deoxyribonucleic acid (DNA) synthesis (Nishi, 1961; Hoshino *et al.*, 1962). It has been suggested that because a change in nucleotide composition of RNA during germination could be measured (Hoshino *et al.*, 1962), the ungerminated spores are characterized by the possession of "dormant nucleic acids" which become active by molecular modification.

After their activation, spores enter the swelling stage (Mandels and Darby, 1953; Sisler and Coy, 1954; Yanagita, 1957). They become rounded with a dedifferentiated, uniform cytoplasm swollen with imbibed water. Only the powdery mildew conidia which already have a high water content (70%) do not swell (Yarwood, 1950). The dedifferentiation of the sporal content is also revealed cytochemically by the progressive disappearance of the fat globules (Kordes, 1923; Evans and Harrar, 1930) and a change in appearance of the nuclei (macroconidia of *Neurospora;* Kihara, 1962) as a probable preparation for their first division (G. E. Baker, 1945). The increased basophilia of the sporal cytoplasm reflects the active nucleic acid synthesis detected in the swelling stage of the conidiospores of *A. niger* (Yanagita, 1957).

The short dedifferentiative, swelling phase characterized by a uniform spore content is rapidly followed by an intracytoplasmic reorganization concerned with the creation of a polar center of growth activity. This process culminates in the emergence of a germ tube as the morphological expression of a simplified redifferentiation (initial morphogenesis). A significant increase in the activity of proteinase has been measured at this stage of the germination of *Penicillium griseofulvum* (Morton *et al.*, 1960). In its further extension, the germ tube keeps the growth point in its tip (apical growth: see Reinhardt, 1892; Smith, 1924) so that rapidly a hyphal type of differentiation appears with a meristematic, apical zone and an increasingly vacuolated, distal portion. The redifferentiation may be bipolar as in the spores of *Helminthosporium sativum* which emit either one or two germ tubes (Hrushovetz, 1956). Moreover, a certain "competence" of the spore content appears to be required for germination, as shown by the multicellular spores of *Pestalotia* in which only the basal cell forms a germ tube (Weston, 1951; Chevaugeon, 1961).

Parallel to these cytomorphological changes, the type of metabolism also changes after spore germination, as demonstrated by the differential effect of griseofulvin, which, while not affecting emergence of the germ tube, prevents its further extension (Brian et al., 1946). Similarly, *Myrothecium verrucaria* needs biotin for its growth, but only in the stage following germ tube emergence (Mandels, 1955).

2. Spores with a Dormant Stage

Mature ascospores of Ascobolaceae (Discomycetes) and Sordariaceae (Pyrenomycetes) are not able to germinate in a fresh and enriched medium. Surrounded by their thick, chitinous, melanized walls (see Lowry and Sussman, 1958), they remain in a pronounced dormancy period which is the first of the three stages (viz. dormancy, activation, and germination) in the development of the ascospores of *Neurospora* recognized by Goddard (1935).

Dormancy can be broken by brief exposure to high temperature (50–60°C for 10–60 minutes) as shown for *Ascobolus* ascospores by Dodge (1912) and Gwynne-Vaughan and Williamson (1927) and for *Neurospora* ascospores by Shear and Dodge (1927) and Goddard (1935, 1939). This heat activation is reversible, i.e., activated ascospores become dormant again if prevented from germinating (Goddard, 1935). They can be partially reactivated in *N. crassa* (Emerson, 1954). Fresh ascospores of *N. crassa* (Emerson, 1948) and *N. tetrasperma* (Sussman, 1953a,b) can also be activated chemically with furfural and related unsaturated heterocyclic compounds. Emerson (1954) has suggested that furfural duplicates the action of a natural catalyst which is normally produced during spore dormancy or prematurely induced to form or become active by heat treatment. Alternatively, a natural inhibitor could be present in fresh ascospores and inactivated by heat or by those chemicals which induce germination (Cochrane, 1958).

As for the factors of dormancy, permeability neither to water nor to gases appears to be implicated in *N. tetrasperma* (Lowry et al., 1956). However, the activating effect of alkali on ascospores of *Ascobolus* spp. (Yu, 1954) may be related to permeability to water. In *N. tetrasperma,* dormant ascospores are relatively impermeable to cations (Lowry et al., 1957), which are adsorbed by the surface and can gain access inside only during germination (Sussman et al., 1958). Mechanical factors might also be implicated in *Onygena equina* where ascospore dormancy develops only after the heavy spore wall is laid down whereas immature spores can germinate without a dormant period (Brierley, 1917).

Activation of the ascospores of *N. tetrasperma* is characterized by a prominent increase in their respiratory rate (Goddard and Smith, 1938) and ability to decarboxylate pyruvic acid through activation of a latent carboxylase (Goddard, 1939). However, it was later demonstrated that the activation process could not be explained in terms of activation of pyruvic carboxylase, ethanol dehydrogenase, and cytochrome oxidase (Sussman et al., 1956) or of increased amounts of cytochrome c available to the respiratory apparatus of ascospores after their activation (Holton, 1960). The locus of metabolic activation might rather consist in the induction of an enzyme system through which trehalose, the main endogenous substrate of dormant ascospores, is metabolized (Sussman, 1961). However, recent work suggests that removal of a barrier between trehalase and its substrate could explain the breaking of dormancy (Budd et al., 1966).

Thermal and chemical activations correspond to at least two distinctive steps in the activation stage as revealed by their differential sensitivity toward metabolic inhibitors. Thus sodium azide prevents heat-activation and its characteristic respiratory rise but does not interfere with furfural activation (Emerson, 1954). Moreover, aged dormant spores can still be chemically activated, but only if they are first heated (Sussman, 1954).

Germination as the stage following activation is defined not only morphologically by germ tube emergence, but also metabolically as demonstrated by its complete inhibition by iodoacetate, which is incapable of reducing the increased respiration characterizing the activation stage (Goddard, 1948). Activated ascospores are ready to germinate if placed in the right environmental conditions. Thus, the washed ascospores of *N. tetrasperma* can germinate even in distilled water (Sussman, 1954) by utilizing trehalose as their endogenous substrate (Sussman and Lingappa, 1959). Those of the related sphaeriale *Sordaria fimicola* germinate only poorly in these conditions and are, therefore, nutritionally dependent (Bretzloff, 1954; Butler, 1956).

After the dedifferentiative step which can include ascosporal swelling (Gwynne-Vaughan and Williamson, 1927; Hawker, 1950), polar or bipolar redifferentiation of the spore contents culminates in the protrusion of one (*Sordaria* spp.) or two (*Neurospora* spp.) germ tubes, thereby achieving the metabolic and morphological transition from the germinative to the mycelial type of growth.

B. *Intermediate or Vegetative-Reproductive Morphogenesis*

This accessory phase of morphogenesis is the simplest type of reproduction in fungi, characterized by the direct modification of vegetative cells into more or less differentiated structures such as oidia, vegetative chlamydospores, sclerotia, or synnema.

1. Oidia

The formation of yeastlike or oidial forms by rounding off and ultimate separation of vegetative cells depends on environmental conditions such as partial anaerobiosis (aspergilli, etc.) or is associated with the well-known phenomenon of dimorphism (see Chapter 7).

2. Vegetative Chlamydospores

These have all the characteristics of resting bodies, such as thick walls, dense, oily contents, longevity, and limited powers of germination.

Little is known of the exact factors inducing their formation, but they are generally formed in old cultures where the medium is almost depleted of essential nutrients (Hawker, 1957). They appear in great numbers on *Fusarium solani* growing in the presence of strains of certain bacteria (Venkat Ram, 1952). In *Colletotrichum atramentarium,* conidia evolve to appressoria instead of chlamydospores in the presence of inhibitory substances from *Bacillus subtilis* (Schmiedeknecht, 1959). *Candida albicans* forms its chlamydospores only when the concentration of glucose in the medium is low (Nickerson and Mankowski, 1953), a condition unfavorable for oidial production. Similarly, in *Fusarium oxysporum* f. sp. *gladioli,* chlamydospore formation is favored by a low C:N ratio as well as by darkness (Carlile, 1956). These low carbon requirements are in contrast with the well-known situation in the phycomycete *Mucor racemosus,* where chlamydospores are best formed on media of high sugar concentration (Hawker, 1957).

Finally, from the descriptive features given above, it can be inferred that in prospective chlamydospores the metabolic pathways may be directed toward increased synthesis of fatty materials and wall polysaccharides.

3. Sclerotia

The exact nature of sclerotia may differ depending upon whether they are solely organs of vegetative reproduction and survival, or whether they will bear the fructifications of the fungus, their formation being only a first step toward sporulation, as in species of *Sclerotinia* and *Claviceps* and in certain penicillia.

They develop by various processes of branching and coalescence of closely interwoven hyphae, completed by a differentiation of the outer cells to give a protective layer (Isaac, 1949; Townsend and Willetts, 1954).

Sclerotium formation depends on adequate physical environmental factors, such as temperature and light, which do not necessarily coincide with those favorable for growth (Hawker, 1957). Continuous white light promotes sclerotium formation in *Fusarium oxysporum* (Carlile, 1956) but has no effect on sclerotial aspergilli (Rudolph, 1962) and may even be inhibitory to *Botrytis* spp. (Paul, 1929; O. T. Page, 1956). Kaiser (1962) found that microsclerotia of *Verticillium alboatrum* formed only on colonies illuminated with red to green light and that blue light was inhibitory, as already shown for aspergilli (Tarurenko, 1954).

Among nutritional factors, the C:N ratio is important in controlling the formation of sclerotia. Thus, an increase in nitrogen inhibits their production in *Botrytis cinerea* while increasing that of conidia (Peiris, 1947). Fewer sclerotia were formed on glucose than on sucrose in several aspergilli (Rudolph, 1962). In *Verticillium,* manganese ions stimulate simultaneously melanin and microsclerotia formation, as does a diffusible morphogenetic factor produced by this fungus (Brandt, 1962).

Contrary to the claims of Robbins and Kavanagh (1938) that thiamine induced the formation of numerous sclerotia by the basidiomycete *Sclerotium rolfsii,* Lilly and Barnett (1948a) conclude that the known vitamins do not have a specific effect on sclerotial production. This by no means excludes the formative action of unknown stimulating substances from natural extracts (Nakata, 1929) or of diffusible morphogenetic factors (Brandt and Reese, 1964).

In repeating and expanding Peiris' work on the effects of the C:N ratio, Townsend (1957) showed that under some conditions, numerous but immature sclerotial initials were induced but that under others only a few, but mature, sclerotia were formed. Thus it appears that the processes of initiation and maturation are distinct and not favored by the same set of environmental conditions. In fact, it has been shown that O_2 uptake of *Claviceps purpurea* sclerotia is insensitive to malonate inhibition whereas subsequent fruit-body formation on them is completely blocked by this Krebs cycle inhibitor (Garay, 1958).

4. Synnemata

The synnema, or coremium, is a differentiated structure consisting of an erect bundle of hyphae which eventually bears the spores. Taber (1961) describes two morphogenetic types of synnemata: (1) those which produce spores at the apex, as in *Graphium* and *Stysanus* spp., classified as having determinate growth; (2) those which produce spores at the base and possess an apical growing point, as in *Isaria cretacea,* classified as having indeterminate growth.

Morphogenesis of the synnema can be divided into four phases: differentiation of certain hyphae of the assimilative mat into those capable of developing into synnemata, orientation of the hyphae away from their origin, continued growth, and branching and sporulation of the hyphae (Taber, 1959). Synnema morphogenesis is under genetic control as revealed by a variant of *Isaria cretacea* which does not produce synnemata under any condition, not even in heterokaryosis with the parent strain (Taber, 1959).

Nutritional control of synnematal development has been thoroughly studied (Taber, 1960). Sucrose, mannitol, and acetate are specific inhibitors of synnematal morphogenesis. No more exogenous thiamine and biotin are required for this process than for maximal vegetative mat growth. However, Magrou *et al.* (1951) had shown that *Sphaerocybe concentrica* produced its characteristic coremes only on media containing thiamine or a mixture of its two constituents, pyrimidine and thiazole. Addition of an auxin, indoleacetic acid, which inhibits endogenous respiration of *I. cretacea*, to the sucrose medium retards vegetative mat growth (primary vegetative growth) and initiates synnema growth (secondary vegetative growth) (Taber, 1960). These data suggest that morphogenesis of synnemata is a function of endogenous metabolism and constitutes a good example of experimental control of fungal morphogenesis.

The relationship between synnematal development and nutrients appears to be similar in *Hirsutella gigantea* (Stilbaceae), an insect parasite with synnemata resembling the *Isaria* type, to that described in *Graphium ulmi* (Taber, 1961). In *H. gigantea,* Loughheed (1961) made the interesting observation that phosphoglyceric acid and gibberellic acid are more effective stimulants of synnemata formation in the dark than in the light.

Factors in the formation of coremia were also studied in other ascomycetes: these factors include desiccation of the culture, pH change in the medium, accumulation of metabolic products in *Trichophyton mentagrophytes* (Hejmánek and Hejmánková-Uhrová, 1956); effect of illumination on the size and form of coremia in *Penicillium claviforme* (Carlile *et al.,* 1961). In the latter, a photosensitive stage (blue light) early in the elongation of the coremium stalk is followed by a light-insensitive phase of elongation, well-illustrating Loughheed's (1961) conclusion that "the diversity of factors influencing synnemata formation indicates that their morphological differentiation is a multistep process which may be affected at several points."

C. *Final or Reproductive Morphogenesis: Asexual Sporulation ("Imperfect" Stage)*

The main type of asexual spore produced by ascomycetes is the conidium or conidiospore, which is a deciduous bud formed on a specialized hypha. [For the method of conidial formation in the Hyphomycetes, see Hughes (1953).] By contrast, the so-called macroconidium often corresponds to an arthrospore formed by the constriction of a preexisting hypha (Vuillemin, 1910).

1. Conidia

The most generally essential condition for the formation of conidiospores in several species of *Penicillium* is the absence, or the exhaustion, of assimilable nitrogen from the medium while carbohydrate in high concentration is still present. In such conditions, sporulation could even be induced in submerged cultures of *P. griseofulvum* when pure glucose was replaced by a crude glucose derived from maize starch by acid hydrolysis (Morton *et al.*, 1958). The morphogenetic stimulus could be due to the presence in crude glucose of both anhydroglucose and traces of Ca^{++} (Armstrong *et al.*, 1963).

In nitrogen-starved *Penicillium griseofulvum*, the intracellular proteinase enzymes increased to levels several times higher than in growing mycelium (Morton *et al.*, 1960). Under some conditions the induction of sporulation could be associated with this rise in proteinase, but there was no simple causal relation between the two processes, although they occurred simultaneously after transfer of the mold to nitrogen-free medium. Indeed, in *Aspergillus niger*, *Scopulariopsis brevicaulis*, and *Gibberella fujikuroi*, increased proteinase during nitrogen starvation was not accompanied by sporulation. The inducing effect of nitrogen starvation may be related to the fact that there is considerable reorganization of nitrogenous constituents at sporulation as shown in *A. niger*, where the amino acid composition of mycelium differs from that found after sporulation (Stokes and Gunness, 1946). However, the mycelial proteins of *P. roquefortii* do not differ in their albumen and globulin contents from the spore protein (Taha and Knight, 1962). In *A. flavus*, the appearance of conidia is coincident with a marked fall in mycelial nitrogen, easily interpreted as resulting from transport to the sporulating structures (Pillai and Srinivasan, 1956). Correspondingly, there is also a transfer of phosphate from the mycelium to the conidia during their formation in *A. niger* as shown by the 80% P decline in the mycelium with at least some of this P appearing in the spores (Bajaj *et al.*, 1954). Acid-soluble polyphosphate is accumulated in sporulating *Aspergillus* (Kulayev and Belozersky, 1957), and the conidia of *A. niger* contain in their metachromatic granules a fairly large amount of polyphosphate as a P reservoir (Nishi, 1961). These translocations and interconversions of phosphorus compounds are mediated by enzymes such as the polyphosphatases, which catalyze the depolymerization of high-polymer polyphosphates to lower polymers. Their activity increases in the sporulating mycelium of *A. niger* (Lindeberg and Malmgren, 1952). Moreover, the conidia of *A. niger* are highly basophilic. The basophilic substances, probably nucleoproteins, are translocated from the vesicles into conidia during morphogenesis (Yanagita and Kogané, 1962).

The conditioning effects of trace elements on sporulation and its associated pigmentation in *A. niger* is well known (Foster, 1949). Depending on their concentration, these elements exert a prosporulating effect, as with traces of copper (Mulder, 1938) or an antisporulating effect, as with excess zinc (Roberg, 1928). Lack of iron had the same restrictive effect on sporulation of *A. niger* as the absence of oxygen (Sauton, 1910). Manganese and iron stimulated sporulation in *Penicillium* (Bhattacharyya and Basu, 1962). Dimethylglyoxime and other metal-reacting oximes and quinolines were found to be effective in reducing spore production of *Sclerotinia fructicola, Alternaria* sp., *Penicillium* sp., and *A. niger* (Rich and Horsfall, 1948).

A calcium requirement has been demonstrated for sporulation of *Penicillium notatum* in submerged culture (Foster *et al.*, 1945). At least 35 ppm of Ca^{++} was necessary for the maximum degree of sporulation by this mold, and strontium or barium could partially replace calcium for the morphogenetic effect (Hadley and Harrold, 1958a). However, the sporulation of *P. notatum* in normal subaerial cultures did not require the presence of calcium, and Hadley and Harrold concluded that "in submerged cultures of *Penicillium*, it appears that the function of the different agencies inducing sporulation is to impart an element of heterogeneity into the system which stimulates mycelium in some yet undefined way, to manifest the capacity for sporulation which develops during growth." Concerning the development of sporulation in *P. notatum*, they showed that the requirement for calcium appears to be confined to the 6-hour period immediately preceding initial sporulation and is associated with the differentiation of phialides and conidia. A culture's development is therefore divisible into an initial calcium-independent phase of physiological differentiation or maturation, the length of which is a function of inoculum load and a calcium-dependent phase of morphological differentiation of the now mature mycelium, lasting 6 hours and independent of the inoculum load. A stage of "ripeness to spore," corresponding to the end of the maturation period has also been recognized in submerged cultures of *P. griseofulvum* (Morton *et al.*, 1958). Finally, a sporulating factor(s) was found to be liberated in the filtrates of mature cultures of *P. notatum* and also of five other *Penicillium* species and *A. niger* (Hadley and Harrold, 1958b). This nonspecific substance(s) is thermolabile and its effects are not reproduced by glucose-1-phosphate or fructose-1:6-phosphate, the perithecial stimulants in *Melanospora (Sordaria) destruens* (Hawker, 1948).

Vitamins have often been mentioned as stimulating asexual sporulation in fungi (Lilly and Barnett, 1951), but this effect is not too specific as it is generally accompanied by increased growth. Relatively high doses of inositol added to its culture medium cause *Ophiostoma multiannulatum* to grow almost entirely in the form of conidia (Fries, 1949). In other cases, excess of a vitamin may be inhibitory to sporulation, as with riboflavin in *Cercospora personata* [*Mycosphaerella berkleyii*] (Shanta, 1961). Antivitamins such as pyrithiamine can also be effective antisporulants (Lilly and Barnett, 1948b).

Too little attention has been paid to the unraveling of those metabolic pathways involved in the processes critical for conidial formation. In *A. niger*, the functioning of the complete glycolytic pathway and the citric acid cycle seems to be required for conidial formation as revealed by the differential sensitivity of conidiation toward appropriate metabolic inhibitors (fluoride, arsenite, malonate, etc.) at concentrations that have no effect on mycelial growth (Behal and Eakin, 1959b). However, induction of the glyoxylate cycle as an alternative pathway to the citric acid cycle in *A. niger* grown on an acetate medium increased the relative rate of conidiogenesis (Turian and Seydoux, 1961). The stimulation of macroconidial formation in *Trichophyton mentagrophytes* grown under increased CO_2 tensions (Chin and Knight, 1957) may also be related to induced changes in metabolic pathways (Chin and Knight, 1963). In *Fusarium oxysporum* f. sp. *cubense*, similar patterns of distribution of the glycolytic and oxidative enzymes were found among four particulate fractions of mycelium and microconidia. The specific activities of diphosphopyridine nucleotidase and cytochrome oxidase were higher in the mycelium and those of succinic dehydrogenase and isocitratase higher in the microconidia (Maruyama and Alexander, 1962a), which are noticeably richer in nucleic acids (Maruyama and Alexander, 1962b). Budding conidia of *Ophiostoma multiannulatum* were also found to have a higher DNA content than hyphae; thus, as expected, aminopterin, actinomycin, or puromycin, which can interfere with normal synthesis of DNA or protein, produced long hyphal cells in this species (von Hofsten, 1962). In connection with lipid metabolism, it was shown that the formation of ketones from fatty acids was definitely associated with the spores, and not with the mycelium, of *P. roquefortii* (Gehrig and Knight, 1958). Disturbance in the metabolism of methionine caused by 6-ethylthiopurine prevented conidial differentiation at the extremities of the sterigmata in *A. niger*. Another purine analog, 6-hydroxy-2-mercaptopurine (thioguanine) inhibited only conidiophore maturation (Behal and Eakin, 1959a). Further use of antimetabolites may help to clarify the nature of the subtle metabolic shifts associated with each of the morphogenetic stages in the fungi.

Among the physical factors that control spore formation, light has frequently been shown to influence asexual sporulation (Fikry, 1932; Etzhold,

1960; Ingold, 1962). It has a positive effect on the size and septation of macroconidia of *Fusarium* spp. (Harter, 1939; Snyder and Hansen, 1941; Carlile, 1956) and stimulates conidial formation in many imperfect fungi (Johnson and Halpin, 1954). In *Alternaria,* formation of sterigmata was induced by light, while dark periods were required for conidial differentiation on these sterigmata (von Witsch and Wagner, 1955). Ultraviolet light can also promote sporulation in many fungi (Stevens, 1928) such as *Fusarium oxysporum* (Carlile, 1956), *Helminthosporium oryzae* (Leach, 1961), *Alternaria dianthi* (Joly, 1962). Light-induced formation of asexual structures in concentric rings (zonation) is of frequent occurrence in *Penicillium* (Sagromsky, 1952), *Monilia* spp. (Jerebzoff, 1958; and Volume I, Chapter 27). The light stimulus for sporulation could check the growth of the hyphal tips, triggering an enzymatic mechanism implicated in spore formation.

Abnormalities such as proliferations of sterigmata and enlarged, multinucleated conidia have been observed in *Aspergillus repens* and *A. echinulatus* grown at temperatures above optimum or in high humidity (Thielke, 1958; Thielke and Paravicini, 1962). Under similar conditions, proliferations of the conidiophores had also been described in *Eurotium herbariorum* (Barnes, 1928). Exclusive conidial growth of *O. multiannulatum* could be maintained only in aerated liquid media incubated at about 30°C, while below 20°C hyphal growth was favored (von Hofsten and von Hofsten, 1958).

Oxygen tension appears to be critical for normal sporulation in *Aspergillus* spp. Anaerobic conditions lead to conidiophore proliferations in *A. niger* (C. W. Miller and Anderson, 1961). Sterigmata proliferations, considered as dedifferentiations induced by respiratory deficiency, were also observed in *A. amstelodami* (Bleul, 1962b). Furthermore, submerged cultures exhibited morphogenetic changes in *Aspergillus* and *Penicillium* spp. (Thirumalachar, 1957) and in *Penicillium,* the presence of O_2 was found to be necessary for the strong spore-forming effect of light (Gutter, 1957).

The most powerful stimulus to sporulation in *Penicillium* and other fungi comes from emergence of mycelium from submerged into aerial conditions. In a critical reevaluation of the role of oxygen in this morphogenetic induction, Morton (1961) demonstrated that in *P. griseofulvum* and *P. chrysogenum* the aerial stimulus is not associated with the supply of O_2. Concentration of CO_2 and water loss from the mycelium are also not influential. The primary aerial stimulus to sporulation may be associated with some physicochemical change at the cell surface (probably synthesis of a surface-active protein) induced by the abrupt formation of an air/water interface. This explanation also finds support in previous observations that certain surface-active substances can stimulate endosporulation in *Penicillium* sp. (Converse, 1957) while others such as digitonin reduced aerial sporulation in *A. niger* (Steinberg, 1940), as confirmed in *P. griseofulvum* (Morton, 1961), and in the suggestion that spore surfaces in *P. cyclopium* and *P. spinulosum* are of a waxy or lipidic nature (Douglas et al., 1959). Finally the observed increase in dehydrogenase activity of the aerial portion of *P. griseofulvum* (Morton, 1961) reveals that important metabolic changes occur when the mycelium breaks the surface of the medium (see also in *Neurospora,* Section II, D, 1, c).

All the above studies on the control of asexual sporulation, i.e., maintenance of the molds in a vegetative, mycelial condition or induction of their sporulation, have been made with fungi having a normal genetical background, fully compatible with spore formation. Mutations can disturb this morphogenetic capacity as shown in the sterile M (mycelial) form of many fungi exhibiting the "dual phenomenon" (Hansen, 1938) and the sectors without conidia and conidiophores, or with only abnormal conidiophores appearing in the colonies of penicillia (Reese et al., 1949; R. Müller, 1953) or other fungi such as aspergilli (see Fincham and Day, 1963). These so-called morphological mutants have lost the capacity to sporulate normally even in environmental conditions known as optimal. Therefore, if at first sight the environmental factors may appear to exert a determining (inductive or repressive) effect on sporulation, in the last analysis they act only through the secondary control of metabolic pathways directed primarily by the genetic potential of every normal fungus. It must be pointed out, however, that the sequential nature of this morphogenetic control does not exclude the possibility of restoring morphological mutants to normality by supplementing them with a critical but deficient metabolic intermediate. Thus, certain basic amino acids (lysine, histidine) were beneficial to nitrite-requiring mutants of aspergilli with abnormal sporulating structures (Steinberg and Thom, 1942).

2. *Arthrospores*

See macroconidia of *Neurospora* (Section II, D, 1, c).

D. *Final or Reproductive Morphogenesis: Sexual Sporulation ("Perfect" Stage)*

1. *Differentiation of Sex Organs*

a. *Ascogonia—antheridia.* In a few species of *Penicillium,* the differentiation of ascogonia (♀) among tangles of aerial hyphae is accompanied by that of antheridia (♂) as in Brefeld's well-known illustration (1874) of *"P. glaucum"* showing two short bodies arising from adjacent cells and coiling spirally about each other. In the *Penicillium luteum* series, Emmons (1935) also described perithecial initials as coiling bodies, the antheridial branch being sometimes much thinner than the ascogonial (*P. vermiculatum*). In *P. wortmannii,* a slightly differentiated branch of the vegetative mycelium functions as an ascogonium and no paired organs are to be found whereas in six other species, among which is *P. brefeldianum* (Dodge, 1933), a single substitute type of ascogonium arises in the crotch of a system of dichomotized hyphal branches (Emmons, 1935).

In aspergilli the perithecium arises from a single branch which coils in various ways to become the ascogonium (Dangeard, 1907; Dale, 1909). No antheridial differentiation and no fertilization were demonstrated in these studies (Thom and Raper, 1945).

All these types of perithecial initials in the *Penicillium-Aspergillus* group have in common a high stainability (Dodge, 1933; Emmons, 1935), probably indicative of their richness in nucleoproteins. The factors in their appearance and development have received much less attention than their descriptive morphology. Moreover, the formation of the whole fruiting structure, the perithecium, has generally been considered as the developmental criterion rather than the appearance of the initial sex organs.

The abundance of assimilable carbohydrate has often been considered to be the most general condition favoring sexual reproduction in these fungi (Klebs, 1928; Thom and Raper, 1945). However, in *Aspergillus manginii,* the perithecial initials do not form on high sugar concentrations (M. Moreau, 1959). An initial low concentration of soluble sugar was also conducive to perithecial formation in *P. vermiculatum* and *P. wortmannii* and perithecial growth was best with polysaccharides as C sources while peptone was the most favorable N source (Basu and Bhattacharyya, 1962). In *A. amstelodami,* peptone in alkaline media favors conidial formation (Schönborn, 1955). The concentration of nitrogen (NH_4NO_3 or other N source) is more important than the concentration of glucose in determining the production of perithecia in *P. vermiculatum* (DasGupta and Nandi, 1957). From these rather conflicting results it appears that a definite carbon/nitrogen balance is the most general condition controlling sexual expression in different penicillia and aspergilli.

Among physical factors, continuous light was shown to reduce the perithecia:conidia ratio in *A. amstelodami* (Bleul, 1962a).

An element of duality could be suspected in the developmental alternative, well illustrated in the penicillia and aspergilli between the asexual differentiation of propagative conidia (asexual sporulation) and the differentiation of sexual organs, ascogonia and antheridia, leading finally to ascospore production (sexual sporulation). This dualism has been well demonstrated in *Aspergillus glaucus* propagated by conidia for several generations. In these conditions, the production of perithecia and ascospores gradually fell until the fungus lost its capacity for sexual reproduction and became imperfect (Jinks, 1954, 1956; Chapter 19). A similar increased emphasis upon asexual sporulation by prolonged selection of conidia was obtained in *Cercospora musae* [*Mycosphaerella musae*] (Calpouzos, 1954). In *A. glaucus,* the cytoplasm that has thus progressively changed its determination of sexual capacity can, nevertheless, be restored to its original state by propagation through the last-formed ascospores. Mather and Jinks (1958) concluded, therefore, that sexual reproduction always involves a cytoplasmic restoration so that despite developmental alterations the standard basic cytoplasmic pattern is once again established.

Among other ascomycetes differentiating both ascogonia and antheridia at the beginning of sexual sporulation is *Venturia inaequalis* (Killian, 1917; Keitt and Palmiter, 1938) in which extracts of other fungi have been shown to stimulate (Wilson, 1927), and low concentrations of NO_3^- to inhibit (Ross, 1959), initiation of perithecia. In *Pleospora gaeumannii* both ascogonium and antheridium exhibit strong stainability (E. Müller, 1951) and in *P. bromi,* the optimum pH range for formation of pseudothecial primordia is pH 6.0–6.3 (Frauenstein, 1962). Furthermore, light is required for perithecial primordium formation in *Hypomyces solani* under certain laboratory conditions (R. Baker and Ware, 1962).

In several species of *Chaetomium,* a cell of an ascogonial coil is fertilized by a slender antheridial hypha (Greis, 1941; Whiteside, 1957). *C. cochliodes* (Hawker, 1942) and *C. convolutum* (Lilly and Barnett, 1949) fruit better in the presence of aneurin. The existence of a definite "fruiting factor," other than the recognized B-group vitamins, has been observed in the extracts of jute (Buston and Basu, 1948). Suitable doses of calcium could reproduce in part the jute effect in *C. globosum* and *C. brasiliense* (Basu, 1951, 1952). The formation of perithecia in *C. globosum* is associated with the presence of organic phosphates, especially phosphoglyceric acid, in the medium (Buston and Khan, 1956; McDonough and Rickard, 1960); unfortunately, the exact stage of development at which the chemical stimulus can evoke the fruiting response is unknown.

Contrasting with the wealth of descriptive knowledge accumulated about sexual development of the discomycete *Pyronema* since the time of Harper, Dangeard, and Claussen (E. J. Moore, 1963), our insight into the morphogenetic factors at work in this interesting fungus is still very poor. According to Robinson (1926), initiation of the sexual organs in *P. confluens* [*P. omphalodes*] occurred only on exhaustion of the nitrate ion from the medium (also in *Venturia* and *Neurospora*), and at least 6 hour's exposure to light was required for normal differentiation of groups of antheridia plus ascogonia in the tufts of short aerial hyphae (for pigment relationships, see Section II, D, 4). Kerl (1937) showed that, in certain cultural con-

11. Morphogenesis in Ascomycetes

ditions, antheridial and ascogonial cells of *P. omphalodes* can dedifferentiate back to vegetative hyphae. With ascogonia, however, there was a progressive diminution of this regenerative ability up to fertilization.

Ascobolus magnificus also differentiated an antheridium and a septated ascogonium including one central cell as the initial of the future ascogenous hyphae and an apical trichogynous cell (Dodge, 1920). On the monoecious mycelium of the species, the sexual elements tend to develop into antheridia on the distal branches and into oogonia on the older branches nearer the base of the mycelium (Gwynne-Vaughan and Williamson, 1932). Antheridia could be induced class-specifically in *Ascobolus stercorarius* (Bistis and Raper, 1963).

b. Ascogonia—microconidia. In *Podospora anserina,* the female organs or ascogonia consist of coiled structures terminating in slender trichogynes while the male structures are small flask-shaped antheridia out of whose necks minute spermlike bodies, often called microconidia, are successively pushed (Ames, 1934). Similar sharp differentiation between the sexual organs has been described in pyrenomycetes such as *Mycosphaerella tulipiferae* (Higgins, 1936), *Podospora minuta* (Page, 1939), *Bombardia lunata* (Zickler, 1937, 1953), and *Gelasinospora calospora* (Sloan and Wilson, 1958; Goos, 1959).

As in *Neurospora, Glomerella,* and *Sordaria,* detailed genetic study of *Podospora anserina* has led to the isolation of mutants blocked at given stages of their sexual morphogenesis (Rizet and Engelmann, 1949). On the physiological side, it has been shown that *P. anserina* grown in glucose or fructose media, which are favorable to dark pigment production, formed ascogonia which degenerated while with saccharose, a poor C source for pigment production, normal sexual morphogenesis occurred. Thus, contrary to *Neurospora,* no correlation between the differentiation of ascogonia-protoperithecia and the formation of pigment, assumed to be melanin, could be ascertained either in the wild type or in different mutants of *P. anserina* (Esser, 1956). Moreover, this study illustrates Klebs' principle (1900) that relatively poor nutritional conditions, such as growth on saccharose for *P. anserina,* are more favorable to sexual reproduction.

Among discomycetes, microconidial formation has been especially studied in the Sclerotiniaceae (Drayton, 1932, 1937; Groves and Drayton, 1939). In *Sclerotinia gladioli,* the receptive bodies containing deeply stained, coiled ascogonial hyphae on the stromatic tissue are the only structures capable of fertilization by the microconidia (Drayton, 1934). It was later shown that thermoperiods exert an influence on the production of the sexual stage in *S. trifoliorum* (Sproston and Pease, 1957). In *Coccomyces hiemalis,* the elongated coiled ascogonium, under some hormonal incitement, extends up to the acervuli differentiating the microconidia (Backus, 1934). *Pseudopeziza ribis* differentiates its microconidia at lower temperatures than its macroconidia, which form at 20–24°C (Blodgett, 1936).

Bistis (1956, 1957) has contributed two major morphogenetic studies concerning the sexual reaction of *Ascobolus stercorarius* which results from the interaction between a single oidium (fertilizing, microconidial-like agent, Dowding, 1931a) and a mycelium (ascogonial parent). The ontogeny of the ascogonium includes in its first stages (1) induction of the ascogonial primordium, (2) maturation of the ascogonium, and (3) directional growth of the trichogyne toward the oidium. There is evidence that sex hormones are active during this sexual process (Bistis, 1956). Protoplasmic differentiation in the ascogonium has been studied further, and it has been shown that the stalk cells of the mature ascogonium alone retain the ability to bud out lateral vegetative branches and that the main stem and the trichogyne are apparently capable only of carrying out their sexual function (Bistis, 1957). Dedifferentiation was, however, still possible through transfer of one complete ascogonial primordium to a fresh agar plate on which the tip grew out as a vegetative hypha and produced a normal colony (see also *Neurospora,* Dodge, 1932; and *Pyronema,* Kerl, 1937).

c. *Ascogonia—macroconidia—microconidia.* Neurospora, the red bread mold, has proved to be a particularly suitable tool for the study of the factors determining the expression of morphogenesis. This is due to the fact that it is possible to use a combined genetic and biochemical approach to problems of morphogenesis on one and the same organism, which can be grown under very precisely controlled environmental conditions on a chemically defined medium.

Following the pioneer studies on sexuality in the newly described *Neurospora sitophila* (Shear and Dodge, 1927; Dodge, 1928), the stages in the development of female sex bodies or protoperithecia (incipient perithecia) from the initial ascogonial coil were studied in detail in this species and *N. crassa* (F. Moreau and Moreau, 1930; Dodge, 1935a; Backus, 1939) as well as *N. tetrasperma* (Colson, 1934).

Both multinucleate macroconidia and uninucleate microconidia of heterothallic *N. sitophila* and *N. crassa* function as the usual donors of nuclei to the female receptive organs of the opposite mating type (spermatization, see Backus, 1939). As such they can be considered to be male cells and their differentiation can thus be visualized and studied as the morphogenetic alternative to ascogonia-protoperithecia rather than as simple asexual spores (macroconidia considered as arthrospores). Moreover, factors determining their epigenetic initiation can be investigated independently of the genetically determined outbreeding device enforcing cross-fertility (heterothallism) because both types of sexual structure are differentiated on a single strain (bisexuality). Furthermore, the direct morphogenetic sequence from the ascogonium → protoperithecium → perithecium with four-spored asci can be adequately followed in the homothallic *N. tetrasperma.*

Several types of morphological mutants are known in *Neurospora.* Some have lost the ability to form conidia, e.g., the purely mycelial, aconidial or "fluffy" strains (Lindegren and Lindegren, 1941). Others can form only microconidia (albino strains of *N. sitophila,* Dodge, 1932; "peach" mutant of *N. crassa,* Barratt and Garnjobst, 1949). According to segregation tests, an aconidial character (*con*) is situated in the mating-type chromosome (Sheng and Ryan, 1948). In addition, temperature-sensitive genes affecting conidiation are known in *Neurospora* (Grigg, 1960a), and it was shown that the ability of a culture of *N. crassa* to produce a macroconidium or a microconidium is determined (irreversibly) at a particular, not always coincident, period during development (Grigg, 1960b). Female-sterile mutants, incapable of forming protoperithecia, are also known (see Westergaard and Hirsch, 1954), and it has been shown that the abundance of protoperithecia formed by any strain of *N. sitophila* is genetically controlled by factors which segregate at meiosis (Aronescu, 1933; Dodge, 1946). Further mutational studies will be necessary to disclose the sequential blockage in the sexual morphogenesis of *Neurospora* as already described in *Podospora* or *Glomerella.*

Among the numerous biochemical mutants *Neurospora* (see Wagner and Mitchell, 1955) certain may also be useful tools for investigation of morphogenetic problems. Such is the case with the inositolless mutants because of their colonial morphology (Beadle, 1944) similar to the "paramorphic" growth induced by *l*-sorbose (Tatum *et al.,* 1949) suggesting that inositol might have a morphogenetic role in *N. crassa* (Shatkin and Tatum, 1961) as in *Ophiostoma* (Fries, 1949; Section II, C, 1).

The establishment of the perithecia-promoting minimal medium (P-min. medium) for *Neurospora* by Westergaard and Mitchell (1947) not only fostered the field of biochemical genetics by providing biologists extending the brilliant discoveries of Beadle and Tatum (1941) with a better-defined crossing medium, but also fostered morphogenetic studies by becoming a reference medium to test for the degree of fertility of *Neurospora.* While testing their new medium, Westergaard and Mitchell (1947) made the important observation that *N. crassa,* though grown on this optimal medium, produced no perithecia at 35°C. Hirsch (1954) confirmed this thermoinhibition and found that tyrosinase and melanin are reduced or absent in such sterile mycelia. He further showed that any other conditions which interfered with melanin production (increased nitrogen, tyrosinase inhibitors, etc.) also had an inhibitory effect on the formation or normal functioning of protoperithecia. Hirsch suggested a causal connection between tyrosine metabolism and induction of the female sex bodies. However, this requires further genetic studies of the loci responsible for protoperithecial and melanin formation, and Hirsch wisely concluded, "The process of protoperithecia formation requires the function of certain genes some of which may be associated with melanin formation, but these genes act only under proper environmental conditions." An investigation of tyrosine metabolism in *N. crassa* has added further biochemical confirmation of Hirsch's hypothesis by showing that there was no tyrosinase activity in the female-sterile strains available (Barbesgaard and Wagner, 1959). Melanin production has recently been envisaged as being a reflection of the protein turnover associated with the differentiation process in *Neurospora* (Horowitz et al., 1961).

The idea put forward by Westergaard and Hirsch (1954) that in the formation of female sex organs one or more of the precursors of melanin may have a hormonelike effect has not been directly confirmed. Hirsch (1954) was, indeed, unsuccessful in his attempts to demonstrate the presence, in extracts of one strain of *N. crassa*, of hormones or morphogenetic substances capable of inducing the formation of protoperithecia in another strain. In fact, sex hormones have never been unequivocally shown to be present in *Neurospora* (F. Moreau and Moruzi, 1931; F. Moreau and Moreau, 1938; Aronescu, 1933; Dodge, 1935a; Lindegren, 1936; Sansome, 1946; see Raper, 1952). More recent evidence has been given of the presence, in the filtrate of a strain of *N. crassa* grown in a balanced NH_4^+–NO_3^- medium, of substances that act partially as sex inducers of the opposite mating type strain (Ito, 1959, 1961).

In the search for further criteria of differential metabolism in the alternate morphogenetic states (protoperithecial (25°C)-conidial (37°C)) of *N. crassa*, we detected at first a striking accumulation of succinic acid in the conidial, "male" filtrates. This was indicative of a metabolic block at the succinic dehydrogenase step and could be proved by the finding in cell-free extracts of the conidial mycelia of only 20% of the succinic dehydrogenase of the protoperithecial mycelia (Turian, 1960). It could then be inferred that conidial differentiation was in some way connected with a lesion in the Krebs cycle while protoperithecial morphogenesis apparently required full functioning of this important metabolic pathway. Owens (1955) had already measured succinic oxidase activity in conidial homogenates of *N. sitophila* but had not compared it with that from protoperithecial mycelia. Instead, confirmation of our suggestion can be found in Zalokar's independent demonstration (1959a) of very low succinic dehydrogenase activity in the mitochondria isolated from conidia of *N. crassa* compared to that from vegetative mycelia. Additional support came from the successful use of an efficient Krebs cycle inhibitor, malonate, which strongly repressed protoperithecial differentiation in *N. crassa* and *N. tetrasperma* while favoring a conidial development (Turian, 1962c). Chemocontrol of *Neurospora* morphogenesis could thus be substituted for the thermocontrol used thus far. Induction of the glyoxylic acid cycle as an alternative to the Krebs cycle, by imposing acetate as a single source of C for *Neurospora* achieved approximately the same goal, i.e., pure conidial growth (modest growth improvable with a 1:8 supplement of sucrose) without any protoperithecial differentiation (Turian, 1961a,b). Such induction of conidia was accompanied by a drop in the succinic cytochrome c reductase activity of the mitochondria isolated from the conidial cultures in comparison with that from sucrose-grown cultures (Turian and Seydoux, 1962). Isocitratase, the key enzyme of the glyoxylic cycle, was also induced in a microconidial albino strain of *N. sitophila* (from Dodge, 1932) grown on acetate medium but with only 33% efficiency compared to the macroconidial wild strain (Turian *et al.*, 1962). Fair activity of isocitratase could be measured in extracts of the conidial cultures obtained at 37°C on sucrose, a strong repressor (as glucose) of isocitratase at 25°C. This endogenously induced enzyme activity was ascribed to a derepression effect through negative feedback to the isocitrate branching of the thermoinhibited Krebs cycle (Turian, 1961b, 1963). CO_2 ($NaHCO_3$), presumably by repressing the decarboxylation steps in the Krebs cycle (see Cantino and Horenstein, 1956), also induced in sucrose cultures, but already at 25°C, isocitratase activity; this effect was unfavorable for protoperithecial, but favorable for conidial, differentiation (Turian, 1963).

A certain proportion of the glyoxylic acid formed by isocitratase activity appears to be transaminated by α-alanine to form glycine (Turian and Combépine, 1963), an important precursor for the increased nucleic acid biosyntheses required for conidial proliferation. Another amino acid, methionine, appears to play a role in conidial formation, as revealed by its successful counteraction of the anticonidial effect of its analog, ethionine (Strauss, 1958). In a more general way, media rich in organic nitrogen are favorable for conidiation in *Neurospora* (Horowitz, 1947; Hirsch, 1954).

Whatever the importance of isocitratase activity in opening an alternate pathway to the Krebs cycle and thus creating internal conditions unfavorable for female differentiation, it does not appear to be the only possible way of producing glyoxylate, the important glycine precursor always detected in conidial homogenates (Owens, 1955; Turian, 1961b). Abundant conidial production can indeed occur under conditions of relatively low isocitratase activity by growing *N. crassa* at 25°C on the Westergaard-Mitchell sucrose medium enriched in citrate or succinate. Under these conditions, the main oxidative alternate pathway in the conidia appears to be provided by the hexose monophosphate or pentose shunt (Turian, 1962a) and the glyoxylate generated through the splitting of some of the pentose produced (Turian, 1963). The heavy conidial production on the citrate–sucrose–nitrate medium could be prevented by the addition of ammonium ions (Turian, 1964), known to be repressors of the nitrate reductase (Kinsky, 1961), and therefore antagonizing the best source of TPNH (reduced triphosphopyridine nucleotide) regeneration normally coupled with the functioning of the pentose shunt (nitrate reductase in *Neurospora*: TPNH-Mo-flavoprotein, Nicholas and Nason, 1954).

The observed stimulatory effect of nitrate upon conidiation in *Neurospora* growing in defined conditions (sugar and organic acids as H donors) fits with Hirsch's observation (1954) that this ion inhibits some stage in the differentiation of the protoperithecia (nitrate exhaustion from the medium is a prerequisite for their formation). Moreover, when the mycelial felts break the surface of the culture solution and emerge into a more aerobic environment where they start forming conidia, there is a predominance of the assimilatory type of nitrate reduction requiring only the functioning of FAD (flavine adenine dinucleotide) and molybdenum to regenerate TPNH (Walker and Nicholas, 1962). The dispensability of the cytochrome system in this process may explain the lower cytochrome oxidase activity measured in conidial homogenates compared to protoperithecial ones (Turian, 1960). In this connection, it is also important to mention that a very active DPNase (diphosphopyridine nucleotidase) has been detected in the conidia of *N. crassa* (Zalokar and Cochrane, 1956) and that the TPN rather than the DPN type of glutamic dehydrogenase functions in these "male" cells (Sanwal and Lata, 1961). Thus it appears that a flavine type of metabolism, coupled through TPNH → TPN regeneration to the direct oxidation of sugars through the hexose monophosphate shunt, predominates during conidial differentiation in *Neurospora*. Such a tentative conclusion is in good agreement with the highly aerobic nature of this morphogenetic process as suggested by the fact that conidia never form on submerged mycelia (Went, 1901; Zalokar, 1957), but always on specialized, aerial hyphae (Zalokar, 1959b).

Protoperithecia can differentiate under less strict aerobic conditions than conidia as revealed by observations on the effects of O_2 deficiency on perithecia formation (Denny, 1933; see Section II, D, 4). However, their associated respiratory processes not only require normal functioning of the Krebs cycle (see above), but appear to be cytochrome mediated. Thus, certain nuclear gene mutants (C_{115} and C_{117}) which mimic the cytoplasmic mutant *poky* (slow growth, aberrations in cytochrome system) cannot normally function as protoperithecial parents in crosses with the wild

11. Morphogenesis in Ascomycetes

type. Interestingly enough, they also have an abnormally high quantity of FAD (Wagner and Mitchell, 1955).

There is no necessary relationship between the formation of conidia by *Neurospora* and the usually associated biosynthesis of carotenoids (Haxo, 1949), as exemplified by albino but fully conidiated mutants (Hungate, 1945; Sheng and Sheng, 1952) but a repression of conidial formation accompanied drastic inhibition of carotenogenesis through diphenylamine treatment of *N. crassa* grown on the Fries liquid medium (Turian, 1957). On our new conidiogenic media such as the citrate–sucrose–nitrate (see above), pure white, partially conidiated phenocopies of the albino strains could however be obtained with the wild type of *N. crassa* grown in the presence of diphenylamine (Turian, 1962d). In the conidia, the relative amounts of the carotenoids spirilloxanthine, lycopene, and an acidic pigment (neurosporaxanthine) where shown to be prominently higher than in the mycelium (Zalokar, 1954).

Finally, by analogy with other fungi such as the phycomycete *Allomyces* (Turian, 1962b), some kind of relationship between the nucleic acids and sexual morphogenesis could be expected in *Neurospora*. The average RNA: DNA ratio in macroconidia is $8 \cdot 7$ (UV method, Owens *et al.*, 1958) and tends to be higher in protoperithecial compared to conidial mycelia (Turian, 1961c). Minagawa *et al.* (1959) found that the base ratio of total RNA in hyphae and conidia is the same. Composition of ribosomal and soluble RNA is also identical in both morphological types (Henney and Storck, 1963). Protoperithecial mycelia would be interesting to analyze in this light.

d. Ascogonia. No antheridium has been found near the coiled ascogonium of *Ophiostoma adiposum* (Sartoris, 1927), *O. fimbriatum* (Mittmann, 1932; see, however, "functionless antheridium," Andrus and Harter, 1933), *Ceratocystis picea* (Bakshi, 1951), *C. moniliformis* (F. Moreau and Moreau, 1952) and *C. ulmi* (Rosinski, 1961). In *Ceratostomella fimbriata* (*O. fimbriatum*), there is good evidence that perithecial formation occurs only when the ratio of thiamine to the amount of nutrients in the medium is relatively high (Barnett and Lilly, 1947a). Thiamine is also required for perithecial production in *C. pluriannulata* (Robbins and Ma, 1942) and *C. variospora* (Campbell, 1958). While calcium favors, excess nitrogen prevents, sexual morphogenesis in *C. fimbriata* (Campbell, 1960).

In *Glomerella cingulata,* the two initials of the perithecium are at first indistinguishable from one another. They arise from adjacent cells chiefly at, or near, the point where a hypha from a conidial-type culture crosses a hypha from the perithecial culture (McGahen and Wheeler, 1951). Some kind of chemical stimulation has been reported to be involved in that morphogenetic process (Markert, 1949). Then the initials elongate differentially and the longest begins to coil around the other and soon envelops it. The inner coil is made up of three to five uninucleate, thick cells, rich in intensely staining cytoplasm. It corresponds to the ascogonial structure in which the dikaryotic condition originates after the fusion of its receptive tip cell with a conjugation hypha of the conidial culture (McGahen and Wheeler, 1951). Thus, in the *Ipomoea* strain of *G. cingulata,* no typical antheridium is differentiated simultaneously with the ascogonial structure. The effect of environmental conditions on ascogonial differentiation is still poorly known in *Glomerella*. The induction of tyrosinase activity coincides with the cessation of growth and therefore with the initiation of the differentiative processes (Sussman and Markert, 1953). On the other hand, genetic factors A_2 and B' have been shown to control the first steps of perithecial initiation (Wheeler, 1954) and there is preliminary evidence for a diffusible metabolite which induces the formation of perithecia in *G. cingulata* (Driver and Wheeler, 1955).

Sexual morphogenesis in *Sordaria fimicola* and related species is generally initiated by a single coiled ascogonium (Dangeard, 1907; Ritchie, 1937; C. Moreau, 1953). However, male cells such as microconidia have occasionally been described (Greis, 1936; Gäumann, 1940; Olive and Fantini, 1961). Self-sterility may be induced at different stages of the sexual process in *S. fimicola* (Greis, 1942; Heslot, 1958; Carr and Olive, 1959). Fertility could be recovered through heterokaryon formation between irradiation-induced self-sterile mutants of homothallic *S. macrospora* (Esser and Straub, 1956). Extracts of fertile strains did not induce formation of perithecial bodies in the sterile mutants (Esser and Straub, 1958). Thus, as in *Glomerella,* the various steps of sexual reproduction in *Sordaria* are gene controlled. In one of the particular crosses to produce fertile heterokaryotic mycelia in *S. fimicola,* one self-sterile strain produced no ascogonia and therefore had its sexual morphogenesis blocked at an earlier stage than the other strain capable of producing protoperithecia only when grown alone (Olive, 1958).

The formation of the perithecia of *Sordaria fimicola* can occur under conditions that are not strictly aerobic, as in submerged cultures (Bretzloff, 1951). In such cultures, the addition of boric acid (10^{-5}) to the Fries sucrose medium resulted in a doubling of the production of coiled ascogonia and young perithecia in *S. macrospora* (Turian, 1955). Physiological studies had previously shown that a strain of *S. fimicola* was entirely unable to produce any trace of sexual organs or fruit-body initials in a biotin-free medium (Barnett and Lilly, 1947b). Small quantities of certain phosphoric esters of glucose and fructose could stimulate the formation of perithecia in *S. destruens* (Hawker, 1948). In this species, an essential, minimal, internal concentration of both thiamine and biotin may be largely responsible for the increase in respiration which precedes the formation of perithecial initials (Hawker, 1957).

2. Fertilization (Plasmogamy)

In this intermediate phase of sexual morphogenesis, the complementary nuclei are brought together through plasmogamy of the ascogonium with an antheridium, microconidium, or an oidium, a germinated or ungerminated micro- or macroconidium, or even an ascospore germ tube or a hyphal tip.

The coordination of the morphogenetic events preceding the physical contact between sex organs is most likely due to the secretion of diffusible sex hormones by the two mates (Raper, 1952, 1960). Thus, in *Neurospora sitophila*, trichogynes branch freely in the direction of conidia of the opposite mating type (Backus, 1939), and in *Bombardia lunata*, the trichogyne exhibits a strong positive chemotropic response with respect to spermatia discharged from spermogonia (Zickler, 1953). In *Glomerella cingulata*, plasmogamy is accomplished by a copulation hypha of the conidial culture fusing with the tip cell of the ascogonial coil (McGahen and Wheeler, 1951).

Several genes can block this sexual step in *Glomerella* (Wheeler and McGahen, 1952). Cultures that carry any of these genes produce an abundance of perithecial initials or protoperithecia, but these never develop. Genes affecting the sexual process in *G. cingulata* could do so by controlling the synthesis of specific chemical substances required for the completion of the various morphogenetic steps (Wheeler, 1954); a sexual hormone was found to be responsible for selfing in this fungus (Driver and Wheeler, 1955).

In the heterothallic species of *Ascobolus*, there is indirect evidence of hormonal action in the sexual process (Dodge, 1912, 1920). Bistis (1956, 1957) has presented new evidence in favor of its existence in demonstrating the directed growth of the trichogyne and sexual activation of oidia in *A. stercorarius*. Plasmogamy can occur only between a trichogyne and a sexually activated oidium (or a hypha). In the sexual conditioning process some changes occur in the oidial wall which result in its breaking at the point of contact with the trichogyne wall, itself locally dissolved (Bistis, 1957).

In the yeast *Hansenula wingei* the mating cells in contact also fuse by a softening of the cell wall, followed by formation of a conjugation tube and dissolution of the cross walls between the two cells. Inhibitors which prevent metabolism prevent the fusion process. This process requires synthesis of a new protein assumed to be the wall-softening enzyme(s), the synthesis of which is induced in each cell by contact with its mate (Brock, 1959, 1961). It appears that in other yeasts a contact between haploid cells is not a necessary prerequisite for the formation of conjugation tubes, as shown in *Saccharomyces cerevisiae* where some diffusible substance induces the process (Levi, 1956).

3. Embryogenesis

It is common knowledge that embryogenesis immediately follows fertilization, and ascomycetes do not break this rule even though their fertilization is accomplished in two steps due to their peculiar, deferred karyogamy. The intercalated proliferation of ascogenous hyphae can be visualized as the first embryonic device for the multiplication of the initial "diplo-zygote" formed at plasmogamy. Finally, the popular analogy between fungal spores and plant seeds, if restricted to the sexual spores, here ascospores, may be valid in comparing the ascosporal wall to the seed integument and the uni- or pluricellular ascosporal content to the embryo.

a. Ascogenous Hyphae. As perithecial development progresses after plasmogamy, the ascogonial coil becomes more complex, often producing lateral branches. In *Glomerella,* only one binucleate cell in each ascogonial coil proliferates to produce the ascogenous hyphae (Wheeler *et al.,* 1948). Proliferation by means of croziers is characteristic of the entire development leading up to the formation of asci. An indication that the development of the ascogenous system is distinct from other processes of the protoperithecial to perithecial transformation was obtained in *Neurospora* by inhibition of the former by independent mechanisms (Lindegren *et al.,* 1939). Later, genes (pl, f, l) controlling the transformation of ascogonium-containing protoperithecia to perithecia with a complete ascogenous system were described in the apogamous *Sordaria macrospora* (Esser and Straub, 1958).

The physiological processes involved in the proliferation of ascogenous hyphae are unknown and, in some studies, may have been confused with those responsible for the formation of the young asci. Thus, certain cases of aborted asci may have been due to failure of development of the ascogenous system.

b. Asci. In late stages of development, the ascogenous hyphae bend to form a three-celled hook or crozier, its central, binucleate cell being the ascus initial. Cytological stages of ascus development have been well studied in *Neurospora crassa* (McClintock, 1945; Singleton, 1953). Almost immediately after the formation of the ascus initial, the two nuclei within it fuse together (karyogamy). The diploid fusion nucleus then undergoes meiosis resulting in the formation of the haploid nuclei of the presumptive ascospores. Prominent centrioles in the postmeiotic division may play a role in ascospore delimitation in *Neurospora* (Singleton, 1953) and *Sordaria* (Heslot, 1958). A rather unorthodox view of the ascus of *N. crassa* as a complex structure formed by association of several hyphae which cooperate in forming spores has been presented (Mitchell, 1960).

In the immature perithecium of *Glomerella,* thin-walled, multinucleate cells, fill the portion that is not occupied by the ascogenous system. As the asci mature, these cells disintegrate and slowly disappear while serving a nutritive function (McGahen and Wheeler, 1951). Karyogamy and meiosis in the young asci of this fungus are under genetic control; mutant genes (B^2 and dw^1) produce nuclear disintegrations leading to ascus abortion in perithecia otherwise normal in appearance (Wheeler, 1954).

In *Sordaria macrospora,* mutant genes (*s, min, pa*) permit apparently normal formation of the asci while preventing any further intra-ascal differentiation into ascospores (Esser and Straub, 1958). The process of formation of asci is thus developmentally distinct from the subsequent one of ascospore differentiation. It also includes the differentiation of various apical devices (Chadefaud, 1942, 1960) related to the mechanics of final ejection of the ripe ascospores (Ingold, 1953).

c. Ascospores. The cytological processes of ascospore differentiation have received much attention from the period of the pioneer investigations by Guilliermond (1904), Faull (1905), Fraser and Brooks (1909), and others, to the most recent electron microscopical studies of ascospore initiation in yeasts (Conti and Naylor, 1960) and the discomycete *Dasyscyphus* (R. T. Moore and McAlear, 1962). Of importance to the field of morphogenesis are also studies of the development of the wall structure of ascospores such as in *Neurospora tetrasperma* (Lowry and Sussman, 1958). Autonomously functioning rib-forming bodies may participate in this process in *N. crassa* (Lindegren and Scott, 1937).

Since Dodge's description (1934) of "indurated asci" free of ascospores in *N. tetrasperma* (see also Dodge *et al.,* 1950), ascospore abortion has been observed in many ascomycetes: *Podospora anserina* (Rizet and Engelmann, 1949), *Ascobolus stercorarius* (Bistis and Olive, 1954), *Sordaria macrospora* (Esser and Straub, 1958), *S. fimicola* (Carr and Olive, 1959). Giant and dwarf ascospores have been observed in *Podospora* (Dowding, 1931b; Page, 1936), *S. fimicola* (Page, 1933), *N. tetrasperma* (Dodge, 1935b). The size of ascospores in *N. crassa* was shown to be controlled by a polygenic system, a part of which is linked with the albino locus on chromosome I (Lee and Pateman, 1961). In *Venturia inaequalis,* five mutant genes can determine abnormal differentiation of ascospores (Boone and Keitt, 1956). Giant ascospore formation can be artificially induced by treatment of *S. macrospora* with ether or chloral hydrate (Zickler, 1931) or of *P. anserina* with ether, chloroform, or benzene

(Rizet, 1942). Dimorphism of ascospores has been studied genetically in *Chromocrea spinulosa* (Mathieson, 1952) and is also known in *Bulgaria inquinans* (Forster, 1941). In *S. fimicola* (Olive, 1956; Heslot, 1958) and *N. crassa* (Ito, 1957), ascospore color mutants (lack or dilution of melanic pigment in the wall) are known. Partially fertile mutants of *S. fimicola*, with slow-maturing ascospores of variable color, have been obtained (El-Ani et al., 1961). Maturation of ascospores in the asci can also be chemically repressed with neutralized boric acid in *S. macrospora* (Turian, 1954, 1955), phenyl mercuric chloride (Hutton, 1954), maleic hydrazide, or nucleic acids in *V. inaequalis* (Ross, 1959).

The hydrogen-ion concentration is important for normal ascospore maturation. Thus, in the cleistocarps of *Eurotium herbariorum* and *Penicillium javanicum* and perithecia of *Chaetomium globosum*, asci did not mature at pH values below neutrality (Lockwood, 1937). The beneficial effect of calcium on sporulation, e.g., on perithecial production by *C. globosum* (Basu, 1951) might well be due to its effect in counteracting acidity (Hawker, 1957). Certain critical concentrations of vitamins are required for normal differentiation of ascospores. In *S. fimicola*, there is a relationship between the amount of biotin and the number of mature ascospores produced. In the lower concentrations of biotin, the cytoplasm of most the abnormal asci was not even delimited into ascospores and consequently disintegrated (Barnett and Lilly, 1947b). A similar relationship has been found in *C. convolutum* which for any given concentration of nutrients requires certain concentrations of thiamine and biotin in order to develop mature perithecia with normal ascospores (Lilly and Barnett, 1949). In *N. crassa*, a high concentration of sucrose in Czapek's medium, unless balanced by increased doses of yeast hydrolyzate, prevents normal differentiation of the ascospores (Girbardt, 1952).

Vitamins also are required for ascospore formation in yeasts (Tremaine and Miller, 1954) as are also certain ions such as K^+ and Mg^{++} (McClary et al., 1959). Acetate is a very favorable substrate for inducing sporulation in these proto-ascomycetes (Stantial, 1935; Adams, 1949; Fowell, 1952). This morphogenetic effect of acetate might well be correlated with its predictable inducing effect on isocitratase. The activity of this enzyme has been shown to be awakened (endogenous induction) at the stage of ascospore differentiation in *N. tetrasperma* (Turian et al., 1962) and, by analogy, it is possible that the effect of acetate in yeasts also is connected in some way with the induction of the glyoxylic acid by-pass of the Krebs cycle. Such enzyme induction should necessarily precede morphogenetic expression for, according to McClary et al. (1959), most of the important metabolic events lie in the presporulation phase while sporulation may be mainly concerned with the intracellular protein degradation and resynthesis postulated for spore maturation in bacteria (Hardwick and Foster, 1952). Changes in amino acid content could thus be expected to occur during yeast sporogenesis; in fact an accumulation of free proline has recently been detected in sporulated *Saccharomyces cerevisiae* (Ramirez and Miller, 1963). Finally, it is worth mentioning that Miller *et al.* (1959) found no evidence of difference in the respiratory ability of sporulated and nonsporulated yeast cells.

4. Fruit Bodies

Two elaborate categories of ascomycetous fruit bodies are the flasklike perithecia of pyrenomycetes and the cup-shaped apothecia of discomycetes (cup fungi).

Since the thorough study by Dangeard (1907) of the development of perithecia, many other detailed, descriptive studies have been concerned with these structures (Varitchak, 1931; Chadefaud, 1960). It has been established that while the dikaryotic ascogenous hyphae grow out from the ascogonium, the haploid, mycelial sheath which envelops it begins to develop as the wall of the perithecium. The apothecium has also received detailed attention from Corner (1929) as to the exact derivation of its parts. This wealth of descriptive knowledge is in sharp contrast to our lack of information concerning the formative factors controlling the morphogenesis of both perithecia and apothecia. These are only superficially known from the studies of the effects of different environmental factors on fruit-body formation (see Lilly and Barnett, 1951; Hawker, 1957; Cochrane, 1958). Most often these effects could not be clearly distinguished from those on the reproductive organs previously mentioned.

Perithecial formation does not require strict aerobic conditions in *Neurospora sitophila* (Denny, 1933) and *Sordaria fimicola* (Bretzloff, 1951). It conforms to Klebs' principle (1900) that reproduction takes place under more restricted environmental conditions than growth. In many pathogenic fungi, perithecial formation can occur only on natural substrata; for example, the entomogenous *Cordyceps militaris* requires unautoclaved pupae (Shanor, 1936), and several plant parasites their hosts (Hansen and Snyder, 1944). Apple leaf medium offered the best conditions for perithecial development in *Venturia inaequalis* (Keitt and Palmiter, 1938) and *Leptosphaeria rusci* produced a number of perithecia on a synthetic medium containing cellulose but none on a glucose medium (Lacoste, 1960). In *Gnomonia vulgaris,* a peptone-malt extract medium at pH 5.2 is optimal for perithecial production if the temperature is below 20°C (Henriksson and Morgan-Jones, 1951). Low temperature and light are both necessary for the formation of perithecia in many species of *Leptosphaeria* (Lacoste, 1963).

Robinson (1926) found that light is necessary for both orange pigmentation and apothecial formation in *Pyronema omphalodes* and postulated a causal relationship between these two processes. However, an albino *Pyronema* was later found to be capable of normal reproduction (Bean and Brooks, 1932) and an albino mutant with neither colored nor colorless polyenes still required light to produce apothecia (Carlile and Friend, 1956). Thus, carotenoids cannot be the photoreceptors in the photomorphogenetic response of *Pyronema*. Contrary to Robinson's hypothesis, pigmentation and apothecial morphogenesis are distinct and unrelated photochemical effects in normal, orange *Pyronema* (Carlile and Friend, 1956). Light is necessary for apothecial formation of *Ascobolus immersus* grown on an urea-containing synthetic medium (Yu-Sun, 1964). Stipe apices of *Sclerotinia sclerotiorum* also require light to develop their single apothecium. In darkness, these stipes only grow in length without branching. Decapitated stipes cease to grow in length and lateral branches develop, demonstrating removal of the apical dominance which normally is effective in the apothecial stipe of this discomycete (Henderson, 1962).

III. CONCLUSIONS

In the complex processes of morphogenesis, overly simple formulas can scarcely be expected. It does seem, however, that further investigations of the relationships between metabolic pathways and alternate morphogenetic situations such as ascogonia-antheridia or ascogonia-conidia in ascomycetous fungi, offer promising lines of investigation.

The indispensable connection between the ultrastructural components of the cell and these phenomena must not be forgotten. The ergastoplasm, through its ribosomal constituents, is tied to the RNA system in the synthesis of the specific proteins, associated with the successive morphogenetic stages. And thus we return to the main control center, the nucleus, with its DNA as the ultimate source of morphogenetic information.

ADDENDUM

Further information concerning aspects of morphogenesis in ascomycetous fungi can be found in recent reviews [W. J. Nickerson and S. Bartnicki-Garcia, *Ann. Rev. Plant Physiol.* 15:327-344 (1964); H. H. Baldwin and H. P. Rusch *Ann. Rev. Biochem.* 34:565-594 (1965)].

Prominent among recent photomorphogenetic studies [see also M. J. Carlile, *Ann. Rev. Plant Physiol.* 16:175-202 (1965) and R. M. Page, Volume I, Chapter 23) are the observations of the prevention of the photo-inhibition of conidiation in *Alternaria solani* by flavins [R. J. Lukens, *Am. J. Botany* 50:720-724 (1963)], of the effect of high concentrations of glucose and peptone on the formation of conidia in the light and of sclerotia in the dark by *Aspergillus japonicus* [L. A. F. Heath and H. O. W. Eggins, *Experientia* 21:385-386 (1965)], of the effect of near UV in stimulating perithecial development in *Hypomyces* [C. R. Curtis, *Phytopathology* 54:1141-1145 (1964)] while inhibiting both melanin synthesis and microsclerotial development in

11. Morphogenesis in Ascomycetes

Verticillium [W. H. Brandt, *Can. J. Botany* 42:1017-1023 (1964)], and the unraveling of ultraviolet-absorbing substances associated with light-induced sporulation in several ascomycetes [C. M. Leach, *Mycologia* 55:151-163 (1963); *Can. J. Botany* 43:185-200 (1965); *Mycologia* 57:291-300 (1965); C. M. Leach and E. J. Trione, *Plant Physiology* 40:808-812 (1965)].

Section II, D, 1, c

Genetic and epigenetic factors controlling female sterility [P. H. Fitzgerald, *Heredity* 18:47-62 (1963)] and other morphological mutants of *Neurospora crassa* [J. C. Murray and A. M. Srb, *Can. J. Botany* 40:337-349 (1962)] have been studied. A new periodical colonial mutant of *N. crassa* named "clock" [A. S. Sussman, R. J. Lowry and Th. Durkee, *Am. J. Botany* 51:243-252 (1964)] shows a rhythmic alternation of surface and aerial growth [D. E. Bianchi, *J. Gen. Microbiol.* 35:437-445 (1964)] and can produce conidia only under bright, continuous light [M. D. Berliner and P. W. Neurath, *J. Cellular Comp. Physiol.* 65:183-194 (1965)]. Similar morphological mutants have been obtained in *Ascobolus immersus* [C. C. Yu-Sun, *Genetics* 50:987-998 (1964)].

The relationship of cell wall to morphology in *N. crassa* has recently been studied by correlating the levels of structural polymers of the cell wall with wild-type and colonial morphology [P. R. Mahadevan and E. L. Tatum, *J. Bacteriol.* 90:1073-1081 (1965)].

Concerning enzymes and conidiation in *Neurospora*, β-glucosidase [B. M. Eberhardt, *J. Cellular Comp. Physiol.* 58:11-16 (1961)] and trehalase [E. P. Hill and A. S. Sussman, *J. Bacteriol.* 88:1556-1566 (1964)] were shown to be more active in conidia than in the mycelium. B. Weiss [*J. Gen. Microbiol.* 39:85-94 (1965)] completed an electron microscope and biochemical study of *N. crassa* during development. The mitochondrial oxidative phophorylation system showed no variation in the protoplasts of conidia, young germinated conidia, and branched mycelia; succinate dehydrogenase also did not alter. Non-conidiating, mycelial cultures of *N. crassa* (ammonium medium, see Turian, 1964) have a much greater glycolytic activity than conidiating cultures (nitrate medium) as measured by the production of alcohol, alcohol dehydrogenase, and pyruvate decarboxylase activities (in the aconidial "fluffy" mutant, glycolytic activity was relatively high in both media); chemical inhibition of glycolysis induced conidiation in the wild type while interference with oxidative metabolism suppressed it [G. Turian and N. Matikian, *Nature* in press (1966); B. Weiss and G. Turian, *J. Gen. Microbiol.* 44, in press (1966)].

Sections II, D, 2 and 3

The conjugation process in *Hansenula wingei* has been further studied by T. D. Brock from both a biochemical [*J. Bacteriol.* 90:1019-1025 (1965); *Proc. Natl. Acad. Sci. U.S.* 54:1104-1112 (1965)] and an ultrastructural [S. F. Conti and T. D. Brock, *J. Bacteriol.* 90:524-533 (1965)] point of view, while J. J. Miller and O. Hoffmann-Ostenhof [*Z. Mikrobiol.* 4:273-294 (1965)] produced a thorough review of spore formation and germination in *Saccharomyces*.

REFERENCES

Adams, A. M. (1949). A convenient method of obtaining ascospores from bakers' yeast. *Can. J. Res.* C27:179-189.

Alexopoulos, C. J. (1952). "Introductory Mycology," 482 pp. Wiley, New York (and 1962, 613 pp.).

Allen, P. J. (1965). Metabolic aspects of spore germination in fungi. *Ann. Rev. Phytopathol.* 3:313-342.

Ames, L. M. (1934). Hermaphroditism involving self-sterility and cross-fertility in the Ascomycete *Pleurage anserina. Mycologia* **26**:392-414.
Andrus, C. F., and L. L. Harter. (1933). Morphology and reproduction in *Ceratostomella fimbriata. J. Agr. Res.* **46**:1059-1078.
Armstrong, J. J., D. J. F. England, and J. A. Morton. (1963). Stimulation of sporulation in *Penicillium* by anhydroglucose. *Nature* **197**:723.
Aronescu, A. (1933). Further studies in *Neurospora sitophila. Mycologia* **25**:43-54.
Backus, M. P. (1934). Initiation of the ascocarp and associated phenomena in *Coccomyces hiemalis. Contrib. Boyce Thompson Inst.* **6**:339-379.
Backus, M. P. (1939). The mechanics of conidial fertilization in *Neurospora sitophila. Bull. Torrey Botan. Club* **66**:63-76.
Bajaj, V., S. P. Damle, and P. S. Krishnan. (1954). Phosphate metabolism of mold spores. I. Phosphate uptake by the spores of *Aspergillus niger. Arch. Biochem. Biophys.* **50**:451-460.
Baker, G. E. (1945). Conidium formation in species of Aspergilli. *Mycologia* **37**:582-600.
Baker, R., and B. Ware. (1962). Induction of perithecial primordia in *Hypomyces solani* f. *cucurbitae. Phytopathology* **52**:359.
Bakshi, B. K. (1951). Development of perithecia and reproduction structures in two species of *Ceratocystis. Ann. Botany (London)* [N.S.] **15**:53-61.
Barbesgaard, P., and S. Wagner. (1959). Further studies on the biochemical basis of protoperithecia formation in *Neurospora crassa. Hereditas* **45**:564-572.
Barnes, B. (1928). Variations in *Eurotium herbariorum* (Wigg.) Link induced by the action of high temperatures. *Ann. Botany (London)* **42**:783-812.
Barnett, H. L., and V. G. Lilly. (1947a). The relation of thiamin to the production of perithecia by *Ceratostomella fimbriata. Mycologia* **39**:699-708.
Barnett, H. L., and V. G. Lilly. (1947b). The effects of biotin upon the formation and development of perithecia, asci and ascospores by *Sordaria fimicola* Ces. and de Not. *Am. J. Botany* **34**:196-204.
Barratt, R. W., and L. Garnjobst. (1949). Genetics of a colonial microconidial strain of *Neurospora crassa. Genetics* **34**:351-369.
Basu, S. N. (1951). Significance of calcium in the fruiting of *Chaetomium* species, particularly *Chaetomium globosum. J. Gen. Microbiol.* **5**:231-238.
Basu, S. N. (1952). *Chaetomium brasiliensis* Batista and Pontual; nutritional requirements for growth and fruiting. *J. Gen. Microbiol.* **6**:199-204.
Basu, S. N., and J. P. Bhattacharyya. (1962). Studies on the growth and sporulation of some species of *Penicillium. J. Gen. Microbiol.* **27**:61-73.
Beadle, G. W. (1944). An inositolless mutant strain of *Neurospora* and its use in bioassays. *J. Biol. Chem.* **156**:683-689.
Beadle, G. W., and E. L. Tatum. (1941). Genetical control of biochemical reactions in *Neurospora. Proc. Natl. Acad. Sci. U.S.* **27**:499-506.
Bean, W. J., and F. T. Brooks. (1932). A note on a white form of *Pyronema confluens. New Phytologist* **31**:70-71.
Behal, F. J., and R. E. Eakin. (1959a). Inhibition of mold development by purine and pyrimidine analogs. *Arch. Biochem. Biophys.* **82**:439-447.
Behal, F. J., and R. E. Eakin. (1959b). Metabolic changes accompanying the inhibition of spore formation in *Aspergillus niger. Arch. Biochem. Biophys.* **82**:448-452.
Bessey, E. A. (1950). "Morphology and Taxonomy of Fungi," 791 pp. Blakiston, Philadelphia, Pennsylvania.

Bhatnagar, G. M., and P. S. Krishnan. (1959). Studies on the germination of spores of *Aspergillus niger*. *Arch. Mikrobiol.* 33:395-405.
Bhatnagar, G. M., and P. S. Krishnan. (1960a). Enzymatic studies on the spores of *Aspergillus niger*. Part I. Catalase. *Arch. Mikrobiol.* 36:131-138.
Bhatnagar, G. M., and P. S. Krishnan. (1960b). Enzymatic studies on the spores of *Aspergillus niger*. Part II. Phosphatases. *Arch. Mikrobiol.* 36:169-174.
Bhattacharyya, J. P., and S. N. Basu. (1962). The effect of trace elements, other nutritional factors and pH on the growth and sporulation of *Penicillium* species. *J. Sci. Ind. Res. (India)* 21C:263-268.
Bistis, G. N. (1956). Sexuality in *Ascobolus stercorarius*. I. Morphology of the ascogonium; plasmogamy; evidence for a sexual hormonal mechanism. *Am. J. Botany* 43:389-394.
Bistis, G. N. (1957). Sexuality in *Ascobolus stercorarius*. II. Preliminary experiments on various aspects of the sexual process. *Am. J. Botany* 44:436-443
Bistis, G. N., and L. S. Olive. (1954). Ascomycete spore mutants and their use in genetic studies. *Science* 120:105-106.
Bistis, G. N., and J. R. Raper. (1963). Heterothallism and sexuality in *Ascobolus stercorarius*. *Am. J. Botany* 50:880-891.
Bleul, J. (1962a). Studien zur Morphologie und Physiologie der Sterigmenproliferation bei *Aspergillus amstelodami* (Mangin) Thom and Church. *Arch. Mikrobiol.* 44:23-46.
Bleul, J. (1962b). Eine Sektorenvariante mit proliferierten Sterigmen von *Aspergillus amstelodami* (Mangin) Thom and Church. *Arch. Mikrobiol.* 44:105-112.
Blodgett, E. W. (1936). *Phytopathology* 26:115-152 (quoted by V. W. Cochrane, 1958).
Boone, D. M., and G. W. Keitt. (1956). *Venturia inaequalis* (Cke.) Wint. VIII. Inheritance of color mutant characters. *Am. J. Botany* 43:226-233.
Brandt, W. H. (1962). Manganese stimulation of melanin synthesis and microsclerotia development in *Verticillium*. *Plant Physiol.* 37:XXX.
Brandt, W. H., and J. E. Reese. (1964). Morphogenesis in *Verticillium*: a self-produced, diffusible morphogenetic factor. *Am. J. Botany* 51:922-927.
Brefeld, O. (1874). II. Die Entwicklungsgeschichte von *Penicillium*. "Botanische Untersuchungen über Schimmelpilze," pp. 1-98.
Bretzloff, C. W. (1951). Fungus fruiting in submerged cultures. *Science* 114:418-419.
Bretzloff, C. W. (1954). The growth and fruiting of *Sordaria fimicola*. *Am. J. Botany* 41:58-67.
Brian, P. W., P. J. Curtis, and H. G. Hemmings. (1946). *Brit. Mycol. Soc. Trans.* 29:173-187 (quoted by V. W. Cochrane, 1958).
Brierley, W. B. (1917). *Ann. Botany (London)* 31:127-132 (quoted by V. W. Cochrane, 1958).
Brock, T. D. (1959). Biochemical basis of mating in yeast. *Science* 129:960.
Brock, T. D. (1961). Physiology of the conjugation process in the yeast *Hansenula wingei*. *J. Gen. Microbiol.* 26:487-497.
Budd, K., A. S. Sussman, and F. I. Eilers. (1966). Glucose-C^{14} metabolism of dormant and activated ascospores of *Neurospora*. *J. Bacteriol.* (in press).
Burgert, I. A. (1934). *Phytopathology* 24:384-396 (quoted by V. W. Cochrane, 1958).
Buston, H. W., and S. N. Basu. (1948). Some factors affecting the growth and sporulation of *Chaetomium globosum* and *Memnoniella echinata*. *J. Gen. Microbiol.* 2:162-172.

Buston, H. W., and A. H. Khan. (1956). The influence of certain micro-organisms on the formation of perithecia by *Chaetomium globosum*. *J. Gen. Microbiol.* **14**: 655-660.
Butler, E. E. (1956). *Mycologia* **48**:345-348 (quoted by V. W. Cochrane, 1958).
Calpouzos, L. (1954). Controlled sporulation of *Cercospora musae* Zimm. in pure culture. *Nature* **173**:1084-1085.
Campbell, R. N. (1958). Nutrient requirements for the production of perithecia by *Ceratocystis variospora* and other species. *Am. J. Botany* **45**:263-270.
Campbell, R. N. (1960). Effects of nitrogen and calcium on perithecial formation by *Ceratocystis fimbriata*. *Phytopathology* **50**:631.
Cantino, E. C., and E. A. Horenstein. (1956). Stimulatory effect of light upon growth and CO_2 fixation in *Blastocladiella*. I. The S. K. I. cycle. *Mycologia* **48**:777-799.
Carlile, M. J. (1956). A study of the factors influencing non-genetic variation in a strain of *Fusarium oxysporum*. *J. Gen. Microbiol.* **14**:643-654.
Carlile, M. J., and J. Friend. (1956). Carotenoids and reproduction in *Pyronema confluens*. *Nature* **178**:369-370.
Carlile, M. J., B. G. Lewis, E. M. Mordue, and J. Northover. (1961). The development of coremia. I. *Penicillium claviforme*. *Brit. Mycol. Soc. Trans.* **44**:129-133.
Carr, A. J. H., and L. S. Olive. (1959). Genetics of *Sordaria fimicola*. III. Cross-compatibility among self-fertile and self-sterile cultures. *Am. J. Botany* **46**:81-91.
Chadefaud, M. (1942). Etudes d'asques. II. Structure et anatomie comparées de l'appareil apical des asques chez divers discomycètes et pyrénomycètes. *Rev. Mycol.* [N.S.] **7**:57-88.
Chadefaud, M. (1960). "Traité de botanique systématique." Vol. I, 1016 pp. Masson, Paris.
Chevaugeon, J. (1961). L'auto-incompatibilité, conséquence régulière de la différenciation chez le *Pestalozzia annulata*. *Compt. Rend.* **252**:4183-4185.
Chin, B., and S. G. Knight. (1957). Growth of *Trichophyton mentagrophytes* and *Trichophyton rubrum* in increased carbon dioxide tensions. *J. Gen. Microbiol.* **16**: 642-646.
Chin, B., and S. G. Knight. (1963). Stimulation of glucose metabolism in *Trichophyton mentagrophytes* during incubation in increased carbon dioxide tension. *J. Gen. Microbiol.* **30**:121-126.
Cochrane, V. W. (1958). "Physiology of Fungi," 524 pp. Wiley, New York.
Colson, B. (1934). The cytology and morphology of *Neurospora tetrasperma*. *Ann. Botany (London)* **48**:211-224.
Conti, S. F., and H. B. Naylor. (1960). Electron microscopy of ultrathin sections of *Schizosaccharomyces octosporus*. III. Ascosporogenesis, ascospore structure and germination. *J. Bacteriol.* **79**:417-425.
Converse, J. L. (1957). *J. Bacteriol.* **74**:106-107 (quoted by H. F. Linskens, 1959).
Corner, E. J. H. (1929). Studies in the morphology of Discomycetes. II. The structure and development of the ascocarp. *Brit. Mycol. Soc. Trans.* **14**:275-291.
Dale, E. (1909). On the morphology and cytology of *Aspergillus repens* DeBary. *Ann. Mycol., Berlin* **7**:215-225.
Dangeard, P. A. (1907). Recherches sur le développement du périthèce chez les Ascomycètes. *Botaniste* **10**:1-385.
DasGupta, A., and P. N. Nandi. (1957). Role of nitrogen concentration on production of perithecia in *Penicillium vermiculatum* Dang. *Nature* **179**:429-430.
Delp, C. J. (1954). *Phytopathology* **44**:615-626 (quoted by V. W. Cochrane, 1958).

Denny, F. E. (1933). Oxygen requirements of *Neurospora sitophila* for formation of perithecia and growth of mycelium. *Contrib. Boyce Thompson Inst.* **5**:95-102.
Dodge, B. O. (1912). Methods of culture and the morphology of the archicarp in certain species of Ascobolaceae. *Bull. Torrey Botan. Club* **39**:139-197.
Dodge, B. O. (1920). The life history of *Ascobolus magnificus*. *Mycologia* **12**:115-134.
Dodge, B. O. (1928). Production of fertile hybrids in the Ascomycete *Neurospora*. *J. Agr. Res.* **36**:1-14.
Dodge, B. O. (1932). The non-sexual and the sexual functions of microconidia of *Neurospora*. *Bull. Torrey Botan. Club* **59**:347-360.
Dodge, B. O. (1933). The perithecium and ascus of *Penicillium*. *Mycologia* **25**:90-104.
Dodge, B. O. (1934). A lethal for ascus abortion in *Neurospora*. *Mycologia* **26**:360-376.
Dodge, B. O. (1935a). The mechanics of sexual reproduction in *Neurospora*. *Mycologia* **27**:418-438.
Dodge, B. O. (1935b). A recessive factor lethal for ascospore formation in *Neurospora*. *Bull. Torrey Botan. Club* **62**:117-128.
Dodge, B. O. (1946). Self-sterility in "bisexual" heterocaryons of *Neurospora*. *Bull. Torrey Botan. Club* **73**:410-416.
Dodge, B. O., J. R. Singleton, and A. Rolnick. (1950). Studies on lethal E gene in *Neurospora tetrasperma* including chromosome counts also in races of *Neurospora sitophila*. *Proc. Am. Phil. Soc.* **94**:38-52.
Doran, W. L. (1922). Effect of external and internal factors on the germination of fungus spores. *Bull. Torrey Botan. Club* **49**:313-336.
Douglas, H. W., Collins, A. E., and D. Parkinson. (1959). Electric charge and other surface properties of some fungal spores. *Biochim. Biophys. Acta* **33**:535-537.
Dowding, E. S. (1931a). The sexuality of *Ascobolus stercorarius* and the transportation of the oidia by mites and flies. *Ann. Botany (London)* **45**:621-637.
Dowding, E. S. (1931b). The sexuality of the normal, giant and dwarf spores of *Pleurage anserina* (Ces.) Kuntze. *Ann. Botany (London)* **45**:1-14.
Drayton, F. L. (1932). The sexual function of the microconidia in certain Discomycetes. *Mycologia* **24**:344-348.
Drayton, F. L. (1934). The sexual mechanism of *Sclerotinia gladioli*. *Mycologia* **26**:46-72.
Drayton, F. L. (1937). The perfect stage of *Botrytis convoluta*. *Mycologia* **29**:305-318.
Driver, C. H., and H. E. Wheeler. (1955). A sexual hormone in *Glomerella*. *Mycologia* **47**:311-316.
El-Ani, A. S., L. S. Olive, and Y. Kitani. (1961). Genetics of *Sordaria*. IV. Linkage group I. *Am. J. Botany* **48**:716-723.
Emerson, M. R. (1948). Chemical activation of ascospore germination in *Neurospora crassa*. *J. Bacteriol.* **55**:327-330.
Emerson, M. R. (1954). Some physiological characteristics of ascospore activation in *Neurospora crassa*. *Plant Physiol.* **29**:418-428.
Emmons, C. W. (1935). The ascocarps in species of *Penicillium*. *Mycologia* **27**:128-150.
Esser, K. (1956). Wachstum, Fruchtkörper- und Pigmentbildung von *Podospora anserina* in synthetischen Nährmedien. *Compt. Rend. Trav. Lab. Carlsberg, Ser. Physiol.* **26**:103-116.

Esser, K., and J. Straub. (1956). Fertilität im Heterocaryon aus zwei sterilen Mutanten von *Sordaria macrospora* Auersw. *Z. Induktive Abstammungs- Vererbungslehre* **87**:625-626.

Esser, K., and J. Straub. (1958). Genetische Untersuchungen an *Sordaria macrospora* Auersw., Kompensation und Induktion bei Genbedingten Entwicklungsdefekten. *Z. Vererbungslehre* **89**:729-746.

Etzhold, H. (1960). Die Wirkung des Lichtes auf einige Pilze und ihre spektrale Grenze zum Langwelligen hin. *Arch. Mikrobiol.* **37**: 226-244.

Evans, M. M., and G. Harrar. (1930). *Phytopathology* **20**:993-997 (quoted by V. W. Cochrane, 1958).

Faull, J. H. (1905). Development of ascus and spore formation in Ascomycetes. *Proc. Boston Soc. Nat. Hist.* **32**:77-83.

Fikry, A. (1932). *Ann. Botany (London)* **46**:29-70 (1932) (quoted by V. W. Cochrane, 1958).

Fincham, J. R. S., and P. R. Day. (1963). "Fungal Genetics," 300 pp. Blackwell, Oxford.

Forster, C. L. (1941). Ascospore dimorphism of *Bulgaria inquinans*. *Nature* **147**:238.

Foster, J. W. (1949). "Chemical Activities of Fungi," 648 pp. Academic Press, New York.

Foster, J. W., L. E. Daniel, H. B. Woodruff, and J. L. Stokes. (1945). Conidiospore formation in submerged cultures of *Penicillium notatum*. *J. Bacteriol.* **50**:365-368.

Fowell, R. R. (1952). Sodium acetate agar as a sporulation medium for yeast. *Nature* **170**:578.

Fraser, H. C. I., and W. E. Brooks. (1909). Further studies on the cytology of the ascus. *Ann. Botany (London)* **23**:537-549.

Frauenstein, K. (1962). Untersuchungen zur Biologie von *Pleospora bromi* Died. *Phytopathol. Z.* **44**:1-38.

Fries, N. (1949). *Ophiostoma multiannulatum* (Hedge. and Davids) as a test object for the determination of pyridoxin and various nucleotide constituents. *Arch. Botan.* **1**:271-287.

Garay, A. S. (1958). Der Zusammenhang zwischen Fruchtkörperbildung und Atmung im Falle des Mutterkorns unter besonderer Berücksichtigung der Bedeutung der Fumarsäure. *Physiol. Plantarum* **11**:48-55.

Gäumann, E. A. (1940). Neuere Erfahrungen über die Entwicklungsgeschichte der Ascomyceten. Sammelreferat. *Z. Botan.* **35**:433-513.

Gäumann, E. A. (1949). "Die Pilze. Grundzüge ihrer Entwicklungsgeschichte und Morphologie," 382 pp. Birkhäuser, Basel (and 1964, 541 pp.).

Gehrig, R. F., and S. G. Knight. (1958). Formation of ketones from fatty acids by spores of *Penicillium roqueforti*. *Nature* **182**:1237.

Girbardt, M. (1952). Zur Frage der Fertilität bei *Neurospora crassa* und *Neurospora tetrasperma* in Abhängigkeit von Aussenfaktoren. *Flora (Jena)* **139**:477-525.

Goddard, D. R. (1935). The reversible heat activation inducing germination and increased respiration in the ascospores of *Neurospora tetrasperma*. *J. Gen. Physiol.* **19**:45-60.

Goddard, D. R. (1939). The reversible heat activation of respiration in *Neurospora*. *Cold Spring Harbor Symp. Quant. Biol.* **7**:362-376.

Goddard, D. R. (1948). *Growth* **12**: Suppl., 17-45 (quoted by V. W. Cochrane, 1958).

Goddard, D. R., and P. E. Smith. (1938). Respiratory block in the dormant spores of *Neurospora tetrasperma*. *Plant Physiol.* **13**:241-264.

Goos, R. D. (1959). Spermatium-trichogyne relationship in *Gelasinospora calospora* var. *autosteira*. *Mycologia* **51**:416-428.
Gottlieb, D. (1950). The physiology of spore germination in fungi. *Botan. Rev.* **16**: 229-257.
Gottlieb, D. (1964). Germination of fungus spores. *Endeavour* **23**:85-89.
Greis, H. (1936). Entwicklungsgeschichte von *Sordaria fimicola* (Rob.). *Botan. Arch.* **38**:113-151.
Greis, H. (1941). Befruchtungsvorgänge in der Gattung *Chaetomium*. *Jahrb. Wiss. Botan.* **90**:233-254.
Greis, H. (1942). Mutations- und Isolationsversuche zur Beeinflussung des Geschlechtes von *Sordaria fimicola*. *Z. Botan.* **37**:1-116.
Grigg, G. W. (1960a). Temperature-sensitive genes affecting conidiation in *Neurospora*. *J. Gen. Microbiol.* **22**:667-670.
Grigg, G. W. (1960b). The control of conidial differentiation in *Neurospora crassa*. *J. Gen. Microbiol.* **22**:662-666.
Groves, J. W., and F. L. Drayton. (1939). The perfect stage of *Botrytis cinerea*. *Mycologia* **31**:485-489.
Guilliermond, A. (1904). Contribution à l'étude de la formation des asques et de l'épiplasme des Ascomycètes. *Rev. Gen. Botan.* **16**:49-65.
Gutter, Y. (1957). *Bull. Res. Council Israel* **D5**:273-286 (quoted by H. F. Linskens, 1959).
Gwynne-Vaughan, H. C. I., and H. S. Williamson. (1927). *Ann. Botany (London)* **41**:489-495 (quoted by V. W. Cochrane, 1958).
Gwynne-Vaughan, H. C. I., and H. S. Williamson. (1932). The cytology and development of *Ascobolus magnificus*. *Ann. Botany (London)* **46**:653-670.
Hadley, G., and C. E. Harrold. (1958a). The sporulation of *Penicillium notatum* Westling in submerged liquid culture. I. The effect of calcium and nutrients on sporulation intensity. *J. Exptl. Botany* **9**:408-417.
Hadley, G., and C. E. Harrold. (1958b). The sporulation of *Penicillium notatum* Westling in submerged liquid culture. II. The initial sporulation phase. *J. Exptl. Botany* **9**:418-425.
Hansen, H. N. (1938). The dual phenomenon in imperfect fungi. *Mycologia* **30**:442-455.
Hansen, H. N., and W. C. Snyder. (1944). *Science* **99**:264-265 (quoted by V. W. Cochrane, 1958).
Hardwick, W. A., and J. W. Foster. (1952). On the nature of sporogenesis in some aerobic bacteria. *J. Gen. Physiol.* **35**:907-927.
Harter, L. L. (1939). Influence of light on the length of the conidia in certain species of *Fusarium*. *Am. J. Botany* **26**:234-243.
Hawker, L. E. (1942). Effect of vitamin B_1 on concentration of glucose optimal for certain fungi. *Ann. Botany (London)* [N.S.] **6**:631-636.
Hawker, L. E. (1948). Stimulation of the formation of perithecia of *Melanospora destruens* Shear by small quantities of certain phosphoric esters of glucose and fructose. *Ann. Botany (London)* [N.S.] **12**:77-79.
Hawker, L. E. (1950). "Physiology of Fungi," 360 pp. Oxford Univ. Press (Univ. London), London and New York.
Hawker, L. E. (1957). "The Physiology of Reproduction in Fungi," 128 pp. Cambridge Univ. Press, London and New York.
Haxo, F. T. (1949). Studies on the carotenoid pigments of *Neurospora*. I. Composition of the pigment. *Arch. Biochem.* **20**:400-421.

Hejmánek, M., and N. Hejmánková-Uhrová. (1956). Unusual forms of variability in *Trichophyton mentagrophytes*. *Folia Biol. (Prague)* **2**:149-156.

Henderson, R. M. (1962). An inhibitory growth correlation in the apothecial stipe of *Sclerotium sclerotiorum*. *Nature* **195**:826.

Henney, H., and R. Storck. (1963). Nucleotide composition of RNA from *Neurospora crassa*. *J. Bacteriol.* **85**:822-826.

Henriksson, L. E., and J. F. Morgan-Jones. (1951). The effect of temperature, pH and malt extract upon growth and perithecial development of two *Gnomonia* species. *Svensk Botan. Tidskr.* **45**:648-657.

Heslot, H. (1958). Contribution à l'étude cytogénétique et génétique des Sordariacées. *Rev. Cytol. Biol. Vegetales* **19**: Suppl. 2, 1-235.

Higgins, B. B. (1936). Morphology and life history of some Ascomycetes with special reference to the presence and function of spermatia. III. *Am. J. Botany* **23**:598-602.

Hirsch, H. M. (1954). Environmental factors influencing the differentiation of protoperithecia and their relation to tyrosinase and melanin formation in *Neurospora crassa*. *Physiol. Plantarum* **7**:72-97.

Holton, R. W. (1960). Studies on pyruvate metabolism and cytochrome system in *Neurospora tetrasperma*. *Plant Physiol.* **35**:757-766.

Horowitz, N. H. (1947). Methionine synthesis in *Neurospora*. The isolation of cystathionine. *J. Biol. Chem.* **171**:255-264.

Horowitz, N. H., M. Fling, H. Macleod, and Y. Watanabe. (1961). Structural and regulative genes controlling tyrosinase synthesis in *Neurospora*. *Cold Spring Harbor Symp. Quant. Biol.* **26**:233-238.

Hoshino, J., A. Nishi, and T. Yanagita. (1962). Alanine metabolism in conidiospores of *Aspergillus niger* in the early phase of germination. *J. Gen. Appl. Microbiol.* **8**: 233-245.

Hrushovetz, S. B. (1956). Cytological studies of *Helminthosporium sativum*. *Can. J. Botany* **34**:321-327.

Hughes, S. J. (1953). Conidiophores, conidia and classification. *Can. J. Botany* **31**: 577-659.

Hungate, M. V. G. (1945). A genetic study of albino mutants of *Neurospora crassa*. Master's thesis, Stanford University.

Hutton, K. E. (1954). Eradication of *Venturia inaequalis* (Cooke) Wint. *Nature* **174**: 1017-1018.

Ingold, C. T. (1953). "Dispersal in Fungi," 197 pp. Oxford Univ. Press, London and New York.

Ingold, C. T. (1962). The reaction of fungi to light and the problem of photoperception. *Symp. Soc. Exptl. Biol.* **16**:154-169.

Isaac, I. (1949). A comparative study of pathogenic isolates of *Verticillium*. *Brit. Trans. Mycol. Soc.* **32**:137-157.

Ito, T. (1957). Gene locus of the pigment development factor of ascospores in *Neurospora crassa*. *Res. Bull. Obihiro Zootech. Univ.* **2**:238-243.

Ito, T. (1959). Fruit body formation of red bread mold *Neurospora crassa* III. Effect of nitrogen sources with special reference to the ionic ratio of ammonium and nitrate in the medium. *Botan. Mag. (Tokyo)* **72**:238-246.

Ito, T. (1961). Fruit body formation of red bread mold *Neurospora crassa* IV. Effect of ammonium and nitrate ion in the medium on size of the perithecium. *Botan. Mag. (Tokyo)* **79**:379-385.

Jerebzoff, S. (1958). Relation entre la quantité d'énergie lumineuse reçue par *Monilia fructicola* et la croissance de ses conidiophores fertiles. *Compt. Rend.* 246:1728-1731.

Jinks, J. L. (1954). Somatic selection in fungi. *Nature* 174:409.

Jinks, J. L. (1956). Naturally occurring cytoplasmic changes in fungi. *Compt. Rend. Trav. Lab. Carlsberg, Ser. Physiol.* 26:183-203.

Johnson, T. W., and J. E. Halpin. (1954). Environmental effects on conidial variation in some *Fungi imperfecti*. *J. Elisha Mitchell Sci. Soc.* 70:314-426.

Joly, P. (1962). Recherches sur les genres *Alternaria* et *Stemphylium*. III. Action de la lumière et des ultra-violets. *Rev. Mycol.* [N.S.] 27:1-16.

Jones, F. R. (1919). *U.S. Dept. Agr., Tech. Bull.* 759:1-58 (quoted by V. W. Cochrane, 1958).

Kaiser, W. J. (1962). Influence of light on the production of microsclerotia by *Verticillium albo-atrum*. *Phytopathology* 52:362.

Keitt, G. W., and D. H. Palmiter. (1938). Heterothallism and variability in *Venturia inaequalis*. *Am. J. Botany* 25:338-345.

Kerl, I. (1937). Über Regenerationsversuche an Fruchtkörpern und andere entwicklungsphysiologische Untersuchungen bei *Pyronema confluens*. *Z. Botan.* 31:129-174.

Kihara, M. (1962). Nuclear number in germinating conidia of *Neurospora*. *Neurospora Newsletter* 2:8-9.

Killian, C. (1917). Über die Sexualität von *Venturia inaequalis* (Cooke) Ad. *Z. Botan.* 9:353-398.

Kinsky, S. C. (1961). Induction and repression of nitrate reductase in *Neurospora crassa*. *J. Bacteriol.* 82:898-904.

Klebs, G. (1900). Zur Physiologie der Fortpflanzung einiger Pilze. *Jahrb. Wiss. Botan.* 35:80-203.

Klebs, G. (1928). "Die Bedingungen der Fortpflanzung bei einigen Algen und Pilzen," 541 pp. Fischer, Jena.

Kordes, H. (1923). *Botan. Arch.* 3:282-311 (quoted by V. W. Cochrane, 1958).

Kulayev, I. S., and A. N. Belozersky. (1957). A study of the physiological role of polyphosphates in the development of *Aspergillus niger*, using radiophosphorus (P_{32}). *Biochemistry (USSR) (English Transl.)* 22:545-554.

Lacoste, L. (1960). La reproduction du *Leptosphaeria rusci* (Wallr.) Sacc. en culture pure. *Compt. Rend.* 250:3698-3700.

Lacoste, L. (1963). Action de la température et de l'éclairement sur la reproduction en culture pure de diverses espèces du genre *Leptosphaeria* Ces. et de Not. *Compt. Rend.* 256:2668-2671.

Leach, C. M. (1961). The sporulation of *Helminthosporium oryzae* as affected by exposure to near ultraviolet radiation and dark periods. *Can. J. Botany* 39:705-715.

Lee, B. T. O., and J. A. Pateman. (1961). Studies concerning the inheritance of ascospore length in *Neurospora crassa*. I. Studies on large-spored strains. *Australian J. Biol. Sci.* 14:223-230.

Levi, J. D. (1956). Mating reaction in yeast. *Nature* 177:753-754.

Lilly, V. G., and H. L. Barnett. (1948a). Growth rates, vitamin deficiencies and sclerotia formation by some Sclerotiniaceae. *Proc. West Va. Acad. Sci.* 20:69-74.

Lilly, V. G., and H. L. Barnett. (1948b). The effect of pyrithiamin upon sporulation of three thiamin-deficient fungi. *Am. J. Botany* 35:801.

Lilly, V. G., and H. L. Barnett. (1949). The influence of concentrations of nutrients, thiamin and biotin upon growth and formation of perithecia and ascospores by *Chaetomium convolutum. Mycologia* 41:186-196.

Lilly, V. G., and H. L. Barnett. (1951). "Physiology of the Fungi," 464 pp. McGraw-Hill, New York.

Lindeberg, G., and H. Malmgren. (1952). Enzymatic break-down of polymetaphosphate. VI. Influence of nutritional factors on the polymetaphosphatase production of *Aspergillus niger. Acta Chem. Scand.* 6:27-37.

Lindegren, C. C. (1936). Heterocaryosis and hormones in *Neurospora. Am. Naturalist* 70:404-405.

Lindegren, C. C., and M. A. Scott. (1937). Formation of the ascospore wall in *Neurospora. Cellule Rec. Cytol. Histol.* 45:361-371.

Lindegren, C. C., V. Beaufield, and R. Barber. (1939). Increasing the fertility of *Neurospora* by selective inbreeding. *Botan. Gaz.* 100:592-599.

Lindegren, C. C., and G. Lindegren. (1941). X-ray and ultraviolet induced mutations in *Neurospora*. I. X-ray mutations. *J. Heredity* 32:405-412.

Lockwood, L. B. (1937). Hydrogen ion concentration and ascus formation. *Mycologia* 29:289-290.

Loughheed, T. C. (1961). The effect of nutrition on synnemata formation in *Hirsutella gigantea* Petch. *Can. J. Botany* 39:865-873.

Lowry, R. J., and A. S. Sussman. (1958). Wall structure of ascospores of *Neurospora tetrasperma. Am. J. Botany* 45:397-403.

Lowry, R. J., A. S. Sussman, and B. von Böventer-Heidenhain. (1956). *Mycologia* 48:241-252 (quoted by V. W. Cochrane, 1958).

Lowry, R. J., A. S. Sussman, and B. von Böventer-Heidenhain. (1957). Physiology of the cell surface of *Neurospora* ascospores. *Am. J. Botany* 41:21-30.

McClary, D. O., W. L. Nulty, and G. R. Miller. (1959). Effect of potassium versus sodium in the sporulation of *Saccharomyces. J. Bacteriol.* 78:362-368.

McClintock, B. (1945). Preliminary observations of the chromosomes of *Neurospora crassa. Am. J. Botany* 32:671-678.

McDonough, M. W., and B. Rickard. (1960). The influence of certain simple nitrogenous compounds on growth and sporulation of *Chaetomium globosum. Ann. Botany (London)* [N.S.] 24:475-481.

McGahen, J. W., and H. E. Wheeler. (1951). Genetics of *Glomerella*. IX. Perithecial development and plasmogamy. *Am. J. Botany* 38:610-617.

Magrou, J., H. Marneffe, and F. Mariat. (1951). Action morphogène de facteurs vitaminiques sur certains champignons. *Ann. Inst. Pasteur* 80:443-450.

Mandels, G. R. (1955). *Am. J. Botany* 42:921-929 (quoted by V. W. Cochrane, 1958).

Mandels, G. R. (1956). *J. Bacteriol.* 71:684-688 (quoted by V. W. Cochrane, 1958).

Mandels, G. R., and R. T. Darby. (1953). A rapid cell volume assay for fungitoxicity using fungus spores. *J. Bacteriol.* 65:16-26.

Markert, C. L. (1949). Sexuality in the fungus *Glomerella. Am. Naturalist* 83:227-231.

Maruyama, Y., and M. Alexander. (1962a). Localization of enzymes in the mycelium and microconidia of *Fusarium oxysporum. J. Bacteriol.* 84:307-312.

Maruyama, Y., and M. Alexander. (1962b). Distribution of protein and nucleic acids in hyphae and microconidia of *Fusarium. Arch. Mikrobiol.* 41:401-407.

Mather, K., and J. L. Jinks. (1958). Cytoplasm in sexual reproduction. *Nature* 182:1188-1190.

Mathieson, M. J. (1952). Ascospore dimorphism and mating type in *Chromocrea spinulosa* (Fuckel) Petch n. comb. *Ann. Botany (London)* [N.S.] 16:449-466.
Miller, C. W., and N. A. Anderson. (1961). Proliferations of conidiophores and intrahyphal hyphae in *Aspergillus niger*. *Mycologia* 53:433-436.
Miller, J. J., O. Hoffmann-Ostenhof, E. Scheiber, and O. Gabriel. (1959). The metabolism of yeast sporulation. III. Respiration of sporulating and growing cells. *Can. J. Microbiol.* 5:153-159.
Minagawa, T., B. Wagner, and B. S. Strauss. (1959). The nucleic acid content of *Neurospora crassa*. *Arch. Biochem. Biophys.* 80:442-445.
Mitchell, M. B. (1960). Ascus formation and recombinant frequencies in *Neurospora crassa*. *Genetics* 45:507-517.
Mittmann, G. (1932). Kulturversuche mit Einsporstämmen und zytologische Untersuchungen in der Gattung *Ceratostomella*. *Jahrb. Wiss. Botan.* 77:185-219.
Moore, E. J. (1963). The ontogeny of the apothecia of *Pyronema domesticum*. *Am. J. Botany* 50:37-44.
Moore, R. T., and McAlear, J. H. (1962). Observations on ascospore initiation in the Discomycete *Dasyscyphus* sp. *J. Gen. Microbiol.* 28:211-213.
Moreau, C. (1953). "Les genres *Sordaria* et *Pleurage*. Leurs affinités systématiques," 330 pp. Lechevalier, Paris.
Moreau, F. (1952-1953). "Les Champignons. Physiologie, Morphologie, Développement et Systématique," Vol. I, 940 pp. and Vol. II, 2120 pp. Lechevalier, Paris.
Moreau, F., and Moreau, Mme. F. (1930). Le développement du périthèce chez quelques Ascomycètes. *Rev. Gen. Botan.* 42:65-98.
Moreau, F., and Moreau, Mme. F. (1938). La formation hormonale des périthèces chez les *Neurospora*. *Compt. Rend.* 206:369-370.
Moreau, F., and Moreau, Mme. F. (1952). Sur le développement du *Ceratocystis moniliformis* (Hedgcock) nov. comb. *Rev. Mycol.* 17:141-153.
Moreau, F., and C. Moruzi. (1931). Recherches expérimentales sur la formation des périthèces chez les *Neurospora*. *Compt. Rend.* 192:1476-1478.
Moreau, M. (1959). *L'Aspergillus mangini*. Ses exigences nutritives, ses conditions de développement. *Fruits (Paris)* 14:315-328.
Morton, A. G. (1961). The induction of sporulation in mould fungi. *Proc. Roy. Soc.* B153:548-569.
Morton, A. G., D. J. F. England, and D. A. Towler. (1958). The physiology of sporulation in *Penicillium griseofulvum* Dierckx. *Brit. Mycol. Soc. Trans.* 41:39-51.
Morton, A. G., A. G. F. Dickerson, and D. J. F. England. (1960). Changes in enzyme activity of fungi during nitrogen starvation. *J. Exptl. Botany* 11:116-128.
Mulder, E. G. (1938). Influence of copper on growth of microorganisms. *Ann. Fermenations* 4:513-533.
Müller, E. (1951). Ueber die Entwicklung von *Pleospora Gäumannii* nov. sp. *Ber. Schweiz. Botan. Ges.* 61:165-174.
Müller, R. (1953). Studien über die Sektoren-bildung bei *Penicillium*. *Flora (Jena)* 140:209-252.
Nakata, K. (1929). Studies on *Sclerotium rolfsii*. Part VII. The results of successive cultures and selections within pure lines of the fungus. *Bull. Sci. Fak. Terk. Kjusu Univ.* 3:292-299 (abstract in *Rev. Appl. Mycol.* 9:613).
Nicholas, D. J. D., and A. Nason. (1954). Mechanism of action of nitrate reductase from *Neurospora*. *J. Biol. Chem.* 211:183-197.
Nickerson, W. J., and Z. Mankowski. (1953). Role of nutrition in the maintenance of the yeast-shape in *Candida*. *Am. J. Botany* 40:584-592.

Nishi, A. (1960). Enzymatic studies on the phosphorus metabolism in germinating spores of *Aspergillus niger*. *J. Biochem.* 48:758-767.

Nishi, A. (1961). Role of polyphosphate and phospholipid in germinating spores of *Aspergillus niger*. *J. Bacteriol.* 81:10-19.

Olive, L. S. (1956). Genetics of *Sordaria fimicola*. I. Ascospore color mutants. *Am. J. Botany* 43:97-107.

Olive, L. S. (1958). On the evolution of heterothallism in fungi. *Am. Naturalist* 42:233-251.

Olive, L. S., and A. A. Fantini. (1961). A new heterothallic species of *Sordaria*. *Am. J. Botany* 48:124-128.

Owens, R. G. (1955). Metabolism of fungus spores. II. Cytochrome oxidase, succinoxidase and pyruvate carboxylase systems in homogenates of conidia of *Neurospora sitophila*. *Contrib. Boyce Thompson Inst.* 18:145-152.

Owens, R. G., H. M. Novotny, and M. Michels. (1958). Composition of conidia of *Neurospora*. *Contrib. Boyce Thompson Inst.* 19:355-374.

Page, O. T. (1956). The influence of light and other environmental factors on mycelial growth and sclerotial production by *Botrytis squamosa* Walk. *Can. J. Botany* 34:881-890.

Page, W. M. (1933). A contribution to the life-history of *Sordaria fimicola* (4-spored form) with special reference to the abnormal spores. *Brit. Mycol. Soc. Trans.* 17:296-300.

Page, W. M. (1936). Note on abnormal spores in *Podospora minuta*. *Brit. Mycol. Soc. Trans.* 20:186-187.

Page, W. M. (1939). Contributions to the life history of certain coprophilous fungi. *Brit. Mycol. Soc. Trans.* 23:253-268.

Paul, W. R. C. (1929). A comparative morphological and physiological study of a number of strains of *Botrytis cinerea*, with special reference to their virulence. *Brit. Mycol. Soc. Trans.* 14:118-134.

Peiris, J. W. L. (1947). The *Botrytis* disease of *Gladiolus*, together with a physiological study of certain Botrytis species. Ph.D. thesis, University of London.

Pillai, N. C., and K. S. Srinivasan. (1956). *J. Gen. Microbiol.* 14:248-255 (quoted by V. W. Cochrane, 1958).

Ramirez, C., and J. J. Miller. (1963). Accumulation of free proline during yeast sporogenesis. *Nature* 197:722-723.

Raper, J. R. (1952). Chemical regulation of sexual processes in the Thallophytes. *Botan. Rev.* 18:447-545.

Raper, J. R. (1960). The control of sex in fungi. *Am. J. Botany* 47:794-808.

Reese, E., K. Sanderson, R. Woodward, and G. M. Eisenberg. (1949). Variations and mutations of *Penicillium chrysogenum*. *J. Bacteriol.* 57:15-25.

Reinhardt, M. O. (1892). Das Wachstum der Pilzhyphen. *Jahrb. Wiss. Botan.* 23:479-566.

Rich, S., and J. G. Horsfall. (1948). Metal reagents as antisporulants. *Phytopathology* 38:22.

Ritchie, D. (1937). The morphology of the perithecium of *Sordaria fimicola* (Rob.) Ces. and de Not. *J. Elisha Mitchell Sci. Soc.* 53:334-342.

Rizet, G. (1942). Sur l'obtention d'irrégularités dans les asques et les spores de Pyrénomycètes du genre *Podospora* par l'action de quelques anesthésiques. *Bull. Soc. Linneenne Normandie* [9] 2:123-130.

Rizet, G., and C. Engelmann. (1949). Contribution à l'étude génétique d'un Ascomycète tétrasporé, *Podospora anserina* (Ces.) Rehm. *Rev. Cytol. Biol. Vegetales* 11:201-304.

Robbins, W. J., and F. Kavanagh. (1938). Vitamin B_1 or its intermediates and the growth of certain fungi. *Am. J. Botany* 25:229-236.
Robbins, W. J., and R. Ma. (1942). Vitamin deficiencies of *Ceratostomella* and related fungi. *Am. J. Botany* 29:835-843.
Roberg, M. (1928). Über Wirkung von Eisen-, Zink- und Kupfer-Salzen für *Aspergillus*. *Centr. Bakteriol. Parasitenk., Abt. II* 74:33-370.
Robinson, W. (1926). The conditions of growth and development of *Pyronema confluens* Tul. (*P. omphalodes* (Bull.) Fuckel). *Ann. Botany (London)* 40:245-272.
Rosinski, M. A. (1961). Development of the ascocarp of *Ceratostomella ulmi*. *Am. J. Botany* 48:285-293.
Ross, R. G. (1959). *Proc. Can. Phytopathol. Soc.* 26:14 (quoted by E. Müller, 1961, *Fortschr. Botan.* 23:420).
Rudolph, E. D. (1962). The effect of some physiological and environmental factors on sclerotial *Aspergilli*. *Am. J. Botany* 49:71-78.
Ryan, F. J. (1948). The germination of conidia from biochemical mutants of *Neurospora*. *Am. J. Botany* 35:497-503.
Saccas, A. (1951). *Rev. Pathol. Vegetale Entomol. Agr. France* 30:65-96 (quoted by V. W. Cochrane, 1958).
Sagromsky, H. (1952). Der Einfluss des Lichtes auf die rhytmische Conidienbildung von *Penicillium*. *Flora (Jena)* 139:300-312.
Sansome, E. R. (1946). Heterocaryosis mating-type factors and sexual reproduction in *Neurospora*. *Bull. Torrey Botan. Club* 73:397-409.
Sanwal, B. D., and M. Lata. (1961). Glutamic dehydrogenase in single-gene mutants of *Neurospora* deficient in amination. *Nature* 190:286-287.
Sartoris, G. B. (1927). A cytological study of *Ceratostomella adiposa* (Butl.) comb. nov., the black-rot fungus of sugar-cane. *J. Agr. Res.* 35:577-585.
Sauton, B. (1910). *Compt. Rend.* 151:241-243 (quoted by V. W. Cochrane, 1958).
Schmiedeknecht, M. (1959). Appressorien und Chlamydosporen von *Colletotrichum atramentarium* (Berk. et Br.) Taub. *Arch. Mikrobiol.* 34:374-378.
Schönborn, W. (1955). Energetische Untersuchungen an Pilzen und Bakterien. *Arch. Mikrobiol.* 22:408.
Shanor, L. (1936). The production of mature perithecia of *Cordyceps militaris* (L.) Link in laboratory culture. *J. Elisha Mitchell Sci. Soc.* 52:99-104.
Shanta, P. (1961). Growth requirements of *Cercospora personata*. *Phytopathol. Z.* 41:59-73.
Shatkin, A. J., and E. L. Tatum. (1961). The relationship of *m*-inositol to morphology in *Neurospora crassa*. *Am. J. Botany* 48:760-771.
Shear, C. L., and B. O. Dodge. (1927). Life-histories and heterothallism of the red bread-mold fungi of the *Monilia sitophila* group. *J. Agr. Res.* 34:1019-1042.
Sheng, T. C., and F. J. Ryan. (1948). Mutation involving the production of conidia and the requirement for leucine in a mutant of *Neurospora*. *Genetics* 33:221-227.
Sheng, T. C., and G. Sheng. (1952). Genetic and non-genetic factors in pigmentation of *Neurospora crassa*. *Genetics* 37:264-269.
Singleton, J. R. (1953). Chromosome morphology and the chromosome cycle in the ascus of *Neurospora crassa*. *Am. J. Botany* 40:475-492.
Sisler, H. D., and C. E. Coy. (1954). *Am. J. Botany* 41:338-345 (quoted by V. W. Cochrane, 1958).
Sloan, B. J., and G. B. Wilson. (1958). The function of the microspores of *Gelasinospora calospora* var. *autosteira*. *Mycologia* 50:111-116.
Smith, J. H. (1924). On the early growth rate of the individual fungus hyphae. *New Phytologist* 23:65-79.

Snyder, W. C., and H. N. Hansen. (1941). The effect of light on the taxonomic characters in *Fusarium*. *Mycologia* 33:580-591.

Sproston, T., and D. C. Pease. (1957). Influence of thermoperiods on production of the sexual stage of the fungus *Sclerotinia trifoliorum* Eriks. *Trans. N.Y. Acad. Sci.* [2] 20:199-204.

Stantial, H. (1935). The sporulation of yeast. *Trans. Roy. Soc. Can. Sect. III* 29:175-188.

Steinberg, R. A. (1940). Action of some organic compounds on yield, sporulation, and starch formation of *Aspergillus niger*. *J. Agr. Res.* 60:765-773.

Steinberg, R. A., and C. Thom. (1942). Reversions in morphology of nitrite-induced "mutants" of Aspergilli grown upon amino acids. *J. Agr. Res.* 64:645-652.

Stevens, F. L. (1928). Effects of ultra-violet radiation on various fungi. *Botan. Gaz.* 86:210-225.

Stokes, J. L., and M. Gunness. (1946). The amino-acid composition of microorganisms. *J. Bacteriol.* 52:195-207.

Strauss, B. S. (1958). Cell death and "unbalanced growth" in *Neurospora*. *J. Gen. Microbiol.* 18:658-669.

Sussman, A. S. (1953a). The effect of furfural upon the germination and respiration of ascospores of *Neurospora tetrasperma*. *Am. J. Botany* 40:401-404.

Sussman, A. S. (1953b). The effect of heterocyclic and other compounds upon the germination of ascospores of *Neurospora tetrasperma*. *J. Gen. Microbiol.* 8:211-216.

Sussman, A. S. (1954). Changes in the permeability of ascospores of *Neurospora tetrasperma* during germination. *J. Gen. Physiol.* 38:59-77.

Sussman, A. S. (1961). The role of trehalose in the activation of dormant ascospores of *Neurospora*. *Quart. Rev. Biol.* 36:109-116.

Sussman, A. S. (1965). Physiology of dormancy and germination in the propagules of cryptogamic plants. *In* "Handbuch der Pflanzenphysiologie" (A. Lang, ed.), Vol. 15, pp. 933-1025. Springer, Berlin.

Sussman, A. S., and B. T. Lingappa. (1959). Role of trehalose in ascospores of *Neurospora tetrasperma*. *Science* 130:1343.

Sussman, A. S., and C. L. Markert. (1953). The development of tyrosinase and cytochrome oxidase activity in mutants of *Glomerella cingulata*. *Arch. Biochem. Biophys.* 45:31-40.

Sussman, A. S., J. R. Distler, and J. S. Krakow. (1956). Metabolic aspects of *Neurospora* activation and germination. *Plant Physiol.* 31:126-135.

Sussman, A. S., R. W. Holton, and B. von Böventer-Heidenhain. (1958). Physiology of the cell surface of *Neurospora* ascopores. Entrance of anions and non-polar compounds. *Arch. Mikrobiol.* 29:38-50.

Taber, W. A. (1959). Studies on *Isaria cretacea*. Nutritional and morphological characteristics of two strains and morphogenesis of the synnema. *Can. J. Microbiol.* 5:513-535.

Taber, W. A. (1960). Studies on *Isaria cretacea*. Morphogenesis of the synnema and endogenous nutrition. *Can. J. Microbiol.* 6:53-63.

Taber, W. A. (1961). Nutritional factors affecting the morphogenesis of the synnema. *Recent Advan. Botany* 4:289-293.

Taha, E. E., and S. G. Knight. (1962). Physiological and chemical studies on mould proteins. III. Extraction and fractionation of the proteins of mould mycelia. *Arch. Mikrobiol.* 41:37-43.

Takebe, I., and N. Shimizu. (1959). Some aspects on the nutritional requirement of conidiospores of *Aspergillus niger* for the initiation of germination. *Ann. Rept. Inst. Food Microbiol.* **12**:29-31.
Tarurenko, E. (1954). The influence of light on the development of mould fungi. *Mikrobiologiya* **23**:29-33 (abstract in *Rev. Appl. Mycol.* **34**:803).
Tatum, E. L., R. W. Barratt, and V. M. Cutter, Jr. (1949). Chemical induction of colonial paramorphs in *Neurospora* and *Syncephalastrum*. *Science* **109**:509-511.
Thielke, C. (1958). Studien zur Entwicklungsphysiologie von *Aspergillus*. I. Sterigmenproliferation bei *Aspergillus repens*. *Planta* **51**:308-320.
Thielke, C., and R. Paravicini. (1962). Studien zur Entwicklungsphysiologie von *Aspergillus*. III. Die Entwicklung mehrkerniger Ascosporen und die Modifizierbarkeit von Conidien und Ascosporen bei *Aspergillus echinulatus*. *Arch. Mikrobiol.* **44**: 75-86.
Thirumalachar, M. S. (1957). Morphogenesis of some fungi in submerged cultures. *Indian Phytopathol.* **10**:1-7.
Thom, C., and K. B. Raper. (1945). "A Manual of the *Aspergilli*," 373 pp. Williams & Wilkins, Baltimore, Maryland.
Tomkins, R. G. (1932). *Brit. Mycol. Soc. Trans.* **17**:147-149 (quoted by V. W. Cochrane, 1958).
Townsend, B. B. (1957). Nutritional factors influencing the production of sclerotia by certain fungi. *Ann. Botany (London)* [N.S.] **21**:153-166.
Townsend, B. B., and H. J. Willetts. (1954). The development of sclerotia of certain fungi. *Brit. Mycol. Soc. Trans.* **37**:213-221.
Tremaine, J. H., and J. J. Miller. (1954). Effect of six vitamins on ascospore formation by an isolate of bakers' yeast. *Botan. Gaz.* **115**:311-322.
Turian, G. (1954). L'acide borique, inhibiteur de la différenciation des ascospores chez *Sordaria*. *Experientia* **10**:183.
Turian, G. (1955). Recherches sur l'action de l'acide borique sur la fructification des *Sordaria*. *Phytopathol. Z.* **25**:181-189.
Turian, G. (1957). Recherches sur l'action anticaroténogène de la diphénylamine et ses conséquences sur la morphogenèse reproductive chez *Allomyces* et *Neurospora*. *Physiol. Plantarum* **10**:667-680.
Turian, G. (1960). Déficiences du métabolisme oxydatif et différenciation sexuelle chez *Allomyces* et *Neurospora*. *Pathol. Microbiol.* **23**:687-699.
Turian, G. (1961a). L'acétate et son double effet d'induction isocitratasique et de différenciation conidienne chez les *Neurospora*. *Compt. Rend.* **252**:1374-1376.
Turian, G. (1961b). Cycle glyoxylique, transaminase alanine-glyoxylate et différenciation sexuelle chez *Allomyces* et *Neurospora*. *Pathol. Microbiol.* **24**:819-839.
Turian, G. (1961c). Unpublished results.
Turian, G. (1962a). The hexosemonophosphate shunt as an alternate metabolic pathway for conidial differentiation in *Neurospora*. *Neurospora Newsletter* **2**:15.
Turian, G. (1962b). Differential synthesis of nucleic acids in sexual differentiation of *Allomyces*. *Nature* **196**:493-494.
Turian, G. (1962c). Effet conidiogène du malonate chez *Neurospora crassa*. *Proc. 8th Intern. Congr. Microbiol., Montreal, 1962* Vol. A2.9 p. 18. Univ. of Toronto Press, Toronto.
Turian, G. (1962d). Unpublished observations.
Turian, G. (1963). Sur le mécanisme de l'induction isocitratasique chez *Allomyces* et *Neurospora*. *Pathol. Microbiol.* **26**:553-563.

Turian, G. (1964). Synthetic conidiogenous media for *Neurospora crassa*. *Nature* **202**:1240.

Turian, G., and G. Combépine. (1963). Activité comparée de la transaminase alanine-glyoxylate de *Neurospora* cultivé en présence de saccharose ou d'acétate. *Helv. Chim. Acta* **46**:2453-2457.

Turian, G., and J. Seydoux. (1961). Acétate et conidiogenèse chez *Aspergillus niger*. Unpublished results.

Turian, G., and J. Seydoux. (1962). Déficience d'activité de la déshydrogénase succinique dans les mitochondries isolées du *Neurospora* en condition d'induction isocitratasique par culture sur acétate. *Compt. Rend.* **255**:755-757.

Turian, G., J. Seydoux, and D. Volkmann. (1962). Activité isocitratasique et type de sporulation chez *Neurospora tetrasperma* et chez *N. sitophila*, souche normale et mutant microconidien. *Pathol. Microbiol.* **25**:737-751.

Varitchak, B. (1931). Contribution à l'étude du développement du périthèce des Ascomycètes. *Botaniste* **23**:1-183.

Venkat Ram, C. S. (1952). Soil bacteria and chlamydospore formation in *Fusarium solani*. *Nature* **170**:889.

von Hofsten, V. (1962). Deoxyribonucleic acid content of morphologically different cell-types of *Ophiostoma multiannulatum*. *Nature* **193**:897-898.

von Hofsten, A., and B. von Hofsten. (1958). Factors influencing cell division and vegetative morphogenesis of *Ophiostoma multiannulatum*. *Physiol. Plantarum* **11**:106-117.

von Witsch, H., and F. Wagner. (1955). Beobachtungen über den Einfluss des Lichtes auf Mycel- und Conidienwachstum bei *Alternaria brassicae* var. *dauci*. *Arch. Mikrobiol.* **22**:307-312.

Vuillemin, P. (1910). Matériaux pour une classification rationnelle des *fungi imperfecti*. *Compt. Rend.* **101**:882.

Wagner, R. P., and H. K. Mitchell. (1955). "Genetics and Metabolism," 444 pp. Wiley, New York.

Walker, C. G., and D. J. D. Nicholas. (1962). An iron requirement for a dissimilatory nitrate reductase in *Neurospora crassa*. *Nature* **189**:141-142.

Wellman, R. H., and S. E. A. McCallan. (1942). *Contrib. Boyce Thompson Inst.* **12**:431-450 (quoted by V. W. Cochrane, 1958).

Went, F. A. F. C. (1901). *Monilia sitophila* (Mont.) Sacc., ein technischer Pilz Javas. *Centr. Bakteriol., Parasitenk., Abt. II* **7**:544-550.

Westergaard, M., and H. K. Mitchell. (1947). *Neurospora* V. A synthetic medium favoring sexual reproduction. *Am. J. Botany* **34**:573-577.

Westergaard, M., and H. M. Hirsch. (1954). Environmental and genetic control of differentiation in *Neurospora*. *Proc. Symp. Colston Res. Soc.* **7**:171-183.

Weston, W. H., Jr. (1951). *Trans. N.Y. Acad. Sci.* [2] **13**:305-308 (quoted by V. W. Cochrane, 1958).

Wheeler, H. E. (1954). Genetics and evolution of heterothallism in *Glomerella*. *Phytopathology* **44**:342-345.

Wheeler, H. E., and J. W. McGahen. (1952). Genetics of *Glomerella*. X. Genes affecting sexual reproduction. *Am. J. Botany* **39**:110-119.

Wheeler, H. E., L. S. Olive, C. T. Ernest, and C. W. Edgerton. (1948). Genetics of *Glomerella*. V. Crozier and ascus development. *Am. J. Botany* **35**:722-728.

Whiteside, W. C. (1957). Perithecial initials of *Chaetomium*. *Mycologia* **49**:420-425.

Wilson, E. E. (1927). Effects of fungus extracts upon initiation and growth of perithecia of *Venturia inaequalis* in pure cultures. *Phytopathology* **17**:835-836.

11. Morphogenesis in Ascomycetes

Yanagita, T. (1957). Biochemical aspects on the germination of conidiospores of *Aspergillus niger*. *Arch. Mikrobiol.* **26**:329-344.

Yanagita, T., and F. Kogané. (1962). Growth and cytochemical differentiation of mold colonies. *J. Gen. Appl. Microbiol.* **8**:201-213.

Yanagita, T., and S. Yamagishi. (1958). Comparative and quantitative studies of fungitoxicity against fungal spores and mycelia. *Appl. Microbiol.* **6**:375-381.

Yarwood, C. E. (1950). *Am. J. Botany* **37**:636-639 (quoted by V. W. Cochrane, 1958).

Yu, C. C. C. (1954). The culture and spore germination of *Ascobolus* with emphasis on *A. magnificus*. *Am. J. Botany* **41**:21-30.

Yu-Sun, C. C. C. (1964). Nutritional studies of *Ascobolus immersus*. *Am. J. Botany* **51**:231-237.

Zalokar, M. (1954). Studies on the biosynthesis of carotenoids in *Neurospora crassa*. *Arch. Biochem. Biophys.* **50**:71-80.

Zalokar, M. (1957). Variations in the production of carotenoids in *Neurospora*. *Arch. Biochem. Biophys.* **70**:561-567.

Zalokar, M. (1959a). Enzyme activity and cell differentiation in *Neurospora*. *Am. J. Botany* **46**:555-569.

Zalokar, M. (1959b). Growth and differentiation of *Neurospora* hyphae. *Am. J. Botany* **46**:602-610.

Zalokar, M., and V. W. Cochrane. (1956). Diphosphopyridine nucleotidase in the life cycle of *Neurospora crassa*. *Am. J. Botany* **43**:107-110.

Zickler, H. (1931). Über die künstliche Erzeugung von Miktohaplonten. *Biol. Zentr.* **51**:540.

Zickler, H. (1937). Die Spermatienbefruchtung bei *Bombardia lunata*. *Ber. Deut. Botan. Ges.* **55**:114-119.

Zickler, H. (1953). Zur Entwicklungsgeschichte des Ascomyceten *Bombardia lunata* Zckl. *Arch. Protistenk.* **98**:1-70.

CHAPTER 12

Morphogenesis in Basidiomycetes

W. A. Taber

*Department of Biology
Texas A & M University
College Station, Texas*

I. INTRODUCTION

The word morphogenesis refers to the process of development by which cells and tissues acquire their characteristic form. In all except spherical unicellular organisms it is an expression of directed but unequal growth. Descriptive studies of changes in form are referred to as developmental morphology, a subject that is not treated fully in this chapter. Appropriate references to developmental morphology are Corner (1934, 1937), Pantidou (1962), and Gäumann (1952).

The fact that determination of form is ultimately under genetic control is self evident, but it is not evident how the information contained in the genetic code is transmitted, how some may be withheld until its expression is advantageous, or how the influence of the external environment manifests itself. Something of the mode of transfer of information *intracellularly* from the nucleus to the site of synthesis, the ribosome, is now known (Davis, 1961), and concepts such as end-product inhibition, repression, derepression, positive feedback, and operator gene control probably will be found to play a role in morphogenesis. For the present, however, it is expedient to view the subject of morphogenic regulators in the terms of Sinnott (1956), who suggests that there is an external and internal environment and that in broadest terms each may be divided further into physical, chemical, and biological components.

It is perhaps paradoxical that few morphogenic studies have been made on the basidiomycete carpophore even though it is the largest regularly shaped fungus structure. Perhaps this is due in part to the mistaken belief that basidiomycete fruit bodies are difficult to grow in the laboratory.

In fact more than 150 species of agarics, polypores, and boletes have been grown in the laboratory, although not all on synthetic media (Buller, 1909, 1922, 1924, 1931, 1933, 1934; Denyer, 1960; Lohwag, 1952; Badcock, 1943; Pantidou, 1962; Tamblyn and Dacosta, 1958; Yurchenco and Warren, 1961).

There are many entities in the Basidiomycetes that either have been, or should be, the subject of morphogenic studies. These include hyphal branching systems, smut cell form, the rust haustorium, appresorium and vesicle, clamp connection, rhizomorphs, pseudorhiza, hyphal strands, and the primordium, stipe, pileus, hymenium, and spore of the fruit body or carpophore. The carpophore should present a particularly rewarding subject for study since it has several sites of growth, a regular and complex form, and an $(n + n)$ somatic cell which is genetically similar to a diploid cell of higher plants and animals. The hymenomycete carpophore is the principal subject of this chapter.

II. MORPHOGENETIC ENTITIES

A. Hyphal Branching

Fungal somatic cell growth may be considered to consist of two types: primary growth, which is that of cells in direct contact with the nutrient medium and their immediate aerial branches, and secondary growth, which is that of cells not in direct contact with the substrate and which obtain their nutrients from primary hyphae. In both instances, growth occurs by extension of the tip and eventually gives rise to new lateral growing points which form branches (cf. Volume I, Chapter 26). The branching system of *Coprinus disseminatus* has been studied by Butler (1961), who found regularity and interdependence in the development of the system. Growth was monopodial; that is, the tip continued to grow after subapical branching had occurred. Apical extension was most rapid in hyphae having the greatest diameter. Since the ratio of surface area to volume decreases with increasing diameter, the limiting factor in apical extension probably is not absorption but either the amount of metabolism in the apical cell or the rate of translocation to it. Butler has provided convincing evidence that hyphal branching is controlled rather than a product of random growth.

B. Mycelial Strands

Mycelial strands (see also Chapter 3, Section III, A) and rhizomorphs resemble one another superficially but have been distinguished by Garrett on developmental grounds (Butler, 1957). Mycelial strands consist of loose aggregates of hyphae which increase in thickness by accretion of hyphae from the base while the rhizomorph develops as a completely autonomous organ possessing an apical growing point. Hein (1930) working with *Agaricus campestris* noted that strands began to develop from the inoculation point, but after most of the substrate had been occupied. He attributed strand development to one or more of the following factors: adhesion, crowding, branching, air currents, CO_2 tension, moisture under certain conditions, chemotropism, and thigmotropism. The strands increased in diameter through aggregation and through actual fusion and resorption of hyphae.

Strand development of *Merulius lacrymans* [*Serpula lacrimans*] through non-nutrient substrate was studied by Butler (1957). Strand development proceeded behind the advancing mycelial margin and arose from a narrow region. Growth of strands was subject to influence from variations in distance from the food base. Slender, thigmotropically sensitive tendril hyphae developed from the main hyphae of the strand (Falck, 1912; Butler, 1958) and contributed to the strand. These tendrils developed at the clamp connection nodes of the main hyphae and at the narrow tips of earlier branches. Butler believes that a form of apical dominance maintains the predictable branching hierarchy and that a nutritional mechanism could be the actual regulatory device. Tendril hyphae are thought to lie along the main hyphae as a result of the nutritional advantage conferred by this proximity. *Agaricus bisporus* also produces strands which bear tendrils (Mathew, 1961). Nutrition may play a role since mycelial strand development was inversely correlated with the concentration of nutrients of the medium and directly correlated with moisture content. Unlike the rhizomorph, mycelial strand development proceeds behind the margin (Butler, 1957).

C. Rhizomorph

Four morphological types of rhizomorphs (see also Chapter 3, Section III, A) have been described by Townsend (1954), who also noted that growth of these highly organized structures was suppressed by light. Development of the rhizomorph has been investigated by Garrett (1953). Development began late but, once established, the rhizomorph grew up to 5 times more rapidly than the mycelium of the colony mat. Nutrition plays an important role in morphogenesis of the rhizomorph. An interaction was found to exist between the concentrations of carbon and nitrogen source. Within a certain range, increasing the amounts of both favored development. The range of nutritional conditions favoring rhizomorph initiation and development is narrower than that permitting mycelial growth. Seven days after placing a 4-mm agar disk cut from near the margin of a colony onto an appropriate nutrient agar, rhizomorph initials developed in a circle about the disks. Those developing most rapidly preempted the flow of nutrients by translocation pull and suppressed subsequent development of others. This was further demonstrated by cutting a strip of agar out of an agar plate along the diameter and inoculating one side of the agar. Unorganized hyphae eventually bridged the gap and established a new colony on the far side. If the bridging hyphae were cut, rhizomorphs subsequently developed from the new colony; if not, the rhizomorphs on the old colony continued to grow but presumably hoarded the nutrients and thus prevented formation of new ones on the far side. The function of the rhizomorph under natural conditions is thought to be the translocation of nutrients from one locale to another. Abundant evidence will be presented throughout this chapter that translocation in regular hyphae is of utmost importance to morphogenesis of secondary hyphal structures. This is perhaps a foregone conclusion since secondary hyphae are not in contact with the exogenous nutrients and hence must either obtain exogenous nutrients via translocation from primary hyphae or endogenous nutrients, synthesized by primary hyphae, via translocation (cf. Volume I, Chapter 16).

Either high O_2 tension or low CO_2 tension is required for rhizomorph development (Snider, 1959).

D. Smut Vegetative Cell Form

The regulation of cell form by nutrients has been studied by Spoerl *et al.* (1957) and Wachter and Spoerl (1961). Various nitrogenous compounds caused *Ustilago sphaerogena* to grow either as short rods or as long hyphalike cells. Cell division is thought to be the process which is affected by the chemicals. Formation of irregular hyphalike cells might be abnormal since the function of cell division may be to maintain a constant ratio between volume of nucleus and cell.

E. Rust Vesicle

The obligate parasite *Puccinia graminis* forms an appressorium on the leaf, enters through the stoma, and develops a substomatal vesicle of quite definite form. Formation of the vesicle is favored by high temperature and high light intensity (Sharp *et al.*, 1958; Rowell *et al.*, 1958). Nutrition may also be involved since these conditions also favor photosynthesis in the host.

F. Gasteromycete Fruit Body

Sphaerobolus stellatus will fruit on a synthetic medium containing starch, $MgSO_4$, thiamine, asparagine, and a low concentration of phosphate providing the temperature does not exceed 20–25°C, and providing incubation occurs under a light intensity of at least 100 lux (Alasoadura,

1963). The band of light allowing fruiting is between 440 and 480 mμ. A high concentration of phosphate and presence of glucose or sucrose permits good vegetative growth, but not fruiting.

G. Hymenomycete Carpophore

1. Primordium

With the exception of *Sphaerobolus* (Alasoadura, 1963) the agarics and polypores are the only fleshy basidiomycetes which have been studied morphogenetically. In general the primordium of the ground agarics develops into a minute "bud" which often possesses gills while but a few millimeters high (Corner, 1934; Bonner *et al.*, 1956). Expansion of the nonphototropic button occurs at night (Corner, 1947). Placing primordia in a saturated atmosphere did not cause them to expand during the day, an observation suggesting that light or some factor other than moisture is required. The button is not characteristic of all agarics, however. The lignicolous *Lentinus lepideus* forms a primordium with a potentially indeterminate growing point resembling that of a polypore. The polypores and boletes typically form a primordium which develops into a cylindrical stipe with an organized growing point, and the pileus develops out of the tip after the stipe is mature. Unlike the button, the light-sensitive stipe expands during the day, profiting by phototropic stimuli. In all cases, however, there must exist a morphological and physiological change from continued growth of primary hyphae to establishment of secondary hyphae which can grow upright in an organized and integrated manner, thereby forming the primordium. That a real metabolic or physiological change has taken place can be demonstrated with *Lentinus lepideus* by a comparison of the form of growth that results from inoculating fresh nutrient media with tissue from a stipe or with vegetative, primary mycelium taken from the colony mat just adjacent to the stipe (Fig. 1). The stipe tissue gave rise to a colony from the lower end which was in contact with the agar and to a pileus from the upper end. The vegetative mycelium, however, produced only a colony which after many days gave rise to primordia—but from the vicinity of newly formed hyphae, not from the original inoculum site (Taber, 1963). This change in the capacity of hyphae is an aspect of morphogenesis that should lend itself well to laboratory experimentation.

2. Stipe and Pileus

a. Agaricaceae. For convenience of treatment, distinction is made between families, as in Ainsworth and Bisby (1961), because of the striking difference in the form of maturation of the commonly studied ground and coprophilous Agaricaceae and the lignicolous Polyporaceae (see Section II,

F, 1). However, the existence of lignicolous agarics like *Collybia velutipes, Lentinus lepideus,* and *Schizophyllum commune* and of new interpretations of family characteristics, reduces the usefulness of the distinction.

(1) *Schizophyllum commune.* This fungus has been the subject of intensive genetic and nutritional studies by J. R. Raper and his group

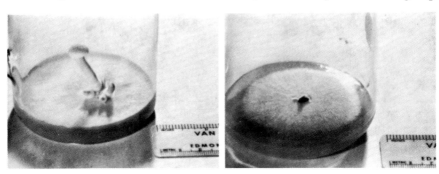

FIG. 1. *Left*: Fruit body of *Lentinus lepideus* which has developed 17 days after transfer of stipe tissue to fresh agar. The stipe tissue tip did not grow further, but gave rise to a pileus above and colony below. *Right*: Vegetative colony which resulted from transferring colony tissue adjacent to stipe used to inoculate culture on left. By 17 days fruit bodies had not developed although eventually 4 did develop, but from the vicinity of new hyphae, not from inoculum tissue (Taber, 1963).

(Raper, 1959, 1961a,b; Raper and San Antonio, 1954; Raper and Krongelb, 1958; Papazian, 1950). Fruiting typically requires formation of a heterokaryon resulting from fusion of two sexually compatible strains (Raper, 1961a).

S. commune grows readily and fruits on a medium of the following composition (Raper and Krongelb, 1958): glucose 20 gm; peptone, or DL-asparagine 2.0 gm; $MgSO_4$ 0.5 gm; KH_2PO_4 0.46 gm; K_2HPO_4 1 gm; thiamine·HCl 12 µg; agar 20 gm; distilled water to 1 liter. The inoculum, peptone, and agar undoubtedly supply the trace elements. The pyrimidine moiety of thiamine alone will not permit fruiting. Good fruiting is associated with restricted growth (e.g., restriction of colony growth with Rose Bengal dye) although not all compounds that restrict colony growth favor fruiting. Addition of yeast extract to the above medium delayed fruiting, presumably by prolonging the time which was favorable for growth. Fruiting took place between 5 and 42 days. Schopfer and Blumer (1940) found that thiamine is required but that some other natural compound is also required for copulation. Exhaustion of exogenous nutrients was found by Wakefield to favor fruiting (see Hawker, 1950).

Various carbon and nitrogen sources appear to support carpophore formation (Niederpreum, 1963). Asparagine, urea, glutamine, glutamic acid, serine, alanine, arginine, and ammonium phosphate were favorable nitrogen sources, and sucrose, maltose, trehalose, cellobiose, glucose, fructose, mannose, galactose, xylose, mannitol, glycerol, and ethanol were good carbon sources. By contrast, acetate and citrate were not satisfactory.

Of physical factors, only light appears to have been considered in detail. Light is required for normal fruiting, and 30–50 foot-candles of fluorescent light for 9 hours per day was sufficient. Niederpreum (1963) concluded that high CO_2 tension and high humidity inhibited fruiting.

(2) *Agaricus bisporus* (syn. *A. campestris* var. *bisporus, A. hortensis*). This fungus fruits readily on certain natural substrates which have been covered with soil or inorganic material such as gravel (Eger, 1961). The advantages conferred by such an environment may be due to both nutritional and physical properties, and a specific role of autotrophic microorganisms in the covering layer was proposed.

Light is inhibitory to fruit-body formation (Koch, 1958) and the carpophore once formed is not phototropic (Ingold, 1953). Buller has proposed that soil mushrooms are not phototropic whereas lignicolous and coprophilous ones are (Buller, 1924), but there is at least one exception (Galleymore, 1949).

Although other aspects of morphogenesis have been neglected (probably because of culturing difficulties), the mechanics of fruit body maturation has been examined in detail (Bonner et al., 1956). Development begins when the button is but 2 mm high. The button will eventually grow to a height of 10 cm. The gills and gill gaps are present at this early stage although the hyphae of the stipe are still irregularly arranged. By the time the button is 2 cm tall, all tissues are formed, so maturation of the stipe consists of elongation of existing cells. The area of most rapid increase in cell length is just behind the cap (Fig. 2). This was established

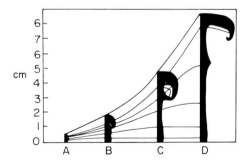

FIG. 2. A diagrammatic growth curve of *Agaricus campestris* showing region of expansion. The lines are drawn through homologous points. Reproduced from Bonner et al. (1956).

by placing carmine markings equidistantly along the button and noting the changes in distance between them as elongation continued. A threefold increase in height was accompanied by a similar increase in the length of cells in the region of rapid elongation. The slight increase in diameter of the stipe was accounted for by a commensurate increase in cell diameter. Elongation was accompanied by uptake of both water and nutrients into the carpophore. Expansion of the cap was effected by a gradient of expansion of the cells, the greatest amount occurring at the margin. When the area of elongation was excised and placed on moist agar it was capable of small but definite expansion. This would suggest that these cells were irreversibly committed to this form of development. Accumulation of volatile substances, some of which are not CO_2, may retard fruiting (Stoller, 1952). Buller (1909) concluded that pileus formation was controlled by internal factors since inverted buds developed normally.

The carbon dioxide level is critical, indicating that CO_2 plays some role in formation of the fruit body (Tschierpe and Sinden, 1964). These investigators found that normal fruiting of *A. bisporus* took place in an atmosphere of 0.05–0.06% air volume of CO_2; increasing the proportion to 0.1–0.18% of air volume retarded formation of fruit bodies as well as the number of fruit bodies.

Gases other than CO_2 may be involved, however, and evolution of ethylene, acetaldehyde, acetone, ethanol, and ethyl acetate as well as carbon dioxide by *A. bisporus* has been detected (Lockard, 1962).

(3) *Psilocybe mexicana*. The fruiting ability of this fungus has been studied by Heim *et al.* (1958) in the course of their investigation of the *in vitro* production of the hallucinogenic substances psilocybin and psilocyn. The carpophore develops on natural substrates, and a short exposure to light is required.

(4) *Coprinus lagopus*. The nutritional requirements for fruiting have been examined by Madelin (1956a,b). Fruiting occurred on a medium of the following composition: glucose 10 gm; DL-alanine 1 gm; K_2HPO_4 2 gm; $MgSO_4 \cdot 7\ H_2O$ 0.2 gm; thiamine·HCl 500 μg; agar 20 gm; distilled water to 1 liter. The minimal pH allowing growth was 4.5. It was also observed that, as the dry weight of the carpophore increased, the dry weight of the colony mycelium decreased. Fruiting occurred over a narrower range than vegetative growth (Madelin, 1956a), suggesting again that fruiting obeyed Klebs' laws of reproduction (Lilly and Barnett, 1951). Madelin found that glucose, maltose, fructose, starch, and xylose were acceptable carbon sources. Sucrose supported abundant mycelial growth but not fruiting, and growth did not occur on nitrate nitrogen. Ammonia nitrogen was used for vegetative growth but not fruiting, but Scheller-Correns (1957) reported that nitrate nitrogen was used. It is not possible

to determine from the literature whether the conflict between these reports is due to strain differences or to experimental conditions. Scheller-Correns observed fruiting on potassium nitrate, glycine, alanine, aspartic acid, valine, asparagine, and glutamic acid, the last two being best. Fruit bodies were not formed on phenylalanine, β-alanine, cysteine, serine, threonine or methionine, α-aminobutyric acid, leucine, isoleucine, arginine, or urea.

Approximately 25°C was optimal for growth and fruiting. Light was required for rapid carpophore formation, but a short exposure was sufficient (Scheller-Correns, 1957; Voderberg, 1950). After 14 days' growth in the dark, 10 seconds' exposure to 8 foot-candles, or 5 seconds at 2.5 foot-candles, was sufficient (Scheller-Correns, 1957). The culture became light sensitive on about the 7th or 8th day. White light was best, followed by blue, then blue-green, light. Green light was intermediate in effectiveness and yellow, orange, and red were almost without effect. Similar results were obtained by Borriss (1934a). Madelin (1956b) observed that fruiting took place on the 15th day when the culture was grown in the dark and by 7–13 days when grown in the light. This stimulation by light was not translocated to portions of the colony not exposed to light. The light receptor appears not to be a carotene (Schneiderhohn, 1955), and a yellow pigment was found which was not riboflavine.

Temperature also influences the development of the stipe (Borriss, 1934b). At 20°C in the dark, the stipe is exceptionally long and the pileus is but a knob whereas at 26°, the stipe is shorter and the pileus normal. Growth in darkness tends to produce "etiolated" carpophores, and both light and mechanical stimulation tend to minimize this response (Stiefel, 1952). Nematodes are not required to induce mechanical stimulation since the laboratory cultures were free of them (Borriss, 1934b). Borriss (1934a) studied the sequence of development of the carpophore and noted that development occurred in two phases: the fruit body separates from the vegetative mycelium during the first phase, and it develops (expands) independently of the mycelium during the second phase. It is believed that water was not taken up during the second phase, and interaction between the stipe and pileus is postulated. If the pileus were removed during the first phase, stipe elongation ceased (possibly because the site of evaporation which provided force for upward translocation had been removed), but they developed independently during the second phase. Translocation, which is dependent upon the pileus, occurs during the first phase, but not the second. Under constant environmental conditions there occurred a periodicity or endogenous rhythm of fruit body growth during the first phase. Elongation was believed not to be due to changes in turgor, elasticity, osmotic values, or absorbing power. Fruit body formation was not dependent upon a specific humidity (Borriss, 1934a).

(5) *Coprinus sassii*. Strains of this fungus were found to be amphithallic, producing both homothallic and heterothallic mycelium (Bille-Hansen, 1953a).

Fruit bodies were formed when the culture was incubated in the light at 17–19°C on a medium consisting of maltose 10 gm; $MgSO_4$ 0.5 gm; $Ca(NO_3)_2$ 0.5 gm; K_2HPO_4 0.25 gm; thiamine·HCl 50 µg; agar 10 gm; distilled water to 1 liter. The inoculum was an agar disk, and 15 ml of medium was dispensed per 100-ml Erlenmeyer flask. When asparagine was used as the nitrogen source, vegetative growth was luxurious but fruiting did not occur. Neither sucrose nor glucose was a satisfactory carbon source for fruiting. Fruiting of *C. heptemerus* and *C. congregatus* was also studied (Bille-Hansen, 1953b). The stipe of *Coprinus cinereus* (*C. lagopus*?) is phototropic (see Chapter 21).

(6) *Collybia velutipes*. Dikaryons synthesized from various monokaryons differed in capacity to form fruit bodies (Aschan, 1954a; Aschan-Aberg, 1960a,b). *C. velutipes* is tetrapolar. Fruit bodies are occasionally formed by haploid mycelia, however. A study of dikaryotization and capacity of strains to form fruit bodies has been conducted by Aschan-Aberg. Normal fruit bodies developed only when the two pairs of genes which most influence the dikaryotization process are different at both the A and B loci. If the alleles at the B locus are identical whereas those at the A locus are not, clamps are formed only at the contact zone and these hyphae give rise only to primordia or half-developed fruit bodies under the culture conditions used. Formation of fruit bodies has been shown by Zattler (see Aschan-Aberg 1960a) to have a genetic basis, segregating as though depending on one Mendelian pair of genes. Thus genetic factors other than mating type are involved in fruiting.

Nutritional requirements for fruiting have been examined (Aschan, 1954a,b; Aschan-Aberg, 1958). A synthetic medium (Min_1) has the following composition: glucose 20 gm; ammonium tartrate 9 gm; KH_2PO_4 7 gm; $MgSO_4·7 H_2O$ 2.5 gm; ferric citrate 5 mg; thiamine 50 µg; $MnSO_4·4 H_2O$ 20 mg; $ZnSO_4·7 H_2O$ 20 mg; NaCl 100 mg; $CaCl_2$ 100 mg; distilled H_2O to 1 liter, pH 5.3. Although growth will occur in the pH range of 4.0 to 8.0, fruiting occurs in a narrower range. A pH of 4.6 was the lowest allowing fruiting according to Aschan (1954b), and 5.2 was the lowest observed by Plunkett (1953). Once primordia were formed, however, fruit bodies formed at lower pH's. Fruiting occurred in 25 days when 25 ml of this medium contained in 125-ml Erlenmeyer flasks were inoculated with an agar disk (Aschan-Aberg, 1958). Thiamine was required for growth (Marczynski, 1943) although the concentration is not critical (Aschan, 1954b). Addition of folic acid and other B vitamins did not influence fruiting (Aschan-Aberg, 1958), nor did hydolyzed nucleic acid, yeast extract, tryptophan, and agar. Glucose was the best carbon source, followed by sucrose then maltose. Indoleacetic acid stimulated fruiting slightly (Aschan-Aberg, 1958). This substance can force formation of the stipelike synnema of *Isaria cretacea* (Taber, 1960). Ammonium tartrate was the best nitrogen source examined, followed by ammonium chloride and asparagine. The efficacy of nitrogen sources depended in part on their influence on pH as growth commenced. Plunkett (1953) obtained fruiting on a medium containing a high ratio of sucrose to asparagine. In general, it would appear that high concentrations of the carbon source and low concentrations of nitrogen source are favorable for fruiting. However, it is difficult to translate this into terms of metabolism or physiology.

Some influences of the physical environment have been identified. *C. velutipes* will develop primordia and stipe in the dark, but normal development of the pileus requires light. When cultures are exposed to light through Wratten and Jena glass filters, it was found that wavelengths longer than 470 mμ are without effect on pileus development (Aschan-Aberg, 1960b). Aiki (cited by Aschan-Aberg, 1960b) found that pilei were formed in violet, but not green, orange, or red, light. Blue-sensitive processes are often assumed to be mediated by yellow pigments, but Aschan-Aberg did not detect carotenes or riboflavine in the fruits although only strains which were yellowish were capable of fruiting.

A pretreatment of 1 week of darkness followed by light decreased the time required for fruiting from 5 to 4 weeks (Aschan-Aberg, 1958). The culture was incubated at 25° in the dark and 15° in the light. Plunkett (1956) concluded that darkness restrains cap expansion without preventing stipe elongation. Only a weak phototropic response of stipes and young fruit bodies has been observed (Taber, 1963).

Carbon dioxide tension may be important in fruiting, for a flowing air stream favored fruiting (Plunkett, 1956) as a result of removing CO_2 or other staling substances. It was found that 5% CO_2 atmosphere retarded stipe growth and lower concentrations retarded pileus development. Both darkness and high CO_2 tension restrained cap expansion without preventing stipe elongation. Long (1962) found that a high CO_2 tension (3%) caused light-induced cultures to grow as if they were in the dark; that is, the cap did not expand. Carbon dioxide appears to be the gas involved since the presence of KOH removes the inhibitory effect (Plunkett, 1956). The beneficial effect of moving air is to remove CO_2 since maturation of *C. velutipes* is not favored by low humidity. *Polyporus brumalis* (see Section II, G, 2, b i), on the other hand, responds favorably to air flow because the resulting low humidity accelerates translocation.

Chloramphenicol, an inhibitor of protein synthesis, prevented fruit body formation only when primordia were less than 1 cm high, an observation indicating again that expansion may involve a minimum of cell synthesis (Long, 1962).

(7) *Lentinus tuber-regium.* This carpophore develops from a sclerotium, and light is required for fruit body but not sclerotium development (Galleymore, 1949).

(8) *Lentinus lepideus.* Buller (1933) observed that this fungus requires light for pileus development. He postulated that, since ground agarics such as *Agaricus campestris* grow on an essentially horizontal surface, response to light is not necessary for orientation whereas tree agarics require such orientation. Oddly, response to gravity occurs only in the light, but the stipe of *L. lepideus* continues to grow in the dark (Taber, 1963). The development of the primordium has been discussed in Section II, G, 1. The fungus fruits readily on potato-dextrose agar when incubated at 20°C in the light (Fig. 1).

(9) *Armillaria mellea.* Translocation in this fungus has been studied by Schutte (1956) and reviewed by Hill (Volume I, Chapter 16).

(10) *Pleurotus ostreatus.* This agaric fruits on a partially synthetic medium containing cellulose, peptone, salts, and thiamine after 40–150 days' incubation, if illuminated (Koch, 1958).

b. *Polyporaceae.* (1) *Polyporus brumalis.* A series of very concise and ingenious experiments by Plunkett (1956, 1958, 1961) on this fungus, and on *Collybia velutipes,* have revealed much of what is known of the role of the physical environment on carpophore morphogenesis. *P. brumalis* is dimetic, having thin-walled generative hyphae and thick-walled branching binding hyphae. This fungus does not form a button but develops a tubular stipe whose undifferentiated growing point of generative hyphae grows into the air for some distance before fanning out and differentiating into tissues which then form the cap and hymenial layer. This is a strikingly different mode of growth and development from that of many ground Agaricaceae which produce a miniature mushroom in the primordium; this mushroom then matures by expansion of the preformed pseudo-tissue. *P. brumalis* fruits on 4% malt extract broth. It has an unusually restricted pH range for growth of from 3.1 to 5.1 and fruits in a narrower range, near pH 4.1. Fruiting occurs readily from 15° to 25°C.

Light is important in the development of the fruit body and, also in its orientation. Carpophore primordia form in the dark although they are more numerous when incubated in the light. Exposure to darkness results in short, thick stipes as contrasted to the effect of such exposure in the case of certain agarics. Continuous exposure of 40 foot-candles of incandescent light was not sufficient to allow normal fruiting, but exposure to 160 foot-candles was. A high transpiration rate, which is brought about by low humidity, leads to rapid translocation which may favor fruiting, but the light stimulation is not a result of acceleration of transpiration rate.

The effect of humidity on fruiting was studied using a chamber similar to that shown in Fig. 3. The water level was kept constant by use of a reservoir, and air of varying humidity was continuously passed through

FIG. 3. Modified Plunkett chamber. Culture medium is sterilized *in situ* in the culture beakers. When cool, the level of liquid in the culture beakers is raised by attachment of reservoir at top, which contains sterile water. Sterile air is passed through the cotton-filled tube on right and is discharged below the supporting plate.

the chamber. The number of fruit bodies produced under a given set of conditions varied too much to be used as an index of fruiting capacity. Plunkett used the ratio of stipe length to pileus diameter ($1/d$) since these two forms of growth are usually competitive. The relative humidity (RH) of air entering and leaving the chamber was measured. In an example the RH of ingoing air was 0, 75, and 96% and of outgoing air was 69.5, 88, and 96.5%, respectively. The flow rates of air were 200, 200, and 5 ml/minute, and the rate of water loss per culture (in $mg/cm^2/hr$) was calculated. Plunkett found that low humidity and, therefore, high transpiration favored pileus development. Water loss from the fungus at 6 times the rate which suppressed pileus development in *C. velutipes* was favorable for pileus expansion. Reducing the water loss from 6.5 to 0.0015 mg/cm^2/hour suppressed pileus expansion. With increasing light intensity the amount of water loss required to effect a given amount of pileus expansion decreased. Thus light and low humidity were additive in favoring expansion but were not interchangeable. In still, nearly water-saturated air, the pileus does not develop but the stipe continues to elongate. Addition of 5% CO_2 to the air or washing it with $KMnO_4$ did not influence expansion, unlike the situation with *C. velutipes,* so it was concluded that moisture was the component of the atmosphere which influenced pileus development. Mader (1943) believed that under some circumstances other volatiles are effective. After Plunkett found that low humidity favored pileus expansion, he designed experiments to determine whether it was due to enhanced translocation into the carpophore (1958). Under conditions of low humidity (high transpiration), the uptake of the dyes fluorescein and trypan blue was rapid. Carpophores which had been killed by chloroform vapor did not take up the dyes. Furthermore, low humidities led to increased dry weight in the growing tip of the stipe. Light did not increase dye uptake in Plunkett's experiments, adding further weight to the supposition that light did not favor cap development through a stimulation of the rate of transpiration.

Some fruit bodies are known to be both phototropic and geotropic, and Buller (1933) postulated that the stipe is negatively geotropic and the dissepiments positively geotropic. Plunkett (1961) provided a different explanation for the role of phototropic and geotropic responses in *P. brumalis*. The stipe was found to be positively phototropic at first and then negatively geotropic. Placing an artificial pileus (cardboard disk, Fig. 4) over the stipe tip shaded it and blocked phototropism and allowed expression of negative geotropism. Thus, from this and other experiments, it was concluded that the stipe is both positively phototropic and negatively geotropic but that when both stimuli are present the phototropic stimulus takes precedence. Under normal conditions response to light brings the stipe tip into the air. Then light stimulates expansion of the tip into the cap which then shields the tip from light, thus allowing expression of the negative response to gravity. Subsequent light would have but little effect since by the time the cap extends the growth potential of the subapical region is all but exhausted. Further, the remaining area of growth under the cap is so close to the top that any curvature in response to light would be almost immediately stopped as a result of renewed shading brought about by the curvature. When cultures were illuminated from below, growth was

12. *Morphogenesis in Basidiomycetes* 401

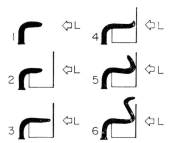

FIG. 4. Demonstration that phototropic response overrides geotropic response. In the presence of unilateral light (*1*) growth proceeds toward the light source and in defiance of gravity. When a shield is placed between light source and stipe (*2–5*), geotropic response is expressed. When light once again strikes the stipe (*6*) the phototropic reaction once again takes over. Reproduced from Plunkett (1961).

toward the light source. The orientation of the pileus was reversed with reference to the substratum, but not to the stipe. That is, the gill area faced upward and the morphological upper surface of the pileus faced downward (Fig. 5). There are, apparently, two positions of null response to gravity: when the stipe is vertical, either pointing upward or downward. The carpophore always grew so as to place the morphologically upper surface of the pileus toward the strongest light source. Changing the position with respect to the gravitational field did not alter this response.

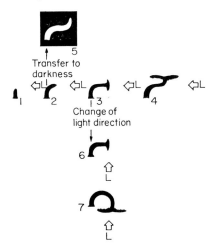

FIG. 5. Demonstration that growth of the stipe proceeds toward a light source until the growth area is shaded by the pileus and that light from below can result in inverted growth. In the latter case, however, development is normal in the sense that the morphologically upper surface of the pileus is closest to the light. Reproduced from Plunkett (1961).

(2) *Serpula lacrimans.* Lippe and Nesemann (1959) determined conditions under which this fungus formed fruit bodies on agar in the laboratory. Fruiting followed 18 weeks' incubation at 16°C on a medium having a pH of 5.8 and the following composition: sucrose, DL-α-alanine, threonine, salts, and agar. With sucrose as the carbon source, 16 of 22 amino acids and amides examined allowed fruiting when used as the sole source of nitrogen. A combination of NH_4Cl and KNO_3 also allowed fruiting if the nitrogen concentration was sufficiently low. Glucose was not a satisfactory carbon source for fruiting. The cultures were illuminated 9 hours per day with fluorescent light and received about 400–600 lux.

(3) *Polyporus versicolor.* This polypore fruits if given light and grown on a medium containing glucose, alanine, thiamine, and salts (Koch, 1958). Fructose and glycerol are satisfactory carbon sources and ammonium chloride, ammonium tartrate, arginine, asparagine, glutamic acid, glycine, and aspartic acid are suitable nitrogen sources. At least 1000 lux per day were required for fruiting.

(4) *Ganoderma lucidum.* Abundant fruit bodies and vegetative growth occurred when cultures were grown 16 weeks at 20°C on an agar medium consisting of: a carbon source 5 gm; nitrogen source 0.425 gm; KH_2PO_4 2.0 gm; $MgSO_4 \cdot 7\ H_2O$ 0.5 mg; $FeCl_3 \cdot H_2O$ 0.8 gm; $ZnSO_4 \cdot 7\ H_2O$ 0.9 gm; $MnSO_4 \cdot 4\ H_2O$ 0.4 gm; $Ca(NO_3)_2$, and thiamine 2 mg each per liter. Calcium was said to be necessary for fruiting, but its beneficial effect may have been due to its interaction with an excessive amount of some other ion.

(5) *Poria ambigua.* This fungus provides the only reported example of the retention of the light stimulus by the mycelium, where it is expressed in subsequent darkness (Robbins and Hervey, 1960). When the inoculum was exposed for a few minutes to bright light and then transferred to darkness, fruiting was induced although a second exposure to light was beneficial. The stimulus of the two light exposures was believed not to be qualitatively different but were additive. When using a rich malt extract medium only one exposure was required. Three growth factors were postulated: (x) formed in the light and required for fruiting; (y) whose formation was interfered with by light and which was required for vegetative growth, and (z) whose formation is favored by light but which is limiting for growth in the dark and in the presence of large amounts of (y).

(6) *Lenzites trabea.* A study of genetic regulation of fruiting has been carried out by Barnett and Lilly (1947). Cultures were grown 6–8 weeks at 25°C on 20 ml of 2% malt extract agar. Absence of clamp connections was used as a criterion of haploidy. The culture characteristics of haplonts and diplonts differed significantly, and dediploidization frequently oc-

curred, giving rise to sectors. When haplonts, isolated as germlings, were crossed many produced fruits. However, 17 of 30 haplonts also fruited. Spore lines obtained from a haplont fruit body were all incompatible with the parent haplont but were compatible with other haplonts.

c. *Nidulariales fruit body.* (1) *Cyathus stercoreus.* This "bird's nest fungus" will fruit on semisynthetic media (Brodie, 1948). Recent studies have shown that light is required for fruit body formation. Lu (1965) found that a certain amount of light (blue light being best) was required to initiate fruiting; a photoinductive constant was calculated and found to be 17,200 foot-candle hours at 25°C. As the light intensity was increased, the fewer hours of exposure were required. Cultures were grown 15 days in the dark and then exposed to light. Under the specified conditions the time required for fruiting (Y) could be calculated by the formula $Y = 17256/I \cdot X$ where I is light intensity, X is number of hours of exposure per day. It was hypothesized that precursors form during growth in the dark and that a photoreceptive precursor brings about photoinduction.

3. Gill and Hymenium

The gill is the site of compact, regularly formed tissue and of differentiated cells such as the basidium, spore, cystidium, basidioles and other sterile elements (cf. Chapter 5). Pressure and localized positive phototropism probably play roles in determining the shape of these structures. Pressure resulting from continued expansion of tissues in the confinement of the underside of the pileus could lead in part to a folding which might lead to the formation of gills or pores; and pressure of adjoining cells and differential laying down of rigid cell walls during growth could lead to the cylindrical form of the basidium and allied cells (see Corner, 1934). In any event, the formation of these various types of cells results ultimately from unequal growth, and about this little is known.

That the gills and spores of many mushrooms orient themselves to the vertical by slight growth adjustments which may be due to differential inflation of cells at the base of the gill (cf. Chapter 21) is well known. The gill possibly is positively geotropic (Plunkett, 1956), so gravity may assist in the regulation of forms, but this does not explain how unequal growth within the cell is effected.

III. MORPHOGENETIC FACTORS

A. Genetical

The genes provide the blueprints of the various proteins and, in addition, provide incompatibility mechanisms which reduce the chance of inbreeding and subsequent loss of "nonessential" reproductive capabilities. But little is known of the actual role of genes in morphogenesis although the mechanisms proposed by Jacob and Monod (1961) for the control of protein synthesis may be involved (cf. Volume I, Chapter 14).

B. Physical

As stated at the beginning of this chapter, morphogenesis in basidiomycetes is a function of a series of unequal growth patterns. Unequal growth cannot occur unless polarization occurs. Known exogenous factors which can influence growth unilaterally are light, gravity, pressure, temperature, moisture, gases, air currents, and, possibly, magnetic fields. Light is the most thoroughly studied of these forces (Table I; see also Volume I, Chapter 23). In *Coprinus sterquilinus* light prevents development of primordia on the surface of dung (Buller, 1924). This has survival value because only primordia seated deeply enough in the substratum to support the fruit body actually can develop into fruit bodies. Response to unilateral light also results in the upward orientation of stipes of gymnocarpic, lignicolous hymenomycetes; in addition, light in some manner institutes differentiation at the stipe tip, thereby starting pileus development. In some species, pileate fruit bodies grow in such a way that the cap is always directed toward the light source. A general observation is that only short wavelengths are active on fungi. The role of gravity was evaluated in Section II, G, 3. That the seven external physical forces play a role in determining form is unquestionable but just how they interact with metabolic processes to bring about unequal syntheses within the cell is completely unknown.

C. Nutritional

Numerous examples of the influence of the nutrient medium on fruit body morphogenesis have been cited in this chapter. Evaluation of nutritional data is difficult because the composition and concentration of nutrients such as carbon, nitrogen, phosphorus, and salts may influence growth through effects on pH and other variables. A favorable concentration of an ion may be due to its interaction with another ion which is present in otherwise too high a concentration. The influence of nutrients may also be the result of the formation of staling substances. These influences are therefore no doubt mostly indirect, and a possible explanation of their role is given below.

D. Endogenous Nutrition and Physiology

Nutrition is the utilization of food stuffs for growth and hence relates to morphogenesis in that it provides the substance and energy for synthesis of primary and secondary hyphae. It is possible that exogenous growth factors play an additional role in morphogenesis by triggering secondary growth. A speculation as to this role is as follows: primary (or essen-

TABLE I
INFLUENCE OF EXOGENOUS PHYSICAL FACTORS ON NORMAL FRUITING

Fungus	Habitat	High CO_2,[a]	Low humidity	Temperature range (°C)	Geotropic response[b]	Primordium development	Light — Stipe elongation	Light — Pileus expansion	Light — Phototropic response	pH range
Agaricus campestris[c]	Ground	Pileus inhibited	Unfavorable	10–24 (21)	Stipe weak	Inhibitory	Inhibitory	Inhibitory	None	6.9–8
Coprinus lagopus[d]	Ground, dung	—	—	ca. 25	Stipe weak	Inhibited	Base suppressed	Required	Strong	4–9
Coprinus sterquilinus	Dung	—	—	—	Stipe and gill weak	Inhibited	Base suppressed	Required	Strong	—
Schizophyllum commune	Tree	Unfavorable	May be favorable	22	—	—	—	Required	—	—
Collybia velutipes	Tree, base	Pileus inhibited	Not favorable	10–20 (15)	Strong	Not required	Not required	Required	Strong	5.2–7.2
Polyporus brumalis	Tree	Not inhibitory	Favorable for pileus	15–25 (20)	Strong	Not required	Not required	Required	Strong	4.1
Lentinus lepideus	Tree	—	—	ca. 20	Strong in light	Not required	Not required	Required	Strong	ca. 5.5

[a] Ca 1% CO_2.
[b] Gill may be positively phototropic and stipe negatively geotropic.
[c] Laboratory cultures in some studies may have been *A. bisporus*.
[d] *Coprinus comatus*, a strict ground form is not phototropic.

tially colony growth) continues as long as no critical exogenous nutrient becomes limiting, and as long as staling does not become excessive. During primary growth, endogenous nutrients such as polyols, carbohydrates, amino sugars, lipids, polyphosphates, and nitrogenous compounds accumulate. Eventually some exogenous nutrient becomes limiting and primary growth, or cellular synthesis, either ceases or becomes drastically reduced. Upon the cessation of primary growth, secondary growth (formation of sporophores) then is initiated and proceeds along the line dictated by the genetic constitution. Endogenous nutrients, and perhaps some exogenous ones, are then used in respiration and synthesis of the secondary hyphae which will make up the fruit body.

If this hypothesis is correct, then it should be possible to detect changes in the content and extent of growth of the primary mycelium. Madelin reported a decrease in dry weight of the mycelium as the fruit body develops, and Aschan-Aberg detected changes in the content of nitrogen and phosphorus compounds. Further, Kulaev et al. (1960) found differences in the chemical composition of the fruit body. Mention has already been made of cessation of colony growth before fruiting.

Hormones or some form of endogenous growth regulators appear to be involved in development of the carpophore (Gruen, 1963; Hagimoto and Konishi, 1959). Gruen determined the influence of the cap on stipe development and obtained evidence that an endogenous growth factor present in the lamellae stimulates stipe elongation. The lamellae were also the site of a substance controlling cap trama expansion. Transmission of the growth factor stimulating stipe growth occurred either through hyphae at the base of the cap adjacent to the lamellae, or directly through the lamellae to the cap-stipe juncture.

E. Biochemical

Biochemical investigations of morphogenesis in the Basidiomycetes have been few. While no single biochemical step can explain morphogenesis, interactions, regulation, and inheritance, must be the ultimate basis of morphogenesis.

IV. MECHANICAL AND MATHEMATICAL ANALYSIS OF FRUIT BODY

Economy of cellular synthesis, and efficiency in use of the environment by extensive growth and dispersal of propagules are certainly manifested in the Hymenomycetes. Mutation and selection have apparently led to development of an efficient means of bringing genetically different nuclei together without necessitating utilization of sex organs, and hence the synthesis of such structures is not required. Irrespective of the form of a given "mushroom," it confers a high degree of efficiency in coping with the environment.

The central stipitate umbrella form of fruit body provides maximal strength with minimal interference with spore dispersal for fungi growing on a horizontal surface. The cap typically tapers toward the margin or is thin and flat, thus avoiding excess weight for the stipe to support. Often the stipe is hollow, thereby conferring the most strength to resist lateral pressure to a beam of given length and amount of structural material. Movement of the gill only 5 degrees from the vertical may result in most of the spores being lost to the neighboring gill rather than being properly dispersed. *Russula,* which has a heavy pileus, may have a solid, short stipe which makes the fruit body rigid and hence prevents swaying, as well as resists downward pressure on the thick pileus (Buller, 1909). Such a stipe cannot respond fully to geotropism and the gill is brought to the vertical by differential growth changes at the base of the gill. Those fruit bodies with a longer and more slender stipe (such as coprophilous ones) respond more readily to forces such as gravity and light.

1. *Russula ochroleuca*

Ingold (1953) analyzed the dimensions of this and other fungi mathematically and concluded that their stipe length and diameter were just sufficient to serve their supportive and disseminative functions. Small-capped agarics tend to have slender stipes and appear to be "tall" while those with large caps have thick stipes and appear to be "short." The weight of the cap, which is proportionate to its volume, is distributed evenly over the cross section of the stipe. A solid structure of constant shape but varying in size, such as the pileus, will vary in volume (or weight) as the cube of the linear dimension whereas the stipe area will vary as the square of its diameter. Therefore, the pileus and stipe diameters will change in proportion to one another with changing size. Further, natural selection will select for shorter stipes among fungi with large pilei. Shorter stipes among small pileate species would not be selected for because this type of structure would impede lateral dispersal of spores. That cellular syntheses and physiological processes often are selected for in accordance with economic considerations is well established (Davis, 1961).

Fruit bodies of most lignicolous species developing from a vertical surface bear either no stipe or a lateral or eccentric stipe. The advantages that are conferred are conservation of stipe material and little interference with spore drop. Unlike soil fungi such as *Agaricus campestris* and *Coprinus comatus,* which possess a thick stipe and pileus, the lignicolous ones are phototropic and geotropic. Phototropism brings the primordium into the open and geotropism assures that it is upright with the result that the gills are vertical.

Evolution has led to development of hymenial layers with increased efficiency in the production of spores. Thus, an evolutionary trend can be visualized leading from the Thelephoraceae with smooth, flat hymenia to polypores with the most hymenial surface area to pileus area (Buller, 1934).

In studying the relative efficiency of the gill and pore in providing large surface area, Buller (1934) expressed the ratio of hymenial surface area (H) to pileus underside surface area (A) as $H:A$. Theoretically the ratio for the Thelephoraceae with no folding would be 1. The $H:A$ ratio for agarics ranged from 7 for *Russula citrina* to 20 for *Agaricus campestris*. The ratio for polypores ranged up to 148 for annuals and almost 500 for perennials such as *Fomes vegetus*.

The examples of mechanical efficiency in fruit body form are many, and since this topic merges with that of developmental morphology, which is not dealt with here, the reader is referred to the volumes of Buller (1909-1934), Thompson (1952), and Wardlaw (1952) and Chapter 21 of this volume.

REFERENCES

Ainsworth, G. C., and G. R. Bisby. (1961). "Ainsworth and Bisby's Dictionary of Fungi," 547 pp. Commonwealth Mycological Institute, Kew, Surrey.

Alasoadura, S. O. (1963). Fruiting in Sphaerobolus with special reference to light. *Ann. Botany (London)* [N.S.] 27:123-145.

Aschan, K. (1954a). Some facts concerning the incompatibility groups, the dicaryotization and the fruit body production in *Collybia velutipes*. *Svensk Botani. Tidskr.* 48:603-625.

Aschan, K. (1954b). The problem of fruit bodies in *Collybia velutipes*. I. Influence of different culture conditions. *Physiol. Plantarum* 7:571-591.

Aschan-Aberg, K. (1958). The production of fruit bodies in *Collybia velutipes*. II. Further studies on the influence of different culture conditions. *Physiol. Plantarum* 11:312-328.

Aschan-Aberg, K. (1960a). Studies on mono- and di-caryotic mycelia of *Collybia velutipes*. *Physiol. Plantarum* 13:280-297.

Aschan-Aberg, K. (1960b). The production of fruit bodies in Collybia velutipes. III. Influence of the quality of light. *Physiol. Plantarum* 13:276-279.

Badcock, E. C. (1943). Method for obtaining fructifications of wood-rotting fungi in culture. *Brit. Mycol. Soc. Trans.* 26:127-132.

Barnett, H. L., and V. G. Lilly. (1947). Production of haploid and diploid fruit bodies in *Lenzites trabea* in culture. *Proc. West Va. Acad. Sci.* 19:34-39.

Bille-Hansen, E. (1953a). Fructification of a coprophilous Coprinus on synthetic medium. *Physiol. Plantarum* 6:523-528.

Bille-Hansen, E. (1953b). Fructification of three coprophilous species of Coprinus using glucose, sucrose, and maltose as carbon source. *Svensk Botan. Tidskr.* 50:81-85.

Bonner, J. T., K. K. Kane, and R. H. Levey. (1956). Studies on the mechanics of growth in the common mushroom, *Agaricus campestris*. *Mycologia* 48:13-19.
Borriss, H. (1934a). Beiträge zur Wachstums und Entwicklungsphysiologie der Fruchtkorper von *Coprinus lagopus*. *Planta* 22:28-69.
Borriss, H. (1934b). Über den Einfluss ausser Faktoren auf Wachstum und Entwicklung der Fruchtkorper von *Coprinus lagopus*. *Planta* 22:644-684.
Brodie, H. J. (1948). Variation in fruit bodies of *Cyathus stercoreus* produced in culture. *Mycologia* 40:614-626.
Buller, A. H. R. (1909). "Researches on Fungi," Vol. I. pp. 1-287. Longmans, Green, New York.
Buller, A. H. R. (1922). "Researches on Fungi," Vol. II, pp. 1-492. Longmans, Green, New York.
Buller, A. H. R. (1924). "Researches on Fungi," Vol. III, pp. 1-611. Longmans, Green, New York.
Buller, A. H. R. (1931). "Researches on Fungi," Vol. IV, pp. 1-329. Longmans, Green, New York.
Buller, A. H. R. (1933). "Researches on Fungi," Vol. V, pp. 1-416. Longmans, Green, New York.
Buller, A. H. R. (1934). "Researches on Fungi," Vol. VI, pp. 1-513. Longmans, Green, New York.
Butler, G. M. (1957). The development and behavior of mycelial strands in *Merulius lacrymans* (Wulf.) Fr. I. Strand development during growth from a food base through a non-nutrient medium. *Ann. Botany (London)* [N.S.] 21:523-537.
Butler, G. M. (1958). The development and behaviour of mycelial strands in *Merulius lacrymans* (Wulf.) Fr. II. Hyphal behaviour during strand formation. *Ann. Botany (London)* [N.S.] 22:219-236.
Butler, G. M. (1961). Growth of hyphal branching systems in *Coprinus disseminatus*. *Ann. Botany (London)* [N.S.] 25:341-352.
Corner, E. J. H. (1934). An evolutionary study in the Agarics: *Collybia apalusarca* and the veils. *Brit. Mycol. Soc. Trans.* 19:39-88.
Corner, E. J. H. (1947). Variation in size and shape of spores basidia and cystidia in Basidiomycetes. *New Phytologist* 46:195-228.
Davis, B. D. (1961). Opening address: Telenomic significance of biosynthetic control mechanisms. *Cold Spring Harbor Symp. Quant. Biol.* 26:1-10.
Denyer, W. B. G. (1960). Cultural studies of *Flammula alnicola* (Fr.) Kummer and *Flammula conissans* (Fr.) Gillet. *Can. J. Botany* 38:909-920.
Eger, G. (1961). Untersuchungen über die Funktion der Deckschicht bei der Fruchtkorperbildung des Kulturchampignons *Psalliota bispora* Lge. *Arch. Mikrobiol.* 39:313-334.
Falck, R. (1912). Die Merulius Fäule des Bauholzes, *Hausschwammforsch.* 6:1-465.
Galleymore, H. B. (1949). The development of fructifications of *Lentinus tuberregium* Fries in culture. *Brit. Mycol. Soc. Trans.* 32:315-317.
Garrett, S. D. (1953). Rhizomorph behaviour in *Armillaria mellea* (Vahl) Quèl. I. Factors affecting rhizomorph initiation by *A. mellea* in pure culture. *Ann. Botany (London)* [N.S.] 17:63-79.
Garrett, S. D. (1956). Rhizomorph behaviour in *Armillaria mellea* (Vahl) Quèl. II. Logistics of infection. *Ann. Botany (London)* [N.S.] 20:193-209.
Gäumann, E. A. (1952). "The Fungi. A Description of their Morphological Features and Evolutionary Development," 420 pp. Hafner, New York.
Gruen, H. E. (1963). Endogenous growth regulation in carpophores of *Agaricus bisporus*. *Plant Physiol.* 38:652-666.

Hagimoto, H., and M. Konishi. (1959). Studies on the growth of fruit body of fungi. I. Existence of a hormone active to the growth of fruit body in *Agaricus bisporus* (Lange) Singer. *Botan. Mag. (Tokyo)* **72**:359-366.

Hawker, L. E. (1950). "Physiology of Fungi," 360 pp. Oxford Univ. Press (Univ. London), London and New York.

Hawker, L. E. (1957). "The Physiology of Reproduction in Fungi," 128 pp. Cambridge Univ. Press, London and New York.

Heim, R., A. Brack, H. Kobel, A. Hofmann, and R. Cailleux. (1958). Déterminisme de la formation des carpophores et des sclérotes dans la culture du *"Psilocybe mexicana,"* agaric halucinogène du mexique, et mise en évidence de la Psilocybine et de la Psilocine. *Compt. Rend.* **246**:1346-1352.

Hein, I. (1930). Studies on the mycelium of *Psalliota campestris*. *Am. J. Botany* **17**:197-211.

Ingold, C. T. (1953). "Dispersal in Fungi," 197 pp. Oxford Univ. Press (Clarendon), London and New York.

Jacob, F., and J. Monod. (1961). On the regulation of gene activity. *Cold Spring Harbor Symp. Quant. Biol.* **26**:193-211.

Koch, W. (1958). Untersuchungen über Mycelwachstum und Fruchtkorperbildung bei einigen Basidiomyceten (*Polystictus versicolor, Polyporus annosus, Pleurotus ostreatus* and *Psaliota bispora*). *Arch. Mikrobiol.* **30**:409-432.

Kulaev, I. S., M. S. Kritskii, and A. N. Belozerskii. (1960). Metabolism of polyphosphates and of other phosphorus compounds during the development of the mushroom *Agaricus bisporus* fruit bodies. *Biochemistry (USSR) (English Transl.)* **25**:735-748.

Lilly, V. G., and H. L. Barnett. (1951). "Physiology of Fungi," 464 pp. McGraw-Hill, New York.

Lippe, T. Z., and G. Nesemann. (1959). Über die Fruchtkorperbildung von *Merulius lacrymans domesticus* Falck. *Arch. Mikrobiol.* **34**:132-148.

Lockard, J. D. (1962). An investigation of the metabolic gases produced by the cultivated mushroom, *Agaricus bisporus* (Lange) Sing. 78 pp. Ph.D. thesis, Pennsylvania State University.

Lohwag, K. (1952). Zu Fruchtkorperbildung Holzzerstorender hoher Pilzen Reinkultur. *Sydowia* **6**:323-335.

Long, T. J. (1962). The effects of chloramphenicol and 8-azaguanine on normal and abnormal sporocarp development in the mushroom *Collybia velutipes*. *Am. J. Botany* **49**:655.

Lu, B. C. (1965). The role of light in fructification of the basidiomycete *Cyathus stercoreus* (Schw) de Toni. *Am. J. Botany* **52**:432-437.

Madelin, M. F. (1956a). Studies on the nutrition of *Coprinus lagopus* Fr. Especially as affecting fruiting. *Ann. Botany (London)* [N.S.] **20**:307-330.

Madelin, M. F. (1956b). The influence of light and temperature on fruiting of *Coprinus lagopus* Fr. in pure culture. *Ann. Botany (London)* [N.S.] **20**:467-480.

Mader, E. O. (1943). Some factors inhibiting the fructification and production of the cultivated mushroom, *Agaricus campestris* L. *Phytopathology*. **33**:1134-1145.

Marczynski, R. (1943). Studies on the nutrition of *Collybia velutipes* (Curt) Quel. (Homobasidiomycetes, Agaricales). *Am. Midland Naturalist* **30**:164-170.

Mathew, K. T. (1961). Morphogenesis of mycelial strands in the cultivated mushroom, *Agaricus bisporus*. *Brit. Mycol. Soc. Trans.* **44**:285-290.

Niederpreum, D. J. (1963). Role of carbon dioxide in the control of fruiting of *Schizophyllum commune*. *J. Bacteriol.* **85**:1300-1308.

Pantidou, M. E. (1962). Cultural studies of Boletaceae. Carpophores of *Phlebopus lignicola* in culture. *Can. J. Botany* **40**:1313-1319.

Papazian, H. P. (1950). Physiology of the incompatibility factors in *Schizophyllum commune*. *Botan. Gaz.* **112**:143-163.

Papazian, H. P. (1956). Sex and cytoplasm in the fungi. *Trans. N.Y. Acad. Sci.* [2] **18**:388-397.

Plunkett, B. E. (1953). Nutritional and other aspects of fruit body production in pure cultures of *Collybia velutipes* (Curt.) Fr. *Ann. Botany (London)* [N.S.] **17**:193-218.

Plunkett, B. E. (1956). The influence of factors of the aeration complex and light upon fruit body form in pure cultures of an agaric and polypore. *Ann. Botany (London)* [N.S.] **20**:563-586.

Plunkett, B. E. (1958). Translocation and pileus formation in *Polyporus brumalis*. *Ann. Botany (London)* [N.S.] **22**:237-250.

Plunkett, B. E. (1961). The change of tropism in *Polyporus brumalis* stipes and the effect of directional stimuli on pileus differentiation. *Ann. Botany (London)* [N.S.] **25**:206-223.

Raper, J. R. (1959). *Schizophyllum umbrinum* Berkeley in culture. *Mycologia* **51**: 474-476.

Raper, J. R. (1961a). Incompatibility bei den Basidiomycetin *Schizophyllum commune*. *Ber. Deut. Botan. Ges.* **74**:326-328.

Raper, J. R. (1961b). Tetrapolarity in *Schizophyllum fasciatum*. *Mycologia* **52**:334-336.

Raper, J. R., and G. S. Krongelb. (1958). Genetic and environmental aspects of fruiting in *Schizophyllum commune* Fr. *Mycologia* **50**:707-740.

Raper, J. R., and J. P. San Antonio. (1954). Heterokaryotic mutagenesis in Hymenomycetes. I. Heterokaryosis in *Schizophyllum commune*. *Am. J. Botany* **41**:69-86.

Robbins, W. J., and A. Hervey. (1960). Light and the development of *Poria ambigua*. *Mycologia* **52**:231-247.

Rowell, J. B., C. R. Olien, and R. D. Wilcoxian. (1958). Effect of certain environmental conditions on infection of wheat by *Puccinia graminis*. *Phytopathology* **48**:371-377.

Scheller-Correns, E. (1957). Über die Fruchtkorperbildung von *Coprinus lagopus* bei verschiedenen Stickstoffquellen. *Arch. Mikrobiol.* **26**:52-54.

Schneiderhohn, G. (1955). Das Aktionsspektrum der Wachstumsbeeinflussung durch licht bei *Coprinus lagopus*. *Arch. Mikrobiol.* **21**:230-236.

Schopfer, W. H., and S. Blumer. (1940). Le pouvoir de synthèse d'un facteur de croissance par *Schizophyllum commune* (haplontes et diplontes). *Protoplasma* **34**:524-532.

Schutte, K. H. (1956). Translocation in the fungi. *New Phytologist* **55**:164-182.

Sharp, E. L., C. G. Schmidt, J. M. Staley, and C. H. Kingsolver. (1958). Some critical factors involved in establishment of *Puccinia graminis* var. tritici. *Phytopathology* **48**:469-474.

Sinnott, E. W. (1956). Botany and morphogenesis. *Ann. J. Botany* **43**:526-531.

Sinnott, E. W. (1960). "Plant Morphogenesis," 550 pp. McGraw-Hill, New York.

Snider, P. J. (1959). Stages of development in rhizomorphic thalli of *Armillaria mellea*. *Mycologia* **51**:693-707.

Spoerl, E., A. Sarachek, and S. B. Smith. (1957). The effect of amino acids upon cell division in *Ustilago*. *Am. J. Botany* **44**:252-258.

Stiefel, S. (1952). Über Erregungsvorgange bei der Einwirkung von photoischen und mechanischen Reizen auf *Coprinus* Fruchtkorper. *Planta* 40:301-312.
Stoller, B. B. (1952). Abnormal growth and fructification of the cultivated mushroom. *Science* 116:320-322.
Taber, W. A. (1960). Studies on *Isaria cretacea*. Morphogenesis of the synnema and endogenous nutrition. *Can. J. Microbiol.* 6:53-63.
Taber, W. A. (1963). Unpublished data.
Tamblyn, N., and E. W. B. Dacosta. (1958). A simple technique for producing fruit bodies of wood destroying Basidiomycetes. *Nature* 181:578-579.
Thompson, D'Arcy W. (1952). "On Growth and Form," 2 Vols., 1116 pp. Macmillan, New York.
Townsend, B. B. (1954). Morphology and development of fungal rhizomorphs. *Brit. Mycol. Soc. Trans.* 37:222-233.
Tschierpe, H. J., and J. W. Sinden. (1964). Weitere untersuchungen über die Bedeutung von Kohlendioxyd für die Fruktifikation des Kulturchampignons, *Agaricus campestris,* var *bisporus* (L) Lge. *Arch. Mikrobiol.* 49:405-425.
Voderberg, K. (1949). Zur fruchtkorperbildung von *Coprinus lagopus*. *Planta* 37:149-160.
Voderberg, K. (1950). Die Abhängigkeit der Fruchtkorperentwicklung bei *Coprinus lagopus* von inneren und ausseren Facktoren. *Planta* 37:612-625.
Wachter, J. P., and E. Spoerl. (1961). Biochemical changes associated with cell division in *Ustilago sphaerogena*. *Exptl. Cell. Res.* 22:31-39.
Wardlaw, C. W. (1952). "Phylogeny and Morphogenesis," 530 pp. Macmillan, New York.
Yurchenco, J. A., and G. H. Warren. (1961). A laboratory procedure for the cultivation and fructification of species of Hericium. *Mycologia* 53:566-574.

Physiology of Reproduction

CHAPTER 13

Sex Hormones in Fungi

LEONARD MACHLIS

*Department of Botany
University of California
Berkeley, California*

I. INTRODUCTION

The participation of hormones [*sensu* Raper (1952), but see Wilson and Bossert (1963)] in the sexual reproduction of fungi is a well-established fact. The purpose of this chapter is to describe the hormones demonstrated or postulated to exist and to indicate the progress made toward chemical identification. The material is organized in relation to the organisms used by the investigators. Several reviews with excellent bibliographies are available. These begin with the detailed and comprehensive review by Raper (1952) on *Chemical Regulation of Sexual Processes in the Thallophytes*. Periodically, Raper (1954, 1957, 1960) has brought this original review, particularly the parts pertaining to the fungi, up to date. Less detailed because of their broader scope are the annual summaries in *Forschritte der Botanik* under the heading of "Physiologie der Fortpflanzung und Sexualität" beginning with Volume 17 in 1954 written by Linskens; the summary tables of sex hormones in both the algae and fungi initially prepared by Raper and subsequently revised before publication by Machlis and Rawitscher-Kunkel, which appeared in the handbook "Growth" edited by Altman and Dittmer (1962); and most recently the review by Machlis and Rawitscher-Kunkel (1963) on *Mechanisms of Gametic Approach in Plants*.

II. SAPROLEGNIALES

The role of sex hormones in saprolegniaceous fungi is a most appropriate place to begin because it was in relation to these organisms that the occurrence of sex hormones in the fungi was first suggested (de Bary,

1881) and because species of *Achlya* were used by Raper and his associates in the now classical studies demonstrating beyond doubt a multihormonal regulatory system.

Sexual reproduction in these organisms involves the development either on the same thallus (homothallic) or on separate thalli (heterothallic) of oogonia with one or several uninucleate eggs (oospheres) and antheridial hyphae. The latter grow and attach to the oogonia, after which an antheridium is cut off by a cross wall. Fertilization tubes grow out from an antheridium and pierce the oogonial wall; then one, or a branch from one, grows to each egg which receives a single nucleus, thereby completing fertilization. The fertilized oospheres develop thick walls, thus becoming oospores. These germinate after a period of rest and usually after karyogamy.

The first part of de Bary's investigation was an extensive study of reproduction by such fungi as *Pythium, Phytophthora, Peronospora, Saprolegnia, Achlya,* and *Aphanomyces.* In the second part, which is a general evaluation and discussion, he proposed that specific chemical substances emanating from the oogonia initiate the development of the antheridial hyphae and, further, direct the growth of these hyphae to the oogonia. No experimental proof of these postulates was presented.

Later, Kauffman (1908) supported de Bary's postulates on the basis of his studies of *Saprolegnia hypogyna,* a species in which oospores usually develop parthenogenetically with only the rare production of antheridia. He found, however, that certain inorganic salts caused the production of many antheridial hyphae. Kauffman concluded that nutrients made possible the synthesis of the hormones inducing antheridial hyphae and directing the growth toward oogonia as postulated by de Bary.

However, it was Couch (1926) who, as part of a study of heterothallism in *Dictyuchus,* first deliberately attempted to demonstrate the operation of hormones in the saprolegniaceous fungi. Although his results were all negative, they can be explained on the basis of subsequent work with related fungi, as Raper (1952) did in some detail. It remained for Bishop (1940) to actually demonstrate sexual hormones in *Sapromyces reinschii,* a species now classified in the order Leptomitales. This work was completed in 1937 (Bishop, 1937) although it was not published until 1940, thus antedating Raper's first paper on sexual hormones (Raper, 1939a).

Raper (1952) has described Bishop's work so well that it would be superfluous to rephrase it. "In connection with a study of heterothallism and sexuality in *S. reinschii,* Bishop gave unequivocal proof that secretions of ♀ plants induced the production of antheridial hyphae on the ♂. In matings of ♂ and ♀ plants on an agar medium, production of antheridial

13. Sex Hormones in Fungi

hyphae on the ♂ prior to contact with the ♀ was frequently observed, and it was regularly the case that antheridial hyphal development was more intense upon that portion of the ♂ mycelium proximal to the ♀ than elsewhere upon the ♂ mycelium. Production of antheridial hyphae on ♂ plants grown sterilely upon an agar medium could be regularly induced by the addition of a filtrate, freed of spores and hyphal fragments by passage through a Berkefeld filter, of ♀ plants grown sterilely in water. No response was observed when the reciprocal test was performed, i.e., ♀ plants in ♂ filtrate. Oogonial initials were occasionally formed on ♀ mycelia before contact with ♂'s when mated upon a semisolid medium, and antheridial hyphae were observed always to grow directly to the exact distal ends of oogonial initials. Production of oogonial initials and the directional growth of antheridial hyphae were considered to result from the activities of diffusible substances, but no specific experimentation was performed to test the validity of this assumption." Bishop concluded ". . . that some substance diffusing from the ♀ mycelium stimulated the development of antheridial hyphae on the ♂ and that these in turn were influenced to grow directly toward the oogonia by some substance diffusing from the oogonia themselves. . . ."

From these beginnings Raper (1939a,b, 1940a,b, 1942a,b, 1950a,b) and Raper and Haagen Smit (1942) exposed the full complexity of the hormonal control in the type of sexual reproduction under discussion. Although the basic work was done with two heterothallic species of *Achlya, A. ambisexualis*, and *A. bisexualis*, Raper showed, as has Barksdale (1960) since, that the basic regulatory system also prevails in homothallic forms. There is neither space nor need to recount in detail these investigations; they are available in the original papers as well as in the reviews referred to earlier. Raper divided the sexual reaction into five major stages: (1) the development of antheridial hyphae on the male plants; (2) the production of oogonial initials on the female plants; (3) the growth of the antheridial hyphae to the oogonial initials; (4) the formation of cross walls in the antheridial hyphae, thus delimiting the antheridia after the antheridial hyphae contact the oogonial initials, as well as the delimitation of the oogonia by the formation of the basal cross walls and the cleavage of the oogonial protoplasm into oospheres; and (5) the development of the fertilization tubes, their penetration into the oogonia, their growth to the oospheres, and finally the transfer of the male nuclei to the oospheres. Evidence was presented that the first stage, i.e., the initiation of antheridial hyphae, was controlled by four specific hormones and that at least one hormone was essential for each of the next three stages. Although the last stage, fertilization, would appear to be hormonally controlled, no evidence was or has been presented for this postulate. The evidence for the hormones rests upon experiments involving the use of filtrates, the physical separation of mated plants by permeable membranes, and a perfusion technique in which water passes slowly from one microaquarium to another, each containing a male or a female plant in an order determined by the objective of a particular experiment.

The first step in sexual reproduction in *Achlya* is the initiation of antheridial hyphae on the male plant. The number of antheridial hyphae initiated is dependent on the amounts of four hormones known collectively as the A complex; the action of each of the hormones can be quantitatively assayed. The vegetative female plant secretes hormones A and A_2 while the male plant secretes A_1 and A_3. These hormones can be separated since hormone A from the female plant and A_3 from the male plant are soluble in acetone and dioxane whereas A_1 and A_2 are acetone-insoluble and water-soluble. Hormones A and A_2 secreted by the female plant can individually or together initiate antheridial hyphal development; hormone A_1 from the male plant cannot initiate, but can quantitatively augment, the activity of the two hormones secreted by the female plant; finally, hormone A_3 from the male plant decreases the response to the other three hormones.

While the antheridial hyphae are developing they secrete hormone B, which induces the formation of oogonial initials on the female plant. A quantitative assay for the activity of this hormone has not been developed. The oogonial initials now secrete hormone C, which does two things: (1) directs the growth of the antheridial hyphae to the oogonial initials and (2) causes the formation and delimitation of the antheridia after the antheridial hyphae make contact with the oogonial initials. Finally, the antheridia secrete hormone D, which causes the delimitation of the oogonia by the development of septa across the oogonial stalks and, further, causes the protoplasts of the oogonia to cleave into the eggs or oospheres.

Raper and Haagen Smit (1942) attempted to isolate and identify hormone A from *A. bisexualis* female without success. It must be recognized that this hormone can cause the initiation of the antheridial hyphae and that the other hormones of the A complex only modify the response quantitatively; their essentiality has not been demonstrated. Although the attempt to characterize hormone A chemically failed, methods were developed for concentrating it. Thus, an impure preparation weighing 0.2 mg concentrated from 1440 liters of filtrate from female plants induced antheridial hyphae on male plants when diluted 10^{13} times.

Further work on this system has been continued by Barksdale (1963). Raper had shown earlier that hormone A is produced in measurable amounts by female strains of *Achlya ambisexualis,* but not at all or very slightly by the male strains. Barksdale in the course of her study of hormone A production by various strains of *Achlya* observed that its concentration in cultures containing both male and female thalli equaled, not that of the female strain when grown alone, but that of the male strain. The failure of hormone A to accumulate in mixed cultures, as it regularly does in the isolated female cultures, led her to seek an explanation. Both heterothallic and homothallic strains of *Achlya* were used, some of the latter behaving as either male or female depending on the strain with which they were mated (Barksdale, 1960). The experiments, which involved a less laborious but also less precise assay method than that developed by Raper, showed quite clearly that the strains capable of producing antheridial initials in interthallic sexual reactions with a female strain remove hormone A from the culture fluid. It is taken up most rapidly by the pure male strain, and the two homothallic strains which produce antheridial hyphae when allowed to react with a female strain but do not produce oogonia when reacted with a male strain; it is taken up less rapidly by the homothallic strains that can produce oogonia when mated with a male strain; and still less rapidly, actually too slowly to be detected, by a pure female strain. Hormone A appears to be absorbed by the mycelium and not merely adsorbed on the hypal walls since it was not possible to recover the hormone by extracting the mycelium with acetone. There is the possibility that the hormone is inactivated on the surface of the mycelium but it is unlikely. Two further results are noteworthy. Hormone A accumulates in the cultures of those strains that take up the hormone slowly or not at all, i.e., by those strains with the least male tendencies. Conversely, as detailed above, those strains that take up the hormone are the ones that have the ability to produce antheridial hyphae. Moreover, the greater the initial concentration of hormone A added to the culture media the more rapidly it is absorbed.

It will be recalled that Raper concluded that the female mycelium secreted hormone A, which causes the initiation of antheridial hyphae, and that subsequently the oogonial initials secrete hormone C, which directs the growth of the antheridial hyphae to the oogonial initials or to a separating cellophane membrane. Furthermore, after the antheridial initials contact an oogonial initial or a membrane, septation of the antheridia is induced. Barksdale's (1963) investigation indicates that hormone A causes those responses attributed to hormone C as well as those of hormone A, thereby reducing the number of hormones known to act in this system. She found that particles of either polystyrene or polyvinyl plastic would adsorb hormone A. These particles were then quite clearly able to attract the antheridial hyphae. When these hormone-treated particles were placed on top of a cellophane membrane overlying the male strain, they induced the formation of antheridial branches beneath the membrane. Many of these branches had cross walls near the tip, including branches that had not made contact with the membrane. In other experiments the number of cross walls formed was found to be a function of the number of antheridial branches, which in turn was related to the concentration of hormone A added to the cultures. Thus, it appears that hormone A is responsible for the activities attributed to hormone C and that thigmotropism of the antheridial hyphae is not a necessary prelude to antheridium formation.

Further substantial progress in the physiology, as well as the biochemistry, of the hormonal system operating in these saprolegniaceous molds is dependent on the isolation and chemical identification of the hormones. This same statement will or could be made for each of the other hormonal systems yet to be discussed.

III. CHYTRIDIALES

One stage of sexual reproduction in two species of *Synchytrium* appears to be hormonally controlled. In a previous review (Machlis and Rawitscher-Kunkel, 1963), this type of reproduction was referred to as physiological anisogamy. These organisms produce motile isogametes, some of which become nonmotile and attract to themselves the remaining motile gametes. E. Köhler (1930) observed this behavior in *S. endobioticum*, as did Kusano (1930) in *S. fulgens*. Köhler remarks that as soon as copulation occurs the swarmers leave. He postulated that the functional females produce a substance that not only attracts the functional males but stimulates them to swim about at a greater velocity than when not in the vicinity of a functional female. There is no experimental evidence to support the suggestion that an attracting substance is secreted.

IV. MUCORALES

In the Mucorales sexuality is manifested by the development of protuberances on adjacent sexually compatible hyphae, usually referred to as zygophores. When they meet, the apex of each is cut off, thus delimiting multinucleate gametangia. Blakeslee (1904), in the course of his discovery of heterothallism in the Mucorales, observed that progametangia of *Rhizopus nigricans* [*R. stolonifer*] were formed after the zygophores were mutually attracted to each other. The chemotropism of the zygophores was named zygotropism by Burgeff (1924), who provided the first experimental evidence for such attraction. He observed that when plus and minus strains of *Mucor mucedo* were allowed to grow toward each other on an agar plate, hyphal swellings, considered to be the beginnings of progame-

13. Sex Hormones in Fungi

tangia, appeared before actual contact had been made. He confirmed this in an experiment in which a membrane was placed over the mycelium of the minus strain growing on nutrient agar. On top of the membrane he placed a block of agar containing the plus strain, which then grew out over the membrane. Zygophores were induced in the two strains and grew toward each other although they were prevented from meeting by the membrane.

Similar experiments with *Rhizopus nigricans* [*R. stolonifer*], *Mucor hiemalis*, and *Phycomyes nitens* failed. However, when two strips of agar, one containing the minus strain of *M. hiemalis* and the other the plus strain, were placed about 2 mm apart, each produced zygophores which grew toward each other through the air. Burgeff postulated that each strain produced a volatile and water-soluble substance that could diffuse through agar media or pass through the air to induce as well as direct the growth of the zygophores. In support of the idea that each mycelium produces an inducing and chemotropic hormone he did an experiment in which air was passed over a plus culture of *R. stolonifer,* through a tube a meter long, and then over a minus culture of *M. mucedo*. In the latter, young sporangiophores were converted into branched zygophores. Although the evidence for volatile hormones is not fully convincing, the experiments are described because of the subsequent recurrence of this theme.

It will be noted that Burgeff did not postulate separate hormones for the induction of zygophores on the one hand and their chemotropic attraction on the other. Experimental proof that these two processes are controlled by separate hormones did not become available until 1960 (Plempel, 1960a).

Burgeff's report, as might be expected, initiated a series of investigations on the hormonal basis of reproduction in the Mucorales which has continued to this day. Verkaik (1930) repeated Burgeff's membrane tests with *M. mucedo* but added nothing significant to what was already known. Ronsdorf (1931) showed that *Phycomyces blakesleeanus* was similar to *M. mucedo* in its behavior. F. Köhler's (1935) efforts to isolate an active principle failed and led him to suggest that the induction was caused by "some kind of mitogenic ray." When Kehl (1937) found that a continuous current of air passing over a nutrient plate containing plus and minus strains of *M. mucedo* appeared to narrow the copulation zone, he concluded that the active principle was transmitted through the atmosphere and tested a number of volatile oils for activity with negative results. In a very detailed, extensive investigation of *Pilobolus crystallinus,* which grows entirely submerged in the agar, in contrast to *Phycomyces* which has aerial zygophores, Krafczyk (1931, 1935) demonstrated that zygophore induction and attraction occurred prior to contact. To demonstrate the zygotropic reaction he placed an agar block with a minus mycelium and one with a plus mycelium next to each other so that the direction of growth of the mycelia was opposite but parallel. As they approached each other along the common edge, the zygophores clearly turned toward each other.

Banbury (1954, 1955) undertook a detailed study of the zygotropic reaction by inoculating agar plates with alternate rows of plus and minus spores of *M. mucedo.* When the mycelia approached each other, zygophores were induced. At this time Banbury cut out rectangular agar blocks that crossed the copulation zone. Each block then contained in the middle a mixture of plus and minus copulating zygophores, and at one end minus zygophores and at the other plus zygophores. Thus, each rectangular block was like a magnet with its two poles. If now, under appropriate conditions of humidity, and with the blocks turned on their sides, a plus end was brought close to a minus end, the zygophores grew toward each other, curving if necessary. If two plus ends or two minus ends were brought close to each other, the zygophores grew away from each other. When such blocks were sealed from each other by glass, mica, or aluminum foil barriers, there was no zygotropism. These last experiments were done to eliminate the possibility that "mitogenic rays," previously postulated by F. Köhler (1935), were the active agent.

Since the agar blocks in the above tests did not touch each other, Banbury concluded that the active principles were volatile. In keeping with others before him (Ronsdorf, 1931; Krafczyk, 1931, 1935; Buller, 1933), Banbury concluded that there must be two hormones involved. He proposed that one of them is produced by the plus zygophores, stimulating growth in the plus and inhibiting growth in the minus, and that the other hormone is produced by the minus zygophores, stimulating growth in the minus and retarding it in the plus. The positive zygotropic response between plus and minus zygophores was interpreted as a consequence of the partial inhibition of growth on the near side of each hypha caused by the higher concentration of hormone emanating from the opposite zygophore. The tendency of like zygophores to grow away from each other is attributed to the growth-promoting effect of the hormone produced by these zygophores. Thus, two like zygophores would grow more on the sides facing each other and thus curve away from each other.

Beginning in 1957, Plempel and his associates (Plempel, 1957, 1960a,b, 1963a,b; Plempel and Braunitzer, 1958; Plempel and Dawid, 1961) initiated a vigorous attack on the hormonal regulating system in *Mucor,* working principally with *M. mucedo.* The experimental results require the postulation of at least six hormones. The plus and minus strains, when grown separately, each release a "progamone" into the nutrient broth during their vegetative growth. When the cell-free broth is then used to culture the opposite strain, i.e., broth from plus mycelium is used as substrate for minus mycelium, the latter then synthesizes the minus "gamone"; similarly the plus mycelium produces plus gamone. These gamones, when used in the quantitative assay, induce the development of the zygophores, the plus gamone being specific for zygophore production by the minus mycelium and the reciprocal being true for the minus gamone. Finally, the zygophores produce zygotropic hormones that direct the growth of the zygophores of the opposite type toward the source of the hormone.

An extensive series of experiments were carried out on the zygotropic hormones to establish whether or not they are volatile and transmitted through the gas phase as suggested by the earlier investigators. The experimental conditions were improved by Plempel's isolation of the substances inducing zygophores in the plus and minus strains (see below). Thus, it became possible to induce zygophores on plus and minus strains grown in separate agar plates.

When this was done by including zygogenic substance in nutrient agar, the placing of agar blocks containing additional active material adjacent to plus or minus zygophores failed to cause bending toward the blocks. From this it was concluded that the purified material containing zygophore-inducing hormones did not include the zygotropic factor. Further, because of the conditions under which the zygophore-inducing material was produced, it seemed likely that the chemotropic factor(s) was formed only after the appearance of the zygophores. Also reported are observations of the reaction when a plus or minus strain of *M. mucedo* is confronted with the opposite strain of *Phycomyces blakesleeanus*. In the latter, the zygophores develop within the agar substrate and rise above it only after contact, whereas in *M. mucedo* they develop upward from the substrate prior to contact. The *Mucor* zygophores always developed first, then, when those of *Phycomyces* formed, the former bent back toward the substrate where they became encircled by the *Phycomyces* zygophores. However, zygospores were not formed. Plempel concludes by suggesting the possibility of a gaseous zygotropic factor for *Mucor,* but ruling it out for *Phycomyces* since it grows entirely in the substrate.

Plempel and co-workers then set about establishing the mechanism involved in the transfer of the zygotropic factor in *M. mucedo*. First they unsuccessfully attempted to induce a zygotropic response by diffusion of presumably active material through agar. Plus and minus mycelia alone and mixed were grown on 3% malt extract absorbed into cotton, and were then induced to form zygophores by the zygogenic substance. Extracts were then obtained by gently pressing the cotton and the mycelium on it. These extracts were tested directly or after various treatments which included: (a) bringing to pH 3 with sulfuric acid, or pH 9 with KOH, and then extracting with petroleum, ether, and acetaldehyde in succession, followed by taking to dryness at 30°C and then dissolving in 0.5 ml water; and (b) concentrating 7.0 ml of the pressed juice by lyophilization to dryness and then dissolving the concentrate in 0.5 ml of water. The several preparations were tested both by solidifying them with agar from which a small cylinder was placed near zygophores, or by placing capillaries containing the solutions next to zygophores. In no instance did any curvature toward the test material occur. Had the factor been present it should have diffused through the agar to the zygophores. It was possible that the factor had been destroyed in the preparative procedures. To check this, cheese cloth circles supported by a wire ring about the size of a petri plate were coated with nutrient agar 2 mm thick. These were seeded with spores from plus strains near one edge on one side and with spores from minus strains on the other side at the other end of a diameter connecting the two inocula. After incubation in a sterile, humid chamber for 3 days, zygophores were induced by the zygogenic substance. If zygotropic substances were produced they should have diffused through the 2-mm thick agar disk and caused the zygophores of the two strains to bend 90 degrees toward the surface of the agar disk. This did not happen. Moreover, young zygophores not yet above the agar surface should have remained in the medium in response to the attraction, but did not. It was concluded that the zygotropic material was not diffusible through agar.

Plempel and associates also tested the possibility that the zygotropic substance is transmitted through the air. The basic experiments were done with a petri dish divided in half by a vertical mica sheet through which holes 3.5 mm in diameter (four across the plate) had been drilled. The mica was held in place between glass blocks glued to the bottom of the plate and by the half-covers which met with the mica between them. Rectangular blocks (12×5 mm) of agar with plus and minus mycelia were prepared, soaked in zygogenic solution, dried on filter paper, and then placed standing on edge next to the holes in the mica so that the direction of growth of the zygophores was at right angles to the nutrient agar surface and in the direction of the holes. When minus zygophores faced plus zygophores across the holes, several of the former grew with the necessary curvature through the hole toward a single plus zygophore and established contact, traversing a distance of 2.5 mm. With a separation of 4 mm, the zygophores of both types nearest to the hole elongated twice as much as those most distant (laterally) from the hole. If for the first 12 hours a minus block faced a minus block the zygophores stopped growing and began changing into sporangiophores with thickened tips. If, after this time, one of the minus blocks was replaced by a plus block, the transformed minus zygophores developed from their tips the long thin hyphae characteristic of zygophores, which then grew up to and through the hole. When two plus blocks or two minus blocks faced each other, no responses in terms of growth toward the holes and accelerated elongation were observed. Instead, most of the zygophores changed into sporangiophores. Additional tests of various kinds served to support the suggestion that the zygotropic hormones are volatile and transmitted through the atmosphere. They greatly increase the growth in length of the zygophores—as much as four to six times compared to those not exposed to the agent—and cause them to bend toward each other.

No mention is made of a tendency of like zygophores facing each other to grow back toward their own nutrient agar surfaces as described by Banbury. The zygotropic response is explained in terms of two gaseous, organ-specific growth substances. These stimulate elongation of the zygophores of the opposite mating type. If a zygophore is exposed to unequal concentrations on its anterior and posterior flanks, either the elongation on the side receiving the higher concentration is inhibited or the other side receiving the lower concentration is enhanced. This work suggests that the zygotropic substances are unstable and readily oxidized in air. This destruction is postulated to be the basis for the maintenance of concentration gradients.

The other major line of attack on the hormonal system in *M. mucedo* has been on the chemistry of the gamones, or zygogenic hormones. In this work, the initial hormonally active nutrient solution was obtained by growing mixed plus and minus cultures. The individual hormones cannot, as yet, be separated chromatographically, indicating that they have very similar structures. The most recent preparation began with 250 liters of active solution which was first extracted with butyl acetate, then concentrated by evaporation at 20°C, and fractionated on a column. The active fraction was treated with benzoyl chloride to yield the benzoate ester. After further chromatographic separation, 29.8 mg of pure gamone ester was obtained. The latter crystallized from ether at −2°C in the form of yellow needles. Upon saponification and chromatography of the products there was obtained a yellow-red, viscous, clear oil with very high biological activity. The elemental analysis of this preparation indicated 67.7% carbon, 7.4% hydrogen, and 24.6% oxygen. The molecular weight determined osmotically gave values of 314 in acetone and 374 in chloroform (± 5%). These figures suggest the formula $C_{20}H_{25}O_5$. Evidence is presented indicating the presence in the molecule of one or more hydroxyls, an ester bond, and a carbon-carbon double bond. From the infrared analysis it is concluded that no aromatic ring is present.

The reported progress made by Plempel and his associates on the chemistry of the gamones of *M. mucedo* is so far the most successful attack made on any sex hormone in plants.

V. BLASTOCLADIALES

The water mold *Allomyces*, in which so far only one hormone is known to function, has been the object of intensive investigation with the purpose of establishing its chemical nature (Machlis, 1958a,b,c; Machlis *et al.*, 1965). In *Allomyces*, the gamete-bearing generation consists of a dichotomously branching mycelium that bears large numbers of small orange, male gametangia and larger, colorless, female gametangia. In water, the gametangia release highly active, motile, orange, male gametes and sluggishly motile, colorless, female gametes. It can be observed that the male gametes cluster in the vicinity of unopened female gametangia.

The first proof that the clustering is a response to a chemotactic agent was obtained by embedding female gametangia in agar and showing that the male gametes are attracted to the gametangia. It was subsequently shown that the male gametes would approach and remain in the vicinity of a dialyzing membrane that had on its other side the supernatant in which female gametangia had released female gametes. The hormone attracting the sperm was named sirenin.

From the normally hermaphroditic plant, predominantly female and predominantly male isolates were genetically selected on the basis of hybridization studies by Emerson and Wilson (1954). The female plants were then used to produce sirenin and the male plants were used for the production of sperm in adequate concentrations for assaying for sirenin. A quantitative assay was developed, based on the number of gametes adhering to a unit area of membrane in response to diffusion of sirenin through the membrane.

Progress on the chemical aspects of the study of sirenin became possible with the development of a system yielding approximately 25 mg of sirenin per week. Briefly, female plants are grown on nutrient agar plates. Agar and plants are fragmented in a blendor and used to inoculate 300 ml of yeast extract-glucose liquid medium. After 2 days' incubation at 25°C the entire contents of a flask is added to 10 liters of glucose-tap water contained in 5-gallon carboys, where further growth takes place at 25°C with vigorous aeration for 30 hours. By this time the plants are coated with gametangia. Upon addition of another 9 liters of tap water there is a copious discharge of gametes together with sirenin. Each day, the active medium from four carboys is transferred to two large 40-liter continuous extractors where extraction with methylene chloride takes place for 24 hours. At the end of each week, the methylene chloride containing the sirenin and other lipid-soluble materials from almost 200 liters of active medium is concentrated by vacuum evaporation at room temperature to a small volume. At this point the material undergoes final purification. It is first fractionated on an alumina column. The active fraction is then treated with p-[(p-nitrophenyl)azo]benzoyl chloride (NABS) to form a colored, crystallizable NABS ester (Hecker, 1955). The ester can be saponified with the recovery of activity, thus making possible the identification of the sirenin ester from others which are also formed. The sirenin ester is separated by thin layer chromatography on a micro scale and by column chromatography on a larger scale. Elemental analysis of the ester showed only carbon, hydrogen, and oxygen to be present. This information, together with estimates of molecular weight based on the UV extinction coefficient for the ester, indicate the best value to date for the empirical formula to be $C_{15}H_{24}O_2$ with a molecular weight of 236.

On the basis of a molecular weight of 236, sperm attraction in the standard bioassay can be detected at a concentration of $10^{-10} M$. Considerable information is available on probable functional groups and structural detail of this molecule, but we prefer to withhold discussion until these aspects are proved beyond doubt.

VI. ASCOMYCETES

Winge (1935) and Nickerson and Thimann (1941, 1943) suggested that the conjugation tubes of certain yeasts might be hormonally directed in their growth toward each other. Experimental evidence that this is so was presented by Levi (1956) for *Saccharomyces cerevisiae*. Plus and minus mating types in liquid culture develop hyphal copulatory processes. When these meet, fusion occurs and a zygote is formed. He showed that when a plus cell is placed close to a minus cell on agar, the latter, but not the plus mating type, develops a copulatory tube. In further experiments he showed that an agar surface from which sexually active cells had been removed could now induce the copulatory process in new minus cells, but not in plus cells. So far, Levi has not been able to prepare an active filtrate, and only once in several trials was the mating reaction induced across a collodion membrane.

The basic pattern of reproduction in the remaining ascomycetes to be discussed involves the development on hyphae of an ascogonium, usually a coiled, septate structure representing the female. From this develops a tube, which may branch in some species. The tube—a trichogyne—eventually contacts the nonmotile male element, whose contents then enter the trichogyne and migrate into the ascogonium. The ascogonium may become ensheathed by hyphae originating from basal cells of the ascogonium or nearby vegetative hyphae. The male elements may be almost any kind of cell from the proper mating type, but specifically, in the work to be reviewed here, they are nonmotile, unicellular bodies cut off from the parent plant and called variously, depending on matters not pertinent to the present review, oidia, spermatia, or conidia.

The most significant investigation with organisms of this type has been that of Bistis (1956, 1957) on *Ascobolus*. Before going into this study, one should note certain less extensive studies in which sexual hormones have been implicated. Raper (1952) has recounted in detail the highly controversial series of papers by several investigators claiming and disclaiming the involvement of hormones in the sexual reproduction of *Neurospora,* specifically the action of hormones in inducing the development of perithecia. From this work no meaningful conclusions can be drawn.

Markert (1949), from certain experiments on *Glomerella,* concluded that a diffusible substance affected perithecial development. Two weakly compatible strains were mated on agar and separated by a permeable membrane from a third strain which was fully compatible with one of the mated strains. He reported that the mated strains produced many more perithecia in the presence of the third strain than in its absence. McGahen and Wheeler (1951) also concluded from their studies on the genetics of *Glomerella* that there may be perithecium-inducing substances. In a strain which produces perithecia in clumps they reported that the formation of one perithecium seemed to stimulate the formation of others in the immediate vicinity, thus leading to the clumped perithecial condition. In another situation, where the clumped perithecial strain was mated with a conidial strain, the perithecia arose chiefly at or near the point where a hypha from the conidial culture crossed one from the perithecial culture. McGahen and Wheeler concluded that the conidial hypha provides a chemical stimulus for the development of the perithecia.

More concrete evidence of hormonal involvement exists in relation to the chemotropic growth of the trichogyne. The first suggestion of a chemotropic growth of a trichogyne was made by Dodge (1912) when describing reproduction in *Ascobolus carbonarius*: "There can be no question, however, as to the specific attraction between the trichogyne and the conidium, and I shall call it the antheridial conidium." A similar observation was made by Backus (1939). He performed no experiments to substantiate his idea that in *Neurospora sitophila* the trichogyne sought out the conidium. Backus also observed that conidia, which by themselves can germinate and grow into a mycelium, would not germinate in the presence of a mycelium of the opposite compatibility strain.

Definite evidence for the chemotropic growth of a trichogyne was provided by Zickler (1937, 1952) in *Bombardia lunata*. In this organism the male element is a spermatium. In contrast to the conidia above they will not germinate and grow vegetatively on nutrient agar, nor do they require sexual activation as do the oidia to be described later in relation to *Ascobolus stercorarius*. Each of the compatibility types produces both ascogonia and spermatia. The trichogyne arising from an ascogonium initially grows in a random fashion and then, if spermatia from the opposite mating type are present, the trichogyne grows directly to the spermatia, making in some cases a full right-angle bend. Zickler suspended spermatia in water and then removed them by filtration. The filtrate, either in capillary tubes or in agar blocks, attracted the trichogynes and did so even after autoclaving. Vegetative hyphae did not respond chemotropically, an observation indicating that the chemotropic factor was specific for the trichogyne. On the other hand, mycelial extracts of the correct mating type were as effective as spermatial extracts in attracting trichogynes. This is not unexpected since almost any part of the appropriate compatibility-type partner can serve as a male element in these organisms.

The work of Bistis referred to earlier provided evidence that in *A. stercorarius* there is a multihormonal mechanism controlling and regulating sexual reproduction. In this work the male element consists of oidia which are multinucleate cells obtainable free of the mycelium on which they are produced. These are capable of growing vegetatively when placed on nutrient agar, but their germination and vegetative growth is inhibited in the presence of mycelium from their own or the opposite compatibility class. An oidium induces ascogonial development only after it itself has been sexually activated by exposure for about 4 hours to a mycelium of the opposite compatibility type. After activation it then induces the development of ascogonial initials which develop into multicellular organs, the terminal cell of which grows out as a trichogyne. Evidence for the chemotropic growth of the trichogyne was obtained by moving an oidium after a trichogyne had started growing toward it. The trichogyne then turned until directed toward the new position of the oidium. This could be repeated until the trichogyne failed to grow. Moreover, it was found that an unactivated oidium is unable to attract a trichogyne.

After fusion, lateral hyphae from the base of an ascogonium and nearby vegetative hyphae grow to the ascogonium and ensheath it. This is considered to be a chemotropic response, but no evidence other than the observation of the approach of these investing hyphae has been presented.

Although the question was later posed (Bistis and Raper, 1963) whether the inhibition of germination was essential to sexual activation, the two responses could not be separated. In this same recent study hyphal fragments were also used as fertilizing elements. These became sexually activated by dilation of the tip, which the authors consider to be the induction of antheridia. Thus, since nongerminated oidia function as antheridia, the process of sexual activation referred to above is actually antheridial induction.

The work reported above makes available for further study a third multihormonal system in the fungi. So far, no effort has been made to isolate and identify any of the hormones involved.

VII. BASIDIOMYCETES

Somatic copulation by the fusion of hyphae is the typical sexual reaction in the Basidiomycetes with the exception of the rusts. As early as 1883, Brefeld described the development of tubular connections between pairs of germinating sporidia of rusts. This we now know is a somatic sexual fusion, but at the time, Brefeld considered it to be nonsexual because the sporidia would always develop into mycelia or conidial colonies in the yeast form as long as there were suitable nutrients. Only when the nutrient solutions were exhausted did the hyphal fusions occur.

Purely vegetative hyphal fusions also are widespread in these fungi. Sexual hormones per se have not been demonstrated, but there is an extensive literature on chemotropism between fungal hyphae, whether sexual or vegetative, resulting in such fusions.

VIII. SUMMARY

The preceding survey of the evidence that hormones regulate sexual reproduction of fungi involves enough different organisms and different types of sexual reproduction to suggest that all sexually reproducing fungi probably use hormonal control mechanisms to a greater or lesser extent. So far, three fungi are known in which the initiation of the sexual process and the coordination of all stages up to plasmogamy are controlled by hormones—*Achlya, Mucor,* and *Ascobolus*. It is to be expected that this list will be increased with time. The need in this field, however, is not as great for evidence of hormones in other organisms as for the determination of the chemical structures of known hormones. Progress in this direction is being made only with the zygogenic hormone of *Mucor*, the sperm-attractant from *Allomyces*, and hormone A of *Achlya*. Once the structures of these hormones are known, then it is likely that they and analogs can be synthesized. With such materials the study of the mechanisms by which these hormones exert their control can begin.

ACKNOWLEDGMENT

The unpublished work on sirenin has been supported by research grants from the National Science Foundation.

REFERENCES

Altman, P. L., and D. S. Dittmer, eds. (1962). Sex hormones: Thallophytes. In "Growth," pp. 532-533. Federation Am. Soc. Exptl. Biol., Washington, D.C.

Backus, M. P. (1939). The mechanics of conidial fertilization in *Neurospora sitophila*. *Bull. Torrey Botan. Club* 66:63-76.

Banbury, G. H. (1954). Processes controlling zygophore formation and zygotropism in *Mucor mucedo*. *Nature* 173:499.

Banbury, G. H. (1955). Physiological studies in the Mucorales. III. The zygotropism of zygophores of *Mucor mucedo*. *J. Exptl. Botany* 6:235-244.

Barksdale, A. W. (1960). Inter-thallic sexual reactions in *Achlya*, a genus of the aquatic fungi. *Am. J. Botany* 47:14-23.

Barksdale, A. W. (1963). The role of hormone A during sexual conjugation in *Achlya ambisexualis*. *Mycologia* 55:627-632.

Bishop, H. (1937). Sexuality in *Sapromyces reinschii*. Ph.D. thesis, Harvard University, Cambridge, Massachusetts.

Bishop, H. (1940). A study of sexuality in *Sapromyces reinschii*. *Mycologia* 32:505-529.

Bistis, G. N. (1956). Sexuality in *Ascobolus stercorarius*. I. Morphology of the ascogonium; plasmogamy; evidence for a sexual hormonal mechanism. *Am. J. Botany* 43:389-394.

Bistis, G. N. (1957). Sexuality of *Ascobolus stercorarius*. II. Preliminary experiments on various aspects of the sexual process. *Am. J. Botany* 44:436-443.

Bistis, G. N., and J. R. Raper. (1963). Heterothallism and sexuality in *Ascobolus stercorarius*. *Am. J. Botany* 50:880-891.

Blakeslee, A. F. (1904). Sexual reproduction in the Mucorineae. *Proc. Natl. Acad. Sci. U.S.* 40:206-319.

Brefeld, O. (1883). "Untersuchungen aus den Gesammtgebiet der Mykologie," Vol. 5, 222 pp. Felix, Leipzig.

Buller, A. H. R. (1933). "Researches on Fungi," Vol. V, Chapter 1, pp. 1-74. Longmans, Green, New York.

Burgeff, H. (1924). Untersuchungen über Sexualität und Parasitismus bei Mucorineen. I. *Botan. Abhandl.* 4:5-135.

Couch, J. N. (1926). Heterothalism in *Dictyuchus*, a genus of the water molds. *Ann. Botany (London)* 40:848-881.

de Bary, A. (1881). Untersuchungen über die Peronosporeen und Saprolegnieen und die Grundlagen eines natürlichen Systems der Pilze. *Abhandl. Senckenberg. Naturforsch. Ges.* 12:225-370.

Dodge, B. O. (1912). Methods of culture and the morphology of the archicarp in certain species of the Ascobolaceae. *Bull. Torrey Botan. Club* 39:139-197.

Emerson, R., and C. M. Wilson. (1954). Interspecific hybrids and the cytogenetics and cytotaxonomy of *Euallomyces*. *Mycologia* 46:393-434.

Hecker, E. (1955). 4′-Nitro-azobenzol-carbonsäure (4)-chlorid als Reagens auf Alkohole. *Chem. Ber.* 88:1666-1675.

Kauffman, C. H. (1908). A contribution to the physiology of the Saprolegniaceae with special reference to the variations of the sexual organs. *Ann. Botany (London)* 22:361-388.

Kehl, H. (1937). Ein Beitrag zur Morphologie und Physiologie der Zygophoren von *Mucor mucedo*. *Arch. Mikrobiol.* 8:379-406.

Köhler, E. (1930). Beobachtungen an Zoosporenaufschwemmungen von *Synchytrium enbodioticum* (Schilb.) Perc. *Zentr. Bakteriol., Parasitenk., Abt. II* **82**:1-10.

Köhler, F. (1935). Beitrag zur Kenntnis der Sexualreaktionen von *Mucor mucedo*. *Planta* **23**:358-378.

Krafczyk, H. (1931). Die Zygosporenbildung bei *Pilobolus crystallinus*. *Ber. Deut. Botan. Ges.* **49**:141-146.

Krafczyk, H. (1935). Die Bildung und Keimung der Zygosporen von *Pilobolus crystallinus* und sein heterokaryotisches Myzel. *Beitr. Biol. Pflanz.* **23**:349-396.

Kusano, S. (1930). Life history and physiology of *Synchytrium fulgens*, with special reference to its sexuality. *Japan. J. Botany* **5**:35-132.

Levi, J. D. (1956). Mating reaction in yeast. *Nature* **177**:753-754.

Linskens, H. (1954-1962). In *"Fortschritte der Botanik"* (E. Bünning and E. Gäumann, eds.), Vols. 17-25. Springer, Berlin.

McGahen, J. W., and H. E. Wheeler. (1951). Genetics of *Glomerella*. IX. Perithecial development and plasmogamy. *Am. J. Botany* **38**:610-617.

Machlis, L. (1958a). Evidence for a sexual hormone in *Allomyces*. *Physiol. Plantarum* **11**:181-192.

Machlis, L. (158b). A procedure for the purification of sirenin. *Nature* **181**:1790-1791.

Machlis, L. (1958c). A study of sirenin, the chemotactic sexual hormone from the watermold *Allomyces*. *Physiol. Plantarum* **11**:845-854.

Machlis, L., and E. Rawitscher-Kunkel. (1963). Mechanisms of gametic approach in plants. *Intern. Rev. Cytol.* **15**:97-138.

Machlis, L., W. Williams, W. H. Nutting, and H. Rapoport. (1965). Unpublished data.

Markert, C. L. (1949). Sexuality in the fungus, *Glomerella*. *Am. Naturalist* **83**:227-231.

Nickerson, W. J., and K. V. Thimann. (1941). The chemical control of conjugation in *Zygosaccharomyces*. *Am. J. Botany* **28**:617-621.

Nickerson, W. J., and K. V. Thimann. (1943). Chemical control of conjugation in *Zygosaccharomyces*. II. *Am. J. Botany* **30**:94-101.

Plempel, M. (1957). Die Sexualstoffe der Mucoraceae. *Arch. Mikrobiol.* **26**:151-174.

Plempel, M. (1960a). Die zgyotropische Reaktion bei Mucorinieen. I. Mitteilung. *Planta* **55**:254-258.

Plempel, M. (1960b). Die Darstellung eines kristallinen Benzoesäure-Esters der Sexualstoffee von *Mucor mucedo*. *Naturwissenschaften* **47**:472-473.

Plempel, M. (1963a). Die Chemischen Grundlagen der Sexualreaktion bei Zygomyceten. *Planta* **59**:492-508.

Plempel, M. (1963b). Die Mucorineen-Gamone. *Naturwissenschaften* **50**:226.

Plempel, M., and G. Braunitzer. (1958). Die Isolierung der Mucorineen Sexualstoffee. I. *Z. Naturforsch.* **13b**:302-305.

Plempel, M., and W. Dawid. (1961). Die zygotropische Reaktion bei Mucorineen. II. Mitteilung. *Planta* **56**:438-446.

Raper. J. R. (1939a). Role of hormones in the sexual reaction of heterothallic *Achlyas*. *Science* **89**:321-322.

Raper, J. R. (1939b). Sexual hormones in *Achlya*. I. Indicative evidence for a hormonal coordinating mechanism. *Am. J. Botany* **26**:639-650.

Raper, J. R. (1940a). Sexuality in *Achlya ambisexualis*. *Mycologia* **32**:710-727.

Raper, J. R. (1940b). Sexual hormones in *Achlya*. II. Distance reactions, conclusive evidence for a hormonal coordination mechanism. *Am. J. Botany* **27**:162-173.

Raper, J. R. (1942a). Sexual hormones in *Achlya*. III. Hormone A and the initial male reaction. *Am. J. Botany* **29**:159-166.
Raper, J. R. (1942b). Sexual hormones in *Achlya*. V. Hormone A', a male secreted augmenter or activator of hormone A. *Proc. Natl. Acad. Sci. U.S.* **28**:509-515.
Raper, J. R. (1950a). Sexual hormones in *Achlya*. VI. The hormones of the A-Complex. *Proc. Natl. Acad. Sci. U.S.* **36**:524-533.
Raper, J. R. (1950b). Sexual hormones in *Achlya*. VII. The hormonal mechanism in homothallic species. *Bot. Gaz.* **112**:1-24.
Raper, J. R. (1952). Chemical regulation of sexual processes in the Thallophytes. *Bot. Rev.* **18**:447-545.
Raper, J. R. (1954). *In* "Sex in Microorganisms" (D. H. Wenrich, I. F. Lewis, and J. R. Raper, eds.), p. 42. Am. Assoc. Advance. Sci., Washington, D.C.
Raper, J. R. (1957). Hormones and sexuality in lower plants. *Symp. Soc. Exptl. Biol.* **11**:143-165.
Raper, J. R. (1960). The control of sex in fungi. *Am. J. Botany* **47**:794-808.
Raper, J. R., and A. J. Haagen Smit. (1942). Sexual hormones in *Achlya*. IV. Properties of hormone A of *A. bisexualis*. *J. Biol. Chem.* **143**:311-320.
Ronsdorf, L. (1931). Über die chemischen Bedingungen von Wachstum und Zygotenbildung bei *Phycomyces blakesleeanus*. *Planta* **14**:482-514.
Verkaik, C. (1930). Über das Entstehen von Zygophoren von *Mucor mucedo* (+) unter Beeinflussung eines von *Mucor mucedo* (−) abgeschiedenen Stoffes. *Koninkl. Ned. Akad. Wetenschap., Proc.* **C33**:656-658.
Wilson, E. O., and W. H. Bossert. (1963). Chemical communication among animals. *Recent Progr. Hormone Res.* **19**:673-713.
Winge, Ö. (1935). On haplophase and diplophase in some Saccharomycetes. *Compt. Rend. Trav. Lab. Carlsberg, Ser. Physiol.* **21**:77-111.
Zickler, H. (1937). Die Vererbung des Geschlechts bei dem Askomyzeten *Bombardia lunata* Zckl. *Z. Induktive Abstammungs-Vererbungslehre* **73**:403-408.
Zickler, H. (1952). Zur Entwicklungsgeschichte des Askomyzeten *Bombardia lunata*. *Arch. Protistenk.* **98**:1-70.

CHAPTER 14

Environmental Influences on Reproduction

LILIAN E. HAWKER

*Department of Botany
University of Bristol
Bristol, England*

I. INTRODUCTION

Reproduction of an organism is the production of new individuals which, in general, resemble the parent(s). This may be brought about *vegetatively*, by development of new individuals from unspecialized detached portions of the parent; *asexually*, by the formation of new individuals from specialized reproductive bodies produced by the parent independently of nuclear fusion; or *sexually*, by a process involving a fusion between two compatible nuclei and a subsequent reduction division. The functions of reproduction in fungi are not only the multiplication of individuals, but also dispersal to new substrata, resistance to temporary adverse conditions, and the provision of a mechanism for variation.

Filamentous fungi increase vegetatively by the linear growth and branching of the hyphae, a process which involves replication of similar units. This can correctly be termed *vegetative reproduction* only when a new mycelium arises from a detached portion of a hypha. Yeasts multiply vegetatively by fission or budding of unicells, a process involving first an enlargement of the individual and then an increase in number. Vegetative cells of other unicellular fungi, such as the chytrids, may increase in size but usually increase in number only through the production of spores. The whole or most of the single-celled thallus of these fungi is used up in asexual or sexual reproduction.

Most fungi reproduce by the production of small detachable bodies, the *spores*. These may be produced asexually or sexually, the same fungus usually producing spores of more than one type. Spores may be produced in very large numbers, and they then serve as a most efficient means of dispersal and migration of the species, or they may be provided with thick, relatively impermeable walls and are then capable of surviving periods unfavorable to vegetative growth.

When a suitable culture medium is inoculated with a fungus, or a natural substrate is successfully colonized, the organism first grows vegetatively. This phase may be quite brief or it may continue indefinitely. A change to the reproductive or sporulating state is the result of a combination of genetic competence to produce spores and the effects of environmental factors. A mycelium which is genetically unable to sporulate will remain sterile under all conditions; one of low fertility will sporulate only when external conditions are particularly favorable; and a highly fertile mycelium may be prevented from sporulating only by sublethal conditions.

The type of spore produced at a particular time may depend upon the age or state of the parent mycelium or may be determined solely by environmental influence. In general, for a given species, the external conditions inducing production of a particular type of spore differ, often considerably, from those favoring another type or from those optimal for vegetative growth. Such differences in requirements for the various phases of growth and reproduction are biologically valuable, since they often lead to the formation of the appropriate dispersal units or resting bodies at the time when these are most needed, that is when conditions are becoming less favorable for vigorous vegetative growth. Moreover, with many fungi, energy is not wasted in producing complex reproductive bodies under conditions optimal for hyphal growth.

Successive stages in the initiation, development, and maturation of particular spores or spore-bearing structures may differ in their environmental requirements. This also is often of obvious biological advantage, as when falling food supply permits further development of only the first-formed fruit-body initials of certain higher fungi, thus allowing the limited food available to be devoted to the maturation of a few fruit bodies rather than to partial development of a larger number.

Owing to the complexity of the natural habitat, most studies of the effect of external factors on reproduction have been concerned with pure cultures. This work has been the subject of a number of reviews including those by Lilly and Barnett (1951), Hawker (1951, 1957), Hawker et al. (1960), Cochrane (1958), and Cantino (1961). This chapter will not include a full review of results from pure culture work but will refer also to the effects of temporary changes in the natural environment. Little is known of the mechanism by which perception of an external stimulus is translated into the visible initiation of the reproductive phase.

II. EFFECTS OF EXTERNAL FACTORS

A. Food Supply

The production of spores, particularly when these are contained in large and complex fruit bodies, inevitably makes heavy demands on available food materials. The cytoplasm of spores is denser than that of vegetative hyphae, and it contains quantities of reserve food substances such as glycogen and oil drops. Electron microscope studies reveal that even such a comparatively simple spore as the sporangiospore of *Rhizopus* possesses a cell wall which is relatively thick and of different construction from that of the hyphae (Hawker and Abbott, 1963). Many spores have very thick, sculptured walls (e.g., teleutospores of rusts or ascospores of *Tuber* sp.); others are surrounded by a gelatinous layer (e.g., ascospores of *Sordaria*) or have complex appendages (e.g., conidia of *Pestalotia*); others are produced on specialized branched hyphae or in or on complex fruit bodies. The formation of spores thus involves not only the use of relatively large quantities of food, but also the synthesis of special substances not normally present in the vegetative hyphae and for which special food substances not necessary for mycelial growth may be required. Thus, it is not surprising that a supply of food adequate to sustain vegetative growth may not permit sporulation and that nutritional requirements for optimal production of mycelium seldom also lead to maximum spore production.

The total amount, nature, and concentration of food materials necessary for reproduction may all be different from those favoring vegetative growth. Moreover, requirements may differ at different stages in a reproductive process or for the production of different types of spore by the same species.

Pure culture studies have shown that the elements required for reproduction are the same as those necessary for vegetative growth, but that the quantities required, and the form in which the various elements must be present, are not necessarily the same for both phases. In addition to water, fungi need atmospheric oxygen, a supply of carbon, in the form of a carbohydrate or other relatively complex organic substance, combined nitrogen in a suitable form, smaller quantities of phosphorus, sulfur, potassium, and magnesium (see Volume I, Chapter 8), and minute amounts of a number of other elements (the so-called trace elements) including iron, zinc, copper, manganese, molybdenum, and possibly calcium (see Volume I, Chapter 8).

1. Concentration of Nutrients

In a very weak nutrient solution a fungus may be able to produce a few, sparsely branched hyphae but may not be able to sporulate. With a slight increase in concentration, spores may be produced. Sporulation is usually inhibited by a concentration considerably below that which inhibits mycelial growth. The transfer of a well-nourished mycelium to water or a weak nutrient solution is a well-known method of inducing spore formation. Fruit bodies of certain basidiomycetes will not develop in either a concentrated solution or a small volume of dilute solution, but will do so in a large volume of the same dilute solution (Plunkett, 1953). Fruit bodies of some ascomycetes, e.g., *Sordaria fimicola,* will not form in a medium containing 5.0% glucose, but will do so if the same amount of sugar is supplied in small increments (Hawker, 1939a).

Many plant parasites (e.g., many rusts) produce resting spores only in late summer or autumn. Reduction in food supply is one possible cause of this. The basidiomycete parasites of standing timber produce their fruit bodies only after a considerable period of vegetative activity, by which time the center of the tree trunk is in an advanced state of decay. Again a likely stimulus to fruit-body formation is the depletion of the cellulose and/or lignin of the heartwood. Some entomogenous fungi, such as *Cordyceps* spp. produce fertile stromata bearing the perithecia only when the softer parts of the host have been consumed and replaced by fungal cells. The production of spores by many fungi in the natural habitat is consistent with the view that sporulation is induced by a reduction in food supply, but it is difficult to prove this under natural conditions.

Concentration of nutrients often has less effect on the production of asexual spores than on sexual reproduction. The range of concentration permitting the formation of conidia of many species may be only slightly narrower than that allowing hyphal growth, e.g., many species of *Penicillium* and *Aspergillus*. Such plant parasites as *Venturia inaequalis,* the cause of apple scab, or *Gnomonia erythrostoma,* the cause of cherry leaf scorch, produce their asexual spores (conidia) during the summer before the host is seriously damaged and while the fungus is growing vigorously with an abundant supply of food. The perithecia, however, are not formed until the host leaves die. Similarly many rusts (e.g., *Puccinia graminis*) produce large quantities of asexual uredospores during the summer but teleutospores only later in the year. The factors distinguishing between production of asexual and "sexual" spores by a parasite growing on the host plant are complex, but reduction in food supply may well be important.

Thus, it is clear that spore formation and, in particular, sexual reproduction, has a greater minimum food requirement than has vegetative growth, but that too high a concentration of nutrients encourages vegetative growth rather than sporulation. These effects of concentration of food materials are biologically valuable since, with many fungi in the natural habitat, vigorous mycelial growth continues until the substratum has been fully exploited. The fall in food supply then induces spore formation at a time when this is most valuable.

2. Nature of Nutrients

a. Carbon. All fungi need oxidizable organic compounds as sources of energy and of most of their carbon requirements. They are unable to synthesize carbohydrates from carbon dioxide and water either by photosynthesis, as do green plants and certain pigmented sulfur bacteria, or by the oxidation of inorganic compounds, as do certain specialized groups of bacteria. Consequently, the fungi are dependent upon relatively complex organic material as a source of energy. In natural habitats they obtain this from living organisms or from organic material of biologic origin. Pure culture experiments show that hexose sugars, notably glucose or fructose, are the most generally suitable carbon compounds for vegetative growth and also for the formation of the asexual spores of many species. In contrast, sexual reproduction of many fungi is checked or completely inhibited by concentrations of glucose and fructose considerably lower than those optimal for vegetative growth, but may be favored by relatively high concentrations of more complex carbohydrates. A strain of *Sordaria fimicola* (syn. *Melanospora destruens*) produced no perithecia on media containing 5.0% glucose, 5.0% fructose, or 2.5% glucose plus 2.5% fructose, but produced large numbers on a similar medium in which hexose sugar was replaced by sucrose or in which the same amount of hexose sugar was supplied in small doses (Hawker, 1939a). Perithecial production on some other di-and polysaccharides was poorer than with sucrose, but superior to that with hexoses alone (Table I). In all media there was an inverse correlation between dry weight of mycelium and intensity of sporulation. Other fungi reacted to particular carbohydrates (Table II). Hawker and Chaudhuri (1946) showed that the effect of a particular carbohydrate depended upon the rate at which the fungus could hydrolyze it (Fig. 1). Thus, substances hydrolyzed rapidly had an effect similar to that of an initial supply of a comparable amount of hexose sugar, those hydrolyzed only very slowly or not at all gave a starvation effect with poor growth and little or no fruiting, but those which were hydrolyzed at an intermediate rate, such that a low concentration of hexoses was maintained over a long period, gave the highest number of fruit bodies. Hawker (1947) showed that this was only partly due to the maintenance of a concentration of hexoses optimal for fruiting and that the ease of phosphorylation was another important factor in determining the effect of a particular carbohydrate.

Other carbon compounds, such as amino acids, proteins, lipids, and even some organic acids and higher alcohols can be used by some fungi as sources of energy, but these are usually less suitable both for vegetative growth and sporulation.

b. *Nitrogen.* No fungi have been proved to fix nitrogen, but most are able to use nitrates or ammonium salts. A few require organic nitrogen, usually in the form of specific amino acids, and it is likely that such fungi are unable to synthesize one or more of the amino acids essential for protein synthesis. As a rule any nitrogenous substance which permits the growth of a particular fungus will also be suitable for sporulation, in contrast to the differential effects of various carbon compounds. The minimum concentration of nitrogen necessary for reproduction may be slightly greater than that allowing vegetative growth. High concentrations of nitrogen usually decrease sporulation, and this depressing effect may often be correlated with the accumulation of toxic metabolic products (staling substances). The rate of vegetative growth usually falls at similar concentrations. The effects of nitrogenous substances on sporulation thus closely follow those on mycelial growth. While the nitrogen supply has a less specific effect than carbon on reproduction, the *ratio* of carbon and nitrogen may be important.

TABLE I

EFFECTS OF NATURE AND CONCENTRATION OF CARBON SOURCE ON THE FORMATION OF PERITHECIA BY *Sordaria fimicola* (*Melanospora destruens*)[a,b]

Nature of carbon source	Amount of carbon compound (gm/100 ml medium)[c]						
	0.0	0.5	1.0	2.0	5.0	10.0	20.0
Arabinose	3.0	10.0	11.8	7.2	—	—	—
Glucose	3.0	7.2	3.2	Few	0	0	0
Fructose	3.0	8.3	3.0	Few	0	—	—
Galactose	3.0	3.5	1.6	1.0	—	—	—
Sucrose	3.0	2.9	3.2	5.2	9.4	9.9	Few
Lactose	3.0	8.8	11.3	10.2	9.8	7.0	—
Maltose	3.0	8.2	5.4	4.7	—	—	—
Raffinose	—	—	2.3	4.6	—	—	—
Starch	3.0	7.7	11.1	13.1	10.2	7.0	—
Inulin	3.0	3.5	3.7	2.0	—	—	—
Mannitol	3.0	3.4	3.2	3.4	3.6	0	—

[a] Data from Hawker (1939a).

[b] Basal medium: KNO_3, 3.5 gm; KH_2PO_4, 1.75 gm; $MgSO_4$, 0.75 gm; lentil concentrate as source of growth substances, 0.5 ml; distilled water, 1 liter; agar, 15 gm. Experiments with pure thiamine and biotin as source of growth substance, instead of lentil extract, gave comparable results.

[c] Figures are mean numbers of perithecia per microscope field at 10 arbitrarily chosen points in each of three to ten plates. Dash indicates that no data are available.

14. Environmental Influences on Reproduction

TABLE II

Percentage Concentration of Various Carbohydrates Optimal for Fruit-Body Formation of Six Species of Ascomycetes[a]

Species	Glucose	Fructose	Sucrose	Maltose	Lactose	Starch
Sordaria fimicola strain 1	0.5	0.5	5.0	0.5	0.5	1.5
Sordaria fimicola strain 2	1.0	—[b]	10.0[c]	—	1.0	2.0
Podospora sp.	1.0	1.0	10.0[c]	2.0	10.0[c]	2.0
Melanospora zamiae	0.5	1.0	0.5	5.0[c]	5.0[c]	0.75
Ceratostomella adiposa	0.5	0.5	0.5	0.75	5.0[c]	0.5
Chaetomium cochlioides	2.0	2.0	2.0	2.0	10.0[c]	10.0[c]
Pyronema omphalodes	5.0	5.0	5.0	1.0	10.0[c]	10.0[c]

[a] Data from Hawker and Chaudhuri (1946).
[b] Dash indicates that no data are available.
[c] This was the highest concentration tested; the optimum concentration might have been higher.

When *Botrytis cinerea* is grown on glucose-peptone agar the production of conidia is favored by a low ratio of glucose to peptone and that of sclerotia by a high ratio (Peiris, 1947). Carlile (1956) showed that chlamydospores of *Fusarium oxysporum* were formed on a glucose, nitrate, salts medium only when the glucose:nitrate ratio was low. The shape and size of spores may also be influenced by the carbon:nitrogen ratio. Reduction in the ratio of glucose to asparagine in the medium reduces the length and number of septa of macroconidia produced by some species of *Fusarium* (Brown and Horne, 1926; Horne and Mitter, 1927) and increases the proportion of small oval conidia to long curved ones produced by species of *Cytosporina, Phomopsis,* and *Diaporthe* (Nitimargi, 1937).

c. *Mineral Elements.* There are many references in the literature to the effect of various mineral elements on sporulation. It is clear, however, that any element required for vegetative growth is also essential for sporulation. As a rule the minimum amount permitting measurable mycelial growth is insufficient for sporulation. Sporulation of many fungi is inhibited by concentrations of minerals, such as the trace element zinc, well below that which stops vegetative growth.

With the possible exception of calcium, no element in addition to those necessary for vegetative growth is known to be necessary for sporulation. Basu (1951) showed that a synthetic medium allowing good growth of *Chaetomium globosum* needed the addition of a small quantity of calcium to make it suitable for the initiation and development of perithecia. Hadley and Harrold (1958) showed that while added calcium was not necessary for vegetative growth of *Penicillium notatum* in submerged culture, conidia developed only after the addition of calcium. It is not clear whether calcium is a real exception to the general rule that sporulation does not require

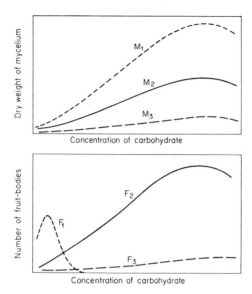

FIG. 1. The curves show three types of effect of concentration of carbohydrate on mycelial growth (M_1–M_3) and on fruiting (F_1–F_3). M_1 and F_1 illustrate typical response to hexose sugars (e.g., *Sordaria fimicola* on glucose). M_2 and F_2 represent the effect of a more complex carbohydrate on a fungus which can break it down at a moderate rate (e.g., *S. fimicola* on sucrose). M_3 and F_3 show the extreme type where the ability of a fungus to break down a complex carbohydrate is so poor that a starvation type of growth results (e.g., *Pyronema omphalodes* on lactose). From Hawker and Chaudhuri (1946).

elements additional to those essential for vegetative growth or whether, more probably, the amount required for the latter is so small that it is not removed by the normal purification techniques. Further work is required not only with calcium, but with other trace elements. Most of the available data on the effect of trace elements on sporulation have been obtained with *Aspergillus niger,* and it is obviously desirable that detailed studies of other fungi should be undertaken.

d. Organic Growth Substances. Many fungi are able to grow and reproduce on defined synthetic media; others will do so on appropriate natural media, but fail to grow on a synthetic medium unless traces of one or more specific organic substances are added. These include a number of known vitamins and some unidentified compounds. It can be shown that all fungi need these growth substances, but that many are able to synthesize their requirements from a sugar-salts medium. Others again can synthesize part of their requirements but grow better in the presence of an external supply. Many can synthesize enough for good vegetative growth but need a further supplement for sporulation. Some fungi are able to synthesize a

14. Environmental Influences on Reproduction

particular vitamin if one or more of its precursors is supplied. Each stage in synthesis of a complex substance is thought to be controlled by a single gene, and loss or damage to any one of these will interrupt the chain of reaction and so make the fungus dependent on an external supply of the finished product or of an appropriate precursor.

The true growth substances, such as thiamine (vitamin B_1), biotin (vitamin H), or pyridoxine (vitamin B_6), are required in only minute quantities and are known to form parts of essential enzyme systems (e.g., thiamine is cocarboxylase). Others (such as certain purines, some amino acids, and inositol) are required in rather larger amounts by those organisms unable to synthesize them and are probably needed in the synthesis of major cell components, such as nucleic acids and proteins, and for the formation of complex spore walls.

None of these known growth substances is a specific "spore-promoting" compound. All are needed for vegetative growth but are usually needed in greater amount for sporulation. So far only a few specific spore-promoting substances are known, e.g., the hormones produced by such fungi as *Achlya* (Raper, 1939, 1952). These are considered in Chapter 13. The effects of known vitamins have been reviewed elsewhere (Hawker, 1957).

The actual growth substance requirements differ among species, between strains of the same species, and even in the same strain under different environmental conditions and with the length of time it has been maintained in artificial culture. Thus, one strain of *Sordaria fimicola* has been reported to grow in a synthetic medium but to require biotin for the formation of perithecia and to require further increases in biotin supply for the production of mature, viable ascospores (Barnett and Lilly, 1947a); another requires thiamine for growth but produces perithecia only with the further addition of biotin; a third requires biotin for growth but fruits only when thiamine is present too (Table III). This last strain (originally identified as *Melanospora destruens*) grew well and produced a few perithecia on a synthetic glucose-salts medium when first isolated but soon needed thiamine for perithecial production and later required biotin also, even for mycelial growth. The vitamin requirements of a fungus are thus determined by its synthetic abilities and may change if its genetic constitution is altered by mutation or otherwise. Such changes are frequent in culture but must occur also in nature. In culture genetic changes are almost invariably in the direction of loss of synthetic ability. A "deficient" mutant is, however, likely to disappear under natural conditions, since it can survive only by colonizing a richer substratum.

Many plant parasites are deficient for one or more known growth substances (i.e., they are unable to synthesize them). These organisms would be at a disadvantage in the presence of less exacting species, and it may well be that their parasitic ability has enabled them to escape from such competition. Mycorrhizal basidiomycetes are usually thiamine-deficient, while many of the woodland saprophytes (the litter fungi) growing in the layer of fallen leaves are able to synthesize this vitamin. The mycorrhizal species have been shown to obtain the vitamin from the living roots, which are a richer source than are the dead leaves. It is claimed that some mycor-

TABLE III

The Effect of Thiamine, Biotin, and Inositol on Growth and Production of Perithecia of Six Isolates of Sordaria fimicola and One of Melanospora zamiae[a]

Isolate		Basal medium (A) without growth substances	A + thiamine	A + biotin	A + thiamine + biotin	A + thiamine + biotin + inositol
S. fimicola	(i)	0, 0[b]	0, 0	mm, 0	mmm, ppp	mmm, ppp
	(ii)	0, 0	0, 0	mm, 0	mmm, ppp	mmm, ppp
	(iii)	0, 0	0, 0	mm, 0	mmm, ppp	mmm, ppp
	(iv)	0, 0	0, 0	m, 0	mm, pp	mm, pp
	(v)	0, 0	0, 0	m, 0	mm, pp	mm, pp
	(vi)	m, 0	mm, p	m, 0	mmm, ppp	mmm, ppp
M. zamiae		0, 0	m, 0	m, 0	m, p	m, p

[a] Data from Hawker (1951).
[b] The first symbol in each column refers to mycelial growth, the second to production of perithecia: *m*, very slight mycelial growth; *mm*, fair mycelial growth; *mmm*, good mycelial growth; *p*, few scattered perithecia; *pp*, fairly numerous perithecia; *ppp*, numerous perithecia. Basal medium: glucose, 5 gm; KNO_3, 3.5 gm; KH_2PO_4, 1.75 gm; $MgSO_4$, 0.75 gm; distilled water, 1 liter.

rhizal basidiomycetes produce fruit bodies only when growing in association with tree roots. It is possible that this is a result of the availability of a continuous supply of thiamine, although other factors are likely to influence this complex relationship.

The localization of spores of some parasites in particular parts of the host (e.g., the grain and anther smuts which produce spores in the ovule or anther, respectively) may be due to nutritional factors, of which the local concentration of vitamins may be one.

It is clear that nutrition plays an important part in initiating the reproductive phase and in the development and maturation of spores and sporophores, but even if all nutritional requirements are satisfied reproduction will still be prevented if other external factors are unfavorable.

B. Water Supply

Both the water content of the substrate and the relative humidity of the atmosphere above the substratum are of importance in controlling growth and reproduction of fungi.

14. Environmental Influences on Reproduction

Since fungi absorb their food in solution it is clear that a supply of water is essential for growth and sporulation. In general, fungi are able to grow only in rather dilute solutions and, as pointed out in the preceding section, sporulation may be inhibited by concentrations considerably below the maximum permitting vegetative growth. Thus, reproduction obviously requires an adequate supply of water and may be more exacting in this respect than is vegetative growth. Aquatic fungi need free water for the production of their zoosporangia. Semiaquatic fungi such as *Pythium* and some species of *Phytophthora* may form their sporangia under slightly drier conditions but require free water for the dispersal of the zoospores.

The delicate sporangiophores and conidiophores of many fungi are particularly sensitive to dry conditions. Most of these develop only when the humidity is relatively high. Many plant parasites (e.g., *Phytophthora infestans* and the downy mildews), protected by the tissues of the host, grow vegetatively within these, but emerge to produce asexual sporangia and conidia only when the humidity is high.

The range of relative humidity (R.H.) permitting sporulation may be very narrow, e.g., 90–100% and 98–100% R.H. for conidia and conidiophores of *Peronospora destructor* (onion mildew; Yarwood, 1943) and *Bremia lactucae* (lettuce mildew; Ogilvie, 1944), respectively. Quite brief and small fluctuations below the optimum humidity may check the development of the sporangia of *Phytophthora infestans* (Orth, 1937), and this effect is much more severe than that of large fluctuations in temperature. The "blight warnings" given to farmers in July and August are based mainly on this effect of high humidity on sporulation.

Nevertheless very damp conditions may not be the best for the final stages of spore formation. For example the conidial (*Monilia*) state of species of *Sclerotinia* causing brown rot of rosaceous fruits consists of branched chains of spores. These form only under conditions of *high* humidity, but a slight *reduction* in humidity is necessary to permit the rounding off and separation of the spores.

In contrast, other species, such as *Venturia pyrina* (the cause of pear scab), bud off their conidia only in the presence of a film of water (Cheal and Dillon Weston, 1938). It is obvious that much work is needed to elucidate the effect of water supply on growth and on the various types and stages of sporulation of different species of fungi.

Water supply, and in particular relative humidity, may determine the kind of spore produced in those fungi having more than one type. Thus, at 25°C and above, the proportion of multispored sporangia to conidial heads produced by *Choanephora cucurbitarum* is greater at a relative humidity of 100 than at lower humidities (Barnett and Lilly, 1955). Humidity also determines the predominance of the asexual or sexual phases in some fungi but the evidence is often contradictory, suggesting that other undetermined factors also are operative. Thus Klebs (1898, 1899, 1900), confirmed by Robinson (1926), reported that high humidity favors the sexually produced zygospores of *Syzygites megalocarpa* and that the optimum for asexual reproduction (by sporangia) is lower. Baker (1931) obtained both spore forms over a range of 0–100% R.H. In contrast sporangia of *Rhizopus sexualis* develop under conditions of low temperature and high humidity unsuitable for zygospore formation. Temperature may, however, be the more important factor with this fungus. The oogonia and antheridia of some species of *Phytophthora* (e.g., *P. cactorum*) form freely on a suitable agar medium, whereas sporangia are few unless the plate is flooded with water.

While most types of sporulation need a damp substratum and a humid atmosphere, some are encouraged by slight drying. The asci of *Eremascus fertilis* form readily in pure culture on a sugary medium if the lid of the petri dish is raised long enough to allow partial drying of the medium. It is not clear, however, whether drying of the substrate or reduction of atmospheric humidity is responsible for increased ascus formation. A comparable example is the formation of sporangia in myxomycetes (e.g., *Badhamia utriculosa*) when the plasmodium is exposed to dry conditions. The production of many types of resting spores under natural conditions is often correlated with drying, but in a complex habitat it is usually impossible to distinguish the effects of reduced water supply from those of high temperature or increased concentration of nutrients.

Fruit bodies of some higher fungi (e.g., *Marasmius* spp., *Schizophyllum commune*, many woody and leathery bracket fungi, and the gelatinous *Auricularia* and *Tremella* in basidiomycetes; and tough stromatic pyrenomycetous species, such as *Daldinia concentrica* or species of *Xylaria*, in ascomycetes) are formed only on a damp substratum but can survive considerable periods of desiccation and will commence to shed spores again with a return to moist conditions.

The shape and size of spores and spore-bearing structures are frequently influenced by humidity. The sporangiophores of *Mucor hiemalis* and some other members of the Mucorales elongate only in a rather moist atmosphere, but those of the related *Phycomyces blakesleeanus*, which have unusually thick rigid cell walls, develop normally in a dry atmosphere if the substrate is kept moist (Ingold, 1954). The conidiophores of such fungi as *Botrytis cinerea* and species of *Penicillium* are long and branching with few spores in a saturated atmosphere but are short and bear numerous spores in a relatively dry one. The shape and size of individual conidia of some species may also be influenced by atmospheric humidity. The cylindrical conidia of *Ramularia vallisumbrosae* are shorter and have fewer septa under conditions of high relative humidity than in a drier atmosphere (Gregory, 1939).

14. Environmental Influences on Reproduction

The form of the complex fruit bodies of higher fungi is influenced by external factors, including humidity. Hopp (1938), grew *Ganoderma applanatum* on blocks of poplar wood under conditions of controlled humidity and obtained normal fruit bodies only when aeration was good and the supply of water to the mycelium was adequate. Under these conditions normal fruit bodies were produced at a relative humidity of 73%, but only abnormal ones occurred at 53 or at 100% R.H. Plunkett (1956) showed that rate of water loss influenced the ratio of stipe length to pileus diameter in the xeromorphic *Polyporus brumalis*. Tremelloid outgrowths of the pileus of species of agarics have been reported and have been variously interpreted as being parasitic or abnormal outgrowths of the fruit body. Keyworth (1942) induced the formation of such outgrowths by passing a stream of air over cultures of *Coprinus ephemerus*. A possible interpretation is that the outgrowths were the result of the drying effect of the air stream. While results of this type must be interpreted with caution unless all environmental factors are strictly controlled, the evidence is consistent with a formative effect of humidity on sporophore development.

C. Hydrogen-Ion Concentration of the Substrate

Studies of the effect of hydrogen-ion concentration on growth and sporulation of fungi are usually concerned with the initial pH of the medium (Table IV). Since the pH alters as the fungus grows, such studies, while

TABLE IV

EFFECT OF pH ON PRODUCTION OF PERITHECIA BY *Sordaria fimicola* ON TWO DIFFERENT SYNTHETIC MEDIA[a]

Initial pH[b]	Basal medium with 0.5% glucose[c]	Basal medium with 0.5% sucrose[c]
2.4	0.0	0.0
3.8	0.0	0.0
4.1	0.0	3.8
4.6	1.2	5.3
5.0	1.7	7.5
5.5	1.8	6.7
6.2	2.0	5.8
7.6	1.9	4.6
8.8	1.5	0.0
9.2	0.0	0.0
9.6	0.0	0.0

[a] Data from Hawker (1947).

[b] All media became less acid during experiments, but the relative acidity remained the same.

[c] Figures refer to number of perithecia taken as the average in ten arbitrarily chosen microscope fields on each of three plates. Basal medium: KNO_3, 3.5 gm; KH_2PO_4, 1.75 gm; $MgSO_4$, 0.75 gm; distilled water, 1 liter.

valuable in determining media suitable for particular species, yield little information on the effect of pH on sporulation. The speed and direction of change with growth depends on the species, the nature and concentration of the food supply, and, to a lesser extent on other external factors.

Most fungi grow over a fairly wide range of initial pH, the limits of the range varying with the species. Sporulation may take place over the whole range or may be more restricted, often to a very narrow range. The range of initial pH which permits sporulation may, however, be very different from the range of pH at which sporulation actually takes place. For example, Lilly and Barnett (1947) showed that although perithecia of *Sordaria fimicola* are eventually formed on a medium with an initial pH as low as 4.0 they do not form until 19 days after inoculation, by which time the pH of the medium has risen to 6.84.

The optimum initial pH for sporulation may also differ from that for vegetative growth of the same species; different types of sporulation may have different optima and the optimum value may change with development of a particular reproductive structure. Thus, the optimum pH for the production of pycnidia, pseudothecia, and chlamydospores of *Mycosphaerella pinodes* is reported to be 5.0, 7.0, and 8.0, respectively (Sørgel, 1953). *Eurotium rugulosum* produces more perithecia and fewer conidia as the initial pH value rises within the limits permitting good growth (Lilly and Barnett, 1951). Plunkett (1953) showed that an initial pH of 4.5 prevented initiation of fruit bodies of *Collybia velutipes* but that when the primordia had been formed at a slightly higher pH they continued to develop even after the pH had fallen as low as 4.2 as a result of the growth of the fungus. Aschan (1954) obtained earlier fruiting of the same species at a pH lower than that optimal for production of the maximum number of fruit bodies. Apparently normal fruit bodies of several ascomycetes (e.g., *Eurotium herbariorum, Chaetomium globosum*) formed over a comparatively wide range of initial pH but contained viable ascospores only over a much narrower range (Lockwood, 1937).

There have been few attempts to analyze the mechanism of action of pH on growth and sporulation. It is known that pH may act in several different ways, such as influencing enzyme action, altering metal solubilities, modifying surface reactions, or preventing or facilitating the entry of vitamins, organic acids, or minerals into the hypha. The influence of pH on sporulation of a particular species may be exerted in a different manner over different parts of the range, and this may in some instances give two optima for the same spore phase.

Effects originally directly attributed to other factors have sometimes been found to be due to pH change brought about by these. For example, Robbins and Schmidt (1945) showed that the effect of temperature on the formation of zygospores of *Phycomyces blakesleeanus* was in fact due to its alteration of the pH of the medium. The beneficial effect of calcium on the sporulation of some fungi (Section II, A, 2, c) may be due to the counteraction of acidity. Antagonism between two species is frequently, but not always, the result of the modification of the pH of the substratum by one species in a manner detrimental to the second.

While a great deal more work is needed to elucidate the mechanism of the effect of pH, it is established that pH is often a critical factor in sporulation.

D. Temperature

1. Range of Temperature Permitting Reproduction

Temperature has a profound effect on both growth and reproduction of fungi. It influences the latter largely as a result of its effect on the many complex chemical and physical processes involved in vegetative growth but also may have a direct specific effect on the production of different types of spores or on the various stages in the initiation, development, and maturation of a particular spore type.

The most striking fact in the effect of temperature on reproduction is that the range permitting sporulation is almost always narrower than that at which mycelial growth occurs. Usually, but not invariably, the range allowing sexual reproduction is narrower than that for the asexual phase, which is itself narrower than that for vegetative growth and spore germination. Table V gives examples of temperature ranges for different phases of a number of fungi.

The shape of the temperature curve for a reproductive process is usually essentially similar to that for growth; that is, the optimum is usually nearer to the maximum than to the minimum. It is usually assumed that the increase in growth with rise in temperature above the minimum up to the optimum value is the result of the effect of temperature on the many chemical metabolic processes which control growth and that the eventual rapid fall in growth after the optimum temperature is reached is due to the effect of high temperature on the physical state of the cytoplasm. This latter effect is to some extent reversible since most fungi are able to survive at temperatures somewhat above that maximal for growth and to resume growth and sporulation on being transferred to more suitable conditions. The relatively narrow range of temperature permitting reproduction suggests that this phase involves some chemical and physical processes which are not necessary for vegetative growth and which are more exacting in their temperature requirements than are those which suffice for the vegetative phase.

Evidence that low temperature may be limiting reproduction through its effect on a particular chemical synthesis is afforded by *Rhizopus sexualis* and some related fungi. Initiation of zygospores of these fungi is inhibited at temperatures of 7–10°C (the exact temperature varying with the species), which permit slow mycelial growth and the production of asexual sporangia (Hawker et al., 1957). Zygospores which have passed the early stages of development at a higher temperature continue to develop even if they are then placed at a temperature low enough to prevent initiation. However, if a current of air is passed over a mature colony bearing numerous zygospores at 20°C and then, after cooling is passed over a young colony at 10°C, the latter will produce zygospores in the path of the stream of air (Hepden and Hawker, 1961). Thus, it is clear that a volatile substance

TABLE V

TEMPERATURE RANGES FOR GROWTH AND REPRODUCTION OF REPRESENTATIVE FUNGI

Fungus	Range for mycelial growth			Range for reproduction			Type of reproduction
	Min.	Opt.	Max.	Min.	Opt.	Max.	
Mucor racemosus (Klebs, 1900)	4–5	—[a]	32–33	6–7	—	30–31	Sporangia
Rhizopus sexualis (Hawker et al., 1957)	1	—	—	5 10	— —	— —	Sporangia Zygospores
Pilobolus microsporus (Gräntz, 1898)	2–4	—	33–34	10–12	—	28–30	Sporangia
Syzygites megalcarpa (Klebs, 1900)	1–2	—	31–32	5–6 5–6	— —	29–30 27–28	Sporangia Zygospores
Saprolegnia mixta (Klebs, 1900)	0–1	—	36–37	1–2 1–2	— —	32–33 26–27	Zoosporangia Oospores
Saccharomyces cerevisiae (Hansen, 1883)	4	—	38	9	—	37–5	Asci
Eurotium repens (Klebs, 1900)	7–8	—	37–38	8–9 —	— —	35–36 33–34	Conidia Cleistocarps
Penicillium sp. (Wiesner, 1873)	2–5	—	43	3	—	40	Conidia
Gnomonia vulgaris (Henricksson and Morgan Jones, 1951)	5	17	30	10	15	19–25	Perithecia
G. intermedia (Henricksson and Morgan Jones, 1951)	5	19	35	5	15–19	19	Perithecia

[a] Dash indicates that no data are available.

14. *Environmental Influences on Reproduction* 451

produced by mature colonies is able to overcome the inhibitory effect of low temperature on the initiation and early development of zygospores. Hepden and Folkes (1960) interpret this as the provision of a methyl donor essential for the synthesis of DNA. Differential staining of vegetative and conjugating hyphae supports this view and shows that vegetative hyphal tips are rich in RNA which, in the zygophores, largely disappears with a corresponding increase in DNA. Cold treatment partially prevents this change in the ratio of RNA to DNA. It is suggested that, in this example, low temperature inhibits reproduction only at a particular stage through its effect on a specific chemical process taking place at this stage and concerned with nucleic acid synthesis.

Another example of the differential effect of temperature on different stages in reproduction is described by Hirsch (1954) for the formation of perithecia in *Neurospora crassa*. In this heterothallic species perithecial initials (protoperithecia) are formed on monosporous colonies but develop into mature perithecia only after fertilization, that is, after the addition to the colony of conidia from a complementary strain. If after fertilization the colony is transferred from 25° to 35°C, none of the protoperithecia develop. Colonies grown continuously at 35°C do not even produce protoperithecia; those initially grown at 35°C and transferred to 25°C after fertilization produce mature perithecia. Continuous growth at 30°C results in protoperithecia which do not develop further. These results, which are summarized in Table VI, indicate that the maximum temperature permitting the formation of protoperithecia is higher than that for the further development of these to give mature perithecia.

TABLE VI

THE EFFECT OF TEMPERATURE ON FORMATION OF PROTOPERITHECIA AND MATURE PERITHECIA BY *Neurospora crassa*[a]

Temperature of incubation before fertilization[b] (°C)	Temperature of incubation after fertilization (°C)	Protoperithecia	Perithecia
25	25	+	+
30	30	+	−
35	35	−	−
25	35	+	−
35	25	+[c]	+

[a] Data from Hirsch (1954).
[b] In general, crosses in *Neurospora* are made by adding conidia of one strain to young cultures of another.
[c] Formed only *after* transfer to 25°C.

In both these examples, it is possible that the specific effect of critical temperature is on particular nuclear stages. Such an effect is indicated even more strikingly in *Ustilago maydis* (Bowman, 1946) where fusions between the sporidia of this smut fungus occur freely only at 20–24°C. Therefore, temperature requirements for nuclear fusion may be particularly exacting.

2. Effect of Temperature on Type of Reproduction

The asexual spores of many fungi form over a wider range of temperature than that suitable for the sexual or perfect phase. In some species, however, the temperature ranges for the two phases differ to such an extent that the type of spore produced depends on the temperature. The cleistocarps of some species of *Aspergillus* (Klebs, 1898, and general laboratory experience) are produced only at relatively high temperatures whereas conidia are most numerous at lower ones. Conidia of *Ceratostomella fimbriata* form freely at 18°C, but perithecia are absent. The latter are numerous at 25°C (Barnett and Lilly, 1947b). According to Baker (1931) *Syzygites megalocarpa* produces zygospores at higher temperatures than those at which sporangia develop. Similarly the sporangia of *Rhizopus sexualis* are produced freely at temperatures low enough to inhibit zygospore initiation but are formed only sparsely at 20°C or over. In contrast, *Thamnidium elegans* produces sporangia at temperatures above those at which zygospores develop. Fungi with more than one type of asexual spore may also produce one type or the other according to the prevailing temperature. Thus *Choanephora cucurbitarum,* in artificial culture (Barnett and Lilly, 1950) at 25°C, produces conidia more freely than multispored sporangia, while sporangia are the more numerous at 30°C, and are the only spore form at 31°C. This fungus produces only conidia in its natural habitat, but this may be due to a complex of factors and not solely to temperature. *Pseudopeziza ribis* (Blodgett, 1936) produces macroconidia over the narrow range of 20–24° and microconidia only at lower temperatures. Many such examples could be cited.

3. Effect of Temperature on the Morphology of Spores and Spore-Bearing Structures

Temperature may also profoundly influence the size and form of spores and sporophores, but there is no general rule as to these effects. Thus sporangia of *Choanephora cucurbitarum* increase in size with increase in temperature (Barnett and Lilly, 1950), but the homologous conidia of *Peronospora parasitica* (Thung, 1926) are smaller ($23 \times 19.5\ \mu$) at 20°C than at 5°C ($27 \times 23\ \mu$). Mrak and Bonar (1938) reported that the *relative* size of asci and ascospores of species of *Debaryomyces* alters with temperature so that at low temperatures the ascospores do not fill the asci.

Wall sculpturing may also depend to some extent on temperature, as with the oogonia of *Achlya colorata* (Reischer, 1949), which are smooth at 20°C and papillate at 15°C. Thus diagnostic characters may be altered by change in temperature.

The many different effects of temperature on reproduction indicate the complexity of the reproductive phases and suggest that temperature may influence a number of metabolic processes any one of which may be limiting under particular circumstances. Interaction with other external factors may mask or alter the nature of the direct temperature effect. Thus, Hawker (1947) demonstrated that the temperature optimal for the formation of perithecia of *Sordaria fimicola* is higher on a sucrose medium than on a comparable glucose one. The effect of temperature may be directly on some metabolic step, as postulated in the example of *Rhizopus sexualis* already given, or it may be indirect as with *Phycomyces blakesleeanus* where temperature was shown by Robbins and Schmidt (1945) to influence zygospore formation by alteration of the pH of the substratum. Further critical investigations are necessary before any general interpretation of the effect of temperature is achieved.

In the natural habitat the effects of temperature can seldom be separated from those of other environmental factors. In a few examples, however, the evidence for temperature effects is fairly clear. In England the oak mildew (*Microsphaera alphitoides* syn. *M. quercina*) is usually present in the conidial form only, but in unusually hot years abundant cleistocarps have been reported (Robertson and Macfarlane, 1946). In general the cleistocarps of other powdery mildews are also more numerous in warm weather but, since in England very warm weather is usually also very dry weather, it is not certain that this abundance of ascocarps is solely due to high temperature. Many rust fungi also tend to be particularly conspicuous in hot summers through the production of numerous spores. The antirrhinum rust (*Puccinia antirrhini*), which first became common in England in the early 1930's, was at first found only in the uredospore state. In the hot summer of 1955 teleutospores were formed abundantly, and these were also reported on plants in a warm greenhouse (Hawker, 1957). It is likely that the teleutospores form only at relatively high temperatures, although other factors also may control their incidence.

E. Aeration

Fungi, with the possible exception of a few aquatic species growing in mud or stagnant water, are strictly aerobic organisms. Some, such as many yeasts, certain species of *Fusarium,* and some members of the Mucorales, produce alcohol under conditions of low oxygen tension and must, therefore, possess the ability to metabolize anaerobically. These fungi usually do not grow or reproduce under such conditions. Even such fungi as the "aero-aquatic" hyphomycetes *Clathrosphaerina* and *Helicodendron,* which colonize decaying leaves in stagnant water, where bacterial activity must render the conditions nearly or completely anaerobic, produce their spores only when the leaves are removed from the stagnant water and exposed to air (van Beverwijk, 1951; Glen-Bott, 1955). Emerson and Cantino (1948) showed that *Blastocladia pringsheimii,* which inhabits decaying vegetable matter in stagnant water, produces its thick-walled resting sporangia only when the concentration of carbon dioxide is at least 95%. Nearly all fungi, however, require adequate aeration for vegetative growth and are even more exacting in their requirements for reproduction. Morton (1961) considered that "the most powerful stimulus to sporulation" of *Penicillium* "is the emergence of the mycelium into aerial conditions." It is common laboratory experience that growth may continue in tightly fitting dishes or plugged tubes but that increased aeration is necessary for sporulation, and there are many references in the literature to this greater requirement for air by reproductive processes (e.g., pycnidia of Sphaeropsidales, Leonian, 1924; apothecia of *Ascobolus* spp., Green, 1930; fruit bodies of *Polyporus brumalis,* Bannerjee and Bakshi, 1944; zygospores of *Rhizopus sexualis,* Hawker, unpublished data).

The effects of aeration on growth and reproduction may be due to one or more of a number of factors. The concentrations of oxygen, carbon dioxide, and various stimulatory and inhibitory gases, and the presence of water vapor, are all important. There is no evidence that atmospheric pressure is important within the range found normally.

1. Oxygen

While all, or nearly all, fungi have an absolute requirement for oxygen in the atmosphere, the actual concentration needed is usually rather low but may be higher for reproduction than for vegetative growth. Pycnidia of *Plenodomus fuscomaculans* (Coons, 1916) and perithecia of *Neurospora sitophila* (Table VII; Denny, 1933) are examples of reproductive bodies which fail to form at low concentrations of oxygen where mycelial growth is normal. Once the essential minimum concentration of oxygen is reached, the effects are usually slight over the whole range permitting sporulation.

2. Carbon Dioxide

It is likely that the deleterious effects of poor aeration on the growth and sporulation of fungi often are due to excess carbon dioxide instead of lack of oxygen. Many observers attribute the frequent failure of fungi to sporulate in large volumes of liquid media, unless these are shaken or otherwise aerated, to the accumulation of carbon dioxide as a result of respiration. Other factors, such as the accumulation of free ammonia or other volatile metabolic products, may be equally important. It has been proved, however, that the sporulation of many fungi is inhibited by lower concentrations of carbon dioxide than are needed to slow or stop vegetative growth, e.g., sporangia of *Mucor mucedo* (Lopriore, 1895), sporangia and conidia

TABLE VII

THE EFFECT OF OXYGEN CONCENTRATION ON FORMATION OF PERITHECIA BY *Neurospora sitophila*[a]

Percentage O_2	Time in days from inoculation to formation of perithecia
20.8	4
9.4	7
3.75	9
1.5	12
0.24	None formed at 30 days

[a] Data from Denny (1933).

of *Choanephora cucurbitarum* (Barnett and Lilly, 1955), ascospores of bakers' yeast (Bright *et al.*, 1949).

Increased concentration of carbon dioxide actually favors the formation of certain resting spores, e.g., the resting sporangia of *Blastocladia*, already referred to, and the chlamydospores of *Mucor racemosus*.

3. Ammonia

In the breakdown of organic nitrogenous compounds, particularly when other sources of carbon are absent or in low concentration, fungi tend to utilize the carbon constituent more rapidly than the nitrogen and the latter accumulates as free ammonia. Brown (1925) showed that such an ammonia residue caused "staling" of a species of *Fusarium* on a medium initially containing a small amount of glucose and with asparagine as the sole nitrogen source. Other observers have obtained similar results with a number of fungi and various nitrogenous substances. Sporulation is often inhibited before vegetative growth stops. The inhibiting effect of poor aeration on sporulation of *Pyricularia oryzae* was attributed by Henry and Andersen (1948) to ammonia released during growth of this fungus.

4. Volatile Fungicides

A number of organic fungicides depend for their efficiency on a volatile substance given off (e.g., the chlorinated nitrobenzenes, marketed as proprietary fungicides). These are usually more effective in preventing sporulation than in inhibiting vegetative growth. Such prevention of sporulation is particularly valuable in the control of diseases caused by such fungi as *Botrytis* spp. where spread of the disease is due to the dissemination of large numbers of air-borne spores. The mechanism of inhibition is not fully understood, but it is remarkable that some fungi are not significantly inhibited by these substances whereas others are effectively controlled.

5. Unidentified Volatile Stimulatory and Inhibitory Substances

It had long been suspected that certain volatile substances produced by the mycelium are concerned in the regulation of conjugation in heterothallic members of the Mucorales, but it was not until 1954 that Banbury (1954, 1955) showed that such substances are responsible for the attraction of the zygophores of complementary strains toward one another.

More recently, Hepden and Hawker (1961) showed that cold-induced inhibition of early stages of zygospore formation in *Rhizopus sexualis* (see Section II, D, 2) could be at least partially counteracted by a volatile substance produced by mature mycelium of the same fungus. Volatile substances produced by related fungi were less effective, and those by unrelated fungi were only slightly effective or had no effect. The nature of the volatile substance has not been elucidated, but there is some evidence that it might be methylamine.

6. Morphogenetic Effects of Aeration

The form of spores or of sporophores may be altered by atmospheric conditions. Thus Lambert (1933) claimed that excess carbon dioxide caused abnormal growth of mushroom sporophores and that excess oxygen gave larger and more compact fruit bodies. Normal expansion of the pileus of *Collybia velutipes* and *Polyporus brumalis* is prevented by poor aeration (Table VIII; Plunkett, 1956). The development of tremelloid outgrowths on the pileus of agarics, attributed by Keyworth (1942) to the drying effect of a stream of air, might also be influenced by other aspects of aeration.

While it is clear that adequate aeration is essential for spore production there is a need for more critical work to analyze the effects of atmospheric factors.

F. Radiation

The effects of visible light and of other radiations on growth and development of fungi have been reviewed by Smith (1936), Marsh *et al.* (1959), Mohr (1961), and Ingold (1962); also see Volume I, Chapters

23 and 24. The most striking effect of visible light is on the initiation and development of spores of a number of species.

1. Visible Light

Many fungi are apparently uninfluenced by visible light. These produce their spores equally well in darkness, continuous light, or alternating darkness and light. However, light may influence the size and shape of spores

TABLE VIII

THE EFFECT OF CARBON DIOXIDE CONCENTRATION ON DIAMETER (MM) OF PILEUS OF *Collybia velutipes*[a]

		Airlike gas streams		
Still air	Moving air	1% CO_2	2% CO_2	4.9% CO_2
1.2	4.7	2.6	1.8	0.96

[a] Data from Plunkett (1956).

and spore-bearing structures of fungi which are able to sporulate freely in the dark, as with *Sordaria fimicola,* which produces equivalent numbers of perithecia in darkness or in light, but those subjected to illumination are significantly larger. The macroconidia of some species of *Fusarium* are also longer in illuminated cultures. The length of the sporangiophores of *Phycomyces* and some other members of the Mucorales is influenced by light even in species which produce sporangia freely in continuous darkness. These and many other spore-bearing structures are strongly phototropic. Such a response is of great importance in spore discharge (Chapter 21).

The *type* of spore produced may also be controlled by illumination. Thus, *Thamnidium elegans* (Lythgo, 1961) produces both sporangioles and terminal multispored sporangia in the light but only sporangioles in continuous darkness.

Many species produce spores in darkness but produce them more freely in the light or in alternating light and dark conditions. These include many Fungi Imperfecti, such as *Botrytis cinerea* and *Trichoderma viride.*

A third group of species has an absolute requirement for light for sporulation, which is completely inhibited by continuous darkness. Fungi of this type occur in most of the major groups, e.g., *Pilobolus* spp. and *Choanephora cucurbitarum* among zygomycetes, *Pyronema omphalodes* and many other discomycetes among ascomycetes, some species of *Fusarium* and some members of the Sphaeropsidales among Fungi Imperfecti, and *Coprinus* spp. among basidiomycetes. Some of these fungi need only a small increment of light to induce sporulation; others require light over a longer period. Some species of *Coprinus* which are unable to produce fruit bodies in continuous darkness need only 2–3 hours' illumination for the initiation and subsequent development to maturity of the fruit bodies. *P. omphalodes* (Robinson, 1926), however, does not require light for the initiation of fruit bodies. Tufts of hyphae arise and eventually give rise to sclerotium-like bodies in complete darkness. If, when these tufts are forming, or just before this point, the colonies are exposed for 6 hours to light of 40 candle-power at a distance of 50 cm, antheridia and ascogonia are formed. These, however, do not give rise to fertile apothecia unless the periods of exposure to light total at least 24 hours. The pink pigment characteristic of normal apothecia is not synthesized in the sterile sclerotia formed in darkness. Fruit bodies of many agarics and polypores are initiated in darkness but develop abnormally unless exposed to light. Many other examples could be given to show that the phase of development which requires light differs in different light-requiring species. No generalization can be made as to whether light is needed for initiation, further development or maturation or for all these stages in reproduction.

A striking effect of light in inducing sporulation is the production of alternating zones of sporing and nonsporing hyphae (see Volume I, Chapter 27) in colonies exposed according to a diurnal periodicity or to artificially arranged alternating periods of light and darkness. This effect is seen in culture and also in the natural habitat. Concentric rings of spore-bearing tufts of *Monilia* spp. on rosaceous fruits damaged by the brown rot fungi and rings of pycnidia of *Phyllosticta* and similar fungi on plant leaves are familiar sights. These are almost certainly due to the diurnal periodicity of alternating light and darkness. The zones of spores are usually developed as a result of light stimulation but may actually form during the dark period on hyphae stimulated during the preceding period of illumination. The rhythmic zonation may continue for some time after the fungus is transferred to complete darkness, e.g., *M. fructigena* (Hall, 1933). Zonation may also be induced by light-inhibition of sporulation in those fungi which sporulate only in darkness.

Some fungi which are unable to sporulate in continuous darkness are also unable to do so in continuous light and need alternating periods of light and darkness. Others sporulate more freely in such alternating periods than in continuous light. Barnett and Lilly (1950) reported a detailed examination of factors controlling the production of both conidia and sporangia by *Choanephora cucurbitarum*. Their strain of this fungus formed conidia only in alternating light and darkness but sporangia were formed independently of the conditions of illumination. They concluded that at least two metabolic reactions (A and B) are influenced by light. Reaction A needs light, but strong light inhibits reaction B. Thus, in continuous bright light only reaction A takes place and conidial formation is inhibited by failure of reaction B. In continuous darkness reaction A is inhibited. For both reactions to take place alternating periods of light and darkness are required. A strain used by Christenberry (1938) formed conidia in complete darkness, although less freely than in alternating light and darkness. The reactions leading to conidial production must be different in the two strains. There are many other examples of striking differences in response to light between members of the same family, different species of the same genus and even strains of the same species. It is clear that, as with growth-substance deficiencies (Section II, A, 2, d), changes in the ability to synthesize some necessary enzyme may make a fungus more dependent upon favorable external factors than was the parent type.

Sporulation in some fungi is actually depressed or completely inhibited by light. Buller (1909–1950) claimed that the initiation of fruit bodies of *Coprinus sterquilinus* is inhibited in light and suggested that this has biological value since only those fruit bodies which are firmly based within the substratum reach maturity. Although the brown rot fungus *Sclerotinia fructigena* fails to form conidia in continuous darkness, sporulation of the closely related *S. fructicola* is inhibited by light.

Exact studies on the most effective wavelength of light are few, but there is considerable evidence that, in general, blue light is the most effective. In experiments with monochromatic light, Leach (1962, 1963) showed that the dosages of light necessary to induce reproduction in *Ascochyta pisi* and *Pleospora herbarum* decreased with decreasing wavelength. Requirements for sexual and asexual reproduction were not identical. Little is known of the mechanism of the light effect with respect to sporulation, but the effect on growth in general is considered in Chapter 23, Vol. I. It is of interest that some instances have been reported of the removal or modification of the light requirement by some other factor (e.g., temperature, humidity, or nutrition). Thus, Plunkett (1956) showed that the pileus of *Polyporus brumalis* does not form under conditions of high humidity and weak illumination but does so if either the light is increased or the humidity is reduced; conidia of *Helminthosporium gramineum* (Houston and Oswald, 1946) are formed in darkness on the infected barley leaf but, in artificial culture on potato-dextrose agar, are not; some members of the Sphaeropsidales (Leonian, 1924) produce pycnidia freely in the dark only at temperatures higher than those which are optimal in the light. Coons (1916) attempted to show that light could be replaced by certain oxidizing agents and reported that a few pycnidia of *Plenodomus fuscomaculans* formed in the dark in the presence of hydrogen peroxide. This result has not been confirmed. More critical studies on the nature of the light stimulus and on factors which may replace it are desirable before generalizations may be made.

2. Nonvisible Radiation

Little is known of the effects of radiation outside the visible spectrum. Sublethal doses of ultraviolet light or of nearby radiation stimulate sporulation of some fungi (Stevens, 1928), but the exact wavelength producing this effect has not been determined.

G. Gravity

Many spore-bearing structures are geotropic. Thus, gravity influences the direction of growth of various parts of these structures.

The upright growth of many simple spore-bearing structures such as sporangiophores and conidiophores is not necessarily due solely to the effect of gravity but may also be influenced by negative chemotropism directing them away from the substratum. Under suitable illumination phototropism also plays a part.

The large fruit bodies of most stipitate discomycetes and higher basidiomycetes are, however, strongly geotropic. The stipes of such discomycetes as *Geoglossum, Helvella,* and *Morchella* and of the agarics and stipitate polypores and hydnaceous species are negatively geotropic. The pilei of these species are usually diageotropic and gravity plays a part, together with light and humidity, in their expansion. The gills of the agarics (with the exception of species of *Coprinus*) and the teeth of species of *Hydnum* are positively geotropic. In such species this geotropism of the spore-bearing surfaces acts as a fine adjustment and ensures that they are placed in such a way that the discharged basidiospores have an uninterrupted fall and so are freed from the parent fruit body (see Chapter 21). The tubes or pores of the polypores are also formed in an exactly vertical position in response to gravity. The hymenia of less complex fruit bodies such as *Auricularia, Stereum,* or *Sparassis* are also influenced by gravity and are formed only on the under surfaces of the fruit bodies. Hymenia in the Clavariaceae are presumably not influenced by gravity, since they develop over the surface of the club-shaped fruit body without any obvious relation to the direction of gravitational stimulus.

The mechanism of response of sporing structures of fungi to gravity is entirely unknown.

H. Poisons, Inhibitors, and Fungistatic Substances

Chemical inhibition of fungal growth and the mechanisms by which various inhibitory substances act have been discussed in Volume I, Chapter 20. Little can be added here concerning the specific effects of such substances on sporulation, since insufficient data exist. In general the inhibiting effects on sporulation are more severe than those on growth. This is to be expected since, as already pointed out, any harmful interference with essen-

14. Environmental Influences on Reproduction

tial metabolic pathways is likely to result in a failure to synthesize the complex materials needed for reproduction.

The accumulation of staling products, metabolic toxic substances produced by some fungi (Section II, A, 2, b), often prevents spore production before growth is seriously slowed.

I. Contact Stimuli

It is a common phenomenon for sporulation to commence when the mycelium of a colony growing in artificial culture reaches the edge of the petri dish. It has been suggested that this is the result of contact with the rim of the dish, but it is more likely to be due to exhaustion of nutrients or even to better aeration near the edge of the dish. It is clear, however, that contact with a solid object does influence sporulation of some species; for example, fruit bodies of many hypogeous gasteromycetes are commonly found pressed against the roots of trees or against stones. These and the hypogeous ascomycetes (in particular, species of *Elaphomyces*) are frequently found in woodlands at the level of the hard clay pan beneath the leaf litter. The mechanism of this response is unknown. Raper (1952) claims that the stimulus of contact with a firm surface, together with the presence of hormonal exudates, causes the differentiation of the oospheres of *Achlya* after contact has been made between the antheridia and the immature oogonium.

J. Wounding

There are several reports of the increased production of conidia in *Fusarium, Alternaria,* and other genera by the cutting or grinding of the mycelium. Again the mechanism by which this stimulatory effect is brought about is entirely unknown.

K. Biotic Factors

Most of the recorded data relating to the effect of external factors on reproduction have been obtained by means of pure cultures. A few studies have been made with two-member cultures. In the natural habitat, however, such simplified conditions seldom occur. The fungus is usually growing in the company of other species of diverse types and competing with these for water, food, and oxygen. Owing to the nature of the habitats in which fungi grow and to their nutritional requirements they must obviously compete with other species of fungi and with other microorganisms, such as bacteria and myxomycetes, and often algae and protozoa also. These other organisms may injure a particular fungus or, more often, inhibit sporulation by more rapid utilization of nutrients and oxygen, by actually overgrowing the fungus, by the secretion of toxic antibiotic substances, by altering the composition and pH of the substratum, or by actively destroying and consuming spores or mycelium.

Other microorganisms may, however, actually stimulate sporulation of some fungi. Contaminant colonies on a petri dish culture are frequently surrounded by zones of intensified sporulation or rings of fruit bodies of the original culture. Asthana and Hawker (1936) listed many examples of this and showed that the formation of rings of perithecia of *Sordaria fimicola* around colonies of a number of unrelated fungi was due to the production of a stimulatory substance by the latter. Later Hawker (1939b) showed that this substance was thiamine. Similarly other growth substances produced by those fungi able to synthesize them may stimulate sporulation in deficient strains.

Reduction of nutrients or modification of the pH of the substratum through the activity of microorganisms may not always be harmful, but may actually stimulate sporulation of a particular fungus even when reducing mycelial growth.

Not only other microorganisms but also animals (including man) and green plants may influence sporulation of fungi in the natural habitat. Grazing animals may remove competitors or may allow light and air to reach microfungi; their dung influences the composition of the soil by providing organic materials which stimulate sporulation; man by his agricultural activities has a profound influence on other species, including fungi; the green plant both competes with and provides food and shelter for fungi and other microorganisms.

Many fungi are associated with green plants in so-called symbiotic relationships. Mycorrhizal species of basidiomycetes produce their fruit bodies only in the presence of tree roots of the appropriate species. Fruit bodies of some species of *Endogone* have been found only in contact with plant roots. Detailed investigations of the effect of the living plant on sporulation of fungi are needed.

L. Interaction of External Factors

Under artificial cultural conditions it can be readily demonstrated that the effects of a particular external factor on both mycelial growth and reproduction may be modified by changes in other such factors. For example, Plunkett (1956) showed that the development and final shape of fruit bodies of *Collybia velutipes* and *Polyporus brumalis* depend upon the interaction of a number of external factors, aeration, humidity, and light, rather than upon any one of these acting alone. Similarly, Barnett and Lilly (1950, 1955) have shown that the effect of light on the sporulation of *Choanephora cucurbitarum* is modified by temperature together with other factors. The formation of perithecia by *Sordaria fimicola* (Hawker, 1947) reaches a maximum at a higher temperature on a sucrose medium than on a comparable glucose one. Many such examples could be quoted, but the reasons for these interaction effects have usually not been fully elucidated.

In the natural habitat it is difficult to distinguish between the effects of the many variable external factors, but it must be assumed that these interact to control the type and intensity of sporulation.

III. POSSIBLE MECHANISMS OF TRANSLATION OF EXTERNAL STIMULI INTO VISIBLE CHANGE OF PHASE

From the few examples given in the preceding sections of this chapter it is clear that a large amount of data is available concerning the effects of various external stimuli on the initiation of the reproductive stage and on the development of the reproductive structures.

It is possible to make some generalizations as to the expected effects of external factors: (1) Conditions favoring maximum mycelial growth may or may not also favor asexual reproduction but are usually unfavorable to sexual reproduction. (2) The range of any particular external condition which will allow sporulation is usually narrower than that permitting mycelial growth and is sometimes narrower for sexual than for asexual reproduction. (3) Sporulation and, in particular, sexual reproduction usually require a higher threshold level of nutrients than does mycelial growth, but sporulation is usually inhibited at concentrations considerably below the maximum for growth; nevertheless the total amount of food necessary for the formation of complex fruit bodies is often greater than that sufficing for hyphal growth and is then best supplied in a large volume of dilute solution or as small increments over the growing period. (4) Conditions favoring initiation of reproduction are not necessarily equally favorable for later stages in the development and maturation of the reproductive bodies; much of the earlier work was reduced in value by failure to study each stage separately. (5) Since the conditions favoring vegetative growth, asexual sporulation and sexual reproduction differ, it is theoretically possible to control the type of growth by suitable manipulation of the environment.

In spite of the theoretical possibility of the control of phase of growth through alterations in external conditions, very little critical work has been done along these lines and few investigators have studied the mechanisms by which an external stimulus is translated into a visible morphogenetic response. Doubtless this scarcity of precise data is due to the inherent difficulties of such work, and it is to be hoped these will be overcome by the use of new techniques.

The few critical investigations carried out, however, indicate that changes in the nature and distribution of the chemical constituents of the hyphae precede reproduction and that changes, or shunts, in the metabolic pathway may be brought about by changes in external conditions. Turian (1957) showed that the formation of the female gametangium and the subsequent differentiation of the gametes of species of *Allomyces* is associated with the establishment of a ribonucleoprotein gradient in the hyphal tips. Hepden and Hawker (1961) showed by differential staining that the ratio of RNA:DNA in the hyphal tips changed during the early stages of zygospore formation in *Rhizopus sexualis*. Later (Hawker and Hepden, 1962) they showed that in some fungi sexual reproduction took place only after an initial period of intense respiration. The work of Cantino and his associates (Chapter 10) with *Blastocladiella emersonii* showed that the presence of relatively high concentrations (ca. 0.1%) of bicarbonate in the medium interfered with the Krebs cycle and altered the metabolic pathway in such a way that resting spores were produced instead of zoosporangia. Nickerson (1954) showed that the formation of chlamydospores by *Candida albicans* depends upon changes of metabolic pathway resulting from changes in the supply of nutrients. Other examples could be cited.

Hawker and Hepden (1962) discussed the probable series of events during the change from vegetative growth to the reproductive phase (Fig. 2). They considered that in young colonies, up to and just beyond the

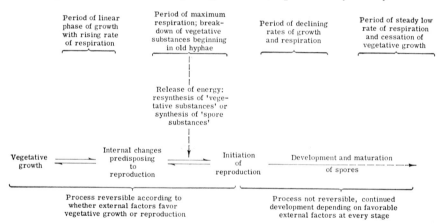

FIG. 2. Diagram to show suggested relation between growth, respiration, and sporulation in a fungus genetically competent to produce spores, growing in a static culture. From Hawker and Hepden (1962).

period of maximum vegetative growth and respiration, internal changes take place predisposing the fungus to reproduction but that these may be inhibited or accelerated by external conditions at any time during that stage. After the peak of respiratory activity has been passed, growth declines and, if external conditions are favorable, spore initials develop. The release of energy by the active respiration presumably promotes the synthesis of relatively large quantities of essential compounds, including novel spore-promoting substances. Up to this point the tendency toward sporulation is reversible, but soon a stage is reached when it is no longer reversible and when the spore or fruit body initials must either go on developing or abort. External conditions determine whether or not further development and maturation takes place.

The accumulation of data relating to the effects of external conditions on particular fungi is of value, but the elucidation of the mechanism of these effects is of greater fundamental interest. Workers on this subject should exploit new chemical and physical techniques to the full and, moreover, should distinguish between the various stages in development when attempting to determine the effect of environment on reproduction.

REFERENCES

Aschan, K. (1954). The production of fruit bodies in *Collybia velutipes*. I. Influence of different culture conditions. *Physiol. Plantarum* 7:571-591.

Asthana, R. P., and L. E. Hawker. (1936). The influence of certain fungi on the sporulation of *Melanospora destruens* Shear, and of some other Ascomycetes. *Ann. Botany (London)* 50:325-344.

Baker, R. E. D. (1931). Observations on the conditions for spore formation in *Sporodinia grandis* Link. *New Phytologist* 30:303-316.

Banbury, G. H. (1954). Processes controlling zygophore formation and zygotropism in *Mucor mucedo* Brefeld. *Nature* 173:499-500.

Banbury, G. H. (1955). Physiological studies in the Mucorales III. The zygotropism of zygophores of *Mucor mucedo* Brefeld. *J. Exptl. Botany* 6:235-244.

Bannerjee, S. N., and K. Bakshi. (1944). On the production of true pilei of *Polyporus brumalis* (Pers.) Fr. in artificial culture. *Current Sci.* 13:102-104.

Barnett, H. L., and V. G. Lilly. (1947a). The effects of biotin upon the formation and development of perithecia, asci and ascospores by *Sordaria fimicola* Ces. and de Not. *Am. J. Botany* 34:196-204.

Barnett, H. L., and V. G. Lilly. (1947b). The relation of thiamine to the production of perithecia by *Ceratostomella fimbriata*. *Mycologia* 39:699-708.

Barnett, H. L., and V. G. Lilly. (1950). Nutritional and environmental factors influencing asexual sporulation of *Choanephora cucurbitarum* in culture. *Phytopathology* 40:80-89.

Barnett, H. L., and V. G. Lilly. (1955). The effects of humidity, temperature and carbon dioxide on the sporulation of *Choanephora cucurbitarum*. *Mycologia* 47:26-29.

Basu, S. N. (1951). Significance of calcium in the fruiting of *Chaetomium* species, particularly *Chaetomium globosum*. *J. Gen. Microbiol.* 5:231-238.

Blodgett, E. C. (1936). The anthracnose of currant and gooseberry caused by *Pseudopezziza ribis*. *Phytopathology* 26:115-152.

Bowman, D. H. (1946). Sporidial fusion in *Ustilago maydis*. *J. Agr. Res.* 72:233-243.

Bright, I. B., P. A. Dixon, and J. W. T. Whymper. (1949). Effect of ethyl alcohol and carbon dioxide on the sporulation of bakers' yeast. *Nature* 164:544.

Brown, W. (1925). Studies in the genus *Fusarium* II. An analysis of factors which determine the growth form of various strains. *Ann. Botany (London)* 39:373-408.

Brown, W., and A. S. Horne. (1926). Studies in the genus *Fusarium* III. An analysis of factors which determine certain microscopic features of *Fusarium* strains. *Ann. Botany (London)* 40:203-221.

Buller, A. H. R. (1909-1950). "Researches on Fungi," Vols. I-VII. Longmans, Green, New York.

Cantino, E. C. (1961). The relationship between biochemical and morphological differentiation in non-filamentous aquatic fungi. *Symp. Soc. Gen. Microbiol.* 11:243-271.

Carlile, M. J. (1956). A study of the factors influencing non-genetic variation in a strain of *Fusarium oxysporum*. *J. Gen. Microbiol.* 14:643-654.

Cheal, W. F., and W. A. R. Dillon Weston. (1938). Observation on pear scab (*Venturia pyrina* Aderh.) *Ann. Appl. Biol.* 25:206-208.

Christenberry, G. A. (1938). A study of the effect of light of various periods and wavelengths on the growth and asexual reproduction of *Choanephora cucurbitarum* (Berk. and Rav.) Thaxter. *J. Elisha Mitchell Sci. Soc.* 54:297-310.

Cochrane, V. W. (1958). "Physiology of Fungi," 524 pp. Wiley, New York.

Coons, G. H. (1916). Factors involved in the growth and pycnidium formation of *Plenodomus fuscomaculans*. *J. Agr. Res.* 5:713-769.

Denny, F. E. (1933). Oxygen requirements of *Neurospora sitophila* for formation of perithecia and growth of mycelium. *Contrib. Boyce Thompson Inst.* 5:95-102.

Emerson, R., and E. C. Cantino. (1948). The isolation, growth and metabolism of *Blastocladia* in pure culture. *Am. J. Botany* 35:157-171.

Glen-Bott, J. I. (1955). On *Helicodendron tubulosum* and some similar species. *Brit. Mycol. Soc. Trans.* 38:17-30.

Gräntz, F. (1898). Ueber den Einfluss des Lichtes auf die Entwicklung einiger Pilze Inaug. Dissert., Leipzig.

Green, E. (1930). Observations on certain Ascobolaceae. *Brit. Mycol. Soc. Trans.* 15:321-322.

Gregory, P. H. (1939). The life history of *Ramularia vallisumbrosae*. Cav. on *Narcissus*. *Brit. Mycol. Soc. Trans.* 23:24-25.

Hadley, G., and C. E. Harrold. (1958). The sporulation of *Penicillium notatum* Westling in submerged liquid culture. I. The effect of calcium and nutrients on sporulation intensity. II. Initial sporulation phase. *J. Exptl. Botany* 9:408-417, 418-425.

Hall, M. P. (1933). An analysis of the factors controlling the growth form of certain fungi, with special reference to *Sclerotinia* (*Monilia*) *fructigena*. *Ann. Botany (London)* 47:538-578.

Hansen, E. (1883). Recherches sur la physiologie et la morphologie des ferments alcooliques. II. *C. R. Lab. Carlsberg.* 2:29-102.

Hawker, L. E. (1939a). The influence of various sources of carbon on the formation of perithecia by *Melanospora destruens*. Shear in the presence of accessory growth factors. *Ann. Botany (London)* [N.S.] 3:455-468.

Hawker, L. E. (1939b). The nature of the accessory growth substances influencing growth and fruiting of *Melanospora destruens* Shear and of some other fungi. *Ann. Botany (London)* [N.S.] 3:657-676.

Hawker, L. E. (1947). Further experiments on growth and fruiting of *Melanospora destruens* Shear in the presence of various carbohydrates, with special reference to the effects of glucose and sucrose. *Ann. Botany (London)* [N.S.] 11:245-259.

Hawker, L. E. (1950). "Physiology of Fungi," 360 pp. Univ. London Press, London.

Hawker, L. E. (1951). Morphological and physiological studies on *Sordaria destruens* (Shear) comb. nov. (Syn. *Melanospora destruens*), *Sordaria fimicola* and *Melanospora zamiae*. *Brit. Mycol. Soc. Trans.* 34:174-186.

Hawker, L. E. (1957). "The Physiology of Reproduction in Fungi." Cambridge Univ. Press, London and New York.
Hawker, L. E., and P. McV. Abbott. (1963). Fine structure of vegetative hyphae of *Rhizopus*. *J. Gen. Microbiol.* 30:444-555.
Hawker, L. E., and S. D. Chaudhuri. (1946). Growth and fruiting of certain ascomycetous fungus as influenced by the nature and concentration of the carbohydrate in the medium. *Ann. Botany (London)* [N.S.] 9:185-194.
Hawker, L. E., and P. M. Hepden. (1962). Sporulation in *Rhizopus sexualis* and some other fungi following a period of intense respiration. *Ann. Botany (London)* [N.S.] 26:619-632.
Hawker, L. E., P. M. Hepden, and S. M. Perkins. (1957). The inhibitory effect of low temperature on early stages of zygospore production in *Rhizopus sexualis*. *J. Gen. Microbiol.* 17:758-767.
Hawker, L. E., A. H. Linton, B. F. Folkes, and M. J. Carlile. (1960). "An Introduction to the Biology of Micro-Organisms." Arnold, London.
Henry, B. W., and A. L. Andersen. (1948). Sporulation by *Piricularia oryzae*. *Phytopathology* 38:265-278.
Hepden, P. M., and B. F. Folkes. (1960). Possible relationship between nucleic acid metabolism and initiation of zygospores of *Rhizopus sexualis*. *Nature* 185:254-255.
Hepden, P. M., and L. E. Hawker. (1961). A volatile substance controlling early stages of zygospore formation in *Rhizopus sexualis*. *J. Gen. Microbiol.* 24:155-164.
Hirsch, H. M. (1954). Environmental factors influencing the differentiation of protoperithecia and their relation to tyrosinase and melanin formation in *Neurospora crassa*. *Physiol. Plantarum* 7:72-97.
Horne, A. S., and J. H. Mitter. (1927). Studies in the genus *Fusarium* V. Factors determining septation and other features in the section Discolor. *Ann. Botany (London)* 41:519-547.
Hopp, H. (1938). Sporophore formation by *Fomes applanatus* in culture. *Phytopathology* 28:356-358.
Houston, B. S., and J. W. Oswald. (1946). The effect of light and temperature on conidium production by *Helminthosporium gramineum* in culture. *Phytopathology* 36:1049-1055.
Ingold, C. T. (1954). Fungi and water. *Brit. Mycol. Soc. Trans.* 37:97-107.
Ingold, C. T. (1962). The reaction of fungi to light and the problem of photoreception. *Symp. Soc. Exptl. Biol.* 16:154-169.
Keyworth, W. G. (1942). The occurrence in artificial culture of tremelloid outgrowth on the pilei of *Coprinus ephemeris*. *Brit. Mycol. Soc. Trans.* 25:307-310.
Klebs, G. (1898, 1899, 1900). Zur Physiologie der Fortpflanzung einiger Pilze. *Z. Wiss. Botan.* 32:1-70; 33:513-597; 35:80-203.
Lambert, E. B. (1933). Effect of excess carbon dioxide on growing mushrooms. *J. Agr. Res.* 47:599-608.
Leach, C. M. (1962). The quantitative and qualitative relationship of ultraviolet and visible radiation on the induction of reproduction in *Ascochyta pisi*. *Can. J. Botany* 40:1577-1602.
Leach, C. M. (1963). The quantitative and qualitative relationship of monochromatic radiation to sexual and asexual reproduction of *Pleospora herbarum*. *Mycologia* 40:151-163.
Leonian, L. H. (1924). A study of factors promoting pycnidium formation in some Sphaeropsidales. *Am. J. Botany* 9:19-50.
Lilly, V. G., and H. L. Barnett. (1947). The influence of pH and certain growth factors on mycelial growth and perithecial formation by *Sordaria fimicola*. *Am. J. Botany* 34:131-138.

Lilly, V. G., and H. L. Barnett. (1951). "Physiology of the Fungi," 464 pp. McGraw-Hill, New York.

Lockwood, L. B. (1937). Hydrogen ion concentration and ascus formation. *Mycologia* 29:289-290.

Lopriore, G. (1895). Über die Einwerkung der Kohlensäure auf das Protoplasma der lebenden Pflanzenzelle. *Z. Wiss. Botan.* 28:531-626.

Lythgoe, J. N. (1961). Effect of light and temperature on growth and development in *Thammidium elegans* Link. *Brit. Mycol. Soc. Trans.* 44:199-213.

Marsh, P. B., E. E. Taylor, and L. M. Bassler. (1959). A guide to the literature on certain effects of light on fungi: Reproduction morphology, pigmentation and phototropic phenomena. *Plant Disease Reptr.* Suppl. 261.

Mohr, H. (1961). Wirkungen Kurzwelligen Lichtes. *Encyclopedie Plant Physiol.* 16:439-531.

Morton, A. G. (1961). The induction of sporulation in mould fungi. *Proc. Roy. Soc.* B153:548-569.

Mrak, E. M., and L. Bonar. (1938). The effect of temperature on asci and ascospores in the genus *Debaryomyces*. *Mycologia* 30:182-186.

Nickerson, W. J. (1954). Experimental control of morphogenesis in micro-organisms. *Ann. N. Y. Acad. Sci.* 60:50-57.

Nitimargi, N. M. (1937). Studies in the genera *Cytosporina, Phomopsis* and *Diaporthe*. VII. Chemical factors influencing sporing characters. *Ann. Botany (London)* 49:19-40.

Ogilvie, L. (1944). Downy mildew of lettuce. *Rept. Agr. Hort. Res. Sta. Long Ashton, Bristol* pp. 90-94.

Orth, H. (1937). Der Einfluss der Luftfeuchtigkeit auf das Keimverhalten der Sporangien von *Phytophthora infestans* (Mont). de Bary, des Energens der Kartoffelfäule. *Z. Pflanzenkrankh. Pflanzenschutz* 47:425-447.

Peiris, J. W. L. (1947). The *Botrytis* disease of *Gladiolus*, together with a physiological study of certain *Botrytis* species. Ph.D. thesis, University of London.

Plunkett, B. E. (1953). Nutritional and other aspects of fruit-body production in pure cultures of *Collybia velutipes* (Curt.) Fr. *Ann. Botany (London)* [N.S.] 17:193-216.

Plunkett, B. (1956). The influence of factors of the aeration complex and light upon fruit-body form in pure cultures of an agaric and a polypore. *Ann. Botany (London)* [N.S.] 20:563-586.

Raper, J. R. (1939). Role of hormones in the sexual reaction of heterothallic *Achlyas*. *Science* 89:321-322.

Raper, J. R. (1952). Chemical regulation of sexual processes in the thallophytes. *Botan. Rev.* 18:447-545.

Reischer, H. S. (1949). The effect of temperature on the papillation of oogonia of *Achlya colorata*. *Mycologia* 41:398-402.

Robbins, W. J., and M. B. Schmidt. (1945). Factor Z_2 and gametic reproduction of *Phycomyces*. *Am. J. Botany* 32:320-326.

Robertson, N. F., and I. Macfarlane. (1946). The occurrence of perithecia of the oak mildew in Britain. *Brit. Mycol. Soc. Trans.* 29:219-220.

Robinson, W. (1926). The conditions of growth and development of *Pyronema confluens* Tul. P. *omphaloides* (Bull.) Fuckel. *Ann. Botany (London)* 40:245-272.

Smith, E. C. (1936). The effects of radiation on fungi, *in* "Biological Effects of Radiation" (B. M. Duggar, ed.), Vol. II, pp. 889-918. McGraw-Hill, New York.

Sörgel, G. (1953). Über den Entwicklungsgang von *Mycosphaerella pinodes* (Berk. and Blox.). Stone. II. Die Einfluss der Wasserstoffonenkonzentration auf die Ausbildung der Fortpflanzungsorgane. *Arch. Mikrobiol.* **19**:372-397.

Stevens, F. L. (1928). Effects of ultra-violet radiation on various fungi. *Botan. Gaz.* **86**:210-225.

Thung, T. H. (1926). Opmerkingen over *Peronospora parasitica* op Kool. *Tijdscht. Plantenziekten* **32**:161-179.

Turian, G. (1957). Recherches sur la morphogenèse sexuelle chez *Allomyces*. *Ber. Schweiz. Botan. Ges.* **67**:458-486.

van Beverwijk, A. L. (1951). Zalewski's *Clathrosphaeria spirifera*. *Brit. Mycol. Soc. Trans.* **34**:280-290.

Wiesner, J. (1873). Ueber den Einfluss der Temperatur auf die Entwicklung von *Penicillium glaucum*. *Akad. wiss. Wien Abt. Math.* **17**:835-836.

Yarwood, C. E. (1943). Onion downy mildew. *Hilgardia* **14**:595-691.

Reproduction and Inheritance

CHAPTER 15

Life Cycles, Basic Patterns of Sexuality, and Sexual Mechanisms [1]

JOHN R. RAPER

Biological Laboratories
Harvard University
Cambridge, Massachusetts

I. INTRODUCTION

The fungi were once characterized, with considerable justification, as "a mutable and treacherous tribe." Probably no other characteristic or activity of the fungi contributed so prominently to this epithet as sex and the phenomena associated with sex. For the better part of a century the problem of sex in fungi has received a great deal of attention among students of the group, and a tremendous literature has accumulated through the years. The problem, however, seems to grow a trifle faster than does the solution and leads to the interesting situation, originally described by Lewis Carroll, in which one loses only little ground by running very fast.

During the early decades of the century, numerous scholarly publications summarized the existing information and integrated it into the more comprehensive problem of sexuality in plants and animals. The more notable of these works were Kniep's "Die Sexualität der niederen Pflanzen," 1928, Gäumann's "Vergleichende Morphologie der Pilze," 1926, and Dodge's translation and revision of this work in 1928 (see Gaümann and Dodge, 1928), Link's highly intellectual review of reproduction published the following year, and Hartmann's "Die Sexualität," published in 1943. In more

---

[1] The present chapter is a somewhat expanded and revised treatment of a paper previously published by the author: Life cycles, sexuality, and sexual mechanisms in the fungi. *In* "Sex in Microorganisms" (D. H. Wenrich *et al.*, eds.), pp. 42-81. Am. Assoc. Advance. Sci., Washington, D.C., 1954.

recent years, several reviews have appeared on sexuality and its many manifestations among the fungi (Whitehouse, 1949a, 1951; J. R. Raper, 1954, 1959, 1960; Ahmad, 1954; Burnett, 1956; Esser and Kuenen, 1965); none of these, unfortunately, treat the subject in the same detail as did the classic works of the 1920's. The implications of sexuality in fungi, however, remain largely unknown to biologists in general.

Essential sexual processes in the fungi, as in all other organisms, may be defined as those processes requisite to and including the juxtaposition and fusion of compatible nuclei and the subsequent sorting out of genetic factors in meiosis. These processes impose a cyclic progression during which plasmogamy, karyogamy, and meiosis are the irreducible cardinal events. The cycle, however, may be varied in three basically different ways: (1) by variations of the temporal relationships between the cardinal events by the intercalation, at different stages, of essential processes of growth; (2) by the imposition of genetic restrictions upon universal compatibility; and (3) by variations in the mechanical means of accomplishing the cardinal events.

These three modes of variation determine three distinct facets of sexuality, all separately definable but inextricably interrelated in the living organism: (1) life cycle, (2) basic pattern of sexuality, and (3) the sexual mechanism per se, respectively. Each facet is understandable only as a time-integrated and dynamic process. A detailed examination of each facet brings to light a number of facts which are little known but which are of considerable biological interest and are essential to an appreciation of the broad implications of sexuality in the fungi.

II. LIFE CYCLES

The fungi are commonly considered to be haploid organisms, with nuclear fusion occurring at the end of the vegetative phase to yield a diploid phase which persists for only a single nuclear generation. Although this is true of many species, particularly among the more primitive groups, the regular occurrence of exceptions to this simple pattern among the lower groups and the various complexities of the life cycles characteristic of the more highly evolved forms make such a generalization meaningless. Life cycles among sexually reproducing fungi run the gamut from completely haploid at the one extreme to completely diploid, except for immediate products of meiosis, at the other. In addition, certain life cycles unique to the fungi involve a highly specialized heterokaryon, the dikaryon, which has evolved as a distinctive nuclear phase (Whitehouse, 1951; J. R. Raper, 1955). The dikaryon greatly increases the range of variability in respect to the life cycle.

Since the dikaryon makes possible life cycles that are peculiar to the fungi, it deserves brief description and illustration at this point (Fig. 1). The essential sexual process is initiated by the fusion of two sexually compatible elements, spores, vegetative cells, or differentiated sexual organs, each containing one or more haploid nuclei (N). This fusion has been termed *plasmogamy* or *cytogamy*. The nuclei provided by the fusing elements may retain their individuality and become associated in one or

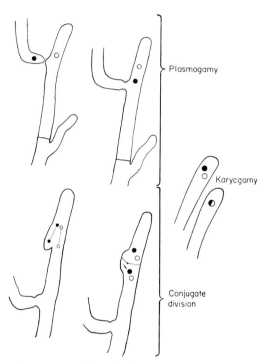

FIG. 1. Schematic representation of the initiation, propagation, and termination of the dikaryotic association of compatible nuclei. The dikaryon occurs in the higher ascomycetes in the ascogenous hyphae and universally in the Basidiomycetes in the "secondary" (dikaryotic) mycelium.

more pairs, each pair known as a *dikaryon* (B). The dikaryon may be propagated for a short, or for an indefinite, period of time by repeated, simultaneous mitotic divisions of its members, the division figures of the two nuclei commonly lying side by side. This process is termed *conjugate division*. Fusion of the two associated nuclei, or *karyogamy*, eventually occurs in terminal binucleate cells to establish the diploid phase (D); meiosis follows immediately, and the haploid nuclei are incorporated into spores. The dikaryotic phase thus serves, when present, to effect a temporal and spatial separation of plasmogamy and karyogamy. It also serves, because of the repeated divisions of its component nuclei, to increase greatly the productivity per sexual fusion both of the number of spores and of possible genetic combinations.

Seven basic types of life cycles can be clearly distinguished; these are diagrammatically represented in Fig. 2 and are designated by the letters *A* to *G*. Changes in nuclear phase are here considered the cardinal events in

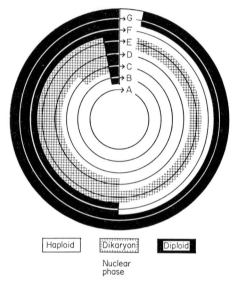

FIG. 2. Schematic comparison of life cycles in fungi. In each cycle, changes in nuclear phase are indicated, in clockwise sequence, by changes in shading. The double vertical line at the top of the diagram represents meiosis, and each of the two narrow sectors adjacent to the line represents a single nuclear generation (from Raper, 1954).

the life cycle. These changes are indicated for each cycle, in clockwise sequence, by differences in shading.

Asexual reproduction, by spores or other specialized organs, occurs at least in certain species belonging to each type and with few exceptions propagates the phase of the cycle from which the specialized reproductive cells are derived; the few exceptions will be mentioned later.

A. Asexual Cycle

Species apparently lacking any sexual expression or alternation of nuclear phase are fairly common throughout the fungi and constitute a sizable proportion of all known species, approximately 20% according to Bessey (1950). Because of the failure to observe rarely occurring sexual stages, the actual number of exclusively asexual species must be somewhat less than reported, but it must still be very large. The entire group known as the Fungi Imperfecti belongs here as well as numerous species which are clearly assignable by morphological characteristics to various groups throughout the perfect fungi, such as *Penicillium notatum*.

Certain of the benefits of sexuality are provided in many sexually sterile species by the association of nuclei of different origins in heterokaryotic mycelia, in which different genetic characters are expressed in much the same way as in dikaryotic mycelia or in diploid organisms (cf. Chapter 17; Pontecorvo, 1946). Heterokaryosis per se allows only for the interaction rather than for the permanent recombination of genetic characters of the associated genomes. Through the intimate association of genetically different nuclei which it affords, however, heterokaryosis serves as the primary requisite for somatic recombination (Chapter 18), which yields haploid recombinant nuclei via the parasexual cycle (Pontecorvo, 1956) and possibly via other means (Ellingboe and Raper, 1962; Ellingboe, 1963). The haploid products of somatic recombination differ only in their relative rarity from the products of the sexual cycle and provide for asexual forms the essential benefits of true sexuality. Somatic recombination has been reported in numerous asexual, as well as in sexual, species belonging to all major groups of the higher fungi, and probably it occurs in all groups of fungi that are able to form heterokaryons. A majority of asexual species have this competence, and it is probable that somatic recombination is a regular and highly significant feature in the biology of most fungi lacking overt sexuality.

B. Haploid Cycle

The most common type of life cycle found in phycomycetes, and more primitive ascomycetes, is completely haploid with the exception of a single, diploid, nuclear generation, the fusion or zygote nucleus. This type of life cycle is the simplest possible one that allows for sexual fusion and genetic recombination and in all probability represents the primitive type from which the more complicated cycles have evolved. The general correlation between this type of cycle and the relative morphological simplicity of the forms exhibiting it, not only in the fungi but also in the algae, tends to support this view.

C. Haploid Cycle with Restricted Dikaryon

A predominantly haploid cycle, which differs from the one discussed above by the separation in space and time of plasmogamy and karyogamy, is characteristic of the higher ascomycetes such as *Neurospora*. At the time of the fusion of the sexual cells or organs, one or more dikaryotic pairs of nuclei are formed, and these, by repeated mitotic divisions in the ascogenous hyphae, provide paired nuclei for a large number of ascal primordia, within which karyogamy and meiosis occur. The multiplication of associated nuclei, though often extensive, is nevertheless restricted both in time and by the complete dependence of the ascogenous hyphae upon the haploid mycelium. The nature of the dikaryotic phase here would suggest for this type of cycle an evolutionary position intermediate between the exclusively haploid cycle and the more complex cycles to be found among basidiomycetes.

D. Haploid-Dikaryotic Cycle

The predominant life cycle in the Basidiomycetes, many of the smuts excluded, differs from the cycle just discussed by the unrestricted and independent growth of the dikaryotic phase. Both the haploid, or homokaryotic, phase and the dikaryotic phase are completely independent and capable of indefinite vegetative growth and are terminated by dikaryotization and fruiting-body formation, respectively. The termination of each phase depends upon the achievement of certain requirements, which are, in each case, largely a matter of chance. The cycle may therefore be considered to comprise two roughly equivalent phases and to terminate in a single diploid nuclear generation, the fusion or definitive nucleus in the basidium.

A number of cases have been described among these forms in which differentiated spores produced by the dikaryotic mycelium reestablish the haploid phase (Brodie, 1931; Nobles, 1942). This occurs through the separation of the members of conjugate pairs of nuclei in the formation of uninucleate conidia or oidia. These specialized cells appear to attain their greatest effectiveness as fertilizing (dikaryotizing) agents, although germination in low percentage does serve to sort out the original dikaryotic components into haploid, vegetative mycelia. Similar cells produced on haploid mycelia behave in an identical manner.

E. Dikaryotic Cycle

The extreme development of the dikaryotic phase is exemplified by the cycle in which the immediate products of meiosis, ascospores or basidiospores, fuse to initiate the dikaryotic phase. Both haploid and true diploid phases are thus reduced to single nuclear generations. This type of cycle is occasionally seen in the yeasts (Guilliermond, 1940) and is of common occurrence among the smuts (Kniep, 1926).

The distinction made here between the haploid-dikaryotic and the dikaryotic cycles emphasizes the two extremes in what, in all probability, is a continuous series. Chance juxtaposition of compatible germinating spores of the haploid-dikaryotic type might result in the typical dikaryotic cycle; on the other hand, the experimental prolongation of the haploid phase, as sprout mycelia in smuts for example, converts the typical dikaryotic cycle into the haploid-dikaryotic.

Of particular interest in this and the haploid-dikaryotic cycle is the failure of the dikaryon in many cases to constitute a physiological summation of its haploid components. This phenomenon is reflected in (1) the host specificity of the two phases in the heteroecious rusts (for example, the haploid phase of the "black stem rust" of wheat is an obligate parasite of the barberry, whereas the dikaryotic phase is an obligate parasite of grasses); (2) the saprophytic habit of the haploid phase versus the obligate parasitic habit of the dikaryotic phase of many smuts (Christensen and Rodenhiser, 1940); and (3) the fruiting requirements of the dikaryotic phase of certain hymenomycetes as compared to the nutritional requirements of the component homokaryons (Schopfer and Blumer, 1940).

F. Haploid-Diploid Cycle

The alternation of haploid and true diploid generations, a common type of cycle in the algae and in the higher plants, is known to occur among fungi only in two groups. The better known of these is the aquatic phycomycetous order Blastocladiales, with certain species of *Allomyces* the best-known examples (Couch and Whiffen, 1942; Emerson, 1941; Harder and Sörgel, 1938; Kniep, 1929, 1930). In *Allomyces* and related genera, the vegetative mycelia of the two generations are identical except for the specialized reproductive organs which they bear. In the second case, a heteromorphic life cycle (i.e., alternation of dissimilar generations) has been reported for *Ascocybe grovesii* (Endomycetales) (Dixon, 1959). In this exceptional form, the haplophase consists of vegetative mycelium and asexual spores, and a diplophase, initiated by the fusion of two vegetative nuclei, persists throughout the formation and differentiation of a specialized ascophore, at the tip of which is borne a fascicle of asci. This cycle, which occurs in a form related to the yeasts, thus differs from the cycle of the typical mycelial ascomycetes by the interposition of a diplophase rather than a dikaryophase between plasmogamy and karyogamy.

G. Diploid Cycle

The cycle that is typical for the animal kingdom, completely diploid except for the immediate products of meiosis, is known to occur among the fungi in a number of yeasts (Guilliermond, 1940; Winge, 1935), and it also occurs in the Myxomycetes, or true slime molds (Alexopoulos, 1962). In both these cases, the haploid phase can be propagated, as in the dikaryotic smuts, by the isolation of ascospores and swarmers, respectively, prior to their fusion to establish the diploid phase.

A diploid life cycle has also been reported in some members of the

Blastocladiales (Couch and Whiffen, 1942; McCranie, 1942). This may be a slight variant of a true diploid cycle, as Wilson (1952) has reported a single mitotic division of the meiotic nuclei prior to the differentiation of gametes. A regular haploid phase of two nuclear generations is unique among the fungi and perhaps should be considered a distinct type of life cycle.

Convincing evidence that a diploid life cycle occurs in, and may be characteristic of, members of the Saprolegniales and Peronosporales has been presented by Sansome (1961, 1963), from studies on *Pythium debaryanum, Phytophthora cactorum,* and *Achlya* sp. The author interprets figures of nuclear division that she observed in differentiating oogonia and antheridia of all of these species to be meiotic; accordingly she considered the vegetative phase to be diploid, with the haploid phase restricted to a single nuclear generation or, at most, to a very few nuclear generations prior to fertilization of the oosphere. Meiosis in the biflagellate water molds had generally been considered to occur in the germination of the oospore (zygote), and the life cycle, consequently, haploid (Ziegler, 1953). Early and definitive resolution of any remaining uncertainties about the basic facts of the life cycle in this large and important group is highly desirable.

III. BASIC PATTERNS OF SEXUALITY

A. Semantic Difficulties

Blakeslee (1904), in the course of an investigation of zygospore formation in the common "black bread mold," *Rhizopus nigricans* [*R. stolonifera*], first demonstrated "bisexuality" in the fungi. The term *heterothallism* was introduced to designate the occurrence, within a given species, of two kinds of individuals, each self-sterile and presumably differing in sexual sign, and the necessity of interaction between mycelia of the two kinds to accomplish sexual reproduction. The term *homothallism* was coined for the antithetical condition, the occurrence of only a single kind of individual, self-fertile and sexually self-sufficient.

The original definitions of homothallism and heterothallism unfortunately, however, were somewhat ambiguous. The derivation of the term heterothallism implies differences of any sort between the individuals required for sexual interaction, whereas the original definition strongly implied differences in sexual sign. That Blakeslee was convinced of the sexual nature of the race differences, in spite of the slight and inconstant morphological differences, is strongly indicated by the work done by him and his associates during three decades toward the definite identification of (+) and (—) as ♀ and ♂, respectively (Satina and Blakeslee, 1928, 1929).

15. Life Cycles, Sexuality, and Sexual Mechanisms

Blakeslee (1920) and other workers determined the pattern of sexuality in most of the members of the Mucorales, the order to which *Rhizopus* belongs. It is of interest in the present discussion that all species of this group having a sexual stage were unambiguously divisible into heterothallic and homothallic species and that, in each heterothallic species, no irregularities in respect to sexual sign were encountered, although individual isolates often varied widely in sexual potency.

In the half century that has elapsed since Blakeslee's first demonstration of obligatory intermycelial reaction for sexual reproduction, similar situations have been reported for some members of every major group of fungi. The requirement for intermycelial reaction, however, is the only feature common to all cases: in some, sexual differences are clearly evident; in others, sexual differences equally clearly do not account for the pattern of self-sterility and cross-fertility. With the discovery of the several patterns of interactions, each differing in some important respect from that originally described in the Mucorales and termed heterothallism, a number of proposals have been made either (a) to differentiate, by appropriate terms, these cases from heterothallism as originally defined, (b) to redefine heterothallism in a more broadly inclusive manner, or (c) to replace the terms and the concept of homothallism versus heterothallism, which have been held by certain authors to be inappropriate or outmoded.

Different authors quite naturally approach the problem of sexuality from different points of view, and the systems of categorization of sexual phenomena in fungi that have been proposed are consequently rather diverse. The treatment that is developed here is thus only one of many possibilities, each of which has its own virtues and weaknesses. A brief comparative note relating the system adopted here to others that have been proposed will be presented later.

Whitehouse (1949a), in a comprehensive review, advanced a logical system of differentiation which promised to clarify considerably the entire subject of sexuality in the fungi. He retained, on rational grounds and with historical justification, the term heterothallism to include all those cases in which intermycelial reaction is a requisite for sexual fusion. Two major types of heterothallism were distinguished: (1) *morphological heterothallism,* to include those cases in which the two interacting thalli differ by production of morphologically dissimilar sexual organs or gametes which are identifiable as ♂ and ♀, and (2) *physiological heterothallism,* to include those cases in which the interacting thalli differ in mating type, or incompatibility, irrespective of the presence or absence of sexual organs or differentiated gametes per se. Homothallism was retained in the original sense: sexual fusion between elements of the same thallus or, in unicellular organisms, between individuals of the same clone. A new term, *secondary homothallism,* was applied to self-fertile heterokaryons. These will be discussed in detail later.

Inevitably, there exist a number of forms which fit uneasily into a simple breakdown of this sort; in a group as varied as the fungi, this situation almost necessarily follows any attempt at categorization in respect to characteristics of the mature thalli. A somewhat less ambiguous system could be erected on the distinction between phenotypic and genotypic determination of sexual or mating behavior or both. The two major groupings here would be based upon the ability or inability of genetically identical nuclei (sister nuclei, daughters of a single primary meiotic product) to participate in sexual fusion. Such a distinction would roughly parallel that between homo- and heterothallism. Wide acceptance and common usage of the homo–heterothallism concept, however, dictate its perpetuation without radical change in spite of its intrinsic shortcomings. Recognition of the pattern of segregation at meiosis as the chief, and frequently the sole, factor in determining the ultimate sexual character or mating behavior, or both, of the thallus results in a far clearer understanding of the homo–heterothallism concept.

Each mature thallus, at the stage in its development at which sexual fusions occur, commonly contains nuclei of only a single kind; that is, it is *homokaryotic* (a number of important exceptions to this generalization will be considered later). These sexually mature thalli thus represent the expressed potentialities determined at meiosis and imparted to the spores that constitute the immediate products of this process. Spores, and the thalli into which they develop, may be divided into three types in respect to the segregation of sexual or mating capacities; (1) segregation of sexual factors, (2) segregation of incompatibility factors, and (3) segregation of neither sexual nor incompatibility factors. In the simple cases under consideration, spores of types 1 and 2 give rise to thalli which are self-sterile but which are cross-fertile in those combinations bringing together complementary sexual or incompatibility factors. Such forms are clearly heterothallic. Spores of type 3, on the other hand, produce thalli of only a single kind, all of which are self-fertile; such forms are homothallic.

A number of complicating phenomena tend to mitigate somewhat the simplicity of this picture. Foremost among these is the regular association, initiated in spore formation in certain species, of two kinds of nuclei of dissimilar incompatibility types in a single thallus which is self-fertile. A form of this kind, in spite of its segregative pattern and the necessity of genetically dissimilar nuclei for sexual fusion, must be termed homothallic because of the self-fertile nature of its thallus.

A second complication is the possibility of final determination of sexual or mating behavior, in forms lacking this determination at meiosis, by environmental factors during the development of the thallus. A physiological differentiation of this sort between individual cells or groups of cells within a single thallus constitutes typical homothallic behavior; if the final differentiation involves different thalli, however, it must be termed heterothallic because of the self-sterile nature of the sexually mature thalli. Students of different groups of fungi have shown somewhat less than complete accord in their integration of phenotypic determination with the homo–heterothallism concept. The general acceptance of the concept of the clone, now frequently ignored except in the study of unicellular forms, would resolve the more important discrepancies in interpretation of these phenomena.

A third mode of deviation from a strict dichotomy between homo- and heterothallism may arise through mutations of factors controlling mating behavior or modifying sexual expression.

These departures from strict homo- and heterothallism will be considered later in connection with detailed accounts of the various patterns of mating behavior.

B. Homothallism

Of the several distinct patterns of sexuality found among the fungi, homothallism is perhaps the most common; it occurs in all major groups and, with the exception of the Basidiomycetes, in a majority of species within each group. The critical differentiation of compatible elements is intramycelial, and differentiation in different cases may involve a portion of the thallus ranging from a single cell to the entire thallus. The spatial relationship between differentiated elements of the fusing pair is also variable. This variability may best be illustrated by certain species in the coenocytic, aquatic phycomycetous order, the Saprolegniales: (1) ♂ and ♀ elements may together constitute a specialized lateral hyphal branch, a stalked oogonium with an antheridial cell either differentiated in the stalk or arising from it; (2) ♂ and ♀ elements may arise from adjacent sections of main hyphae; and (3) ♂ and ♀ elements may arise from different main hyphae, each main hypha being differentiated in its entirety as ♂ or as ♀ (Coker, 1923).

Differentiation of sexual elements within a single thallus is usually reversible, either to the vegetative state or in some cases to sexual organs of the opposite sign. The vegetative development of unfused ♀ gametes of *Allomyces* (Emerson, 1941) and the ability of the differentiated sexual organs of homothallic species of *Achlya* to regenerate normal hermaphroditic plants are typical examples of such reversibility. In at least certain cases, however, reversibility to vegetative growth is dependent upon the degree of differentiation that has been achieved. In *Ascobolus stercorarius,* Bistis

(1957) reports that all cells of the developing ascogonium are capable of reversion, whereas once the ascogonium is fully differentiated only the basal cells retain this capability. A more extensive reversibility, from sexual organs of one sign to organs of the opposite sign, is fairly common in the homothallic water molds. The production of antheridial hyphae from oogonia and the occurrence of small oogonia intercalated in antheridial hyphae have been observed in various species (Coker, 1923; Humphrey, 1892; Maurizio, 1899). It has also been demonstrated in several homothallic species that sexual hormones from strongly sexed plants caused oogonial initials to redifferentiate and produce antheridial hyphae (J. R. Raper, 1950).

One further point in connection with true homothallism is of general biological interest. Sexual fusion normally occurs between elements carrying sister (genetically identical) nuclei. This would imply, a priori, that most fungi are deprived of the benefits occurring in the recombination of genetic factors following sexual fusion between dissimilar elements. Two facts would tend to mitigate this deprivation: (1) the separate histories, often extended, of the two sister nuclei brought together in the sexual act allow considerable opportunity for the accumulation and recombination of minor differences due to induced or spontaneous mutations (Pontecorvo and Roper, 1952; Roper, 1952; Esser and Straub, 1958; El Ani and Olive, 1962); and (2) juxtaposed thalli having totally different origins allow for extensive crossbreeding and even hybridization in forms with motile or nonmotile differentiated gametes (Emerson, 1941, 1950; Emerson and Wilson, 1954) and for occasional crossbreeding in forms lacking free gametes (J. R. Raper, 1950; Salvin, 1942). The extent to which either or both of these phenomena might duplicate in nature the benefits of enforced crossbreeding cannot be accurately assessed. The widespread occurrence of homothallism in fungi, however, is eloquent testimony of the evolutionary success of this pattern of sexuality among these forms.

Superficially, it would appear that in homothallic species, which typically unite genetically identical nuclei, the usual sexual endeavor approaches a total sacrifice of quality for quantity; the exceptional cases which prevent the accomplishment of this biological absurdity appear to provide sufficient variability to allow for adaptation and survival.

C. Heterothallism

A number of distinct, basic patterns of sexuality have been described as responsible for heterothallism among fungi. Beyond the single requirement for heterothallism, that the sexual act involve two individuals, these several patterns are quite distinct.

The distinctions between the various basic patterns imposing intermycelial mating reactions have been recognized by many authors, several of whom have proposed new terms for one or more of the seemingly coordinate patterns to distinguish them from heterothallism as originally defined. Some of these terms have been widely accepted and now constitute useful components of our working vocabulary; others have probably deserved the oblivion to which they have been relegated. It is certainly not the purpose here to add to this burden of awkward descriptive terms, but

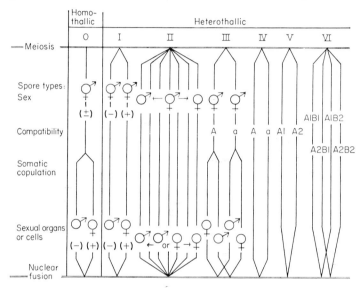

FIG. 3. The genetic devices that underlie the seven distinct patterns of sexuality in fungi. All individuals of species of type O are alike and functionally hermaphroditic; individuals of species of types I to VI are divided, by sexual or incompatibility differences, into two or more distinct mating types among which cross-mating is obligatory. Series of multiple incompatibility factors commonly occur in types V and VI, and the number of distinct mating strains may be of the order of hundreds and of tens of thousands in species of the two types, respectively (modified from Raper, 1954).

rather to differentiate as concisely as possible between a number of patterns which are based upon distinct genetic devices, are quite similar superficially, and accomplish a common purpose.

The basic segregative mechanisms responsible for the different heterothallic patterns are diagrammed in Fig. 3. The order within the comparative listing here is not intended to convey any intimations of phylogenetic or evolutionary significance.

In typical heterothallic species, the immediate products of meiosis, spores of one sort or another in most cases, differ among themselves in respect to either sexual sign or incompatibility factors.

The necessary use here of both sexual and incompatibility factors forces upon the reviewer the most unwelcome chore of attempting to distinguish concisely between the two; the onerous fact that a clear distinction is impossible at the present time unfortunately does not excuse him from making the attempt. *Sexual factors* are those genetic factors which determine the elaboration of morphologically distinguishable ♂ and ♀ plants by determining the formation of differentiated ♂ and ♀ sexual organs or gametes, or both. The criteria for the designation of ♂ and ♀ organs or cells, or both, are largely borrowed from mammalian reproductive processes and include relative size, inclusion of reserve food materials, motility, and particularly the direction of nuclear migration (or transport) in fertilization. *Incompatibility factors,* by contrast, are those extrasexual genetic determinants of mating capacity which operate either in addition to or in the absence of sexual factors. The difficulty of a sharp, universally applicable distinction between the two arises primarily from the occasionally known occurrence of heterothallic species in which demonstrable sexual differences exist in the absence of morphological differentiation. The best-known example is the complex of interbreeding species of the green alga *Chlamydomonas,* which comprises heterogamous, anisogamous, and isogamous forms (Moewus, 1950). In other cases where sexual sign cannot be tested by crossbreeding with sexually differentiated forms, it is impossible to make a certain distinction between sexual and incompatibility control of mating behavior in the absence of clear morphological differences. This difficulty will be apparent in the following description of segregative patterns.

1. Single Alternate Sexual Factors (Pattern I)

The simplest pattern of sexual differentiation yields two classes of progeny, each of which is either immediately distinguishable as ♂ or ♀ or bears differentiated ♂ or ♀ sexual organs or gametes, respectively, or both. Sexual dimorphism is typically rigid in plants belonging to this category.

Relatively few groups of fungi contain species which unquestionably show this type of differentiation. Among the more primitive monoflagellated aquatic fungi, numerous species produce thalli which, at maturity, are differentiated into single gametangia with clear morphological distinction bewteen ♂ and ♀ (Couch and Whiffen, 1942; Harder and Sörgel, 1938; Sparrow, 1960). Such forms are obviously heterothallic; whether the differentiation of the individual as a ♂ or as a ♀ is phenotypically or genotypically determined, however, remains largely untested (Cantino and Hyatt, 1953; Emerson, 1950). In one species, *Dictyomorpha dioica,* however, fusion has been reported to occur only between gametes derived from two sexually compatible strains (Mullins, 1961), and both original mating

15. Life Cycles, Sexuality, and Sexual Mechanisms

types have been recovered in the progeny of the germinated resting spores (Mullins, 1965). Mating competence is evidently genetically determined in this case. Certain groups among these primitive fungi, particularly *Blastocladiella* (Blastocladiales), constitute series grading from clear distinction between ♂ and ♀ thalli to forms that show no morphological difference between the two mating types (Stüben, 1939). The sure distinction here between sexual factors and incompatibility factors is not possible, but it would seem to the reviewer, in disagreement with the views of Whitehouse, that here as elsewhere a common pattern of sexuality most probably is shared by the members of a closely related group.

Sexual dimorphism is also known among the members of two groups of ascomycetes: in many species of the Laboulbeniales (Benjamin and Shanor, 1950; Thaxter, 1908) and in *Ascophaera* (*Pericystis*) (Claussen, 1921; Spiltoir, 1955). Sexual dimorphism has been reported for isolated species belonging to three additional groups of ascomycetes and basidiomycetes: *Hypomyces solani* f. sp. *cucurbitae* (Pyrenomycetes) (Hansen and Snyder, 1946; Hirsch, 1949), *Stromatinia narcissi* (Discomycetes) (Drayton and Groves, 1952), and *Solenia anomala* (Hymenomycetes) (Greis, 1942; Hartmann, 1943, 1955). The occurrence of incompatibility systems as the primary determinant of mating competence in all other known heterothallic species belonging to these groups, however, suggests that "dimorphism" in these cases may be related to mutations affecting the normal pattern of development (El Ani, 1954; J. R. Raper, 1959). Induced mutations that mimic the features described in these species are known in various ascomycetes and basidiomycetes (Barnett, 1953; Esser, 1959; Zickler, 1934, 1937; J. R. Raper and Miles, 1958).

The heterothallic members of the Mucorales, e.g., *Rhizopus*, in which heterothallism was first discovered, have long been cited as the classic examples of sexual segregation among the fungi. Recent work and reexamination of earlier studies, however, leave such an interpretation in some doubt; current views rather favor the determination of mating type in these forms by incompatibility factors (Whitehouse, 1949a).

2. *Multiple Alternate Sexual Factors (Pattern II)*

A somewhat more complicated type of sexual segregation than that immediately preceding involves the determination of several sexual strains, each typically self-sterile but cross-fertile with all others. A heterothallic species of this type constitutes a linear series of sexual strains, each of which, with the exception of the two terminal strains, reacts as ♂ or as ♀ depending upon its position in the series relative to that of its mate; each of the two terminal strains reacts in a single sexual capacity, as ♂ or as ♀. This pattern of sexuality has been found in all heterothallic species of the biflagellate, phycomycetous orders, Saprolegniales, Leptomitales, and Peronosporales, which have been intensively investigated (Bishop, 1940; de Bruyn, 1935, 1937; Couch, 1926; Leonian, 1931; J. R. Raper, 1940, 1947; Barksdale, 1960, 1965).

The mating pattern of a number of strains of *Achlya ambisexualis* best serves to illustrate this type of sexuality (J. R. Raper, 1947). Ten isolates of this species, collected from northern Illinois in 1946, when mated in all possible combinations, were found to belong to six classes. These strains, each self-sterile but cross-fertile in all combinations, could be linearly ordered, in respect to ♂ and ♀ potentialities, as shown in Fig. 4.

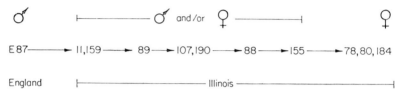

FIG. 4. In *Achlya ambisexualis* (a heterothallic species of type II), there are numerous self-sterile, intergrade strains in addition to pure ♂ and pure ♀ strains. The intergrade strains may be linearly arranged in respect to ♂ and ♀ potentialities, and each strain can react as ♂ or ♀ or both (from Raper, 1947).

In this series each isolate reacted as ♀ to those on its left and as ♂ to those on its right. A strong ♂ strain, E87, collected the following year in England, reacted as ♂ to all six strains from Illinois. Any intergrade mycelium is capable of reacting as ♂ and ♀ in different portions of its thallus when mated simultaneously with strong ♀ and ♂ plants.

Only in a single species, *Dictyuchus monosporus,* has germination of a sufficient number of zygotes been achieved to permit any study of the segregation of sexual characters in plants exhibiting this pattern of sexuality. Couch (1926) found various intergrades in addition to ♂ and ♀ strains among the progeny of ♂ by ♀ crosses.

These preliminary findings are in complete accord with the many reports of multiple sexual strains in this and in other heterothallic species, collected from nature, but the underlying genetic basis for the complex of different sexual strains is still unknown. Earlier suggestions to account for the situation, such as multiple sexual factors or polyploidy (J. R. Raper, 1940, 1954, 1960) assumed the basic life cycle to be haploid. The present indication of a diploid cycle in these forms (Sansome, 1961, 1963) calls immediate attention to other possibilities. The cataloguing of these, however, is bootless; the basis for this unusual pattern of sexuality can be satisfactorily clarified only by adequate genetic analysis.

[*Note Added in Proof:* The handicap of poor germination of the oospores of the biflagellate fungi proves not to constitute an absolute bar to genetic analysis. Mullins and Raper (1965) reported germination in low frequency (< 1%) of oospores of *Achlya ambisexualis* and *Dictyuchus monosporus*. The results of preliminary analyses of small samples of progeny (56 and 36 for the two species, respectively) were consistent with, but not proof of, diploidy. Both samples of progeny included ♂, ♀, and intergrade strains of varied sexual potency, and it was concluded that inheritance of mating competence involves a more complex genetic basis than alternate alleles at a single locus. Barksdale (1966) has also succeeded in germinating oospores of *Achlya* and has made a preliminary study of the inheritance of sexual characters in *A. ambisexualis* and *A. bisexualis*.]

3. Hermaphrodism with Incompatibility Factors at a Single Locus (Pattern III)

This type of heterothallic differentiation produces two self-sterile and cross-fertile strains, each morphologically and functionally hermaphroditic, and depends upon the equal segregation at meiosis of incompatibility factors. Mycelia of each of the two strains characteristically produce both ♂ and ♀ sexual organs; sexual fusion is accomplished, however, only between the ♂ gametes or the ♂ gametangia of one strain with the ♀ elements of the opposite and compatible strain (Dodge, 1932; Drayton, 1932, 1934; Lindegren, 1932; Shear and Dodge, 1927; Wilcox, 1928).

The majority of heterothallic ascomycetes, with the exception of the heterothallic yeasts, as well as many species of the rusts (Basidiomycetes), exhibit this basic pattern of sexuality. In many ascomycetes, *Neurospora,* for example, the ♂, or fertilizing, element is characteristically the microconidium or spermatium; the ♀, an ascogonium. In other ascomycetes, differentiated gametes are not formed, and fusion occurs between morphologically distinct gametangia, antheridia and ascogonia, respectively. In rusts exhibiting this type of sexuality, spermatia effect fertilization when brought into contact with receptive elements of the compatible mycelium, usually a specialized organ known as the "flexuous hypha" (Buller, 1950; Craigie, 1927, 1931, 1942).

The differentiation of sexual cells in plants having this type of heterothallism is phenotypic, and there are numerous cases in which differentiated sexual cells, spermatia or microconidia, of ascomycetes particularly (Dodge, 1932), have been shown to be capable of purely vegetative development. Conversely, in a number of forms, fertilization is accomplished with equal facility by microconidia, by asexual macroconidia or, for that matter, by any cell of the vegetative thallus (Backus, 1939). In some the ability to produce differentiated ♂ cells appears to have been lost, the function of fertilization being completely assumed by asexual or vegetative elements (Dowding, 1933; Dowding and Buller, 1940).

In most cases, differentiation of ♂ and ♀ sexual organs or cells requires no external stimulus, fully functional sexual elements forming upon isolated mycelia of both classes, e.g., *Neurospora sitophila* and *N. crassa* (Dodge, 1932) and *Bombardia lunata* (Zickler, 1937, 1952). In heterothallic species of *Ascobolus,* however, ♂ and ♀ sexual organs are formed and differentiated only upon contact of compatible mycelia or of compatible mycelial elements. (Dodge, 1920; Bistis, 1956).

Secondary homothallism, *sensu* Whitehouse—a phenomenon of fairly common occurrence in this group and in forms of one other pattern in which incompatibility factors constitute the critical determinant of mating behavior (see below)—results from the regular inclusion in the spore of two nuclei carrying opposed incompatibility factors (Ames, 1934; Dodge, 1927; Dowding, 1931; Dowding and Buller, 1940; Rizet and Engelmann, 1949). Binucleate spores of this sort give rise to heterokaryotic mycelia which are self-fertile; in some species, sexual organs are present and appear to be essential, in other species sexual organs may be absent or greatly reduced and apparently nonessential. In several cases, occasional irregularities during spore production yield small, uninucleate spores, each of which develops into a self-sterile but cross-fertile mycelium which behaves exactly as do the individual mycelia of heterothallic species (Ames, 1934; Dowding, 1931). The initial binucleate condition thus predetermines a compatible heterokaryon, the net reaction of which is homothallic.

The detailed means by which compatible elements are juxtaposed in the developing asci differ in two of the more intensively studied species of this sort. In *Neurospora tetrasperma,* the mating type locus lies near the centromere and the segregation of alleles occurs at the first meiotic division; overlapping spindles at the second division then pair nuclei of the two types in the maturing ascus (Dodge *et al.,* 1950). In *Podospora* (*Pleurage*) *anserina,* the mating type locus lies distant from the centromere and the mating type alleles segregate in the second meiotic division in practically all asci; nonoverlapping spindles in the second division thus pair nuclei of the two types (Franke, 1957, 1962).

4. Paired Incompatibility Factors at a Single "Locus" (Pattern IV)

This and the succeeding patterns of sexuality involve no sexual factors and, with the exception of the Mucorales, no differentiated sexual organs. Mating commonly consists of the fusion of two morphologically similar vegetative cells, spores, or gametangia.

In heterothallic species of certain groups, a single pair of incompatibility alleles determines mating type; all individuals of each species therefore belong in one or the other of two mating categories, commonly designated *A* and *a*. The heterothallic yeasts are the best-known examples of this pattern

(Winge, 1935, 1944; Winge and Laustsen, 1939), and a recent review of the sexuality of the heterothallic smuts indicates basic control of mating behavior in many members of this group by a one-locus, two-allele mechanism (Whitehouse, 1951). The heterothallic members of the Mucorales are also most commonly considered to exhibit this pattern of sexuality.

Mutations at the incompatibility locus in certain yeasts (Lindegren and Lindegren, 1944; Winge, 1944; Ahmad, 1952, 1953) may be considered slight deviations of this pattern and may possibly indicate the mode of origin of the following pattern. Either *A* or *a* may occasionally mutate to altered states which permit fusion and ascus production within a single clone. The ascospores of such unions, however, have a low degree of viability. This possibly reflects either a lack of equivalence between the mutated alleles and the originals or the expression of deleterious, semisterility factors in the homozygous condition (Catcheside, 1951). The mating type "locus" in one species of yeast, *Schizosaccharomyces pombe* has been found to be complex, and internal recombination results in several interallelic combinations that display distinctive sexual reactions (Leupold, 1958, 1959). Also, in certain yeasts, numerous factors, such as extra-incompatibility genes, polyploidy, and irregularities in nuclear divisions and distribution, may mask or otherwise profoundly affect sexual expressions (cf. J. R. Raper, 1960, for review and references).

5. *Multiple Incompatibility Factors of a Single Series (Pattern V)*

What would appear to be a much more highly evolved pattern of single "locus" control of mating behavior is characteristic of many basidiomycetes, exclusive of the rusts and smuts. All the forms displaying this pattern of sexuality are mycelial; mating is reciprocal between compatible strains, and each cell of the thallus is potentially capable of donating or receiving a fertilizing nucleus. The term *somatic copulation—Somatagamie* (Renner, 1916)—has been applied to this type of sexual fusion. In these forms, a very large number of completely equivalent factors may be found in various individuals at the single incompatibility "locus," and mating occurs readily between any two haploid strains which carry different factors (Brunswik, 1924; Buller, 1924; Vandendries, 1923; Whitehouse, 1949b). Thus, in lieu of the single pair, *A* and *a,* these forms each comprise an extended series of mating types which may be designated by *A1, A2, A3, A4, . . . , An.* This pattern of mating-type determination has been termed *bipolar sexuality* or, preferably, *bipolar incompatibility.*

Secondary homothallism is quite common among forms that are basically bipolar (Sass, 1929; Skolko, 1944; Lange, 1952; Boidin, 1956). A variety of patterns of nuclear behavior in the developing basidium account, in different species, for the inclusion of compatible nuclei in single basidiospores and the consequent self-fertility of the heterokaryotic mycelia (Skolko, 1944).

6. Multiple Incompatibility Factors of Two Series (Pattern VI)

The final pattern of obligatory, interstrain mating behavior is one found only among basidiomycetes, exclusive of the rusts and related groups. It involves mating-type determination by incompatibility factors of two series; for example, the diploid condition may be designated $A1A2\ B1B2$, and segregation and independent assortment of these factors at meiosis yield progeny of four mating types, $A1\ B1,\ A1\ B2,\ A2\ B1,$ and $A2\ B2$. Mating occurs only in those combinations having different factors of both series, for example, $A1\ B2 \times A2\ B1$ and $A1\ B1 \times A2\ B2$ (Brunswik, 1924; Hanna, 1925; Kniep, 1920, 1922; Mounce, 1922, 1926; Whitehouse, 1949b; J. R. Raper, 1953). This pattern of segregation was first described by Kniep about 1920 and was later termed *tetrapolar sexuality* by Bauch (1931).

In tetrapolar species, as in the bipolar forms discussed above, the total number of mating types in the population is increased tremendously by the occurrence of multiple factors of both series (Kniep, 1922). The number of equivalent factors of each series, however, appears to be consistently different in two large groups of basidiomycetes, the Gasteromycetes, which includes the "puffballs," and so on, and the Hymenomycetes, which includes the "mushroom," "bracket fungi," and the like. In the former group, about 10 factors of each series has been indicated as the extent of the series (Fries, 1940, 1943), whereas, in the latter group more extensive series were early indicated (Kniep, 1922; Brunswik, 1924; Whitehouse, 1949b) and have since been demonstrated. In *Schizophyllum commune,* 122 A factors and 61 B factors have been identified, and the two series, in the total natural population, have been estimated to comprise 350–450 A factors and about 65 B factors (J. R. Raper *et al.,* 1958b; J. R. Raper *et al.,* 1960). Comparably extended series are indicated for certain other tetrapolar species (Fries and Jonasson, 1941; Prévost, 1962; Day, 1963b) and are suspected in all species. In all cases the factors of each series appear to be physiologically equivalent. The device of multiple incompatibility factors allows for almost complete outbreeding while maintaining inbreeding at 50% in bipolar forms and at 25% in tetrapolar forms.

Kniep, in his original work on tetrapolarity, observed that "mutations" occurred at the A and B "*loci*" in frequencies of about 2% and slightly less than 1%, respectively (Kniep, 1923). These changes in the incompatibility factors, repeatedly observed by various workers, however, seemed to occur only in the germling mycelia recently derived from basidiospores, never in well-established mycelia. It was shown beyond reasonable doubt by Papazian (1951) that the *A* factor of *S. commune* consists of at least two linked but distinct loci, that these act together as a physiological unit, and that occasional recombination at meiosis yields new factors. Subsequent analysis of the *A* and *B* factors of this species has demonstrated both to be complex. The *A* factor consists of two loci, α, and β, each with a series of multiple alleles. Nine and 26 alleles have been identified at $A\alpha$ and $A\beta$, respectively, and the two series are estimated to comprise 9 α's and about 50 β's in the natural population (J. R. Raper *et al.*, 1958a; J. R. Raper *et al.*, 1960). The *B* factor is similarly constituted of at least two distinct loci (J. R. Raper *et al.*, 1958a), but there is evidence for a third locus, γ, as well (Raper, 1966). Less extensive analyses have demonstrated complex factors in several other tetrapolar species (Terakawa, 1957, 1960; Takemaru, 1957, 1961; Day, 1960, 1963a,b; Prévost, 1962).

D. Anomalies of Patterns and Expression of Sexuality

A majority of sexually reproducing species that have been adequately examined have been shown to be either homothallic or heterothallic. The literature, however, is burdened with reports of (1) anomalous sexual behavior in forms exhibiting a clear pattern of sexuality and (2) of cases that cannot rationally be assigned to any of the patterns of sexuality above.

In the first category, certain types of anomalous behavior are so common as to be considered characteristic of the basic patterns of sexuality, e.g., (a) low-level self-fertility via mutations of the incompatibility factors in yeasts (Pattern IV, Fig. 3), (b) the factors affecting sexual expression in yeasts (Pattern IV), and (c) secondary homothallism in the higher ascomycetes (Pattern III) and bipolar hymenomycetes (Pattern IV). Anomalous behavior occurs in all the different patterns of sexuality with sufficient frequency to blur somewhat the rather clear distinctions made in their descriptions. A few additional cases will suffice to emphasize this point: (a) in heterothallic water molds (Pattern II), oogonia and antheridia are occasionally formed on aged mycelia of strongly reacting ♂ and ♀ strains grown in isolation (J. R. Raper, 1940; Barksdale, 1960); (b) in *Ascobolus* (Pattern III) plasmogamy can be induced following maturation of the ascogonium between sexual elements of the same incompatibility class (Bistis and Raper, 1963); (c) in the Pyrenomycetes (Pattern III), including *Cochliobolus* (Nelson, 1959, *et prior*) and *Podospora* (Esser, 1959, *et prior*), numerous genetic factors have been shown to modify the pattern of sexuality determined by the incompatibility factors—in the latter species, a distinct genetic system of four loci, *semi-incompatibility*, imposes restrictions on outbreeding and thus operates in opposition to the basic incompatibility system (Esser, 1959); (d) in bipolar and tetrapolar hymenomycetes (Patterns V and VI), haploid mycelia of many species produce sporulating fruiting bodies—in some of these, spore production is poor and germinability is low (J. R. Raper and Krongelb, 1958), but in some such fruiting seems to be an efficient means of reproduction (Smith, 1934; J. R. Raper, 1953).

To these naturally occurring anomalies can be added those resulting from mutations and other genetic ills induced in the laboratory. Such effects have been observed in forms representing several different patterns of sexuality. The example of a single species will serve here to illustrate the range of possibilities. In the typical tetrapolar hymenomycete *Schizophyllum,* numerous deviations from normal sexual behavior have been demonstrated: (a) most morphological mutations, whether spontaneous or induced, result in unilateral mating, the mutant being able to donate, but not to accept, fertilizing nuclei (Papazian, 1950; J. R. Raper and Miles, 1958). (b) A class of dominant mutations prevents nuclear pairing and conjugate division in the dikaryon and leads to sterility (C. A. Raper and Raper, 1964). (c) A number of genetic systems, some comprising single loci and others appearing to be polygenic, determine both fruiting competence and the form of the fruiting bodies (J. R. Raper and Krongelb, 1958). (d) Disomy for, and mutations induced in, the A and B factors lead in monosporous cultures to the establishment of fertile dikaryons (J. R. Raper and Oettinger, 1962; J. R. Raper, Boyd and Raper, 1965).

In the second category, occasional species appear to occupy positions that are intermediate between homothallism and heterothallism. These species exhibit patterns of sexuality ranging from predominantly heterothallic with homothallic tendencies to predominantly homothallic with heterothallic tendencies and together may be considered as bridging the gap between true homothallic and heterothallic conditions. At the one extreme are those yeasts, mentioned earlier, which are basically heterothallic but which produce frequent, low-viability mutants of the incompatibility factors. Mather (1940) has suggested the term *partial heterothallism* for cases of this type. At the other extreme are homothallic species such as *Aspergillus nidulans,* in heterokaryons of which crossed perithecia versus selfed perithecia occur in characteristic ratios that are often quite different from the ratio of 1:1 expected by chance alone (Pontecorvo, 1953). This situation was termed *relative heterothallism.*

Intermediate to these conditions, which are basically heterothallic and homothallic, respectively, a number of patterns of sexual behavior have been reported that are quite ambiguous in respect to these two extremes.

Outstanding among such forms is the ascomycete *Glomerella,* a sexually ambiguous species without peer. Edgerton (1914) described a strong sexual interaction in this species between weakly self-fertile strains. Subsequent intensive work with *G. cingulata* (Andes, 1941; Edgerton *et al.,*

1945; McGahen and Wheeler, 1951; Wheeler, 1950; Wheeler and McGahen, 1952) has revealed an extremely complicated pattern of sexuality which results from the interaction of numerous genetic factors, some exhibiting high mutation rates. As currently interpreted (Wheeler and McGahen, 1952), two loci, A and B, are considered primarily responsible for the basic sexual characteristics, with some twenty other loci modifying the sexual reaction. Two mutant states are known at each of the two primary sexual loci in addition to the two wild-type alleles. Thus all combinations between the three alleles at the two loci, $A+$, $A1$, and $A2$ and $B+$, $B1$, and $B2$, determine nine distinct phenotypes, each having a characteristic pattern of self-sterility or self-fertility on the one hand and interstrain matings on the other. The sexual characteristics of the various strains may be further modified by mutations at loci other than the primary sexual loci, A and B, and two of these, F^1 and st^1, have been described in detail (Wheeler and McGahen, 1952). Each of these mutants imposes self-sterility upon each of the normally self-fertile strains but does not interfere with interstrain reactions provided that the two mates carry neither of the mutations in common.

Self-sterility resulting from induced, recessive mutations, comparable to F^1 and st^1 in *G. cingulata,* has been extensively analyzed in two additional homothallic ascomycetes, *Sordaria fimicola* (Carr and Olive, 1959; El Ani and Olive, 1962) and *S. macrospora* (Esser and Straub, 1956, 1958). These three studies on homothallic forms have shed significant light upon the genetic control of the sexual sequence and have suggested to certain authors a possible mechanism for the origin of heterothallism due to incompatibility (Wheeler, 1954; Olive, 1958; El Ani and Olive, 1962). A comparably drastic alteration of sexual behavior has been achieved in the homothallic, aquatic phycomycete *Allomyces;* effectively dimorphic plants, ♂ and ♀, have been generated via hybridization between two distinct species and followed by selection (Emerson and Wilson, 1954; Machlis, 1958).

An interesting pattern of sexuality that cannot be designated either homothallic or heterothallic as construed here has been reported in the ascomycete *Chromocrea spinulosa* (Mathieson, 1952), and a similar situation probably obtains in *Ceratostomella fimbriata* (Olson, 1949): different alleles at a single (incompatibility?) locus are requisite for sexual activity, with heterozygocity apparently being achieved anew via mutation in each sexual generation.

The patterns of sexuality in *Glomerella* and *Chromocrea* are therefore basically different from any of the well-defined patterns described above. It is possible that here we have on display species in the process of evolving from homothallism to heterothallism, or vice versa, and to accept the concept of partial and relative heterothallism may well be the best that can be done at the present time toward integrating these patterns into the general scheme of sexuality in the fungi.

Other present-day students of sexuality in fungi, however, have viewed the problem in different perspective and with differences in emphasis on the various criteria that can be applied. Thus the systems developed by Ahmad (1954), Burnett (1956), and Esser and Kuenen (1965) bear varying resemblance in nomenclature and in organizational detail to that given above. Conceptually, that of Ahmad most closely resembles the general outline of the above, with new terms paralleling homo- and heterothallism to avoid the ambiguities implicit in the original definitions of these terms. The proposal of Burnett emphasizes the relationship between basic life cycle and the origins of sexually interacting nuclei in the context of a newly rationalized and very esoteric terminology. The scheme of Esser uses as the primary criterion of distinction the ability of the individual (a) both to donate *and* to accept fertilizing nuclei (monoecism) *vs.* (b) only to donate *or* to accept fertilizing nuclei (dioecism); self-fertility, self-sterility and cross-fertility, sexual dimorphism, etc., are then applied as secondary criteria of differentiation. All these systems have merit, and any attempt to formulate a definitive analysis of sexuality in the fungi will be deeply in the debt of their several authors. The present outline has no such pretensions, and the serious student of sexuality can only be referred to these related but divergent treatments of the subject for broader perspective.

IV. SEXUAL MECHANISMS

The final aspect that must be considered to give a comprehensive understanding of sex in fungi is the sexual mechanism, the mechanical means by which compatible elements are brought together under the restrictions imposed by the particular life cycle and pattern of sexuality involved.

The number of possible combinations of basic sexual apparatuses and developmental histories to be found among fungi precludes the consideration of all. Let us rather list a few possible variants at certain critical stages and demonstrate by simple developmental histories the range of variety of specific overall patterns.

Sexual mechanisms may be differentiated on the basis of morphological differences at three critical points in the life cycle. These points are (1) meiosis, (2) the physical union of compatible sexual elements, and (3) the fusion of compatible nuclei.

A. Meiosis

The immediate products of meiosis, with few exceptions among the fungi, are spores of various kinds, such as zoospores, ascospores, and basidiospores.

B. Union of Sexual Elements

In spite of the almost endless variety of sexual apparatuses among the fungi, they may be considered to belong to four basic types, first recognized by Kniep (1928). Each type comprises definite groups of plants, but such groupings have very little correlation with the major phylogenetic groupings. The four basic types are:

1. *Gametic copulation,* in which the two elements brought together in the sexual act comprise uninucleate, free gametes of which one or both may be motile.

2. *Gamete–gametangial copulation,* in which one fusing element is a differentiated uninucleate gamete and the other is a differentiated gametangium which produces no discrete, uninucleate gametes. The differentiated gametes may be either ♂ or ♀ depending upon the group.

3. *Gametangial copulation,* in which both fusing sexual elements are differentiated as gametangia; one or many pairs of nuclei may be involved, and the two gametangia may be differentiated as ♂ and ♀ or they may be morphologically indistinguishable.

4. *Somatic copulation,* in which fusion occurs between undifferentiated vegetative cells or spores. In mycelial forms, fusion is commonly followed by reciprocal nuclear migration, each mate fertilizing the other, and the two compatible nuclei usually retain, once brought together, a dikaryotic association for an indefinite period prior to nuclear fusion.

These four basic types, as exemplified in four well-known representative species, are shown, in surface view, in Fig. 5. Each type may be found in a wide array of morphological variations, but the basic aspects of the sexual progression and nuclear behavior are relatively constant in the variants.

C. Fusion of Compatible Nuclei

After the fusion of the two sexual elements, there exist two possibilities with regard to the subsequent activity of the paired compatible nuclei: they may fuse immediately to establish the diploid phase; or they may become associated in one or more pairs and divide conjugately by mitosis to provide ultimately a large number of paired nuclei, which finally fuse to form the definitive nuclei in the asci or basidia.

The developmental patterns relating these cardinal stages in the sexual cycle may be represented by the various pathways indicated in Fig. 6. The specific combination of events at the critical points in the developmental cycle, meiosis, plasmogamy, and karyogamy, defines about as well as is possible the sexual mechanism for any given species. A few well-known forms will be used here to illustrate the range of possibilities; sexual mechanism and developmental history may be defined in each case by a specific sequence of the numbered stages shown in Fig. 6.

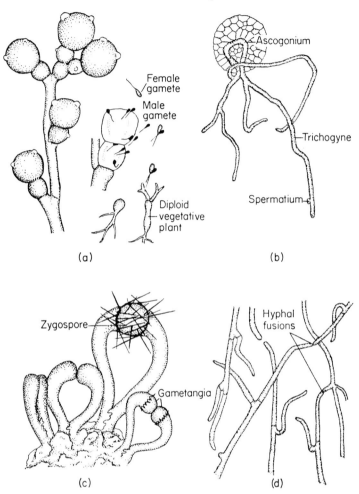

Fig. 5. The four basic modes of sexual fusion in fungi. (a) Gametic copulation, *Allomyces arbuscula*. Motile gametes originating in ♀ gametangium (above) and ♂ gametangium (below) fuse to form a zygote that germinates directly to produce a diploid plant (lower right). (b) Gamete-gametangial copulation, *Neurospora crassa*. A multinucleate ♀ gametangium, the ascogonium, is fertilized via the trichogyne, by the nucleus of a differentiated ♂ gamete, the spermatium. (c) Gametangial copulation, *Phycomyces blakesleeanus*. A pair of multinucleate gametangia, produced at the tips of large, arched processes, fuse to form a heavy-walled zygospore. (d) Somatic copulation, *Schizophyllum commune* (schematic). Two types of hyphal fusion, tip-to-tip and tip-to-peg, are shown in progress (left) and completed (right). The exchange of nuclei in somatic copulation is typically reciprocal, each mate fertilizing the other (modified from Raper, 1954).

15. Life Cycles, Sexuality, and Sexual Mechanisms

The production of gametes as the immediate products of meiosis may occur in a very few species of the monoflagellate Blastocladiales and may prove to be characteristic of biflagellate phycomycetes. In the former case, however, a single mitotic division has been reported as interposed between meiosis and the differentiation of gametes in the single species which has been cytologically investigated (Wilson, 1952). In the latter case, the

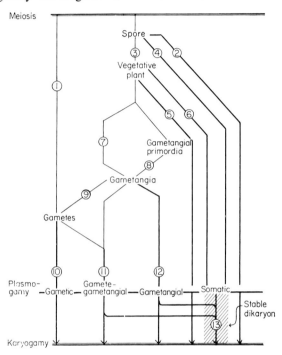

FIG. 6. Summary diagram of developmental sexual histories in fungi. The numbered lines trace developmental variations relating the critical events of plasmogamy, karyogamy, and meiosis (modified from Raper, 1954).

Saprolegniales, Leptomitales, and Peronosporales, the cytological details of gametangial development are obscure, but differentiation of the immediate products of meiosis as gametes now appears to be the likely course of events.

A distinction is necessary at this point between gametes on the one hand and single cells of other types that are capable of sexual fusion on the other. The inability or ability to multiply vegetatively and to retain copulatory competence in the individual progeny provides a convenient criterion. The copulatory cells of *Allomyces* are thus gametes, since, in isolation, they can only reestablish vegetative mycelia. Copulatory spores or vegetative cells of yeasts and smuts and the swarmers of myxomycetes are not gametes according to this criterion, since cells of each of these types can propagate vegetatively to establish a clone of morphologically identical cells, each of which retains its copulatory competence. Sexual fusions in these latter cases are thus interpreted here as somatic copulation.

Most species, however, produce spores immediately after meiosis, and the further developmental sequence is extremely variable. In a number of cases the fusion of these differentiated spores constitutes the sexual act. Of common occurrence in the yeasts is the fusion of ascospores in pairs while still in the ascus to reestablish the diploid phase [2] (Winge and Laustsen, 1939) or, rarely, a dikaryon [4-13] (Guilliermond, 1940); a similar sexual fusion is known in many smuts, in which sporidia, or basidiospores, fuse to establish a stable dikaryon [4-13] (Bauch, 1925; Kniep, 1926).

In many, if not all, of these cases, the spores germinate to establish clones of sexually competent unicells. The developmental sequence would then become [3-5] in the diploid yeasts and [3-6-13] in the smuts.

The spores give rise in other fungi to vegetative thalli or clones of vegetative cells prior to sexual activity. Vegetative cells may participate without any discernible sexual differentiation in either of two ways. In clonal, unicellular forms, such as many of the haploid yeasts, each individual cell may function as a gamete (Guilliermond, 1940), but fusion between such cells must be considered a somatic copulatory process [3-5]. In a large number of extensively developed mycelial forms, including the majority of the species of the Basidiomycetes, all vegetative cells of the thallus are capable of reciprocal somatic copulation to initiate the dikaryon [3-6-13] (Buller, 1924; Kniep, 1920, 1922).

The remaining fungi produce sexual organs or gametangia, and these are almost invariably essential for sexual activity. The entire vegetative thallus may be differentiated at maturity into one or more gametangia, which may develop further in either of two different ways. The gametangia may undergo internal differentiation to produce uninucleate gametes which fuse in pairs, as in *Blastocladiella* [3-7-9-10] (Couch and Whiffen, 1942; Harder and Sörgel, 1938), or the gametangia may fuse without further differentiation, as in numerous monoflagellate phycomycetes, such as *Siphonaria* [3-7-12] (Karling, 1945; Wager, 1913).

In yet other forms, the sexual activity is relegated to gametangia which originate *de novo* as extravegetative structures. Three different patterns of further sexual development are found in these forms: gametangia may produce gametes which fuse in pairs, as in *Allomyces* [3-8-9-10] (Emerson, 1941; Kniep, 1929); gametangia of one sexual sign may produce differentiated gametes which react sexually with gametangia of the opposite sexual sign, as in *Neurospora* (Backus, 1939; Shear and Dodge, 1927) and many rusts [3-8-9-11-13] (Buller, 1950; Craigie, 1942); the gametangia, morphologically differentiated in respect to sexual sign, or not, depending upon the species, may fuse directly with one another, as in *Mucor* and *Rhizopus* [3-8-12] (Blakeslee, 1904, 1920; Burgeff, 1924; Krafczyk, 1935) or *Pyronema* (Claussen, 1912) and *Ascobolus* (Dodge, 1920) [3-8-12-13]. The developmental pattern of phycomycetes and most of the lower ascomycetes (Hemiascomycetes) differs from that of the higher ascomycetes (Euascomycetes) and basidiomycetes following plasmogamy in that their nuclei fuse immediately, whereas in the higher groups dikaryons are regularly formed.

The dozen or so developmental and sexual histories sketched here are the more common types encountered among the fungi. Most forms fit comfortably in one or the other of these patterns, but there are a number of cases that would be categorized variously according to the preferred interpretation of structural and behavioral characteristics.

V. CORRELATIONS OF LIFE CYCLES, SEXUALITY, AND SEXUAL MECHANISMS

The three principal facets of sex in fungi having been examined in some detail, it should now be possible to attempt some correlation between them and to approach some sort of integrated picture of the problem in its entirety. Such a correlation is attempted in Table I. In this table are shown the more frequent combinations of life cycle, sexuality, and developmental sexual history, as well as examples of these, chosen wherever possible from fungi which are relatively well known to biologists other than mycologists. Patterns of sexuality and developmental histories have been bracketed within each type of life cycle; indication of the actual combinations which are known to occur, however, would serve only to obscure the important conclusions that may be drawn from this body of information.

The most striking fact that emerges here is also one of considerable significance, namely, no rigid and inclusive correlation exists between the various combinations of sexual features and the universally accepted phylogenetic groupings. To illustrate this: homothallism, possibly the most primitive of the various patterns of sexuality, occurs in conjunction with all types of life cycles, with practically all developmental histories, and in every major grouping from the most primitive phycomycetes to the most highly evolved basidiomycetes.

In spite of the lack of any parallel progression from simple to complex life cycles, patterns of sexuality, and sexual mechanisms and morphological characteristics, there are certain tendencies that are worthy of mention. There is a very loose correlation between morphological specialization and each of the three major facets of sexuality.

Life cycles, on the whole, become progressively more complex proceeding from primitive to more highly specialized groups. The haploid cycle predominates in the phycomycetes, the haploid with restricted dikaryon cycle in the ascomycetes, and the haploid-dikaryotic and the dikaryotic cycles in the basidiomycetes. The exceptions to this generalization, how-

TABLE I
COMBINATIONS OF LIFE CYCLES, PATTERNS OF SEXUALITY, AND SEXUAL MECHANISM OCCURRING IN FUNGI

Life cycle (cf. Fig. 2)	Pattern of sexuality (cf. Fig. 3)	Sexual mechanism (cf. Fig. 6)	Example
A	None	None	
B	O	3–7–9–10	Synchytrium
		3–7–12	Siphonaria
	I	3–8–9–10	Monoblepharis
		3–8–12	Mucor, Eremascus
	IV	3–5	Zygosaccharomyces
C	O	3–8–12–13	Pyronema, Ascobolus
	III	3–8–9–11–13	Neurospora, Podospora
D	O		
	III	4–13	Saccharomyces sp.
	V	3–8–9–11–13	Uredinales
	VI	3–6–13	Gasteromycetes, Hymenomycetes, Ustilaginales
E	O	4–13	Ustilaginales
	V		
F	O	3–8–9–10	Allomyces
	I	3–7–9–10	Blastocladiella
	V	3–5	Saccharomyces sp.
G[a]	IV	2	Saccharomycodes

[a] Achlya, Dictyuchus, Pythium, etc., patterns O and II, probably belong in this category, but sexual mechanisms cannot be specified on the basis of available information.

ever, are numerous, and, when considered in respect to probable phylogenetic lines, they are more than a little puzzling. Haploid-diploid and diploid cycles, those cycles which would seem to be the most highly advanced of all, occur only in aquatic phycomycetes and in a number of yeasts.

The pattern of sexuality in heterothallic species shows a similar progres-

15. Life Cycles, Sexuality, and Sexual Mechanisms

sion. The role of sexual factors as the critical determinants of mating behavior is for the most part limited to the more primitive forms, particularly aquatic phycomycetes, although there are a few cases of strict sexual dimorphism among ascomycetes. A single pair of incompatibility factors at a single locus possibly occurs in the more complex phycomycetes, the Mucorales, is very common among ascomycetes, and is frequently encountered in the rusts and possibly the smuts of the Basidiomycetes. The essentiality of differentiated sexual organs would seem to follow similar broad phylogenetic lines: they are present and functional in practically all phycomycetes and most ascomycetes, except the yeasts, and absent in all basidiomycetes, except the rusts.

Multiple-factor incompatibility is known only among members of the most highly evolved fungi, the Basidiomycetes, and is unquestionably the most efficient of all means evolved in the fungi to enhance outbreeding.

This might suggest a sort of coupling of the culmination of incompatibility control of mating behavior with a high degree of morphological development, particularly in the tetrapolar species, were it not for the fact that species which are obviously closely related to such tetrapolar forms are strictly homothallic and get along quite nicely with no restrictions imposed by incompatibility factors.

Sexual mechanisms and developmental histories are fairly constant within groups at the level of orders. There is also a tendency, in passing from primitive to highly evolved forms, to progress from gametic copulation through the loss of gametic differentiation in one sex or the other (gamete–gametangial copulation), to loss of gametic differentiation in both sexes (gametangial copulation), to the loss of sexual organs completely and the ability of all vegetative cells to participate in sexual fusions (somatic copulation). The developmental histories of sexual aspects per se, furthermore, show a marked tendency toward simplification, probably through reduction, in most of the more highly evolved groups.

VI. SUMMARY

Sexual reproduction in fungi displays a tremendous range of variability. Recognition of three distinct features is necessary adequately to describe the role of sex in any single species. These facets are: (1) the life cycle, in which the critical events are coincident with the initiation, the progression, and the termination of the essential sexual process; (2) the pattern of sexuality, which determines self-fertility or self-sterility and, in the later case, the exact pattern of inter-individual fertility; and (3) the sexual mechanism, the means by which sexual fusion is accomplished within the restrictions imposed by the life cycle and pattern of sexuality. Seven types of life cycles, seven distinct patterns of sexuality, and about a dozen or more basic kinds of sexual histories allow, in combination, a bewildering array of distinct sexual types.

Although there is a very loose correlation between morphological specialization and each of the three major facets of sexuality, no rigid correlation appears to exist between phylogenetic groupings and the various combinations of sexual features.

REFERENCES

Ahmad, M. (1952). Single-spore cultures of heterothallic *Saccharomyces cerevisiae* which mate with both tester strains. *Nature* **170**:546-547.

Ahmad, M. (1953). Mating of cells of same mating type in heterothallic *Saccharomyces*. *Cellule Rec. Cytol. Histol.* **55**:235-242.

Ahmad, M. (1954). A consideration of the terms and mechanisms of heterothallism. *Pakistan J. Sci.* **5**:59.

Alexopoulos, C. J. (1962). "Introductory Mycology," 2nd ed., 613 pp. Wiley, New York.

Ames, L. M. (1934). Hermaphroditism involving self-sterility and cross-fertility in the ascomycete *Pleurage anserina*. *Mycologia* **26**:392-414.

Andes, J. O. (1941). Experiments on the inheritance of the "plus" and "minus" characteristics in *Glomerella cingulata*. *Bull. Torrey Botan. Club* **68**:609-614.

Backus, M. P. (1939). The mechanics of conidial fertilization in *Neurospora sitophila*. *Bull. Torrey Botan. Club* **66**:63-76.

Barksdale, A. W. (1960). Inter-thallic sexual reactions in *Achlya*, a genus of the aquatic fungi. *Am. J. Botany* **47**:14-23.

Barksdale, A. W. (1965). *Achlya ambisexualis* and a new cross-conjugating species of *Achlya*. *Mycologia* **57**:493-501.

Barksdale, A. W. (1966). Personal communication.

Barnett, H. L. (1953). A unisexual male culture of *Chalara quercina*. *Mycologia* **45**:450-458.

Bauch, R. (1925). Untersuchungen über die Entwicklungsgeschichte und Sexualphysiologie der *Ustilago bromivora* und *U. grandis*. *Z. Botan.* **17**:129-177.

Bauch, R. (1931). Geographische Verteilung und funktionelle Differenzierung der Faktoren bei der multipolaren Sexualität von *Ustilago longissima*. *Arch. Protistenk.* **75**:101-132.

Benjamin, R. K., and L. Shanor. (1950). The development of male and female individuals in the dioecious species *Laboulbenia formicarum*. *Am. J. Botany* **37**:471-476.

Bessey, E. A. (1950). "Morphology and Taxonomy of Fungi," 791 pp. Blakiston, Philadelphia, Pennsylvania.

Bishop, H. (1940). A study of sexuality in *Sapromyces reinschii*. *Mycologia* **32**:505-529.

Bistis, G. N. (1956). Sexuality in *Ascobolus stercorarius*. I. Morphology of the ascogonium; plasmogamy; evidence for a sexual hormonal mechanism. *Am. J. Botany* **43**:389-394.

Bistis, G. N. (1957). Sexuality in *Ascobolus stercorarius*. II. Preliminary experiments on various aspects of the sexual process. *Am. J. Botany* **44**:436-443.

Bistis, G. N., and J. R. Raper. (1963). Heterothallism and sexuality in *Ascobolus stercorarius*. *Am. J. Botany* **50**:880-891.

15. Life Cycles, Sexuality, and Sexual Mechanisms

Blakeslee, A. F. (1904). Sexual reproduction in the Mucorineae. *Proc. Am. Acad. Arts Sci.* 40:205-319.
Blakeslee, A. F. (1920). Sexuality in Mucors. *Science* 51:375-382 and 403-409.
Boidin, J. (1956). Polarité dite "sexuelle" et systématique chez les Basidiomycètes Théléphoracés. *Rev. Mycol.* [N.S.] 21:121-131.
Brodie, H. J. (1931). The oidia of *Coprinus lagopus* and their relation with insects. *Ann. Botany (London)* 45:315-344.
Brunswik, H. (1924). Untersuchungen über die Geschlechts- und Kernverhältnisse bei der Hymenomyzetengattung *Coprinus. Botan. Abhandl.* K. Goebel 5:1-152.
Buller, A. H. R. (1924). Eperiments on sex in mushrooms and toadstools. *Nature* 114:826.
Buller, A. H. R. (1950). "Researches on Fungi," Vol. 7, 458 pp. Roy. Soc. Can., Univ. of Toronto Press, Toronto.
Burgeff, H. (1924). Untersuchungen über Sexualität und Parasitismus bei Mucorineen. I. *Botan. Abhandl.* K. Goebel 4:5-135.
Burnett, J. H. (1956). The mating systems of fungi. I. *New Phytologist* 55:50-90.
Cantino, E. C., and M. T. Hyatt. (1953). Phenotypic "sex" determination in the life history of a new species of *Blastocladiella, B. emersonii. Antonie van Leeuwenhoek, J. Microbiol. Serol.* 19:25-70.
Carr, A. J. H., and L. S. Olive. (1959). Genetics of *Sordaria fimicola*. III. Cross-compatibility among self-fertile and self-sterile cultures. *Am. J. Botany* 46:81-91.
Catcheside, D. G. (1951). "The Genetics of Micro-Organisms," 223 pp. Pitman, New York.
Christensen, J. J., and H. A. Rodenhiser. (1940). Physiological specialization and genetics of the smut fungi. *Botan. Rev.* 6:389-425.
Claussen, P. (1912). Zur Entwicklungsgeschichte der Ascomyceten, *Pyronema confluens. Z. Botan.* 4:1-64.
Claussen, P. (1921). Entwicklungsgeschichliche Untersuchungen über den Erreger der als "Kaltbrut" bezeichneten Krankheit der Bienen. *Arb. Biol. Abt. (Anst.—Reichsanst.), Berlin* 10:467-521.
Coker, W. C. (1923). "The Saprolegniaceae," 201 pp. Univ. of North Carolina Press, Chapel Hill, North Carolina.
Couch, J. N. (1926). Heterothallism in *Dictyuchus*, a genus of water moulds. *Ann. Botany (London)* 40:848-881.
Couch, J. N., and A. J. Whiffen. (1942). Observations on the genus *Blastocladiella. Am. J. Botany* 29:582-591.
Craigie, J. H. (1927). Discovery of the function of pycnia of the rust fungi. *Nature* 120:765-767.
Craigie, J. H. (1931). An experimental investigation of sex in the rust fungi. *Phytopathology* 21:1001-1040.
Craigie, J. H. (1942). Heterothallism in the rust fungi and its significance. *Trans. Roy. Soc. Can., Sect. V* 36:19-40.
Day, P. R. (1960). The structure of the A mating type locus in *Coprinus lagopus. Genetics* 45:641-651.
Day, P. R. (1963a). Mutations affecting the A mating type locus in *Coprinus lagopus. Genet. Res.* 4:55-65.
Day, P. R. (1963b). The structure of the A mating type factor in *Coprinus lagopus*: wild alleles. *Genet. Res.* 4:323-325.
de Bruyn, H. L. G. (1935). Heterothallism in *Peronospora parasitica. Phytopathology* 25:8.

de Bruyn, H. L. G. (1937). Heterothallism in *Peronospora parasitica*. *Genetica* **19**: 553-558.
Dixon, P. A. (1959). Life history and cytology of *Ascocybe grovesii*. *Ann. Botany (London)* [N.S.] **23**:509-520.
Dodge, B. O. (1920). Life history of *Ascobolus magnificus*. Origin of the archicarp from two strains. *Mycologia* **12**:115-134.
Dodge, B. O. (1927). Nuclear phenomena associated with heterothallism and homothallism in the Ascomycete *Neurospora*. *J. Agr. Res.* **35**:289-305.
Dodge, B. O. (1932). The non-sexual and sexual functions of microconidia of *Neurospora*. *Bull. Torrey Botan. Club* **59**:347-360.
Dodge, B. O., J. R. Singleton, and A. Rolnick. (1950). Studies on lethal E gene in *Neurospora tetrasperma*, including chromosome counts also in races of *N. sitophila*. *Proc. Am. Phil. Soc.* **94**:38-52.
Dowding, E. S. (1931). The sexuality of normal, giant, and dwarf spores of *Pleurage anserina*. *Ann. Botany (London)* **45**:1-14.
Dowding, E. S. (1933). *Gelasinospora*, a new genus of Pyrenomycetes with pitted spores. *Can. J. Res.* **9**:292-305.
Dowding, E. S., and A. H. R. Buller. (1940). Nuclear migrations in *Gelasinospora*. *Mycologia* **32**:471-488.
Drayton, F. D. (1932). The sexual function of microconidia in certain Ascomycetes. *Mycologia* **24**:345-348.
Drayton, F. D. (1934). The sexual mechanism of *Sclerotinia gladioli*. *Mycologia* **26**: 46-72.
Drayton, F. D., and J. W. Groves. (1952). *Stromatinia narcissi*, a new sexually dimorphic Discomycete. *Mycologia* **44**:119-140.
Edgerton, C. W. (1914). Plus and minus strains in *Glomerella*. *Am. J. Botany* **1**:244-254.
Edgerton, C. W., S. J. P. Chilton, and G. B. Lucas. (1945). Genetics of *Glomerella*. II. Fertilization between strains. *Am. J. Botany* **32**:115-118.
El Ani, A. S. (1954). The genetics of sex in *Hypomyces solani* f. *cucurbitae*. *Am. J. Botany* **41**:110-113.
El Ani, A. S., and L. S. Olive. (1962). The induction of balanced heterothallism in *Sordaria fimicola*. *Proc. Natl. Acad. Sci. U.S.* **48**:17-19.
Ellingboe, A. H. (1963). Illegitimacy and specific factor transfer in *Schizophyllum commune*. *Proc. Natl. Acad. Sci. U.S.* **49**:286-292.
Ellingboe, A. H., and J. R. Raper. (1962). Somatic recombination in *Schizophyllum commune*. *Genetics* **47**:85-98.
Emerson, R. (1941). An experimental study of the life cycles and taxonomy of *Allomyces*. *Lloydia* **4**:77-144.
Emerson, R. (1950). Current trends of experimental research on the aquatic Phycomycetes. *Ann. Rev. Microbiol.* **4**:169-200.
Emerson, R., and C. M. Wilson. (1954). Interspecific hybrids and the cytogenetics and cytotaxonomy of *Euallomyces*. *Mycologia* **46**:393-434.
Esser, K. (1959). Die incompatibilitätbeziehungen zwischen geographischen Rassen von *Podospora anserina*. II. Die Wirkungsweise der Semi-Incompatibilitäts-Gene. *Z. Vererbungslehre* **90**:29-52.
Esser, K., and R. Kuenen. (1965). "Genetik der Pilze," 497 pp. Springer, Berlin.
Esser, K., and J. Straub. (1956). Fertilität im Heterocaryon aus zwei sterilen Mutanten von *Sordaria macrospora*. *Z. Induktive Abstammungs-Verebungslehre* **87**:625-626.

15. Life Cycles, Sexuality, and Sexual Mechanisms 507

Esser, K., and J. Straub. (1958). Genetische Untersuchungen an *Sordaria macrospora* Auersw., Kompensation und Induktion bei genebedingten Entwicklungsdefekten. *Z. Induktive Abstammungs-Vererbungslehre* 87:729-746.

Franke, G. (1957). Die Cytologie der Ascusentwicklung von *Podospora anserina*. *Z. Induktive Abstammungs-Vererbungslehre* 88:159-160.

Franke, G. (1962). Versuche zu Genomverdopplung des Ascomyceten *Podospora anserina* (Ces.) Rehm. *Z. Vererbungslehre* 93:109-117.

Fries, N. (1940). Researches into the multipolar sexuality of *Cyathus striatus*. *Symbolae Botan. Upsalienses* 4:1-39.

Fries, N. (1943). Über das Vorkommen von geographischen Rassen bei *Crucibulum vulgare*. *Arch. Mikrobiol.* 13:182-190.

Fries, N., and L. Jonasson. (1941). Über die Interfertilität der Stämme von *Polyporus abientinus*. *Svensk Botan. Tidskr.* 35:177-193.

Gäumann, E. A. (1926). "Vergleichende Morphologie der Pilze," 626 pp. Fischer, Jena.

Gäumann, E. A., and C. W. Dodge. (1928). "Comparative Morphology of Fungi," 701 pp. McGraw-Hill, New York.

Greis, H. (1942). Relative Sexualität und Sterilisationsfaktoren bei den Hymenomyzeten *Solenia*. *Biol. Zentr.* 62:46-92.

Guilliermond, A. (1940). Sexuality, developmental cycle and phylogeny of yeasts. *Botan. Rev.* 6:1-24.

Hanna, W. F. (1925). The problem of sex in *Coprinus lagopus*. *Ann. Botany (London)* 39:431-457.

Hansen, H. N., and W. C. Snyder. (1946). Inheritance of sex in fungi. *Proc. Natl. Acad. Sci. U.S.* 32:272-273.

Harder, R. B., and G. Sörgel. (1938). Über einen neuen planoisogamen Phycomyceten mit Generationswechsel und seine phylogenetische Bedeutung. *Nachr. Ges. Wiss. Goettingen. Math.-Phys. Kl. Fachgruppen, VI* 3:119-127.

Hartmann, M. (1943). "Die Sexualität," 426 pp. Fischer, Jena.

Hartmann, M. (1955). Sex problems in algae, fungi, and protozoa. *Am. Naturalist* 89:321-347.

Hirsch, H. E. (1949). The cytogenetics of sex in *Hypomyces solani* f. *cucurbitae*. *Am. J. Botany* 36:113-121.

Humphrey, J. E. (1892). The Saprolegniaceae of the United States with notes on other species. *Trans. Am. Phil. Soc.* 17:63-148.

Karling, J. S. (1945). Brazilian Chytrids. VII. Observations relative to sexuality in two new species of *Siphonaria*. *Am. J. Botany* 32:580-587.

Kniep, H. (1920). Über morphologische und physiologische Geschlechts-differenzierung (Untersuchungen an Basidiomyceten). *Verhandl. Physik.-Med. Ges. Wurzburg* 46:1-18.

Kniep, H. (1922). Über Geschlechtsbestimmung und Reduktionsteilung (Untersuchungen an Basidiomyceten). *Verhandl. Physik.-Med. Ges. Wurzburg* 47:1-28.

Kniep, H. (1923). Über erbliche Änderungen von Geschlechtsfaktoren bei Pilzen. *Z. Induktive Abstammungs-Vererbungslehre* 31:170-183.

Kniep, H. (1926). Über Artkreuzungen bei Brandpilzen. *Z. Pilzk.* 5:217-247.

Kniep, H. (1928). "Die Sexualität der niederen Pflanzen," 544 pp. Fischer, Jena.

Kniep, H. (1929). *Allomyces javanicus*, n. sp. ein anisogamer Phycomycet mit planogameten. *Ber. Deut. Botan. Ges.* 47:199-212.

Kniep, H. (1930). Über den generationswechsel von *Allomyces*. *Z. Botan.* 22:433-441.

Krafczyk, H. (1935). Die Bildung und Keimung der Zygosporen von *Pilobolus crystallinus* und sein heterokaryotisches Myzel. *Beitr. Biol. Pflanz.* 23:349-396.
Lange, M. (1952). Species concept in the genus *Coprinus*. A study on the significance of intersterility. *Dansk. Botan. Ark.* 14:1-164.
Leonian, L. H. (1931). Heterothallism in *Phytophthora*. *Phytopathology* 21:941-955.
Leupold, U. (1958). Studies on recombination in *Schizosaccharomyces pombe*. *Cold Spring Harbor Symp. Quant. Biol.* 23:161-169.
Leupold, U. (1959). Studies on allelism in *Schizosaccharomyces pombe*. *Proc. 10th Intern. Congr. Genet., Montreal, 1958* Vol. 2, pp. 165-166. Univ. of Toronto Press, Toronto.
Lindegren, C. C. (1932). The genetics of *Neurospora*. II. Segregation of sex factors in the asci of *N. crassa, N. sitophila,* and *N. tetrasperma*. *Bull. Torrey Botan. Club* 59:119-138.
Lindegren, C. C., and G. Lindegren. (1944). Instability of the mating type alleles in *Saccharomyces*. *Ann. Missouri Botan. Garden* 31:203-218.
Link, G. K. K. (1929). Reproduction in Thallophytes, with special reference to Fungi. *Botan. Gaz.* 88:1-37.
McCranie, J. (1942). Sexuality in *Allomyces cystogenus*. *Mycologia* 34:209-213.
McGahen, J. W., and H. E. Wheeler. (1951). Genetics of *Glomerella*. IX. Perithecial development and plasmogamy. *Am. J. Botany* 38:610-617.
Machlis, L. (1958). Evidence for a sexual hormone in *Allomyces*. *Physiol. Plantarum* 11:181-192.
Mather, K. (1940). Outbreeding and separation of the sexes. *Nature* 145:484-486.
Mathieson, M. J. (1952). Ascospore morphology and mating type in *Chromocrea spinulosa* (Feukel) Petch n. comb. *Ann. Botany (London)* [N.S.] 16:449-460.
Maurizio, A. (1899). Beiträge zur Biologie der Saprolegnieen. *Z. Fischerei* 7:1-66.
Moewus, F. (1950). Sexualität und Sexualstoffe bei einem einzelligen Organismus. *Z. Sexualforsch.* 1:1-25.
Mounce, I. (1922). Homothallism and heterothallism in the genus *Coprinus*. *Brit. Mycol. Soc. Trans.* 7:256-269.
Mounce, I. (1926). A preliminary note on *Fomes pinicola* and *F. adiposa*—two heterothallic species of wood-destroying fungi. *Phytopathology* 16:757-758.
Mullins, J. T. (1961). The life cycle and development of *Dictyomorpha* gen. nov. (formerly *Pringsheimella*), a genus of aquatic fungi. *Am. J. Botany* 48:377-387.
Mullins, J. T. (1965). Personal communication.
Mullins, J. T., and J. R. Raper. (1965). Heterothallism in biflagellate aquatic fungi: preliminary genetic analysis. *Science* 150:1174-1175.
Nelson, R. R. (1959). Genetics of *Cochliobolus heterostrophus*. IV. A mutant gene that prevents perithecial development. *Phytopathology* 49:384-386.
Nobles, M. K. (1942). Secondary spores in *Corticium effuscatum*. *Can. J. Res.* C20:347-357.
Olive, L. S. (1958). On the evolution of heterothallism in fungi. *Am. Naturalist* 92:233-251.
Olson, E. O. (1949). Genetics of *Ceratostomella*. I. Strains in *Ceratostomella fimbriata* (Ell. and Hals.) Elliot from sweet potatoes. *Phytopathology* 39:548-561.
Papazian, H. P. (1950). Physiology of the incompatibility factors in *Schizophyllum commune*. *Botan. Gaz.* 112:143-163.
Papazian, H. P. (1951). The incompatibility factors and a related gene in *Schizophyllum commune*. *Genetics* 36:441-459.

15. Life Cycles, Sexuality, and Sexual Mechanisms

Pontecorvo, G. (1946). Genetic systems based on heterokaryosis. *Cold Spring Harbor Symp. Quant. Biol.* 11:193-201.

Pontecorvo, G. (1953). The genetics of *Aspergillus nidulans*. *Advan. Genet.* 5:141-237.

Pontecorvo, G. (1956). The parasexual cycle in fungi. *Ann. Rev. Microbiol.* 10:393-400.

Pontecorvo, G., and J. A. Roper. (1952). Genetic analysis without sexual reproduction by means of polyploidy in *Aspergillus nidulans*. *J. Gen. Microbiol.* 6:vii.

Prévost, G. (1962). Etude génétique d'un Basidiomycète: *Coprinus radiatus*. Thesis, "Docteur ès Sciences Naturelles," Univ. of Paris.

Raper, C. A., and J. R. Raper. (1964). Mutations affecting heterokaryosis in *Schizophyllum commune*. *Am. J. Botany* 51:503-513.

Raper, J. R. (1940). Sexuality in *Achlya ambisexualis*. *Mycologia* 32:710-727.

Raper, J. R. (1947). On the distribution and sexuality of *Achlya ambisexualis*. Paper read before Microbiological Section, Botanical Society of America, Chicago, Dec. 1947. *Am. J. Botany* 34:31a (Abstract).

Raper, J. R. (1950). Sexual hormones in *Achlya*. VII. The hormonal mechanism in homothallic species. *Botan. Gaz.* 112:1-24.

Raper, J. R. (1953). Tetrapolar Sexuality. *Quart. Rev. Biol.* 28:233-259.

Raper, J. R. (1954). Life cycles, sexuality and sexual mechanisms in the Fungi. *In* "Sex in Microorganisms" (D. H. Wenrich, I. F. Lewis, and J. R. Raper, eds.), pp. 42-81. Am. Assoc. Advance. Sci., Washington. D.C.

Raper, J. R. (1955). Heterokaryosis and sexuality in fungi. *Trans. N.Y. Acad Sci.* [2] 17:627-635.

Raper, J. R. (1959). Sexual versatility and evolutionary processes in fungi. *Mycologia* 51:107-125.

Raper, J. R. (1960). Control of sex in fungi. *Am. J. Botany* 47:794-808.

Raper, J. R. (1966). "Genetics of Sexuality in Higher Fungi," 283 pp. Ronald Press, New York.

Raper, J. R., D. H. Boyd, and C. A. Raper. (1965). Primary and secondary mutations at the incompatibility loci in *Schizophyllum*. *Proc. Natl. Acad. Sci. U.S.* 53:1324-1332.

Raper, J. R., and G. S. Krongelb. (1958). Genetic and environmental aspects of fruiting in *Schizophyllum commune* Fr. *Mycologia* 50:707-740.

Raper, J. R., and P. G. Miles. (1958). The genetics of *Schizophyllum commune*. *Genetics* 43:530-546.

Raper, J. R., and M. T. Oettinger. (1962). Anomalous segregation of incompatibility factors in *Schizophyllum commune*. *Rev. Biol. (Lisbon)* 3:205-221.

Raper, J. R., M. G. Baxter, and R. B. Middleton. (1958a). The genetic structure of the incompatibility factors in *Schizophyllum commune*. *Proc. Natl. Acad. Sci. U.S.* 44:889-900.

Raper, J. R., G. S. Krongelb, and M. G. Baxter. (1958b). The number and distribution of incompatibility factors in *Schizophyllum commune*. *Am. Naturalist* 92:221-232.

Raper, J. R., M. G. Baxter, and A. H. Ellingboe. (1960). The genetic structure of the incompatibility factors of *Schizophyllum commune*: the A factor. *Proc. Natl. Acad. Sci. U.S.* 46:833-842.

Renner, O. (1916). Zur Terminologie des pflanzlichen Generationswechsel. *Biol. Zentr.* 36:337-374.

Rizet, G., and C. Engelmann. (1949). Contribution à l'étude génétique d'un Ascomycète tetraspore: *Podospora anserina. Rev. Cytol. Biol. Vegetales* 11:201-304.
Roper, J. A. (1952). Production of heterozygous diploids in filamentous fungi. *Experientia* 8:1-4.
Salvin, S. B. (1942). A preliminary report on the intergeneric mating of *Thraustotheca clavata* and *Achlya flagellata. Am. J. Botany* 29:674-676.
Sansome, E. R. (1961). Meiosis in the oogonium and antheridium of *Pythium debaryanum* Hesse. *Nature* 191:827-828.
Sansome, E. R. (1963). Meiosis in *Pythium debaryanum* Hesse and its significance in the life-history of the Biflagellatae. *Trans. Brit. Mycol. Soc.* 46:63-72.
Sass, J. E. (1929). The cytological basis for homothallism and heterothallism in the Agaricaceae. *Am. J. Botany* 16:663-701.
Satina, S., and A. F. Blakeslee. (1928). Studies on biochemical differences between sexes in Mucors. V. *Proc. Natl. Acad. Sci. U.S.* 14:308-316.
Satina, S., and A. F. Blakeslee. (1929). Criteria of male and female in bread molds (Mucors). *Proc. Natl. Acad. Sci. U.S.* 15:735-740.
Schopfer. W. H., and S. Blumer. (1940). Le pouvoir de synthèse d'un facteur de croissance par *Schizophyllum commune* (haplontes et diplontes). *Protoplasma* 34: 524-532.
Shear, C. L., and B. O. Dodge. (1927). Life histories and heterothallism of the red bread-mold fungi of the *Monilia sitophila* group. *J. Agr. Res.* 34:1019-1042.
Skolko, A. J. (1944). A cultural and cytological investigation of a two-spored Basidiomycete, *Aleurodiscus canadensis. Can. J. Res.* C22:251-271.
Smith, A. H. (1934). Investigations of two-spored forms in the genus *Mycena. Mycologia* 26:305-331.
Sparrow, F. K. (1960). "Aquatic Phycomycetes," 2nd ed., 1187 pp. Univ. of Michigan Press, Ann Arbor, Michigan.
Spiltoir, C. F. (1955). Life cycle of *Ascosphaera apis* (*Pericystis apis*). *Am. J. Botany* 42:501-508.
Stüben, H. (1939). Über Entwicklungsgeschichte und Ernährungsphysiologie eines neuen niederen Phycomyceten mit Generationswechsel. *Planta* 30:353-383.
Takemaru, T. (1957). Genetics of *Collybia velutipes*. IV. "Interpolarity" occurring in the strain NL-55. *Botan. Mag.* (*Tokyo*) 70:238-243.
Takemaru, T. (1961). Genetic studies in Fungi. X. The mating system in Hymenomycetes and its genetical mechanism. *Biol. J. Okayama Univ.* 7:133-211.
Terakawa, H. (1957). The nuclear behavior and the morphogenesis in *Pleurotus ostreatus. Sci. Papers Coll. Gen. Educ., Univ. Tokyo* 7:61-88.
Terakawa, H. (1960). The incompatibility factors in *Pleurotus ostreatus. Sci. Papers Coll. Gen. Educ., Univ. Tokyo* 10:65-71.
Thaxter, R. (1908). Contribution toward a monograph of the Laboulbeniales. II. *Mem. Am. Acad. Arts Sci.* 13:217-469.
Vandendries, R. (1923). Nouvelle recherches sur la sexualité de Basidiomycètes. *Bull. Soc. Botan. Belg.* 56:73-97.
Wager, H. (1913). The life cycle and cytology of *Polyphagus euglenae. Ann. Botany* (*London*) 27:173-202.
Wheeler, H. E. (1950). Genetics of *Glomerella*. VIII. A genetic basis for the occurrence of minus mutants. *Am. J. Botany* 37:304-312.
Wheeler, H. E. (1954). Genetics and evolution of heterothallism in *Glomerella. Phytopathology* 44:342-345.

15. Life Cycles, Sexuality, and Sexual Mechanisms

Wheeler, H. E., and J. W. McGahen. (1952). Genetics of *Glomerella*. X. Genes affecting sexual reproduction. *Am. J. Botany* **39**:110-119.
Whitehouse, H. L. K. (1949a). Heterothallism and sex in the fungi. *Biol. Rev. Cambridge Phil. Soc.* **24**:411-447.
Whitehouse, H. L. K. (1949b). Multiple allelomorph heterothallism in fungi. *New Phytologist* **48**:212-244.
Whitehouse, H. L. K. (1951). A survey of heterothallism in the Ustilaginales. *Trans. Brit. Mycol. Soc.* **34**:340-355.
Wilcox, M. S. (1928). The sexuality and arrangement of spores in the ascus of *Neurospora sitophila*. *Mycologia* **20**:3-17.
Wilson, C. M. (1952). Meiosis in *Allomyces*. *Bull. Torrey Botan. Club* **79**:139-160.
Winge, Ö. (1935). On haplophase and diplophase in some Saccharomycetes. *Compt. Rend. Trav. Lab. Carlsberg, Ser. Physiol.* **21**:77-113.
Winge, Ö. (1944). On segregation and mutation in yeast. *Compt. Rend. Trav. Lab. Carlsberg, Ser. Physiol.* **24**:79-96.
Winge, Ö., and O. Laustsen. (1939). *Saccharomycodes ludwigii*, a balanced heterozygote. *Compt. Rend. Trav. Lab. Carlsberg, Ser. Physiol.* **22**:357-370.
Zickler, H. (1934). Genetische Untersuchungen an einem heterothallischen Askomyzeten (*Bombardia lunata* nov. sp.). *Planta* **22**:573-613.
Zickler, H. (1937). Die Vererbung des Geschlechts bei dem Askomyzeten *Bombardia lunata* Zckl. *Z. Induktive Abstammungs-Verebungslehre* **73**:403-408.
Zickler, H. (1952). Zur Entwicklungsgeschichte des Askomyzeten *Bombardia lunata*. *Arch. Protistenk.* **98**:1-70.
Ziegler, A. W. (1953). Meiosis in the Saprolegniaceae. *Am. J. Botany* **40**:60-66.

CHAPTER 16

Mechanisms of Inheritance

1. Mendelian

STERLING EMERSON

*Division of Biology
California Institute of Technology
Pasadena, California*

I. INTRODUCTION

The genetics of fungi is not a self-contained subject. A student of mycology wishing to deal competently with genetic aspects of fungi needs some knowledge of hereditary processes as they occur in higher plants and animals and in bacteria and bacteriophages. He may reasonably expect to find the necessary background information in current textbooks of general genetics, some of which are completely adequate. Students primarily interested in the genetics of insects, mammals, higher plants, bacteria, bacteriophages, or protozoa, on the other hand, may not appreciate the genetic potentialities of fungi, or may not be able to review critically the data from experiments with fungi, because of insufficient knowledge of the sexual, morphological, and cultral characteristics of different kinds of fungi. They may logically expect to find the required background information in a series of volumes dealing with all aspects of the lives of the fungi.

Information pertinent to genetic studies appears throughout the volumes of "The Fungi" in sections reviewing the morphology of vegetative and reproductive structures, nuclear cytology during meiosis and mitosis, sexual cycles and life histories, etc. Inasmuch as those reviews were not necessarily written with the aim of showing their relevance to genetic mechanisms it seems important to do so in this chapter. It is my hope that overlap with other chapters will be small, discrepancies minor, and viewpoints sufficiently dissimilar to warrant the duplication that does occur.

No attempt will be made to catalog all kinds of genetic experiments that have been made with fungi, nor to list all species that have been used in genetic experiments. Instead, species representative of different groups of fungi (exclusive of the slime molds) will be used to illustrate important diversities that occur. Most attention will be paid to those species which have contributed most to the current understanding of genetic mechanisms. A more extensive coverage of various aspects of fungal genetics can be found in a recent book by Fincham and Day (1965).

II. THE BASIC MECHANISM OF MENDELIAN INHERITANCE

Mendelian inheritance, in the sense used in this review, includes all patterns of inheritance of characteristics controlled by the genes in the chromosomes. The observed patterns of inheritance are dependent upon the locations of the genes in the chromosomes and upon the detailed behavior of the chromosomes during the entire life cycle of the species concerned. The basic mechanism of inheritance would be more nearly self-evident if there were a single invariable pattern of behavior of genetic elements within an individual and among all individuals of a species. As it is, the vast bulk of genetic and cytological observation is in accord with a single general mechanism, but one which can be modified by certain influences and severely upset by accidents.

The principal problem encountered in deducing a basic pattern of nuclear and genetic behavior arises from the difficulty in evaluating those observations which are discordant with a postulated basic pattern. Does an untoward event stem directly from the true basic pattern? If so, does it in any way invalidate a postulated pattern? Or does it supply information leading to a more complete understanding of a pattern under consideration? At present there is one generally accepted pattern of nuclear and genetic behavior which satisfactorily accounts for the great majority of observations in all nucleated organisms, including the fungi. There are also, especially in studies of fungi, a number of observed phenomena which are not directly predictable from this accepted pattern. Such phenomena will be examined for their importance to the accepted general mechanism of inheritance after it has been outlined.

A. Critical Stages in Life Cycles

The kinds of information available from genetic experimentation, the ease and accuracy with which genetic observations can be made, and the validity of the inferences drawn from such observations, all depend to a very considerable extent on details of nuclear behavior during the entire sexual cycle of the organism studied. Of the various phases succeeding one another throughout a life cycle, two are essential to studies of Mendelian inheritance: karyogamy and meiosis. Homologous sets of chromosomes from the two parents are brought together in one nucleus at karyogamy, without which there would be no opportunity for segregation of, or recombination between, those genes in which the parents differ. Cytological observations alone are often sufficient to show that karyogamy has occurred, and has brought together two sets of haploid chromosomes. The two meiotic divisions can also be identified cytologically, as can pairing between homologous chromosomes to give an opportunity for crossing over. On the other hand, many of the details of genetic recombination and segregation which occur during meiosis cannot be directly determined, and must be inferred from genetic observation. The mechanism by which genetic recombination occurs is still not understood, though quite a lot is known about it. Hence, from a strictly genetic point of view, meiosis is the most critical stage in the life cycle of a species.

A genetically ideal life cycle would be one in which it would be possible to know the exact genetic constitution of the two sets of homologous chromosomes which pair in the first meiotic division, and one in which the four products of the two meiotic divisions can be recovered and identified as to their relation to those two divisions. Among the fungi these conditions would be closely approximated in a life cycle in which no dikaryotic phase intervened between plasmogamy and karyogamy, in which no diploid phase occurred between karyogamy and meiosis, and in which the four products of meiosis occur together in an order reflecting their relationships to the two meiotic divisions. The nearest approach to ideal among fungi which have been studied genetically is to be found in a few species of ascomycetes with linearly ordered ascospores. One of these, *Neurospora crassa,* will be used to illustrate the basic mechanism of Mendelian inheritance.

B. Basic Pattern of Inheritance in Neurospora crassa

1. Life Cycle

The entire vegetative part of the life cycle of *N. crassa* is haploid, and consists of a freely branched multicellular mycelium in which there are perforated septa through which nuclei freely migrate. Asexual spores are of two kinds: macroconidia, 6–8 μ in diameter (Fig. 1a) with one to eight or more nuclei, usually three or two (Norman, 1951; Huebschman, 1952), and uninucleate microconidia, 3–4 μ in diameter. Strains with appropriate genotypes (Barratt and Garnjobst, 1949) produce microconidia exclusively.

Heterothallism is governed by two alleles at the single mating-type locus. The alleles are remarkably stable, never having been observed to mutate. Strains of both mating types are hermaphroditic in that each can function as either female or male in crosses. The female sex organ is the ascogonium (Fig. 1b), consisting of a rather thick coil of a few oligonucleate cells, ending in a branched receptive hypha (or trichogyne), and enclosed in a wall of sterile hyphae to constitute the incipient ascocarp, or protoperithecium. No specialized male cells are produced, unless microconidia are so considered, but conidia or any vegetative cells can serve as male gametes.

Plasmogamy takes place through the attachment of a branch of the trichogyne to a conidium (Fig. 1b) or other vegetative cell of opposite

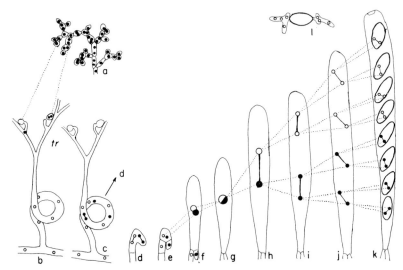

FIG. 1. Nuclear behavior at critical stages in the sexual cycle of *Neurospora crassa*: (a) portion of a conidiophore with macroconidia—the black dots represent nuclei of one mating type; (b) the fertile hypha (ascogonium) of a protoperithecium (incipient ascocarp)—the open circles represent nuclei opposite in mating type to those in the conidia, two of which are shown in association with the trichogyne, *tr*, of the ascogonium; (c) the same, after nuclei from the conidia have migrated into it; (d) conjugate divisions of nuclei of opposite mating type in the crosier; (e) origin of the ascus initial from the penultimate cell of the crosier; (f) and (g) fusion of haploid nuclei to form the diploid zygote nucleus; (h–k) successive nuclear divisions in the ascus—respectively the first meiotic division, the second meiotic division with spindles in tandem orientation, the third division which is a haploid mitosis, and the fourth division which is a haploid mitosis occurring in the young ascospores; (l) ascospore germination to form coenocytic hyphae.

mating type. Nuclei from the male cell migrate through the trichogyne and establish a dikaryotic condition in the coil of the ascogonium (Fig. 1c), from which dikaryotic ascogenous hyphae develop inside the wall of the growing perithecium. (Judging by the number of asci and sterile cells produced in a perithecium it can be estimated that at least seven and not more than ten successive nuclear divisions usually take place in the relatively brief dikaryophase.)

16. Mendelian 517

The cytological details of all nuclear divisions, from those occurring in the crosier (Fig. 1d) to those in the nearly mature ascospores (Fig. 1k), have been very well established by studies of McClintock (1945), Singleton (1953), and others, and have been reviewed by Olive (1965). Only those features which are important to an understanding of genetic mechanisms will be noted here. The haploid set consists of seven chromosomes, each of which can be recognized by morphological characteristics. Karyogamy occurs in the penultimate cell of the crosier (the ascus initial). Meiosis occurs in the first two divisions of the zygote nucleus formed at karyogamy —there are no diploid mitoses intervening. In the second meiotic division the two spindles are parallel to the long axis of the ascus, and well separated (Fig. 1i) so that the two nuclei arising from one first division daughter nucleus are in one half of the ascus, the two from the other daughter nucleus in the other half of the ascus. A third division, a haploid mitosis, then occurs in which there is rarely any overlapping of the diagonally oriented spindles. As a consequence the lines of descent of the nuclei in each of the eight ascospores produced (shown by the dotted lines in Fig. 1, g–k) can be inferred with considerable accuracy from the positions of the spores in the linearly ordered ascus.

2. Genetic Confirmation of Events in the Life Cycle

Whereas, conditions being appropriate, cytological observations can be made at any step in the procession of events making up the life cycle, genetic observations of segregation and recombination are possible only after the completion of all steps in the life cycle upon which these phenomena are dependent. Nevertheless genetic observations can often produce more evidence about details of the life cycle than can be gained by other known means. Evaluation of the significance of genetic observations is probably simplest if the steps in the life cycle are considered in reverse order, beginning with the stage actually examined and progressing to more and more remote phases.

a. Haploidy of the Vegetative Phase. Chromosome counts have demonstrated that haploidy is established at the end of the second meiotic division in the ascus and persists in the vegetative phase. In *N. crassa* there are seven chromosomes, the haploid number, in the eight nuclei about which ascospores are cut out (McClintock, 1945; Singleton, 1953), and in nuclei of the vegetative mycelium (Somers *et al.,* 1960). Genetic confirmation comes from the observation that all alleles which are segregating in crosses produce their full phenotypic expression at or shortly after ascospore germination or, with favorable mutants, in the ascospore itself (Stadler, 1956a,b). In the normal course of events there is no masking of the phenotype of one allele by the presence of its dominant alternative, as would occur in diploid cells. (Infrequently both alternative alleles are included in a single ascospore, as in the pseudo-wild segregants mentioned below in Section II, B, 2, d.) The haploid nature of the vegetative phase is further verified by observed segregation in subsequent crosses of all alleles phenotypically expressed in the parents of such crosses, and of no alleles not so expressed.

b. First and Second Division Segregation. Segregation is known to occur during meiosis in all organisms in which Mendelian inheritance regularly occurs. In linearly ordered asci (see Fig. 1) it is possible to tell whether a pair of alleles have segregated at the first or second meiotic division from the positions within the ascus of spores carrying a particular allele.

(1) *Segregation of alleles at one locus.* The eight linearly ordered ascospores in the ascus occur in three principal patterns, each of which consists of two secondary patterns which differ only in the particular allele occupying particular positions. For example, the patterns produced in the segregation of the alternative alleles b and $+$ (at locus $b/+$) are:

(I) $\begin{cases} b\,b\,b\,b\,+\,+\,+\,+ \\ +\,+\,+\,+\,b\,b\,b\,b \end{cases}$

(II-alt.) $\begin{cases} b\,b\,+\,+\,b\,b\,+\,+ \\ +\,+\,b\,b\,+\,+\,b\,b \end{cases}$

(II-sym.) $\begin{cases} b\,b\,+\,+\,+\,+\,b\,b \\ +\,+\,b\,b\,b\,b\,+\,+ \end{cases}$

First division segregation patterns (I) carry a particular allele in the four spores whose nuclei were derived from one of the two nuclei arising from the first meiotic division, i.e., the four spores at one or the other end of the ascus (Fig. 1). Whenever segregation fails to take place during the first meiotic division the two resulting nuclei are still heterozygous. Segregation at the second division is recognized by the genetic difference between pairs of spores at each end of the ascus. The order in which alleles occur may be the same in both ends of an ascus, resulting in a pattern in which the two kinds of spore pairs occupy alternate positions (II-alt.), or the orders may be reversed, resulting in patterns in which the distribution of each allele is symmetrical (II-sym.).

(2) *Segregation of alleles at two loci.* Ascospore patterns resulting from the segregation of alternative alleles at two heterozygous loci, $b/+$ and $c/+$, can be predicted from the first and second division patterns of each pair of alleles, as illustrated in Table I. Three different ascospore patterns, called tetrad types, are produced. Parental ditype tetrads have two spore-pairs of one parental genotype, two of the other. Nonparental ditype tetrads have two spore-pairs with one recombinant arrangement of parental

TABLE I
Tetrad Patterns Produced by First and Second Division Segregation at Two Loci, $b/+$ and $c/+$

Segregation divisions		Tetrad types		
$b/+$	$c/+$	Parental ditypes	Nonparental ditypes	Tetratypes
I	I	bc bc bc bc ++ ++ ++ ++	b+ b+ b+ b+ +c +c +c +c	— — — — — — — —
I	II-alt.	— — — — — — — —	— — — — — — — —	bc bc b+ b+ +c +c ++ ++
I	II-sym.	— — — — — — — —	— — — — — — — —	bc bc b+ b+ ++ ++ +c +c
II-alt.	I	— — — — — — — —	— — — — — — — —	bc bc +c +c b+ b+ ++ ++
II-sym.	I	— — — — — — — —	— — — — — — — —	bc bc +c +c ++ ++ b+ b+
II-alt.	II-alt.	bc bc ++ ++ bc bc ++ ++	b+ b+ +c +c b+ b+ +c +c	— — — — — — — —
II-alt.	II-sym.	— — — — — — — —	— — — — — — — —	bc bc ++ ++ b+ b+ +c +c
II-sym.	II-alt.	— — — — — — — —	— — — — — — — —	bc bc ++ ++ +c +c b+ b+
II-sym.	II-sym.	bc bc ++ ++ ++ ++ bc bc	b+ b+ +c +c +c +c b+ b+	— — — — — — — —

alleles, two with the reciprocally recombinant arrangement. Tetratype tetrads have one spore-pair with alleles at both loci derived from one parent, one spore-pair with both from the other parent, one spore-pair with one recombination of parental alleles, and one with the complementary recombination.

Whenever the segregation patterns of both pairs of alleles are of the same sort, i.e., both I, both II-alt., or both II-sym., the resulting tetrad type is either parental ditype or nonparental ditype. Whenever the patterns are of different sorts, i.e., one I and one II, or one II-alt. and one II-sym., tetratype tetrads are produced.

(3) *Frequencies of regular segregations.* I am here using the term regular segregation to designate a 4:4 segregation of a pair of alleles, that is, asci in which each alternative allele is present in two spore-pairs. Irregular segregations, then, are those in which one allele is present in more than four spores, its alternative in less than four, resulting in ratios such as 6:2 and 5:3. It should be noted that when irregular segregations of this kind are observed (see discussion of nonreciprocal recombination, Section III) they involve segregation occurring at only one heterozygous locus in asci in which regular segregation occurs at other heterozygous loci.

Observed frequencies of irregular segregations are low, as indicated by the data from three representative studies which are summarized in Table II. A difficulty in estimating the frequencies of regular and irregular segregations arises from the amount of ascospore inviability that seems inevitably

TABLE II

OBSERVED FREQUENCIES OF ASCI WITH REGULAR SEGREGATIONS

Data	Perkins (1962)		Bole-Gowda et al. (1962)		Prakash (1964)	
Heterozygous loci	6		7		11	
Total asci dissected	1406		3264		1940	
Analyzable asci[a]	1310	93.2%	2945	90.2%	1835	94.6%
Regular segregations	1262	96.3%	2909	98.8%	1813	98.8%
4 tetrad members	(1017	77.6%)	—		(1004	54.7%)[b]
					(442	24.1%)
3 tetrad members	(245	18.7%)	—		(367	20.0%)
Irregular segregations	11	0.8%	36	1.2%	22	1.2%
Technical errors	25	1.9%				
Incomplete scoring	12	0.9%	—		—	

[a] Analyzable asci are expressed as percentage of total asci dissected; types of segregation observed are expressed as percentages of analyzable asci.
[b] Both sister spores of all four tetrad members were analyzed.

to occur in all studies involving large numbers of asci. If irregular segregations are disregarded it is possible to deduce the genetic constitution of one missing tetrad member (i.e., one missing spore-pair) in instances in which the genetic constitutions of the other three tetrad members are known. Further, inasmuch as the two members of each spore-pair usually are completely identical in genetic constitution, known constitutions of one member of each of three spore-pairs are sufficient for complete ascus analysis. For many purposes the common practice of using all analyzable asci is certainly justifiable, but irregular segregation at some one locus can be estimated accurately only from asci in which germination is complete. Estimates based on a selected group of asci in which all eight spores were viable are subject to bias only if irregular segregation itself is likely to result in ascospore inviability. Although there is no evidence suggesting that such a relationship exists between irregular segregation (of the kind in question) and ascospore viability, there is also no direct evidence that it does not. [Chromosomal nondisjunction during meiosis ordinarily results in ascospore abortion rather than in inviability of normal appearing ascospores (McClintock, 1945; Perkins et al., 1962) hence is not pertinent to this discussion.]

Technical errors (as noted in Table II) are difficult or impossible to avoid completely, even in the best-regulated experiments. Included here are such happenings as sporadic contamination, errors in dissection, mix-ups between groups of spores discharged from different asci (when that technique is used), errors in transcription, etc. Such things are annoying because one can be almost certain that they do not represent occurrences belonging to the investigation at hand, but not sufficiently certain to omit them from the tabulation of results.

(4) *Frequencies of disordered second division patterns.* Observed frequencies of first and second division segregations would fail to give an accurate estimate of second division segregation frequencies if there was an appreciable frequency of overlapping of spindles in anaphase of the second meiotic division (or the equivalent displacement of nuclei after the second division). As illustrated in Fig. 2, following such spindle overlapping, first division segregations would appear as second division segregations with the alternating pattern, and second division segregations which should lead to the alternating pattern would appear as first division segregations. Second division segregations which should lead to the symmetrical pattern are unaffected.

Data on observed second division segregation frequencies can be subjected to an algebraic treatment which considers three variables: the frequency of actual second division segregation, the fraction of second divisions which should lead to alternating patterns, and the actual fre-

frequency of second division spindle overlapping (S. Emerson, 1963). Data from *N. crassa* indicate, by this treatment, that there are no spindle overlaps and that orientations that should lead to alternating and symmetrical second division patterns occur equally often. Data from *Bombardia lunata* by the same treatment suggest that overlapping second division spindles occur in nearly half of the instances. Although the alge-

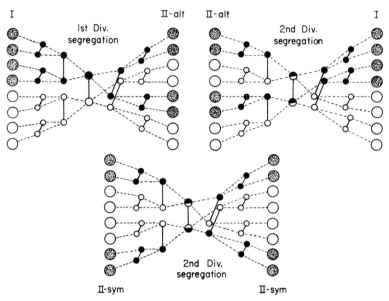

FIG. 2. Changes in spore patterns resulting from overlapping second division spindles. At the left in each diagram, the ascus pattern correctly reflecting the division at which segregation occurred and orientation of alleles on second division spindles; at the right, the patterns resulting from spindle overlapping.

braic approach is indirect, its results are in agreement with cytological observations which show little possibility of spindle overlapping in *Neurospora* (McClintock, 1945; Singleton, 1953) and the considerable occurrence of overlapping in *Bombardia* (Zickler, 1952).

A more direct test for overlapping spindles in the second meiotic division depends on the relationship between crossing over and second division segregation, to be discussed below (Section II, B, 2, c). Following such overlapping there would appear to be a crossover between the centromere and genes on either side of the centromere which are most closely linked to it; and this should occur in each chromosome carrying appropriate genetic markers. With genes close to the centromere in both chromosome arms the appearance would be that of a two-strand double exchange immediately surrounding the centromere. Among 1813 ordered asci analyzed

16. Mendelian

by Prakash (1964) there was only one ascus which could be interpreted as resulting from overlapping second division spindles, and this one only if there had been true crossing over in one arm of each of two chromosomes (of three which were followed) of a kind exactly canceling the expected effects of overlapping. In total, genetic data indicate that there is no, or very little, second division spindle overlapping.

Spindle overlap	II-sym.	II-alt.	I		Tetratype
○○●○○●○○	1035	966	7037	864	280
ᏮᏫᏫ○○○○	28	63	(Undetected)		13
○○ᏮᏫᏫ○○	(Undetected)	0	160	27*	8
ᏮᏫᏫ○○○○	? ← 1 → ?		(Undetected)		0
○○ᏮᏫ○Ꮯ○○	(Undetected)	? ← 5 → ?	3		0
ᏮᏫᏮᏫ○○	(Undetected)	1	(Undetected)		3
ᏮᏫᏮᏫᏮᏫ	1	0	(Undetected)		1
	D. R. Stadler (unpublished)		Howe (1956)		

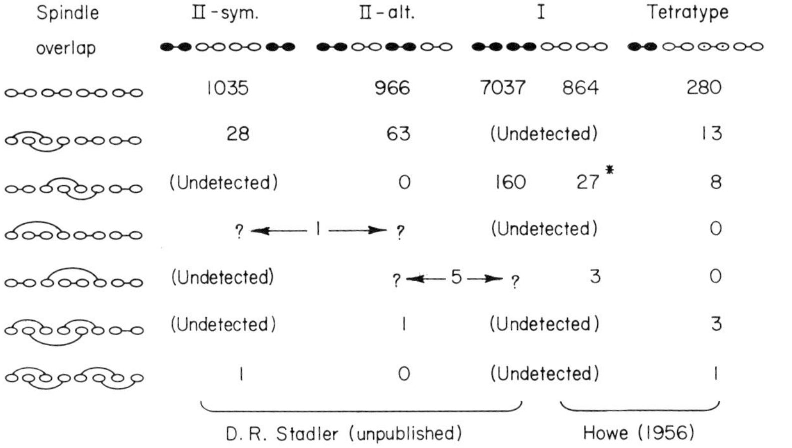

*Including three asci in which ascospore disarrangement was more complex.

FIG. 3. Numbers of observed asci with spore patterns showing different irregularities attributable to the kinds of third division spindle overlapping diagrammed in the leftmost column.

(5) *Frequency of disordered third division patterns.* Spindles of the third (mitotic) division of the ascus in *N. crassa* have an oblique orientation in the ascus, and there is some movement of nuclei following that division and preceding the division of the cytoplasm about the nuclei to form the ascospores (Singleton, 1953). It would thus not be too surprising if some disordering of nuclei occurred at this time. Disordered ascus patterns which are observed in rather low frequency can be most simply interpreted on that basis. Two sets of data which give some idea of the frequencies of disarranged patterns, and of the nuclear displacements probably responsible for them, are summarized in Fig. 3. Segregation at a single locus was followed in Stadler's study, at several loci in one chromosome and at one locus in another chromosome in Howe's study. It should be noted that tetratype tetrads are adapted to the detection of all such disarrangements of spores because of the ease with which members of each spore-pair can be identified.

c. *Linkage and Crossing Over.* Tetrads of meiotic products are not needed for the detection of linkage—on the contrary, as shown by Perkins (1953), linked inheritance is usually more efficiently detected among strictly random products of meiosis than among tetrads. Genes are observed to be linked when recombination between them is significantly less than 50%. (Genes belonging to the same linkage group may be sufficiently distant from each other to prevent detection of linkage in the absence of other genes lying between them.) The linear order of genes within a linkage group is also efficiently determined from random meiotic products in appropriate three-point tests (involving simultaneous segregations at three linked loci) because the frequency of double crossovers (recombinants) does not ordinarily exceed the product of the frequencies of single crossovers in the two intervals involved (Sturtevant, 1913); hence the recombination class which occurs in the lowest frequency is the one made up of double crossovers.

Seven linkage groups have been established in *N. crassa* (Barratt et al., 1954) in agreement with the haploid number of chromosomes. Genetic and cytological studies (McClintock, 1945; St. Lawrence, 1952; Barry, 1961; Perkins et al., 1962) in combination have permitted the identification of particular linkage groups with particular chromosomes as recognized by their morphological characteristics.

(1) *Characteristics of crossing over.* Many of the more important characteristics of the crossing-over process are completely undetectable in studies of random products of meiosis. The most valuable information relating to the mechanism of crossing over depends upon the complete genotypic identification of all members of tetrads of meiotic products.

Following crossing over at a single level in a chromosome, two members of the tetrad are observed to be reciprocal crossovers, the other two noncrossovers. The inescapable inference from this observation is that crossing over occurs at the four-strand stage: that is, when the two homologous chromosomes are both divided into two sister chromatids; and that crossing over involves an exchange between only two of the four chromatids (between one sister chromatid of each of the two homologous chromosomes).

Following such single exchanges, observed ascospore patterns show that segregation at heterozygous loci on one side of the exchange takes place at the first meiotic division, and at the second division at loci on the other side of the exchange. When many different loci in a single linkage group are followed, single crossing over invariably results in second division segregation for loci which are nearest one or the other of the two ends of the linkage map. By this method it is possible to identify one region (point) on the map of each linkage group at which segregation always occurs at the first division. This point is identified with the cytologically observed centromere, which does not divide until the end of the first division, and to which both sister chromatids are attached through anaphase of the first division. Because of this relationship the centromere can be used as a genetic marker in linearly ordered tetrads.

Four different tetrad patterns are observed to result from double crossing over when each exchange takes place between two heterozygous loci, as one between $d/+$ and $e/+$ and one between $e/+$ and $f/+$, as in Fig. 4.

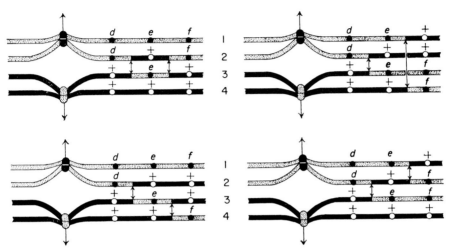

FIG. 4. Genetic compositions of tetrads of chromatids following two-strand (upper left), four-strand (upper right), and two kinds of three-strand (lower left and right) double crossing over. Sister chromatids of one chromosome are shown in black, those of the other stippled. Each pair of sister strands is represented as attached to a still undivided centromere, from which an arrow indicates the pole to which the two chromatids will pass at anaphase of the first meiotic division. At both levels of crossing over the double-headed arrows indicate the two chromatids taking part in crossing over.

One tetrad pattern has two members which are non-crossovers, one carrying alleles from one parent, $d\ e\ f$, the other alleles from the other parent, $+ + +$, and two members which are reciprocal double-crossovers, $d + f$ and $+ e +$. Double exchanges responsible for this tetrad pattern are known as two-strand doubles because only two of the four chromatids have been altered by crossing over. Three-strand double exchanges result in tetrads in which one member is a double crossover, one a non-crossover, and two are single crossovers, one a crossover in one region and one a crossover in the other region. Two different patterns arise from three-strand doubles: they differ in that the non-crossover member in one has alleles from one parent whereas the non-crossover member of the other has alleles from the other parent. All four members of patterns derived from four-strand double exchanges are single crossovers, of which two are reciprocal crossovers in one region, two reciprocal crossovers in the other.

Some additional points should be noted in connection with double exchanges: (1) Segregation at a locus distal to a double exchange ($f/+$ in the diagrams) takes place at the first division following two-strand and four-strand doubles, but at the second division following three-strand doubles. (2) Tetrad types produced by alleles at the heterozygous loci between which both exchanges have occurred (loci $d/+$ and $f/+$ in the diagrams) are parental ditypes following two-strand doubles, nonparental ditypes following four-strand doubles, and tetratypes following three-strand doubles. (3) From the situations noted in (1) and (2) it is evident that when there is no heterozygous locus between two exchanges (when $e/+$ is replaced in the cross by either e/e or $+/+$), two-strand doubles would yield tetrads identical with those produced when no exchanges had occurred. Tetrad patterns resulting from three-strand doubles would be indistinguishable from those arising from single exchanges. Only four-strand double exchanges produce a unique pattern, a nonparental ditype, recognizable as being derived from a double or multiple exchange. Consequently double exchanges can be identified with confidence only when both intervals involved (as $d/+$ to $e/+$ and $e/+$ to $f/+$ in Fig. 4) are so short that the chance of double exchanges within either interval is negligible.

(2) *Crossing over between sister chromatids.* Inasmuch as sister chromatids are genetically identical, crossing over between them cannot be detected under any normal circumstances. Whether or not they occur at all, or at what frequencies if they do occur, is unknown. The above discussion and diagrams (Fig. 4) imply that no sister-chromatid crossing over does occur. It should be noted, however, that the same observed tetrad patterns could result from situations also involving sister-strand exchanges—for example, the possibility exists that only two of the original chromatids are involved in exchanges between homologs, but that exchanges also occur between sister chromatids so that the patterns characterized as following from three-strand and four-strand doubles would also occur.

(3) *Quantitative aspects of crossing over.* A number of quantitative relationships connected with crossing over have been studied by the methods of tetrad analysis. These involve such things as the extent to which an exchange in one interval influences the probability of a second exchange in a neighboring region (exchange interference or chiasma interference), and the extent to which the strands involved in crossing over at one level influence the choice of strands taking part in an adjacent exchange (chromatid interference). Inasmuch as these subjects have recently been

16. Mendelian

reviewed in some detail (S. Emerson, 1963), they will not be discussed further here, except to point out that there is a great deal of heterogeneity among the data obtained in different experiments.

d. The Possibility of Premeiotic Recombination. It is quite generally believed that nothing ordinarily happens during the brief dikaryophase of *Neurospora* which could alter the genetic constitutions of the gamete nuclei (which fuse in the ascus initial) from the constitutions originally possessed by the parental nuclei entering the cross during plasmogamy. This belief is supported by the very general observation that segregation of all genes introduced by the two parents regularly occurs in all asci. Some examples reported by Mitchell (1963), in which there is sporadic segregation of some phenotypes in only a fraction of the asci in certain crosses, seem to contradict the generally accepted interpretation. These interesting observations will be discussed later (Section V).

In a recent general review of crossing over in its many aspects, Westergaard (1964) concluded that there is at present no evidence excluding somatic recombination during the dikaryophase of *N. crassa* as a rare or even common occurrence. It seems to me that the kinds of somatic recombination known to occur in other fungi (see Chapter 18) would have been detected in genetic studies of *Neurospora* if any of them do occur in appreciable frequencies. (1) Diploid recombinant nuclei are expected to be homozygous at loci distal to the mitotic exchange in about half of all instances (see Chapter 18). If such diploid nuclei underwent meiosis in the ascus, in place of the completely heterozygous zygote nucleus expected, they would be detected by the complete failure of segregation of some genes in the asci concerned. (It is possible, of course, that such occurrences might be reported as "technical errors" in the sense used in Table II above.) (2) If one or both of the nuclei fusing at the karyogametic step in the ascus initial were diploid, the resulting zygote nucleus would be triploid or tetraploid, thus leading to polyploid segregation patterns which are easily identified in most instances (S. Emerson, 1956). (3) Somatic recombination resulting from haploidization of somatically diploidized nuclei results in haploid nuclei in which some chromosomes were derived from one parent, some from the other (see Chapter 18). The chance that two such haploidized nuclei of exactly complementary composition would unite at karyogamy is exceedingly remote. All other combinations would result in homozygosity which would again be identified through the failure of expected segregations. (4) Finally, there is no evidence that genetic recombination occurs between nuclei of a heterokaryon. It is true that most heterokaryons studied are homokaryotic for mating type, instead of heterokaryotic as in the dikaryophase. Observations of Coyle and Pittenger (1964) strongly suggest that somatic recombination in *N. crassa* requires the presence within a single nucleus of the participating elements. They found that recombination did occur in pseudo-wild segregants at a time when the nuclei were presumably still polysomic, but did not occur in reconstituted heterokaryons composed of nuclei derived from the pseudo-wilds.

e. Nuclear and Cytoplasmic Contributions at Plasmogamy

(1) *Reciprocal crosses.* As nuclei from conidia of one mating type pass down through the trichogyne into the ascogonial coil on a mycelium of opposite mating type, the possibility exists that no cytoplasm accompanies the nuclei from the conidia. Genetic tests by Mitchell and Mitchell (1952) proved that this inference is true: whereas chromosomal genes are transmitted equally through conidia and ascogonia, extranuclearly determined characteristics (see Jinks, 1964, and Chapter 19 of this volume) are transmitted only through the ascogonium. Reciprocal crosses, in which first one and then the other strain serves as the ascogonial (or maternal) parent, thus readily distinguish between the two modes of inheritance.

(2) *Number of functioning nuclei in the ascogonium.* Cells in the ascogonial coil (Fig. 1b) have been shown to be oligonucleate (M. P. Backus, 1939, for *N. sitophila*), but whether only one or several of these nuclei take part in the further development of ascogenous hyphae has not been established by cytological studies. Genetic observations, of a kind capable of giving only minimal estimates, show that at least two nuclei from the ascogonium do function in some instances. In crosses in which the protoperithecial parent was a heterokaryon with nuclei of two different genotypes, segregation for genes from both kinds of nuclei was observed in four out of eight perithecia examined (Sansome, 1947). In crosses between two appropriately marked heterokaryons (but in which plasmogamy may have occurred before protoperithecial formation) two kinds of nuclei from one parent functioned in 5 of 50 perithecia in one cross and none of 33 in another (Grant, 1945). In none of these tests was it possible to tell whether more than one nucleus of a single genotype functioned in this manner.

(3) *Number of conidia functioning in development of one perithecium.* The cytological illustrations of M. P. Backus (1939) show that the branches of a single trichogyne become attached to different conidia. Whether or not nuclei from more than one such conidium actually function in further development of ascogenous hyphae in a perithecium can be determined only by genetic tests. Grant (1945) conidiated protoperithecia of one mating type with a mixture of equal numbers of conidia of five different genotypes, all complementary in mating type to the protoperi-

thecial parent. From her data, which are summarized in Table III, it can be concluded that nuclei from more than one conidium rarely function in the development of asci in a single perithecium—in her experiments this occurred only once in about 30 perithecia. This frequency is derived from the sum of the squares of the frequencies with which each conidial type functions, giving the frequency, 25.8%, with which two conidia would have identical genotypes; hence any two conidia should be of different types in 74.2% of all instances, or in about 59 of the 79 perithecia tested— if nuclei from more than two conidia functioned in a single perithecium, a still larger proportion should have been detected in this experiment.

TABLE III
NUMBERS OF CONIDIA FUNCTIONING EFFECTIVELY IN THE DEVELOPMENT OF ASCI IN INDIVIDUAL PERITHECIA[a]

Conidial genotypes	Perithecia segregating for genotypes of		Functioning frequencies of conidial	
	One conidial genotypes	Two conidial genotypes	Totals	Squares
Aurescent	27	(1)	0.346	0.1197
Cheesy	22	(2)	0.296	0.0876
Lysine	10	(1)	0.136	0.0185
Pantothenic	14	0	0.173	0.0299
Adenine	4	0	0.049	0.0024
	77	2		0.2581

[a] Equal numbers of conidia were mixed before conidiating trichogynes of opposite mating type. An average of 40 ascospores per perithecium were tested. Data from Grant (1945).

f. Summary. The above description of known cytological and genetic features of the life cycle of *N. crassa* shows that there are still some aspects needing further study and understanding. On the other hand, this life history and its genetic implications are as well established as that of any other fungus, and much better than those of most fungi. From the control of hybridization at plasmogamy to the analysis of the segregating progeny following meiosis, most possible sources of error are known, and their probable magnitudes have been estimated.

It is not my intent to represent *Neurospora* as the best possible species for the study of all genetic phenomena—it is not suited to studies of somatic recombination, or of polyploidy, for example. It is, however, as well adapted to the study of normal meiotic recombination as any species so far studied; and it has been studied more thoroughly than any other species with similar advantages.

III. NONRECIPROCAL RECOMBINATION

Tetrad ratios other than 2:2 in the segregation of alternative alleles at a heterozygous locus were postulated by Lindegren (1953) to result from gene conversion, a phenomenon of "directed mutation occurring at meiosis as a result of the effect of homologous alleles upon each other"—Lindegren (1955). Since then the same phenomenon has been identified in a number of fungal species; Lindegren's interpretation of the phenomenon has been confirmed; and knowledge of the characteristics associated with it have been considerably extended. The term "nonreciprocal recombination," now commonly applied to this phenomenon, derives from the finding (Mitchell, 1955) that recombination between different pairs of heterozygous alleles of a single gene is frequently nonreciprocal: a wild-type recombinant is commonly produced unaccompanied by the expected complementary double mutant. (In the cross $m1 + \times + m2$, in which $m1/+$ and $m2/+$ are heterozygous allelic sites within the locus of one gene, nonreciprocal recombination results in a tetrad such as $m1 +, m1 +, + m2, + +$, in which segregation is 2:2 at one allelic site, 3:1 at the other, with no double mutant member, $m1\ m2$.)

Characteristics of nonreciprocal recombination vary somewhat from species to species, from one gene to another within a species, and even between allelic sites within a gene. On the other hand, the similarities between species, genes and alleles, are equally noteworthy and appear to become more numerous as studies of nonreciprocal recombination are extended.

A. Conversion Ratios at One Allelic Site

In nonreciprocal recombination, the most commonly observed tetrad ratios are $3+:1m$ and $1+:3m$ in four-spored ascomycetes such as *Saccharomyces cerevisiae* (Lindegren, 1953; Roman, 1963). The equivalent ratios, $6+:2m$ and $2+:6m$, are similarly the most commonly occurring in eight-spored ascomycetes such as *Ascobolus immersus* (Rizet et al., 1961; Lissouba et al., 1962), *Neurospora crassa* (Case and Giles, 1958a,b, 1964; Stadler and Towe, 1963), and *Sordaria fimicola* (Kitani et al., 1962).

The ratios $5+:3m$ and $3+:5m$, which are detectable in eight-spored ascomycetes (Olive, 1959), have been observed to occur much less frequently than 6:2 or 2:6 at most allelic sites (Lissouba et al., 1962; Stadler and Towe, 1963; Case and Giles, 1964), and equally frequently at other sites (Kitani et al., 1962). *These ratios (5:3 and 3:5) result from third division segregation in one spore-pair, an occurrence not in accord with the basic genetic mechanisms described in Section II*—hence of consider-

16. Mendelian 531

able importance to the evaluation of relationships between reciprocal and nonreciprocal recombination.

Third division segregation has been observed to occur in two members of the same tetrad (Kitani *et al.*, 1962). Each of nine instances of apparent ascospore disarrangement (see Section II, Fig. 3), following $4+:4m$ segregation of an ascospore color mutant, actually proved to be the result of third division segregations, once members of spore-pairs were identified through the presence of segregating loci on either side of the spore-color locus, and closely linked to it.

B. Intragenic Recombination

Studies of genetic fine structure are based on recombination between different allelic sites within the loci of single genes. In a cross between two different allelic mutants with the same nutritional requirement, as $m1 + \times + m2$, wild-type recombinants, $+ +$, can be selectively isolated by their nutritional independence, making studies of rare occurrences feasible. Analysis of tetrads of *Neurospora crassa* in which interallelic recombination has occurred has been limited, but in the data available, most wild-type recombinants have resulted from gene conversion at one or both sites rather than from reciprocal recombination between them. Of the 132 wild-type spores summarized in Fig. 5, only eight occurred in asci with patterns typical of reciprocal recombination between allelic sites.

The different genotypic constitutions present in segregants with mutant phenotypes are identified in test crosses to strains of each parental genotype. Segregants in which a single mutant allele is responsible for the mutant phenotype (say $m1 +$) produce wild-type recombinants only in crosses to tester strains of opposite genotype ($+ m2$); segregants which are double mutants ($m1\ m2$) fail to yield wild-type recombinants in crosses to either tester strain.

In *Ascobolus immersus* extensive studies have been made of recombination between alleles producing colorless ascospores (Lissouba, 1960; Rizet *et al.*, 1961; Lissouba *et al.*, 1962). The infrequent asci with wild-type (pigmented) spores are identified visually. In this species relative frequencies of reciprocal and nonreciprocal interallelic recombination vary considerably, as shown in the data summarized in Table IV.

1. Polarity

Among tetrads in which wild-type segregants have arisen by nonreciprocal interallelic recombination it is often observed that conversion occurs at different rates at the two heterozygous allelic sites. More surprisingly, observed conversion rates frequently depend less upon the specific site undergoing conversion than upon the particular second heterozygous site with which it is associated. The most striking examples of this sort have been found at loci affecting ascospore color in *A. immersus,* in which there exists a strongly polarized control of gene conversion (Rizet et al., 1961; Lissouba and Rizet, 1960; Lissouba, 1960; Lissouba et al., 1962; Rizet and Rossignol, 1963).

	6 + : 2m1	5 + : 3 m1	4 + : 4 m1	3 + : 5m1	2 + : 6m1
6 + : 2 m2	2 m1 + 2 + m2 4 + + 1 a		4 m1 + 2 + m2 2 + + 28 a, b, d		6 m1 + 2 + m2 3 c
5 + : 3 m2	2 m1 + 3 + m2 3 + + 1 c				
4 + : 4m2	2 m1 + 4 + m2 2 + + 30 a, b, c, d		2 m1 m2 2 m1 + 2 + m2 2 + + 4 b, c	1 m1 m2 4 m1 + 3 + m2 1 c	2 m1 m2 4 m1 + 2 + m2 1 c
3 + : 5 m2		3 m1 + 5 + m2 1 c	2 m1 m2 2 m1 + 3 + m2 1 + + 1 c		
2 + : 6 m2	2 m1 + 6 + m2 5 b, c		2 m1 m2 2 m1 + 4 + m2 1 c		

FIG. 5. Ascus patterns resulting from interallelic recombination, arranged in columns according to segregation ratios occurring at site $m1/+$ and in rows according to segregation ratios at site $m2/+$. The numbers of spores of each genotype are shown in the upper portion of each rectangle; and below, the numbers of such asci observed by (a) Mitchell (1955), (b) Case and Giles (1958b), (c) Case and Giles (1964), (d) Stadler and Towe (1963).

Complete polarization may exist in a large section of a locus. Such a region is known as a *polaron.* In the locus designated as series 46 (Lissouba et al., 1962), six allelic sites (i.e., excluding $m277$) constitute such a polaron. The six sites can be mapped in linear order by the frequencies of recombination occurring between each pair of sites. Analyses of recombinant asci have shown (1) that reciprocal recombination within the polaron is very infrequent; and (2) that in each nonreciprocally recombinant ascus analyzed the 6+:2m segregation invariably occurred at the site located nearer the right end of the map, 4+:4m at the site nearer the left end, whichever pair of sites was involved (see Table IV).

TABLE IV
RELATIVE FREQUENCIES OF RECIPROCAL AND NONRECIPROCAL INTERALLELIC RECOMBINATION AT DIFFERENT LOCI IN *Ascobolus immersus*[a]

Locus	Reciprocal	Nonreciprocal	
	2 $m1$ +, 2 + $m2$, 2 $m1$ $m2$, 2 + +	4 $m1$ +, 2 + $m2$, 2 + +	2 $m1$ +, 4 + $m2$, 2 + +
Series 46			
a[b]	1	154	0
b	6	30	18
Series 75	39	84	34
Series 19			
c[b]	0	89	1
d	230	242	50

[a] Data from Lissouba et al. (1962).
[b] a, Not involving crosses with $m277$; b, crosses with $m277$.
[c] c, Crosses within groups; d, crosses between groups.

A curious quantitative relationship exists in relation to three sites, $m63$, $m46$ and mW, mapping in that order near the center of the polaron just referred to. In separate crosses to wild type, the frequencies of 6+:2m segregations per 1000 asci were 4.8 ± 0.4 for $m63$, 1.9 ± 0.6 for $m46$, and 3.9 ± 0.8 for mW (Lissouba, 1960, Table IX). On the other hand, 6+:2m segregation for $m46$ was 0.53 (confidence limits 0.27–1.14) per 1000 asci in the cross $m63$ + × + $m46$, and for mW only 0.74 (0.39–1.44) in the cross $M46$ × mW (Lissouba, 1960, Table II). Observed frequencies of conversion at both sites are reduced by the presence of the second heterozygous site, but differentially, that on the left apparently being completely suppressed.

Recombination between allelic sites occupying positions in different polarons of a single locus are frequently reciprocal, and polarities often reversed (series 46b, 75, and 19d, in Table IV). Suggestions of even more complex structure of a locus have been reported (Rizet and Rossignol, 1963). In *Neurospora crassa* there are indications of polarity in interallelic recombination between members of two groups of sites within a locus (Case and Giles, 1958a,b, 1964; Stadler and Towe, 1963), but to a much lesser degree than in *Ascobolus*.

2. Recombination between Outside Markers

In many studies of interallelic recombination, use has been made of outside markers—that is, of heterozygous loci closely linked to and on either side of the locus involved in interallelic recombination. In all such studies, whether the interallelic recombination is reciprocal or nonreciprocal, recombination between outside markers is much more frequent among asci in which interallelic recombination has also occurred than among the population of all asci. Recombination between outside markers accompanying interallelic recombination frequently approaches, but rarely exceeds, 50% (Mitchell, 1955; Freese, 1957a,b; Murray, 1963; and many others), even in examples in which normal recombination between the loci used as outside markers is not more than 1 or 2%. In all reported instances, the recombination between outside markers is reciprocal and segregation is 4:4 at both loci irrespective of the kind of interallelic recombination occurring.

TABLE V

Distribution of Wild-Type Interallelic Recombinants Relative to Associations with Outside Markers[a]

Cross[b]	Parental types		Recombinant types	
	tryp +	*+ pan*	*tryp pan*	*+ +*
$\dfrac{tryp\ m1\ +\ +}{+\ +\ m2\ pan}$	643	1749	560	1201
$\dfrac{tryp\ +\ m2\ +}{+\ m1\ +\ pan}$	1691	504	1105	444

[a] Data from Murray (1963).

[b] *m1* and *m2* are alleles of *me-2*, from different groups of sites of which *m1* is from a group nearer *tryp* than is *m2*.

Polarity with respect to the particular type of parental or crossover chromatid most commonly associated with wild-type interallelic recombinants has been observed in all, or nearly all, experiments. In a population of selected wild-type interallelic recombinants, one parental arrangement of outside markers is usually more frequent than the other, and one recombinant type more frequent than its reciprocal. This situation is illustrated in the data summarized in Table V. The data are totals from 53 crosses between 18 alleles, all giving results consistent with respect to polarity, but differing somewhat in the relative frequencies of the different classes.

C. Significance of 4:0 Tetrad Ratios

The complete failure of expected segregation at a particular locus resulting in $4+:0m$ or $0+:4m$ tetrad ratios was observed in *Saccharomyces cerevisiae* by Lindegren (1953) in crosses in which $3+:1m$ and $1+:3m$ ratios also occurred. Similar occurrences in *Saccharomyces* are also reported in the data of R. K. Mortimer (summarized by Roman, 1963). Lindegren concluded that both 3:1 and 4:0 tetrad ratios resulted from gene conversion. Because the preponderance of available genetic evidence indicated that one of the two sister chromatids of each homologous chromosome takes no part in a recombination event (Section II, B, 2, c), and because premeiotic recombination was known to occur in *Saccharomyces* and to result in segregation failure, there has been reluctance to accept 4:0 tetrad ratios as valid products of gene conversion (S. Emerson, 1956; Roman, 1963). There are now a few data in the published literature which lend some credence to the idea that more than two chromatids may be involved in nonreciprocal recombination. Three such examples known to me are summarized in Table VI.

In the ascus listed from cross 1 in Table VI (the type 5 ascus of Case and Giles, 1958b) the failure of *B5* to segregate can hardly be due to premeiotic recombination inasmuch as a distal site within the same locus and a still more distal locus did not also become homozygous (see Chapter 18). Homozygosity at site *B5* could, of course, have resulted from back-mutation—it could also have resulted from gene conversion by a DNA repair mechanism (Section IV, B, and Fig. 10d). In the ascus listed from cross 2 (the single such aberrant ascus among 1457 observed by Case and Giles, 1964) only one chromatid has failed to be involved in non-reciprocal recombination—the chromatid present in the distal spore-pair. It is difficult to think of any interpretation of this ascus other than that three chromatids have been involved in gene conversion within the locus of one gene (see Fig. 10b). Similarly, the ascus with $7+:1g$ segregation listed from cross 3 [the only such ascus observed in about 200,000 examined for irregular segregations of a spore color mutant by Kitani *et al.* (1962)] strongly suggests that more than two chromatids were involved in gene conversion at a single allelic site (see Fig. 10c). If genotypic determinations of all eight members of this ascus were not made, the possibility of phenocopies, such as observed by Stadler (1956a) in *Neurospora,* and Lissouba (1960) in *Ascobolus,* cannot be disregarded.

IV. HYPOTHETICAL MODELS OF RECOMBINATION

An acceptable general hypothesis of genetic recombination must account satisfactorily for a large number of observed characteristics of crossing over, gene conversion, and related chromosome behavior. A number of these characteristics, especially as they relate to tetrad patterns in the fungi, have been referred to earlier (Sections II and III). A more complete survey of factors important to interpretations of genetic recombination as

TABLE VI

Segregations in Which Nonreciprocal Recombination Apparently Involves More Than Two Chromatids[a]

Cross	Genotypes of spore-pairs[a]			
	Distal pair	Second pair	Third pair	Proximal pair
1	$ad + B3\ tr\ (A)$	$ad + B3\ tr + (A)$	$+ + + + (a)$	$+ + + + (a)$
2	$ad\ B23 + B36 + (a)$ $\Big\{$	$\dfrac{ad + B72 + + (a)}{ad + + B36 + (a)}$	$\dfrac{+ + B72 + tr\ (A)}{+ + B72\ B36\ tr\ (A)}$	$+ B23\ B72 + tr\ (A)$ $\Big\}$
3	$+ + (+)$ $\Big\{$	$\dfrac{sp + (+)}{sp\ \ g\ \ (+)}$	$+ + (sm)$	$\dfrac{sp +}{} (sm)$

[a] All genes (except those in parentheses) are linked, and in the order listed.

Cross 1. $ad\text{-}1\ B5\ B3\ tryp\text{-}2 \times + + + +$; $B5$ and $B3$ are mutants at different allelic sites of $pan\text{-}2$ (Case and Giles, 1958b)

Cross 2. $ad\text{-}1\ B23 + B36 + (a) \times + + B72 + tryp\text{-}2\ (A)$; $B23$, $B72$, and $B36$ are mutants at different allelic sites of $pan\text{-}2$ (Case and Giles, 1964)

Cross 3. $sp\ g\ (+) \times + + (sm)$ (Kitani et al., 1962)

observed in all higher organisms has recently appeared in a publication by Westergaard (1964), to which the reader is referred for essential background information and for references to the literature pertaining to it.

Current hypotheses of recombination mechanisms attempt to account for crossing over and gene conversion on a molecular basis. Known characteristics of the structure and behavior of deoxyribonucleic acids (DNA) have been used in developing two different kinds of models of genetic recombination: the "switch" or "copy choice" models, and "repair" models.

A. Copy Choice, or Switch, Models

The copy choice, or switch, interpretations place recombination at a DNA replication occurring while homologous chromosomes are paired. The replicating base chains are postulated to switch from one template to another derived from the chromosome homologous to the first. Both reciprocal and nonreciprocal recombination could result from such switches. This interpretation has been used by most investigators to account for observed patterns of nonreciprocal recombination (Lissouba *et al.,* 1962; Kitani *et al.,* 1962; Stadler and Towe, 1963; Case and Giles, 1964). On the other hand it has been difficult by this hypothesis to account for all the different kinds of segregation patterns that have been observed; and some details in the timing of DNA synthesis are difficult to reconcile with copy choice interpretations. For a summary of the difficulties and apparent inconsistencies that have been encountered in applications of these models the reader is referred to the review of Westergaard just cited.

B. Repair Models

A repair mechanism, whereby mispaired bases in a DNA double helix undergo a replacement of one such base by that complementary to the other, has been suggested as the basis of gene conversion by Holliday (1962, 1964) and by Whitehouse (1963). In both proposed models crossing over and gene conversion are interrelated. Of the two, Holliday's model is the more restrictive, hence better suited to quantitative predictions. The model to be described here is essentially the one he proposed, but with a few additional restrictive modifications to make comparisons of observed and expected recombination patterns somewhat easier.

Knowledge of DNA repair mechanisms, while rapidly increasing, is still too incomplete to be very useful in the evaluation of recombination models. For a report on the current status of this subject the reader is referred to a review by Horowitz and Metzenberg (1966). It should be noted here, however, that the dark repair mechanism takes place in two steps. First there is an enzymatic reaction which removes a considerable number of bases from one strand of a double helix, including the damaged bases (thymine dimers in the most studied cases). There follows a resynthesis (presumably enzymatic) of the excised region, making use of the intact strand of the double helix as a template.

1. The Model

Recombination is postulated to occur during the prophase of the first meiotic division at a time when each homologous chromosome consists of two sister chromatids and after premeiotic DNA synthesis has been completed. At this time each chromatid is assumed to consist of a linear sequence of DNA molecules joined end-to-end through "linkers" (lk in Fig. 6). It is further supposed that alleles capable of undergoing conversion differ from wild type by substitution of a single base pair. In the diagrams in Fig. 6 such a wild-type base pair is represented by A-B, and the mutant allele at that site by X-Y.

Hybrid DNA double helices arise in the following way: the two strands of a double helix sometimes become separated from one another by the dissociation of one end of one strand (here restricted to the end illustrated as an arrowhead in Fig. 6) from the linker, followed by uncoiling of the free end. Simultaneous separations at the same end of corresponding DNA molecules of two nonsister chromatids (Fig. 6, a or d) offers the opportunity for the free ends to reassociate with the complementary strands of the homologous chromatids (Fig. 6, b and e). The two chromatids involved in this switch have parental DNA helices at one end of a molecule and hybrid helices at the other. A half-chromatid chiasma is formed where the uniparental helices become biparental.

The integrity of the chromatids is restored by breakage and reunion of two of the base chains involved in the half-chromatid chiasma. If this half-chromatid crossover occurs between the chains shown to cross in Fig. 6, b and e, the restored chromatids are nonrecombinant for the outside markers $ma/+$ and $co/+$ (parental combinations are $ma\ co$ and $+\ +$). If half-chromatid crossing over involves the other two base chains, true crossing over results, with the production of the reciprocally recombinant chromatids $ma\ +$ and $+\ co$ (Fig. 6, c and f). Reciprocal recombination between outside markers might well occur in half of all instances in which half-chromatid chiasmata occur. In the absence of a heterozygous site within the region of hybrid DNA such crossing over would be unaccompanied by gene conversion.

Mispaired bases result whenever a heterozygous site is present in a region of hybrid DNA. Such a heterozygous site is shown in the diagrams

16. *Mendelian*

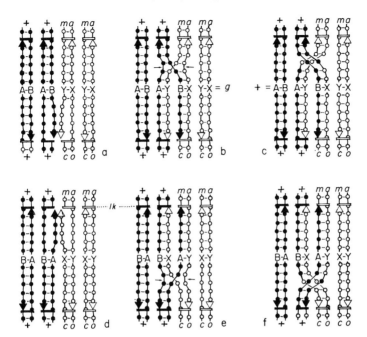

FIG. 6. Diagrams illustrating the origin of hybrid regions in DNA molecules. Chromatids are represented as double-stranded DNA in which base pairs are shown as black dots connected by crossbanding in two sister chromatids, and as open circles in the sister chromatids of the homologous chromosome. Polarity of base chains is indicated by the arrowheads at either end of a molecule. A linear series of such molecules is joined end-to-end by linkers, *lk*. X-Y, the base pair of mutant allele *g*, A-B, base pair at the same site in the wild-type allele, +; *ma*, mutant allele at a linked locus on one side of *g*; *co*, mutant allele at a linked locus on the other side of *g*.

a and d, separation of base chains of common polarity in two homologous chromatids at the linker at one end of the molecule in a, at the other end in d; b and e, reassociation of separated base chains with complementary chains of their homologs to produce regions of hybrid DNA with mispaired bases A-Y and B-X at the included heterozygous site $g/+$ — a half-chromatid chiasma is shown by the crossing of two base chains at the point where DNA molecules become hybrid; c, and f, recombination between the outside markers resulting from the resolution of the half-chromatid chiasma by breakage and reunion of the two outside base chains at points indicated by the small arrows in diagrams b and e, to produce a true, or whole-chromatid, chiasma. Resolution of the half-chromatid chiasma by breakage and reunion of the two base chains shown to cross in diagrams b and e produces no exchange between outside markers—the resultant configuration is not illustrated but can be easily visualized from the diagrams by replacing the crossed lines with vertical lines connecting adjacent open and solid circles.

in Fig. 6, in which the wild-type allele is represented by the base pair A-B, the mutant allele of that site by X-Y. The hybrid sites in the hybrid regions of the two chromatids differ in base constitution, being A-Y in one and B-X in the other. Both hybrid base pairs must be noncomplementary. It should be noted that when the hybrid DNA is at one end of the molecule the relation of A-Y and B-X to outside marker alleles is just the reverse of that occurring when hybridity is at the other end of the molecule, except when crossing over has occurred between the outside markers. The different kinds of conversion patterns expected on this model will be illustrated in connection with specific examples.

2. Conversion at a Single Allelic Site

All possible segregation patterns which can be predicted from the DNA repair model just outlined have been observed in segregations of a spore color mutant (*g,* for *gray spores*) of *Sordaria fimicola* (Kitani et al., 1962). These patterns together with the kinds of DNA repair expected to produce them are summarized in Table VII.

The kind of repair occurring depends on which mispaired base at a heterozygous site is excised (whether A or Y at A-Y, B or X at B-X, in Fig. 6), as well as whether or not any excision occurs at a heterozygous site. Each such alternative has some probability of occurring. The fraction of instances in which there is no correction of mispairing at site A-Y can be represented by $1-p$, the fraction with repair to wild type (A-B) as pr, and to mutant (X-Y) as $p(1-r)$; and at site B-X the uncorrected fraction as $1-q$, the fraction repaired to wild type as qs, and to mutant as $q(1-s)$. Algebraic expressions for the probabilities of occurrences of combinations of alternatives expected to produce each specific segregation pattern are listed in Table VII under the heading "Expected fractions."

From comparisons of observed frequencies of the various patterns with the hypothetical probability of each it can be shown that the two heterozygous sites actually do differ in frequencies of repair, and that they are even more different in the relative frequencies in which such repair results in a wild-type allele rather than a mutant allele. From the relative frequencies of asci with $5+:3g$ and $3+:5g$ segregations,

$$\frac{p(1-q)r + (1-p)qs}{p(1-q)(1-r) + (1-p)q(1-s)} = \frac{108}{20}$$

$$p = \frac{q(32s - 27)}{q(32r + 32s - 54) + 27 - 32r} \quad (1)$$

TABLE VII
ARRAY OF SEGREGATION PATTERNS EXPECTED FROM THE DNA REPAIR MODEL

Nature of repair		Ascus patterns (sites of origin)					Expected fraction[a]	Observed fraction[b]
At site A-Y	At site B-X	A-B	A-Y	B-X	X-Y			
(Y) to B = A-B	(X) to A = A-B	++	++	++	g g		$pqrs$	98/239
(Y) to B = A-B	(B) to Y = X-Y	++	++	g g	g g		$pqr(1-s)$	?
(A) to X = X-Y	(X) to A = A-B	++	g g	++	g g		$pq(1-r)s$	
(A) to X = X-Y	(B) to Y = X-Y	++	g g	g g	g g		$pq(1-r)(1-s)$	13/239
(Y) to B = A-B	None = B-X	++	++	+g	g g		$p(1-q)r$	
None = A-Y	(X) to A = A-B	++	+g	++	g g		$(1-p)qs$	108/239
None = A-Y	(B) to Y = X-Y	++	+g	g g	g g		$(1-p)q(1-s)$	
(A) to X = X-Y	None = B-X	++	g g	+g	g g		$p(1-q)(1-r)$	20/239
None = A-Y	None = B-X	++	+g	+g	g g		$(1-p)(1-q)$	9/150

[a] Algebraic terms: p represents the fraction of all instances in which repair of mispaired bases at site A-Y occurs, r represents the fraction of such repairs resulting in a wild-type allele, such that:

$$pr = \text{fraction of repair to wild type}$$
$$p(1-r) = \text{fraction of repair to mutant}$$
$$1-p = \text{fraction of no repair}$$

q represents the fraction of all instances in which repair at site B-X occurs, s represents the fraction of such repairs resulting in a wild-type allele, such that:

$$qs = \text{fraction of repair to wild type}$$
$$q(1-s) = \text{fraction of repair to mutant}$$
$$1-q = \text{fraction of no repair}$$

[b] Fractions of total conversion patterns at the *grey spore* locus of *Sordaria fimicola*. Data from Kitani *et al.* (1962).

And from the relative frequencies of asci with 5+:3g and 6+:2g segregations,

$$\frac{p(1-q)r + (1-p)qs}{pqrs} = \frac{108}{98}$$

$$p = \frac{q(49s)}{q(49r + 49s + 54rs) - 49r} \quad (2)$$

By equating values for p in Eqs. (1) and (2),

$$q = \frac{s-r}{s - r - 1.102rs + 1.306rs^2} \quad (3)$$

From the relative frequencies of asci with 6+:2g and 2+:6g segregations,

$$\frac{pqrs}{pq(1-r)(1-s)} = \frac{98}{13}$$

$$r = \frac{98 - 98s}{98 - 85s} \quad (4)$$

Hence, for any values of s, unique values are also obtained for r [from Eq. (4)], for q [by substituting s for r in Eq. (3)], and for p [by substituting s for r and for q in either Eq. (1) or (2)]. A summary of the valid corresponding values for the four parameters is shown in the graphs in Fig. 7.

No set of corresponding values for these parameters, however, predicts asci of the pattern ++ +g +g gg in as great a frequency as that observed. On the basis of a set of values predicting a maximum number of asci of that pattern, observed and expected numbers of all ascus patterns are compared in Table VIII. Inasmuch as the observed frequency of the divergent class is based on a somewhat different set of data from that used for frequencies of other classes, the discrepancy from expected can be considered to be unimportant ($P = 0.35$).

The identification of the particular ascospores carrying the alleles which were altered by conversion depends to a considerable extent upon which mechanism of gene conversion is adopted. This difference with respect to 6+:2g, and 5+:3g segregations is shown in Fig. 8, making use of asci in which reciprocal recombination has occurred between the outside markers $ma/+$ and $co/+$ (the cross being $ma\ g\ co \times + + +$) as an aid in identifying the nonrecombinant chromatids. Further, the exact position at which recombination between outside markers has occurred can apparently be determined on one interpretation but not on the other. The patterns presumed to exist if alleles had not been changed by conversion

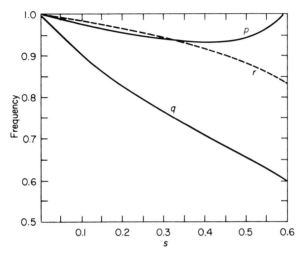

FIG. 7. Expected frequencies of repair at hybrid site A-Y (p), and of those repaired the expected fraction becoming wild type (r); and the expected frequencies of repair at hybrid site B-X (q); all with respect to the fraction of repairs at B-X which become wild type (s).

TABLE VIII

NUMBERS OF ASCI WITH DIFFERENT CONVERSION PATTERNS OBSERVED, AND NUMBERS EXPECTED

Ratio	Pattern				Observed[a]	Expected[b]
6+:2g	++	++	++	gg	98	98.3
2+:6g	++	gg	gg	gg	13	13.0
5+:3g	++	++	+g	gg	108	107.8
3+:5g	++	+g	gg	gg	20	20.0
4+:4g	++	+g	+g	gg	9	4.5
4+:4g	++	++	gg	gg	?	156.0

[a] See Table VII.
[b] Number expected when repair occurs at site A-Y at a frequency of 93.5% ($p = 0.935$) of which 92% are changed to wild-type alleles ($r = 0.92$), and repair at site B-X is 71% ($q = 0.71$) of which 40% become with type ($s = 0.4$).

show crossing over between g and co on a copy choice interpretation (right-hand column of Fig. 8), but equally probably between g and co or between ma and g on the repair interpretation (left-hand column—compare Fig. 6f with 6c).

3. The Polaron

In the earlier discussion of the polaron (Section III) it was noted that observed conversion frequencies at a heterozygous site were strongly influenced by the presence of a second heterozygous site and that the extent of the influence was determined by the relative positions of the two sites. No conversion at all was observed at the site mapping to the left, and

Presumptive pattern	Change due to repair	Observed pattern	Change due to copy choice	Presumptive pattern
		6 + : 2g		
+ + +		+ + +		+ + +
+ + +		+ + +		+ + +
+ + co		+ + co		+ + co
+ g co	⟶	+ + co		+ + co
ma + +		ma + +	⟵	ma g +
ma g +	⟶	ma + +	⟵	ma g +
ma g co		ma g co		ma g co
ma g co		ma g co		ma g co
		5 + : 3g		
+ + +		+ + +		+ + +
+ + +		+ + +		+ + +
+ + co		+ + co		+ + co
+ g co	⟶	+ + co		+ + co
ma + +		ma + +	⟵	ma g +
ma g +		ma g +		ma g +
ma g co		ma g co		ma g co
ma g co		ma g co		ma g co

FIG. 8. Identifications of spores carrying alleles produced by conversion. Linearly ordered asci with 6:2 and 5:3 segregations at $g/+$ are shown in the center column as actually observed. The patterns presumed to show the genotypes existing if no allele had been altered by conversion are represented in the outside columns—those to be altered by DNA repair on the left, those to be altered according to earlier interpretations on the right.

(provided the sites were closely linked) was much less at the site mapping to the right than when it was the only heterozygous site present.

This double relationship is predictable from the DNA repair model described. The *Ascobolus* crosses had the alleles in repulsion: $m1 + \times + m2$. Interallelic recombination was detected by the production of pigmented wild-type (+ +) spores. As pointed out by Holliday (1964), with base-chain separation starting at the right end of the polaron, sites close to the right end would be included in regions of hybrid DNA more often than sites farther to the left. Hence the rightmost of two heterozygous sites could undergo repair without a site to the left being affected. For the site to the left to be included in a heterozygous region of DNA, the site to the right must also be included. With both sites included, the excision of a large number of bases from one chain would frequently remove one base at each mispaired site, especially if they are closely linked. To leave one intact chain to serve as a template in resynthesis, excised bases at both sites must be from the same chain. Removal of the mutant base at the left site would then coincide with removal of the wild-type base at the right site so that the repaired double helix in becoming wild type at the left site would become mutant at the right, thus obscuring the conversion at the left site. It follows then that only sites to the right would appear as wild-type convertants, and a considerable fraction actually converted could be obscured by simultaneous conversion at the closely linked site on the left.

4. Heterozygosis at Three Allelic Sites

Case and Giles (1964) made complete genetic analyses of 1457 asci from crosses involving allelic sites in the *pan-2* locus of *Neurospora*. They observed 13 asci in which interallelic recombination had occurred. Of these, 11 could be straightforwardly interpreted on a copy choice model. These 11 can also be simply interpreted on the repair model (Fig. 9). The two not fitting a simple interpretation of the copy choice model can also be accounted for by the repair model (Fig. 10, a and b). One of these (a) requires base-chain separation at both ends of the DNA molecule with at most only a relatively short central region of parental DNA remaining between two hybrid regions. The second (b) requires involvement of three chromatids in one of which the base chains have again separated at each end of the molecule to become associated with a base chain from one homolog at one end, with one from the other homolog at the other end.

Also included in Fig. 10 are diagrams of the other two asci cited earlier (Section III, C) in which more than two chromatids were involved in interallelic recombination. Both (Fig. 10, c and d) can be simply accounted for by the repair mechanism, but identical events must be assumed to have occurred, each involving two pairs of homologous chromatids.

V. POSSIBILITY OF EPISOMIC INHERITANCE IN FUNGI

Segregations occurring in tetrads of meiotic products are nearly always those that are expected from the known chromosomal behavior in the species studied (Section II). Exceptional patterns of segregation are most frequently those expected to result from gene conversion (Sections III and

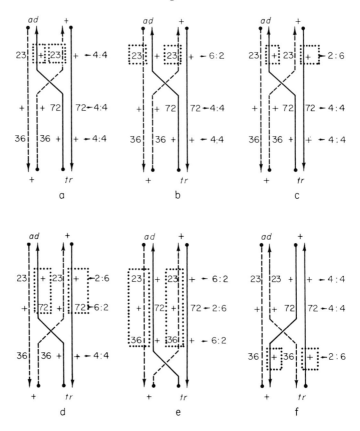

FIG. 9. Interallelic recombination patterns as interpreted on the DNA repair model. Regions of hybrid DNA originate as diagrammed in Fig. 6. Only the two chromatids actually involved are here represented (the two center chromatids in Fig. 6)—the other two retain their respective parental constitutions. Recombination and the failure of recombination between outside markers occur as described in the legend to Fig. 6.

Both bases of a mutant allele are represented by the allelic designation, 23, 72, or 36; and both bases at corresponding sites in wild type are designated by + — the site concerned being evident from the position in the chromatid. Dotted rectangles enclose regions of single base chains which are excised. Excised bases are replaced by the bases characteristic of the alleles opposite them in hybrid DNA.

The patterns illustrated represent those reported by Case and Giles (1964): a, with recombination (between outside markers), asci 98 and 710; b, with recombination, asci 153 and 545, without recombination, asci 497 and 1021; c, without recombination, ascus 583; d, with recombination, ascus 78; e, with recombination, ascus 565, without, ascus 581; f, with recombination, ascus 614.

IV). There remains, however, a relatively small residue of atypical segregations which occur sporadically in crosses in which only standard types of segregation are observed in other tetrads—even for other segregating characteristics in tetrads in which atypical segregations were noted.

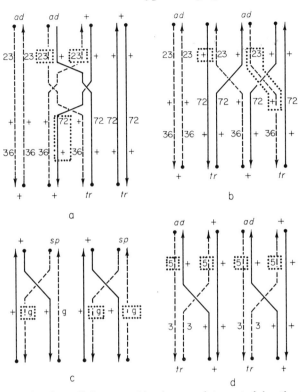

FIG. 10. Complex interallelic recombinations as interpreted by the DNA repair model. Conventions are the same as in Fig. 9 except that all four chromatids are here represented. Illustrated are: a, ascus 529 of Case and Giles (1964), segregation ratios are 6+:2m at site 23, 5+:3m at 72, and 3+:5m at 36—recombination between outside markers did occur in this ascus, but between the two homologous chromatids not involved in interallelic recombination; b, with no recombination between outside markers, ascus 43 from the same study, ratios 4+:4m at 23, 3+:5m at 72, at 36 4+:4m, but with third division segregation—see cross 2 in Table VI; c, the ascus with 7+:1g segregation reported by Kitani et al. (1962)—see cross 3 in Table VI; d, the type 5 ascus of Case and Giles (1958b), ratios 8+:0m at 5, 4+:4m at 3— see cross 1 in Table VI.

Aberrant segregation patterns of this sort often place the investigator in an awkward position: there is frequently no way of knowing in particular instances whether the observed discrepancy is real or was the result of an experimental error of one kind or another. It is usually only when similar aberrations recur in related crosses that he is persuaded that they must be real; and it is probably only in such circumstances that any experimental verification of their validity is possible. The atypical segregations reported by Mitchell (1963) constitute a case in point—possibly also those reported by Threlkeld (1962). Their observations show points of resemblance to examples of episomic inheritance sufficient to warrant consideration of that interpretation.

Episomes (Jacob and Wollman, 1958) are hereditary determiners possessing two modes of inheritance, one in association with definite loci in the linkage map, the other as an extrachromosomal element. The existence of episomes has been definitely established only in bacteria. Genetic and phenotypic properties of known and suspected episomes differ to a considerable extent from one example to another. For a discussion of the general and diverse natures and properties of episomes the reader is referred to reviews by Jacob *et al.* (1960) and by Campbell (1962).

Examples of possible episomic inheritance in *Neurospora* are too poorly established to warrant detailed description at this time. Instead, some of the characteristics exhibited by presumed examples will be noted. (1) An unexpected phenotype appears sporadically in the progenies of related crosses, usually in occasional asci from a few perithecia, and often in fewer than half of the ascospores of an ascus. When carried through further generations of crossing, regular 4:4 segregation occurs in all asci. (2) A characteristic which had previously segregated regularly appears with an altered phenotype in some segregants. When such segregants are carried through a further generation of crossing the characteristic is rapidly lost, failing to appear at all among the progeny from some perithecia, and appearing only in a few spores of a fraction of the asci in other perithecia. (3) A phenotypic characteristic which is transmitted vegetatively as a strictly nuclear element, as determined by the heterokaryon test, is recovered among segregants from a cross in an unstable form, from which stable forms can sometimes be recovered by vegetative isolation.

Because fungi have defined nuclei, which bacteria do not, some differences in episomic inheritance may be expected. In *Neurospora,* divisions of vegetative nuclei differ in important respects from the divisions of nuclei in the ascus. In the two meiotic divisions (also in the third, mitotic, division in the ascus?) the nuclear membrane breaks down and the nucleolus migrates into the cytoplasm, where it degenerates. In mitoses of vegetative nuclei as followed by phase contrast (S. Emerson, 1966) the nuclear membrane persists throughout division, stretching into a threadlike structure between the separating daughter nuclei before breaking, and the nucleolus divides by fission, half being retained in each daughter nucleus. The third characteristic attributed above to episome-like inheritance may be related to this difference in nuclear behavior.

VI. GENETIC CHARACTERISTICS OF SELECTED FUNGI

A. Life Cycles

1. Phases of the Life Cycle

Not all fungi go through the same phases, or stages, in their life cycles. There is, however, a generalized sequence consisting of haplophase, plasmogamy, dikaryophase, karyogamy, diplophase, meiosis, haplophase, and so on. Many fungi do not have all these phases; but all phases that do occur invariably follow one another in that sequence (see Chapter 15). Each phase is of some importance to genetic studies.

a. Haplophase. All genes present in haploid forms are freely expressed without regard to dominance which phenotypically masks the presence of recessives in diploid tissues or phases. Segregation of and recombination between genes are directly observable in the haploid phase of the generation following crossing. If the haplophase were absent (as in higher plants and animals) a backcross of the first (hybrid) diploid generation to a multiple-recessive tester stock would be necessary for obtaining equivalent information. Haploid cells are advantageous for obtaining and isolating mutations and for establishing genotypically pure lines.

b. Plasmogamy. Plasmogamy brings together in a single cell the nuclei of the two parents of a cross. This is the step at which control of hybridization is accomplished. Whether or not reciprocal crosses, in which one parent contributes only a nucleus, the other both nucleus and cytoplasm, can be made depends to a considerable extent on the nature of the cells which unite in plasmogamy.

c. Dikaryophase, Karyogamy, and Diplophase. In the dikaryotic phase of a life cycle, nuclei descended from the two parental nuclei associated in plasmogamy (or from pairs of such parental nuclei) are carried along together until karyogamy. In dikaryotic hyphae in which each cell contains only two nuclei (as in most basidiomycetes) the cytologically observed conjugate divisions of nuclei at each cell division demonstrate that nuclei of both parental origins are in fact carried along together throughout this phase. In fungi with coenocytic hyphae or in those like *Neurospora* with several nuclei per cell, cytological observations alone fail to demonstrate that the pairs of nuclei fusing at karyogamy are actually of different parental origin, though the conjugate divisions in the crosiers support such an inference.

In fungi lacking the diplophase, the dikaryotic phase (or even a heterokaryotic state—Davis, 1966) can often substitute for it in tests for dominance, allelic complementation, etc., but does not necessarily do so. For example, in *Ustilago maydis* (Holliday, 1961b) the dikaryophase is obligately parasitic on maize and cannot be maintained on a synthetic medium, whereas diploid mycelia (arising by fusion of pairs of dikaryotic nuclei and hence carrying exactly the same genes as the parental dikaryotic mycelia) do grow on the synthetic medium.

d. Meiosis and the Products of Meiosis. Inasmuch as all major assortment of genes (segregation and recombination) takes place during the two meiotic divisions, meiosis is the most important and critical step upon which genetic analysis depends in the entire life cycle. Cytological studies have not yet placed the position of meiosis unambiguously in the life cycles of many fungi—to a considerable extent because of the small size of nuclei in many species (see Olive, 1965). In a very few species of fungi, in *Allomyces arbuscula* and *Neurospora crassa* for example, the cytological picture is clear: the position of the two meiotic divisions in the cycle is established; the haploid number of chromosomes has been shown to exist immediately before karyogamy and immediately following meiosis; and the diploid number of chromosomes has been found in diplophase, or in the zygote nucleus.

The products of meiosis are ordinarily recovered in specialized reproductive cells of various sorts: zoospores from resistant sporangia in the Blastocladiales, zoospores from germ-sporangia in *Phytophthora,* germ-sporangiospores in the Mucorales, ascospores in the Ascomycetes, and basidiospores in the Basidiomycetes. The term meiospore, implying some fairly direct relationship to a primary product of meiosis, has been used for such reproductive cells in *Allomyces* (R. Emerson, 1941, 1954), and could appropriately be applied to the equivalent reproductive cells in all fungi.

2. *Other Important Characteristics of Fungi*

a. Heterothallism. The controlled production of hybrids is relatively simple in species in which haploid strains are sexually self-incompatible. In many heterothallic species self-incompatibility is governed by mating-type alleles at one or two loci. Crosses between homothallic strains frequently produce mixtures of biparental and uniparental progeny, among which recombination between parental genes is a principal criterion of a hybrid origin. Strains of homothallic species have been made heterothallic by the introduction of mutations which result either in a failure to produce female gametangia (female sterility) or in meiotic failures in diploid cells which are homozygous for the mutant gene (El-Ani and Olive, 1962).

b. Hermaphroditism. A simple distinction can be made between gene control and extranuclear control (Jinks, 1964; see Chapter 19, this volume) of hereditary traits under circumstances in which one parent contributes only a nucleus, the other both nucleus and cytoplasm, to the hybrid zygote, provided each parent can serve in both capacities.

c. Asexual Spores. The presence of separate uninucleate haploid cells is of considerable help in the establishment of genetically pure lines, in separating the components of a heterokaryon or dikaryon, in the isolation of mutant strains, etc., and in numerous physiological and biochemical studies in which suspensions of living material are needed. Such uninucleate unicellular stages constitute the haplophase in some species, such as *Saccharomyces cerevisiae* and *Ustilago maydis,* whereas in most mycelial species the only single-celled structures are the spores (conidia, oidia, zoospores, etc.). For many purposes these asexual spores can substitute for cells of a unicellular vegetative phase. Uninucleate cells are also technically useful in some hybridization experiments.

d. Meiospores. Origins of the meiospores are most readily determined when the four of common origin are maintained in a separate sac (the ascus in ascomycetes—see Section II, B) or budded off from a separate organ (the basidium in basidiomycetes). The facility with which meiospores of common origin can be isolated and separately cultured depends to some extent on the fruiting structures which bear them, and even more on the characteristics of the asci and basidia and of the meiospores themselves. Many species have meiospores so small that their isolation, even with the aid of micromanipulators, is extremely difficult, and few have spores large enough to make freehand dissections rather easy. Size differences of meiospores among selected species of fungi which have been studied genetically are illustrated in Fig. 11.

For the study of rare meiotic events, large numbers of meiospores must be tested and, to secure the most meaningful information, large numbers of tetrads of meiospores must be examined. To this end, viable mutations whose phenotypes are directly expressed in the meiospores, without recourse to germination and culture, are of an enormous advantage. Such mutations occur reasonably frequently in several species of ascomycetes, most commonly affecting pigmentation of the ascospores.

e. Nutrition. Genetic experimentation is sometimes severely handicapped by the nutritional requirements of the species studied—an extreme example is an obligate parasite whose host is not adapted to controlled culture. A considerable advantage accompanies species which can be grown on relatively simple, chemically defined, media. In such species it is possible to induce a large variety of nutritionally deficient mutants. These in turn can be used in appropriate combinations and by the use of appropriate screening techniques for the selection of extremely rare genetic recombinants (Section III).

f. Reservoir of Genetic Information and of Mutant Stocks. Perhaps the greatest contributor to the successful interpretation of genetic experiments is the knowledge already gained from previous genetic studies; and the greatest aid to the planning and execution of a particular experiment is an

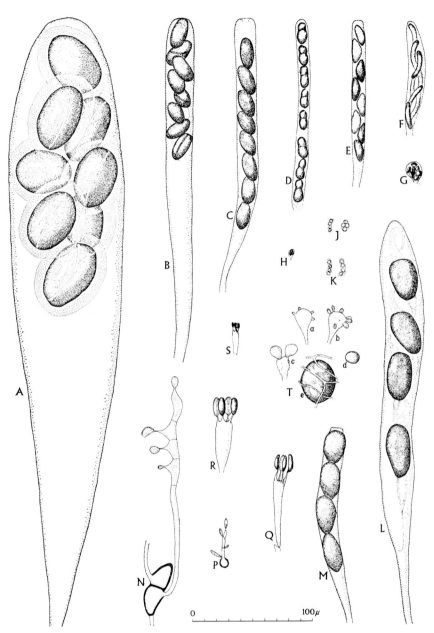

FIG. 11. Relative sizes of meiospores of some ascomycetes and basidiomycetes which have been used in genetic studies: A, *Ascobolus immersus;* B, *Ascobolus magnificus;* C, *Neurospora crassa;* D, *Venturia inaequalis;* E, *Bombardia lunata;* F, *Glomerella cingulata;* G, *Aspergillus nidulans;* H, *Ophiostoma multiannulata;* J, *Saccharomyces cerevisiae;* K, *Schizosaccharomyces pombe;* L, *Podospora anserina;* M, *Neurospora tetrasperma;* N, *Puccinia graminis;* P, *Ustilago maydis;* Q, *Cytidia salicina;* R, *Coprinus fimetarius;* S, *Schizophyllum commune;* T, *Cyathus stercoreus.*

ample collection of well-mapped mutant stocks. These of course are not inherent properties of the organisms studied, but accomplishments of the investigators who studied them—to whom all colleagues are forever indebted.

B. Characteristics of Selected Species of Fungi

1. Chytridiomycetes

Allomyces arbuscula (Blastocladiales, Blastocladiaceae). Haplophase a dichotomously branched coenocytic mycelium, asexual spores absent; monoecious, gametes motile, anisogamous, female gametes 6.0–11.5 µ, male gametes 5.8–8.5 µ. Karyogamy follows cytogamy, dikaryophase absent. Diplophase morphologically similar to haplophase; asexual spores uninucleate, motile, 9–12 µ. Meiosis at germination of oligonucleate resting sporangium; meiotic products randomly mixed. Meiospores motile, 7.5–10.0 µ. Nutrition auxotrophic, thiamine and arginine required. Reviews: R. Emerson (1941, 1954, 1958). Other references: R. Emerson and Wilson (1954), Hatch (1935), Hatch and Jones (1938), Machlis (1953), Machlis and Crasemann (1956), Sörgel (1937), Wilson (1952), and Yaw and Cutter (1951).

The life cycle of this species is unusually well authenticated by excellent cytological studies. Genetic studies include inheritance of morphological characters in species crosses, crosses between members of a polyploid series (haploid chromosome numbers 8, 16, 32), recombination between nutritional mutants. Observed aberrations: female gametes sometimes develop parthenogenetically; presumptive meiospores occasionally develop into diplophase without fusion; occasionally asexual zoospores are produced on haplophase plants.

2. Oomycetes

Phytophthora infestans (Peronosporales, Pythiaceae). Haplophase a freely branching coenocytic mycelium; multinucleate sporangia, 27 ×18 µ, functioning either as conidia with direct germination, or as sporangia which germinate indirectly with production of uninucleate motile asexual spores; heterothallic, one mating type locus, two alleles; hermaphroditic, antheridia and uninucleate oogonium produced on separated hyphal branches. Plasmogamy by direct tubular connection between antheridium and oogonium through which male nucleus migrates. Karyogamy follows cytogamy resulting in one zygote nucleus (based on genetic evidence); dikaryophase lacking. Meiosis occurs in zygote nucleus (genetic evidence only), diplophase lacking. Meiospores motile, many from a single meiotic product of a single zygote, the other three meiotic products apparently degenerate (based on genetic evidence). Nutrition: completes life cycle on artificial media, complex media usually employed. References: Clinton (1911), Crosier (1933, 1934), Galindo and Gallegly (1960), Gallegly and Galindo (1958), Pethybridge and Murphy (1913), Reddick and Crosier (1933), Romero (1963), Rosenbaum (1917), Savage and Gallegly (1960), and Smoot et al. (1958).

This species is an important pathogen, causing late blight of potatoes. Genetic studies were impossible until the discovery of the second mating type: all strains from Africa, Europe, and America north of Mexico are of one mating type; both mating types occur in Mexico. Apparently only one genotype occurs in all meiospores produced from one zygote, e.g., all from one zygote were a complex recombination between different host-range factors and also mating type (Savage and Gallegly, 1960).

3. Zygomycetes

Phycomyces blakesleeanus (Mucorales, Mucoraceae). Haplophase a freely branched coenocytic mycelium; asexual spores are oligonucleate (averaging about 5 nuclei), sometimes heterokaryotic; heterothallic, one mating-type locus, two alleles; gametangia of one kind (isogametangeous), multinucleate. Plasmogamy by direct fusion of gametangia to form the zygospore. Karyogamy between pairs of nuclei in the zygospore, some haploid nuclei remaining unfused; no true dikaryophase. Mitotic divisions of diploid nuclei uncertain. Meiosis occurs during germination of the zygospore at which time there may apparently be a mixture of nuclei of various origins (parental haploid, hybrid diploid, and haploid following meiosis). Meiospores are oligonucleate and are sometimes heterokaryotic. Some genetic evidence suggests that all meiospores may be descended from a single zygote nucleus; fairly frequently all are of one genotype, but four genotypes have been recovered from dihybrids. Nutrition auxotrophic, requiring thiamine as sole supplement. References: Burgeff (1912, 1915a, b, 1925, 1929), Cutter (1942), Robbins and Kavanaugh (1937), Schwartz (1927), Sjöwall (1945, 1946), and Spalla (1963).

There are a considerable number of characteristics of the life cycle of this species which need further elucidation. Genetic studies have been handicapped by difficulties in obtaining satisfactory zygospore germination.

4. Hemiascomycetidae

Saccharomyces cerevisiae (Endomycetales, Saccharomycetaceae). Haplophase unicellular and uninucleate; asexual spores absent; heterothallic, one mating type locus, two mutable alleles; sex organs absent, no specialized gametes. Plasmogamy between vegetative cells, even between meiospores. Karyogamy immediately following plasmogamy, dikaryophase absent. Diplophase morphologically similar to haplophase. Meiosis in vegetative cells which have been induced to sporulate by changes in nutritional conditions. Meiospores (ascospores) are the immediate products of meiosis; four-spored asci usually unordered. Nutrition auxotrophic, biotin and thiamine required; carbohydrate utilization is strain specific. Reviews: S. Emerson (1955, 1956), Lindegren (1949), and Robinow and Bakerspigel (1965).

The biochemistry of this species, which is important in brewing and baking, has been extensively studied. Genetic studies are also extensive, and linkage groups are fairly well established (Hawthorne and Mortimer, 1960), though chromosome number is still not established. Genetic developments of theoretical importance include studies of reciprocal and non-reciprocal somatic recombination (Roman, 1963), genic and extranuclear control of cytochromes (Ephrussi, 1958), tetrad analyses of tetraploids and triploids.

5. Euascomycetidae

The eight-spored ascomycetes that have been studied in genetic experiments are so similar to each other, and to *Neurospora crassa* which has been dealt with rather extensively earlier (Section II), that only important differences between them will be noted. Haplophase is the predominant phase of the life cycles, dikaryophase is very limited, and diplophase usually absent—karyogamy and meiosis occur in the developing ascus.

Aspergillus nidulans (Eurotiales, Eurotiaceae). Asexual spores of haplophase are uninucleate conidia. The species is homothallic, but biparental cleistothecia are preferentially produced in many crosses. Ascospores are small, and asci unordered. Nutrition: no organic supplement other than a carbon source is required. Reviews: Pontecorvo (1953), and Pontecorvo and Käfer (1958).

The life cycle of this species is well established by genetic tests but the cytology is still inadequate. The sporadic occurrence of diploidy has led to the development of useful techniques for the analysis of linkage groups by somatic recombination, resulting either from mitotic crossing over or from haploidization of diploids (see Chapter 18), as contrasted with meiotic crossing over.

Neurospora crassa (Sphaeriales, Sordariaceae). See description in Section II. Nutrition: auxotrophic, requiring biotin. Review: S. Emerson (1955).

Sordaria fimicola (Sphaeriales, Sordariaceae). Homothallic, but difficulties in control of crossing have been overcome by use of mutants causing female sterility and of recessive mutants for ascospore abortion (El-Ani and Olive, 1962). Asci with linearly ordered ascospores. Ascospores nearly as large as in *Neurospora*, 18–28 μ by 8–18 μ. Produces viable ascospore color mutants. Life cycle established by genetic and cytological observations. References: Bretzloff (1954), Carr and Olive (1958, 1959), El-Ani *et al.* (1961), Heslot (1958), Olive (1954, 1959), and Perkins *et al.* (1963).

Glomerella cingulata (Diaporthales, Diaporthaceae). Haplophase with uninucleate cells; homothallic, but crossing preferentially; many strains female sterile; at least four loci involved in self-incompatibility of one sort or another; multiple alleles at two loci. Plasmogamy between trichogyne and conidia. The dikaryophase in a single perithecium apparently arises from a single dikaryotic cell following plasmogamy. Asci unordered. Nutrition: normally a parasite on apple, but can be grown through its entire life cycle on artificial media. References: Chilton *et al.* (1945), Edgerton (1914), Lucas (1946), Lucas *et al.* (1944), McGahen and Wheeler (1951), McGahen *et al.* (1950), Stoneman (1898), Struble and Keitt (1950), Wheeler (1954a,b), Wheeler and McGahen (1952), and Wheeler *et al.* (1948).

Ascobolus immersus (Pezizles, Pezizaceae). Haplophase heterothallic, one mating-type locus, two alleles; asexual spores absent. Asci unordered, few per apothecium; ascospores very large (see Fig. 11); ascospore color mutants abundant. Nutrition: auxotrophic, requiring biotin and thiamine. References: Ames (1930), Buller (1909), Lissouba (1960), Lissouba *et al.* (1962), and Yu-Sun (1964a,b); further references to genetic studies in Sections III and IV. Genetic interest in this species has related principally to nonreciprocal recombination.

Venturia inaequalis (Pleosporales, Venturiaceae). Haplophase a mycelium of uninucleate cells; asexual spores are uninucleate conidia; both antheridia and ascogonia produced; heterothallic and hermaphroditic. Plasmogamy by fusion between antheridium and ascogonial coil. Asci have ascospores in a single row (Fig. 11, D), but both genetic and cytological observations indicate that the order in which spores occur does not accurately reflect the division at which segregations have occurred. Nutrition: haplophase mycelium has been grown on an undefined artificial medium on which protoperithecia were produced, but crossing has been accomplished only in tissues of the host plant, the apple. Several months are required for completion of the life cycle. References: E. J. Backus and Keitt (1940), Keitt and Boone (1954), Keitt and Langford (1941), Keitt and Palmenter (1938), Keitt *et al.* (1943), Killian (1917), Shay and Keitt (1945), and Williams and Shay (1957). Genetic interest in this species has centered chiefly in host-pathogen interrelationships.

Four-spored higher Ascomycetes, such as *Podospora anserina* and

Neurospora tetrasperma, have heterokaryotic ascospores. These large spores (Fig. 11, L and M) usually contain nuclei derived from two products of meiosis. Genetic analyses are therefore somewhat complex, but interesting.

Podospora (Pleurage) anserina (Sphaeriales, Sordariaceae). References: Ames (1932, 1934), Dowding (1931), Rizet (1941, 1952), and Rizet and Engelmann (1949). One of the first thorough mathematical treatments of tetrad analysis is presented in the last reference cited. Particular interest attaches to studies of the barrage phenomenon in this species.

Neurospora tetrasperma (Sphaeriales, Sordariaceae). References: Colson (1934), Cutter (1946), Dodge (1927), Howe (1964), Sansome (1946), and Seaver (1937).

6. Heterobasidiomycetidae

Puccinia graminis (Uredinales, Pucciniaceae). Haplophase a mycelium composed of uninucleate cells, parasitic on the barberry plant; heterothallic and hermaphroditic; male gametes are minute pycnia produced in the same organ in the host leaf as the female elements, the receptive hyphae. Plasmogamy by unions between receptive hyphae and pycnia which are transported by insects. Dikaryophase begins in the barberry leaf where it produces dikaryotic asexual spores, aeciospores, which infect wheat plants; dikaryotic asexual spores, uredospores, produced on wheat reinfect that host; two-celled dikaryotic sexual spores, teliospores, are produced by the dikaryophase on wheat. Karyogamy by fusion of the two nuclei in cells of the teliospores. Meiosis at germination of teliospores to produce linear, four-celled basidia. Meiospores are basidiospores budded off each cell of the basidium, and into which the four haploid nuclei from meiosis migrate. Nutrition: obligately parasitic. Some other species of the Pucciniaceae have been successfully cultured in tissue cultures of the host plants (Cutter, 1959, 1960). References: Buller (1950), Craigie (1927, 1928, 1959), Hiratsuka and Cummins (1963), Johnson (1954), and Loegering and Powers (1962).

Ustilago maydis (Ustilaginales, Ustilaginaceae). Haplophase unicellular, uninucleate (in culture, probably brief or absent in nature); no specialized gametes or sex organs. Plasmogamy between haploid cells. Dikaryophase is the dominant phase, obligately parasitic on maize; hyphae of dikaryotic cells; asexual spores absent; sexual spores are unicellular brandspores or teleutospores. Karyogamy between the two nuclei in the brandspore. Meiosis in the zygote nucleus during germination of the brandspore to form a four-celled linear basidium. Meiospores are basidiospores developing from buds on basidial cells into which the nuclei migrate; haploid mitoses sometimes occur in nuclei produced at meiosis before buds are formed, and more than one basidiospore may be derived from a single cell of the basidium. Nutrition: the dikaryophase is obligately parasitic on the maize plant; haplophase and a diploid phase arising by nuclear fusion in dikaryophase can be cultured on defined media. References: Hanna (1929), Holliday (1961a,b, 1962), Hüttig (1932), Rowell (1954, 1955a,b), Sleumer (1932), Stakman and Christensen (1927), and Wolf (1953). Genetic analyses have been made both by tetrad analysis and by somatic recombination. Diploid lines produce brandspores in which meiosis occurs normally.

7. *Homobasidiomycetidae*

Aside from members of the Agaricaceae few higher basidiomycetes have been used in genetic studies. Many species of the Agaricaceae have been studied, but principally to determine the inheritance of mating type, which is controlled by multiple alleles at either one locus (bipolar sexuality) or two loci (tetrapolar sexuality).

The life cycles of all agarics are very similar. Haplophase consists of a mycelium of uninucleate cells. Plasmogamy occurs by hyphal fusion followed by nuclear migration. Mycelium of the dikaryophase is similar to that of the haplophase except for dikaryotic cells in which the nuclei divide conjugately with the fairly regular production of clamp connections in many species. Karyogamy occurs by the union of the two nuclei in the young basidium. The zygote nucleus immediately enters meiosis. Meiospores are the basidiospores formed from buds on the basidium into which the four haploid nuclei produced in meiosis migrate.

Coprinus fimetarius (lagopus) (Agaricales, Agaricaceae). References: Bohn (1934), Brunswik (1926), Day (1963), Hanna (1925), Oort (1930), Quintanilha (1933, 1934, 1935a,b, 1937, 1938a,b, 1938/1939) and Quintanilha and Balle (1938, 1940). A considerable amount of tetrad analysis has been done with this species. Most of the characteristics and behavior of "illegitimate matings," and of apparent recombination of genes and increased mutation rates in heterocaryons were first worked out in this species and later confirmed and extended by observations in *Schizophyllum*. The bipartite nature of the two mating type "loci," so well established in *Schizophyllum* has more recently been observed in *Coprinus*.

Schizophyllum commune (Agaricales, Agaricaceae). References: Bakerspigel (1959), Ehrlich and McDonough (1949), Kniep (1928), Papazian (1950a,b, 1951), Raper (1953, and Chapter 15 of this volume), Raper and SanAntonio (1954), Raper *et al.* (1958a,b), and Schopfer and Blumer (1940).

REFERENCES

Ames, L. M. (1930). A study of homothallic and heterothallic Ascomycetes. *Mycologia* **22**:318-332.

Ames, L. M. (1932). An hermaphroditic self-sterile but cross-fertile condition in *Pleurage anserina*. *Bull. Torrey Botan. Club* **59**:341-345.

Ames, L. M. (1934). Hermaphroditism involving self-sterility and cross-fertility in the Ascomycete *Pleurage anserina*. *Mycologia* **26**:392-414.

Backus, E. J., and G. W. Keitt. (1940). Some nuclear phenomena in *Venturia inaequalis*. *Bull. Torrey Botan. Club* **67**:765-770.

Backus, M. P. (1939). The mechanism of conidial fertilization in *Neurospora sitophila*. *Bull. Torrey Botan. Club* **66**:63-67.

Bakerspigel, A. (1959). The structure and manner of division of the nuclei in the vegetative mycelium of the basidiomycete *Schizophyllum commune*. *Can. J. Botany* **37**:835-842.

Barratt, R. W., and L. Garnjobst. (1949). Genetics of a colonial microconidiating mutant strain of *Neurospora crassa*. *Genetics* **34**:351-369.

Barratt, R. W., D. Newmeyer, D. D. Perkins, and L. Garnjobst. (1954). Map construction in *Neurospora crassa*. *Advan. Genet.* **6**:1-93.

Barry, E. G. (1961). A complex chromosome rearrangement in *Neurospora crassa*. Ph.D. thesis, Stanford University.

Bohn, W. (1934). Einige Untersuchungen über die Tetradenaufspaltung bei den Basiciomyceten. *Z. Induktive Abstammungs- Vererbungslehre* **67**:434-445.

Bole-Gowda, B. N., D. D. Perkins, and W. N. Strickland. (1962). Crossing over and interference in the centrosome region of linkage group I. of *Neurospora. Genetics* **47**:1243-1252.

Bretzloff, C. W. (1954). The growth and fruiting of *Sordaria fimicola*. *Am. J. Botany* **41**:58-67.

Brunswik, H. (1926). Die Reduktionsteilung bei den Basidiomyzeten. *Z. Botan.* **18**: 481-498.

Buller, A. H. R. (1909). "Researches on Fungi," Vol. I, 274 pp. Longmans, Green, New York.

Buller, A. H. R. (1950). "Researches on Fungi," Vol. VII, 458 pp. Univ. of Toronto Press, Toronto.

Burgeff, H. (1912). Über Sexualität, Variabilität, und Vererbung bei *Phycomyces nitens*. *Ber. Deut. Botan. Ges.* **30**:679-685.

Burgeff, H. (1915a). Untersuchungen über Variabilität, Sexualität und Erblichkeit bei *Phycomyces nitens* Kurz. I. *Flora (Jena)* [N.F.] **7**:259-316.

Burgeff, H. (1915b). Untersuchungen über Variabilität und Ehblichkeit bei *Phycomyces nitens*. II. *Flora (Jena)* [N.F.] **8**:353-448.

Burgeff, H. (1925). Über Arten und Artkreuzung in Gattung Phycomyces Kunze. *Flora (Jena)* [N.F.] **18/19**:40-46.

Burgeff, H. (1929). Variabilität, Vererbung und Mutation bei *Phycomyces Blakesleeanus* Bgff. *Z. Induktive Abstammungs- Vererbungslehre* **49**:26-94.

Campbell, A. M. (1962). Episomes. *Advan. Genet.* **11**:101-145.

Carr, A. J. H., and L. S. Olive. (1958). Genetics of *Sordaria fimicola*. II. Cytology. *Am. J. Botany* **45**:142-150.

Carr, A. J. H., and L. S. Olive. (1959). Genetics of *Sordaria fimicola*. III. Crosscompatibility among self-fertile and self-sterile cultures. *Am. J. Botany* **46**:81-91.

Case, M. E., and N. H. Giles. (1958a). Evidence from tetrad analysis for both normal and aberrant recombination between allelic mutants in *Neurospora crassa*. *Proc. Natl. Acad. Sci. U.S.* **44**:378-390.

Case, M. E., and N. H. Giles. (1958b). Recombination mechanisms at the *pan-2* locus in *Neurospora crassa*. *Cold Spring Harbor Symp. Quant. Biol.* **23**:119-135.

Case, M. E., and N. H. Giles. (1964). Allelic recombination in Neurospora: Tetrad analysis of a three-point cross within the *pan-2* locus. *Genetics* **49**:529-540.

Chilton, S. J. P., G. B. Lucas, and C. W. Edgerton. (1945). Genetics of Glomerella. III. Crosses with a conidial strain. *Am. J. Botany* **32**:549-554.

Clinton, G. P. (1911). Oöspores of the potato blight fungus, *Phytophthora infestus*. *Conn. Univ., Storrs Agr. Exptl. Sta., Ann. Rept. 1909-1910* pp. 753-774.

Colson, B. (1934). The cytology and morphology of *Neurospora tetrasperma* Dodge. *Ann. Botany (London)* **48**:211-224.

Coyle, M. B., and T. H. Pittenger. (1964). Somatic recombinants from pseudo-wild types of Neurospora recovered from 4:4 acsi. *Genetics* **50**:242-243. (abstr.).

Craigie, J. H. (1927). Experiments on sex in rust fungi. *Nature* **120**:116-117.

Craigie, J. H. (1928). On the occurrence of pycnia and aecia in certain rust fungi. *Phytopathology* **18**:1005-1015.

Craigie, J. H. (1959). Nuclear behavior in the diploidization of haploid infections of *Puccinia helianthi*. *Can. J. Botany* **37**:843-855.

Crosier, W. (1933). Culture of *Phytophthora infestans*. *Phytopathology* **23**:713-720.

Crosier, W. (1934). Studies in the biology of *Phytophthora infestans* (Mont.) de Bary. *Cornell Univ., Agr. Expt. Sta. Mem.* **155**.

Cutter, V. M., Jr. (1942). Nuclear behavior in the Mucorales. II. The Rhizopus, Phycomyces, and Sporodinia patterns. *Bull. Torrey Botan. Club* **69**:592-616.

Cutter, V. M., Jr. (1946). The chromosomes of *Neurospora tetrasperma*. *Mycologia* **38**:693-698.

Cutter, V. M., Jr. (1959). Studies on the isolation and growth of plant rusts in host tissue cultures and upon synthetic media. I. *Gymnosporangium*. *Mycologia* **51**:248-295.

Cutter, V. M., Jr. (1960). Studies on the isolation and growth of plant rusts in host tissue cultures and upon synthetic media. II. *Uromyces aritriphylii*. *Mycologia* **52**:726-742.

Davis, R. H. (1966). Heterokaryosis. *In* "The Fungi" (G. C. Ainsworth and A. S. Sussman, eds.), Vol. 2, Chapter 17. Academic Press, New York.

Day, P. R. (1963). The structure of the A mating type factor in *Coprinus lagopus*. *Genet. Res.* **4**:323-325.

Dodge, B. O. (1927). Nuclear phenomena associated with heterothallism in the ascomycete *Neurospora J. Agr. Res.* **35**:289-305.

Dowding, E. S. (1931). The sexuality of normal, giant and dwarf spores of *Pleurage anserina* (Ces.) Kutze. *Ann. Botany (London)* **45**:1-14.

Edgerton, C. W. (1914). Plus and minus strains in the genus *Glomerella*. *Am. J. Botany* **1**:244-254.

Ehrlich, H. G., and E. S. McDonough. (1949). The nuclear history in the basidia and basidiospores of *Schizophyllum commune* (Fries). *Am. J. Botany* **36**:360-363.

El-Ani, A. S., and L. S. Olive. (1962). The induction of balanced heterothallism in *Sordaria fimicola*. *Proc. Natl. Acad. Sci. U.S.* **48**:17-19.

El-Ani, A. S., L. S. Olive, and Y. Kitani. (1961). Genetics of *Sordaria fimicola*. IV. Linkage group I. *Am. J. Botany* **48**:716-723.

Emerson, R. (1941). An experimental study of the life-cycle and taxonomy of Allomyces. *Lloydia* 4:77-144.
Emerson, R. (1954). The biology of water molds. *In* "Aspects of Synthesis and Order of Growth" (D. Rudnick, ed.), pp. 171-208. Princeton Univ. Press, Princeton, New Jersey.
Emerson, R. (1958). Mycological organization. *Mycologia* 50:589-621.
Emerson, R., and C. M. Wilson. (1954). Interspecific hybrids and cytogenetics and karyotaxonomy of Euallomyces. *Mycologia* 46:393-434.
Emerson, S. (1955). Biochemical genetics. *In* "Hoppe-Seyler/Thierfelder Handbuch der physiologisch- und pathologisch-chemischen Analyse" (K. Lang and E. Lehnartz, eds.), 10th ed., Vol. 2, Part 2, pp. 443-537. Springer, Berlin.
Emerson, S. (1956). Notes on different causes of aberrant tetrad ratios in Saccharomyces. *Compt. Rend. Trav. Lab. Carlsberg., Ser. Physiol.* 26:71-86.
Emerson, S. (1963). Meiotic recombination in fungi with special reference to tetrad analysis. *In* "Methodology in Basic Genetics" (W. J. Burdette, ed.), pp. 167-206. Holden-Day, San Francisco, California.
Emerson, S. (1966). Unpublished observations.
Ephrussi, B. (1958). The cytoplasm and somatic cell variation. *J. Cellular Comp. Physiol.* 52: Suppl., 35-53.
Fincham, J. R. S., and P. R. Day. (1965). "Fungal Genetics," 2nd ed., 326 pp. Blackwell, Oxford.
Freese, E. (1957a). The correlation effect for a histidine locus in *Neurospora crassa*. *Genetics* 42:671-684.
Freese, E. (1957b). Über die Feinstruktur des Genoms im bereich eines PAB locus von *Neurospora crassa*. *Z. Induktive Abstammungs- Vererbungslehre* 88:388-406.
Galindo, J. A., and M. E. Gallegly. (1960). The nature of sexuality in *Phytophthora infestans*. *Phytopathology* 50:123-128.
Gallegly, M. E., and J. Galindo. (1958). Mating types and oöspores of *Phytophthora infestans* in nature in Mexico. *Phytopathology* 48:274-277.
Grant, H. (1945). A genetic analysis of the life cycle of *Neurospora crassa*. Unpublished thesis, Stanford University.
Hanna, W. F. (1925). The problem of sex in *Coprinus lagopus*. *Ann. Botany (London)* 39:431-457.
Hanna, W. F. (1929). Studies in the physiology and cytology of *Ustilago zeae* and *Sorosporium reilianum*. *Phytopathology* 19:415-442.
Hatch, W. R. (1935). Gametogenesis in *Allomyces arbuscula*. *Ann. Botany (London)* 49:623-649.
Hatch, W. R., and R. C. Jones. (1938). An experimental study of alternation of generations in *Allomyces arbuscula*. *Mycologia* 36:369-381.
Hawthorne, D. C., and R. K. Mortimer. (1960). Chromosome mapping in Saccharomyces: centromere-linked genes. *Genetics* 45:1085-1110.
Heslot, H. (1958). Contribution à l'étude cytogénétique et génétique des Sordariacees. *Rev. Cytol. Biol. Vegetales* 19: Suppl. 2, 1-235.
Hiratsuka, Y., and G. B. Cummins. (1963). Morphology of the spermagonia of the rust fungi. *Mycologia* 55:487-507.
Holliday, R. (1961a). The genetics of *Ustilago maydis*. *Genet. Res.* 2:204-230.
Holliday, R. (1961b). Induced meiotic crossing-over in *Ustilago maydis*. *Genet. Res.* 2:231-248.
Holliday, R. (1962). Mutation and replication in *Ustilago maydis*. *Genet. Res.* 3:472-486.

Holliday, R. (1964). A mechanism for gene conversion in fungi. *Genet. Res.* **5**: 282-304.
Horowitz, N. H., and R. L. Metzenberg. (1966). Biochemical aspects of genetics. *Ann. Rev. Biochem.* **34**:527-264.
Howe, H. B., Jr. (1956). Crossing over and nuclear passing in *Neurospora crassa*. *Genetics* **41**:610-622.
Howe, H. B., Jr. (1964). Sources of error in genetic analysis in *Neurospora tetrasperma*. *Genetics* **50**:181-189.
Huebschman, C. (1952). A method for varying the average number of nuclei in the conidia of *Neurospora crassa*. *Mycologia* **44**:599-604.
Hüttig, W. (1932). Die Grundlagen zur Immunitätszüchtung gegen Brandpilze (Ustilagineen). *Zuechter* **4**:209-219.
Jacob, F., and E. L. Wollman. (1958). Les épisomes, éléments génétiques ajoutés. *Compt. Rend.* **247**:154-156.
Jacob, F., P. Schaeffer, and E. L. Wollman. (1960). Episomic elements in bacteria. *Symp. Soc. Gen. Microbiol.* **10**:67-91.
Jinks, J. L. (1964). "Extra Chromosomal Inheritance," 177 pp. Prentice-Hall, Englewood Cliffs, New Jersey.
Johnson, T. (1954). Selfing studies with physiological races of wheat stem rust, *Puccinia graminis* var. *tritici*. *Can. J. Botany* **32**:506-522.
Keitt, G. W., and D. M. Boone. (1954). Induction and inheritance of mutant characters in *Venturia inaequalis* in relation to its pathogenicity. *Phytopathology* **44**: 362-370.
Keitt, G. W., and M. H. Langford. (1941). *Venturia inaequalis* (Ckl.) Wint. I. A groundwork for genetic studies. *Am. J. Botany* **28**:805-820.
Keitt, G. W., and D. H. Palmiter. (1938). Heterothallism and variability in *Venturia inaequalis*. *Am. J. Botany* **25**:338-345.
Keitt, G. W., M. H. Langford, and J. R. Shay. (1943). *Venturia inaequalis* (Ckl.) Wint. II. Genetic studies on pathogenicity and certain mutant characters. *Am. J. Botany* **30**:491-500.
Killian, K. (1917). Über die Sexualität von *Venturia inaequalis* (Cooke) Ad. *Z. Botan.* **9**:353-398.
Kitani, Y., L. S. Olive, and A. S. El-Ani. (1962). Genetics of *Sordaria fimicola*. V. Aberrant segregation at the g locus. *Am. J. Botany* **49**:697-706.
Kniep, H. (1928). "Die Sexualität der niederen Pflanzen," 544 pp. Fischer, Jena.
Lindegren, C. C. (1949). "The Yeast Cell" Educational Publishers, St. Louis, Missouri.
Lindegren, C. C. (1953). Gene conversion in *Saccharomyces*. *J. Genet.* **51**:625-637.
Lindegren, C. C. (1955). Non-Mendelian segregation in a single tetrad of *Saccharomyces* ascribed to gene conversion. *Science* **121**:605-607.
Lissouba, P. (1960). Mise en évidence d'une unité génétique polarisée et essai d'analyse d'un cas d'interférence négative. *Ann. Sci. Nat.: Botan. Biol. Vegetale* [12] **12**:641-720.
Lissouba, P., and G. Rizet. (1960). Sur l'existence d'une unité génétique polarisée ne subissant que des échanges non réciproques. *Compt. Rend.* **250**:3408-3410.
Lissouba, P., J. Mousseau, G. Rizet, and J. L. Rossignol. (1962). The fine structure of genes in the ascomycete *Ascobolus immersus*. *Advan. Genet.* **11**:343-380.
Loegering, W. Q., and H. R. Powers, Jr. (1962). Inheritance of pathogenicity in a cross of physiological races 111 and 36 of *Puccinia graminis* f. sp. *tritici*. *Phytopathology* **52**:547-556.

Lucas, G. B. (1946). Genetics of *Glomerella*. IV. Nuclear phenomena in the ascus. *Am. J. Botany* 33:802-806.
Lucas, G. B., S. J. P. Chilton, and C. W. Edgerton. (1944). Genetics of *Glomerella*. I. Studies on the behavior of certain strains. *Am. J. Botany* 31:233-239.
McClintock, B. (1945). Neurospora. I. Preliminary observations of the chromosomes of *Neurospora crassa*. *Am. J. Botany* 32:671-678.
McGahen, J. W., and H. E. Wheeler. (1951). Genetics of *Glomerella*. IX. Perithecial development and plasmogamy. *Am. J. Botany* 38:610-617.
McGahen, J. W., H. E. Wheeler, and S. J. P. Chilton. (1950). Factors conditioning sexuality in *Glomerella* from *Ipomoea*. *Phytopathology* 41:25-26.
Machlis, L. (1953). Growth and nutrition of water molds of the subgenus of *Euallomyces*. I, II, III. *Am. J. Botany* 40:189-195, 450-460, and 460-464.
Machlis, L., and J. M. Crasemann. (1956). Physiological variation between generations and among water molds in the subgenus *Euallomyces*. *Am. J. Botany* 43: 601-611.
Mitchell, M. B. (1955). Aberrant recombination of pyridoxine mutants of *Neurospora*. *Proc. Natl. Acad. Sci. U.S.* 41:215-220.
Mitchell, M. B. (1963). Indications of pre-ascus recombination in *Neurospora* crosses. *Genetics* 48:553-559.
Mitchell, M. B., and H. K. Mitchell. (1952). A case of "maternal" inheritance in *Neurospora crassa*. *Proc. Natl. Acad. Sci. U.S.* 38:442-449.
Murray, N. E. (1963). Polarized recombination and fine structure within the *me-2* gene of *Neurospora crassa*. *Genetics* 48:1163-1183.
Norman, A. (1951). Inactivation of *Neurospora* conidia by ultraviolet radiation. *Exptl. Cell Res.* 2:454-473.
Olive, L. S. (1954). Cross-karyology and segregation in a homothallic fungus. *Bull. Torrey Botan. Club.* 81:95-97.
Olive, L. S. (1959). Aberrant tetrads in *Sordaria fimicola*. *Proc. Natl. Acad. Sci. U.S.* 45:727-732.
Olive, L. S. (1965). Nuclear behavior during meiosis. *In* "The Fungi" (G. C. Ainsworth and A. S. Sussman, eds.), Vol. 1, Chapter 7. Academic Press, New York.
Oort, A. J. P. (1930). Die zexualität von *Coprinus fimetarius*. *Rec. Trav. Botan. Neerl.* 27:85-148.
Papazian, H. P. (1950a). A method of isolating the four spores from a single basidium in *Schizophyllum commune*. *Botan. Gaz.* 112:139-140.
Papazian, H. P. (1950b). Physiology of the incompatibility factors in *Schizophyllum commune*. *Botan. Gaz.* 112:143-163.
Papazian, H. P. (1951). The incompatibility factors and a related gene in *Schizophyllum commune*. *Genetics* 36:441-459.
Perkins, D. D. (1953). The detection of linkage in tetrad analysis. *Genetics* 38:187-197.
Perkins, D. D. (1962). Crossing over and interference in a multiply marked chromosome arm of Neurospora. *Genetics* 47:1253-1274.
Perkins, D. D., M. Glassey, and B. A. Bloom. (1962). New data on markers and rearrangements in Neurospora. *Can. J. Genet. Cytol.* 4:187-205.
Perkins, D. D., A. S. El-Ani, L. S. Olive, and Y. Kitani. (1963). Interference between exchanges in tetrads of *Sordaria fimicola*. *Am. Naturalist* 97:249-252.
Pethybridge, G. H., and P. A. Murphy. (1913). On pure cultures of *Phytophthora infestans* de Bary, and the development of oöspores. *Sci. Proc. Roy. Dublin Soc.* 13:566-588.

Pontecorvo, G. (1953). The genetics of *Aspergillus nidulans*. *Advan. Genet.* **5**:141-238.

Pontecorvo, G., and E. Käfer. (1958). Genetic analysis based on mitotic recombination. *Advan. Genet.* **9**:71-104.

Prakash, V. (1964). Chromatid inheritance in *Neurospora crassa*. *Genetics* **50**:297-321.

Quintanilha, A. (1933). Le problème de la sexualité chez les Basidiomycètes. Recherches sur le genre "*Coprinus*," *Bol. Soc. Broteria.* [2] **8**:3-99.

Quintanilha, A. (1934). La descendance des copulations illégitimes chez les Hyménomycètes. *Compt. Rend. Soc. Biol.* **117**:737-739.

Quintanilha, A. (1935a). Cytologie et génétique de la sexualité chez les Hyménomycètes. *Bol. Soc. Broteria.* [2] **10**:289-332.

Quintanilha, A. (1935b). Cytologie des copulations illégitimes chez *Coprinus fimetarius*. *Compt. Rend.* **201**:1143-1145.

Quintanilha, A. (1937). Contribution à l'étude génétique du phénomène de Buller. *Compt. Rend.* **205**:745-747.

Quintanilha, A. (1938a). Troisième contribution à l'étude génétique de phénomène de Buller. *Compt. Rend. Soc. Biol.* **129**:730-734.

Quintanilha, A. (1938b). Duexième contribution à l'étude génétique du phénomène de Buller. *Compt. Rend. Soc. Biol.* **127**:1245-1248.

Quintanilha, A. (1938/1939). Étude génétique du phénomène de Buller. *Bol. Soc. Broteria.* [2] **13**:425-486.

Quintanilha, A., and S. Balle. (1938). Étude génétique des phénomènes de nanisme chez les Hyménomycètes. *Compt. Rend. Soc. Biol.* **129**:191-194.

Quintanilha, A., and S. Balle. (1940). Étude génétique des phénomènes de nanisme chez les Hyménomycètes. *Bol. Soc. Broteria.* [2] **14**:17-46.

Raper, J. R. (1953). Tetrapolar sexuality. *Quart. Rev. Biol.* **28**:233-259.

Raper, J. R., and J. P. SanAntonio. (1954). Heterocaryotic mutagenesis in hymenomycetes. I. Heterocaryosis in *Schizophyllum commune*. *Am. J. Botany* **41**:69-86.

Raper, J. R., G. S. Krongelb, and M. G. Baxter. (1958a). The number and distribution of incompatibility factors in *Schizophyllum*. *Am. Naturalist* **92**:221-223.

Raper, J. R., M. G. Baxter, and R. B. Middleton. (1956b). The genetic structure of the incompatibility factors in *Schizophyllum commune*. *Proc. Natl. Acad. Sci. U.S.* **44**:889-900.

Reddick, D., and W. Crosier. (1933). Biological specialization in *Phytophthora infestans*. *Am. Potato J.* **10**:129-134.

Rizet, G. (1941). La formation d'asques hybrides dans les confrontations de souches "self-steriles" et de souches "self-fertiles" chez le *Podospora anserina*. *Rev. Mycol.* [N.S.] **6**:128-133.

Rizet, G. (1952). Les phénomènes de barrage chez *Podospora anserina*. I. Analyse génétique des barrages entre souches S. et s. *Rev. Cytol. Biol. Vegetales* **13**:50-91.

Rizet, G., and C. Englemann. (1949). Contribution à l'étude génétique d'un Ascomycète tetraspore: *Podospora anserina* (Ces.) Rehm. *Rev. Cytol. Biol. Vegetales* **11**:201-304.

Rizet, G., and J. L. Rossignol. (1963). Manuscript of report at 11th Intern. Congr. Genet., The Hague, 1963.

Rizet, G., P. Lissouba, and J. Mousseau. (1961). Les mutations d'ascospores chez l'ascomycète *Ascobolus immersus* et l'analyse de la structure fine des gènes. *Bull. Soc. Franc. Physiol. Vegetale* **6**:175-193.

Robbins, W. J., and F. Kavanaugh. (1937). Intermediates of vitamin B_1 and growth of Phycomyces. *Proc. Natl. Acad. Sci. U.S.* **23**:499-502.
Robinow, C. F., and A. Bakerspigel. (1965). Somatic nuclei and forms of mitosis in fungi. *In* "The Fungi" (G. C. Ainsworth and A. S. Sussman, eds.), Vol. 1, Chapter 6. Academic Press, New York.
Roman, H. (1963). Genic conversion in fungi. *In* "Methodology in Basic Genetics" (W. J. Burdette, ed.), pp. 209-221. Holden-Day, San Francisco, California.
Romero, S. (1963). Oogonia germination in *Phytophthora infestans*. *Phytopathology* **53**:899-903.
Rosenbaum, J. (1917). Studies of the genus Phytophthora. *J. Agr. Res.* **8**:233-276.
Rowell, J. B. (1954). Functional role of the factors for sexual compatibility in haploid lines of *Ustilago zeae*. *Phytopathology* **44**:504 (abstr.).
Rowell, J. B. (1955a). Functional role of compatibility factors and an in vitro test for sexual compatibility with haploid lines of *Ustilago zeae*. *Phytopathology* **45**: 370-374.
Rowell, J. B. (1955b). Segregation of sex factors in a diploid line of *Ustilago zeae* induced by alpha radiation. *Science* **121**:304-306.
St. Lawrence, P. (1952). The association of particular linkage groups with their respective chromosomes in *Neurospora crassa*. Ph.D. thesis, Columbia University [*Dissertation Abstr.* **14**:7-8 (1954) (abstr.)].
Sansome, E. R. (1946). Maintenance of heterozygosity in a homothallic species of the *Neurospora tetrasperma* type. *Nature* **157**:484-485.
Sansome, E. R. (1947). The use of heterokaryons to determine the origin of the ascogeneous nuclei in *Neurospora crassa*. *Genetica* **24**:59-63.
Savage, E. J., and M. E. Gallegly. (1960). Problems of germination of oospores of *Phytophthora infestans*. *Phytopathology* **50**:573 (abstr.).
Schopfer, W. H., and S. Blumer. (1940). Le pouvoir de synthèses d'un facteur de croissance par *Schizophyllum commune* (haplontes et diplontes). *Protoplasma* **34**:524-532.
Schwartz, W. (1927). Die Zygoten von *Phycomyces blakesleeanus*. Untersuchungen über die Bedingungen ihrer Bildung und Keimung. *Flora (Jena)* [N.F.] **21**:1-39.
Seaver, B. (1937). Additional data on the sex in monospore races of *Neurospora tetrasperma*. *Mycologia* **29**:258-265.
Shay, J. R., and G. W. Keitt. (1945). The inheritance of certain mutant characters in *Venturia inaequalis*. *J. Agr. Res.* **70**:31-41.
Singleton, J. R. (1953). Chromosome morphology and chromosome cycle in the ascus of *Neurospora crassa*. *Am. J. Botany* **40**:124-144.
Sjöwall, M. (1945). "Studien über Sexualität, Vererbung, und Zytologie bei einigen diozischen Mucoraceen," p. 97. Carl Bloms, Lund, Sweden.
Sjöwall, M. (1946). Über die zytologischen Verhältnisse in dem Keimschlauchen von *Phycomyces blakesleeanus* and *Rhizopus stolonifer*. *Botan. Notiser* pp. 331-334.
Sleumer, H. O. (1932). Über Sexualität und Zytologie von *Ustilago zeae* (Beckm.) Unger. *Z. Botan.* **25**:209-263.
Smoot, J. J., F. J. Gough, H. A. Lamey, J. J. Eichenmuller, and M. A. Gallegly. (1958). Production and germination of oöspores of *Phytophthora infestans*. *Phytopathology* **48**:165-171.
Somers, C. E., R. P. Wagner, and T. C. Hsu. (1960). Mitosis in vegetative nuclei of *Neurospora crassa*. *Genetics* **45**:801-810.
Sörgel, G. (1937). Untersuchungen über den Generationswechsel von *Allomyces*. *Z. Botan.* **31**:400-446.

Spalla, C. (1963). Richerche sulla reproduzione sessuale in Mucorales. Studio della reproduzione sessuale in *Phycomyces blakesleeanus* e in *Choanephora circinans* comparazione di *Cunninghamiella blakesleeana, C. elongans, Mucor heimalis* e *M. racemosus. Riv. Patol. Vegetale* 3:189-198.

Stadler, D. R. (1956a). A map of linkage group VI of *Neurospora crassa. Genetics* 41:528-543.

Stadler, D. R. (1956b). Double crossing-over in *Neurospora. Genetics* 41:623-630.

Stadler, D. R., and A. M. Towe. (1963). Recombination of allelic cysteine mutants in Neurospora. *Genetics* 48:1323-1344.

Stakman, E. C., and J. J. Christensen. (1927). Heterothallism in *Ustilago zeae. Phytopathology* 17:827-834.

Stoneman, B. (1898). A comparative study of the development of some anthracnoses. *Botan. Gaz.* 26:69-120.

Struble, F. B., and G. W. Keitt. (1950). Variability and inheritance in *Glomerella cingulata* (Stonem.) S. and U.S. from apple. *Am. J. Botany* 37:563-576.

Sturtevant, A. H. (1913). The linear arrangement of six sex-linked factors in *Drosophila*, as shown by their mode of association. *J. Exptl. Zool.* 14:43-59.

Threlkeld, S. F. H. (1962). Some asci with nonidentical sister spores from a cross in *Neurospora crassa. Genetics* 47:1187-1198.

Westergaard, M. (1964). Studies on the mechanism of crossing over. I. Theoretical considerations. *Compt. Rend. Trav. Lab. Carlsberg* 34:359-405.

Wheeler, H. E. (1954a). Genetics and evolution of heterothallism in *Glomerella. Phytopathology* 44:342-345.

Wheeler, H. E. (1954b). Two additional mating reaction genes in *Glomerella. Phytopathology* 44:510 (abstr.).

Wheeler, H. E., and J. W. McGahen. (1952). Genetics of *Glomerella*. X. Genes affecting sexual reproduction. *Am. J. Botany* 39:110-119.

Wheeler, H. E., L. S. Olive, C. T. Ernest, and C. W. Edgerton. (1948). Genetics of *Glomerella*. V. Crosier and ascus development. *Am. J. Botany* 35:722-728.

Whitehouse, H. L. K. (1963). A theory of crossing-over by means of hybrid deoxyribonucleic acid. *Nature* 199:1034-1040.

Williams, E. B., and J. R. Shay. (1957). The relationship of genes for pathogenicity and certain other characters in *Venturia inaequalis* (Cke.) Wint. *Genetics* 42:704-711.

Wilson, C. M. (1952). Meiosis in *Allomyces. Bull. Torrey Botan. Club.* 79:139-159.

Wolf, F. T. (1953). The utilization of carbon and nitrogen compounds by *Ustilago zeae. Mycologia* 45:516-522.

Yaw, K. E., and V. M. Cutter, Jr. (1951). Crosses involving biochemically deficient mutants of *Allomyces arbuscula. Mycologia* 43:156-160.

Yu-Sun, C. C. C. (1964a). Nutritional studies of *Ascobolus immersus. Am. J. Botany* 51:231-237.

Yu-Sun, C. C. C. (1946b). Biochemical and morphological mutants of *Ascobolus immersus. Genetics* 50:987-998.

Zickler, H. (1952). Zur Entwicklungs Geschichte des Askomyceten *Bombardia lunata* Zckl. *Arch. Protistenk.* 98:1-70.

CHAPTER 17

Mechanisms of Inheritance

2. Heterokaryosis

ROWLAND H. DAVIS

*Department of Botany
University of Michigan
Ann Arbor, Michigan*

I. INTRODUCTION

The generally accepted definition of heterokaryosis is the coexistence of genetically different nuclei in cytoplasmic continuity with one another. Heterokaryosis is potentially a fundamental aspect of the biology of filamentous fungi, by virtue of their unique structure and mode of growth. The cells of an actively growing mycelium, whether multinucleate or uninucleate, are continuous with one another along hyphae through septal pores, and cytoplasmic streaming allows translocation of the products of nuclear activity, and in many cases, of the nuclei themselves. Therefore, many nuclei may come to take part in the determination of phenotype at a given point in the cytoplasm. In fact, the cell cannot be accepted without qualification as the unit of organization here. Instead, any mycelium must be viewed simultaneously as an integrated organism and as a population of nuclei in a morphologically patterned cytoplasmic environment. A large part of this review will be devoted to synthesizing these points of view.

The genetic system of fungi, as a consequence of coenocytic organization, is a very plastic one. As in haploid unicellular organisms, the large nuclear populations available to species of haploid fungi allow mutation to play a significant role in short-term adaptation. Genetic recombination mechanisms will, of course, increase variability over that available through mutation alone. However, the association of mutant and "normal" nuclei in a multinucleate cytoplasm makes dominant-recessive relations between genes possible. As a result, potentially valuable genetic variation is shielded from adverse natural selection, much as it is in heterozygous diploid organisms. The fact that fungi embody these attributes of haploid and diploid organisms is a major factor in the evolution of the group (cf. J. R. Raper, 1955).

The formation of heterokaryons may come about in several ways. One of the most common is through the occurrence of mutation. Since the nuclear population of any visible mycelium is large enough to assure mutation of at least one genetic locus of some nuclei, it is improbable that any fungal mycelium of this size is genetically homogeneous. Thus, mutation leads automatically to heterokaryosis, but the new nuclear types will, barring selection in their favor, be so low in frequency as to be undetectable on a gross level.

Heterokaryosis may be brought about in nature and in the laboratory by the fusion of vegetative cells; this is a method commonly used in genetic analysis. Since fusion of cells within a single hyphal system is very common, it is not surprising that related strains, differing by only a few genetic markers, will fuse and give rise to a heterokaryotic mycelium. While heterokaryosis may be limited to mycelium derived from the zone of fusion, there is much evidence (Dowding and Buller, 1940; Snider and Raper, 1958; Swiezynski and Day, 1960b) in various species that nuclear migration from the point of fusion throughout the original mycelia may take place. Since nuclei may divide in the course of migration, widesperad heterokaryotization may follow the fusion of a few hyphae. In nature, the most obvious heterokaryon formation by fusion of cells is the development of the dikaryon of many basidiomycetes; here, the heterokaryon is made up of binucleate cells, the nuclei of which are of different mating type, and which ultimately yield diploid nuclei prior to meiosis.

Finally, heterokaryosis may be a natural consequence of spore formation in many fungi. This takes place by the inclusion of nonidentical nuclei in a single spore subsequent to the meiotic divisions (e.g., *Neurospora tetrasperma, Podospora anserina*). In this way, heterokaryotic associations may be maintained for many sexual generations. In the asexual phase, this may be accomplished through the formation of multinucleate asexual spores.

II. THE STUDY OF HETEROKARYONS

A. Criteria for Heterokaryosis

Experimental tests as criteria for heterokaryosis are required to answer two related questions. The first is whether two genetically different strains have established heterokaryotic association. The second is whether a mycelium of unknown genetic constitution is a heterokaryon.

In both cases, the most rigorous test for heterokaryosis follows naturally from the definition of the term. A mycelium may be judged to be a heterokaryon if two (or more) distinct nuclear types can be shown to have coexisted in a single hypha or multinucleate conidium. This requires the isolation of the nuclear components in homokaryotic form from a culture derived from a single cytoplasmic unit; this is a test used in the original description of heterokaryosis by Burgeff (1912, 1914), followed by the studies of Hansen and Smith (1932). These authors went one step further: after resolving a naturally occurring heterokaryon into its components, they were able to resynthesize the heterokaryon from them and show that its phenotype and potentialities resembled those of the original mycelium.

If it is possible to isolate two homokaryotic components from single hyphal tips or single conidia, it excludes the possibility that a mycelium is in fact an intermingled pair of homokaryotic mycelia. If this test is negative, however, it is not necessarily significant, because (a) one nuclear type may be very rare; (b) the distribution of nuclei is such that they remain segregated despite the overlapping of phenotypic effects, or (c) one or both nuclear types may fail to survive in the homokaryotic condition [see particularly Burgeff (1914), who even then was able to appreciate the operation of a balanced-lethal system in heterokaryons]. In the latter case, a study of spore viability, or a series of matings to well-characterized homokaryons may be necessary to establish genetic heterogeneity.

Another difficulty which must be recognized is the segregation of cytoplasmically inherited variability. The only way in which to distinguish this from nuclear segregation is to see that the difference does not behave in a Mendelian manner in matings, or that it does not segregate with known genetic differences in the resolution of a heterokaryon through asexual transfers (Jinks, 1959). Many workers have overlooked this possibility when characterizing natural variation in fungi.

As mentioned previously, a coenocytic organization allows two or more types of nuclei to cooperate in the genetic determination of a single cytoplasm. Since dominance and recessiveness characterize such systems, a wild-type (normal) nucleus may mask the deficiencies of a mutant nucleus, and a heterokaryon will resemble the wild type. If two nuclei carrying nonallelic mutations are combined in a heterokaryon, the resulting phenotype will approach the wild-type condition. The latter behavior is designated "complementation." In fact, heterokaryons have been used widely in tests of allelism, as well as in the study of complex loci, alleles of which may complement to some extent through interaction of mutant proteins (see Catcheside, Volume I). The major initial work on complementation was that of Dodge (1942), with *Neurospora tetrasperma,* followed by that of Beadle and Coonradt (1944), with *N. crassa.* Dodge found that two slow-growing mutants were able to complement one another in heterokaryotic association to yield a rapidly growing mycelium. His proof of heterokaryosis was the isolation of both original strains and the heterokaryon in cultures derived from single multinucleate conidia. He interpreted the more vigorous growth of the heterokaryon as parallel to hybrid vigor, and proposed that a mutual supplementation of growth factors occurred between the components.

Beadle and Coonradt (1944) extended these findings to heterokaryons constituted of well-characterized nutritional mutants (e.g., pantothenate- and lysine-requiring strains) and came to the same conclusions. Complementation of genetic deficiencies was seen to be a regular consequence of heterokaryotic association. The criterion that these workers used for the heterokaryotic condition was based upon the observation that hyphal tip cultures from the heterokaryon, when mated with normal homokaryotic strains, showed that the presumed heterokaryon had indeed contained two nuclear types. However, they, and many workers since that time, have used the phenotypic consequences of heterokaryosis (complementation) as a good indication of nuclear association in a common cytoplasm. In order for complementation to be useful in this sense, it requires that the strains involved be different from each other and from the wild-type homokaryon; a combination of a wild-type and a recessive mutant strain, for instance, will not give phenotypic evidence of the latter's presence.

There are cases where complementation is clearly observed between two nutritional mutants, but one of the nuclear types is perhaps so rare, or the tendency of the nuclei to remain segregated in different hyphal tips is so great, that heterokaryosis is difficult to prove directly (e.g., J. R. Raper and San Antonio, 1954). In such cases, complementation is often the *only* indication of heterokaryosis, and the criterion is not reliable when applied to very restricted areas of the mycelium (Grindle, 1963; K. B. Raper and Fennell, 1953).

B. Measurement of Nuclear Ratios

In the study of heterokaryosis, an assessment of nuclear ratio is generally necessary. Because no method of recognizing genetically different nuclei by cytological means is available, the determination of frequencies is in most cases indirect, and involves certain assumptions.

The most common method of nuclear ratio determination is through an analysis of asexual spore frequency. In species where conidia are uninucleate [e.g., *Aspergillus nidulans, Penicillium notatum* (Pontecorvo, 1946)] or where all of several nuclei in a conidium are derivatives of one original nucleus [e.g., *A. oryzae* (Pontecorvo, 1946), *Fusarium oxysporum* (Garber et al., 1961)], the application of this method is quite straightforward. All that is required is plating of spores on media which allow discrimination of the significant genetic differences. However, several complications prevail. First, it must be assumed that nuclei of the mycelial population are not differentially incorporated into conidia (cf. Barron, 1963). Second, conidia, the formation of which in these species effects an absolute segregation of genetic differences, indicate nothing regarding the randomness of nuclear distribution in the mycelium. This is particularly serious in species of *Aspergillus* and *Penicillium,* because heterokaryotic inocula have a tendency to sector into homokaryotic regions (Pontecorvo, 1946; and see below). A test of the degree to which a mycelium is a mosaic of homokaryotic regions may be made by sampling spore populations from various points on its surface; some idea of the randomness of nuclear distribution may be obtained by determining frequencies of homokaryotic and heterokaryotic conidial heads (Pontecorvo, 1953; K. B. Raper and Fennell, 1953).

In *Neurospora crassa,* which has been used widely in the study of heterokaryosis, the situation is rather different. Conidial ratios are used to measure nuclear ratios, as they are in *Aspergillus* and *Penicillium,* and the same assumptions are made regarding the correspondence of nuclear ratios in mycelium and conidia. However, in most strains the macroconidial populations contain a large proportion of multinucleate units; the nuclear number varies from one to ten or more. The average number of nuclei per conidium in turn varies from approximately two to six, depending upon the conditions of growth (Huebschman, 1952), and may be determined cytologically. The multinucleate conidia allow a test of the randomness of nuclear associations, since, for any nuclear ratio, unique proportions of heterokaryotic and homokaryotic conidia may be predicted on the assumption of random nuclear distribution and compared to estimates of conidial frequencies found by plating techniques. Such an analysis has been performed by several workers (Prout *et al.,* 1953; Atwood and Mukai, 1955; Klein, 1958), and frequent small departures from random distribution, in the direction of excess homokaryotic conidia, were noted. These departures, however, were postulated to arise during conidial formation, and if this is accepted, a relatively random distribution of nuclei in the mycelium finds support in these experiments. This point is further substantiated by the work of Pittenger and Atwood (1956), who observed a remarkable stability of nuclear proportions during the growth of heterokaryons and concluded that nuclear mixing during growth is very efficient in this species.

The determination of nuclear ratios from conidial ratios of *Neurospora* according to the assumptions of random distribution of nuclei may be found in the article by Prout *et al.,* (1953). Atwood and Mukai (1955) have derived a simpler formula for nuclear ratio estimation, however, which takes into account the departures from randomness mentioned above. Since it is applicable in more cases, it has been more widely used.

A more direct method for determining nuclear ratios has been developed by Snider (1963) for the basidiomycete *Schizophyllum commune*. Because this species has no asexual spores, it was necessary to plate macerates of mycelia and to analyze the data as is done with conidial platings. The advantage of this method is that it circumvents the assumption that conidial and mycelial nuclear ratios are the same. Such a technique is probably applicable to other species in which the number of nuclei per cell, as in *S. commune*, is very low.

III. DOMINANCE IN HETEROKARYONS

The fact that the percentage of a nuclear type (or of any given allele) may vary continuously between 0 and 100% in heterokaryons makes fungi somewhat different from diploids, where only three ratios of two alleles (2:0, 1:1, and 0:2) may prevail. That the phenotype of a heterokaryon will vary with the ratio of the nuclear components was postulated in the classical investigations of Burgeff (1914) on varieties of *Phycomyces,* and of Hansen and Smith (1932) and Hansen (1938) on *Botrytis cinerea*. In both cases, the range of variation found between the pure extreme types from which heterokaryons were constituted was presumed on good evidence to be a reflection of the nuclear ratios of mycelia. Beadle and Coonradt (1944) formalized these relationships in *Neurospora crassa* and showed that wild-type growth rate of heterokaryons may be achieved with far less than 100% of nuclei carrying the wild-type allele of certain nutritional mutations. However, they indicate that the wild-type alleles of certain morphological mutations must be present in proportions greater than 50% for normal growth rates to be sustained. When two such mutants (nonallelic) were used to construct a heterokaryon, the heterokaryon failed under all circumstances to grow at a wild-type rate—presumably because the wild-type alleles of the mutations used could not both be in excess of 50% simultaneously.

While little has been done to study dominance quantitatively, several examples of the relationship between phenotype and nuclear ratio are available. Pittenger and Atwood (1956) showed that the wild-type allele of the *pan-1* (pantothenate-requiring) gene of *Neurospora* need be present in only 5% of the nuclei of a $pan\text{-}1^+ + pan\text{-}1^-$ heterokaryon to sustain normal growth rates. Furthermore, a direct relation was found between growth rate and nuclear ratio in the range 0–4% $pan\text{-}1^+$ nuclei.

A similar analysis has been performed by the author (Davis, 1957) on two nonallelic albino mutations (*al-1* and *al-2*) in *N. crassa*. Here, the carotenoid content of the conidial mass is related to the ratio of $al\text{-}1^+ \ al\text{-}2^-$ and $al\text{-}1^- \ al\text{-}2^+$ nuclei of the mycelium (Fig. 1). The optimal carotenoid content, which occurs at approximately 0.4 $al\text{-}1^- \ al\text{-}2^+$ nuclei, is similar to that of wild type strains.

In some species, such as *Aspergillus nidulans*, it is possible to study the colors of uninucleate conidia of heterokaryons constituted from spore-color mutants. In many cases, the spore color is determined by the genetic constitution of the nucleus the conidium contains, whereas with some mutations, the dominance relations of the heterokaryon extend to the phenotype of the individual spores elaborated by it, even though they contain single, haploid nuclei (Pontecorvo, 1946, 1953).

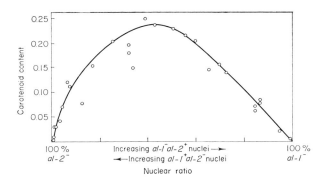

Fig. 1. Relationship of carotenoid content to nuclear ratio in *Neurospora* heterokaryons constituted of nuclei carrying nonallelic albino mutations, $al\text{-}1^-$ and $al\text{-}2^-$. $Al\text{-}1^-$ nuclei carry the wild-type allele of the other gene, and vice versa. Carotenoid content was measured as absorbance at 470 mμ in arbitary units for extracts of comparable amounts of material for each heterokaryon.

IV. GENETICS OF HETEROKARYON FORMATION

In filamentous fungi, vegetative nuclear associations may be studied in many species without particular reference to the sexuality of the organism. Because sexuality almost invariably involves the formation of a diploid nucleus, however, a heterokaryotic stage intervenes between the fusion of mating cells and the fusion of their nuclei. This stage may be very transitory; it may be extended somewhat when the pairs of haploid nuclei in the female sexual structure divide a number of times before nuclear fusions occur; or it may be a major phase of vegetative propagation of the organism. The last pattern is characteristic of most basidiomycetes, where sexual fusions of homokaryotic mycelia lead to the formation of a highly specialized heterokaryon, the dikaryon. In the dikaryon, the nuclei remain associated in pairs and the mycelium is capable both of indefinite vegetative growth and the development of fruiting bodies and sexual spores.

In heterothallic fungi, mating-type loci determine the possibility or outcome of sexual fusions. Usually, different alleles at one or more such loci are required if the mating is to culminate in the meiotic process. The selective advantage of such a system may be understood in its restriction of inbreeding. Because these loci in many ascomycetes may have an effect upon the fusion of gametes, it is not surprising that they may also have an effect upon the formation of vegetative heterokaryons. In the basidiomycetes, where sexual and vegetative activities overlap so much during the life cycle, the mating type loci exert profound effects upon the behavior of heterokaryons (cf. Chapter 15, pp. 491-493).

In addition to mating type loci, a number of genes have been described in ascomycetes and basidiomycetes whose effects are seen only in the formation or stability of vegetative heterokaryons. These, of course, may operate in any species, whether homothallic or heterothallic.

A. Ascomycetes

In *Neurospora crassa,* nuclei of like mating type (sexually incompatible) will readily form vegetative heterokaryons, while those of opposite mating type (sexually compatible) will not (for review, see Sansome, 1946; Whitehouse, 1949). In the latter case, if a heterokaryon is formed, complementation is poor because of highly disparate nuclear ratios (Gross, 1952), and the heterokaryon dissociates quite regularly if selective conditions do not stringently enforce the maintenance of the heterokaryotic condition. It is not surprising that heterokaryons with nuclei of like mating type are seen, since all nuclei of any homokaryon are of like mating type. That vegetative associations of sexually compatible nuclei do not occur with equal facility in this species, however, points to a special property of the female reproductive structure, where nuclei of opposite mating type necessarily coexist.

In *N. tetrasperma,* on the other hand, mating type heterokaryons are formed readily, and this accounts for the "secondary homothallism" of this species. Following meiosis, nuclei of opposite mating type are included in single spores (cf. Sansome, 1946), and cultures derived from single ascospores are self-fertile. This behavior suggests that the ability of mating type loci to restrict vegetative associations in *N. crassa* may be separable from their role in determining sexual associations. Few other ascomycetes have been investigated extensively in regard to this problem, although both patterns seen in *Neurospora* spp. are probably widespread.

Aside from the influence of mating type genes, any discussion of the genetic control of heterokaryosis in ascomycetes depends heavily upon what has been done with *Neurospora crassa.* The work done on this species, however, undoubtedly has relevance to all filamentous fungi.

Studies by Garnjobst and her co-workers have revealed two pairs of alleles (C/c and D/d) in *N. crassa* which influence heterokaryon formation. Here, identity of the alleles at both loci is required for strains to establish heterokaryotic association. A difference at either or both loci leads to poor or no complementation between auxotrophic strains (Garnjobst, 1953, 1955). Microscopic examination revealed that the fusion of cells of heterokaryon-negative combinations was not prevented, but instead, that fusion led to the death of one or both cells involved (Garnjobst and Wilson, 1956). In further studies (Wilson et al., 1961), an active substance was isolated from *CD* mycelia which would cause the death of cells of unlike genotype (with respect to the *C* and *D* loci) when injected into them. The evidence strongly indicates that the substance is a protein, possibly one which acts as an antigen in cells of a different genetic constitution. These loci have no noticeable effect upon sexual compatibility. It should be noted that the fitness of these genes and proteins in nature may not be based primarily upon their influence upon heterokaryon formation, but possibly upon other effects entirely. It is interesting that the same drastic response of cells which follows the fusion of unlike genotypes with respect to *C* and *D* is also seen upon the fusion of vegetative cells which are of different mating type (Garnjobst and Wilson, 1956).

Another study in *N. crassa* by Holloway (1955) has indicated the existence of at least four pairs of alleles with effects on the behavior of heterokaryons. The phenotypes of the various mixed cultures and heterokaryons were sufficiently different to allow a description of the genes' effects in regard to (1) heterokaryon formation, (2) the onset of heterokaryotic growth, (3) vigor of growth, and (4) maintenance of heterokaryosis. The relationship or identity of these genes and those described by Garnjobst is not known.

An allelic pair, *I/i,* has been described by Pittenger and Brawner (1961), the effects of which resemble one of those described by Holloway. Heterokaryons constituted of *I* and *i* nuclei are stable in their nuclear ratio only when the former type is in a frequency of less than 30%. When the frequency of *I* nuclei is greater than 30%, there is regularly a nonadaptive increase of *I* (with respect to nutritional deficiencies carried by it) leading to homokaryosis and a cessation of growth. No nutritional regime has been found to alter this pattern, nor have extracts of the *I* strain been found to inhibit the growth of *i* mycelia. Although this pattern has been denoted "heterokaryon incompatibility," it may be a symptom of competition for intracellular metabolites in the same fashion as that in *pan* + *pan m* heterokaryons (see Section V, B).

It is quite clear to *Neurospora* geneticists that many genetic effects, aside from those described above, prevail in heterokaryotic associations; thus, it is regularly found that stocks of different genetic background rarely form heterokaryons which complement well. Such a situation is known to exist in other species. For example, in an extensive study of heterokaryon compatibility among independent strains of the *Aspergillus nidulans* group, Grindle (1963) found few pairs which were able to form heterokaryons. If, in line with a suggestion made above, heterokaryon incompatibility were a pleiotropic effect of genes having other functions, evolutionary diversification of a fungal species would lead naturally to heterokaryon incompatibility.

B. Basidiomycetes

In basidiomycetes, specialized gametangia are reduced or absent entirely (particularly the female). The first step in the sexual process takes place, therefore, as the formation of a heterokaryon between cells which are—or are capable of becoming—strictly vegetative entities. As noted before, the heterokaryon thus formed is itself capable of indefinite vegetative propagation.

The mating type system of many basidiomycetes is highly developed, characteristically with one or two loci each of which have many alleles. The effects of these genes appear not to restrict cell fusions and the formation of heterokaryons but to determine the phenotype of the heterokaryon so formed. In the case of species where there are two mating type loci, A and B (e.g., *Schizophyllum commune, Coprinus lagopus*), the remainder of the sexual process will be carried out normally only in the dikaryon, where there are different alleles at both loci. In a very general sense, this is equivalent to the heterokaryotic cells in the fertilized female sexual structure of heterothallic ascomycetes. Two properties of the dikaryon and its formation may be noted. First, upon the fusion of sexually compatible mycelia, nuclear migration from each mycelium into the other takes place, leading to widespread "dikaryotization" of the two mycelia. Second, the further growth of the mycelia is characterized by conjugate nuclear division in binucleate cells, often with clamp connections, which ensures a strict equality of the two nuclear types in new cells. As might be expected, genetic complementation between the two nuclear types may be observed easily with the proper materials (cf. J. R. Raper, 1953).

In confrontations of *S. commune* mycelia having common A factors and different B factors, nuclear migration takes place at a rate similar to that seen in the sexually compatible pairing (Snider and Raper, 1958). However, the propagation of a "common-A" heterokaryon leads to a mycelium which is less vigorous than the homokaryon, and which has cells that are uninucleate, like those of the homokaryon, rather than binucleate. Few or no clamp connections are seen. The nuclear ratios vary widely from point to point in the common-A mycelium; perhaps as a consequence of the disparate ratios or the irregular distribution of nuclei, complementation between the nuclei is poor or nonexistent (J. R. Raper and San Antonio,

1954). In *C. lagopus*, the common-*A* heterokaryon does show complementation between nuclei, and is occasionally fertile (Swiezynski and Day, 1960a).

The heterokaryon formed by fusions of mycelia having common *B* factors and different *A* factors shows a very different behavior from the common-*A* heterokaryon. First, nuclear migration is very restricted, and, in order to propagate the heterokaryon, isolations must be made from the area of fusion of the two homokaryotic mycelia. This is true both of *S. commune* (Parag and Raper, 1960) and of *C. lagopus* (Swiezynski and Day, 1960a). When propagated, however, the common-*B* heterokaryon is relatively stable during growth (though sectoring may occur) and in both species mentioned, genetic complementation occurs. In addition, true or imperfect clamp connections form during the growth of these heterokaryons, and for reasons which may not be the same in different instances, fruiting is occasionally seen (Parag and Raper, 1960; Swiezynski and Day, 1960a).

Heterokaryons formed between strains having common *A* and common *B* factors (common-*AB*) are, formally, the only ones comparable to those of heterothallic ascomycetes in which mating type genes are in common. Although complementation was seen between nuclei of like mating type in *S. commune*, there was originally difficulty in obtaining other evidence that two nuclei were present in heterokaryotic association (J. R. Raper and San Antonio, 1954). Recently, Middleton (1964) has obtained better evidence of heterokaryosis between nuclei of like mating type, and similar results have been obtained by Swiezynski and Day (1960a) for *C. lagopus*. Common-*AB* heterokaryons are similar in morphology to the homokaryon in *S. commune*. It appears that nuclear migration is very much restricted in common-*AB* heterokaryons, as in the common-*B*, and nuclear ratios are disparate and irregular, much as they are in the common-*A*. However, as noted above, the nuclei do show genetic complementation.

It is clear that nuclear migration and complementation are not well correlated in *S. commune*. This may be seen in a comparison of common-*AB*, common-*B* and common-*A* heterokaryons. In the first two, migration is restricted, but complementation is good; in the last, migration is extensive, but complementation is poor. Complementation may be more directly related to the ability of mycelia to translocate cytoplasmic constituents from cell to cell; if they are not able to do so, complementation will be poor unless the cells contain nuclei of both types (see Middleton, 1964). Further comparison indicates that different *A* factors are required for the initiation of clamp connections (as in the common-*B* or the dikaryon); different *B* factors are required for extensive nuclear migration (as in common-*A* or dikaryon confrontations) (Fincham and Day, 1963).

Few studies have been reported which deal with genes restricting heterokaryon formation in basidiomycetes which can be understood apart from the sexual compatibility system. This would be expected, inasmuch as vegetative heterokaryosis is a necessary phase of the reproductive cycle, in contrast to many ascomycetes, where vegetative heterokaryosis may be primarily restricted to nuclei which are *sexually* incompatible. However, in *Rhizoctonia solani,* a homothallic basidiomycete, Whitney and Parmeter (1963) have described patterns of heterokaryon formation among natural isolates. They found that two groups of strains could be distinguished between which heterokaryon formation took place, but within each of which recognizable heterokaryon formation did not take place. Heterokaryons, when formed, were quite stable, but the relation of these results with sexuality in heterothallic basidiomycetes is not clear. The results are distinct from the ascomycete pattern, however, where a similarity, rather than a difference, between strains is required for stable heterokaryosis.

V. NUCLEAR RATIOS AND GROWTH OF HETEROKARYONS

A. General Remarks

Heterokaryosis, because it allows a continuous variation of nuclear ratio and phenotype between various extremes, is well fitted to serve the requirements of short- and long-term adaptation. A major point of interest is how significant changes of nuclear ratio take place during growth. Certain points relevant to any species will be mentioned here, and these will subsequently be used in the analysis of specific patterns known to occur in various fungi.

The first thing to be recognized is the relationship possible between the *genetic* mosaicism of a heterokaryon (varying between the conditions of dikaryosis in basidiomycetes, through random distribution of nuclei, to obvious sectors) and the *phenotypic* mosaicism among regions or among cells. The degree of phenotypic heterogeneity of a heterokaryon may be different for different characters, since the various effects of a single nucleus in a mycelium are not necessarily coextensive. Any phenotypic heterogeneity among cells of a growing heterokaryon will be magnified by selective conditions which favor one or both homokaryons; competition between regions will lead to changes in nuclear ratios or distribution. Thus, what is termed nuclear selection, where it occurs, is probably in most cases selection in favor of cells of a certain range of nuclear ratio. However, some workers have thought of nuclear selection as a matter of differential division rates of nuclei within a single cell (Rees and Jinks, 1952).

The features of mycelial growth that are relevant to an analysis of nuclear selection are as follows:

1. Hyphal Fusion

The ability of a heterokaryon to retain a well-mixed nuclear population, and thus phenotypic uniformity, depends in part on fusions among hyphae near the frontier and the number of nuclei per cell. Any statistical tendency toward segregation of nuclear types during branching of hyphae will be reversed to a greater or lesser extent by fusions (Pontecorvo, 1946, 1953; Pittenger and Atwood, 1956; Kiritani, 1959).

2. Cytoplasmic Streaming

The growth of filamentous fungi is correlated with cytoplasmic streaming; this will tend to randomize the nuclear population if the nuclei move freely with the stream (Pittenger and Atwood, 1956). Even if nuclei are not carried easily with the cytoplasm, the movement of cytoplasm will facilitate phenotypic homogeneity over large regions. If this is so, selection on a "cellular" level will be dampened.

In this connection, it has been demonstrated in cutting experiments (Ryan *et al.*, 1943) that the growth of hyphae at the frontier of a culture of *Neurospora crassa* is dependent upon about 1 cm of the mycelium proximal to them. This indicates nonautonomy of the hyphal tips in their own growth. Moreover, the author (Davis, 1957) has made experiments indicating that the dependence of hyphal tip growth upon proximal regions is less as the growth rate is reduced; that is, hyphal tips become more autonomous under these conditions. If this is accepted, variation of nuclear ratio among hyphal tips will lead, at lower growth rates, to greater selective differences among them.

3. Nuclear Division

Nuclear division is, of course, the ultimate focus of selection, and aside from differences among nuclei in division rate per se, changes in nuclear ratios must reflect differences in division rates among regions of different nuclear constitution. In many fungi, particularly ascomycetes, nuclear division takes place rapidly in hyphal tips and for a greater or lesser distance behind them. In fact, division is reported to be simultaneous for the many nuclei in hyphal tips of *Penicillium cyclopium* (Rees and Jinks, 1952), a finding which indicates that the timing of nuclear division is determined by the common cytoplasmic milieu. The effectiveness with which environmental conditions influence nuclear ratios may depend upon the spatial relation of the zone of division and the zone of the mycelium performing biosynthetic activities upon which division depends. The more these zones overlap, the more quickly the nuclear ratio would be expected to respond to selection. However, no critical experiments have been done on this point.

B. Nuclear Behavior in Neurospora Heterokaryons

Beadle and Coonradt (1944), without critical evidence, proposed that *N. crassa* heterokaryons would automatically adjust nuclear ratios during growth to the optimal range for highest growth rate. They felt that the nuclear ratio of individual hyphae would vary considerably; that natural selection of those within the optimal range would take place, and that the nuclear ratio of the heterokaryon as a whole would thus be determined. Within the optimal range, the nuclear ratio would be free to vary, although some of their experiments are based upon the assumption that this variation within a single culture is limited. This general construct has been designated the "hyphal selection" hypothesis; it entails the basic assumption that the growth rates of hyphae are determined by their own nuclear ratio.

The hyphal selection hypothesis was subsequently tested by Pittenger and Atwood (1956). By methods allowing control of the initial nuclear ratio of nutritionally mutant types (Atwood and Pittenger, 1955; Pittenger et al., 1955) within the suboptimal range, they were able to demonstrate stable, suboptimal growth rates of heterokaryons, where the growth rate was limited by the scarcity of one of the nuclear components. Within the optimal range, nuclear ratios were also stable. These findings indicate either that the nuclear ratios of all hyphae at the frontier are extremely similar (allowing no selection) or that the hyphae at the frontier are not autonomous. Pittenger and Atwood supported the latter view by demonstrating considerable variation among hyphal tips after isolation from the frontier, and concluded that, in the intact heterokaryon, growth rates of frontier hyphae are determined by the "proportions within a larger domain" proximal to them. They explain that cytoplasmic streaming could account for this relationship, and that all that is required beyond this is that the nuclear types have the same rate of division. With this material, then, the hyphal selection hypothesis was contraindicated, and the well-integrated nature (i.e., lack of phenotypic mosaicism) of these heterokaryons of *N. crassa* was demonstrated.

The generality of these conclusions for *N. crassa* heterokaryons depends upon how well the nuclear types used represent the species. In fact, Pittenger and Atwood found that nuclear ratios of $nic\text{-}2^- + nic\text{-}2^+$ heterokaryons could not be maintained in the suboptimal range of $nic\text{-}2^+$ nuclei. Therefore, adaptive hyphal selection may operate in this case.

It has become increasingly clear that another type of behavior (Ryan and Lederberg, 1946; Ryan, 1946; Davis, 1960b; Pittenger and Brawner, 1961) is common, which can be understood neither in terms of hyphal selection nor in terms of stability. In these cases, a nonadaptive change of nuclear ratio is seen, and one example of this behavior familiar to the author is summarized below.

Two strains of *N. crassa* were used in this work, one the common *pan* (pantothenate-requiring) strain, the other a one-gene mutant derived from it, *pan m*. The difference between them is that *pan m* is able to grow normally on pantothenate concentrations on which *pan* cannot grow at all; *pan m* could be shown to take pantothenate from the medium at lower concentrations (Davis, 1960a). Therefore, on limited concentrations of pantothenate, *pan m* would be expected to have a selective advantage over *pan*. However, heterokaryons constituted of the two nuclei, when grown on limited pantothenate, regularly display a cyclic pattern of growth: rapid growth, correlated with a high proportion of *pan m* nuclei, alternates with slowing or cessation of growth in which there is a nonadaptive increase of the *pan* component (Davis, 1960b). This behavior is not seen, either in respect to growth rate or to nuclear ratio, if pantothenate concentration is unlimiting—under such conditions, both are constant for long distances. Also, both nuclear types maintain stable ratios with nuclear types carrying the wild-type allele of the *pan* mutation.

It is clear from these data that the cyclic behavior is a manifestation of competition for intracellular pantothenate or its derivatives. Thus, *pan* nuclei are more efficient in utilizing intracellular pantothenate for growth, even though *pan m* nuclei are responsible for its uptake from the medium. This leads to overgrowths of the *pan* component during which intracellular pantothenate becomes depleted and the heterokaryon ceases growth. This is followed by the initiation of growth by a few hyphae (Davis, 1960b) with higher proportions of *pan m* nuclei.

The renewed growth of the heterokaryon is best understood in terms of the hyphal selection hypothesis. It is precisely at a stationary frontier, where hyphal fusion and streaming of cytoplasm are much reduced, that phenotypic mosaicism would be expected to develop, and selection to favor hyphae with advantageous nuclear ratios. However, an explanation of the overgrowth of the *pan* nucleus during the other phase must start with the premise that pantothenate concentration is, at best, uniform throughout the active part of the mycelium (but probably more concentrated in regions with more *pan m* nuclei). Under these conditions, either *pan* nuclei divide faster in all cells, or phenotypic mosaicism develops among regions only with respect to utilization of pantothenate (and not to its rate of uptake). While intracellular pantothenate lasts, therefore, *pan* nuclei, or cells with more *pan* nuclei, are at an advantage.

Many such cases have been described (see above), the original one being that of Ryan and Lederberg (1946), who used heterokaryons of leucine-requiring and back-mutant (leucine-independent) strains. In all these cases, the nuclei were closely related and showed, in heterokaryons, the opposite of the behavior expected on the basis of the homokaryotic phenotypes.

In *Neurospora*, then, several varieties of behavior have been observed. *Neurospora* stands out in that purposeful selection in favor of one component of a heterokaryon during growth is not as easy a thing to achieve as it is in some other species (see below). This is probably a reflection of the fast growth of *Neurospora*, with its correlates: a relative homogeneity of the nuclear distribution and of the phenotypes of growing hyphae (Pittenger and Atwood, 1956).

C. Nuclear Behavior in Heterokaryons of Other Species

Many other species which have been studied in regard to nuclear selection show behavior which is usually compatible with the hyphal selection hypothesis.

The experience of those working with *Aspergillus* and *Penicillium* spp. has shown that the maintenance of the heterokaryotic condition usually requires that the heterokaryon have a selective advantage over both homokaryotic components (Pontecorvo, 1946, 1953; Jinks, 1952a). If the homokaryotic components have an equal (or greater) selective advantage, pronounced sectoring appears very early in growth. This behavior is interpreted to mean that the frontier is composed of homo- and heterokaryotic hyphae; the latter are continually resolving into the homokaryotic components with hyphal branching. Because hyphal fusions do not occur frequently enough to compensate for the segregation of nuclear types, only selection in favor of the heterokaryon will maintain a mixed nuclear population (Pontecorvo, 1946, 1953). This conclusion entails the assumption that considerable phenotypic heterogeneity develops at the frontier in these species and that differential rates of nuclear division are a property of hyphae, not of the nuclei themselves.

A more complex behavior was demonstrated by Jinks (1952a), who was able, by continuous variation of the composition of the medium, to show regular adjustments in the nuclear ratio of *Penicillium cyclopium* heterokaryons. The changes were those expected on the basis of the growth rates of the homokaryotic components. While this behavior is consistent with the hyphal selection hypothesis, Rees and Jinks (1952) felt that the two nuclear types in a given cell would have different probabilities of division, and that nuclear selection was thus direct. Much the same pattern of nuclear ratio change in response to selection has been observed by Kiritani (1959) in *Aspergillus oryzae,* by Rizet and Engelmann (1949) in *Podospora anserina,* by Tuveson and Garber (1961) in *Fusarium oxysporum* f. *pisi,* and by Tuveson and Coy (1961) in *Cephalosporium mycophilum*. It is undoubtedly a common pattern throughout the fungi.

In *C. mycophilum,* certain heterokaryons constituted of nuclei carrying nonallelic nutritional deficiencies were found to be incapable of continued growth on unsupplemented medium (Tuveson and Coy, 1963). This indicates that segregation of nuclear types during growth is so pronounced that even selection in favor of the heterokaryon is ineffective. This is not the complete explanation, however, because there is also evidence of nonadaptive overgrowth of one nuclear type. While this overgrowth may be eliminated by the addition of nutrients required by the other nuclear type, the segregation of nuclei in hyphal tips is still seen. However, heterokaryosis does prevail here, since rare heterokaryotic hyphal tips can be isolated. Moreover, diploid formation can be observed, and, in fact, diploids may be selected for on unsupplemented medium.

Patterns of nuclear behavior in the basidiomycetes *Schizophyllum commune* and *Coprinus lagopus* have been described in Section IV, B in relation to the phenotypic effects of mating type genes. Most of these patterns appear to be explainable in terms of the efficiency of nuclear mixing and of cytoplasmic streaming during growth. The most stable type of heterokaryon, as noted before, is the dikaryon. Nuclear selection may play a role in the behavior of the other types of heterokaryon, however, and where it occurs, it appears to be adaptive (Middleton, 1964; Swiezynski and Day, 1960a).

D. Nuclear Behavior and the Expression of Mutations

Because both the mechanics of growth and the nuclear types involved determine nuclear relationships in heterokaryons, no single rule can encompass all behavior. It is instructive to consider, however, the patterns discussed above in regard to their effect upon the expression of mutations which occur in a growing mycelium. First, where hyphal selection prevails, mutations conferring a higher growth rate will tend to form sectors, and those which do not will become buried in the population of normal nuclei (see Pontecorvo, 1946). Second, where a stability of ratios is maintained despite environmental circumstances, recessive mutations will be masked in their expression, but will be maintained. They may be expected to accumulate at a rate proportional to the mutation rate. Finally, where potentially advantageous mutations are selected against, as in the case of *pan m* in *Neurospora,* the accumulation of mutations, and certainly their expression, will be counteracted (Davis, 1960a). If such behavior is at all common, it may explain the stability of many fungal species. An intimation of factors operating to this end is seen in *Schizophyllum commune.* Homokaryons of this species are quite stable; few mutations gain expression in the normal course of growth. In the common-*A* heterokaryon, however, many morphological mutants may be observed in older regions of the mycelium (see particularly J. R. Raper *et al.,* 1958). The mutants found are recessive, and are rarely seen in other conditions. The appearance of these mutants has been shown not to be the result of an elevated mutation rate (Dick and Raper, 1961). It must be concluded that the multiplication and phenotypic expression of the mutant nuclei is allowed in the common-A heterokaryon, and correspondingly suppressed in mycelia homokaryotic for mating type loci (common-AB). The reason for this difference is related, in part, to the fact that complementation (dominance relationships) between nuclei is very poor in the common-A heterokaryon, in contrast to the homokaryon (see p. 576). Thus the expression of these recessive mutants may be facilitated because of the interference with dominance relationships. Further, most of the mutants isolated from common-A heterokaryons are unable to accept migrating nuclei from other mycelia, even, perhaps, from the cells nearby in the mycelium from which the mutants arose. Under the conditions of aged common-A mycelia, mutant expression would require only that certain mutant cells have the ability to grow more than the cells around them. Because the mutants may *contribute* nuclei to other cells, however, a single mutational event may come to be represented by many secondary areas of mutant phenotype in a common-A heterokaryon, where migration is efficient. In the common-AB mycelium, migration is not as efficient and mutants would be restricted to an area near their point of origin.

VI. HETEROKARYOSIS AS A MECHANISM OF NATURAL VARIATION

While the demonstration of heterokaryosis may be credited to Burgeff (1912, 1914; see Bistis, 1960), the significance of heterokaryosis in nature was first fully appreciated by Hansen and Smith (1932), working with isolates of *Botrytis cinerea*. Their paper and others following it (Hansen, 1938; Hansen and Snyder, 1943) were important in showing that heterokaryosis, and the dissociation of nuclear components upon conidial formation, could substitute to a certain extent in imperfect fungi for syngamy and meiosis. Some of the early work of Hansen and his co-workers is open to question in that it did not eliminate the possibility that cytoplasmic, rather than nuclear, differences were operating. This possibility has been given some force by Jinks (1959), who showed in imperfect aspergilli, that heterokaryons and mycelia containing variable non-Mendelian elements are indistinguishable by the criteria used by Hansen and his co-workers. However, heterokaryosis must be assigned a major role in the variation of imperfect fungi and, by analogy, the significance is the same for all coenocytic fungi in their vegetative growth. While Hansen (1938) concentrated upon pairs of common morphological variants of imperfect fungi found in heterokaryotic association (the "dual phenomenon"), it became increasingly clear, particularly with the work of Beadle and Coonradt

(1944), that many genetic differences may become associated in an adaptive way. In terms of population genetics, this allows a system of balanced (or "adaptive") polymorphism to develop, in which heterokaryons become selectively more advantageous than homokaryons containing any single nuclear type available to the species. This pattern results from the accumulation of recessive mutations with time, together with complementation among pairs of nuclei. Selection will operate to shift the frequencies of nuclear types in the species and within individual thalli (see Section V, C). Because the heterokaryotic condition is favored, however, neither component will be totally lost through continued selective pressure. In thinking of heterokaryosis as a substitute for sex, it should be noted (Jinks, 1952a; Buxton, 1956) that the variability of the natural population in the absence of sexual or parasexual recombination is limited by the nuclear types already available and the mutations derived from them. And, equally as important, heterokaryosis in nature will be further limited by any genes which arise to prevent it. The latter point appears to be very significant in light of the experiments of Grindle (1963) (see p. 576). Thus heterokaryosis is more legitimately a substitute for heterozygosity in maintaining variability than for sex in creating it.

For a system of this sort to be of great adaptive significance, it requires the regular expression of variation. In the imperfect fungi, and in the asexual phase of perfect fungi, this is accomplished through the formation of asexual spores containing relatively few nuclei. It was clear to Hansen (1938) that the ease with which the components of a heterokaryon could be dissociated by single conidial isolations depended in part upon the number of nuclei per conidium. One extreme of this point is seen in *Aspergillus nidulans,* which has uninucleate conidia, and in which, consequently, no heterokaryotic spores are formed. As nuclear number increases, the probability decreases that a spore from a heterokaryon will contain all of one type of nucleus, although a large proportion of homokaryotic spores are seen in most fungi studied. A balance is achieved in many species such that the heterokaryotic associations are maintained in asexual dissemination while the components are also expressed as homokaryons.

In fungi whose conidia are uninucleate, or the nuclei of which derive from a single nucleus by mitosis, any tendency for the spores to remain joined after abstriction will encourage the maintenance of heterokaryotic associations. Jinks (1952b) was able to demonstrate heterokaryosis in a culture of *Penicillium cyclopium* derived from an airborne inoculum, and concluded that a group or pair of uninucleate, genetically different spores was its probable origin.

The dynamics of selection during serial mass conidial transfers were studied by Davis (1959) in *Neurospora crassa*, a species with multinucleate conidia. The experiments showed that absolute selection against one homokaryotic conidial type would remove it from the population only slowly; ten to twenty transfers were required to rid the population of it entirely. This could happen, however, only if the heterokaryotic conidia had no selective advantage over the homokaryon being selected for. Algebraic considerations and experimental tests showed that the slightest advantage of the heterokaryons would entail the permanence of the "non-adaptive" nuclear type. Since this "heterokaryotic vigor"—to a greater or lesser degree—may be expected to be the rule in nature, it will not be surprising to find heterokaryosis in most natural populations of fungi, and for much the same reasons that a large amount of heterozygosis is found in populations of sexually reproducing diploid organisms (Dobzhansky, 1953; Davis, 1959).

REFERENCES

Atwood, K. C., and F. Mukai. (1955). Nuclear distribution in conidia of *Neurospora* heterokaryons. *Genetics* **40**:438-443.

Atwood, K. C., and T. H. Pittenger. (1955). The efficiency of nuclear mixing during heterokaryon formation in *Neurospora crassa*. *Am. J. Botany* **42**:496-500.

Barron, G. L. (1963). Distribution of nuclei in a heterocaryon of *Penicillium expansum*. *Nature* **200**:282-283.

Beadle, G. W., and V. L. Coonradt. (1944). Heterocaryosis in *Neurospora crassa*. *Genetics* **29**:291-308.

Bistis, G. N. (1960). The concept of heterokaryosis in the fungi: the historical record. *Am. Naturalist* **94**:443-444.

Burgeff, H. (1912). Über Sexualität, Variabilität, und Vererbung bei *Phycomyces nitens*. *Ber. Deut. Botan. Ges.* **30**:679-685.

Burgeff, H. (1914). Untersuchungen über Variabilität, Sexualität und Erblichkeit bei *Phycomyces nitens* Kunze. *Flora (Jena)* **107**:259-316.

Buxton, E. W. (1956). Heterokaryosis and parasexual recombination in pathogenic strains of *Fusarium oxysporum*. *J. Gen. Microbiol.* **15**:133-139.

Davis, R. H. (1957). Unpublished work.

Davis, R. H. (1959). Asexual selection in *Neurospora crassa*. *Genetics* **46**:1291-1308.

Davis, R. H. (1960a). Adaptation in pantothenate-requiring *Neurospora*. I. A gene modifying pantothenate mutants. *Am. J. Botany* **47**:351-357.

Davis, R. H. (1960b). Adaptation in pantothenate-requiring *Neurospora*. II. Nuclear competition during adaptation. *Am. J. Botany* **47**:648-654.

Dick, S., and J. R. Raper. (1961). Origin of expressed mutations in *Schizophyllum commune*. *Nature* **189**:81-82.

Dobzhansky, T. (1953). "Genetics and the Origin of Species," 364 pp. Columbia Univ. Press, New York.

Dodge, B. O. (1942). Heterocaryotic vigor in *Neurospora*. *Bull. Torrey Botan. Club* **69**:75-91.

Dowding, E. S., and A. H. R. Buller. (1940). Nuclear migration in *Gelasinospora*. *Mycologia* **32**:471-488.

Fincham, J. R. S., and P. R. Day. (1963). "Fungal Genetics," 300 pp. F. A. Davis, Philadelphia, Pennsylvania.
Garber, E. D., E. G. Wyttenbach, and T. S. Dhillon. (1961). Genetics of phytopathogenic fungi. V. Heterocaryons involving formae of *Fusarium oxysporum*. *Am. J. Botany* **48**:325-329.
Garnjobst, L. (1953). Genetic control of heterocaryosis in *Neurospora crassa*. *Am. J. Botany* **40**:607-614.
Garnjobst, L. (1955). Further analysis of genetic control of heterocaryosis in *Neurospora crassa*. *Am. J. Botany* **42**:444-448.
Garnjobst, L., and J. F. Wilson. (1956). Heterocaryosis and protoplasmic incompatibility in *Neurospora crassa*. *Proc. Natl. Acad. Sci. U.S.* **42**:613-618.
Grindle, M. (1963). Heterokaryon incompatibility of unrelated strains in the *Aspergillus nidulans* group. *Heredity* **18**:191-204.
Gross, S. R. (1952). Heterokaryosis between opposite mating types in *Neurospora crassa*. *Am. J. Botany* **39**:574-577.
Hansen, H. N. (1938). The dual phenomenon in the Fungi Imperfecti. *Mycologia* **30**:442-455.
Hansen, H. N., and R. E. Smith. (1932). The mechanism of variation in the Fungi Imperfecti. *Phytopathology* **22**:953-964.
Hansen, H. N., and W. C. Snyder. (1943). The dual phenomenon and sex in *Hypomyces solani* f. cucurbitae. *Am. J. Botany* **30**:419-422.
Holloway, B. W. (1955). Genetic control of heterocaryosis in *Neurospora crassa*. *Genetics* **40**:117-129.
Huebschman, C. (1952). A method for varying the average number of nuclei in the conidia of *Neurospora crassa*. *Mycologia* **44**:599-604.
Jinks, J. L. (1952a). Heterokaryosis: A system of adaptation in wild fungi. *Proc. Roy. Soc.* **B140**:83-99.
Jinks, J. L. (1952b). Heterokaryosis in wild *Penicillium*. *Heredity* **6**:77-87.
Jinks, J. L. (1959). The genetic basis of "duality" in imperfect fungi. *Heredity* **15**:525-528.
Kiritani, K. (1959). Selection of fitter type nuclei in heterocaryons of *Aspergillus oryzae*. *Z. Vererbungslehre* **90**:182-189.
Klein, D. T. (1958). Randomness of nuclear distribution in conidia of *Neurospora* heterokaryons. *Z. Vererbungslehre* **89**:323-327.
Middleton, R. B. (1964). Evidences of common-AB heterokaryosis in *Schizophyllum commune*. *Am. J. Botany* **51**:379-387.
Parag, Y., and J. R. Raper. (1960). Genetic recombination in a common-B cross of *Schizophyllum commune*. *Nature* **188**:765-766.
Pittenger, T. H., and K. C. Atwood. (1956). Stability of nuclear proportions during growth of *Neurospora* heterokaryons. *Genetics*. **41**:227-241.
Pittenger, T. H., and T. G. Brawner. (1961). Genetic control of nuclear selection in *Neurospora* heterokaryons. *Genetics* **46**:1645-1663.
Pittenger, T. H., A. W. Kimball, and K. C. Atwood. (1955). Control of nuclear ratios in *Neurospora* heterokaryons. *Am. J. Botany* **42**:954-958.
Pontecorvo, G. (1946). Genetic systems based on heterocaryosis. *Cold Spring Harbor Symp. Quant. Biol.* **11**:193-201.
Pontecorvo, G. (1953). The genetics of *Aspergillus nidulans*. *Advan. Genet.* **5**:141-238.
Prout, T., C. Huebschman, H. Levene, and F. J. Ryan. (1953). The proportions of nuclear types in *Neurospora* heterocaryons as determined by plating conidia. *Genetics* **38**:518-529.

Raper, J. R. (1953). Tetrapolar sexuality. *Quart. Rev. Biol.* **28**:233-259.
Raper, J. R. (1955). Heterokaryosis and sexuality in fungi. *Trans. N.Y. Acad. Sci.* [2] **17**:627-635.
Raper, J. R., and J. P. San Antonio. (1954). Heterokaryotic mutagenesis in Hymenomycetes. I. Heterokaryosis in *Schizophyllum commune*. *Am. J. Botany* **41**:69-86.
Raper, J. R., J. P. San Antonio, and P. G. Miles. (1958). The expression of mutations in common-A heterokaryons of *Schizophyllum commune*. *Z. Vererbungslehre* **89**:540-558.
Raper, K. B., and D. I. Fennell. (1953). Heterokaryosis in *Aspergillus*. *J. Elisha Mitchell Sci. Soc.* **69**:1-29.
Rees, H., and J. L. Jinks. (1952). The mechanism of variation in *Penicillium* heterokaryons. *Proc. Roy. Soc.* **B140**:100-106.
Rizet, G., and C. Engelmann. (1949). Contribution à l'étude génétique d'un Ascomycète tétrasporé: *Podospora anserina* (Ces.) Rehm. *Rev. Cytol. Biol. Vegetales* **11**: 201-304.
Ryan, F. J. (1946). Back-mutation and adaptation of nutritional mutants. *Cold Spring Harbor Symp. Quant. Biol.* **11**:215-227.
Ryan, F. J., and J. Lederberg. (1946). Reverse mutations and adaptation in leucineless *Neurospora*. *Proc. Natl. Acad. Sci. U.S.* **32**:163-173.
Ryan, F. J., G. W. Beadle, and E. L. Tatum. (1943). The tube method of measuring the growth rate of *Neurospora*. *Am. J. Botany* **30**:784-799.
Sansome, E. R. (1946). Heterokaryosis, mating-type factors, and sexual reproduction in *Neurospora*. *Bull. Torrey Botan. Club* **73**:397-409.
Snider, P. J. (1963). Estimation of nuclear ratios directly from heterokaryotic mycelia in *Schizophyllum*. *Am. J. Botany* **50**:255-262.
Snider, P. J., and J. R. Raper. (1958). Nuclear migration in the Basidiomycete *Schizophyllum commune*. *Am. J. Botany* **45**:538-546.
Swiezynski, K. M., and P. R. Day. (1960a). Heterokaryon formation in *Coprinus lagopus*. *Genet. Res.* **1**:114-128.
Swiezynski, K. M., and P. R. Day. (1960b). Migration of nuclei in *Coprinus lagopus*. *Genet. Res.* **1**:129-139.
Tuveson, R. W., and D. O. Coy. (1961). Heterocaryosis and somatic recombination in *Cephalosporium mycophylum*. *Mycologia* **53**:244-253.
Tuveson, R. W., and D. O. Coy. (1963). Hyphal tip isolation as a criterion for heterocaryosis in *Cephalosporium mycophylum*. *Mycologia* **55**:402-414.
Tuveson, R. W., and E. D. Garber. (1961). Genetics of phytopathogenic fungi. IV. Experimentally induced alterations in nuclear ratios of heterocaryons of *Fusarium oxysporum* f. *pisi*. *Genetics* **46**:485-492.
Whitehouse, H. L. K. (1949). Heterothallism and sex in the fungi. *Biol. Rev. Cambridge Phil. Soc.* **24**:411-447.
Whitney, H. S., and J. R. Parmeter. (1963). Synthesis of heterokaryons in *Rhizoctonia solani* Kühn. *Can. J. Botany* **41**:879-886.
Wilson, J. F., L. Garnjobst, and E. L. Tatum. (1961). Heterokaryon incompatibility in *Neurospora crassa*—microinjection studies. *Am. J. Botany* **48**:299-305.

CHAPTER 18

Mechanisms of Inheritance

3. The Parasexual Cycle

J. A. ROPER

*Department of Genetics
The University
Sheffield, England*

I. INTRODUCTION

Less than twenty years ago the standard sexual cycle was the only known mechanism of genetic recombination. A possible exception to this statement had been provided by Griffith's (1928) work on transformation in pneumococci, but at that time transformation was a little understood phenomenon. Microbial species in which no sexual cycle was known were described as asexual or, in the case of fungi, imperfect. Such species were not amenable to rigorous genetic analysis. In fact, in the absence of convincing cytological studies, there could be no absolute certainty that these species enjoyed the same fundamental mode of inheritance as higher organisms; however, this doubt was probably applied more to bacteria and viruses than to the asexual fungi. Lack of knowledge of recombination processes seriously restricted certain fields of study in the imperfect fungi; for instance, control of virulence in asexual phytopathogens, the planned breeding of improved industrial strains, the study of genetic diversity within related groups, and so on. Not only that, imperfect fungi posed a problem in neo-Darwinian terms. How did they meet the challenge of evolutionary forces?

The fruitful union of genetics, microbiology, and biochemistry has had far-reaching consequences in biology as a whole. One of these consequences has been the discovery of what Haldane (1955) called "alternatives to sex." That is, the discovery of processes, other than the standard sexual cycle, which lead to genetic recombination. These "alternatives to sex" have almost invariably been revealed by a genetic approach using large numbers of cells, coupled with the powerful selective tools provided by nutritional mutants and selective, chemically defined media. In no instance has there been prior microscopic evidence to suggest that recombination might be found.

Later, extensive analyses, largely genetic, have allowed a comparison between these newly discovered processes of recombination and the standard sexual cycle. There is now an almost bewildering array of recombination mechanisms known in microorganisms. Most of these processes are fairly well analyzed in formal genetic terms and, in some cases, the chromosome mechanics are well understood. One of these novel processes of recombination, and one of the most thoroughly elucidated, was discovered in fungi and has been termed by Pontecorvo (1954) the parasexual cycle.

II. THE PARASEXUAL CYCLE, AND ITS INDIVIDUAL STEPS, IN *Aspergillus nidulans*

The parasexual cycle was discovered in the homothallic ascomycete *Aspergillus nidulans,* where it coexists with the standard sexual cycle. The existence of both cycles in one species has made it possible to confidently define the features of the parasexual cycle.

The essential steps of the parasexual cycle are: (1) heterokaryosis, (2) fusion of unlike nuclei in the hyphae, (3) segregation and recombination at mitosis. For clarity, certain of these three essential steps require subdivision.

A. *Heterokaryosis*

An obvious prerequisite for recombination is fusion of haploid nuclei (or parts of nuclei). This normally requires, as a first step, inclusion of the genetically different nuclei in the same cytoplasm. This is achieved through heterokaryosis.

Wild-type *A. nidulans* has green, haploid uninucleate conidia. It grows perfectly on a minimal medium of mineral salts with a sugar (for example, Czapek-Dox medium with 1% glucose). Strains differing from wild type in nutritional requirement, conidial color, or resistance to inhibitory substances are readily prepared by the standard techniques of microbial genetics (see, for example, Pontecorvo *et al.,* 1953a; Roper and Käfer, 1957). All the mutant properties just mentioned are particularly valuable in the exploitation of the parasexual cycle.

Any pair of strains selected for study will generally differ from wild type, and from each other, in one or several nutritional requirements; one or both strains will differ from wild type in conidial color. A "balanced" heterokaryon is most easily prepared by mixing 10^6 or so conidia of each

18. The Parasexual Cycle

of the two parent haploids in a few milliliters of liquid minimal medium supplemented with sufficient of the required nutrients to allow germination, but not full growth, of the parent haploids. The mat of mycelium which results after 2–3 days is teased out on solid minimal medium. From certain points of the teased-out mycelium balanced heterokaryotic growth escapes on further incubation. Such growth is usually readily recognized by its mosaic of conidial heads of different color and often by its rather typical growth form. The conidial color markers of *A. nidulans* are autonomous, each conidium having its color determined solely by the nucleus it carries. When the conidial colors are sufficiently contrasted, in a green + white or green + yellow heterokaryon, "mixed" heads produced by heterokaryotic conidiophores are often seen. The absence of mixed heads and/or an extreme infrequency of one conidial class does not necessarily indicate a low degree of effective heterokaryosis. From such heterokaryons it is often possible to obtain a high frequency of hybrid perithecia and a yield of vegetative diploids comparable to that from heterokaryons showing less disproportion of conidial types.

Heterokaryons, at least in *A. nidulans*, have hyphae carrying widely differing frequencies of the two nuclear types (Clutterbuck and Roper, 1966). Maintenance of the balanced heterokaryotic state, a form of intracellular symbiosis, is probably by interhyphal selection at the growing edge of the colony. At present it is not possible to profitably apply to a heterokaryon the mathematical tools of population genetics, despite the analogy between a heterokaryon and a polymorphic population in equilibrium (cf. Chapter 17, on heterokaryosis).

B. Formation of Diploids; Recognition and Isolation

Sansome (1946) described gigas forms of *Penicillium notatum* resulting from camphor treatment of individual haploid strains. There was evidence (Sansome, 1949) that these gigas forms had diploid nuclei which, considering their origin, were necessarily entirely homozygous. While such diploids are valuable in various forms of analysis they are of relatively little use in genetic analysis. The original purpose, for which *A. nidulans* diploids were synthesized, was to study problems of allelism (Roper, 1953a) and these studies could be made only with heterozygous diploids.

A successful search was therefore made (Roper, 1952) for heterozygous diploid nuclei which might arise by the vegetative fusion of pairs of unlike nuclei rather than by some mechanism, such as spindle failure, which would give totally homozygous diploids. There were no strong theoretical grounds for expecting such fusions though there was some earlier experimental evidence, in animals, that the search might prove successful (e.g., Pontecorvo, 1943). The technique adopted was to search for the conidial products of the fusion of unlike nuclei in heterokaryons. The vast majority of the conidia produced by a balanced heterokaryon formed between different nutritional mutants would be of one or other parental type, and would be unable to grow on minimal medium. However, making the reasonable assumption that most mutant alleles would be recessive, conidia with heterozygous diploid nuclei would, like the heterokaryon, grow on minimal medium. This approach provided a powerful tool for the selection of heterozygous diploids, if they should arise, from the mass of parental mutant conidia. At the same time the approach was limited to a search for the required type, heterozygotes.

Young, but established, subcultures of heterokaryons were treated with camphor vapor. A few crystals of d-camphor were placed in the inverted dish and the heterokaryons were incubated for 5 hours. The camphor was then removed and incubation was continued for several days. Conidia were then harvested and plated at high density on minimal medium. The conidial densities, usually between 10^6 and 3×10^7 per dish, were adjusted so that auxotrophs showed little or no germination which might have suppressed growth of the prototrophic heterozygotes (Roper, 1950; Grigg, 1952). Under these conditions resynthesis of heterokaryons, in *A. nidulans*, is generally slight. In any case, heterokaryons can usually be distinguished by their growth form and also by their mosaic of conidial colors. The selective platings yielded rare prototrophs which were wild type both in nutritional requirement and in conidial color. As a rare event, the heterokaryon showed a sector of diploid growth. These sectors are only conspicuous when the phenotype of the heterozygous conidia is different from that of both parent haploids.

In later experiments it was found that camphor treatment was unnecessary and it is now almost never used. The distribution of diploid conidia, in the heterokaryon, is clonal. Thus the frequency of recovery of diploids does not necessarily reflect the frequency of nuclear fusion. Any approach to this important problem must generally use statistical analysis of the type devised by Luria and Delbrück (1943) and must take careful account of the selective or other forces exerted by environmental agents which are investigated. The evidence suggests (Pontecorvo and Roper, 1953) that camphor increases the yield of diploids, but not necessarily the rate of nuclear fusion. Treated heterokaryons gave between 3 and 300 diploid colonies per 10^6 conidia plated, but an untreated control gave only 0.25 per 10^6. Barron (1962) found difficulty in isolating diploids of *Penicillium expansum* from untreated heterokaryons, but not from heterokaryons which had received camphor treatment. Ishitani *et al.* (1956a) have exploited the multinucleate conidia of *Aspergillus sojae* and *A. oryzae* to study the influence of factors affecting the frequency of recovery of diploids. By this approach they avoid certain of the difficulties discussed above. Conidia from heterokaryons received no treatment, camphor treatment, or treatment with ultraviolet light. The conidia were then plated and the resulting colonies were examined for the occurrence of diploids, either as whole colonies or as sectors. Camphor treatment increased the frequency of diploids, but not so dramatically as did UV. At UV doses giving a survival of 10^{-2}, the frequency of diploids rose from < 1 in 10^7 to > 1 in 10^2. The mechanism of action of agents affecting recovery rate of diploids, or rate of nuclear fusion, is far from clear. If suitable experimental designs can be devised the field should yield important results. Clearly, such results have relevance to the question of the formation of diploids in nature.

By the techniques outlined above it has proved a simple matter to prepare a heterozygote of any required genotype. The only limitation is that imposed by the need, in the parent haploids, for suitable markers required to synthesize the balanced heterokaryons and select and identify the heterozygotes. While it would certainly be possible to synthesize a heterozygote from mutants which both differed from wild type, and each other, only in conidial color, it would be a laborious exercise.

No strict record has been kept of success or failure to synthesize heterozygotes in *A. nidulans;* in the author's experience at least 95% of heterokaryons yield diploid colonies from the plating of between 10^7 and 10^8 conidia. In no instance has a heterokaryon failed to eventually yield diploids.

C. The Properties of Heterozygous Diploids

Proof of diploidy, in the first instances, rested on a number of criteria which can now be amplified by more recent findings.

1. The Phenotype

Green-spored prototrophic strains were derived from a heterokaryon whose components each carried several mutant alleles determining nutritional requirements and mutant conidial color. The phenotype of these postulated diploids was consistent with the initial view, generally supported by data from heterokaryons, that most mutant alleles would be recessive. The alternative explanation, that the green prototrophs derived from simultaneous spontaneous mutation, at several loci in one strain, seemed too unlikely to be considered seriously.

2. Deoxyribonucleic Acid Measurements in Haploids and Diploids

Measurements of DNA per nucleus provide an estimate of the degree of ploidy, and with this in mind Heagy and Roper (1952) estimated the DNA in known haploid and putative diploid conidia. The necessary assumptions were that the conidia of both types should be in the same stage of the mitotic cycle and that not only haploid but also diploid conidia should be uninucleate. This latter point has since been confirmed for the diploid conidia.

The results given in Table I are entirely consistent, within the limits of experimental error, with a 1:2 ratio for the DNA of haploid and diploid conidia.

TABLE I
DEOXYRIBONUCLEIC ACID OF HAPLOID AND DIPLOID CONIDIA OF *Aspergillus nidulans*

Strain	DNA phosphorus (10^{-6} gm/10^9 conidia)[a]
Green haploid	4.04
Green diploid	9.39
White haploid	4.22
White diploid	7.75

[a] Results quoted from Heagy and Roper (1952), were corrected for a typographical error of 10^6.

3. Conidial Size

As the conidia of *A. nidulans* are spherical and occur in long chains, it is a simple matter to find the mean conidial diameter of a strain by measuring several chains. Roper (1952) found that the conidia of diploid strains are significantly larger than those of haploids. The ratio of the diameters is almost exactly 1.3:1; the volumes have the ratio 2:1. These results were extended by Pontecorvo et al. (1954), who used conidial size as an unambiguous criterion of haploidy versus diploidy.

Ishitani et al. (1956b) showed that haploid and diploid conidia of *A. sojae* did not differ significantly in size. However, the mean number of nuclei per conidium in haploids was twice that in diploids. Thus the cell volume supported by one haploid nucleus is half that supported by one diploid nucleus. Conidia produced by heterokaryons of *A. sojae* were significantly larger than conidia of the component haploid mutant strains. However, the conidia from heterokaryons had a higher mean number of nuclei than did the component haploids and the ratio of cell volume to nuclear number was the same for both heterokaryon and pure strains. Clutterbuck and Roper (1966) have found similar results for the hyphal tip cells of *A. nidulans*. The mean cell volume per haploid nucleus is about half that per diploid nucleus. Preliminary evidence in triploids shows a roughly 3:1 increase of cell volume per nucleus as compared with haploids. It would be of considerable interest to try to vary, by changes in media, the mean cell volume per nucleus in a plastic system like fungal hyphae. This might provide one approach to the study of conditions which initiate and control mitosis.

4. The Perithecia of Diploids

Haploid strains produce 8-spored asci whose ascospores are usually of high viability. Diploid strains may produce abundant perithecia, but each perithecium contains few asci. Some of these asci have other than 8 spores, the most common exceptional class being 16-spored asci.

Elliott (1960) has made a cytological study of meiosis in haploids and diploids. Eight bivalents are seen, both in haploids and diploids, at first meiotic metaphase. In immature perithecia of diploids true croziers are not seen; instead, there are coiled hyphae made up mainly of uninucleate cells. There was no evidence of tetraploid meiosis; each ascus of a diploid perithecium develops from a single diploid nucleus. Meiosis proceeds normally up to first meiotic metaphase, but then frequently fails. As Elliott has pointed out, "the sterility of the diploids poses an intriguing problem. There is a striking difference in fertility between a diploid and the cross of its two parents. The diploid state of the mycelium itself must somehow be inimical to the proper functioning of the sexual processes." Elliott's analysis revealed nothing about the origin of 16-spored asci which are still an interesting problem.

Genetic segregation at meiosis has been studied by Garber et al. (1961), who plated the ascospores of diploid perithecia and recovered diploids and, in much lower frequency, haploids. This is not in agreement with the present author's experience. In view of the extremely low yield and viability of ascospores from diploids a definitive analysis probably requires micromanipulation of single ascospores so that contaminating conidia are entirely excluded.

5. Mitotic Segregation

In the earliest studies it was mitotic segregation which provided the unequivocal evidence of diploidy. This evidence distinguished between true diploidy and, for instance, a persistent heterokaryotic condition.

Heterozygous diploids are relatively stable at mitosis and their colonies carry mainly diploid conidia of parental kind. However, the diploid colonies show occasional sectors, patches, or single conidial heads of genotype different from the heterozygous parent. These segregant sectors are detected by various means such as conidial color. Most are diploid, but some are haploid. They arise by "accidents" of mitosis which result in segregation. By analysis of the mitotic segregants it was possible to show that the supposed heterozygotes did, in fact, carry all the mutant alleles present in the original haploids.

The processes of mitotic segregation are extremely important in the parasexual cycle and are given extended treatment below.

D. Mitotic Crossing-Over

1. The Mechanism of Mitotic Crossing-Over

To illustrate mitotic crossing-over a heterozygote of the genotype shown at the head of Table II will be used. This is heterozygous for seven recessive mutant alleles and is therefore phenotypically wild type.

Conidial platings from this diploid yield green and very rare white or yellow colonies. Close inspection of the green colonies reveals the color segregants mentioned above. The segregants are isolated, purified and checked for ploidy by conidial size. Whole colonies of white or yellow are ignored as they represent segregation prior to plating. A maximum of one yellow and one white segregant per colony is picked so as to avoid clones. Most of these color segregants are diploid, and most of the diploids arise by mitotic crossing-over. Only diploid mitotic cross-overs are considered in this section; other classes of segregants are discussed in Section II, E.

For the present purposes consideration of just the yellow segregants will be adequate. All the yellow diploids would require biotin (*bi* is distal to *y*). Some would require *p*-aminobenzoic acid (*paba* is proximal to *y*) as well as biotin. Some would require proline (*pro* is proximal to *paba*) as well as *p*-aminobenzoic acid and biotin. Except for extremely rare instances, the segregants would not require riboflavine or adenine. By haploidization (Section II, E) all these yellow segregants could be shown to be still heterozygous for those mutant alleles for which they had not become homozygous.

Results such as these led to the view (Pontecorvo and Roper, 1953) that these segregants arose by mitotic crossing-over, a process elegantly analyzed by Stern (1936) in the insect *Drosophila*. The modalities of this process, both in *Drosophila* and *A. nidulans,* are as follows. Mitotic crossing-over is a rather rare event occurring at the 4-strand stage of mitosis. At any one event, crossing-over is almost invariably confined to a single exchange in one chromosome arm out of the whole chromosome complement. The subsequent behavior of the centromeres is mitotic; that is, the centromeres divide and the chromatids of each homolog go to opposite poles. If the segregation of chromatids is appropriate the resulting nuclei are homozygous for certain markers for which they were previously heterozygous. Specifically, the nuclei become homozygous for all alleles linked in coupling and distal to the point of exchange. Markers proximal to the exchange, and markers on other chromosome arms, remain heterozygous. Table II details the results of mitotic exchange at various points in the right arm of chromosome I.

This laborious and extensive tabulation has been given to emphasize several points including, first, the number of segregant nuclei which go

18. The Parasexual Cycle

TABLE II
THE CONSEQUENCES OF MITOTIC CROSSING-OVER

		Chromosome I					Chromosome II	
	1	ribo	pro	paba	y	bi	+	+
	2	●					●	
Diploid	3	+ D + C + B + A +					w	ad
	4	●					●	

Class	Region of cross-over, assumed between chromatids 2 and 3	Segregation of chromatids	Resulting segregant						
1.	A	1 + 3	ribo	pro	paba	y	bi	+	+
			+	+	+	+	bi	w	ad
2.	A	2 + 3	ribo	pro	paba	y	+	+	+
			+	+	+	+	bi	w	ad
3.	A	2 + 4	ribo	pro	paba	y	+	+	+
			+	+	+	+	+	w	ad
4.	B	1 + 3	ribo	pro	paba	y	bi	+	+
			+	+	+	y	bi	w	ad
5.	B	2 + 3	ribo	pro	paba	+	+	+	+
			+	+	+	y	bi	w	ad
6.	B	2 + 4	ribo	pro	paba	+	+	+	+
			+	+	+	+	+	w	ad
7.	C	1 + 3	ribo	pro	paba	y	bi	+	+
			+	+	paba	y	bi	w	ad
8.	C	2 + 3	ribo	pro	+	+	+	+	+
			+	+	paba	y	bi	w	ad
9.	C	2 + 4	ribo	pro	+	+	+	+	+
			+	+	+	+	+	w	ad
10.	D	1 + 3	ribo	pro	paba	y	bi	+	+
			+	pro	paba	y	bi	w	ad
11.	D	2 + 3	ribo	+	+	+	+	+	+
			+	pro	paba	y	bi	w	ad
12.	D	2 + 4	ribo	+	+	+	+	+	+
			+	+	+	+	+	w	ad

NOTE: The diploid is shown at the 4-strand stage of mitosis and exchanges are assumed between chromatids 2 and 3. Linkage arrangements shown are based entirely on meiotic results (summarized by Käfer, 1958). Symbols: ●, centromere; *y*, yellow conidia; *w*, white conidia; *ribo*, requirement for riboflavine; *pro*, proline; *paba*, *p*-amino benzoic acid; *bi*, biotin, *ad*, adenine. Only nuclei carrying at least one cross-over chromatid are shown; when chromatids 1 and 4 segregate together, the genotype is entirely unchanged.

undetected. Classes 2, 5, 8, and 11 have the complementary products of crossing-over; except for the rare cases where position effect is involved (see below) these go undetected because they have the same phenotype and overall genotype as the parent diploid. Classes 3, 6, 9, and 12 have become homozygous for one or more dominant alleles, and these classes also normally go undetected because they are not phenotypically distinguishable from the parent. Only classes 1, 4, 7, and 10 show mutant properties, and class 1 is likely to go undetected without laborious testing. Classes 4, 7, and 10 are yellow segregants which are visually detected.

A comparison can be made of classes 4, 7, and 10 with the meiotically determined order of loci and centromere in the right arm of chromosome I. This comparison illustrates how mitotic crossing-over can be used to determine the order of genes on a chromosome arm relative to each other and their centromere. For such analysis it is essential to have the recessive alleles in coupling (as in the present example) and to use a selective marker as distal as possible on the chromosome arm. Had there been two markers to the right of the y locus their order could not have been determined as both would always have become homozygous when yellow segregants were selected. It could have been said only that both were distal to y.

Mitotic crossing-over permits, then, the ordering of genes and their centromere on individual chromosome arms. In *A. nidulans* the results of such analysis have always been in absolute agreement with meiotically derived results. However, analysis by mitotic crossing-over has limitations. It analyzes only chromosome arms and does not show how they are associated into whole linkage groups. This association can be shown through haploidization (Section II, E). A further limitation is the need for appropriate recessive or semidominant mutant alleles, distally located, to provide the means for selection of mitotic cross-over classes. The final limitation is that analysis of the type shown in Table II does not afford an immediate measure of recombination frequencies such as are obtained through meiosis. This limitation can to some extent be circumvented in a way described later (Section II, F).

2. *The Reciprocity of Mitotic Crossing-Over*

Experiments such as those described above do not afford unequivocal evidence that mitotic crossing-over is reciprocal, since the postulated complementary products of a single mitotic cross-over are not recovered in the same nucleus (strands 2 + 3 in Table II). Sometimes "twin" spots are formed. These are neighboring tissues formed by daughter nuclei following a segregation of chromatids 1 + 3 and 2 + 4, where chromatids 2 and 3 have exchanged segments. However, it is never possible to say that these apparently complementary products must have arisen from one event of crossing-over.

The proof of reciprocity was found by Roper and Pritchard (1955). By using a novel selection method it was possible to select cross-over classes which included those having the reciprocal products of one crossover event in a single nucleus. The experimental design, shown in Fig. 1,

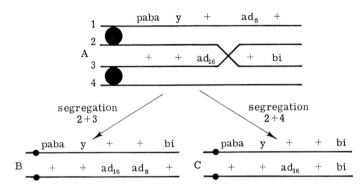

FIG. 1. Recovery of the complementary products of mitotic crossing-over.

is based on the fact that nonidentical, recessive, allelic mutations generally show a position effect. That is, $m1 +/+ m2$ is mutant and $m1\ m2/++$ is normal. A diploid of genotype A was synthesized; it carried several linked markers and also the closely linked alleles *ad16* and *ad8* in *trans* arrangement. The phenotypes of the various haploid and diploid arrangements of *ad16* and *ad8* are shown in Table III. These alleles, which determine a requirement for adenine, are phenotypically distinguishable and, although very closely linked, can be separated by meiotic crossing-over (Pritchard, 1955). The aim was to try to obtain mitotic crossing-over between them.

Conidia of diploid A were plated on a medium which had no adenine.

TABLE III
PHENOTYPES OF VARIOUS COMBINATIONS OF *ad16* AND *ad8* ALLELES

Strain		Phenotype on minimal medium
ad16	+	Reduced growth
+	*ad8*	No growth
ad16	*ad8*	No growth
ad16 / +	+ / *ad8*	Reduced growth
ad16 *ad8* / + +		Full growth

About 1 in 10^7 of the plated conidia gave a colony. The majority of these selected, adenine-independent types were shown, by recovery of haploids and out-crossing, to have either genotype B or C. These results support the mechanism of mitotic crossing-over and segregation as it has been outlined above. This technique is of some value in itself; it allows analysis of half-tetrads and also leads to the recovery of nuclei carrying two mutant alleles in *cis* arrangement, an almost impossibly laborious task by conventional methods.

3. The Frequency of Mitotic Crossing-Over

There are substantial difficulties in the way of estimating the absolute frequency of mitotic crossing-over. Ideally it would be necessary to have distal markers on all chromosome arms, to make statistical allowances for the clonal distribution of segregants, to know the details of centromere segregation following crossing-over, and to know (or compensate for) possible differential viabilities of segregants and parent heterozygote. The nearest approach to this ideal comes from the painstaking work of Pontecorvo and Käfer (1958) and Käfer (1961), who suggest that mitotic crossing-over occurs at about 1 in every 50 mitotic divisions.

E. Haploidization and Nondisjunction

Among the segregants isolated from a diploid are three classes which do not arise by mitotic crossing-over. These are haploids, nondisjunctional diploids, and aneuploids.

1. Haploids

Haploid segregants were first detected by Pontecorvo and Roper (1953), but the analysis was inadequate to show details of their origin. Later analysis, Pontecorvo et al. (1954), showed that haploids arise by a process, independent of crossing-over, in which the members of each homologous pair of chromosomes assort independently of other pairs. Thus, recombinants are obtained between, but not within, linkage groups. An example of haploidization is shown in Table IV. Haploids, derived from suitably marked diploids, provide a very easy means for the initial assigning of a gene to its linkage group since *markers on the same linkage group stay completely linked and never recombine at haploidization.*

2. Nondisjunctional Diploids

This class of segregants was considered in detail by Pontecorvo and Käfer (1958). They are segregants which have become homozygous for one, or very rarely two, whole chromosomes while remaining heterozygous for all others. A typical nondisjunctional diploid derived from the heterozygote at the head of Table IV would have the genotype

$$\frac{ribo\ pro\ paba\ y\ bi\ \ +\ +}{ribo\ pro\ paba\ y\ bi\ \ w\ ad}$$

In *A. nidulans* nondisjunctional diploids are found at considerably lower frequency than are diploid mitotic cross-over classes (Käfer, 1961).

TABLE IV
An Example of the Results of Haploidization[a]

Diploid	$\dfrac{ribo\quad pro\quad paba\quad y\quad bi}{+\qquad +\qquad +\qquad +\quad +}$	$\dfrac{+\ \bullet\ +}{w\qquad ad}$

Haploid classes	Detection
1. *ribo pro paba y bi* ; + +	By color
2. *ribo pro paba y bi* ; *w ad*	By color
3. + + + + + ; *w ad*	By color
4. + + + + + ; + +	Usually undetected

[a] Symbols as in Table II.

These diploid segregants clearly arise by the failure of the two chromatids of one chromosome to separate at mitosis. Very rarely, two chromosomes become homozygous by this means. The probable detailed origin of nondisjunctional diploids, like that of the haploids, is explained through aneuploidy.

3. Aneuploids

When conidia of a heterozygous diploid are plated at very low density, so that intercolony competition is minimized, a proportion of unstable types is found (Pontecorvo and Käfer, 1958). These unstable types are almost always aneuploid. Käfer (1961) has carried out a laborious and rewarding analysis of aneuploids derived from parent diploids heterozygous for up to 26 mutant alleles distributed on both homologues of all eight linkage groups.

Two main classes of aneuploids were obtained. Hyperdiploids, mainly of $2n + 1$ type but, more rarely, $2n + 2$, $2n + 3$, or $2n + 4$. Hyperhaploids, mainly $n + 1$ but, again more rarely, $n + 2$, $n + 3$, and $n + 4$. Hyperdiploids had a total frequency, averaged for two diploids, of about 1 in 150 colonies; hyperhaploids, similarly averaged, had a frequency of about 1 in 1000 colonies.

All the analyzed aneuploids showed reduced growth rate and gave normal-growing sectors. The sectors differed in genotype from the central aneuploid part of the colony, as shown by a change in conidial color and/or nutritional requirement. The majority of hyperdiploids, the $2n + 1$ class, differed from the heterozygote by the addition of *any* one extra chromosome. Each trisomic had a distinct phenotype. These hyperdiploids can be represented by the simplified genotype a/a/+; b/+; c/+; d/+; e/+; f/+; g/+; h/+. The breakdown products were diploids, still heterozygous for the linkage groups bearing markers *b* to *h*, but either homozygous (a/a) or heterozygous (a/+) for the linkage group previously trisomic. Sectors of types a/a and a/+ were formed in a 1:2 ratio. *The former class, a/a, is indistinguishable from a directly isolated nondisjunctional diploid.*

The hyperhaploids sector in similar fashion but to give, ultimately, haploids. The most frequently isolated hyperhaploid (as opposed, perhaps, to the most frequently occurring in the parent colony) is the $n + 1$ class, which may segregate, without crossing-over, to give two haploid classes. In the case of higher hyperhaploids a stepwise loss of single chromosomes could be detected; this was shown by the unmasking of recessive alleles as the homologs, carrying dominant alleles, were lost. *Thus some haploids have been shown to arise from hyperhaploids by the stepwise loss of chromosomes.*

These results have led Käfer to suggest that a single basic mechanism may explain the origin of both nondisjunctional diploids and most haploids. (It cannot be entirely excluded that certain haploids arise by an alternative one-step process, but the indications are that this process, if it occurs at all, is very infrequent.) The first postulated step is formation from a diploid nucleus, by infrequent nondisjunction, of daughter nuclei which are usually $2n + 1$ and $2n - 1$. The hyperdiploid then reverts to a diploid, in one-third of the cases a homozygous nondisjunctional type. Hyperhaploids of type $2n - 1$ ($= n + 7$), $n + 6$, $n + 5$ have not been isolated; this could reflect the inability of such classes to produce conidia. However, they are postulated as intermediates in the stepwise loss of chromosomes from the hyperhaploids, until the stable haploid condition is reached. It is not yet clear whether the secondary steps, the loss of chromosomes from hyperdiploids and hyperhaploids, are more frequent than the first step, nondisjunction. The aneuploids are at a great selective disadvantage and a high rate of sectoring of stable types may reflect this disadvantage rather than a high frequency of chromosome loss.

On the basis of her analysis Käfer has estimated that nondisjunction occurs at about 1 in every 50 mitoses.

F. *A Comparison of the Parasexual Cycle and the Sexual Cycle*

1. *A Comparison of the Processes*

Table V sets out a summarized comparison of the parasexual and sexual cycles. At first sight the parasexual cycle may appear far more laborious than the sexual cycle for laboratory use, since mitotic recombinants are rare. However, the use of more recently devised techniques (Section II, G) makes mitotic analysis a very simple matter.

For the assigning of a new marker to its linkage group, haploidization has overwhelming advantages, especially since Forbes (1959) has devised tester strains carrying markers on all chromosomes. Mitotic crossing-over

TABLE V
A SUMMARIZED COMPARISON OF THE PARASEXUAL AND SEXUAL CYCLES IN *Aspergillus nidulans*

Sexual cycle	Parasexual cycle
1. Heterokaryosis	1. Heterokaryosis
2. Nuclear fusions in specialized structures to yield "selfed" and "hybrid" zygotes	2. Rare nuclear fusion in vegetative cells. Heterozygotes selected by color and/or nutrition. Homozygotes, if formed, are not detected
3. Zygote persists one nuclear generation only	3. "Zygote" may persist through many mitotic divisions
4. Recombination at meiosis: crossing-over, at 4-strand stage, in all chromosome pairs, random assortment of members of each chromosome pair, and reduction to haploid state	4. Recombination by rare "accidents" of mitosis: (a) mitotic crossing-over, at 4-strand stage, usually only one exchange in a single chromosome arm; (b) haploidization, probably usually via aneuploidy. Independent of crossing-over, random assortment of members of each chromosome pair
5. Products of meiosis readily recognized and isolated	5. Recombinants occur among vegetative cells. Recognized by use of suitable markers

is often simpler than ascus analysis for centromere location, provided suitable selective markers are available. The ordering of genes on a chromosome arm by mitotic crossing-over may also be easier than through meiosis. Linked genes which freely recombine at meiosis may well have their order resolved through mitotic crossing-over. Subject to the differences discussed in Section II, F, the meiotic and mitotic linkage maps of *A. nidulans* are entirely consistent.

2. *A Comparison of Relative Frequencies of Crossing-Over from Meiotic and Mitotic Analysis*

From a very extensive analysis Pontecorvo and Käfer (1958) have compared the relative frequencies of meiotic and mitotic crossing-over for several regions of three chromosome arms. They used two diploids carrying various coupling and repulsion arrangements of the mutant alleles to check for differential viability of the various segregants, but significant viability differences were not found. Their approach was as follows. Consider the right arm of chromosome I. Mitotic crossing-over anywhere between y and its centromere, followed by appropriate segregation of chromatids, produces a yellow diploid segregant. The use of the markers *pro* and *paba* permitted Pontecorvo and Käfer to say in which region of the centromere to y interval the exchange had taken place. Recombinants for the whole interval may then be apportioned, as percentages, to the various regions. The meiotic results can be expressed similarly so that the whole interval centromere to y is expressed as 100%. The summarized results are given in Table VI. Pontecorvo and Käfer point out that the comparison shows "a concentration of mitotic cross-overs within 28 (meiotic) units from the centromere. But the 'right' arm of linkage group I shows that the concentration is not in the immediate vicinity of the centromere, but in a small region 20 units away." The significance of the different "linkages" derived meiotically and mitotically is not clear. Several fundamental problems associated with crossing-over have still to be tackled, and one possible approach to some of these problems may be through a comparison of meiotic and mitotic linkage data.

TABLE VI
A Comparison of Meiotic and Mitotic Linkage Data[a]

Linkage group I, "left" arm (85 meiotic units total)

Marker	su	ribo1	an1	ad14	
Interval	I	II	III	IV	
Mitotic	23	7.4	6.2	63.4	
Meiotic	45.8	22.4	8.2	23.6	

Linkage group I, "right" arm (44 meiotic units)

Marker		pro1	paba1	y
Interval	V	VI	VII	
Mitotic	5.5	72.0	22.5	
Meiotic	46.1	18.0	35.8	

Linkage group II, "left" arm (46 meiotic units)

Marker	Acr1	w2	
Interval	VIII	IX	
Mitotic	14.7	85.3	
Meiotic	54.3	45.7	

[a] Results are summarized from Pontecorvo and Käfer (1958). Meiotic data from various workers are summarized by Käfer (1958).

18. The Parasexual Cycle

The analysis by Pontecorvo and Käfer has provided valuable data on the frequency of multiple exchanges at mitotic crossing-over and on the coincidence of crossing-over and nondisjunction or haploidization.

When a segregant can be explained only as a "double event," it is usually impossible to determine whether it arose by two successive, independent events or by the coincidence of events. This leads to what is probably an overestimate of coincidence. With this qualification, the summarized cases of coincidence were as follows:

Two cross-overs in two different chromosomes	13 out of 1332
Two cross-overs in two different arms of one chromosome	4 out of 701
Two cross-overs in one arm	1 out of 422
One cross-over and haploidization	2 out of 449
One cross-over and nondisjunction	3 out of 701

G. Techniques for the Facilitation of Mitotic Analysis

The synthesis of heterozygotes is a simple matter. The hard labor of analysis, from the early diploids, lay in the detection and isolation of the rare segregants. Initially, analysis via mitotic crossing-over was restricted to the chromosome arms bearing the conidial color markers w and y. This restriction does not, of course, extend to haploidization since the members of *all* pairs of chromosomes reassort when haploids are formed. To facilitate analysis two approaches are necessary: (1) to find markers permitting selection, on as many chromosome arms as possible; (2) either to increase the rate of segregation or to create conditions in which segregants have a selective advantage. Both approaches have been made in *A. nidulans;* in certain instances the use of suitable mutant alleles has fulfilled both needs at once. A few of the most important methods in current use are summarized below.

1. Visual Selection by Conidial Color

This has already been discussed in detail. Greatest efficiency is achieved when the conidial color markers are autonomous.

2. Automatic Selection by Suppressors

An example extensively used by Pontecorvo and Käfer (1958) will illustrate this method. A mutant allele, *ad20,* determines a requirement for adenine for full growth. A recessive suppressor, *su-1 ad20,* restores normal growth even in the absence of adenine (Pritchard, 1955). In the absence of adenine a diploid of constitution *ad20/ad20 su-1 ad20/+* shows reduced aconidial growth characteristic of the haploid mutant *ad20*. The above diploid produces vigorous well-conidiating sectors which are either *ad20 su-1 ad20* haploids or *ad20/ad20 su-1 ad20/su-1 ad20* diploids.

By taking small inocula from the sectors it is usually possible to isolate pure segregants.

3. Automatic Selection for Resistance to Inhibitory Substances

A spontaneous mutant allele, *Acr1*, confers resistance to acriflavine (Roper and Käfer, 1957). The allele is semidominant so that at certain concentrations of acriflavine the sensitive fails to grow while the heterozygote, *Acr1/+*, grows much less well than either the diploid *Acr1/Acr1* or the haploid *Acr1*. Diploid conidia are plated at low density. After 4–5 days the center of the colony (*Acr1/+*) still shows stunted growth, but it has vigorous sectors which are *Acr1/Acr1* or *Acr1* types. Isolates from these sectors are almost invariably pure.

In the case of a recessive allele for acriflavine resistance, *acr2*, a slightly different approach is used. Low density platings are made on "complete" medium without acriflavine and covered with a further thin layer of medium to prevent early conidiation. After incubation for 24 hours the colonies have not yet conidiated but most have produced *acr2/acr2* or *acr2* segregants. A top layer of medium with acriflavine is poured on the colonies, and the segregants, but not the parent heterozygote, grow through this layer and form well-conidiating sectors.

4. Selection by Position Effect

This method is potentially very useful but is likely to have limited application in species whose formal enetics is poorly known. The method has been detailed in Section II, D and has been used by Käfer (1958).

5. Selection for Single or Multiple Auxotrophs

These techniques could prove extremely useful in the analysis of a species which, for example, has poor conidial markers.

Forbes (1952) has described a technique which preferentially selects auxotrophs from prototrophs. It depends on the greater resistance of the former to SO_2 treatment. For example, conidia from a heterozygote *ad/+* are treated with SO_2. Among the survivors are greatly increased proportions of the relatively resistant adenine-requiring diploids and haploids.

Macdonald and Pontecorvo (1953) showed that under "starvation" conditions, conidia of a biotin-requiring mutant die off more quickly than do most multiple auxotrophs requiring biotin and a second nutrient. Diploids of genotype, for example, *bi/bi ad/+* require only biotin for growth. If conidia of such diploids are plated on medium without biotin they die off relatively quickly, whereas a much higher proportion of segregants (*bi/bi ad/ad* and *bi ad*) survive. The segregants are recovered by adding appropriate nutrients to the plates after the starvation period.

6. "Increase" of Mitotic Segregation

A real or apparent, but in any case effective, increase of segregation can be achieved by treatment of diploids with a variety of agents, physical and chemical. These are reviewed by Käfer (1963) and by Holliday (1961). Certain of these agents, particularly high-energy radiations, carry substantial risk of producing chromosomal aberrations (see, for example, Tector and Käfer, 1962). These agents are of importance in probing fundamental problems of segregation (Fratello *et al.*, 1960; Käfer, 1963; Morpurgo, 1963) but are generally better avoided for purposes of analysis unless they have been thoroughly checked for undesirable effects.

At present the most effective agent, apparently entirely free of "side effects," is *p*-fluorophenylalanine (Morpurgo, 1961; Lhoas, 1961). On appropriate levels of the inhibitor (usually about 1 in 10,000 w/v) diploid colonies grow very slowly. However, these stunted colonies produce vigorous sectors which are invariably haploid and are readily isolated in pure condition.

III. THE PARASEXUAL CYCLE IN FUNGI OTHER THAN
Aspergillus nidulans

Since the discovery of the parasexual cycle a considerable number of fungal species, in several genera, have been studied in a search for all or part of the cycle. In a few instances the search has yielded negative results. In the majority of cases heterozygous diploids and mitotic segregation have been found. It is extremely difficult to assess and summarize the overall results since the studies have been for different purposes (phytopathology, genetics, antibiotic yield, etc.) and of different depths.

In *Neurospora crassa* intensive searches for vegetative heterozygotes have yielded negative results (Roper, 1953b). Weijer and Dowding (1960) have put forward evidence for vegetative recombination in *Neurospora* heterokaryons which could, if confirmed, suggest the formation of unstable diploids. However, Case and Giles (1962), using a similar experimental approach, have failed to find mitotic reassortment in *Neurospora* heterokaryons. In *Colletotrichum lagenarium* Dutta and Garber (1960) failed to find heterozygous diploids from 10^8 spores of each of three heterokaryons. Camphor treatment did not help. In *Penicillium digitatum* (Garber, 1963), diploids have not yet been found, but Garber reports considerable doubts about heterokaryosis in this species and the failure of heterokaryosis could explain the absence of diploids.

Cases in which diploids and mitotic reassortment have been found include *Aspergillus niger* (Pontecorvo, 1952; Pontecorvo *et al.* 1953b; Hutchinson, 1958; Lhoas, 1961), *A. rugulosus* (Boam and Roper, 1965), *A.*

fumigatus (Berg and Garber, 1962; Strømnaes and Garber, 1963), *A. sojae* (Ishitani *et al.*, 1956a), *Penicillium chrysogenum* (Pontecorvo and Sermonti, 1953, 1954; Sermonti, 1957), *P. italicum* (Garber, 1963), *P. expansum* (Barron, 1962), *Ustilago maydis* (Holliday, 1961), *Cephalosporium mycophilum* (Tuveson and Coy, 1961), *Emericellopsis salmosynnemata* (Fantini, 1962), *Verticillium alboatrum* (Hastie, 1962). *Fusarium oxysporum* (Buxton, 1956, 1962; Tuveson and Garber, 1959), and *Cochliobolus sativus* (Tinline, 1962). Not all of these will be discussed in detail.

In *Aspergillus niger* and *A. rugulosus* the evidence strongly favors a parasexual cycle as shown in *A. nidulans*. The analysis in *A. sojae* is not extensive but is entirely compatible with a "normal" parasexual cycle. However, in *A. fumigatus*, Strømnaes and Garber have found it "impossible to produce a coherent picture of linkage and independent segregation." Some possible reasons for this difficulty, even with a "normal" cycle, are discussed below.

In *Penicillium chrysogenum* and *P. expansum* the evidence again favors a "normal" cycle. However, Garber, using *P. italicum*, found difficulties in analysis of the same type as for *A. fumigatus*.

In most of the other species mentioned above the evidence is entirely compatible with a "normal" parasexual cycle but is not yet sufficient for a definitive statement.

The case of *Ustilago* should be mentioned in some detail. Holliday (1961) has selected diploid solopathogenic strains both from unreduced zygotes and by nutritional selection (the haploid parents were auxotrophs) from gall tissue transplanted to selective media. Spontaneous mitotic recombination was observed in only one of the two diploids studied but UV vastly increased segregation to give only diploid segregants. These segregants were compatible with mitotic crossing-over, and reciprocal products were frequently found. Haploid segregants were not detected, but one unstable strain, giving stable diploids homozygous for one chromosome, was isolated. This unstable strain was tentatively interpreted as aneuploid.

The failure to find the parasexual cycle, or the discovery of abnormal segregation, might be considered first. Failure to establish heterokaryons means failure of the first step in the cycle. However, when two strains derive from an immediate common ancestor, failure of heterokaryosis is interpreted cautiously. Pontecorvo and Sermonti (1954) have discussed the difficulties met by several workers in preparing heterokaryons of *Penicillium;* but, with further experience and new techniques, these difficulties have been entirely overcome. The failure to isolate heterozygous diploids of *Neurospora crassa* is now compelling though one can never exclude possible future success. In any case, in view of Tinline's success with *Cochliobolus,* there is no reason to suppose that heterothallic ascomycetes will necessarily give negative results. A further reason for caution about

Neurospora crassa stems from the work of Sansome (1956), who by camphor treatment, readily induced "gigas" forms of this species. There was strong evidence that these unstable forms were, in fact, diploid. It is extremely difficult to interpret apparent anomalies in segregation patterns such as have been found in *Aspergillus fumigatus* and *Penicillium italicum*. They could reflect a real difference in mitotic segregation mechanism, but in the absence of a sexual cycle a meiotic cross-check is impossible. As Strømnaes and Garber (1963) have said, "Linkage studies by the parasexual cycle in imperfect fungi must be viewed with caution when relatively few data are available." Some causes of abnormal segregation are already known, and most prominent among these is chromosomal aberration (Käfer, 1962). The results of Arditti-Muchnik (1961) may also be highly relevant; diploids of *Penicillium,* combining aged multiple mutants, gave only parental haploid segregants, perhaps due to chromosomal aberrations. Diploids combining freshly isolated mutants gave normal segregation. Selective advantage of certain segregants is also a recognized hazard. For instance, it is usually impossible to isolate morphologically abnormal segregants from heterozygotes with normal morphology (Bainbridge and Roper, 1963). However, no combination of these factors affecting segregation offers any ready explanation for the results obtained with *Aspergillus fumigatus.*

No sweeping statements can yet be made about the occurrence or nonoccurrence of the parasexual cycle in particular fungal groups. *A. nidulans* has proved to be extremely favorable material for the study of this cycle in having spherical, uninucleate conidia, colonial growth, and autonomous conidial color markers. In addition, the perfect stage has allowed a crosscheck of all mitotic analyses. But many fungal species pose technical problems and, in any species, the initial steps in the search for a parasexual cycle are laborious. It will be some time before any general statements can be made; in this connection the extensive surveys being made by Garber and his associates are particularly welcomed. Nevertheless, we can now be confident that the parasexual cycle is not confined to *A. nidulans*. The author's view is that, while we may have to be prepared for certain differences in the cycle from species to species, the cycle is likely to be widespread among the filamentous fungi.

IV. APPLICATIONS AND IMPLICATIONS OF THE PARASEXUAL CYCLE

A. Recombination Mechanisms in Microorganisms

Apart from the standard sexual cycle, there are now five different and well-defined processes which lead to recombination in microorganisms. The discovery of more obviously cannot be excluded. In bacteria transformation, transduction, and conjugation are known. A fourth mechanism is responsible for recombination in viruses. The fifth is the fungal parasexual cycle.

The most conspicuous formal differences between the bacterial processes and the parasexual cycle lie in the nature and stability of the "zygote." Transformation and transduction give a zygote which carries the whole genome of one parent but only a small fraction of the genome of the other. Conjugation also usually gives an incompletely diploid zygote. [Far a review of bacterial and viral genetics see Hayes (1963).] The same may be true for the zygote phase of *Streptomyces coelicolor* (Hopwood and Sermonti, 1962). In all these cases the zygote is usually very unstable. On the other hand, the heterozygous diploids of fungi are complete diploids. We cannot exclude the possibility that some primary aneuploids are formed; but, if this is so, they have escaped detection in cases where we could reasonably have hoped to find them. The diploids are also relatively stable at mitosis. The evidence points to a lower stability of diploids of imperfect species than of perfect species, but in both cases the stability is adequate for the diploids, as such, to be thoroughly studied.

Two *Aspergillus* species, *A. nidulans* and *A. rugulosus,* have both a perfect stage and the parasexual cycle; *Ustilago maydis* has a perfect stage and vegetative diploids which show mitotic crossing-over; *Emericellopsis salmosynnemata* and *Cochliobolus sativus* both have a perfect stage and yield diploids which show mitotic reassortment. This multiplicity of recombination mechanisms (the same is true for certain bacteria) poses important questions relevant to the major problem of the evolution of genetic systems themselves.

B. The Parasexual Cycle in Nature

The imperfect fungi have posed a problem for the neo-Darwinian concept of evolution. In fact, this problem could extend to certain of the perfect fungi as the perfect stage may, for one or other reason, fail in nature.

A fungal colony contains millions of nuclei which must always include a wide spectrum of spontaneous mutants. Heterokaryosis probably provides an ample means for the storage of hereditary variation, expressed or potential. Furthermore, heterokaryosis offers a plastic system which can quickly accommodate environmental changes by an overall change in nuclear ratio (Pontecorvo, 1946; Jinks, 1952). In the case of *Aspergillus nidulans* at least, this adaptive change is probably achieved through interhyphal rather than intrahyphal selection (Clutterbuck and Roper, 1966). However, heterokaryosis has two serious deficiencies in the propagation and full exploitation of the available heritable variation. In species with uninucleate conidia it would be necessary to reestablish heterokaryosis in each single spore culture, either by mutation or by anastomosis with a neighboring culture of different genotype. Even in species with multinucleate conidia, where there is the potential of perpetuating heterokaryosis via the conidia, it is often found that only a small proportion of the conidia produced by a heterokaryotic mycelium are themselves heterokaryotic (e.g., Tinline, 1962). The second deficiency of heterokaryosis may be far more serious. Heterokaryosis, by itself, can never provide new genotypes which reassort the available hereditary variation.

The parasexual cycle could provide the missing link for the imperfect fungi and could even offer a significant supplement for fungi with a perfect stage. But the outstanding questions, entirely unanswered, are: does the cycle operate in nature, and does it operate with adequate efficiency? Pontecorvo (1958) has made tentative calculations and suggests that recombination occurring via the parasexual cycle in *A. nidulans* may be of the order of 500-fold less than that occurring in the sexual cycle. However, in certain asexual species the yields of diploids and segregants, at least in the laboratory, are much higher than in *A. nidulans*. Further speculation is probably unprofitable; there may well be unknown environmental factors operating in nature which either enhance or reduce the efficiency of the parasexual cycle. There is a clear need for experimental evidence. Even a few experiments, using "unnatural" mutants under simulated natural conditions, might be revealing.

The above discussion has centered around the possible formation of diploids and segregants from established heterokaryons and has hardly considered the question of heterokaryon formation. Heterokaryons are formed by mutation and/or by anastomoses between strains carrying nuclei of different genotypes. Formation of heterokaryons by mutation is inevitable, and, if the parasexual cycle operates at all in nature, such heterokaryons might provide a significant contribution to variation. But such a closed system, operating only within a culture, might raise problems of isolation between the micropopulations. In *Neurospora crassa* there are a number of genes known which control ability versus inability of pairs of strains to form heterokaryons (Garnjobst, 1953; Holloway, 1955) though these genes provide no barrier to recombination via the sexual cycle. Grindle (1963) has made an extensive study of the ability of different isolates of the *A. nidulans* group to form heterokaryons, and he finds compatibility groups. Pairs of isolates within a group readily form heterokaryons, as judged by the formation of visibly heterokaryotic conidial heads between one wild-type isolate and a conidial color mutant of the other. Pairs of isolates from different compatibility groups form few or no mixed heads. This criterion of heterokaryosis is not absolute but certainly reflects the relative ease of heterokaryon formation between pairs of natural isolates. This suggests possible barriers to parasexual recombination and gene flow between some populations of the same group. Ultimately, the population genetics of microorganisms is likely to be at least as exciting as the population genetics of higher organisms, especially in view of the versatility of recombination processes in microorganisms.

The time is not yet ripe to consider the further step, the possible natural formation of interspecific diploids. Uchida et al. (1958) have attempted to produce interspecific diploids between *Aspergillus oryzae* and *A. sojae*. The results are promising but not decisive. Both in the laboratory and in nature there are obvious possible barriers to interspecific parasexual recombination at heterokaryosis, nuclear fusion or recombination. But any success along these lines would open immense possibilities for the study of homologies and natural relationships (Roper, 1962).

C. *The Parasexual Cycle in Genetic and Physiological Analysis*

The use of the parasexual cycle for formal genetic analysis, in perfect and imperfect species, has already been detailed. It remains only to mention certain special situations where the use of diploids and their segregants offers particular advantages.

The most valuable area has so far been in the study, direct or indirect, of problems related to subcellular architecture and function. For example, Roberts (1963) has compared the efficiency of interallelic complementation in heterokaryons and diploids. Roper (1958) has used diploids to probe aspects of nucleocytoplasmic interactions; segregation in diploids occurs in what is presumably a cytoplasmic continuum, and the system allows investigation of genotypic change without the introduction of potentially different cytoplasm from another strain.

Discovery of the parasexual cycle has focused attention on the possibilities of mitotic analysis in higher organisms in which comparable segregation processes, in tissue culture, could revolutionize genetic analysis (Pontecorvo, 1962).

D. *The Breeding of Improved Industrial Strains*

Most of the industrially important fungi are imperfect. Strain improvement has generally been achieved through repeated induced mutation coupled with modification of media. The success of this approach has been remarkable; it continues to pay dividends even in the very highly developed strains of *Penicillium chrysogenum*.

The parasexual cycle has undoubted implications in this field. The combining of desirable genes from two strains is no longer impossible, and genetic studies should certainly help in the elucidation of biosynthetic pathways. Fantini (1962) has made preliminary studies of antibiotic yield of diploids and segregants of *Emericellopsis,* but the most thoroughly studied species from this point of view is *P. chrysogenum*. Sermonti (1959, 1961) has reviewed the extensive studies of himself and his colleagues. The general conclusion is that parasexual breeding may not yield immediate results; highly selected strains probably have a delicate balance of "good" genes and ideas based on readily recombining such genes from two strains may be naive. Sermonti (1959) has expressed the view that the use of diploids themselves, rather than segregants, might be valuable: "The heterozygous diploid lends stability to strains and hybrid-vigour lends productivity." Macdonald and colleagues (1963, 1964) have also undertaken extensive analyses of the genetics of penicillin production. Macdonald (1963) has summarized his experiences as follows: "In crosses between strains of high penicillin yield and divergent lineage recombination is restricted, possibly because of difference in chromosome morphology between the parents. However, there is reason to believe that, by using strains of closer relationship, practical advantages might be obtained. Strains have been produced which combine a suitable titre from one parent with additional desirable properties from the other parent."

The use of polyploids themselves, as Sermonti has pointed out, may have advantages in some systems. For instance Ikeda *et al.* (1957) have shown the superiority of diploid, triploid, and tetraploid strains of *Aspergillus oryzae* in protease production.

E. Phytopathology and the Parasexual Cycle

The implications of the parasexual cycle for asexual phytopathogens is obviously tied up with the occurrence, or otherwise, of the cycle in nature. For the present it is possible to speak only of laboratory results. Several of the species mentioned in Section III are either plant pathogens themselves or are closely related to pathogens.

The most revealing work in this field has been that of Buxton (1956, 1962). By parasexual analysis Buxton has shown genetic control of pathogenicity and host range in *Fusarium*. Whatever the implications of this for natural variation of phytopathogens, it is now clear that fundamental laboratory studies are a possibility.

V. CONCLUSIONS

It is only fourteen years since the discovery of heterozygous diploids in filamentous fungi, a discovery which sparked a series of studies leading to the formulation and elucidation of the parasexual cycle. This cycle certainly exists in a number of filamentous fungi and, in the author's view, it is likely to exist in many.

The cycle has found considerable application in many fields—in formal genetic studies of perfect and imperfect species, in some specialized areas of biochemical genetics, in phytopathology, and in programs aimed at the planned breeding of improved strains. In one area, that of natural variation, we still have no idea of the role, if any, of the cycle. That is one of the exciting possibilities awaiting development.

REFERENCES

Arditti-Muchnik, R. (1961). Induced somatic segregation and chromosome mapping in *Penicillium chrysogenum*. *Aspergillus News Letter* **2**:7.

Bainbridge, B. W., and J. A. Roper. (1963). Unpublished data.

Barron, G. L. (1962). The parasexual cycle and linkage relationships in the storage rot fungus *Penicillium expansum*. *Can. J. Botany* **40**:1603-1613.

Berg, C. M., and E. D. Garber. (1962). A genetic analysis of color mutants of *Aspergillus fumigatus*. *Genetics* **47**:1139-1146.

Boam, T. B., and J. A. Roper. (1965). Unpublished data.

Buxton, E. W. (1956). Heterokaryosis and parasexual recombination in pathogenic strains of *Fusarium oxysporum*. *J. Gen. Microbiol.* **15**:133-139.

Buxton, E. W. (1962). Parasexual recombination in the banana-wilt Fusarium. *Brit. Mycol. Soc. Trans.* **45**:274-279.

Case, M. E., and N. H. Giles. (1962). The problem of mitotic recombination in *Neurospora*. *Neurospora Newsletter* **2**:6-7.

Clutterbuck, A. J., and J. A. Roper. (1966). A direct determination of nuclear distribution in heterokaryons of *Aspergillus nidulans*. *Genet. Res.* **7**:185-194.

Dutta, S. K., and E. D. Garber. (1960). Genetics of phytopathogenic fungi. III. An attempt to demonstrate the parasexual cycle in *Colletotrichum lagenarium*. *Botan. Gaz.* **122**:118-121.

Elliott, C. G. (1960). The cytology of *Aspergillus nidulans*. *Genet. Res.* **1**:462-476.

Fantini, A. A. (1962). Genetics and antibiotic production of *Emericellopsis* species. *Genetics* **47**:161-177.

Forbes, E. (1952). The use of SO_2 for selecting auxotrophs in filamentous fungi. *Microbial Genet. Bull.* **6**:26-28.

Forbes, E. (1959). Use of mitotic segregation for assigning genes to linkage groups in *Aspergillus nidulans*. *Heredity* **13**:67-80.

Fratello, B., G. Morpurgo, and G. Sermonti. (1960). Induced somatic segregation in *Aspergillus nidulans*. *Genetics* **45**:785-800.

Garber, E. D. (1963). Personal communication.

Garber, E. D., G. W. Bryan, B. Capon, L. B. Liddle, and M. W. Miller. (1961). Evidence for parthenogenesis in *Aspergillus nidulans*. *Am. Naturalist* **95**:309-313.

Garnjobst, L. (1953). Genetic control of heterokaryosis in *Neurospora crassa*. *Am. J. Botany* **40**:607-614.

Griffith, F. (1928). The significance of pneumococcal types. *J. Hyg.* **27**:113-156.

Grigg, G. W. (1952). Back mutation assay method in microorganisms. *Nature* **169**: 98-100.

Grindle, M. (1963). Heterokaryon compatibility of unrelated strains in the *Aspergillus nidulans* group. *Heredity* **18**:191-204.

Haldane, J. B. S. (1955). Some alternatives to sex. *New Biol.* **19**:7-26.

Hastie, A. C. (1962). Genetic recombination in the hop-wilt fungus *Verticillium albo-atrum*. *J. Gen. Microbiol.* **27**:373-382.

Hayes, W. (1963). "The Genetics of Bacteria and their Viruses," 544 pp. Blackwell, Oxford.

Heagy, F. C., and J. A. Roper. (1952). Deoxyribosenucleic acid content of haploid and diploid *Aspergillus* conidia. *Nature* **170**:713.

Holliday, R. (1961). Induced mitotic crossing-over in *Ustilago maydis*. *Genet. Res.* **2**:231-248.

Holloway, B. W. (1955). Genetic control of heterokaryosis in *Neurospora crassa*. *Genetics* **40**:117-129.

Hopwood, D. A., and G. Sermonti. (1962). The genetics of *Streptomyces coelicolor*. *Advan. Genet.* **11**:273-342.

Hutchinson, J. M. (1958). A first five-marker linkage group identified by mitotic analysis in the asexual *Aspergillus niger*. *Microbial Genet. Bull.* **15**:17.

Ikeda, Y., K. Nakamura, K. Uchida, and C. Ishitani. (1957). Two attempts upon improving an industrial strain of *Aspergillus oryzae* through somatic recombination and polyploidization. *J. Gen. Appl. Microbiol. (Tokyo)* **3**:93-101.

Ishitani, C., Y. Ikeda, and K. Sakaguchi. (1956a). Hereditary variation and genetic recombination in Koji-molds (*Aspergillus oryzae* and *Asp. sojae*). VI. Genetic recombination in heterozygous diploids. *J. Gen. Appl. Microbiol. (Tokyo)* **2**: 401-430.

Ishitani, C., K. Uchida, and Y. Ikeda. (1956b). The relation of DNA content to cell size in *Aspergillus*. *Exptl. Cell Res.* **10**:737-740.

Jinks, J. L. (1952). Heterokaryosis: A system of adaptation in wild fungi. *Proc. Roy. Soc.* **B140**:83-106.

Käfer, E. (1958). An 8-chromosome map of *Aspergillus nidulans*. *Advan. Genet.* **9**:105-145.

Käfer, E. (1961). The processes of spontaneous recombination in vegetative nuclei of *Aspergillus nidulans*. *Genetics* **46**:1581-1609.

Käfer, E. (1962). Translocations in stocks of *Aspergillus nidulans*. *Genetica* **33**:59-68.

Käfer, E. (1963). Radiation effects and mitotic recombination in diploids of *Aspergillus nidulans*. *Genetics* **48**:27-45.

Lhoas, P. (1961). Mitotic haploidization by treatment of *Aspergillus niger* diploids with *para*-fluoro-phenylalanine. *Nature* **190**:744.

Luria, S. E., and M. Delbrück, (1943). Mutations from virus sensitivity to virus resistance. *Genetics* **28**:491-511.

Macdonald, K. D. (1963). Personal communication.

Macdonald, K. D., and G. Pontecorvo. (1953). "Starvation" technique. *Advan. Genet.* **5**:159-170.

Macdonald, K. D., J. M. Hutchinson, and W. A. Gillett. (1963). Formation and segregation of heterozygous diploids between a wild-type strain and derivatives of high penicillin yield in *Penicillium chrysogenum*. *J. Gen. Microbiol.* **33**:385-394.

Macdonald, K. D., J. M. Hutchinson, and W. A. Gillett. (1964). Properties of heterozygous diploids between strains of *Penicillium chrysogenum* selected for high penicillin yield. *Antonie van Leeuwenhoek J. Microbiol. Serol.* **30**:209-224.

Morpurgo, G. (1961). Somatic segregation induced by p-fluoro-phenylalanine. *Aspergillus News Letter* **2**:10.

Morpurgo, G. (1963). Quantitative measurement of spontaneous and induced somatic segregation in *Aspergillus nidulans*. *Microbial Genet. Bull.* **19**:16-17.

Pontecorvo, G. (1943). Meiosis in the striped hamster (*Cricetulus griseus*). *Proc. Roy. Soc. Edinburgh* **B62**:32-42.

Pontecorvo, G. (1946). Genetic systems based on heterocaryosis. *Cold Spring Harbor Symp. Quant. Biol.* **11**:193-201.

Pontecorvo, G. (1952). Non-random distribution of multiple mitotic crossing-over among nuclei of heterozygous diploid *Aspergillus*. *Nature* 170:204.
Pontecorvo, G. (1954). Mitotic recombination in the genetic systems of filamentous fungi. *Caryologia* (Suppl.) 6:192-200.
Pontecorvo, G. (1958). "Trends in Genetic Analysis," 145 pp. Columbia Univ. Press, New York.
Pontecorvo, G. (1962). Methods of microbial genetics in an approach to human genetics. *Brit. Med. Bull.* 18:81-84.
Pontecorvo, G., and E. Käfer. (1958). Genetic analysis by means of mitotic recombination. *Advan. Genet.* 9:71-104.
Pontecorvo, G., and J. A. Roper. (1953). Diploids and mitotic recombination. *Advan. Genet.* 5:218-233.
Pontecorvo, G., and G. Sermonti. (1953). Recombination without sexual reproduction in *Penicillium chrysogenum*. *Nature* 172:126.
Pontecorvo, G., and G. Sermonti. (1954). Parasexual recombination in *Penicillium chrysogenum*. *J. Gen. Microbiol.* 11:94-104.
Pontecorvo, G., J. A. Roper, L. M. Hemmons, K. D. Macdonald, and A. W. J. Bufton. (1953a). The genetics of *Aspergillus nidulans*. *Advan. Genet.* 5:141-238.
Pontecorvo, G., J. A. Roper, and E. Forbes. (1953b). Genetic recombination without sexual reproduction in *Aspergillus niger*. *J. Gen. Microbiol.* 8:198-210.
Pontecorvo, G., E. Tarr-Gloor, and E. Forbes. (1954). Analysis of mitotic recombination in *Aspergillus nidulans*. *J. Genet.* 52:226-237.
Pritchard, R. H. (1955). The linear arrangement of a series of alleles of *Aspergillus nidulans*. *Heredity* 9:343-371.
Roberts, C. F. (1963). The genetic analysis of carbohydrate utilization in *Aspergillus nidulans*. *J. Gen. Microbiol.* 31:45-58.
Roper, J. A. (1950). Back-mutation in *Aspergillus nidulans*. *Microbial Genet. Bull.* 3:7-8.
Roper, J. A. (1952). Production of heterozygous diploids in filamentous fungi. *Experientia* 8:14-15.
Roper, J. A. (1953a). Pseudo-allelism. *Advan. Genet.* 5:208-215.
Roper, J. A. (1953b). Unpublished data.
Roper, J. A. (1963). Unpublished data.
Roper, J. A. (1958). Nucleo-cytoplasmic interactions in *Aspergillus nidulans*. *Cold Spring Harbor Symp. Quant. Biol.* 23:141-154.
Roper, J. A. (1962). Genetics and microbial classification. *Symp. Soc. Gen. Microbiol.* 12:270-288.
Roper, J. A., and E. Käfer. (1957). Acriflavine resistant mutants of *Aspergillus nidulans*. *J. Gen. Microbiol.* 16:660-667.
Roper, J. A., and R. H. Pritchard. (1955). The recovery of the complementary products of mitotic crossing-over. *Nature* 175:639.
Sansome, E. R. (1946). Induction of "gigas" forms of *Penicillium notatum* by treatment with camphor vapour. *Nature* 157:843.
Sansome, E. R. (1949). Spontaneous mutation in standard and "gigas" forms of *Penicillium notatum* strain 1249 B 21. *Brit. Mycol. Soc. Trans.* 32:305-314.
Sansome, E. R. (1956). Camphor-induced *gigas* forms in *Neurospora*. *Brit. Mycol. Soc. Trans.* 39:67-78.
Sermonti, G. (1957). Analysis of vegetative segregation and recombination in *Penicillium chrysogenum*. *Genetics* 42:433-443.

Sermonti, G. (1959). Genetics of Penicillin production. *Ann. N.Y. Acad. Sci.* **81**:950-966.
Sermonti, G. (1961). The parasexual cycle in *Penicillium chrysogenum* and its application to the production of penicillin. *Sci. Rept. Ist. Super. Sanita* **1**:449-454.
Stern, C. (1936). Somatic crossing-over and segregation in *Drosophila melanogaster*. *Genetics* **21**:625-730.
Strømnaes, Ø., and E. D. Garber. (1963). Heterocaryosis and the parasexual cycle in *Aspergillus fumigatus*. *Genetics* **48**:653-662.
Tector, M. A., and E. Käfer. (1962). Radiation-induced chromosomal aberrations and lethals in *Aspergillus nidulans*. *Science* **136**:1056-1057.
Tinline, R. E. (1962). *Cochliobolus sativum*. V. Heterokaryosis and parasexuality. *Can. J. Botany* **40**:425-437.
Tuveson, R. W., and D. O. Coy. (1961). Heterokaryosis and somatic recombination in *Cephalosporium mycophilum*. *Mycologia* **53**:244-253.
Tuveson, R. W., and E. D. Garber. (1959). Genetics of phytopathogenic fungi. II. The parasexual cycle in *Fusarium oxysporum* f. *pisi*. *Botan. Gaz.* **112**:74-80.
Uchida, K., C. Ishitani, Y. Ikeda, and K. Sakaguchi. (1958). An attempt to produce interspecific hybrids between *Aspergillus oryzae* and *A. sojae*. *J. Gen. Appl. Microbiol. (Tokyo)* **4**:31-38.
Weijer, J., and E. S. Dowding. (1960). Nuclear exchange in a heterokaryon of *Neurospora crassa*. *Can. J. Genet. Cytol.* **2**:336-343.

CHAPTER 19

Mechanisms of Inheritance

4. Extranuclear Inheritance

J. L. JINKS

Department of Genetics
University of Birmingham
Birmingham, England

I. INTRODUCTION

The fungi have become the favorite group for the study of extranuclear or, more precisely, extrachromosomal, heredity. As a result, there is a greater number and variety of phenomena ascribable to extrachromosomal heredity in the fungi than in any other group. There are two reasons for this. First, the demonstration of extrachromosomal heredity requires the step by step elimination of all alternative explanations such as chromosomal heredity and nonheritable causation. The ease with which the growth and reproduction of fungi may be controlled in the laboratory and the variety of methods for propagating fungi provide many opportunities for distinguishing between extrachromosomal heredity and the alternative explanations. Secondly, extrachromosomal variation appears to arise more readily in fungi than in any other group so far examined.

II. PROPERTIES OF EXTRACHROMOSOMAL VARIANTS

There is naturally a tendency to concentrate attention on the particular property of an extrachromosomal variant which is most diagnostic of its extrachromosomal basis. Such variants, however, have now been described in sufficient numbers for us to recognize some general characteristics. These will be our principal concern in this section.

A. *The Origin of Extrachromosomal Variants*

Extrachromosomal variants, like their chromosomal counterparts, can arise spontaneously or in response to specific treatments. Examples of

TABLE I
EXAMPLES OF SPONTANEOUS VARIANTS THAT SHOW EXTRACHROMOSOMAL INHERITANCE

Species	Variant	Characteristics	References
Saccharomyces cerevisiae	petite	Slow growth, respiratory defective	Ephrussi (1953)
Neurospora crassa	mi-1, 2, 3 and 4	Slow growth, respiratory defective	M. B. Mitchell et al. (1953), Pittenger (1956)
Aspergillus nidulans	nonsexual	No perithecia	Jinks (1954)
	purple	Purple pigmentation	Grindle (1963)
	alba	Nonpigmented, few perithecia	Mahoney and Wilkie (1962)
Aspergillus glaucus	conidial	Few perithecia	Sharpe (1958)
	vegetative death	Death of hyphae	Jinks (1956, 1959)
Podospora anserina	senescent	Death of hyphae	Rizet (1957)

spontaneous extrachromosomal variants are the *mi* mutants of *Neurospora crassa*, each of which has been recovered once only, and the *purple, alba,* and *nonsexual* variants of *Aspergillus nidulans* which have been recovered repeatedly in one or more strains (Table I). Probably the most widespread in its occurrence is the *petite* mutant of the yeast *Saccharomyces cerevisiae*. This variant is present in most samples of bakers' yeast with a frequency of 1 or 2%.

No reliable estimates of spontaneous mutation rates are available for any extrachromosomal hereditary determinant. It is known, however, that some variants are recovered considerably more frequently than others. But it is possible that some of these more frequently occurring variants, for example, *nonsexual* and *vegetative death,* arise from a variety of different changes in the extrachromosomal system. Hence until methods are available for distinguishing between similar phenotypic changes which are due to changes in the same extrachromosomal determinant and those due to changes in different determinants (see Section III, C, 2), we cannot estimate the mutability of a particular determinant.

A few extrachromosomal variants, for example those listed in Table II, have been induced by various treatments. These variants fall into two classes. The first class includes those whose induction occurs with the

TABLE II
INDUCED VARIANTS THAT SHOW EXTRACHROMOSOMAL INHERITANCE

Species	Variant	Mutagenic treatment	References
Saccharomyces cerevisiae	petite	Euflavine, acriflavine	Ephrussi and Hottinguer (1951)
		Tetrazolium chloride	Laskowski (1954)
		Elevated temperature	Ycas (1956)
		UV irradiation	Pittman (1957), Raut and Simpson (1955), Wilkie (1963)
		Anaerobiosis	Lindegren and Hino (1957) Harris (1956)
		5-Fluorouracil	Moustacchi and Marcovich (1963)
Aspergillus nidulans	crimson	*a*	Arlett (1957)
	fawn		Upshall (1966)
	mycelial	Acridine dyes	Croft (1964, 1966a)
	minute		Faulkner and Arlett (1964)
	red	UV irradiation	Arlett *et al.* (1962)
	mycelial	Acriflavine	Roper (1958)
	nonsexual	Elevated temperature	Arlett (1960)
	compact	Elevated temperature	Arlett (1960)
Aspergillus glaucus	compact	UV irradiation	Jinks (1963)
Neurospora crassa	S.G.	Acriflavine	Srb (1958)

a The other known properties of these mutants fit equally a chromosomal or an extrachromosomal interpretation.

low frequency characteristic of induced chromosomal gene mutation. The mutagenic agents which induce these variants are nonspecific in that they simultaneously increase the rate of mutation at a number of chromosomal and extrachromosomal sites. A characteristic example is the *red* variant of *Aspergillus nidulans*. It is induced by ultraviolet (UV) irradiation at a very low frequency (10^{-3}) along with other extrachromosomal mutants, e.g., *compact,* and a wide range of chromosomal gene mutations (Fig. 1a,b, and c).

The second class includes variants whose induction occurs with very high frequencies. The mutagenic agents which induce these variants are often specific in that under the conditions used they induce only one extrachromosomal variant. The classic example is the *petite* mutant of yeast, which can be induced by growing normal cells in euflavine or acriflavine at concentrations which do not kill. There is, therefore, no lethality among the treated cells and hence no selection. Under optimal conditions all the treated cells and the daughter cells they produce are mutant. Other treatments such as growth in tetrazolium chloride and at 40°C are only slightly less effective in inducing the *petite* mutant. Even UV irradiation which kills most of the cells exposed to it yields the remarkably high rate of 23% *petite* mutants among the survivors.

Other mutants, for example, *crimson, fawn, mycelial,* and *minute,* have been specifically induced in *Aspergillus nidulans* with comparable high frequencies, by various acridine dyes. The evidence that these are extrachromosomal in origin, however, is equivocal since aneuploidy can account for many of their properties (Fig. 1d).

No other mutant has been induced with such high frequencies. Nevertheless the same treatments are implicated in the induction of two other extrachromosomal variants, namely, a different *mycelial* mutant of *A. nidulans* and the *S.G.* mutant of *N. crassa* (Table II). Elevated temperatures also have a marked mutagenic effect in *A. nidulans*. In all, four variants differing from wild type in density of perithecial production and compactness of growth have been repeatedly induced with frequencies around 2% following growth at high temperatures.

FIG. 1. (a-d) Colonies obtained by germinating samples of asexual spores produced by persistently unstable extrachromosomal variants of *Aspergillus* spp. In each case a typical variant colony is indicated by an arrow. In each case the colonies with the alternative morphology are wild type in appearance. The variants are: (a) the *red* variant of *Aspergillus nidulans;* (b) a *compact* variant of *Aspergillus nidulans;* (c) a *compact* variant of *Aspergillus glaucus;* (d) the *minute* variant of *Aspergillus nidulans*. (e) A normal unaged colony of *Aspergillus glaucus* (top) and an aged colony of the same strain showing vegetative death (bottom). (f) Ten colonies of a high selection (top) and ten colonies of a low selection (bottom) for perithecial density in *Aspergillus nidulans*. In the low selection, perithecial production is confined to the small sectors indicated by the arrows.

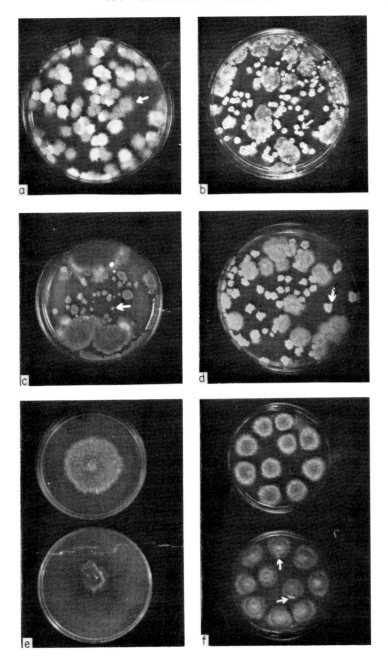

Although not mutagenic in the usual sense, certain methods of stock culture maintenance inevitably lead to a high frequency of particular variants. Aging, achieved by rigorously excluding all sexually produced spores from the inocula used to maintain a stock, results in the degenerate condition known as *vegetative death* in *A. glaucus* and *as senescence* in *Podospora anserina* (Table III). Strains of *A. glaucus* which are not al-

TABLE III

A. Percentage Frequency of Vegetative Death in Aged and Non-Aged Clones of Three Strains of *Aspergillus glaucus* (Jinks, 1956)

Clone	Strains		
	1	3	6
Aged	3.0	1.6	53.1
Non-aged	0.0	0.0	0.8

B. Percentage Frequency of Vegetative Death in an Aging Clone of Strain 1 of *Aspergillus glaucus* (Jinks, 1959)

Age of clone (weeks)	Percentage of propagations showing vegetative death
0–8	0
10	0
12	5
14	10
16	50

lowed to age, by being regularly propagated by sexual spores, rarely, if ever, show *vegetative death*. The variant usually appears after 4 months to 2 years of aging. Once it appears its frequency increases rapidly until half or more of all propagations made from apparently normal colonies produce the variant phenotype (Fig. 1e).

Another variant of *P. anserina*, s^s, is also induced under unusual circumstances. The strains of this species can be classified into two groups, S and s, on the following basis. An S and an s strain when confronted always form a "barrage," but pairs of S or of s strains do not. Following crosses between S and s strains the sexual progenies contain colonies with the S reaction but not with the s reaction. Instead colonies are recovered, called s^s, which form barrages with neither S nor with s strains. This novel behavior is subsequently inherited as an extrachromosomal variant (see Section II, C, 1). The induction of the modified barrage reaction is so far unique although it has a superficial resemblance to the phenomenon known as *paramutation* in maize.

In summary, extrachromosomally inherited variants arise spontaneously and in response to a variety of treatments. Some of these treatments are well-known chromosomal gene mutagens; others are unusual either in their nature or in the highly specific effect they produce. In the latter cases the mode of induction of the variants is often critical evidence for their extrachromosomal basis.

B. Kinds of Extrachromosomal Variants

Almost every morphological, physiological, and biochemical property of a fungus may be altered as a result of an extrachromosomal mutation. Indeed, where an exhaustive analysis of a single mutant has been made all these properties have been found to have changed. For example, the *petite* mutant is slow growing and sexually sterile and has a defective respiratory system. Because of the latter the growth of the mutant is not affected by anaerobic conditions nor by respiratory poisons, both of which reduce the growth of normal cells. The mitochondria of *petite* cells are structurally abnormal, and they do not show the staining reactions of the mitochondria of normal cells. Furthermore, they lack various substrates and enzymes which are associated with the mitochondria in normal cells. All the missing substances are components of the respiratory system.

The *mi-1* or *poky* mutant of *N. crassa* has been described in detail and shows remarkable similarities to *petite*. The differences between them can be explained by the fact that a viable mutant of *N. crassa* must be able to respire, while a viable mutant of yeast need not. The changes in the respiratory system of *mi-1* are, therefore, relatively less severe. Some of the enzymes missing in *petite* are present but in abnormally high or low amounts in *mi-1*, and they approach more normal concentrations as the mycelium ages.

The phenotypes of the other extrachromosomal mutants are known only superficially. They all simultaneously affect a range of properties, such as rate of growth, pigmentation, sporulation, and sexual fertility, and it seems likely that further analysis would reveal complex biochemical and cytological changes comparable with those found in *petite*.

Some of the variation which has been attributed to extrachromosomal changes is continuous, involving no major phenotypic changes (Fig. 2). Such variation can be demonstrated only by careful measurement of quantitative differences between colonies for rate of growth, density of sporulation and speed of spore germination. This kind of variation has been demonstrated within clones of *A. nidulans, A. glaucus,* and yeast. Although the variation is continuous the extreme phenotypes may differ in many important properties and these differences persist in successive propagations. They may even be accentuated by selecting the most extreme phenotypes after each propagation (Figs. 1f, 2, and 3).

Extrachromosomal variants vary enormously in their stability. Some, e.g., *petite* and *poky,* are completely stable. Others, e.g., *compact,* are extremely unstable. This instability reveals itself in two ways. First, it results in persistent sectoring so that colonies of these variants are a mosaic of normal and mutant growth. Secondly, it leads to segregation among colonies raised from the asexual spores or from the single

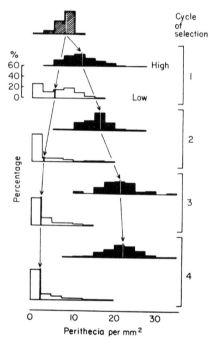

FIG. 2. The changes in perithecial density in four successive cycles of selection for high and low density in a homokaryotic clone of *Aspergillus nidulans.* The arrows indicate the change in the mean density in successive cycles, the distributions show the variation in density within the initial clone and within the propagants from the selected colonies. All this variation is traceable back to a colony obtained from a single haploid asexual spore in the initial propagation. Based on results obtained by J. H. Croft, Department of Genetics, University of Birmingham.

hyphae produced by single homokaryotic colonies (see Section II, D). The instability of some variants is so marked that it is often diagnostic of their extrachromosomal origin.

C. *Behavior at Sexual Reproduction*

The behavior of extrachromosomal differences at sexual reproduction is characteristically non-Mendelian. The deviations from Mendelian expectations are of two kinds: (1) differences between the offspring of reciprocal crosses due to complete or almost complete maternal determination of the phenotype of the offspring; (2) no segregation or irregular segregation following a cross between two contrasting phenotypes.

1. Differences between Reciprocal Crosses

The earliest and still one of the most reliable criteria of extrachromosomal heredity is the occurrence of persistent differences between the

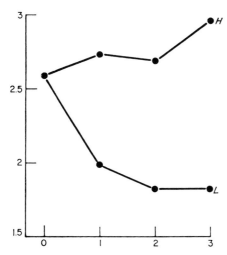

FIG. 3. The changes in growth rate that result from selection for high (H) and low (L) rates of growth in a homokaryotic clone of *Aspergillus glaucus*. This response to selection involves extrachromosomal changes only. From Jinks (1957).

progeny of reciprocal crosses. This criterion may be applied wherever a cross between two contrasting strains can be made in two ways which are reversed for the source of the male and female gametes or for mating type. It is, therefore, readily applicable to some species of fungi where it has been used to establish the extrachromosomal basis of the variants listed in Table IV.

In each case in Table IV the difference between the reciprocal crosses is due to maternal inheritance, the progeny being identical to the strain which was used as the "maternal" parent. To take an example, in *N. crassa* the colonies of both the *A* and the *a* mating types produce *protoperithecia* (the maternal reproductive structure) and *microconidia* (which can be used as the paternal gametes). Reciprocal crosses are, therefore, achieved by bringing microconidia of one mating type into contact with the protoperithecia of the other (Fig. 4). With but very rare exceptions, all the progeny of reciprocal crosses between the *mi* and *S.G.* variants of *N. crassa* and wild-type strains of the opposite mating type have the phenotype of the protoperithecial parent: that is, they have the phenotype of the parent which contributes the bulk of the extrachromosomal material and all the nutrition of the sexually produced spores. The different phenotypes of the reciprocal progenies are maintained through repeated crosses in which they are used as the protoperithecial parent and through indefinite periods of vegetative growth. These demonstrations of persistence are important since they virtually eliminate the possibility that the maternal determina-

TABLE IV
VARIANTS THAT SHOW DIFFERENCES BETWEEN RECIPROCAL CROSSES WHEN CROSSED TO WILD-TYPE STRAINS OR TO A CONTRASTING PHENOTYPE

Species	Designation or characteristic of variant	References
Puccinia graminis	Physiologic race	Johnson (1946)
Puccinia anomala [*P. hordei*]	Physiologic race	d'Oliviera (1939)
Podospora anserina	Modified barrage reaction s^s	Rizet (1952)
	Senescent	Rizet *et al.* (1958)
Neurospora crassa	*mi-1* (*poky*)	M. B. Mitchell and Mitchell (1952)
	mi-3	M. B. Mitchell *et al.* (1953)
	mi-4	Pittenger (1956)
	S.G.	Srb (1958)
Coprinus lagopus	Abnormal tetrad formation	Day (1959)

tion of the progeny phenotype is due solely to the maternal nutrition of the developing sexual spores.

To produce a persistent, heritable difference between the progeny of reciprocal crosses the parents of a cross must contribute unequally to the extrachromosomal complement of the progeny. In many cases the basis of this inequality is obvious in that one parent, the mother, contributes a much greater volume of extrachromosomal material to the zygote than the other parent, the father. In plants ranging from the algae to the gymnosperms, however, there is a visible postzygotic elimination of extrachromosomal material contributed by one of the two parents of a cross. In *Chlamydomonas reinhardii* this elimination leads to uniparental transmission of some extrachromosomally inherited traits even though both parents contribute equally to the extrachromosomal material of the zygote (Sager, 1954). Clearly, quality as well as quantity of extrachromosomal material is important in producing a difference between the progeny of reciprocal crosses.

2. Non-Mendelian Segregation at Sexual Reproduction

In most sexual fungi meiosis occurs just prior to sexual spore formation. Hence any chromosomal gene differences between the pair of haploid nuclei which fuse to give the diploid zygotic nucleus segregate among the sexual progeny (Figs. 4 and 5). And at each chromosomal locus at which the pair of haploid nuclei differ, half the sexual progeny will carry the allele contributed by one haploid nucleus and half the allele contributed by the other. The validity of this expectation has been repeatedly confirmed with only rare exceptions. A regular failure of the expectation has, therefore, been used to indicate extrachromosomal heredity.

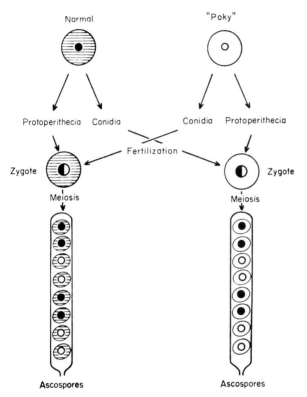

FIG. 4. Reciprocal crosses between a *poky* and a normal strain of *Neurospora crassa* using the female (protoperithecia) and male (conidia) gametes produced by colonies of each strain. When *poky* is used as the female parent, all the progeny are *poky* and in the reciprocal cross all the progeny are normal. In both cases segregation is 1:1 for any chromosomal gene difference (indicated by ● and ○ nuclei) between the strains. Based on M. B. Mitchell and H. K. Mitchell (1952).

The non-Mendelian segregation of extrachromosomally inherited differences takes many forms. One of these is the failure to segregate in the sexual progeny of a cross. Such a failure occurs whenever a difference in phenotype shows strict maternal inheritance (see Section II, C, 1). For example, in *N. crassa* single gene-controlled differences segregate 1:1 in the sexual progeny derived from every zygote irrespective of the direction in which the cross is made. On the other hand, the *mi* mutant:normal or the *S.G.*:non-*S.G.* differences do not segregate in either reciprocal cross. All the sexual progeny are either mutant or normal according to which strain was the protoperithecial parent (Fig. 4).

A failure to segregate at meiosis may occur also where there are no differences between reciprocal crosses or in species in which reciprocal

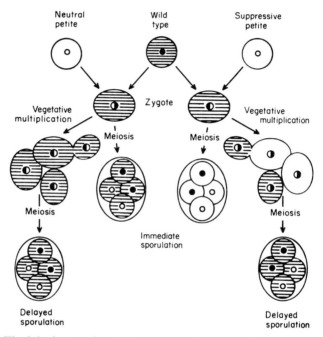

FIG. 5. The inheritance of *petite* in a cross between *petite* and normal strains of *Saccharomyces cerevisiae*. Two forms of *petite*, neutral and suppressive, can be recognized on the outcome of such crosses. *Neutral petite* variants never appear in the progeny of crosses to normal. *Suppressive petite* is the predominant phenotype in the progeny of crosses to normal if the zygotes are sporulated immediately, but if sporulation is delayed and the zygotes multiply vegetatively before sporulation, then all the progeny of zygotes still capable of sporulation are normal. In all cases segregation is 1:1 for any chromosomal gene difference (indicated by ● and ○ nuclei) between the strains. Based on Ephrussi *et al.* (1955).

crosses cannot be made. A typical example is the *petite* variant of yeast. In yeast the diploid zygote is produced by the copulation of two apparently identical haploid cells. The zygote is capable of multiplication by mitotic division, but prior to sexual spore production the nucleus of the zygote undergoes meiosis. Copulation between a wild-type cell and a cell of certain *petite* strains known as *neutral petite* produces a zygote whose phenotype is wild type. And the four haploid sexual spores produced by each zygote are invariably wild type. If these wild-type progeny are crossed once more with *neutral petite* the sexual offspring are still exclusively wild type and repeating this procedure for a further two generations does not alter this result.

A number of other variants listed in Table V including *nonsexual* variants of *A. nidulans* and *low sexual* variants of *A. glaucus* belong in the same category as *neutral petite*. In addition, however, the *low sexual*

TABLE V

VARIANTS THAT DO NOT APPEAR IN THEIR OWN SEXUAL PROGENY OR IN THE PROGENY OF OUTCROSSES TO WILD-TYPE STRAINS

Species	Variants	References
Saccharomyces cerevisiae	neutral petite	Ephrussi (1953)
Aspergillus nidulans	nonsexual	Jinks (1954)
Aspergillus glaucus	low-sexual	Jinks (1956)

variants possess an even more remarkable property, namely, that they do not appear in the sexual progeny produced by selfing (see Section IV, A). It is possible that other extrachromosomal variants in this category would also fail to appear in their own selfed sexual progenies, but this expectation cannot be tested because they are self-sterile. The *neutral petite* and *nonsexual* variants (Table V), for example, can yield sexual progeny only when outcrossed to wild-type strains and all the progenies are wild type.

A second kind of non-Mendelian behavior which has been encountered involves the segregation of the extrachromosomal variant in the sexual progeny of outcrosses to a contrasting phenotype, but with irregular and variable frequencies. The so-called *suppressive petite* variants provide a typical example. On crossing normal and *suppressive petite* strains the immediate phenotype of the zygotes is normal. If the zygotes sporulate at this stage the sexual progeny contains both normal and *petite* segregants, but in proportions which vary from the products of one zygote to another. If instead the zygotes undergo a period of vegetative multiplication, a progressively larger proportion develop a *petite* phenotype and hence become sexually sterile. The remaining fertile zygotes, however, now produce sexual progenies which are predominantly or exclusively normal (Fig. 5).

Three further instances of this kind of non-Mendelian behavior have been found in the fungi, all in *Aspergillus* species (Table VI). In each of these examples the relative proportions of normal and mutant segregants varies widely among the sexual progeny from different perithecia.

D. Behavior during Somatic Growth

Petite and the *mi* mutants are indistinguishable from chromosomal gene mutants in their somatic properties. They are stable, and their phenotypes survive repeated propagations by vegetative hyphae or asexually produced spores unchanged. Other extrachromosomally inherited variants are remarkable for their extreme instability during somatic growth. This may be illustrated by reference to a particular example, the *red* variant (Fig. 6).

1. Persistent Somatic Instability

The *red* variant arose from a single ultraviolet irradiated spore which

TABLE VI

VARIANTS THAT SHOW IRREGULAR AND VARIABLE SEGREGATION RATIOS IN THE SEXUAL PROGENY OF OUTCROSSES TO WILD TYPE STRAINS

Species	Variant	References
Saccharomyces cerevisiae	suppressive petite	Ephrussi et al. (1955)
Aspergillus glaucus	conidial	Sharpe (1958)
Aspergillus nidulans	purple	Grindle (1963)
	alba	Mahoney and Wilkie (1962)

in *A. nidulans* is uninucleate and haploid. The colony produced by this spore was a mixture of normal regions and mutant regions, the latter being characterized by red pigmentation, faster growth, and lower sporulation and perithecial density (Fig. 1a). Single and mass hyphal transfers of this colony gave other colonies which were also mosaics although occasionally a single hyphal transfer gave a stable wild-type colony. Similarly, asexual spores, whether taken from the more normal or from the more mutant regions of the colony, gave rise to colonies with both normal and mutant phenotypes. In general the asexual spores from the more normal regions gave more normal colonies, those from the more mutant regions gave more colonies with the mutant phenotype. But almost all these colonies, whether initially normal or mutant in phenotype, proved to be mosaics with differing proportions of normal to mutant growth. Thus apart from the rare stable wild-type segregant all the colonies sectored and the asexual spores gave colonies which segregated and sectored in their turn (Fig. 6).

In the *red* variant the ability to sector and segregate has survived seven years of propagation by mass hyphal transfers. Furthermore, this ability has been transmitted to the majority of colonies raised from single asexual spores produced by the *red* variant.

Although basically similar to the *red* variant the other somatically unstable variants listed in Table VII may differ from it in one of two ways, namely, in their persistence and in the continuity of their segregation.

a. Persistence. In addition to *red* there are other variants, for example, *purple*, in which the somatic instability of the variant is transmitted to the majority of colonies obtained from hyphae and single asexual spores. But there are also variants, for example, *compact* (Table VII) in which the somatic instability of the variant is lost in the majority of propagations, however made. Every *compact* colony sooner or later produces fast-growing sectors which are wild type in appearance. All propagations made from these sectors, whether by hyphae or by asexual spores, give pure-breeding, wild-type colonies. The mutant portions of the sectored colonies, on the other hand, give both mutant and wild-type

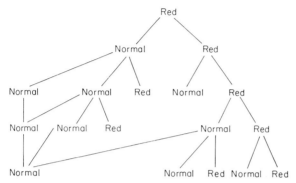

FIG. 6. The pedigree of a persistently segregating variant *red* of *Aspergillus nidulans*. Each propagation is made by a single, haploid, uninucleate asexual spore. This pattern of behavior has survived unchanged through continual propagations since 1956. Other persistently segregating variants behave similarly (Table VII). From Jinks (1964b).

TABLE VII

VARIANTS THAT SHOW PERSISTENT INSTABILITY DURING VEGETATIVE GROWTH AND AT ASEXUAL REPRODUCTION

Species	Designation or characteristic of variant	References
Aspergillus nidulans	red	Jinks (1958), Arlett *et al.* (1962)
	low sexual	Jinks (1954, 1956)
	compact	Grindle (1963)
	purple	Grindle (1963)
	alba	Mahoney and Wilkie (1962)
Aspergillus glaucus	low sexual	Jinks (1956, 1957)
	vegetative death	Jinks (1956, 1959)
	compact	Jinks (1963)
	conidial	Sharpe (1958)
Penicillium sp.	mycelial	Jinks (1960)
	low sporulation	Jinks (1960)
Nectria stenospora	tassellated	Gibson and Griffin (1958)

colonies when propagated by hyphae or by asexual spores. All the colonies with the mutant phenotype retain the ability to sector and their asexual spores repeat the segregation, but all the wild-type colonies are stable and pure breeding (Fig. 1).

Since the wild-type sectors which are invariably produced by every colony of the *compact* variants rapidly outgrow the variants, the leading edge of the colonies become entirely wild type. Hence, only by transferring hyphae and spores from the mutant portions of the colonies and selecting those propagants with mutant phenotypes can these variants be retained. Nevertheless, a *compact* strain has been maintained in this way for many years.

b. *Continuity of the Segregation.* The sectors and segregants which continually emerge from the *red, purple, conidial,* and *compact* variants differ discontinuously, and the colonies produced by their asexual spores can be unambiguously classified into two groups on colonial morphology. In other cases there is a persistent instability, but it is not accompanied by a discontinuous sectoring or segregation. Nevertheless a persistent, continuous segregation among propagants derived from a single colony by hyphal or asexual spore transfers can be demonstrated in a number of ways. First, if the variation among such propagants is measured for a metrical trait, for example rate of growth or perithecial density, it is significantly in excess of that which can be ascribed to error variation (Fig. 2). Secondly the extreme phenotyes of the continuous distribution can be selected and propagated by samples of single hyphae or of single asexual spores. The variation within the samples from the same extreme colony are again in excess of that ascribable to error variation. Furthermore, the samples from the opposite extreme colonies differ significantly and to about the same extent as their selected parental colonies; that is, the difference between the selected colonies persists in their hyphal and asexual spore propagants. If this selection of extremes is continued for a number of successive propagations colonies are obtained from the opposite selections which differ discontinuously from one another in their colonial morphology (Figs. 1f and 2).

For the purpose of discussion the unstable variants have been divided into two classes, those which lead to discontinuous, and those which lead to continuous, variation. In practice no such clear distinction exists. In many cases it is a matter of convenience only whether one classifies the variation into discontinuous groups on colonial morphology or measures some metrical trait and treats the data statistically. An account of the persistent instability of the *red* variant, for example, can be given in terms of the two morphological classes *red* and normal. On the other hand, it can also be described in terms of the continuous variation in rate of growth, sporulation, and perithecial density; the conclusions are the same. Similarly, while the variation in perithecial density shown by some strains of *A. nidulans* and *A. glaucus* can be readily analyzed as a continuously varying character, it can also be analyzed in terms of colonial morphology, although as many as five classes may be required to give an adequate description of the observed patterns of variation. Even where, as with the *red* variant, a simple, unambiguous morphological classification is possible, within each class there is considerable variation. Thus the percentage of *red* segregants in the asexual progenies of colonies classified as normal varies from 0 to 15% while those colonies classified as *red* produce asexual progenies containing 10–95% *red* segregants. The distribution of the percentage of *red* segregants is continuous both within and between the morphological classes. And even if a discontinuous grouping of these percentages is attempted, between 5 and 7 classes are required. Thus the difference between the morphologically normal and *red* segregants of the *red* variant is that the normal colonies rarely give more than 10–15% *red* segregants in their asexual progenies while the *red* colonies rarely give less. Between 10 and 15% there is a threshold: above it the morphology is distinctly mutant, below it the morphology is indistinguishable from normal. Although an underlying continuity has so far been demonstrated only for the discontinuous segregation of the *red* variant, the indications are that this is generally true for all the discontinuously segregating variants.

2. Somatic Reassortment

Homokaryotic strains of fungi differing in one or more chromosomal genes can often coexist in a heterokaryotic state and, apart from rare exceptions due to mitotic recombination, the homokaryotic strains may be reextracted from this association with their phenotypes and chromosomal gene complements unchanged. If, however, the homokaryotic strains also differ in an extrachromosomally inherited trait the latter emerges from the heterokaryotic association in new combinations with the chromosomal gene complements. The kinds of new combinations vary with the nature of the extrachromosomally inherited difference. The simplest situation is typified by the extrachromosomally inherited *nonsexual* variants of *A. nidulans* (Table VIII). In *A. nidulans* the homokaryotic components of a heterokaryon can be reextracted by germinating the uninucleate asexual spores produced by the latter. The homokaryons extracted from a heterokaryon between a sexual and a nonsexual strain are identical with the original strains for the known chromosomally inherited traits by which they differ. All the colonies reextracted from the heterokaryon, however, are highly sexual irrespective of their chromosomal gene complements. Hence the nonsexual component of the heterokaryon has been converted to sexuality during the association.

A different situation is found with heterokaryons between the *mi* and normal strains of *N. crassa* (Table VIII). For example, from a heterokaryon between a lysine-requiring (lys^-) mutant of the mi-4 variant and a non-lysine-requiring (lys^+) normal strain, four kinds of stable homokaryotic colonies could be extracted, namely, lys^-mi-4, lys^- normal, lys^+ mi-4, and lys^+ normal. For the $lys^-:lys^+$ and the other known genes by which the original strains differed, the reextracted homokaryons fell into only two classes. These were identical with the two strains which formed

TABLE VIII

VARIANTS THAT SHOW REASSORTMENT WITH KNOWN CHROMOSOMAL GENE MARKERS WHEN IN HETEROKARYOTIC ASSOCIATION WITH A NORMAL STRAIN

Species	Designation or characteristic of variant	References
Aspergillus nidulans	nonsexual	Jinks (1954)
	mycelial	Roper (1958)
	red	Arlett et al. (1962)
	purple	Grindle (1963)
	alba	Mahoney and Wilkie (1962)
Aspergillus glaucus	low-sexual	Jinks (1956, 1957)
	slow growth	Jinks (1956, 1957)
	nonpigmented	Jinks (1957)
	adaptability to mercuric chloride	Jinks (1958)
	vegetative death	Jinks (1959)
Saccharomyces cerevisiae	suppressive petite	Wright and Lederberg (1957)
Nectria stenospora	tassellated	Gibson and Griffin (1958)
Neurospora crassa	*mi*-variants	Pittenger (1956)
Penicillium sp.	mycelial	Jinks (1960)
	low sporulation	Jinks (1960)

the heterokaryon. In contrast the mi-4:normal extrachromosomal difference had reassorted with the two chromosomal gene complements while associated in the heterokaryon.

The *petite*:normal difference also reassorts in a heterokaryon. In yeast, heterokaryons can be made by employing strains in which the conjugation of haploid cells is not accompanied by nuclear fusion. During the vegetative budding of the heterokaryon haploid cells are produced, and hence monokaryotic strains can be reextracted from the association. These are identical with the original haploid strains for all known chromosomal gene differences. If, however, one of the conjugating strains is *petite* and the other normal, the haploid strains which are recovered from the heterokaryon are sometimes *petite* and sometimes normal irrespective of whether their chromosomal gene complements are derived from the original *petite* or the original normal strain.

The somatically unstable variants, for example *red* and *purple*, behave much the same as the *mi* and *petite* mutants when in heterokaryotic association with a normal strain (Fig. 7). Heterokaryons between a green-spored (W) non-compact (CO) *red* variant and a non-red strain carrying the gene mutations *white spores* (w) and *compact growth* (co) produce asexual progenies which fall into four classes, namely, WCO *red*, WCO non-red, wco *red,* and wco non-red. Thus the two chromosomal gene

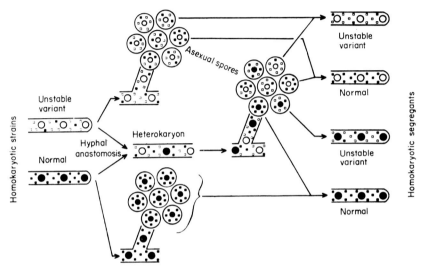

FIG. 7. The heterokaryon test between an unstable, persistently segregating variant (for example the *red* variant of *Aspergillus nidulans*) and a normal strain. The two strains are also distinguished by two or more chromosomal gene markers (indicated by ● and ○ nuclei). At asexual spore formation the variant produces normal and variant segregants while the normal strain produces only normal spores. The heterokaryon produces asexual spores with the variant and with the normal constitution. But most important it produces spores with the nucleus of the normal strain ● and the unstable variant constitution. This class of spore can arise only if the determination of the unstable variant is extranuclear. From Jinks (1964b).

differences W:w and CO:co are extracted in their original combinations, but the red:non-red difference shows reassortment. Because of the instability of the *red* variant, however, WCO non-red colonies can arise from WCO *red* colonies without reassortment. Hence, wco *red* is the only one of the four classes to emerge from the heterokaryon which could not have arisen without the reassortment of the extrachromosomal difference.

The demonstration of the somatic reassortment of extrachromosomal differences in what is now known as the heterokaryon test can be extended to basidiomycetes by employing the dikaryotic stage of the life cycle. Thus two monokaryotic strains can be associated in the dikaryotic state and subsequently reextracted either through the production of uninucleate asexual spores, e.g., oidia, or by micrurgery (see Harder, 1927; Papazian, 1958). There have been a number of claims that monokaryons associated in a dikaryon reemerge with temporary or even permanently altered phenotypes (Harder, 1927; Aschan, 1952). This suggests that some of the initial differences between the monokaryons were extrachromosomal in origin. Unfortunately, none of these examples is conclusive, but they indicate the prospective usefulness of this test for detecting extrachromosomal differences between monokaryotic strains of basidiomycetes.

3. Invasion

There are a few extrachromosomal variants which transmit their mutant phenotype to normal colonies with which they happen to be in contact. Among these variants are *barrage* and *senescence* in *Podospora anserina* and *conidial* and *vegetative death* in *Aspergillus glaucus* (Table IX). If

TABLE IX
EXAMPLES OF VARIANTS THAT ARE INVASIVE WHEN GROWN IN HYPHAL CONTACT WITH A NORMAL STRAIN

Species	Variant	References
Coprinus macrorhizus	*fluffy*	Dickson (1935)
Aspergillus glaucus	*conidial*	Sharpe (1958)
	vegetative death	Jinks (1959)
Podospora anserina	*barrage*	Rizet et al. (1958)
	senescence	Marcou (1961)
Pestalotia annulata	*growth rhythm*	Chevaugeon and Lefort (1960)

hyphae of a variant such as *vegetative death* are inoculated alongside a colony which is distinguished from it by a number of chromosomal gene differences and by growing normally, in about 70% of cases the latter shows all the characteristics of *vegetative death* within 5 days. The symptoms of *vegetative death* appear first at the points of contact between the normal and variant hyphae and then spread to the remainder of the normal colony. The asexual spores produced on the affected portions of the normal colony give rise to homokaryotic colonies possessing only the known chromosomal genes of the initially normal strain, but many of these colonies have all the characteristics of *vegetative death*. The absence of spores containing the nucleus of the variant in the affected portions suggests that there is no nuclear migration from the variant to the normal hyphae. The absence of nuclear migration during the invasive spread of the variant phenotype has also been demonstrated for *conidial, senescence,* and *barrage*. On the other hand, for *vegetative death* and *senescence* it has been shown that anastomosis between the variant and normal hyphae leading to a localized heterokaryon formation is the route by which the extrachromosomal agent responsible for the conversion from normal to variant enters the normal colony. Thus the characteristics of *vegetative death* fail to spread to the normal colony unless heterokaryotic cells are produced at the point of contact between variant and normal hyphae. Furthermore, no agent has so far been extracted from the hyphae of *vegetative death* nor from the medium in which this variant has grown that will produce even a temporary effect on the hyphae of normal colonies.

It would appear, therefore, that at the time of heterokaryon formation at the points of contact between normal and variant hyphae there is a mixing of the two extrachromosomal complements. The extrachromosomal agent responsible for the variant phenotype then replaces its counterpart in every normal hypha to which it can gain access. That is, the agent is suppressive.

Confirmation of this interpretation comes from observations on stable heterokaryons between a homokaryon showing *vegetative death* and a normal partner. The heterokaryons are initially normal, but they begin to show the phenotype of *vegetative death* after 5 days. In the asexual progeny of the heterokaryon the variant:normal difference showed reassortment with the known chromosomal gene differences which distinguished the initially variant and normal homokaryons. The majority of colonies in the asexual progeny had the variant phenotype and this proportion increased with the age of the heterokaryon. Thus in the heterokaryon the extrachromosomal determinant of *vegetative death* gradually replaced its normal counterpart (Fig. 1e).

E. Conclusions

In this section we have described the properties of some variants which are extrachromosomally inherited. These properties are often sufficiently different from those of chromosomal gene mutants to be diagnostic of their extrachromosomal origin. Thus whether we examine the induction, inheritance, or somatic growth of the variants we find patterns of behavior that are difficult to explain without the assumption of extrachromosomal control.

III. THE NATURE OF THE EXTRACHROMOSOMAL SYSTEM

The determinants of extrachromosomal heredity must reside within the extrachromosomal material of the cell. Attempts to locate their sites within this material have been made by both cytological investigations and breeding experiments. The evidence produced is suggestive rather than conclusive and many determinants have been inferred from breeding experiments, for which there is still no known physical basis. Even in these cases, however, it is possible to deduce some of the properties of the determinants and their behavior at cell division and reproduction.

A. Location of Extrachromosomal Determinants

Petite was the first fungal variant to implicate an extrachromosomal organelle, namely, the mitochondrion, in extrachromosomal heredity. This was confirmed by the *mi* mutants of *Neurospora*. Together they constitute a formidable case for the participation of extrachromosomal determinants in the control of the structure and function of mitochondria. They also raise the possibility that the determinants which exercise this control may be borne on the mitochondria themselves (Ephrussi and Slonimski, 1955).

To qualify as a bearer of hereditary determinants a structure must satisfy a number of criteria. The first of these is that the structure must always arise by the division of, or as the result of generation by, a similar structure. That is, it must not arise *de novo*. A direct proof that a structure satisfies this criterion requires the demonstration that a cell which has lost the structure cannot subsequently produce it. Structures such as mitochondria whose presence in the cell is apparently essential for survival cannot be subjected to this test. We have to rely, therefore, on indirect evidence such as observations of the method of replication of mitochondria in normal cells. It is widely accepted on the basis of microscopical observations that in somatic cells mitochondria replicate by fission. This conclusion is supported by experiments in which the mitochondria of rapidly growing *Neurospora* cells were pulse-labeled with radioactive choline. When the mitochondria increased in number all were found to contain the label, a result which is compatible with the formation of new mitochondria by the growth and division of existing mitochondria (Luck, 1963). On the other hand, there are claims that during gametogenesis in higher plants mitochondria are generated from simpler, nonmitochondrial material. It has been suggested, for example, that during gametogenesis the membranes of mitochondria develop from the general membranous system of the cell which includes the nuclear and outer cell membranes and the endoplasmic reticulum.

If this interpretation of events during gametogenesis is correct, it suggests that the extrachromosomal determinants which control mitochondrial development might lie outside the mitochondrion and perhaps reside in the membrane system. During the generation of mitochondria at gametogenesis, however, these determinants could become part of the mitochondrial structure, thus conferring on the mitochondria a genetic continuity which extended throughout somatic life and ended only at gametogenesis.

Irrespective of whether we accept this interpretation there can be no restriction on the genetic continuity of the determinants themselves. To account for the persistence of the abnormal mitochondria of *petite* and *poky* from one generation to the next there must be a corresponding persistence of the extrachromosomal determinants which control mitochondrial development.

Recent demonstrations that mitochondria contain nucleic acids in the form of DNA as well as RNA lend additional support to the view that the mitochondria carry hereditary information. (Chèvremont, 1963; Luck and Reich, 1964; Gibor and Granick, 1964). In *Neurospora,* as in the other species examined, the DNA of the mitochondria appears to be double-stranded and possesses a unique buoyant density (Luck and Reich, 1964). The presence of nucleic acid, however, does not completely resolve the problem of the genetic continuity of the mitochondria. Its presence could be explained by assuming that extramitochondrial nucleic acids provide the information for the generation of mitochondria and in the process become incorporated into their structure.

The presence of DNA in the mitochondria either as a permanent or as a semipermanent constituent accounts for all the properties of the extrachromosomally inherited respiratory mutants of yeasts and *Neurospora.* It also explains the action spectrum for the UV induction of these mutants in yeast which has a maximum that coincides with the maximum absorption bands for DNA (Raut and Simpson, 1955; Wilkie, 1963).

The fungi provide no evidence which implicates other extrachromosomal structures in extrachromosomal heredity. The green plants and protozoa, however, provide considerable evidence that structures such as plastids, kinetosomes, and kinetoplasts possess genetic continuity and are themselves subject to the control of extrachromosomal determinants (Jinks, 1964a). Furthermore, these structures also appear to contain a DNA of the kind found in mitochondria (see Gibor and Granick, 1964, for review). While this evidence makes an important contribution to our understanding of the physical basis of extrachromosomal heredity it has no direct relevance to any known extrachromosomal variant of fungi. However, it is clear that a consistent picture is emerging in which there is an association of extrachromosomal DNA with organelles which, from genetic studies, appear to be in part under extrachromosomal hereditary control and which have themselves long been suspected of being carriers of hereditary information.

B. *The Nature of Extrachromosomal Change*

To explain the origin, persistence, and segregation of extrachromosomally inherited variants it is necessary to postulate a change in some extrachromosomally located cell component. There are a number of ways in which this change from a normal to a variant condition could occur: for example: (i) a change in the relative frequency or activity of the cell component (in practice this is indistinguishable from, and may be identical with, so-called alternative "steady states"); (ii) the physical loss of the cell component; (iii) a change in the structure and function of the cell component; (iv) the introduction of an extrachromosomally located cell component from an extraneous source.

If, of course, the presence of extrachromosomal DNA is responsible for the hereditary properties of cell components then these four categories of change clearly relate to the DNA borne by the cell component.

These changes have their counterpart at the chromosomal level; for example, (ii) is a deletion, and (iii) a point mutation or structural rearrangement. The last of them, (iv), is equivalent to the introduction of an alternative form of a chromosomal gene by reassortment, recombination, transduction, or transformation.

All four kinds of change have been postulated at one time or another to explain particular examples of extrachromosomal variation. The first two [(i) and (ii)] were originally favored as explanations of the early observations on *neutral petite* and variation in sexuality in *Aspergillus*. The stable *nonsexual* variants arise as extreme segregants in strains which show a continuous range of phenotypes differing in sexuality. Similarly, *petite* arises spontaneously as a stable lower extreme of a continuous variation in colony size. Thus the intermediate segregants were explained by an irregular distribution of an extrachromosomal component so that some cells and spores contained more than others. The stable mutants, on this explanation, would then be the extreme products of this irregular distribution in that they would arise from cells and spores which received no representative of the component.

On the basis of this explanation we can make two predictions: (1) Until the last representative of the extrachromosomal component has been lost from a cell lineage, no change in phenotype which has occurred in the extrachromosomal system should be irreversible; hence the intermediate phenotypes should be reversible. (2) Since the stable variants have lost all representatives of the component, their phenotypes should not revert to normal nor to an intermediate phenotype until this component has been reintroduced by conjugation or anastamosis with a normal cell. Both predictions have been verified for *neutral petite* and *nonsexual*. While this suggests that an explanation based on (i) and (ii) gives an adequate account of the origin and breeding behavior of these variants, an explanation based on (iii) is also adequate if we assume that there is a change in function or structure of the extrachromosomal component which makes it inert. The segregation, of which the stable variants are the extreme products, could then be explained by assuming that the active and inert forms of the component are distributed unequally among cells and spores. The stable variants would then arise from cells or spores, which by chance, receive only the inert form. Thus we cannot discriminate between the first three models of extrachromosomal change on the basis of variants such as *neutral petite* and *nonsexual*. The behavior of some suppressive variants, however, allows us to draw this distinction.

A number of extrachromosomal variants including *suppressive petite, poky, vegetative death, senescence, red,* and *mycelial* are suppressive in that following conjugation between a normal cell and a cell of one of these variants the phenotype and breeding behavior of the resulting mixture is predominantly or exclusively like that of the variant. It is difficult to explain this dominance in action and in replication of the extrachromosomal complement of the variant if the latter merely lacks a component which is present in normal cells. Rather we must postulate the presence of an extrachromosomal component in the variant cells with properties that are not found in any component of a normal cell.

Among fungal variants there exist all degrees of suppressiveness as measured by the frequency and speed with which colonies initiated by the fusion of normal and variant cells take on the properties of the variant. In fact the many different forms of *petite* alone cover the whole range of degrees of suppressiveness as measured in this way. No sharp distinction can, therefore, be drawn between suppressive and nonsuppressive variants. Indeed the same extrachromosomal variant may be suppressive or suppressed according to the genotype it is associated with when brought into contact with a normal extrachromosomal complement (see Section III, D, 4). This continuity between suppressive and nonsuppressive mutants suggests a similarity in their underlying basis. If, therefore, suppressive and nonsuppressive variants arise from similar changes in the extrachromosomal system we must accept that these changes are of the kind envisaged in model (iii).

Category (iv) of extrachromosomal change covers a variety of phenomena. Under this heading can be included, for example, the substitution of one form of an extrachromosomal component for another as a result of their heterokaryotic association or as a result of the invasive spread of one form into a mycelium containing an alternative form (Sections II, D, 2 and 3). A further relevant example is the transformation of spheroblasts of a *petite* strain of yeast to a stable, respiratory normal form by the incorporation of mitochondria extracted from a normal strain. The particular importance of this example resides in the fact that it provides the most direct evidence so far that the difference between *petite* and normal cells resides exclusively in a permanent difference in their mitochondria since no other constituent of the normal cell is involved in the transformation (Tuppy and Wildner, 1965).

Another phenomenon that belongs here is exemplified by the "killer trait" in *Paramecium aurelia*. Its extrachromosomal determinant, kappa, has a number of properties in common with viruses and *Paramecium* can be infected with kappa by being exposed to suspensions of the debris from animals which contain it. It seems likely at the present time that a number of "contagious diseases" of fungi, for example, the killer factor in yeast (Makower and Bevan, 1963) and the agent of "die back" in the cultivated mushroom (Holling *et al.*, 1963) which are extrachromosomal components with a number of viral properties, also belong in this same category.

There is a further class of extrachromosomal determinants, as yet unknown in fungi, which could produce the kind of change included in type (iv). These are the viral and nonviral episomes of bacteria. Episomes can alternate between a chromosomal and extrachromosomal site in the cell and can be transmitted as a chromosomal locus or as an extrachromosomal body possessing genetic continuity. The existence of viral episomes which have in addition an extracellular phase has been demonstrated in the bacterium *Escherichia coli*. The evidence for nonviral episomes is more widespread but also more conjectural. Episomes in their chromosomal or extracellular phase are, therefore, a possible source of determinants in the kind of situation envisaged in (iv), although there is no evidence that determinants from this source are involved in any instance of extrachromosomal inheritance in fungi.

C. *Properties of Extrachromosomal Determinants*

An adequate model of the extrachromosomal system must not only account for the origin of extrachromosomal variants (Section II, B), but also for their more important properties such as somatic segregation and suppression.

1. *Somatic Segregation*

Somatic segregation due to extrachromosomal causes is encountered in three situations (Fig. 8). It may occur (a) spontaneously, a homokaryotic clone giving rise to a continuous array of phenotypes the abnormal extreme of which is often a stable variant; (b) following the induction of an extrachromosomal variant, when there may be an initial period of instability of varying duration during which both normal, variant, and intermediate phenotypes emerge as segregants; (c) following cell conjugation or anastomosis between strains which differ in an extrachromosomally inherited trait, when there is a segregation into the components of the mixture and the appearance of intermediate phenotypes.

In each of these situations two contrasting phenotypes appear, among the segregants produced at mitotic cell divisions, which show extrachromosomal inheritance. If, therefore, we accept that the difference between the contrasting phenotypes is of the type we have called (iii) (Section II, B), then the cells from which they segregate must contain two alternative forms of an extrachromosomal determinant, that is, they must be heteroplasmic. Hence on this interpretation heteroplasmons, like their chromosomal equivalent, heterozygotes, arise in two ways; by a spontaneous or induced

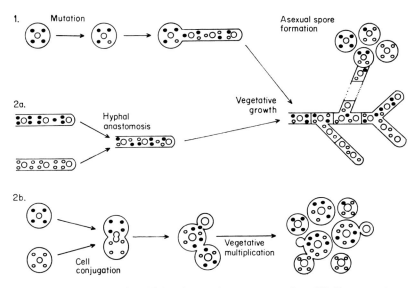

FIG. 8. The two ways in which a heteroplasmon may arise: (1) By a spontaneous or an induced mutation in one or more, but not in all, of the representatives of an extrachromosomal determinant present in a cell. (2) By the fusion of cells from homoplasmic strains which differ for an extrachromosomally inherited trait. The fusion may occur when (a) there is anastomosis between the vegetative cells of a fungus or (b) when haploid cells conjugate to give diploids, as for example in yeasts. Irrespective of the mode of origin the consequence is always the same, namely an unstable extrachromosomal complement which segregates at cell division, hyphal branching, and asexual spore formation. From Jinks (1964b).

mutation in one or more, but not in all, of the homologs of a determinant present in a cell and by conjugation of cells containing alternative forms of a determinant. Thus the same mechanism will suffice to explain the "unstable state" that often accompanies the induction of extrachromosomal mutations and the similar instability of known heteroplasmons synthesized from two different homoplasmons (Section II, D, 2). By itself, however, it will not explain why the unstable state initiated at the induction of a variant should persist indefinitely as it does, for example, in the *red* variant (Section II, D, 1). We have already seen how the persistent segregation of the *red* variant produces a continuous range of phenotypes which vary from homoplasmic normal to an extreme mutant phenotype but fall short of producing a pure-breeding homoplasmic mutant segregant (but see Section III, D, 4). While every other property of the *red* variant fits a heteroplasmic model, this absence of the homoplasmic mutant component among the segregants is anomalous. It seems likely, therefore, that the homoplasmic mutant is lethal and hence it can survive only in the heteroplasmic state.

While the initiation of a heteroplasmic state appears to initiate somatic segregation it is not sufficient to cause the latter, as the following considerations will show. Let us consider the simplest heteroplasmic state, namely, a cell which contains one normal A and one mutant a homolog of a determinant. Let us assume that the replication and distribution of these homologs at cell division is *regular,* that is it follows the same rules as the chromosomes at a mitotic cell division. Thus prior to cell division each homolog will replicate, and one A and one a homolog will pass to each daughter cell (Fig. 9). Hence if the division is regular there is no segregation. Let us now assume that division is *irregular*. Prior to division the heteroplasmic cell has the constitution $AAaa$. These four homologs could be distributed between daughter cells in a number of irregular ways. The distribution could be numerically unequal, one cell receiving 4 or 3 and the other 0 or 1 homologs, respectively, or it could be qualitatively unequal one cell receiving 2 A and the other 2 a homologs. But clearly irregularities of one or both kinds must be assumed to explain segregation of a heteroplasmon at mitotic cell divisions. This conclusion holds irrespective of the complexity of the segregation pattern which results from assuming more than two homologs per cell and unequal rates of replication for the two forms of the determinant (Fig. 9).

Attempts have been made to estimate the number of homologs of a determinant per asexual spore and distribution of mutant and normal homologs of a determinant at spore formation using the *red* variant. Identically maintained colonies of this variant, each initiated by a single asexual spore produce asexual progenies whose compositions vary from 5% normal:95% *red* segregants to 100% normal segregants. These differences in the composition of asexual progenies are far in excess of anything which can be ascribed to extraneous causes. They must, therefore, be due to inherent differences between the spores which produce the parental colonies. It follows then that each parental colony whose asexual progeny contains a distinct proportion of normal:*red* segregants must have arisen from an asexual spore with a distinct composition in terms of the relative numbers of normal to mutant homologs of the determinant it contains. Since we can recognize at least seven classes of asexual progenies which differ significantly in their proportions of normal:*red* segregants, we can infer that the *red* variant can produce a corresponding number of classes of asexual spores. That is, spores containing seven different proportions of mutant to normal homologs are produced.

If we now make the further assumption that the total number of homologs per spore is constant, then six homologs of the *red* determinant must be present to lead to seven different proportions of mutant to normal homo-

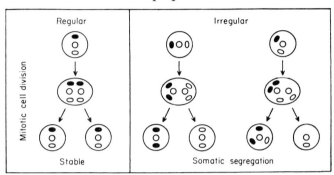

FIG. 9. The consequences of regular and irregular distribution of normal (●) and mutant (○) homologs of an extrachromosomal determinant at the division of a heteroplasmic cell. The irregularity may be qualitative or quantitative, but unless the distribution is irregular there is no segregation for the extrachromosomal difference. From Jinks (1964b).

logs. One possible asexual progeny which contains only pure-breeding *red* segregants, corresponding with a spore containing only mutant homologs, is never recovered. It is presumed to be lethal (Section III, C, 1). Nevertheless it raises the number of spore constitutions which must be accounted for to eight, and hence the number of homologs per spore to seven. The frequencies of these eight spore constitutions in a random sample of asexual spores of the *red* variant are given in Table X. Included for comparison are the frequencies expected if the seven homologs that go into each spore were chosen at random from a large pool of mutant and normal homologs. The correspondence between the observed frequencies and those predicted in this way suggests that we can account for the somatic segregation of the *red* variant, and hence, presumably, of other variants, by a model in which (1) there is more than one homolog of each determinant per cell; (2) there is a heteroplasmic state in the cells which initiate the segregation; and (3) there is an irregular or, in this case, a random distribution of normal and mutant homologs at mitotic cell divisions.

2. *Interaction between Extrachromosomal Determinants*

So far in this discussion of the heteroplasmic state we have avoided the complications which arise from the interactions between alternative forms of a determinant and between different determinants. These interactions are of two kinds, suppression and synergism. Examples of both have been described in the fungi.

a. Suppression. Suppression occurs in the majority of heteroplasmons whether initiated by mutation or by cell fusion. Where the heteroplasmon is composed of a mutant and normal homoplasmon it is usually the mutant component which is suppressive (Section III, B). There are two aspects

TABLE X

THE FREQUENCY WITH WHICH THE EIGHT PROPOSED SPORE CONSTITUTIONS REQUIRED TO ACCOUNT FOR THE SEGREGATIONAL BEHAVIOR OF THE red VARIANT ARE RECOVERED IN A RANDOM SAMPLE OF ASEXUAL SPORES OF THIS VARIANT[a] (Jinks, 1964a)

Spore constitution normal:mutant homologs	Observed frequency	Expected frequency
7:0	0	0.20
6:1	1	1.37
5:2	3	4.10
4:3	10	6.83
3:4	7	6.83
2:5	2	4.10
1:6	2	1.37
0:7	0	0.20

[a] The frequencies expected on a binomial distribution are given for comparison.

to the suppression of one form of a determinant by an alternative form, namely, a superiority in action that is akin to dominance and a superiority in rate of replication. In the case of the *poky* mutant the altered biochemical properties of the mutant determinant may be responsible for its suppressiveness (H. K. Mitchell and Hertzenberg, 1955). The mitochondria of *poky*, in contrast to those from normal cells, possess a potent enzyme which destroys cytochromes. This enzyme destroys both *poky* and normal cytochromes when they are brought together *in vitro*. The suppression of the normal component in a heteroplasmon could, therefore, result from the destruction of the products of its activities. There are two observations which are opposed to this interpretation of suppression. First, the *in vivo* activity of the enzyme in *poky* is insufficient to prevent the accumulation of cytochromes in its own hyphae. Secondly, the suppressive action of *petite* is independent of the modified biochemical activities of *petite* cells (Sherman and Ephrussi, 1962). For the present, therefore, we shall regard suppression as a superiority in the action and replication of one form of a determinant relative to an alternative form rather than as the ability to destroy the products of an alternative form.

We have previously equated heteroplasmons and heterozygotes, but suppression in heteroplasmons has no counterpart in heterozygotes. Thus homologous chromosomes in a heterozygote do not compete in reproduction; the mechanical properties of chromosome replication and division ensure that they keep in step. Greater similarity might, therefore, be expected between heteroplasmons and heterokaryons since in the latter the nuclei of the homokaryotic components are free to compete in action and reproduction. But even in heterokaryons, competition rarely, if ever, leads to a mutant component ousting its normal partner; on the contrary, the outcome is usually the reverse. It appears, therefore, that suppressiveness is a property which is largely confined to extrachromosomal mutants.

Before accepting this conclusion, however, we should reconsider the origin of extrachromosomal mutants. Earlier we concluded that the immediate effect of a mutation is the initiation of a heteroplasmon. On this basis the recognition and isolation of such a mutant is more likely to be successful if the phenotype of the heteroplasmon is readily distinguishable from that of the wild-type homoplasmon. Hence the technical problems of recognition and isolation could impose an automatic selection for mutants which are suppressive in the heteroplasmic state.

b. Synergism. A synergistic interaction in heterozygotic and heterokaryotic associations is critical evidence for the functional independence of chromosomal gene mutations. This is equally valid for extrachromosomal mutants in heteroplasmic association. Thus if two extrachromosomal mutants are defective in independent functions, each will contribute to a heteroplasmon the normal function which is lacking in its partner. Therefore, we would expect a heteroplasmon between two functionally independent mutants to have a more normal phenotype than either of its homoplasmic components.

Evidence of the functional independence of extrachromosomal mutants has been sought only among the *mi* variants of *Neurospora*. All possible heteroplasmons were made between these variants and one, that between *poky (mi-1)* and *mi-4,* had a near wild-type growth rate (Pittenger, 1956). After 1000 cm of growth, however, even this heteroplasmon reverted to the type of growth characteristic of its mutant components. And at all times the biochemical properties of the heteroplasmon were those of its mutant components. Nevertheless, the initial period of rapid growth leaves no doubt that in a heteroplasmon *mi-1* and *mi-4* can partially compensate for one another's functional defects.

Both *mi-1* and *mi-4* are suppressive when in heteroplasmic association with wild-type strains. Hence the period of mutual compensation is short lived because of the mutual suppression of the normal functions contributed by each mutant by the defective function contributed by its partner.

This investigation of the interactive properties of the *mi* variants is the first step in the analysis of the functional relationships within the extrachromosomal system of a fungus. It is important because the results indicate that the techniques which are at present successfully elucidating the structure and function of the chromosomal system can be adapted to yield similar information at the extrachromosomal level. The best evidence that this is so, however, comes from the alga *Chlamydomonas* where the application of standard procedures for studying gene structure and function, that is, complementation tests and linkage studies, have been applied to the extrachromosomal system with remarkable success (Sager and Ramanis, 1965).

D. Interrelationships of the Chromosomal and Extrachromosomal Systems

Evidence that the chromosomal and extrachromosomal systems are interdependent in action and reproduction has been obtained wherever an adequate investigation has been made. This evidence is of four kinds.

1. Chromosomal-Extrachromosomal Mimics

Chromosomal and extrachromosomal mutations often lead to similar phenotypic changes. For example, there are chromosomally inherited mutants whose phenotypes are identical with *petite,* the *mi* variants, *vegetative death,* and *nonsexual.* In the case of the *petite* and *mi* variants the similarity between the effects of the extrachromosomal and chromosomal mutations extends to the biochemical level. It is clear from such examples that the cooperation of both chromosomally and extrachromosomally inherited components is essential for the production of a normal phenotype, a mutation in either component being sufficient to disrupt the action of both components.

2. Interdependence in Action

Gene mutations are known which suppress the phenotypic effect of the extrachromosomally inherited *poky* mutant and the *mycelial* variants of *A. nidulans* (M. B. Mitchell and Mitchell, 1956; Roper, 1958). In both cases a single chromosomal gene mutation can restore the variant phenotype to wild type although some of the biochemical defects of the *poky* variant are present in a much reduced form in the suppressed state. If, by appropriate breeding procedures, these mutant genes are replaced by their wild-type alleles the phenotypic effects of the *mycelial* and *poky* mutants are restored immediately. Hence the gene suppressors have no permanent effect on the extrachromosomal determinants.

The suppressor of *poky* (*f*) is highly specific. It has no effect on any of the other mutants, either chromosomal or extrachromosomal, which affect the respiratory system of *N. crassa.* Thus while *poky, mi-2,* and *mi-3* are sufficiently related functionally not to show a synergistic interaction when in heteroplasmic association, they are sufficiently different to be distinguishable on their reaction to *f*.

The properties of various combinations of chromosomal genes with *poky* have been investigated by Silagi (1965). The combination with the genes *fluffy, peach,* and a gene for fatty acid requirement all grew more slowly than either *poky* or the mutant genes alone. A combination of *poky* with a gene which promotes fast growth, however, grew almost at the wild-type rate of growth, but the cytochrome system of the combination was still that typical of *poky*.

Suppression of chromosomal gene action by the extrachromosomal complement is also found in *Neurospora*. Since all the known extrachromosomally inherited differences in this species show strict maternal inheritance (Section II, C, 1) it is possible to transfer the chromosomal genes of one strain into the extrachromosomal complement of another by repeatedly back-crossing the former to the latter as the maternal parent. In this way the phenotypic effect of chromosomal genes can be compared in their original and in a different extrachromosomal complement. Two such comparisons involving the gene mutations *ac* and *s* have been described (Srb, 1958). The mutant *ac* produces colonies which lack conidia in the extrachromosomal complement of *N. sitophila* and wild-type colonies in the extrachromosomal complement of *N. crassa*. Similarly, the mutant *s* gives large colonies in the extrachromosomal complement of the common laboratory strain of *N. crassa,* but small colonies in that of a Philippine Islands strain of *N. crassa*.

Yeast also provides examples, the most remarkable being the extrachromosomally determined suppression of the chromosomal gene "super suppressor" (Cox, 1965). "Super suppressor" is itself a remarkable gene in that it simultaneously suppresses the action of auxotrophic mutants at a number of chromosomal loci. Breeding tests on stable reversions to auxotrophy (an adenine requirement) in a super-suppressed adenine-requiring strain (adenine-independent) show that the revertants still possess the super-suppressor gene but that they also possess a mutant extrachromosomal component that inactivates this gene.

3. *Chromosomal Control of Extrachromosomal Stability*

The frequency with which extrachromosomally inherited variants arise is subject to the control of chromosomal genes. For example, the incidence of such widely occurring variants as *petite, nonsexual,* and *vegetative death* differs by up to a hundredfold from one strain to another. The frequency of the spontaneous mutant *alba* also differs among strains of *A. nidulans,* the difference being under the control of different alleles at a single chromosomal locus *f* (Mahoney and Wilkie, 1962).

4. Chromosomal Control of Extrachromosomal Reproduction

The persistent segregation of the *red* variant can be explained by assuming that it is a vegetatively stable heteroplasmon between a lethal mutant and its wild-type homolog. The persistence of the segregation and hence the stability of the heteroplasmon is under chromosomal gene control. Thus nine gene mutations are known which bring about a cessation of the persistent segregation into normal and *red* phenotypes. They do so, however, in two distinct ways. Five of the mutants have the effect of making the *red* variants a pure-breeding mutant. Thus, following their introduction into the variant, subsequent vegetative propagations produce colonies with *red* phenotypes all of whose vegetative and asexual transfers are also uniformly *red* in phenotype. Thus these mutants suppress the lethality of the homoplasmic *red* state. The other four mutants have the effect of making the *red* variant change to a pure-breeding, wild-type strain. It appears, therefore, that five of the mutant genes favor the action and replication of the mutant component of the heteroplasmon. On the other hand, in the presence of the wild-type alleles of these mutant genes the two components of the heteroplasmon reach a vegetatively stable equilibrium (Arlett *et al.*, 1962; Grindle, 1963).

In conclusion, the analyses of chromosomal-extrachromosomal interactions in fungi show that the action, stability, and reproduction of extrachromosomal components are ultimately subject to chromosomal gene control. But equally, they show that the action of chromosomal genes are ultimately dependent on the cooperation of extrachromosomal factors. Hence there is interdependence between the two systems rather than the control of one by the other.

IV. THE ROLE OF EXTRACHROMOSOMAL VARIATION

The extrachromosomal system in cooperation with the chromosomal system determines the phenotype. Hence, presumably it plays a role in collaboration with chromosomal genes in development, variation, adaptation, speciation, and evolution.

A. Development

The participation of the extrachromosomal system in the development and differentiation of fungal colonies has been demonstrated in a number of ways. The most obvious demonstration is provided by extrachromosomal mutations which lead to the loss of particular developmental pathways. For example, the *nonsexual, alba, conidial,* and *petite* mutations block the development of their respective sexual stages, the *red* mutant in addition reduces conidiophore and conidial production while the most extreme *mycelial* mutants block the development of all forms of sporulation, leaving only sterile hyphae. These and the many similar examples leave no doubt that the cooperation of a normal extrachromosomal complement is essential for normal development.

A similar conclusion can be drawn from the extensive investigations of the control of perithecial production in the sexual aspergilli (Jinks, 1954, 1956, 1958; Mather and Jinks, 1958; Sharpe, 1958; Mahoney and Wilkie, 1962; Croft, 1964, 1966b). In these fungi there is considerable spontaneous variation in perithecial production within clones and even between different regions of the same colony. And while the cause of the variation has been variously attributed to all the categories of extrachromosomal change which have been recognized (Section III, B), there is complete agreement that the differences between high and low perithecia-producing colonies belonging to the same clone are under the immediate control of the extrachromosomal system. Once they arise, colonies with high and low yields of perithecia usually remain unchanged in phenotype through vegetative growth and vegetative propagations. Where, however, propagations by the asexual spores, sexual spores, and hülle cells from the same colony have been compared for their ability to form perithecia, the extrachromosomal determinant of perithecial density is not distributed at random among different kinds of cells or between the same kind of cell taken from different regions of a colony (Jinks, 1956; Mather and Jinks, 1958; Croft, 1964, 1966b). For example, perithecial production by colonies obtained from sexual spores and hülle cells usually is uniformly high irrespective of whether inocula have been taken from colonies forming few or many perithecia. The asexual spores on the other hand give rise to colonies whose perithecial production varies from high to low with the average level depending on the immediate source of the spores. If the spores are taken from a colony forming many perithecia they usually give rise to colonies which are predominantly, but not exclusively, high yielding. If, on the other hand, they are taken from a colony forming few perithecia they give rise to predominantly low-yielding colonies. However, if the asexual spores from a low-yielding colony are taken only from the immediate vicinity of a perithecium they give rise to colonies which are mainly high yielding. It appears, therefore, that the sexual fruiting bodies, that is, the perithecia and their surrounding hülle cells, are produced only by cell lineages that contain the extrachromosomal constituent which determines high perithecial production. Asexual spores and vegetative mycelium, on the other hand, can be produced whether this constituent is present or not.

The progressive loss of developmental capacity which accompanies aging and senescence provides further evidence of the participation of the extrachromosomal system in development. In *A. glaucus* this loss usually follows the sequence, loss of sexual stage, then loss of asexual stage, and finally cessation of growth. At all stages prior to the last this process is readily reversed by a transfusion of normal extrachromosomal material by heterokaryotic association with a vigorous strain (Fig. 10). The final stage is the extrachromosomally inherited condition which we have called *vegetative death*. A comparable progressive loss of vigor in *Podospora anserina* also culminates in a similar extrachromosomally inherited condition known as

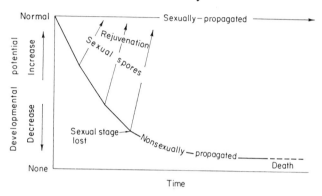

FIG. 10. The successive stages in the degeneration of an aging clone of *Aspergillus*. There is no loss of vigor nor of developmental potential in the clone maintained by regular propagation by sexual spores. The aging clone maintained by asexual spores or vegetative cells loses both vigor and developmental potential and in time dies. Until it loses the ability to produce sexual spores, however, it can be restored to full vigor by propagation with sexual spores. Once the latter are no longer produced this method of restoration is lost. After this stage is reached an aged clone can still be restored by a transfusion of the extrachromosomal complement of a vigorous clone by means of a heterokaryotic association (based on Jinks, 1954; Mather and Jinks, 1958; Jinks, 1959; Croft, 1964). A similar sequence has been described for aging clones of *Podospora anserina* by Marcou (1961).

senescence. Thus in these examples only changes in the extrachromosomal system are involved in the gradual restriction of developmental potential.

The changes which occur in aging aspergilli can be prevented and even reversed by frequent recourse to propagations by sexually produced spores. Hence the extrachromosomal changes that have occurred in an aging clone that can still produce some viable sexual spores are not transmitted to its sexual progeny, that is, the sexual progeny show rejuvenation (Mather and Jinks, 1958) (Fig. 10). These changes can also be prevented and even reversed by keeping an aging clone as a number of independently growing colonies and choosing only the most vigorous to initiate the next batch of independent colonies at each transfer, using hyphae or asexual spores as inocula. The demonstration that rejuvenation can be achieved by sexual reproduction, selection, and the transfusion of normal extrachromosomal material has led to two alternative explanations of the processes involved.

The first explanation assumes that within an aging clone there is variation among hyphae for the ability to support the growth and development of the more complex structures such as conidiophores and sexual fruiting bodies. This variation is extrachromosomal. Since the most complex structures develop only on hyphae which retain the highest level of extrachromosomal organization, the cells and spores in these structures should have extrachromosomal complements which are above average. Hence using these cells and spores for propagation will produce colonies with better than average phenotypes. That is, rejuvenation by sexual reproduction results from a passive selection of those cells which retain the capacity to differentiate the sexual fruiting body. This explanation, of course, also follows directly from the earlier interpretation of the observation that sexual spore and hülle cells, whether taken from colonies forming many or few perithecia, always give colonies that are predominantly of the former phenotype (page 653). The second explanation assumes that during differentiation changes are actively brought about in the extrachromosomal complement. Those that occur in the germ line restore the developmental capacity of the sexual progeny (Mather and Jinks, 1958).

Successive analyses of rejuvenation in aspergilli have not completely ruled out either explanation (Jinks, 1956; Faulkner, 1962; Croft, 1964, 1966b). However, insofar as they have shown that rejuvenation is a property of all the kinds of cells and spores which are produced in the immediate vicinity of a sexual fruiting body, it would appear that either (1) any extrachromosomal change that occurs must precede sexual reproduction and must be shared by cell lineages which are associated with the sexual stage, but which are not in the direct line of descent of the sexual spores or, (2) the sexual stage develops only in those regions of the colony which by chance segregation of extrachromosomal material possess the appropriate extrachromosomal content.

B. Variation and Adaptation

The extrachromosomal variants that have been studied in the laboratory, like their chromosomal counterparts, usually have major defects and hence they are unlikely to play a significant role in the variation and adaptation of fungi in nature. Even those variants which arise in response to specific environmental treatments do not seem to be adapted to the conditions which produced them. Indeed *petite* does not appear to have an advantage over wild type under any of the many treatments which specifically induce this variant. Nevertheless polymorphisms which are extrachromosomal in origin occur among fungi in nature.

For example: (1) The differences in the pathogenicity reactions of certain races of *Puccinia graminis* and *P. anomala* [*P. hordei*] are extrachromosomally inherited (Section II, C). (2) The chromosomal-extrachromosomal interaction which produces the modified barrage phenomenon s^S in *Podospora anserina* shows that strains of this fungus which are recovered from nature differ in their extrachromosomal complements. A similar conclusion can be reached for the interaction involving the common and Philippine Islands strains of *N. crassa*. (3) The "dual phenomenon" is the most widely distributed system of variation found in fungi (Hansen, 1938). Because of its similarity to artificial heterokaryons synthesized in the laboratory, the dual phenomenon has been attributed to naturally occurring heterokaryosis. However, the overall similarity between heterokaryons and heteroplasmons in their modes of origin, segregation upon asexual spore production, and their sectoring during vegetative growth, makes it difficult to distinguish between them without recourse to the refined tests described in Section II, C. It is not surprising, therefore, that when such tests are applied to newly isolated strains of *Penicillium* and *Aspergillus* species exhibiting the dual phenomenon, they are found to be heteroplasmons as often as heterokaryons (Jinks, 1960). If this finding applies generally, then heteroplasmons may occur as frequently as heterokaryons in nature. And if this is so it must imply that heteroplasmons have a role in variation and adaptation of the kind which has been envisaged for heterokaryons.

C. Speciation and Evolution

From the results of intensive investigations of various plant and animal genera it has been concluded that the extrachromosomal system plays an important role in producing barriers to outcrossing and hence in the emergence of species and higher taxonomic units (Caspari, 1948). This conclusion is based primarily on the nature of race and species differences in *Epilobium, Streptocarpus, Oenothera, Funaria,* and *Culex*. The hybrids between certain races and species of these genera are lethal, stunted, or sterile and these abnormalities have been traced to deleterious interactions between the chromosomal genes of one parent and the extrachromosomal complement of the other.

No comparable investigations of race and species relationships have been carried out using fungal material although the extensive analyses of the inheritance of pathogenicity in rust fungi have shown that differences between physiological races can have an extrachromosomal basis (Section II, C, 1). There are also clear cases of extrachromosomal-chromosomal interactions between strains and species of *Neurospora*. But these extrachromosomal differences in *Puccinia* and *Neurospora* do not present a barrier to successful outcrossing. Hence there is as yet no direct demonstration that the extrachromosomal system has played a role in the speciation and evolution of the fungi.

V. GENERAL REMARKS

The possibility of extrachromosomal, as opposed to chromosomal, determination deserves serious consideration whenever a variant phenotype is encountered either from nature or the laboratory. The mode of origin of a variant, if it arises under controlled laboratory conditions, can itself be a valuable guide in distinguishing between extrachromosomal and chromosomal causation, as may also its degree of stability during somatic growth and at asexual reproduction. But any doubt may be unambiguously resolved by a variety of tests which are currently being used with fungal material to distinguish between extrachromosomal and chromosomal inheritance.

The extent to which some of the variation traceable to the extrachromosomal system is heritable is a matter of definition. Variation which occurs between somatic cells of a clone but does not segregate in the sexual progeny of the same clone is not heritable in the strict sense. But a strict definition of heredity is even more out of place in the fungi than elsewhere, for not only are nonsexual methods of reproduction and multiplication both important and highly evolved in this group, but many of the most successful fungal species have no alternative to these methods of reproduction. Hence among such imperfect fungi persistence of a variant phenotype through somatic cell division is the only form of heredity which is known.

While fungi have been used for the systematic study of extrachromosomal heredity for a relatively short time, they have already made significant contributions to our understanding of the specific induction of mutations; the biochemical consequences of mutations, somatic segregation of heteroplasmons, and extrachromosomal changes during development, senescence, and sexual reproduction. A beginning has been made in the study of extrachromosomal variation in wild fungi and its role in adaptation and speciation. Preliminary results suggest that it has a role, and future investigations will determine its extent.

Acknowledgments

I am indebted to my colleagues of the Department of Genetics, University of Birmingham, for helpful discussion and particularly to Dr. M. Grindle and J. H. Croft for unpublished results and photographs. This work was supported by the Agricultural Research Council of Great Britain.

REFERENCES

Arlett, C. F. (1957). Induction of cytoplasmic mutations in *Aspergillus nidulans*. *Nature* **179**:1250-1251.

Arlett, C. F. (1960). A system of cytoplasmic variation in *Aspergillus nidulans*. *Heredity* **15**:377-388.

Arlett, C. F., M. Grindle, and J. L. Jinks. (1962). The red cytoplasmic variant of *Aspergillus nidulans*. *Heredity* **17**:197-209.

Aschan, K. (1952). Studies on dediploidisation mycelia of the basidiomycete *Collybia velutipes*. *Svensk. Botan. Tidskr.* 46:366-393.
Caspari, E. (1948). Cytoplasmic inheritance. *Advan. Genet.* 2:1-66.
Chevaugeon, J., and C. Lefort. (1960). Sur l'apparition régulière d'un "mutant" infectant chez un Champignon du genre *Pestalozzia*. *Compt. Rend.* 250:2247-2249.
Chèvremont, M. (1963). Cytoplasmic deoxyribonucleic acids. Their mitochondrial localization and synthesis in somatic cells under experimental conditions and during the normal cell cycle in relation to the preparation for mitosis. *Symp. Intern. Soc. Cell Biol.* 2:323-333.
Cox, B. S. (1965). A cytoplasmic suppressor of super-suppressor in yeast. *Heredity* 20:505-522.
Croft, J. H. (1964). Variation and development in *Aspergillus nidulans* and in *Collybia velutipes*. Ph.D. thesis, University of Birmingham Library, England.
Croft, J. H. (1966a). Somatically unstable mutants of *Aspergillus nidulans*. II. Specific induction by acridine dyes. In preparation.
Croft, J. H. (1966b). A reciprocal phenotypic instability affecting development in *Aspergillus nidulans*. *Heredity* 21: in press.
Day, P. R. (1959). A cytoplasmically controlled abnormality of the tetrads of *Coprinus lagopus*. *Heredity* 13:81-87.
Dickson, H. (1935). Studies in *Coprinus sphaerocarpus*. II. *Ann. Botany (London)* 49:181-204.
d'Oliviera, B. (1939). Studies on *Puccinia anomala*. I. Physiological races on cultivated barley. *Ann. Appl. Biol.* 26:56-82.
Ephrussi, B. (1953). "Nucleo-Cytoplasmic Relations in Micro-Organisms," 127 pp. Oxford Univ. Press (Clarendon), London and New York.
Ephrussi, B., and H. Hottinguer. (1951). Cytoplasmic constituents of heredity: On an unstable cell state in yeast. *Cold Spring Harbor Symp. Quant. Biol.* 16:75.
Ephrussi, B., and P. P. Slonimski. (1955). Yeast mitochondria. Subcellular units involved in the synthesis of respiratory enzymes in yeast. *Nature* 176:1207-1209.
Ephrussi, B., H. Hottinguer, and H. Roman. (1955). Suppressiveness: A new factor in the genetic determination of the synthesis of respiratory enzymes in yeast. *Proc. Natl. Acad. Sci. U. S.* 41:1065-1071.
Faulkner, B. M. (1962). The role of the cytoplasm in sexual reproduction in fungi. Ph.D. thesis, University of Birmingham Library, England.
Faulkner, B. M., and C. F. Arlett. (1964). The minute cytoplasmic variant of *Aspergillus nidulans*. *Heredity* 19:63-73.
Gibor, A., and S. Granick. (1964). Plastids and mitochondria: Inheritable systems. *Science* 145:890-897.
Gibson, A., and D. M. Griffin. (1958). A study of variation in *Nectria stenospora*. *Australian J. Biol. Sci.* 11:548-556.
Grindle, M. (1963). Nuclear and cytoplasmic variation in fungi. Ph.D. thesis, University of Birmingham Library, England.
Hansen, H. N. (1938). The dual phenomenon in imperfect fungi. *Mycologia* 30:442-455.
Harder, R. B. (1927). Zur frage nach der Rolle von Kern und Protoplasma in Zell geschelen und bei der Übertragung von Eigenschaften. *Z. Botan.* 19:337-407.
Harris, M. (1956). Occurrence of respiration deficient mutants in baker's yeast cultivated anaerobically. *J. Cellular Comp. Physiol.* 48:95-112.
Holling, M., D. G. Gandy, and F. T. Last. (1963). A virus disease of a fungus: Die back of cultivated mushrooms. *Endeavour* 22:112-117.

19. Extranuclear Inheritance

Jinks, J. L. (1954). Somatic selection in fungi. *Nature* **174**:409.
Jinks, J. L. (1956). Naturally occurring cytoplasmic changes in fungi. *Compt. Rend. Trav. Lab. Carlsberg, Ser. Physiol.* **26**:183-203.
Jinks, J. L. (1957). Selection of cytoplasmic differences. *Proc. Roy. Soc.* **B146**:527-540.
Jinks, J. L. (1958). Cytoplasmic differentiation in fungi. *Proc. Roy. Soc.* **B148**:314-321.
Jinks, J. L. (1959). Lethal, suppressive cytoplasms in aged clones of *Aspergillus glaucus*. *J. Gen. Microbiol.* **21**:397-409.
Jinks, J. L. (1960). The genetic basis of "duality" in *imperfect* fungi. *Heredity* **14**:525-528.
Jinks, J. L. (1963). Cytoplasmic inheritance in fungi. *In* "Methodology in Basic Genetics" (W. J. Burdette, ed.), pp. 325-343. Holden-Day, San Francisco, California.
Jinks, J. L. (1964a). "Extrachromosomal Inheritance." 177 pp. Prentice-Hall, Englewood Cliffs, New Jersey.
Jinks, J. L. (1964b). "Somatic Segregation of Extrachromosomally Inherited Differences in Fungi." Pergamon Press, London.
Johnson, T. (1946). Variation and the inheritance of certain characters in rust fungi. *Cold Spring Harbor Symp. Quant. Biol.* **11**:85-93.
Laskowski, W. (1954). Induction par le chlorure de tétrazolium de la mutation "petite colonie" chez la levure. *Heredity* **8**:79-88.
Lindegren, C. C., and S. Hino. (1957). The effect of anaerobiosis on the origin of respiratory deficient yeast. *Exptl. Cell Res.* **12**:163-168.
Luck, D. J. L. (1963). Genesis of mitochondria in *Neurospora crassa*. *Proc. Natl. Acad. Sci. U. S.* **49**:233-240.
Luck, D. J. L., and E. Reich. (1964). DNA in mitochondria of *Neurospora crassa*. *Proc. Natl. Acad. Sci. U. S.* **52**:931-938.
Mahoney, M., and D. Wilkie. (1962). Nucleo-cytoplasmic control of perithecial formation in *Aspergillus nidulans*. *Proc. Roy. Soc.* **B156**:524-532.
Makower, M., and E. A. Bevan. (1963). The inheritance of a killer character in yeast. *Genetics Today* **1**:202.
Marcou, D. (1961). Notion de longévité et nature cytoplasmique du déterminant de la sénescence chez quelques champignons. *Ann. Sci. Natl.: Botan. Biol. Vegetale* [12] **2**:653-764.
Mather, K., and J. L. Jinks. (1958). Cytoplasm in sexual reproduction. *Nature* **182**:1188-1190.
Mitchell, H. K., and L. A. Hertzenberg. (1955). Enzymatic degradation of cytochrome c. *In* "Methods in Enzymology" (S. P. Colowick and N. O. Kaplan, eds.), Vol. 2, pp. 167-169. Academic Press, New York.
Mitchell, M. B., and H. K. Mitchell. (1952). A case of maternal inheritance in *Neurospora crassa*. *Proc. Natl. Acad. Sci. U. S.* **38**:442-449.
Mitchell, M. B., and H. K. Mitchell. (1956). A nuclear gene suppressor of a cytoplasmically inherited character in *Neurospora crassa*. *J. Gen. Microbiol.* **14**:84-89.
Mitchell, M. B., H. K. Mitchell, and A. Tissières. (1953). Mendelian and non-Mendelian factors affecting the cytochrome system of *Neurospora crassa*. *Proc. Natl. Acad. Sci. U. S.* **39**:606-613.
Moustacchi, E., and H. Marcovich. (1963). Induction de la mutation petite colonie chez la levure par le 5-fluorouracile. *Compt. Rend.* **256**:5646-5648.
Papazian, H. P. (1958). The genetics of basidiomycetes. *Advan. Genet.* **9**:41-69.

Pittenger, T. H. (1956). Synergism of two cytoplasmically inherited mutants in *Neurospora crassa*. *Proc. Natl. Acad. Sci. U. S.* **42**:747-752.

Pittman, D. D. (1957). Induction of respiratory deficiency in tetraploid *Saccharomyces* by ultraviolet radiation. *Exptl. Cell Res.* **11**:654-656.

Raut, C., and W. C. Simpson. (1955). The effect of x-rays and of ultra-violet light of different wave lengths on the production of cytochrome deficient yeast. *Arch. Biochem. Biophys.* **57**:218.

Rizet, G. (1952). Les phenomènes de barrage chez *Podospora anserina*. I. Analyse génétique de barrage entre souches S et s. *Rev. Cytol. Biol. Vegetales* **13**:51-92.

Rizet, G. (1957). Les modifications qui conduisent à la senescence chez *Podospora* sont-elles de nature cytoplasmique? *Compt. Rend.* **244**:663-665.

Rizet, G., D. Marcou, and J. Schecroun. (1958). Deux phenomènes d'hérédité cytoplasmique chez l'ascomycète *Podospora anserina*. *Bull. Soc. Franc. Physiol. Vegetale* **4**:136-149.

Roper, J. A. (1958). Nucleo-cytoplasmic interactions in *Aspergillus nidulans*. *Cold Spring Harbor Symp. Quant. Biol.* **23**:141-154.

Sager, R. (1954). Mendelian and non-Mendelian inheritance of streptomycin resistance in *Chlamydomonas reinhardi*. *Proc. Natl. Acad. Sci. U. S.* **40**:356-363.

Sager, R., and Z. Ramanis. (1965). Recombination of non-chromosomal genes in *Chlamydomonas*. *Proc. Natl. Acad. Sci. U. S.* **53**:1053-1061.

Sharpe, H. S. (1958). A closed system of cytoplasmic variation in *Aspergillus glaucus*. *Proc. Roy. Soc.* **B148**:355-359.

Sherman, F., and B. Ephrussi. (1962). The relationship between respiratory deficiency and suppressiveness in yeast as determined with segregational mutants. *Genetics* **47**:695.

Silagi, S. (1965). Interaction between an extrachromosomal factor, Poky and nuclear genes in *Neurospora crassa*. *Genetics* **52**:341-347.

Srb, A. M. (1958). Some consequences of nuclear cytoplasmic recombinations among various Neurosporas. *Cold Spring Harbor Symp. Quant. Biol.* **23**:269-278.

Tuppy, H., and G. Wildner. (1965). Cytoplasmic transformation. Mitochondria of wild-type baker's yeast restoring respiratory capacity in the respiratory deficient petite mutant. *Biochem. Biophys. Res. Commun.* **20**:733-738.

Upshall, A. (1966). Somatically unstable mutants of *Aspergillus nidulans*. *Nature*: **209**:1113-1115.

Wilkie, D. (1963). The induction by monochromatic ultra-violet light of respiratory-deficient mutants in aerobic and anaerobic cultures of yeast. *J. Mol. Biol.* **7**:527-533.

Wright, R. E., and J. Lederberg. (1957). Extranuclear transmission in yeast heterokaryons. *Proc. Natl. Acad. Sci. U. S.* **43**:919-923.

Ycas, M. (1956). A hereditary cytochrome deficiency appearing in yeast grown at an elevated temperature. *Exptl. Cell Res.* **10**:746.

CHAPTER 20

Incompatibility

KARL ESSER[1]

Institut für Allgemeine Botanik
Ruhr-Universität Bochum, Germany

I. DEFINITIONS

Since most terms in this branch of biology are often used in different senses and various phenomena are characterized by different terms, we begin with definitions of the basic phenomena according to the usage employed in this chapter.

The intrinsic value of *sexual reproduction* consists in the sequence of karyogamy and meiosis. The male and female nuclei need not come from morphologically different structures, as in most Euascomycetes. In the simplest case, there may be only physiological differences such as migrating abilities; i.e., the male nucleus migrates into the cell containing the resting female nucleus (Holobasidiomycetes).

Inbreeding, in general, involves sexual propagation between individuals that are more closely related than those of a random sample of a naturally occurring population. The most extreme case of inbreeding is the self-fertilization of an hermaphroditic organism.

Outbreeding occurs when sexual propagation takes place between individuals which are less closely related than those taken at random from a naturally occurring population.

Monoecism and *dioecism* are not defined on the basis of morphology since the essential criterion of sexuality is, as indicated above, merely karyogamy and meiosis. They are defined on a physiological basis according to whether an organism contributes one or two nuclei to the sexual process. On the basis of this assumption a *monoecious* individual can

---

[1] Supported by a grant from the Deutsche Forschungsgemeinschaft, Bad Godesberg, Germany.

act as a donor of nuclei (male) as well as a receptor of nuclei (female) for karyogamy. An individual which possesses only one or the other potency is termed *dioecious*.

Incompatibility (formerly self-sterility) characterizes every genotypically determined inhibition of karyogamy within a sexually reproducing system of monoecious individuals, with the exception of those due to defects of the gametes or gametic nuclei (e.g., sterility due to chromosomal aberrations). When the restriction of mating competence between male and female nuclei is due to like alleles of one or more loci, we speak of *homogenic incompatibility*. When the inhibition of zygote formation between incompatible partners is due to heterogeneity of all incompatibility loci, we speak of *heterogenic incompatibility*.

II. INTRODUCTION

For half a century the phenomenon of incompatibility has been of great interest to geneticists. Although the first research on incompatibility was done mostly on higher plants, within the last few years the interest of biologists has shifted more and more to the fungi, since these organisms can be more easily and rapidly analyzed. The work done with fungi especially has led to a deeper insight into the genetics of incompatibility and its general meaning in evolution, as it is now known that incompatibility as a whole is the product of two alternative genetic systems which act antagonistically in evolution. Before we discuss this problem we must familiarize ourselves with the main facts of sexual incompatibility.

Within the limits of this chapter we can treat incompatibility only very briefly and generally. Reviews which cover this field very comprehensively and include references to original publications not mentioned here include those by Whitehouse (1949a,b, 1951a,b), J. R. Raper (1954, 1960, 1963), Lewis (1954, 1956), Burnett (1956), Papazian (1958), Esser (1962, 1966), J. R. Raper and Esser (1964), and Esser and Kuenen (1965).

III. INCOMPATIBILITY SYSTEMS

Among fungi, incompatibility is found only in the Ascomycetes (approximately 50 species) and in the Basidiomycetes (approximately 370 species). The occurrence of sexual incompatibility within the Myxomycetes and Phycomycetes has not been established with certainty.

Lists of the distribution of compatible and incompatible species in Eumycetes have been published in the past: Whitehouse (1949a, Euascales; 1949b, Holobasidiomycetes; 1951b, Ustilaginales); Quintanilha and Pinto-Lopes (1950, Holobasidiomycetes); Craigie (1942, Uredinales); Nobles *et al.* (1957, Holobasidiomycetes); Esser (1966, Euascales, Holo- and Phragmobasidiomycetes). A summary is given in Table I.

Two incompatibility systems, for which we have introduced the terms homogenic and heterogenic incompatibility (Esser 1959b), exist in the fungi.

A. Homogenic Incompatibility

Homogenic incompatibility was discovered independently by Bensaude (1918) in *Coprinus fimetarius,* Kniep (1918, 1920) in *Schizophyllum commune,* and Dodge (1920) in *Ascobolus stercorarius.* The overwhelming majority of incompatibility phenomena described up to the present belong to this system (see Table I). Homogenic incompatibility may be controlled by either one or two factors. In the first case, there are at least two mating types, and in the second case at least four. Hence one usually distinguishes between the bipolar and tetrapolar mechanism.

1. The Bipolar Mechanism

In the simplest case, there are only two alleles of the mating type locus which determine sexual behavior. They are generally designated as $+$ and $-$ or A and a (*Neurospora*) or a and α (yeasts). According to the definition of homogenic incompatibility, all mycelia with the same mating type are self- and cross-incompatible ($+ \times +; - \times -$). Fertilization occurs only between different mating types ($+ \times -$). Since each mating type can act as donor and receptor of nuclei, there are two reciprocal crosses between $+$ and $-$ mycelia possible.

Homogenic incompatibility in the Euascomycetes and Uredinales is exclusively determined by the bipolar mechanism. Within the Basidiomycetes the bipolar mechanism is relatively frequent in the Ustilaginales (see Table I). In some basidiomycetes multiple alleles of the incompatibility factors have been found. Therefore in these species more than two mating types exist. Their mating behavior obeys the same rule: genetically like mating types are incompatible, genetically unlike mating types are compatible.

2. The Tetrapolar Mechanism

Tetrapolar incompatibility occurs mainly in Holobasidiomycetes and in some Uredinales (cf. Table I). This mechanism is determined by factors, usually unlinked, called A and B. The alleles of these loci are designated by subscripts. In the simplest case there are four mating types: A_1B_1, A_2B_2, A_1B_2, and A_2B_1. The sexual behavior among these types is determined by the Kniep rule (Kniep, 1920): Neither pair of factors can undergo karyogamy in the homozygous state. However in a great number

TABLE I
SYSTEMS, MECHANISMS, AND DISTRIBUTION OF SEXUAL INCOMPATIBILITY WITHIN THE FUNGI[a]

System:	Heterogenic						Homogenic		
Mechanism: Number of factors:	Bipolar 1			Tetrapolar 2 (partially genetical complex)		Unknown	Semi-incompatibility Each at a time, 2	Unknown	
Occurrence	Euasco-mycetes	Holo-basidio-mycetes	Phragma-basidio-mycetes	Holo-basidio-mycetes	Ustilagi-nales	Basidio-mycetes	Euasco-mycetes	Euasco-mycetes	Basidio-mycetes
Number of species	47	92	37	170	4	62	1	2	4
Multiple alleles	Unknown	21	1(?)	36	2	—	Unknown	—	—

[a] From Esser and Kuenen (1965).

of species multiple alleles of the mating type factors exist. In *Schizophyllum*, for example, J. R. Raper et al. (1958b) found 96 alleles of the A factor and 56 for the B factor.

a. Holobasidiomycetes. The ten possible combinations between the four mating types can be placed in four different groups, according to their mating reactions (J. R. Raper, 1961).

(1) Compatible: $A_1B_1 \times A_2B_2$ and $A_1B_2 \times A_2B_1$. Mycelia with different A and B factors undergo plasmogamy and exchange nuclei. In the zone of contact they form a dikaryon, which possesses clamp connections. After plasmogamy the nuclei of each partner migrate part way into the hyphae of the other. Clamp connections may therefore be formed at some distance from the mating zone. Under suitable cultural conditions fruiting bodies occur on the dikaryon.

(2) Hemicompatible A: $A_1B_1 \times A_1B_2$ and $A_2B_1 \times A_2B_2$. Mycelia with common A and noncommon B factors show plasmogamy, exchange of nuclei, and nuclear migration. However, no clamp connections are formed. In general, such heterokaryons with sparse growth do not form fruiting bodies.

(3) Hemicompatible B: $A_1B_1 \times A_2B_1$ and $A_1B_2 \times A_2B_2$. An exchange of nuclei but no nuclear migration occurs between mycelia with common B and noncommon A factors. The heterokaryon exists only in the mating zone, where both partners form defective clamp connections. In general, fruiting bodies are not formed.

(4) Incompatible: $A_1B_2 \times A_1B_1, A_2B_2 \times A_2B_2, A_1B_2 \times A_1B_2, A_2B_1 \times A_2B_1$. Between mycelia with common A and common B factors, plasmogamy and exchange of nuclei takes place only to a very small extent and in the zone of contact. Nuclear migration and clamp connections do not occur and fruiting bodies are not formed.

From these genetic results and from ontogenetic observations, one assumes that the A factors are instrumental in the formation of clamp connections and that the B factors are responsible for nuclear migration.

The action of the A and B factors can be modified in two ways: (a) C. A. Raper and Raper (1964) found several genes which suppress the action of the incompatibility factors. The genes inhibit the formation of fruiting bodies in dikaryons. (b) As a result of disomy or of mutation at the incompatibility loci homokaryons may behave like heterokaryons or dikaryons (Prud'Homme and Gans, 1958; J. R. Raper and Oettinger, 1962).

b. Ustilaginales. The existence of tetrapolar incompatibility in ustilaginales has been disputed for some time (see Table I). The experiments of Rowell (1955), however, have fully confirmed the older claims of Bauch (1930, 1931, 1932, 1934). The reaction of the four mating types is somewhat different from that in Holobasidiomycetes. Hemicompatibility exists only in common B crosses. Common A crosses are incompatible as are common A common B crosses. Only the dikaryons originating from noncommon A-B crosses are compatible and able to infect host plants.

3. Genetic Structure of the Incompatibility Factors

Because of the work of Papazian (1951) and of Raper and his collaborators (J. R. Raper, 1953, 1961; Vakili, 1953; J. R. Raper and Miles, 1958; J. R. Raper et al., 1958a, 1960), we know that the A and B factors in *Schizophyllum commune* consist of at least two subunits, which have been named α and β. Up to 26 different α and β have been found in each factor. Other authors have confirmed these findings for additional basidiomycetes (Table II). The α and β subunits are closely linked but can be separated by crossing over. The distance between the subunits of one factor varies between 0.068 and 19.4 Morgan units in different organisms (Table II).

TABLE II
List of Experimental Results Concerning the Complex Structure of A- and B-Factors of Tetrapolar Incompatible Basidiomycetes[a,b]

Organism	Frequency of recombination within factor (%)	
	A	B
Collybia velutipes	0.5–1.3	19.4
Coprinus lagopus	0.068–0.88	—
Coprinus sp.	—[c]	7.4
Lentinus edodes	—	7.5
Pleurotus spodoleucus	—	8.3
Pleurotus ostreatus	—	—
Schizophyllum commune	0.9–22.8	2.0
Schizophyllum commune	18.3	1.9

[a] From Esser and Kuenen (1965).
[b] On the basis of data so far reported, there are at least two subunits for each factor between which reciprocal recombination is possible.
[c] Dash indicates that distance has not been determined.

The physiological specificity of the A and B factors is determined by a specific combination of the subunits. A factors and B factors exhibit the same physiological reaction if they possess like subunits. The physiological specificity of A or B factors is different when they have different subunits. For example, $A_{\alpha 1\ \beta 1}$ is different from $A_{\alpha 2\ \beta 1}$. Two mating types are incompatible only when their A and B factors consist of identical subunits. Compatibility between two strains is determined when a single subunit difference exists in each factor, e.g., $A_{\alpha 1\ \beta 2}\ B_{\alpha 3\ \beta 3} \times A_{\alpha 2\ \beta 2}\ B_{\alpha 2\ \beta 3}$.

From these findings we assume that the A and B factors are complex genetic units consisting of two closely linked genes. Both genes (α and β) have similar functions. They contribute the genetic information for the functioning of a specific incompatibility factor, e.g., A_1. Raper has called A and B "physiological units." The demonstration that A and B are physiological units lies in the fact that an alteration in only one of the subunits (i.e., in α or β) changes the factor specificity. Therefore, we are still able to term this incompatibility mechanism "tetrapolar" since the determinants of the mechanism are the two physiological units A and B, whose action is determined respectively by two closely linked genes.

4. Pseudocompatibility

There are some monoecious higher fungi in which fruiting body production originating on monosporous mycelia is not due to self-compatibility. The phenomenon of pseudocompatibility (called also "secondary homothallism," Dodge, 1927) directs the mating competence in some four-spored Euascomycetes (e.g., *Podospora anserina, Neurospora tetrasperma, Gelasinospora tetrasperma*) and in some bispored holobasidiomycetes (e.g., *Agaricus bispora*).

The most detailed information on pseudocompatibility is obtained from the genetic analysis of *Podospora anserina* (Rizet and Engelmann, 1949; Franke, 1957, 1962). As seen in Fig. 1a, each of the four linearly arranged ascospores contain two of the four products of meiosis. The $+/-$ alleles show a postreduction frequency of 97%; the asci must therefore contain heterokaryotic spores, which form heterokaryotic mycelia. These produce male and female sex organs (spermatia and ascogonia) with $+$ and $-$ nuclei which fertilize each other according to the mechanism of bipolar incompatibility. The remaining 3% of the asci, in which the $+/-$ genes are prereduced, form spores which germinate to form self-incompatible $+$ or $-$ mycelia. The high postreduction frequency of the mating-type alleles along with the cytological peculiarities of nuclear distribution, when taken together, mimic compatibility.

At first glance *P. anserina* seems not well suited for genetic analysis. This difficulty can be overcome, however, since in 1–2% of all asci there occur one or more pairs of small, uninucleate spores instead of a single binucleate spore (see Fig. 1b, c). This brings the total number of spores in an ascus to 5, 6, 7, or even 8. The uninucleate small spores can be distinguished easily from the normal binucleate spores. Since the small spores contain either a $+$ or a $-$ nucleus the resulting mycelia are self-incompatible and react exactly like other bipolar ascomycetes. The situation in other pseudocompatible ascomycetes is similar (Dodge, 1927, 1928; Dowding, 1933; Dowding and Bakerspigel, 1956).

Pseudocompatibility in the Holobasidiomycetes may be due to the heterokaryotic constitution of the basidiospores which contain two products of meiosis, either by chance or by positive affinity between unlike nuclei

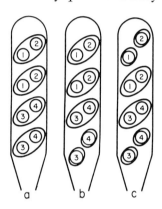

FIG. 1. Schematic representation of the distribution of the four products of meiosis in the asci of *Podospora anserina*. The meiotic products are designated by figures drawn in the nuclei of the spores. For details, see text. From Esser (1959a).

(Sass, 1929; Oikawa, 1939; Skolko, 1944). Pseudocompatibility occurs mostly in bipolar species, but it is possible also within tetrapolar species (Lamoure, 1957).

5. Physiology

There are no clear explanations of the action of the incompatibility factors responsible for the mechanism of the homogenic system. Only more or less speculative models are under discussion. Nor is there a single explanation for homogenic incompatibility in the Ascomycetes and Basidiomycetes, because homogenic incompatibility blocks fertilization at different stages in the two systems. In ascomycetes and uredinales the sexual reaction takes place between well differentiated sex organs and blocks occur before plasmogamy. In the Holobasidiomycetes and Ustilaginales there are only undifferentiated hyphae or single cells involved in the sexual reaction, and the block may occur before as well as after plasmogamy. In general, the two groups are discussed separately, but with respect to gene physiology it is not necessary to distinguish between bipolar and tetrapolar sexuality.

In higher plants (see Lewis, 1954) there are two alternative models:

the complementary stimulant and the oppositional inhibitor, both of which are based on the incompatibility of like genes. To explain the two mechanisms, the following assumptions are made: The complementary mechanism acts only in compatible combinations, whereby the formation of a zygote is stimulated by the complementary action of the gene products of the genetically different partners. In the incompatible combination, both partners form like gene products, which are not able to complement. The oppositional mechanism, however, is effective only in the incompatible combinations and depends on an inhibition of zygote production due to a reaction of like gene products. This inhibition does not occur in the compatible crosses where unlike gene products are formed.

In Euascomycetes, where only bipolar incompatibility is known, the physiological action of the + and − genes is usually explained by the complementary mechanism. None of the results obtained by different authors on various organisms contradicts such a mechanism (e.g., *Bombardia lunata*, Zickler, 1952; *Neurospora crassa*, Kuwana, 1954, 1955, 1956, 1958; Ito, 1956; *Ascobolus stercorarius*, Bistis, 1956, 1957; Bistis and Raper, 1963). One might therefore suggest that the + and − mating types form complementary gene products which act according to the "key-lock system." The results of Ito also support this mechanism, for he found that protoperithecia of one mating type may be induced by a culture filtrate of the other mating type to form perithecia which are sterile because of the absence of the male nucleus.

More complex and difficult to explain is the bipolar and tetrapolar mechanism in holobasidiomycetes. The one fungus which has been analyzed comprehensively in this respect is the tetrapolar basidiomycete *Schizophyllum commune*. (For literature concerning this work, mostly by Raper and his group, see the reviews of Papazian and Raper cited above.) While earlier results seemed to support an oppositional mechanism, later work contradicts both mechanisms.

Most experimental work which has been done to reveal the physiological action of the incompatibility genes has been genetically or morphologically oriented. In order to escape from this dead end, one must attack the problem anew with biochemical experiments devised to detect the products of gene activity and to characterize their action. A first step in this direction was made with immunological experiments with *Schizophyllum commune* (J. R. Raper and Esser, 1961); these experiments have shown that a dikaryon and its monokaryotic components possess different protein spectra. Since the strains used in these experiments were isogenic, the protein differences may have resulted from the action of incompatibility genes.

There are no reliable experiments dealing with the action of incompatibility genes in heterobasidiomycetes.

B. Heterogenic Incompatibility

Heterogenic incompatibility occurs only between different races of one species. As Table I shows, only few cases are known and only one case (*Podospora anserina*) has been subjected to thorough genetic analysis. That heterogenic incompatibility has been seldom described may be because the geneticist tries to work with inbred lines of the highest degree of isogeneity. When heterogenic incompatibility was first described and analyzed in *P. anserina* (see Esser, 1962), it was possible to explain some previously unexplained cases of cross-sterility in this way. More detailed analyses of interracial crosses in different fungi might provide more examples of this incompatibility system. Heterogenic incompatibility occurs in self-fertile, compatible species as well as in species whose mating competence is primarily determined by homogenic incompatibility.

1. Compatible Species

Heterogenic incompatibility seems to determine the mating relations in two species of *Sordaria* for which Olive (1956) analyzed crosses between different races of *S. fimicola*. Through the use of different spore colors as markers, he was able to show that not all races of the self-fertile species can be crossed, e.g., the races A_1 and C_1. However, both races were fertile with a third race (C_4). One can thus assume that the lack of perithecial formation in the cross between A_1 and C_1 is due not to cross-sterility (caused by chromosomal divergences, etc.), but to heterogenic incompatibility. Since the monosporous mycelia of each race are fully fertile the interrace incompatibility must be due to genic differences between the two races. Heterogenic incompatibility has also been found between races of *S. macrospora* (Esser, unpublished). The genetic mechanism for neither case is not known yet.

2. Incompatible Species

When heterogenic incompatibility is linked with homogenic incompatibility, the former controls sexual reproduction in interracial, and the latter in intraracial, crosses. The mode of action of the genes responsible for heterogenic incompatibility may be illustrated in *Podospora anserina*.

Each geographical race of this fungus contains two mating types, $+$ and $-$, and reacts according to the bipolar mechanism of homogenic incompatibility. Since *P. anserina* is pseudocompatible this reaction is sometimes masked, as we have seen above. Each mycelium originating from a homokaryotic spore (due to prereduction of the $+/-$ genes, or to the formation of small, uninucleate spores) forms male and female sex organs. Since zygote formation can occur only in the $+ \times -$ combination, one may observe in the zone of contact between a + and — strain a line of perithecia which are a mixture of the reciprocal crossings: ♀ + × ♂ — and ♀ — × ♂ + (Fig. 2, left half).

In crosses between different races, however, one usually observes the following deviations from the reciprocal incompatibility between + and — strains: (1) A *nonreciprocal incompatibility*, which has been called semi-

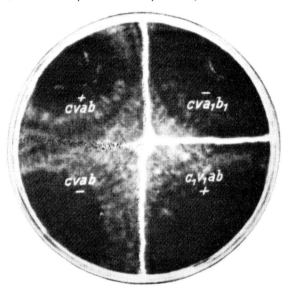

FIG. 2. The operation of heterogenic incompatibility in *Podospora anserina*. From Esser (1956).

incompatibility. The female sex organs of one partner cannot be fertilized by the male gametes of the other. The reciprocal cross, however, is compatible (see Fig. 2, upper and lower halves). (2) A *reciprocal incompatibility* between + and — strains (cf. Fig. 2, right half). Zygote formation is blocked in both reciprocal crosses.

An essential tool for the identification of semi-incompatibility is the so-called "barrage" formation. This phenomenon, which occurs regularly in interracial crosses, consists of a pigment-free zone in the line of contact between different strains of the two races. In the barrage zone the hyphal tips do not form the black melanin pigments. Barrage formation, which was first observed by Rizet (1952),[2] never occurs between strains of the

---

[2] In Rizet's first work on barrage, he found that the phenomenon was inherited through genes and extrachromosomal factors. This case is exceptional, however, as all barrages found in connection with heterogenic incompatibility are inherited strictly chromosomally.

same race. Furthermore, the formation of a barrage is independent of mating type and occurs between + as well as between — strains. Since no fruiting bodies are formed in the barrage zone, two lines of perithecia are formed in compatible crosses, each originating from the ascogonia of one of the partners. In a semi-incompatible cross there is only one line of perithecia, as may be seen in Fig. 2.

Figure 2 also shows the genetic mechanism of heterogenic incompatibility. Semi-incompatibility is due to a digenic difference, e.g., ($ab \times a_1b_1$ or $cv \times c_1v_1$). Reciprocal incompatibility is provoked in the cross $a\ b\ c_1v_1 \times a_1\ b_1\ cv$ by an overlapping of the two mechanisms of semi-incompatibility: $ab \times a_1b_1$ blocks the fertilization of the $a_1\ b_1\ cv$ female sex organs while $cv \times c_1\ v_1$ blocks the fertilization of the $a\ b\ c_1\ v_1$ ascogonia. All four genes are unlinked, and multiple alleles have not been found.

The action of the genes responsible for heterogenic incompatibility affects both the sexual and the vegetative phases. By a specific combination of the $a\ b\ c\ v$ alleles the viability of nuclei is affected in both homokaryons and heterokaryons. (1) Homokaryotic mycelia of the genotype $a_1\ b$ or $c_1\ v$ which occur as recombination types among the F_1 of semi-incompatible crosses exhibit very sparse growth. Most of the nuclei degenerate and the mycelia die after a few days. (2) The combination of genes a_1 and b or c_1 and v are also incompatible in heterokaryons when both genes are located in different nuclei, e.g., $ab + a_1b_1$. These heterokaryons do not show anomalous growth. However, the division rate of the nuclei which carry the gene a_1 decreases rapidly and after a few days the heterokaryon becomes an ab homokaryon. The same occurs in the heterokaryon $cv + c_1v_1$, where the homokaryon cv is formed because of the c_1v incompatibility.

These results suggest that heterogenic incompatibility must be attributed to incompatibility between two genes at different loci ($a_1 \leftrightarrow b$ and $c_1 \leftrightarrow v$). Furthermore, this incompatibility between two genes is due to the effect of b on a_1 (or of v on c_1), since the nuclei carrying the genes a_1 and c_1 show a reduced viability when b or v is present in the same genome or in a common cytoplasm.

These facts permit us also to explain the asymmetrical formation of fruiting bodies in semi-incompatible crosses in the following way: semi-incompatibility (e.g., in the cross $ab \times a_1b_1$, see Fig. 2) consists of an inhibition of plasmogamy in the cross $a_1b_1 \times ab$. Microscopic observations have shown that the trichogynes are quite normally attracted by the male sex organs, but there is no fusion between the trichogyne tip and the male gametes. (The trichogyne branches are further attracted by spermogonia in the vicinity, and so on.) Fertilization is normal in the reciprocal combination. After plasmogamy between the trichogyne tip and male gamete, the nucleus of the latter migrates through the trichogyne, whose own nuclei degenerate rapidly, and initiates the dikaryotic phase in the ascogonium. One may now assume that the inhibition of plasmogamy is the effect of a product of gene b. The gene b can manifest itself only when localized in the male gamete (in the cross ♀ $a_1 b_1$ × ♂ ab). In the reciprocal cross, where b is localized in the nuclei of the trichogyne, it cannot be expressed since these nuclei begin to degenerate once contact with the male gamete is formed. Semi-incompatibility of the cross cv × $c_1 v_1$ may similarly be explained by the action of gene v blocking plasmogamy in the cross ♀ $c_1 v_1$ × ♂ cv.

Genes b and v are both active in reciprocal incompatibility in the cross $abc_1 v_1$ × $a_1 b_1 cv$ because each blocks the fertilization process in one direction.

As for the biochemical characterization of the b and v genes, it is known that their gene products do not diffuse into the medium and that they can act only within the cytoplasm (see action in the vegetative phase, above) or when hyphal elements are in close contact. In mixed cultures of semi-incompatible strains, there is an inhibition of protein synthesis, which expresses itself as an immunological alteration of protein specificity (Esser, 1959b).

Bernet (1963a,b), who studied heterogenic incompatibility in two other races of *Podospora anserina*, was able recently to confirm our results. He found three pairs of alleles which behaved in certain combinations like the *a b c v* genes, producing semi-incompatibility and complete incompatibility, as well as influencing viability in the vegetative phase. The single difference between the findings of Bernet and our own observations is that gene D, which acts comparably to our genes b and v, can act only at a temperature of 20°C. It is not known yet whether the genes found by Bernet are allelic to ours or whether more loci are responsible for the same phenomenon.

We can say in summary, that heterogenic incompatibility in *P. anserina* consists of an incompatibility of two nonallelic genes and, because of the ontogenetic peculiarities of the fertilization procedure, this incompatibility manifests itself only in one of two reciprocal crosses. These genes also act in the vegetative phase and reduce the viability of nuclei.

As mentioned above (page 670), there are described in the literature several other cases which may be related to heterogenic incompatibility. A survey of these cases is given by Esser and Kuenen (1965). Unfortunately, no genetic analysis has been made which can provide clues to the underlying genetic mechanism.

IV. INCOMPATIBILITY AND EVOLUTION

Through evolution the characteristics of all living organisms are continuously changed. The essential factors of evolution are mutability recombination, and selection. Spontaneously occurring mutations can be distributed and fixed within a population only if they lead to a selective advantage. This process naturally depends on environmental conditions. The basis for the distribution of changes in the genetic material is provided above all by sexual reproduction. Through the continuous sequence of karyogamy and meiosis, the genetic information is continuously recombined. (This function can also be provided for, to a limited degree, by mitotic recombination.) Nuclei are obtained by these processes which are better adapted to environmental conditions.

The efficiency of sexual reproduction as a means of genetic recombination is enhanced when fertilization between genetically like nuclei is diminished or made impossible. The prevention of inbreeding in most animals is achieved by dioecism. Among higher plants and fungi, however, this breeding system may be rare. Dioecism is replaced by homogenic incompatibility in many monoecious species. The different mechanisms of homogenic incompatibility in higher plants and fungi have one feature in common in spite of genetic and physiological differences: the incompatibility of like gametic nuclei. Inbreeding is diminished by this phenomenon, and outbreeding enhanced. The wild strains of homogenic incompatible species are therefore largely heterogenic (haploids) or heterozygous (diploids). This is not true in species which are pseudocompatible where, because of the self-fertility of most of the monosporic cultures, the outbreeding effect of homogenic incompatibility is canceled. This explains the fact that races of *Podospora anserina* isolated from nature are highly homogeneous, with the exception of the mating-type genes (Esser, 1959a).

The mechanism of heterogenic incompatibility stands in opposition to that of homogenic incompatibility. Heterogenic incompatibility restricts outbreeding and promotes inbreeding since, in this case, genetically different gametic nuclei are incompatibile. The exchange of genetic material between races is therefore diminished. The effect of heterogenic incompatibility is enhanced when this breeding system is linked with pseudocompatibility as in *P. anserina*, where both heterogenic incompatibility and pseudocompatibility act in the same direction.

We can state in conclusion: Within species whose sexual behavior is determined by homogenic incompatibility or dioecism there is a continuous recombination of the genetic material because of the restriction of inbreeding. Spontaneously occurring mutations will be distributed with relative rapidity within the whole species, which takes part as a whole in

20. Incompatibility

evolution. The outbreeding effect can be suspended by pseudocompatibility as well as by heterogenic incompatibility, or by both acting together. In the latter cases, mutations are transferred from one race to another only to a very limited extent, and thus the races become isolated. The race, instead of the species, becomes the smallest unit of evolution.

REFERENCES

Bauch, R. (1930). *Arch. Protistenk.* **70**:417.
Bauch, R. (1931). *Arch. Protistenk.* **75**:101.
Bauch, R. (1932). *Ber. deut. Botan. Ges.* **50**:17.
Bauch, R. (1934). *Z. Induktive Abstammungs-Vererbungslehre* **67**:242.
Bensaude, M. (1918). Recherches sur le cycle évolutif et la sexualité chez les Basidiomycètes. Thèse, Université de Nemours, France.
Bernet, J. (1963a). *Compt. Rend.* **256**:771.
Bernet, J. (1963b). *Ann. Sci. Nat.: Botan. Biol. Vegetale* [12] **4**:205.
Bistis, G. N. (1956). *Am. J. Botany* **43**:389.
Bistis, G. N. (1957). *Am. J. Botany* **44**:436.
Bistis, G. N., and J. R. Raper. (1963). *Am. J. Botany* **50**:880.
Burnett, J. H. (1956). *New Phytologist* **55**:50.
Craigie, J. N. (1942). *Trans. Roy. Soc. Can., Sect. V* [3] **36**:19.
Dodge, B. O. (1920). *Mycologia* **12**:115.
Dodge, B. O. (1927). *J. Agr. Res.* **35**:289.
Dodge, B. O. (1928). *Mycologia* **20**:226.
Dowding, E. S. (1933). *Can. J. Res.* **9**:294.
Dowding, E. S., and A. Bakerspigel. (1956). *Can. J. Botany* **34**:231.
Esser, K. (1956). *Z. Induktive Abstammungs-Vererbungslehre* **87**:595.
Esser, K. (1959a). *Z. Vererbungslehre* **90**:29.
Esser, K. (1959b). *Z. Vererbungslehre* **90**:445.
Esser, K. (1962). *Biol. Zentr.* **81**:161.
Esser, K. (1966). *In* "Handbuch der Pflanzenphysiologie" (W. Ruhland, ed.), Vol. 18. Springer, Berlin.
Esser, K., and R. Kuenen. (1965). "Genetik der Pilze," 497 pp. Springer, Berlin.
Franke, G. (1957). *Z. Induktive Abstammungs-Vererbungslehre* **88**:159.
Franke, G. (1962). *Z. Vererbungslehre* **93**:109.
Ito, T. (1956). *Botan. Mag. (Tokyo)* **69**:369.
Kniep, H. (1918). *Flora (Jena)* **111**:380.
Kniep, H. (1920). *Verhandl. Physik.-Med. Ges. Wurzburg* **46**:1.
Kuwana, H. (1954). *J. Genet.* **29**:163.
Kuwana, H. (1955). *Med. Biol. (Tokyo)* **36**:187.
Kuwana, H. (1956). *Ann. Rept. Sci. Works, Fac. Sci., Osaka Univ.* **4**:117.
Kuwana, H. (1958). *Botan. Mag. (Tokyo)* **71**:841.
Lamoure, D. (1957). *Compt. Rend.* **244**:2841.
Lewis, D. (1954). *Advan. Genet.* **6**:235.
Lewis, D. (1956). *Brookhaven Symp. Biol.* **9**:89.
Nobles, M. K., R. Macrae, and B. P. Tomlin. (1957). *Can. J. Botany* **35**:377.
Oikawa, K. (1939). *Sci. Rept. Tohoku Univ., Fourth Ser.* **14**:245.
Olive, L. S. (1956). *Am. J. Botany* **43**:97.
Papazian, H. P. (1951). *Genetics* **36**:441.
Papazian, H. P. (1958). *Advan. Genet.* **9**:41.

Prud'Homme, N., and M. Gans. (1958). *Compt. Rend.* **247**:2419.
Quintanilha, A., and J. Pinto-Lopes. (1950). *Bol. Soc. Broteriana* **24**:115
Raper, C. A., and J. R. Raper. (1964). *Am. J. Botany* **51**:379.
Raper, J. R. (1953). *Quart. Rev. Biol.* **28**:233.
Raper, J. R. (1954). *In* "Sex in Microorganisms," p. 42. Am. Assoc. Advance, Sci., Washington, D.C.
Raper, J. R. (1960). *Am. J. Botany* **47**:794.
Raper, J. R. (1961). *Ber. Deut. Botan. Ges.* **74**:326.
Raper, J. R. (1963). *Mycologia* **55**:79.
Raper, J. R., and K. Esser. (1961). *Z. Vererbungslehre* **92**:439.
Raper, J. R., and K. Esser. (1964). *In* "The Cell" (J. Brachet and A. E. Mirsky, eds.), Vol. 6, p. 139. Academic Press, New York.
Raper, J. R., and P. G. Miles. (1958). *Genetics* **43**:530.
Raper, J. R., and M. T. Oettinger. (1962). *Rev. Biol. (Lisbon)* **3**:205.
Raper, J. R., and M. G. Baxter, and R. B. Middleton. (1958a). *Proc. Natl. Acad. Sci. U. S.* **44**:889.
Raper, J. R., G. S. Krongelb, and M. G. Baxter. (1958b). *Am. Naturalist* **92**:221.
Raper, J. R., M. G. Baxter, and A. H. Ellingboe. (1960). *Proc. Natl. Acad. Sci. U. S.* **46**:833.
Rizet, G. (1952). *Rev. Cytol. Biol. Vegetales* **13**:51.
Rizet, G., and C. Engelmann. (1949). *Rev. Cytol. Biol. Vegetales* **11**:201.
Rowell, J. B. (1955). *Phytopathology* **45**:370.
Sass, J. E. (1929). *Am. J. Botany* **16**:663.
Skolko, A. J. (1944). *Can. J. Res.* **22**:251.
Vakili, N. G. (1953). On the genetics of the *A* factor in *Schizophyllum commune*. Thesis, University of Chicago.
Whitehouse, H. L. K. (1949a). *Biol. Rev. Cambridge Phil. Soc.* **24**:411.
Whitehouse, H. L. K. (1949b). *New Phytologist* **48**:212.
Whitehouse, H. L. K. (1951a). *Indian Phytopathol.* **4**:91.
Whitehouse, H. L. K. (1951b). *Brit. Mycol. Soc. Trans.* **34**:340.
Zickler, H. (1952). *Arch. Protistenk.* **98**:1.

Dissemination

CHAPTER 21

Spore Release[1]

C. T. INGOLD

*Birkbeck College
University of London
London, England*

I. INTRODUCTION

Fungi are typically land organisms and this account of spore liberation will be concerned solely with terrestrial forms. Dispersal in the relatively small number of aquatic species will not be considered.

In the main, fungi are dispersed by spores, although other types of propagule, including unspecialized mycelial fragments, may also be involved. In the overall dispersal story of spores three fairly distinct episodes can usually be recognized: liberation, transport, and deposition. In this chapter only the first of these claims our attention.

It is convenient to distinguish between those fungi in which spores are violently or actively discharged by forces operating internally, those in which the momentum of falling rain drops, blown sand, driving mist, or just wind is canalized to effect the take-off, and those in which some animal, insect or mammal, picks up the spores and carries them away.

Although this chapter is concerned only with the liberation of spores, it is impossible to consider this in isolation. It will be necessary from time to time to discuss how the mechanism of spore liberation in particular fungi is related to further dispersal.

II. ACTIVE DISCHARGE

Spores may be violently discharged from the parent body by the bursting of spore-containing cells, by sudden changes in shape of turgid spores

[1] I contributed a chapter on a closely similar subject to Volume III of "Plant Pathology—An Advanced Treatise" published by Academic Press in 1960. I have tried to make the present contribution distinctly different; in particular, none of the figures chosen to illustrate this chapter is the same.

or of turgid structures associated with the spores, by rapid twisting movements produced as the result of drying in filamentous sporophores, and by the sudden breaking of tensile water in spores or conidiophores, distorted on drying, which are thereby permitted to return to their original form.

In any consideration of spore discharge the distance of projection is of special interest. This depends on the initial velocity of the projectile and on its size, shape, and density. For small objects of the dimensions of fungal spores, air resistance is a master factor in determining distance (d). It can be shown for spherical projectiles of the same density that $d = Kr^2$, where r is the radius of the projectile and K is a constant (Ingold, 1960). In violently discharged fungal spores and spore masses there is a general positive correlation between size and distance of shooting.

A. Liberation Due to Bursting of Turgid Cells

It is among the higher ascomycetes that the water-squirting type of discharge is most widely developed. The mature ascus consists of a single cell lined by an almost equally thin layer of enucleate cytoplasm. Within this, occupying most of the volume, is an elongated vacuole of sap in which the ascospores are suspended near the apex of the ascus. Finally it bursts in a regular manner by the hinging backward of a lid, the separation of a cap, or the development of an apical pore, and the spores are squirted out apparently simultaneously or in obvious succession. The distance of discharge varies considerably in different species. It is rarely less than 0.2 cm and is commonly of the order of 1.0–2.0 cm. In the coprophilous species *Dasyobolus immersus* and *Podospora fimicola* distances as great as 30 cm have been recorded (Buller, 1909; Ingold, 1933). With objects the size of fungal spores there is no significant difference between the distance of horizontal and vertical discharge, since air resistance is the overriding factor limiting the range of the ascus gun (Ingold, 1960).

In most ascomycetes the asci are organized in hymenia either more or less exposed at maturity in apothecia or concealed within perithecia or biologically similar pseudothecia.

Among the larger members of Pezizales and Helotiales the apothecium often takes the form of a cup or vase a centimeter or more across and either sessile or stalked. The hymenium lines the interior and is thus exposed to rain, but a temporary wetting does not adversely affect the layer of asci. In an apothecium of this kind the elongated asci, forming a close palisade with the intervening paraphyses, are at right angles to the general hymenial surface. With such a structure it might be expected that cross fire would lead to a considerable wastage by discharge of spores onto opposite hymenial surfaces. Buller (1934) has shown, however, that this does not occur because of the positive phototropism of the asci, as a result of which they point toward the overhead illumination. The phototropic curvature of the ascus may occur at a considerable distance from its free end, or may be limited to its extreme apex so that response to light is indicated merely by the slight displacement of the lid (e.g., in *Dasyscyphus protractus*) to the more strongly lighted side of the apex. However, even curvature to this slight degree is apparently enough to deflect the issuing ascus jet in the general direction of the light. In some stalked apothecia (e.g., *Aleuria repanda*) the whole structure, as well as the individual ascus, is positively phototropic (Bayliss-Elliott, 1927). Although phototropism of asci seems to be a very general phenomenon in ascomycetes, there are species in which no such response is evident (e.g., *Bulgara inquinans*). Indeed, apart from Buller's observations, covering only a few genera, there is very little precise information.

The same general arguments relating to the escape of spores from cuplike apothecia apply equally to the individual pits in the complex apothecium of *Morchella,* which can, perhaps, be regarded as a polypore among ascomycetes. It has been pointed out that the differences between *Morchella* and a hymenomycete polypore are essentially related to the fundamental contrasts between the ascus and the basidium as spore guns.

Phototropism is also a feature of species in which asci are so freely exposed that there is no possibility of the kind of cross-fire wastage that might obtain in a cuplike apothecium. This is so for the minute apothecia of coprophilous discomycetes belonging to such genera as *Ascobolus, Dasyobolus,* and *Saccobolus*. Curvature toward light is particularly obvious in *Dasyobolus immersus* because the asci are so large and, when ripe, project so far beyond the general level of the hymenium. Biologically, however, the phototropism of asci in coprophilous fungi of this kind may be of real significance for liberation. On such an irregular surface as dung, with small depressions and minute caves, phototropism of the asci may allow spores to be shot toward light and thus into open spaces away from the substratum.

In the extensive exposed hymenium of an apothecium a number of asci can discharge their spores at the same time. Probably most apothecia are capable of "puffing," a phenomenon figured by Micheli as early is 1729. During a prolonged still period a very large number of asci may reach a condition when they are so turgid as to be unstable. If the apothecium is then touched, subjected to a blast of relatively dry air, or strongly lit by a shaft of light, these asci explode simultaneously, and audibly if the fungus is close enough to the ear, shooting into the air thousands of spores and droplets of ascus sap which form a visible cloud like smoke. With a vaselike apothecium as in *Sarcoscypha protracta* the spores are puffed out in a cylindrical beam (Fig. 1), because of the phototropism of the asci, much as the parabolic mirror of a searchlight sends a parallel shaft of light into

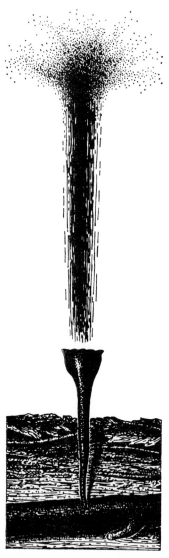

Fig. 1. *Sarcoscypha protracta*. Apothecium, attached to buried wood, puffing. Natural size. After Buller (1934).

the night sky. However, in the fraction of a second the initial velocity of the discharged ascospores is reduced to zero and they diffuse smokewise in the eddy system of the turbulent air. Buller (1934) has pointed out that a beam of puffed spores travels farther than the distance to which an individual ascus can shoot its spores, because when very many asci burst simultaneously they set the whole body of air above the apothecium in motion.

The biological importance of puffing is difficult to assess. It is important to realize that under normal conditions there exists in contact with the ground a layer, usually a few millimeters to a few centimeters deep, of nonturbulent air which is either quite still or in laminar flow. Above this layer the air is commonly turbulent and spores which reach this air have a reasonable chance of effective dispersal. Under calm conditions, particularly at night, the nonturbulent layer may become much deeper. A puffing apothecium may have an advantage in throwing its spores higher with a greater chance of encountering turbulent air. Also the conditions which bring about puffing in nature tend to be associated with turbulence, mechanical or thermal, so that a puffing apothecium usually liberates its spores when conditions for their dispersal are generally favorable.

Not all apothecia are capable of puffing. Falck (1948) has divided discomycetes into two biological groups: the tactiosensitive species which puff readily, and radiosensitive ones in which spore discharge is greatly stimulated by strong illumination, but in which puffing does not occur. It seems doubtful, however, that such a sharp distinction can really be drawn.

In pyrenomycetes the asci occur in a flask-shaped structure communicating to the outside by a narrow opening (ostiole). Developmental morphology has shown that there are two quite distinct types of structure: the perithecium and the pseudothecium. Biologically these two are essentially similar, and indeed, their mature structure is so alike that unless development is closely followed it is difficult to tell one from the other. Luckily for the taxonomist the pseudothecium seems always to be associated with the bitunicate nature of the ascus, a character easy to determine.

The mode of action of a typical perithecium may be illustrated by *Sordaria fimicola* (Ingold and Hadland, 1959). Within, and attached to a basal cushion, are many asci in all stages of development. In some pyrenomycetes paraphyses are present, but in *S. fimicola* these have largely disappeared at maturity. Asci occupy the interior almost completely, but any interstices are filled with mucilage. This is a general feature of these fungi. No gas phase is present in an active perithecium. Communication with the outside is by a narrow neck canal, lined with recurved periphyses. Up this canal a single ascus elongates until its tip protrudes beyond the ostiole. It then bursts, shooting its spores to a distance of up to 10 cm; the empty envelope, still attached to the basal cushion, retracts into the perithecium where it soon gelatinizes. Another ascus then elongates, and so the process goes on. In most pyrenomycetes there is room for only one ascus at a time in the neck canal. Puffing, so striking in discomycetes, is impossible in pyrenomycetes. In contrast to the great range in size of apothecia, perithecia (or pseudothecia) are always small, being rarely more, and never much more, than 1 mm diameter. The difference in range of size between apothecia and perithecia is clearly related to how the two mechanisms work.

A variant of the behavior described for *Sordaria* is the detached-ascus type which has been reported for a small number of ascomycetes. In this the asci become detached from the basal cushion of the perithecium and are squeezed out in single file through the neck canal. On reaching the ostiole discharge occurs, but the empty ascus is squeezed out by the one following it. Discharge of this kind is found in a number of long-necked species such as *Ceratostomella ampullacea* (Ingold, 1933) and *Endothia parasitica* (Rankin, 1914). This type permits very rapid shooting. In *C. ampullacea* only a second or two separates the discharge of successive asci. Such rapid shooting would be impossible if a single ascus had to elongate up the relatively long neck and discharge its spores before the next one could get under way.

Although spore discharge is in general characteristic of the higher ascomycetes, it is not infrequently replaced by passive, or at least nonviolent, liberation. For instance, in *Daldinia concentrica* spores are usually shot to a distance of about 1.5 cm, but sometimes a spore tendril is produced instead. In the production of this it seems that the ascus reaches the ostiole but its contents merely ooze out there. The next ascus piles its spores behind the first lot, and as this process is repeated a spore tendril is gradually formed. Sometimes, however, tendrils of spores are developed in a somewhat different manner. In species of the large genus *Chaetomium* the asci break down while still within the perithecium and there is produced an increasing mass of spores and mucilage which, in some species, oozes out in the form of a tendril like paste squeezed from a tube. A number of pycnidial fungi also liberate their spores as long tendrils (e.g., *Diatrype stigma,* imperfect state). However, in pyrenomycetes, where the asci break down within the perithecium, a spore tendril is not always formed. In *Ceratocystis* species the exuding mass of ascospores mixed with slimy fluid accumulates as a droplet held in place by a rosette of specialized radiating hyphae.

Among other ascomycetes violent spore discharge also occurs in Taphrinales, Myriangiales, and Erysiphales. In the last order one or several asci occur in a minute completely closed cleistothecium, the wall of which must first be broken open before the ascus can project its spores. In *Sphaerotheca mors-uvae,* for example, in spring following the winter's rest, the single swelling ascus breaks through the cleistothecium wall and protrudes considerably. It then bursts apically, shooting its spores into the air. In *Podosphaera leucotricha,* however, the cleistothecium wall is somewhat elastic

21. Spore Release

and, as the ascus protrudes, this wall tends to pinch inward. At a certain stage the jaws of the opened cleistothecium suddenly snap together projecting the whole ascus into the air to a distance of a few centimeters. The ascus itself then bursts, scattering its spores. Thus there are two violent steps in the process of spore liberation in this fungus (Woodward, 1927).

Having considered the different types of ascocarp in relation to spore liberation, we may pass to a more detailed consideration of spore discharge from the ascus. In many species the spores, particularly if spherical or ovoid, appear to be discharged simultaneously as, for example, in the larger discomycetes. However, even in these, although the interval between the first and last leaving the ascus may be a minute fraction of a second, the spores are actually shot away in succession. This almost inevitably follows from the fact that their diameter exceeds that of the apical opening through which they escape. This successive escape does not necessarily involve the separation of each spore from its neighbor, particularly if it is surrounded by a mucilagenous sheath. In some species the spores are so firmly stuck together that, although the spore mass may be drawn out at the moment of leaving the ascus, it soon rounds off in the air as a single spherical droplet. An example of this is *Dasyobolus immersus,* in which each spore has its own mucilage sheath and all eight spores stick tightly together. In *Saccobolus* spp. the spores are even more firmly cemented by a common envelope of mucilage. In some, probably many, ascomycetes all possible types of projectile from 1-spored to 8-spored are formed. This question has been studied particularly in *Sordaria fimicola* (Ingold and Hadland, 1959). It will be seen later that the tendency of spores to stick together is of importance in relation to the distance of discharge.

Many asci discharge their spores in obvious succession. This is especially true where the spores are very elongated. In discomycetes this kind of successive discharge has been reported in *Geoglossum* spp. and among pyrenomycetes in a number of species (e.g., *Cordyceps militaris, Epichloe typhina, Leptosphaeria acuta,* and *Pleospora scirpicola*). In *Geoglossum,* for example, the ascus at maturity develops a minute apical pore into which an elongated spore is pushed, temporarily stoppering it. This then gathers speed and is shot away in a flash. Immediately, and before its hydrostatic pressure is lost, the ascus is plugged by the next spore and so on until all eight have been discharged (Ingold, 1939).

It has been suggested that the shape of ascospores may sometimes be specially related to their discharge through an apical pore. In very many species a transverse cut half way between the apex and the base of the spore divides it into two equal halves (bipolar symmetrical type). However, in quite a large number of species, scattered widely taxonomically, a cut at the midway position would divide the spore into an upper larger part and a lower small one (bipolar asymmetrical). Such an ascospore is relatively blunt at the apex and pointed at its base. The reverse type with the relatively sharp end at the apex is almost unknown among ascomycetes. It seems probable that the bipolar asymmetrical spore with relatively blunt apex is of special value in discharge and tends to be shot farther than one which is bipolar symmetrical (Ingold, 1954).

Most ascomycetes have wind-dispersed spores, and the distance, or rather the height, to which they are shot is important in getting through the laminar layer of air close to the ground. This distance of discharge, commonly a centimeter or two, has a profound effect on the construction of the ascocarp, particularly in discomycetes. The upward-facing hymenium is advantageous; the downward-facing one is ruled out. Further the closely opposed hymenial surfaces which are such a feature of hymenomycetes are clearly impossible.

For the distinctive coprophilous fungi, the first step in dispersal involves reaching the grass around the dung. The grass with its load of spores may then be eaten by a herbivore. Some of the more specialized coprophilous species manage the initial step by violent discharge alone, the necessary distance of throw being achieved by using relatively large projectiles. In extreme cases not only are the spores exceptionally big, but they are also bound together by mucilage to form a single projectile. The discomycete *Dasyobolus immersus* and the pyrenomycete *Podospora fimicola* are outstanding examples which shoot their spores to a distance of 30 cm. This distance of discharge is related mainly to the size of the spore masses.

The relationship between size of projectile and distance of discharge is clearly shown by *Sordaria fimicola*, a common coprophilous species. Although many of the spores stick together in eights on discharge, projectiles with fewer spores are also formed. Spores escape from the ascus in single file through a relatively narrow apical pore, although, because of their mucilaginous sheaths, they tend to stick together. However, as they emerge at high speed a break may occur at any or all of the seven mucilaginous links between adjacent spores. The actual arrangement of spores in the ascus jets has been studied by catching them near the edge of a horizontal transparent Perspex disk rotating very rapidly a few millimeters above discharging perithecia (Ingold and Hadland, 1959). The jets are thereby spread out horizontally on the underside of the disk and can subsequently be examined microscopically. The average distance of horizontal discharge of the eight types of projectile, each containing a different number of spores, has been determined. This distance increases with the number of spores, but not quite to the extent suggested by the formula $d = Kr^2$. This is probably because the projectiles with the larger numbers of spores are not spherical during most of their flight, but elongated, although by the time their horizontal velocity is reduced to zero they have no doubt become roughly spherical under the influence of the surface tension of associated ascus sap. Certainly projectiles appear as rounded masses when, having lost their horizontal velocity, they settle onto a glass slide.

Apart from ascomycetes, violent spore discharge associated with bursting turgid cells occurs only as a few scattered instances. In Mucorales there is a single but very striking example: *Pilobolus,* species of which are morphologically and physiologically highly specialized in relation to the coprophilous habitat. The strongly phototropic sporangiophore, delimited from the parent mycelium by cross walls, is a turgid cell. There is a basal trophocyst with a cylindrical hypha leading from it to a crystal-clear subsporangial bulb. The sporangium, with the upper part of its wall blackened, is separated from the sporangiophore by a substantial columella. At maturity the sporangiophore ruptures along a line of weakness just below the columella and immediately the subsporangial bulb contracts, squirting a jet of sap together with the sporangium and its columella at a mean initial velocity of 10.8 m/sec (Page and Kennedy, 1964) to a distance of up to 200 cm. The upper part of the sporangial wall is unwettable, whereas the lower part is freely wettable, with the result that the upper part projects from the drop of sap when it comes to rest on an object such as a blade of grass. When the drop dries, the sporangium becomes firmly cemented to the object with the black part of the wall effectively covering and presumably protecting the spores. Recently, by a most ingenious procedure, Page (1964) has succeeded in photographing the issuing jet of sap bearing the sporangium at almost the very instant of discharge before it has travelled more than 2–3 mm.

In Entomophthorales there are two well-known examples of discharge by a water-squirting mechanism. In *Entomophthora muscae,* immediately following the death of the parasitized fly, tufts of conidiophores project in the thousands between the segments of the abdomen. Each conidiophore is a turgid cell which bursts to discharge its conidium just as in *Pilobolus.* In late summer flies killed by the fungus are often found stuck to window panes, each fly surrounded by a white halo of discharged spores about 4 cm in diameter.

In *Basidiobolus ranarum,* which grows on the excrement of frogs and toads, and which has a dispersal story subsequent to spore discharge in which insects and amphibians play successive roles, the conidiophore closely resembles the sporangiophore of *Pilobolus.* It is positively phototropic and there is a well-developed subconidial bulb. This finally bursts along a line of weakness which, however, is near the *base* of the bulb. Immediately as rupture occurs the wall of this bulb contracts, squirting sap backward and flying off on the recoil rocketwise with its spore. In flight the contracted subconidial bulb usually separates from the conidium. Conidia are usually thrown to a distance of 2–3 cm and the subconidial bulb to about half that distance (Ingold, 1934).

Another isolated example of what is probably a sap-squirting mechanism has been reported in the imperfect fungus *Nigrospora* (Fig. 2). The penul-

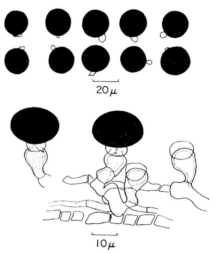

Fig. 2. *Nigrospora sphaerica. Above*: discharged spores showing attached drop of cytoplasm. *Below*: conidiophores: below the black conidium is a small "supporting cell" and below this the "ampulliform cell," which appears to supply the liquid jet for discharge. After Webster (1952).

timate cell of the short conidiophore, extended apically into a narrow projection which presses through the ultimate "supporting" cell and impinges on the base of the spore, bursts to supply a liquid jet which carries the single black conidium to a distance of several centimeters (Webster, 1952).

B. Liberation Due to Rounding Off of Turgid Cells

Spore discharge associated with the sudden rounding off of turgid cells in an unstable form occurs in a number of fungi. It happens in several members of Entomophthorales. For example, in *Entomophthora coronata* a single and relatively large conidium is borne at the end of a straight conidiophore the tip of which projects into the conidium as a distinct columella. Strains are set up and the conidium tends to round off. As this happens, the reentrant part bulges outward and, as a result, the conidium bounces off to a distance of 2–3 cm (Martin, 1925).

A similar mechanism has been described for the downy mildew *Sclerospora philippinensis* (Weston, 1923). Here the area of contact between the spore and its sterigma is relatively small and the tip of the latter does not project into the spore; there is merely a flat contact. It is rounding off in this region that seems to bring about discharge, but the spores are shot to a distance of only a millimeter or so.

In most rusts (Uredinales) the aeciospores are violently discharged. Within the aecium the spores are polyhedral because of mutual pressure. There is a tendency for them to round off if conditions are sufficiently damp. This happens suddenly and spores bounce out either singly or in groups to a distance of several millimeters. Accompanying the spores there are often minute germ-pore plugs. It has been suggested that these also may have a significance for discharge in producing reentrant regions in the spores which may suddenly bulge outward (Dodge, 1924).

The claim has been made (Hammarlund, 1925) that in Erysiphales conidia are actively discharged by rounding off where they are in contact in the unbranched row. Critical reexamination of this question is needed.

A spectacular example of sudden release of tension among turgid cells bringing about spore discharge is found in the gasteromycete *Sphaerobolus*. In this, by the instantaneous eversion of a cup of turgid tissue under stress, a spore mass is shot to a distance of up to 400 cm (Buller, 1933).

C. Ballistospore Discharge

In most basidiomycetes, particularly hymenomycetes, the gelatinous fungi (Dacrymycetales, Tremellales, and Auriculariales), and rusts (Uredinales), basidiospores are discharged by a mechanism which still remains a mystery. Each basidiospore is poised asymmetrically on a sterigma. Very near the point of attachment to the sterigma, the spore has a minute projection (hilum). Just before discharge a drop of fluid appears at the hilum, grows to a certain and definite size but considerably less than that of the spore. The basidiospore is then shot away to a distance of 0.01–0.02 cm, carrying the drop with it and leaving behind a still erect and apparently closed sterigma from which no fluid exudes. This type of spore, in which discharge is associated with this series of events, is referred to as a ballistospore (Derx, 1948). Ballistospores are also produced by the very common "mirror yeasts" (Sporobolomycetaceae). The secondary sporidia of certain smuts (especially *Tilletia*) are also ballistospores.

It has been suggested that ballistospore discharge occurs by a rounding-off process at a flat junction between the basidiospore and its sterigma just as in *Sclerospora,* but this does not explain the asymmetrical placing of the spore nor the phenomenon of drop secretion. Another idea is that a water-squirting mechanism is involved. A difficulty here is that the four spores of the typical unicellular hymenomycete basidium are shot away in strict succession with several seconds elapsing between discharge of sister spores. If a water-squirting mechanism is to function the basidium must be quickly sealed off after each spore is liberated and, indeed, the sterigma does appear to be closed at its apex immediately after the spore has left it. On the basis of a ciné film of ballistospore discharge in *Sporobolomyces,* it has been claimed that the drop is formed actually at the junction with the sterigma and that this drop is shot away carrying the spore with it. In the film one series of frames shows, as an unusual occurrence, the sudden disappearance of the drop leaving the spore behind on the sterigma (Müller, 1954). Presumably the drop has been shot away. Another theory is based on the suggestion that the surface energy of the drop might be mobilized to bring about discharge, but it is not at all clear how, precisely, this could happen (Ingold, 1939).

In a recent contribution to this problem Olive (1964) claims that what appears at the hilum is not a drop but a gas-filled bubble formed between the inner and outer layers of the spore wall in the hilar region. It is suggested that the spore is dislodged by bursting of this bubble.

Earlier in this chapter the point has been made that the ascus discharges its spores to a distance of 0.2 cm up to 30 cm. The basidium is a spore gun of much shorter range, normally only 0.01–0.02 cm. The greatest distance of ballistospore throw recorded is 0.1 cm for the secondary conidium of *Tilletia* (Buller, 1933).

In hymenomycetes the basidia are usually grouped together in extensive hymenia arranged on complex sporophores. Because the basidium is such a short-range gun, it cannot shoot its spores through the boundary layer into the turbulent air above. Hence the upward-facing hymenium is largely ruled out in hymenomycetes. Further, unlike a hymenium of asci, one composed of basidia is adversely affected by wetting. These two factors seem to have conditioned the gross architecture of most hymenomycete sporophores.

The construction of hymenomycete fruit bodies in relation to spore liberation has been closely studied by Buller (1909, 1922, 1924, 1931). Here only a brief account to illustrate the basic principles can be given, and this will be based mainly on the agaric *Oudemansiella radicata* as a concrete example (Fig. 3).

The gills are covered by basidia in various stages of development. Some mycologists recognize both basidia and paraphyses in the hymenium, but in many hymenomycetes it seems that what were considered paraphyses are really young basidia. In some agarics, however, notably in *Coprinus,* paraphyses are clearly differentiated elements of the hymenium. Some species also have larger and more widely scattered cells of a distinctive appearance in the hymenium. These are cystidia. In some species of *Coprinus,* (especially *C. atramentarius* and *C. lagopus*) they are relatively enormous and clearly are of importance in propping apart the closely packed gills during development. In others (e.g., *Oudemansiella radicata*), although they are striking structures, their functional significance is far from obvious.

In an agaric the hymenial surfaces are for the most part nearly vertical and the spores discharged from their basidia are shot horizontally. In *O.*

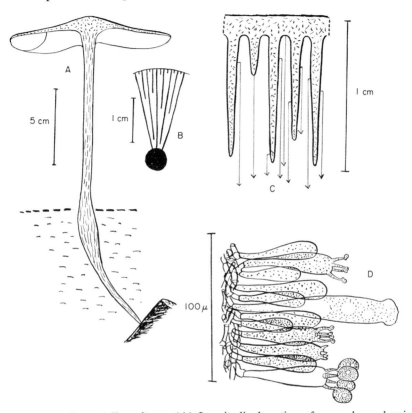

FIG. 3. *Oudemansiella radicata*. (A) Longitudinal section of sporophore showing attachment of pseudorhiza to buried wood. (B) Gill pattern of a sector seen from below, the cut-off stalk being indicated by a black blob. (C) Tangential vertical section of pileus; the hymenium is indicated by thick black line; trajectories of liberated spores are shown by thin lines ending in arrowheads. (D) Part of hymenium, highly magnified.

radicata the distance is 0.02–0.03 cm. The spores are sticky, and if they come to rest on a surface they are likely to be permanently stuck. Clearly the distance between opposing gills must be greater than the distance of discharge. Usually it is considerably greater, a certain margin of safety being allowed. If the gills of a toadstool were all of the the same length, they would be much closer nearer the stipe than at the circumference of the cap.

If it is assumed that near the stipe the gills are the minimum distance apart for successful spore liberation, then on passing outward a position will be reached when the distance is twice this. From this point outward it would be theoretically possible to introduce another shorter gill, neglecting its thickness for the sake of the present argument. Again still nearer the circumference even shorter gills could be introduced when the space between the original long gills had increased to four times the presumed minimum distance. A pattern very much of this type is found in many agarics.

It is clear that if successful spore liberation is to occur the gills must be quite vertical, for if a significant tilting occurred many discharged spores, falling under the influence of gravity, would either come to rest on the same gill lower down or fall onto the opposite gill surface.

Verticality of gills is secured in the following manner: the stout stipe is normally negatively geotropic, giving a roughly vertical orientation to the gills which hang down from the pileus. However, this is only a coarse adjustment. In addition there is a fine one. Each individual gill is positively geotropic and if it is displaced slightly out of the vertical, growth movements occur, presumably of the cell-inflation type, in the region where it joins the cap until it is again essentially vertical.

In agarics generally spore discharge occurs fairly uniformly over the whole gill surface. However, in most species of *Coprinus* a unique condition obtains. The hymenium ripens progressively from the free edge of the gill outward and upward toward the cap tissue. The spores are responsible for color on the gill. During maturation they pass from white through pink to nearly black. As a consequence in a specimen which has just begun to shed spores, the part near the free edge of the gill is black shading off through pink to white next to the cap. In each region of the hymenium, after all the spores are discharged the spent tissue is removed by a process of autodigestion. The result of this is that spores never have far to fall between opposing hymenial surfaces before escaping into the free air below the gills. Correlated with this, the gills are not geotropic. *Coprinus* spp. are referred to as ink caps because under damp conditions the black fluid formed during autodigestion runs down the free edges of the gills and accumulates around the circumference of the pileus. This fluid always contains some spores, but the vast majority fall freely into the air below the pileus.

The principles underlying the polypore type of fruit body are essentially the same as those in the agaric. Generally speaking among agarics sporophores with central stipes are commoner and bracket fruit bodies with lateral attachment are rarer, whereas among polypores the reverse is true.

We may consider such a typical bracket polypore as *Polyporus betulinus*, common on dead birch (*Betula*) trees. At an early stage the sporophore primordium is almost spherical and then expands more or less horizontally as the result of a diageotropic response. Later pores form on the underside and by positively geotropic growth elongate downward, spores being discharged while the pores are still growing, a process which may continue for a month or more in the late summer and early autumn. The tubes are about 0.02–0.04 cm in diameter and may be 1–2 cm long. Spores are discharged horizontally from the hymenium lining the pores, fall vertically, and on emerging below the pileus are carried away by air currents. As with the gills of an agaric the vertical orientation of the tubes must be precise if effective spore liberation is to occur. It has been shown experimentally (Taggart, 1961) that if the tubes of *P. betulinus* are tilted very slightly out of the vertical, the decrease in spore liberation is exactly what would be expected on purely geometrical grounds.

The polypore reaches its extreme expression in the large perennial shelf-fungi such as *Ganoderma applanatum* and *Fomes fomentarius*. The great majority of fungus sporophores are short-lived: fleshy agarics and boletes are active for only a few days, and the corky, leathery, and gelatinous Basidiomycetes for only a few weeks or months and rarely survive into a second season. In *G. applanatum,* however, the sporophore is perennial and the vertical pores continue to grow downward for a number of years. Further, the hymenium remains active in these tubes for two or three years, by which time they may be 4–5 cm long but only 0.01–0.02 cm in diameter. Spores are discharged horizontally to a distance of 0.005–0.010 cm, roughly into the middle of the tubes. These spores may have to fall a considerable distance down these tubes of extremely small bore. The margin of safety, to which reference has already been made in connection with the agaric sporophore, is reduced to practically nothing. Nevertheless, very few discharged spores appear to get stranded on the hymenial surfaces lining the tubes. Some have thought that a system of this kind could not operate in practice and have wondered if static electric forces might be involved in maintaining spores in midstream as they fall down the tubes. Indeed, it has been shown (Gregory, 1957) that the spores of *Ganoderma* normally carry a negative charge, although the existence of a constant repelling charge of the same sign on the hymenium has not been demonstrated. However, work on *Polyporus betulinus* (Taggart, 1961) and *Merulius lacrymans* [*Serpula lacrimans*] (Swinbank et al., 1964) suggests that the charge on basidiospores is of such magnitude that it can have no measurable effect on their fall down the hymenial tubes, and this is probably equally true for *Ganoderma*. The fact that the sporophore of *Ganoderma* can operate effectively with such narrow and long pores is almost certainly associated with the extreme rigidity of its tissues and its firm and broad attachment to such a rigid structure as a tree trunk. In fact the effectiveness of the *Ganoderma* bracket as a spore-liberating mechanism is undoubted. From a fair-sized specimen of *G. applanatum* spores rain down at the rate of several millions a minute and this may be maintained, day and night, for the full 6 months of the annual spore-fall period.

Modern mycological taxonomists no longer recognize the Friesian families Agaricaceae and Polyporaceae as natural. Indeed, by concentrating on microscopic features unlikely to have survival value, a number of "natural" series has been recognized in each of which there are agaric and polyporoid members. Although a series of this kind might be read in either direction, it is easier to think of an agaric giving rise to a polypore than the reverse. The polypore may thus be regarded as an advanced type of spore-liberating mechanism providing in its cul-de-sac hymenial tubes conditions of high humidity and complete stillness necessary for the discharge and subsequent escape of the spores.

Among hymenomycetes there are other ways in which the hymenium can be disposed: covering downward-projecting positively geotropic teeth in hydnoid types (e.g., *Hydnum*), as a relatively smooth downward-facing hymenium as in the Thelephoraceae (e.g., *Stereum*), covering positively geotropic vertical axes in branched clavarioid fungi, or a simple erect club in unbranched types (e.g., *Clavariadelphus pistillaris*). In the clavarioid types the hymenium covers most of the surface except for the more basal regions of the sporophore. Unlike all other hymenomycete fruit bodies, the hymenium is given no protection from rain.

Before leaving hymenomycetes it is worth emphasizing that generally the spore-producing surfaces are arranged at some distance above the ground either elevated by stipes in fungi of the toadstool type, or borne on brackets attached to sticks or branches usually significantly above ground level. Thus discharged spores have a reasonable chance of being dropped into turbulent air with its potentiality for dispersal.

So far as other ballistospores are concerned little need be said. The teliospores of Uredinales germinate to produce curved, septate basidia with the basidiospores on the convex side. Thus the spores tend to be thrown outward and, since teliospores are often attached to dead stems and leaves, discharged spores are often liberated above general ground level with consequent advantage for subsequent dispersal.

It is pertinent to enquire how the ballistospores of mirror yeasts (Sporobolomycetaceae) get into the air. It seems that these fungi are essentially epiphyllous on higher plants generally. They are, therefore, well placed to liberate spores into the normally turbulent layers of the air in spite of the short distance of ballistospore discharge. Indeed, it has been shown that the "mirror yeasts" (*Sporobolomyces* and *Tilletiopsis*) contribute massively to the air spora in country districts in the humid hours after midnight and before dawn.

D. Liberation Due to Hygroscopic Mechanisms

Hygroscopic movements are occasionally responsible for violent spore discharge. An example is *Peronospora tabacina,* and no doubt some other members of Peronsporales behave in the same manner. The branched conidiophore or sporangiophore bears many finely poised spores at its apices. With sudden change from high to low humidity the main axis of the conidiophore dries and as it does so twists violently, shaking off its spores (Pinckard, 1942).

In *Botrytis cinerea* Jarvis (1962) considers that, although actual spore discharge due to hygroscopic movements of the conidiophore may only rarely occur, the conidia are released by these movements from organic connection and come to lie in loose masses associated with the terminal branches of the conidiophores. They are then in a condition to be blown away.

In some Mycetozoa, particularly in *Trichia* spp., spirally thickened elaters in the dehisced sporangium undergo hygroscopic movements on drying which violently eject some of the associated spores (Ingold, 1939).

E. Discharge Due to Rupture of Tensile Water

Among green land cryptogams, mechanisms occur in which the release of strains by the breaking of tensile water produces sudden energetic movements which scatter the spores (Ingold, 1939). In pteridophytes the annulus of the fern sporangium, and in bryophytes the elaters associated with the spores in the capsules of leafy liverworts, are familiar examples of mechanisms of this kind. It has been shown recently that, in a number of dematiaceous fungi, conidia are set free in an essentially similar manner.

In *Deightoniella torulosa* (Meredith, 1961) the end cell of the conidiophore, which bears a single conidium, has a thickened wall. Because the thickening is uneven, evaporation leads to a temporary distortion so that the upper region of the end cell is drawn downward. However, this cell, because of the rigidity of its wall, is tending all the time to return to its original form, and the fluid contents are under increasing tension as evaporation proceeds. Finally a break occurs either because the cohesion between the water molecules or their adhesion to the cell wall is overcome. When this happens a minute gas bubble makes its appearance and instantaneously enlarges as the distorted cell returns to its original shape with a sudden jerk which throws off the attached conidium to a distance of several centimeters (Fig. 4).

In *Zygosporium oscheoides* (Meredith, 1962) much the same thing happens (Fig. 4). In this fungus two spores are poised, each on a thin-walled sporogenous cell, at the end of a specialized curved cell. In this the wall on the convex side is heavily thickened while on the concave side it remains relatively thin. Evaporation leads to reduction in volume which results in increased curvature of the cell. The water inside is under tension and when the inevitable break occurs and a gas phase makes its appearance, the cell suddenly returns to its former shape, slinging off the two conidia in the process.

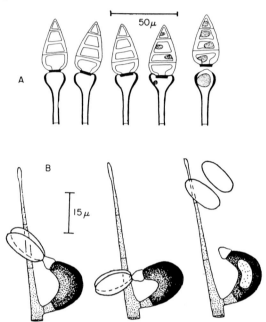

FIG. 4. (A) *Deightoniella torulosa*. Successive changes in form, associated with spore discharge, in the terminal cell of the conidiophore. Interval between final and penultimate stages is a tiny fraction of a second. Gas bubbles are shown stippled. After Meredith (1961). (B) *Zygosporium oscheoides*. Changes in form associated with spore discharge. The time interval between the second and third stages is a minute fraction of a second. The gas vacuole in the dark curved cell is shown white. After Meredith (1962).

In *Cordana musae* (Meredith, 1962) a group of terminal conidia is apparently discharged in the same manner as in *Deightoniella,* although there is some reason to believe that occasionally the separation of a gas phase within the conidium itself may be effective in discharge.

It now seems that this type of mechanism is of fairly common occurrence (Meredith, 1965).

F. External Conditions and Violent Spore Discharge

The principal external conditions affecting violent spore discharge are temperature, light, water supply, and the humidity of the air. In considering any of these it is, however, difficult to discriminate between the effect on spore liberation itself and on spore maturation.

Probably, in general and within the limits of normal fluctuation, increase of temperature produces increased spore liberation. For example, in *Schizophyllum commune* (Zoberi, 1962) temperature affects spore discharge in much the same manner as it does growth, the optimum for basidiospore discharge being, however, somewhat lower than for vegetative growth. Further at 30°C, although growth is still vigorous, spore liberation ceases completely.

Most of the evidence suggests that in Hymenomycetes light has no influence on spore discharge, although in *Corticium filamentosa* (Carpenter, 1949) discharge appears to be inhibited by light and is, therefore, nocturnal.

In many Ascomycetes, however, light has a pronounced effect. This has been studied particularly in *Sordaria fimicola* (Ingold and Dring, 1957; Ingold, 1958). Spore discharge does occur in darkness, but the rate is greatly increased in light. However, only light of wavelengths below 520 mµ is effective. When the fungus is subjected to a regimen of 12 hours' light and 12 hours' darkness in each day period, there is a marked diurnal periodicity. Further when a sporulating culture, conditioned for a day or so to darkness, is given a brief treatment with bright light (e.g., 10,000 lux for 50 seconds) there is a considerable but temporary increase in the rate of discharge 2–3 hours later. In *Sordaria verruculosa* the same thing happens, but the effect is not so striking and the interval between stimulus and response is much longer, ca. 9–12 hours (Ingold and Marshall, 1963). In another pyrenomycete, *Hypoxylon fuscum,* however, the position is quite different. This species is nocturnal due to the fact that light directly inhibits spore discharge. Neither in *S. fimicola* nor in *H. fuscum* is there an inherent rhythm. However, in *Daldinia concentrica,* taxonomically very close to *Hypoxylon,* discharge is also essentially nocturnal, but there is a pronounced endogenous rhythm (Ingold and Cox, 1955). Periodic discharge with a nighttime peak goes on for a week or more when a perithecial stroma is placed in continuous darkness and, for a shorter time, in continuous light.

Rhythms of spore discharge conditioned by light are also a feature of some other fungi. Thus under a regime of 12 hours' light and 12 hours' of darkness each day both *Pilobolus* and *Sphaerobolus* discharge their spore masses during the light periods. In some species of *Pilobolus* at least, and particularly in *P. sphaerosporus,* the rhythm continues for a few days after the periodic conditions have ceased to operate. In *Pilobolus,* a daily alternation of high and low temperature, like a daily alternation of light and darkness, can also induce rhythmic discharge which again persists for a day or two under conditions of stable temperature (Schmidle, 1951; Uebelmesser, 1954).

In water-squirting mechanisms of spore liberation and in those involving the rounding off of cells, turgidity is essential. Further, whatever may be the precise mechanism of basidiospore discharge, it seems certain that it too is dependent on turgor of the basidia. It is not surprising, therefore, that, for most fungi which actively discharge their spores, water supply is a vital factor. Further, since in the majority of fungi, in contrast to vascular plants, there is little provision for translocation of water, spore liberation is usually very dependent on an immediately available supply of external water. In practice this means a dependence on rain or heavy dew. The fleshy Hymenomycetes with short-lived sporophores are produced mainly in early autumn when conditions are generally damp, but before significant frost occurs. Leathery and gelatinous forms dry under conditions of low humidity and spore discharge ceases, to be renewed almost immediately when they are again soaked by rain. Many ascomycetes, particularly pyrenomycetes, are also of this drought-enduring type liberating spores only for short periods after being wetted by rain. A very few fungi can, however, continue to discharge spores even during prolonged dry periods. *Daldinia* is an outstanding example (Ingold, 1946). In this, relying on a water reserve in the stroma, spores can be liberated for weeks without any extraneous water. The same is true of the large perennial bracket fungi *Ganoderma applanatum* and *Fomes fomentarius*. In both of these the sporophore, if still attached to its tree trunk, can go on liberating spores during long periods of drought (Buchwald, 1938). Another special case is *Epichloe typhina*, in which the perithecial stroma is closely associated with the living tissues of the parasitized grass stem immediately above a node. Water for spore discharge is derived from the host's transpiration stream. If this is interrupted, however, discharge quickly comes to an end (Ingold, 1948). Gelatinous ascomycetes such as *Bulgaria inquinans* store water which can be used for spore discharge in jelly. An apothecium of *B. inquinans,* when isolated from its substratum and hung in relatively dry air, sheds spores for several days and only when it has shriveled to about a quarter of its original size does discharge cease (Ingold, 1959).

Although to some extent connected with the factor of water supply, it is, perhaps justifiable to consider the humidity of the ambient air as a separate factor since it may have a more direct and immediate effect on discharge. In an experimental study of discharge in *Sordaria fimicola* it has been shown that the substitution of a very dry (35% relative humidity) for a saturated (100% RH) air stream leads to a temporary acceleration of ascospore discharge (Ingold and Marshall, 1962). It is difficult to envisage how reduced humidity can operate in promoting ascus discharge, and in the work referred to it should be emphasized that the actual supply of water to the fruiting structure was completely adequate. Any significant drying of an apothecium or a perithecium would inevitably lead to the cessation of discharge.

In hymenomycetes lowering the humidity of the ambient air in contact with the hymenium adversely affects spore liberation. In *Schizophyllum* (Zoberi, 1962) reduced humidity temporarily reduces the rate of spore discharge. If, however, the air stream is not too dry and does not operate for too long, a return to humid conditions reverses the inhibition. The same is true for *Polyporus brumalis* and for the release of ballistospores from a culture of the "mirror yeast," *Sporobolomyces roseus.*

In such genera as *Deightoniella* and *Zygosporium,* where water rupture on drying is involved in spore discharge, and in species of *Peronospora,* where a hygroscopic twirling of the conidiophore scatters the spores, humidity of the air is the major factor in discharge. In these fungi spore release in nature occurs in the morning with the normal decrease in atmospheric humidity.

Ingold and Marshall (1964) have reported that the substitution of an air stream containing 0.2–2.5% carbon dioxide for air freed from this gas circulating over the perithecia of *Sordaria fimicola* always led to a marked increase in the rate of spore discharge.

III. PASSIVE SPORE LIBERATION

A. Blow-Off of Spores

Many fungi have dry spores which, although not violently discharged, are fairly easily set free by sufficiently strong air currents. Numerous conidial fungi are of this nature, for example species of *Cladosporium, Penicillium, Aspergillus,* and *Trichothecium.* The conidia tend to be raised above the substratum on erect conidiophores, and this, no doubt, gives some advantage in the take-off. There are also many dry-spore types among the fungi which attack field crops. The conidia (zoosporangia) of *Phytophthora* and of Peronosporales, the conidia (oidia) of Erysiphales, the uredospores of rusts and the chlamydospores of loose smuts (*Ustilago* spp.) are all readily detachable dry spores. In these plant pathogens the spores, being borne on stems and leaves, are normally well above ground level and once detached are suitably placed for aerial dispersal. Also leaf flutter and stem vibration are, no doubt, effective in promoting spore liberation if the spores are not too firmly attached. Among the larger fungi dry-spore species are common in Gasteromycetes such as *Podaxis, Calvatia,* and *Battarrea.* Another interesting case is to be seen in the hymenomycete *Asterophora lycoperdoides* in which basidiospore production is suppressed, but the whole upper part of the pileus becomes a dry powdery mass of stellate chlamydospores. In Ascomycetes a familiar example is *Xylaria hypoxylon* with its erect white branches covered with conidia freely exposed and easily blown away.

There has been little experimental study of spore liberation where no violent discharge is involved. However, the take-off of spores from some molds has been investigated using horizontal tube cultures through which air of known humidity could be passed at controlled speeds (Zoberi, 1961). With *Trichothecium roseum* the stronger the air currents, in the range 1.7–10.0 meters/second, the greater the number of spores liberated. At the higher wind speeds, e.g., 5 meters/second, the number of spores blown off fell very rapidly with time. Again the humidity of the air stream had a very significant effect, many more spores being set free into a dry as compared with a damp air stream of the same velocity. This seems to be a fairly general feature of dry-spore molds.

B. Spore Liberation by Falling Drops

Falling water drops may play an important part in spore liberation. Among conidial fungi there are dry-spore and slime-spore types. The spores of slime-spore fungi cannot be blown off their conidiophores by winds of normal velocity and, in nature, splash liberation or insect dispersal of these fungi seems to be the rule.

Although rain splash has been recognized for a long time as a mechanism of spore liberation, it is only quite recently that the process has received systematic study (Gregory *et al.*, 1959). Water drops of known size were allowed to fall from a given height onto an aqueous spore suspension forming a film on a glass slide. It was found that a drop 5 mm in diameter, falling from a height of 7.4 m onto a film 0.1 mm thick of a rich suspension of the spores of *Fusarium solani* produced over 5000 reflected droplets ranging from 5 μ to 2400 μ across and the larger of these were scattered horizontally over a considerable area. In splash dispersal the bigger droplets fall back rapidly onto the substratum, but the smaller ones may contribute spores to the air spora. A study was also made, using ultra high speed cinematography, of splash liberation of slime spores from the conidial stromata of *Nectria cinnabarina* on a twig. Under these more natural conditions the general picture of splash dispersal was essentially similar. In many slime-spore fungi rain splash is probably the normal means of spore liberation, but also for certain dry-spore fungi rain splash may play an essential part. Work on the coffee leaf-rust (*Hemileia vastatrix*) suggests that winds have little significance in the liberation of uredospores from the leaves, but that rain splash scatters them in quantity (Nutman *et al.*, 1960; Bock, 1962).

Even in fungi where spores are readily blown off by wind or thrown off by hygroscopic twirling, falling rain may play a subsidiary part in spore liberation. Quite apart from the direct action of the falling drop itself, the shock waves ahead of it may be effective in liberating dry spores, for example from a forest of *Botrytis* conidiophores (Jarvis, 1962).

There are also some rather specialized examples of the action of rain drops in spore liberation. The vaselike sporophores of *Cyathus* and *Crucibulum* appear to be splash cups, like the gemmae cups of the liverwort *Marchantia*, from which the hard seedlike peridiola (essentially resistant packets of spores) are splashed to a distance of several feet by large raindrops (Brodie, 1951a). A very similar system operates in connection with the liberation of slimy oidia in *Polyporus conchifer* (Brodie, 1951b). Again in species of *Lycoperdon* and *Geastrum* the mature fruit body has a capsule containing a springy capillitium system saturated with dry spores. The capsule has a papery unwettable wall and opens by an apical ostiole. A large drop of water falling on the capsule wall momentarily depresses it, and in consequence a visible puff of spore-bearing air is blown out through the ostiole (Gregory, 1949). In a heavy thundershower with large rain drops falling, the operation of the puff-ball mechanism is most spectacular.

The myxomycete *Lycogala epidendrum* behaves in just the same manner as *Lycoperdon,* but there is at first no definite ostiole. However, a direct hit by a large enough drop bursts open the sporangium, producing an apical rupture through which spores are puffed by successive bombardment (Dixon, 1963).

It has recently been shown that the perithecia of *Chaetomium* spp. can be splash-dispersed (Dixon, 1961). Large drops of water falling on a fruiting culture are broken up and reflected from the surface carrying perithecia, which are very loosely attached to the parent mycelium and hardly at all to the substratum, to a distance of several feet. Perhaps the extraordinary structure of the perithecia in this genus may in some manner be related to splash dispersal. It must, however, be borne in mind that the effectivenes of splash liberation from a richly fruiting culture in the laboratory and from a natural stand of perithecia in the field may be rather different.

C. Mist Pick-up

Another mechanism of spore liberation involving very small air-borne water droplets, such as might be present in a driving mist, has been suggested. When an aqueous mist is blown over sporulating molds some of the mist droplets are impacted on the fungal structure; others, however, may just touch the sporulating apparatus, pick up a few spores, and drive on (Fig. 5). In this type of passive liberation, dry-spore rather than slime-spore types may be involved. There is at present little to indicate how effective this mechanism may be in nature. It seems to operate in relation to *Cercosporella herpotrichoides,* causing eye-spot of wheat (Glynne, 1953), and possibly also, as a subsidiary method of spore liberation, in *Cladosporium* (Gregory, 1961).

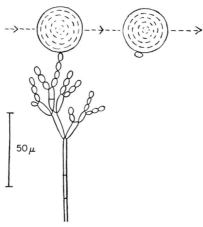

FIG. 5. Mist pick-up. Diagram of how a mist droplet might pick up a spore of *Cladosporium*.

IV. LIBERATION OF SPORES BY ANIMALS

A. *Insect and Spore Liberation*

Insects are quite often responsible for the liberation of spores and also for their dispersal, although, in general, fungi are anemophilous and there are relatively few examples of definite entomophily. The whole subject of insect dispersal of fungal spores has been rather fully discussed (Leach, 1940), and here only a brief outline will be given.

In one group of the larger fungi, the Phallales, structure is obviously related to insect dispersal. In these fungi (e.g., *Phallus impudicus*) the minute spores, embedded in a sugary slime with a strong and unpleasant smell, are displayed at maturity usually on top of a conspicuous stipe. Insects, mostly various kinds of fly, are attracted and eat the slime. Spores are carried away on the legs of the insect and also pass, apparently uninjured, through the alimentary canal. Unfortunately in Phallales no one has succeeded in germinating the spores. *Aseroe rubra* is an especially interesting species. Around a disk of spore slime at the summit of the thick stipe is a whorl of red sterile bifurcate rays. The whole structure is biologically like an entomophilous flower with a central fertile region surrounded by "petals."

Other fungi in which minute, insect-dispersed spores are intermixed with nectar are the rusts (pycnial stage) and ergot (*Claviceps purpurea,* conidial stage). Again in *Ceratocystis ulmi* (the fungus of Dutch elm disease) the conidial (*Graphium*) stage is produced on the walls of the brood chambers of bark beetles at the interface of wood and bark in killed elm trees. On hatching, emerging beetles are already contaminated and may fly off to infect living trees. The association with beetles in connection with "blue stain" of felled conifers caused by *Ceratocystis ips* is rather similar, but here the perithecial stage is produced in the brood channels, not the conidial. Superficially both stages are remarkably alike. In each a slimy drop of spores is formed at the end of a hairlike stalk which in the *Graphium* stage is a sheaf of fungal hyphae constituting a compound conidiophore, whereas in the *Ceratocystis* stage it is the long narrow neck of a perithecium. Indeed, the stalked spore drop (Ingold, 1961) is a very distinctive spore-presentation mechanism, probably in the main associated with insect dispersal, which has been evolved independently in very diverse fungi (Fig. 6).

Another type of insect dispersal is found in the anther smuts, e.g., *Ustilago violacea* on *Lychnis alba.* In an infected pistillate plant the staminal rudiments in the flower are stimulated to develop into stamens which, when their anthers dehisce, liberate minute, sticky, dark purple chlamydospores of the fungus. Like the much larger pollen grains of normal staminate flowers, they are picked up and distributed by night-flying moths. A totally different fungus, *Botrytis anthophila,* which attacks clover, also sporulates only on the anthers and this too is dispersed by pollinating insects, in this case bees.

There are many examples of fungal spores rather casually dispersed by insects. Thus the conidial stage of *Sclerotinia fructigena,* causing a "brown rot" of apples, pears, and plums, is fairly regularly spread by wasps which casually pick up spores from rotting fruit and introduce them into healthy specimens.

B. *Mammals and Spore Liberation*

In the coprophilous fungi, although animals are intimately concerned in the dispersal story, they are not involved in actual spore liberation. In the hypogeal fungi, however, rodents are concerned in the whole process. These fungi have macroscopic sporophores below ground, particularly in woods. The mature fruit bodies frequently become strong-smelling at maturity. Rodents are attracted, grub up and eat the sporophores, the spores passing through the alimentary canal. Hypogeal types occur in the three major groups of fungi; for example, *Endogone* in Phycomycetes, *Tuber* and *Elaphomyces* in Ascomycetes, and *Hymenogaster* and *Rhizo-*

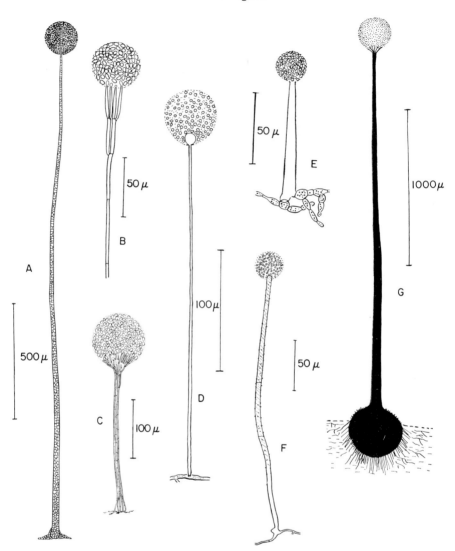

Fig. 6. Stalked spore drop in various fungi. (A) Sorocarp of *Dictyostelium discoideum*. (B) Conidiophore with conidia in *Gliocladium roseum*. (C) Compound conidiophore with conidia in *Graphium cuneiferum*. (D) Sporangial drop and sporangiophore of *Mucor ramannianus*. (E) Dehisced ascus of *Dipodascus uninucleatus*. (F) Ascophore with mass of ascospores of *Cephaloascus fragrans*. (G) Perithecium of *Ceratocystis adiposa* with escaped mass of ascospores. Spore-bearing apparatus shown in longitudinal optical section except in *Ceratocystis*.

21. Spore Release

pogon in Basidiomycetes. Very little is known about the details of the dispersal of these fungi. However, it has been found that the characteristic chlamydospores of *Endogone* are frequently to be found in the gut of smaller rodents in North America. (Dowding, 1955; Bakerspigel, 1956).

REFERENCES

Bakerspigel, A. (1956). *Endogone* in Saskatchewan rodents. *Am. J. Botany* 43:471-475.

Bayliss-Elliott, J. S. (1927). *Aleuria repanda* Pers. *Brit. Mycol. Soc. Trans.* 12:166-169.

Bock, K. R. (1962). Dispersal of uredospores of *Hemileia vastatrix* under field conditions. *Brit. Mycol. Soc. Trans.* 45:63-74.

Brodie, H. J. (1951a). The splash-cup mechanism in plants. *Can. J. Botany* 29:224-234.

Brodie, H. J. (1951b). The splash-cup of *Polyporus conchifer*. *Can. J. Botany* 29:593-596.

Buchwald, N. F. (1938). Om Sporeproduktionens størrelse nos Tøndersvampen. *Friesia* 2:42-69.

Buller, A. H. R. (1909). "Researches on Fungi," Vol. I, pp. 1-287. Longmans, Green, New York.

Buller, A. H. R. (1922). "Researches on Fungi," Vol. II, pp. 1-492. Longmans, Green, New York.

Buller, A. H. R. (1924). "Researches on Fungi," Vol. III, pp. 1-611. Longmans, Green, New York.

Buller, A. H. R. (1931). "Researches on Fungi," Vol. IV, pp. 1-329. Longmans, Green, New York.

Buller, A. H. R. (1933). "Researches on Fungi," Vol. V, pp. 1-416. Longmans, Green, New York.

Buller, A. H. R. (1934). "Researches on Fungi," Vol. VI, pp. 1-513. Longmans, Green, New York.

Carpenter, J. B. (1949). Production and discharge of basidiospores by *Pellicularia filamentosa* (Pat.) Rogers on *Hevea* rubber. *Phytopathology* 39:238-261.

Derx, H. G. (1948). *Itersonilia*, nouveau genre de Sporobolomycètes à mycelium bouclé. *Bull. Botan. Gardens Buitenzog* [3] 18:465-472.

Dixon, P. A. (1961). Spore dispersal in *Chaetomium globosum* (Kunze). *Nature* 191:1418-1419.

Dixon, P. A. (1963). Spore liberation by water drops in some Myxomycetes. *Brit. Mycol. Soc. Trans.* 46:615-619.

Dodge, B. O. (1924). Aecidiospore discharge as related to the character of the spore wall. *J. Agr. Res.* 27:749-756.

Dowding, E. S. (1955). *Endogone* in Canadian rodents. *Mycologia* 47:51-57.

Falck, R. (1948). "Grundlinien eines orbis-vitalen Systems der Fadenpilze." North Holland Publ., Amsterdam.

Glynne, M. D. (1953). Production of spores by *Cercosporella herpotrichoides*. *Brit. Mycol. Soc. Trans.* 36:46-51.

Gregory, P. H. (1949). The operation of the puff-ball mechanism of *Lycoperdon perlatum* by raindrops shown by ultra-high-speed Schlieren cinematography. *Brit. Mycol. Soc. Trans.* 32:11-15.

Gregory, P. H. (1957). Electrostatic charges on spores of fungi in air. *Nature* 180:330.

Gregory, P. H. (1961). "The Microbiology of the Atmosphere," 251 pp. Wiley (Interscience), New York.
Gregory, P. H., E. J. Guthrie, and M. E. Bunce. (1959). Experiments on splash dispersal of fungus spores. *J. Gen. Microbiol.* **29**:328-354.
Hammarlund, C. (1925). Zur Geretik, Biologie und Physiologie einiger Erysiphaceen. *Hereditas* **6**:1-126.
Ingold, C. T. (1933). Spore discharge in Ascomycetes: I. Pyrenomycetes. *New Phytologist* **32**:178-196.
Ingold, C. T. (1934). The spore discharge mechanism of *Basidiobolus ranarum*. *New Phytologist* **33**:274-277.
Ingold, C. T. (1939). "Spore Discharge in Land Plants," 178 pp. Oxford Univ. Press (Clarendon), London and New York.
Ingold, C. T. (1946). Spore discharge in *Daldinia concentrica*. *Brit. Mycol. Soc. Trans.* **29**:43-51.
Ingold, C. T. (1948). The water-relations of spore-discharge in *Epichloe*. *Brit. Mycol. Soc. Trans.* **31**:277-280.
Ingold, C. T. (1954). Ascospore form. *Brit. Mycol. Soc. Trans.* **37**:19-21.
Ingold, C. T. (1958). On light-stimulated spore discharge in *Sordaria*. *Ann. Botany (London)* [N.S.] **22**:129-135.
Ingold, C. T. (1959). Jelly as a water-reserve in fungi. *Brit. Mycol. Soc. Trans.* **42**:475-478.
Ingold, C. T. (1960). Dispersal by air and water—the take-off. *Plant Pathol.* **3**:137-168.
Ingold, C. T. (1961). The stalked spore-drop. *New Phytologist* **60**:181-183.
Ingold, C. T., and V. J. Cox. (1955). Periodicity of spore discharge in *Daldinia*. *Ann. Botany (London)* [N.S.] **19**:201-209.
Ingold, C. T., and V. J. Dring. (1957). An analysis of spore discharge in *Sordaria*. *Ann. Botany (London)* [N.S.] **21**:465-477.
Ingold, C. T., and S. A. Hadland. (1959). The ballistics of *Sordaria*. *New Phytologist* **58**:46-57.
Ingold, C. T., and B. Marshall. (1962). Stimulation of spore discharge by reduced humidity in *Sordaria*. *Ann. Botany (London)* [N.S.] **26**:563-568.
Ingold, C. T., and B. Marshall. (1963). Further observations on light and spore discharge in certain Pyrenomycetes. *Ann. Botany (London)* [N.S.] **27**:481-491.
Ingold, C. T., and B. Marshall. (1964). Stimulation of spore discharge in *Sordaria* by carbon dioxide. *Ann. Botany (London)* [N.S.] **28**:325-329.
Jarvis, W. R. (1962). The dispersal of spores of *Botrytis cinerea* Fr. in a raspberry plantation. *Brit. Mycol. Soc. Trans.* **45**:549-559.
Leach, J. G. (1940). "Insect Transmission of Plant Diseases," 615 pp. McGraw-Hill, New York.
Martin, G. W. (1925). Morphology of *Conidiobolus villosus*. *Botan. Gaz.* **80**:311-318.
Meredith, D. S. (1961). Spore discharge in *Deightoniella torulosa* (Syd.) Ellis. *Ann. Botany (London)* [N.S.] **25**:271-278.
Meredith, D. S. (1962). Spore discharge in *Cordana musae* (Zimm.) Höhnel and *Zygosporium oscheoides* Mont. *Ann. Botany (London)* [N.S.] **26**:233-241.
Meredith, D. S. (1965). Violent spore release in *Helminthosporium turcicum*. *Phytopathology* **55**:1099-1102.
Micheli, P. A. (1729). Nova Plantarum Genera. Florence.
Müller, D. (1954). Die Abschleuderung der Sporen von *Sporobolomyces*—Spiegelhefe-gefilmt. *Friesia* **5**:65-74.

Nutman, F. J., F. M. Roberts, and K. R. Bock. (1960). Method of uredospore dispersal of the coffee leaf-rust fungus, *Hemileia vastatrix*. *Brit. Mycol. Soc. Trans.* 43:509-515.

Olive, L. S. (1964). Spore discharge mechanism in Basidiomycetes. *Science* 146:542.

Page, R. M. (1964). Sporangium discharge in *Pilobolus*: a photographic study. *Science* 146:925-927.

Page, R. M., and D. Kennedy. (1964). Studies on the velocity of discharged sporangia of *Pilobolus kleinii*. *Mycologia* 56:363-368

Pinckard, J. A. (1942). The mechanism of spore dispersal in *Peronospora tabacina* and certain other downy mildew fungi. *Phytopathology* 32:505-511.

Rankin, W. H. (1914). Field Studies on the *Endothia* canker of chestnut in New York State. *Phytopathology* 4:233-260.

Schmilde, A. (1951). Die Tagesperiodizität der asexuellen Reproducktion von *Pilobolus sphaerosporus*. *Arch. Mikrobiol.* 16:80-100.

Swinbank, P., J. Taggart, and S. A. Hutchinson. (1964). The measurement of electrostatic charges on spores of *Merulius lacrymans* (Wulf.) Fr. *Ann. Botany (London)* [N.S.] 28:239-249.

Taggart, J. (1961). Sporulation in fungi with special reference to the Hymenomycetes. Ph.D. Thesis, Univ. of Glasgow.

Uebelmesser, E. R. (1954). Über den endonomen Tagesrhythmus der Sporangienträgerbildung von *Pilobolus*. *Arch. Mikrobiol.* 20:1-33.

Webster, J. (1952). Spore projection in the hyphomycete *Nigrospora sphaerica*. *New Phytologist* 51:229-235.

Weston, W. H., Jr. (1923). Production and dispersal of conidia in the Philippine *Sclerosporas* of maize. *J. Agr. Res.* 23:239-278.

Woodward, R. C. (1927). Studies on *Podosphaera leucotricha* (Ell. Ev.) Salm. *Brit. Mycol. Soc. Trans.* 12:173-204.

Zoberi, M. H. (1961). Take-off of mould spores in relation to wind speed and humidity. *Ann. Botany (London)* [N.S.] 25:53-64.

Zoberi, M. H. (1962). Effect of temperature and humidity on ballistospore discharge. *Brit. Mycol. Soc. Trans.* 47:109-114.

CHAPTER 22

Dispersal

P. H. GREGORY

*Rothamsted Experimental Station
Harpenden, Herts., England*

A fungus is a nucleated cytoplasmic mass which undergoes displacement in a centrifugal direction, either free or inside tubes which it constructs as it advances peripherally. While these tubes are elongating under cytoplasmic pressure, the fungus gradually quits the central part of the thallus whose elements become progressively vacuolated and finally empty and dead. As a result a fungal thallus, whatever its shape, always comprises a peripheral living zone which continues to grow, and a central skeletal zone formed of empty dead tubes. Growth of the thallus is limited only by exhaustion of the cytoplasmic mass, which eventually passes completely into the propagative or reproductive spores.
—Translation from M. Langeron, "Précis de Mycologie," p. 32. Masson, Paris, 1945.

I. INTRODUCTION

The role of dispersal in fungal economy should be viewed in light of the dynamic concept of Buller (1933) summarized in the above quotation. Activity is normal to fungi. Resting spores serve for survival, but most fungi also release spores whose dispersal continues the activity of the nucleated cytoplasmic mass which is the essential fungus.

Dispersal is here treated broadly to include *effective* dispersal processes, as well as *ineffective* dispersal which continues after the spore is dead.

Dispersal has two obvious functions in fungus economy: (1) it serves to start new mycelia ("colonies") on fresh substrates, either near or at a distance from the parent mycelium; (2) it transmits genetic material between established mycelia. Genetic transfer is familiar in rust fungi, where spermatization leads to diploidization. The possibility that a dispersed spore might function in establishing heterokaryosis by fusing directly with an existing mycelium is less familiar, but Jinks (1952) found heterokaryons in wild *Penicillium,* and genetic transmisison between established mycelia may be commoner than we now think. Often we know that a spore form is dispersed but do not know which of these functions it serves. We do not know, for example, whether the spores of the giant puffball *Calvatia* [*Lycoperdon*] *gigantea* are more significant in starting new puffball mycelia or in communicating between existing mycelia. Many kinds of spores germinate with difficulty (cf. Sussman, Chapter 23), or for other reasons seem ineffective in starting new mycelia, and the observation of Ferguson (1902) that mushroom basidiospores germinated more readily when in contact with living hyphae of the same species may be significant in this context. We have scarcely any idea of the conditions necessary for starting new mycelia of many larger fungi, and there is little information on how heterokaryosis is established, if it occurs in nature at all. An existing mycelium might even be the seat of a changing population of nuclei (Gregory, 1952).

Spore dispersal is closely tied to spore-liberation mechanisms. Energy is needed to move a fungus spore over the surface of the earth, and dispersal is most commonly effected by those energy sources, such as rain splash, insects, or wind, to which the fungus has become highly adapted. Incidental mechanisms must often transport spores, but they do this less often than the specialized mechanisms, a fact illustrated very clearly in recent work on how the fungus spore content of the air changes with changing weather and at different times of day, and especially by the remarkable predominance of basidiospores (including Sporobolomycetaceae) resulting from the efficiency of the ballistospore discharge mechanism (Section III, B). The problem of the relative importance of adapted and incidental transfer should become clearer in what follows.

Dispersal produces changes measured by three characteristics: (1) a gradient in space usually showing as a decrease in number of mycelia established (or spores arriving) at increasing distances from the source of liberation (Gregory, 1945; Wolfenbarger, 1946, 1959); (2) a logistic increase in mycelia established (or spores arriving) at a given distance with passage of time (Fracker, 1936; van der Plank, 1963); (3) an increase in the area occupied by the products of a given source with passage of time. This last characteristic has been little studied, and some tentative values, based on necessarily incomplete historical records, are suggested below for the rate of increase in geographical range of fungi dispersed by different methods.

II. MODES OF DISPERSAL

A. Growth of Mycelium

The spread by radial growth of mycelium needs no comment beyond indicating that "fairy rings" progress steadily, colonizing pastures like a culture on a petri dish. Spatial extension by radial growth of natural mycelium can be measured in tens of centimeters per year. Rings of *Agaricus tabularis* averaged 30 cm per year (Shantz and Piemiesel, 1917), but basidiomycetes which form rhizomorphs or strands, such as *Serpula lacrimans,* progress much faster. Garrett (1953) found that rhizomorphs of *Armillaria mellea* grew away from a food base at 2.5 cm per week, a growth rate 5 or 6 times faster than that of unorganized mycelium.

B. Movement in Water

Dispersal by self-motility of zoospores of the lower fungi in water films on leaf surfaces and in soil is measured in millimeters or at most centimeters per generation. Dispersal of *Synchytrium endobioticum* by zoospores is a phenomenon of soil microbiology rather than geography, but progress can be faster in flowing water and in rain-splash droplets (Chapter 21). Behavior of tetraradiate spores of aquatic hyphomycetes in flowing water suggests that analogies will be found in flowing water with the impaction phenomena (Section II, F, 5, c) observed in wind-dispersed spores (Webster, 1959).

C. Ballistic Trajectories

The ballistic trajectories of ascospores and basidiospores have lengths limited to centimeters and fractions of a millimeter, respectively, but these trajectories, which normally serve merely to liberate spores from the parent body into the air where they can be dispersed by wind (Chapter 21), must not be confused with ultimate dispersal distance, as has sometimes been done.

The trajectories of large propagules produced by such fungi as *Pilobolus, Sphaerobolus,* and Nidulariaceae are little affected by air movement, and their range is restricted. However, after alighting on herbage they have a phase of secondary dispersal (in the sense of Dobbs, 1942) while in the gut of grazing animals before being deposited in feces.

D. Animal Vectors

Animals, especially man and insects, are important vectors of fungi, sometimes accidentally (Talbot, 1952), but often as a result of complex adaptation. The topic has been reviewed by Brues (1946), Steinhaus (1946), and Ingold (1953). The role of insects as vectors of fungi causing plant disease is reviewed by Leach (1940), Gäumann (1950), Austwick (1958), and Carter (1962).

Nematodes can transport adhesive spores, both of fungi that prey on them and the appendaged pycnospores of *Dilophospora alopecuri* which produces "twist" of grasses.

Dispersal by insect vectors has many advantages for the fungus, not least that in feeding or gathering nectar and pollen the insect may effectively inoculate the fungus into a site favorable for growth. The range of dispersal depends on the behavior of the insect. Specialized insect-dispersed fungi may be recognized by some or all of the following characters. Like the entomophilous pollens, their spores are usually small and sticky, and they form one biological group of the "slime-spored fungi" (Mason, 1937), the other group being the rain-splashed fungi referred to below (Section II, E). They are typically produced in small drops of mucilage which may be held in position by setae as in the pycnia of the rusts, and with both pycnospores and ascospores of *Ceratocystis ulmi*. The droplets may be raised on stalks, and may be sugary or strongly scented.

Insects may act as vectors incidentally while gathering nectar or pollen. Sturgis (1898) considered that *Phytophthora phaseoli* is disseminated to ovaries of lima beans mainly by foraging bees. *Candida reukaufii* is a peculiar yeast (formerly classified as *Anthomyces* or *Nectaromyces*) living in the nectaries of many flowers and hibernating in the stomachs of bumble bees (*Bombus* spp.) whose foraging flights effect dispersal to nectaries in spring (Lodder and Kreger-van Rij, 1952). Other nectar feeders spread *Botrytis anthophila* to anthers of red clover (*Trifolium*), *Ustilago* species to flowers of the Caryophyllaceae, and *Fusarium moniliforme* f. sp. *fici* to fruits of the fig. Feeding activities of insects can diploidize basidiomycetes (Craigie, 1931; Brodie, 1931).

Many fungi attract insects to their spore masses by scent, e.g., *Endophyllum euphorbiae-sylvaticae, Puccinia obtegens [P. punctiformis], Phallus impudicus, Clathrus ruber,* and the species of *Sclerotinia* on Ericaceae.

Oak wilt, caused by *Ceratocystis fagi,* is spread mainly by beetles (see Stakman and Harrar, 1957) which are attracted to fragrant stromata under cracking bark and become contaminated with ascospores and conidia. Local spread goes on slowly by root grafts, and details of the part played by beetles in bringing about new infections are obscure, but it is clear that haploid mycelia of this heterothallic fungus are diploidized by insects. Information given by Fowler (1952) makes it possible to estimate that the rate of spread from the oldest infections in the United States cannot have averaged much more than about 50 km per year.

Nutman *et al.* (1960) showed that uredospores of *Hemileia vastatrix* are not so readily airborne as those of the cereal rusts, and in coffee plantations they are usually dispersed locally by rain splash. Crowe (1963) added that the rust is carried to more remote plantations by hymenopterous parasites (*Leptacis* and *Synopeas*) which burrow into uredosori in search of mycophagous cecidiomyid larvae (a four-member food chain involved in dispersal).

22. Dispersal

Insect dispersal is more highly developed in symbiotic relationships where the insect actively inoculates a vegetable substrate and provides food for itself. Wood wasps (*Sirex* spp.) have sacs, opening to the ovipositor, containing oidia of *Stereum sanguinolentum* which are extruded on the eggs as they are laid; thus the fungus is introduced into sound wood during oviposition, and the larva is probably partly mycophagous (Parkin, 1942).

Female ambrosia beetles (e.g., *Xyleborus,* Scolytinae) make beds of wood chips which they inoculate with specific microfungi, including species of *Leptographium, Ceratocystis,* and *Oedocephalum,* carried somehow by the adult beetles (Steinhaus, 1946; Bakshi, 1950), and the resulting mycelium spreads to the wooden walls surrounding the larval galleries where it is regularly grazed.

Leaf-cutting ants (Myrmicineae) of tropical America cultivate species of *Pholiota* and *Xylaria* in fungus gardens consisting of beds of leaf fragments. Before a queen leaves the nest for the mating flight she takes a pellet of inoculum in her infrabuccal pouch; then after mating she burrows into the ground and starts a new fungus culture (see Steinhaus, 1946). Characteristic fungi (*Termitomyces*) occur also in termite nests, but they may be mere commensals, not actively transported by the termites (Heim, 1942).

Blue-stain fungi of conifers have a symbiotic relationship with bark beetles (e.g., *Ips* spp.), whose galleries are lined with the *Graphium* state, or with perithecia of the *Ceratocystis* state. Both conidia and ascospores are extruded in sticky masses raised on stalks to contaminate insects passing through the galleries. Although the fungus is apparently not eaten, the relationship is regarded as symbiotic, with the fungus making the environment more suitable for brood development.

The relation between *Ceratocystis ulmi,* the cause of elm disease, and bark beetles (*Scolytus*) appears similar. Zentmeyer et al. (1944) studied the infection gradient of the fungus after local dispersal by beetles and demonstrated a linear relation between the logarithm of the distance and percentage infection (as probits); spread was also affected by wind direction at the time the beetles emerged. When discovered in France in 1918, the fungus was apparently already widespread and so its progress in Europe cannot be recorded, but its spread through North America is better documented (Clinton and McCormick, 1936; Holmes, 1958). Evidently there were several introductions on logs from Europe around 1930, and its range in 1937 suggests an upper limit of about 50 km per year for the rate of extension of the disease by beetles into new areas. Powered transport enabled the fungus to cross ocean barriers, together with its vectors, which then dispersed it more slowly across the continent.

Fungi that parasitize insects (Laboulbeniales, *Basidiobolus*) are dispersed by the wanderings of the host. The activity of the hosts of some Entomophthoraceae is not checked until shortly before death, and the last act of the fungus-riddled insect may be to climb to the end of a twig where conidia are easily liberated into the wind.

Birds, although able to carry enormous spore loads, have been incriminated in dispersal of fungus spores less often than insects. However, woodpeckers and creepers shot in infected chestnut plantations often carried pycnospores (but not ascospores) of *Endothia parasitica,* and over half a million pycnospores were found on a single woodpecker (Heald and Studhalter, 1914).

The most striking example of a plant pathogen being spread by birds was provided by the observation of Kouyeas and Anastassiadis (1962) that magpies (*Pica pica*) made nests in citrus trees with twigs infected with *Deuterophoma tracheiphila* and set up intense foci of infection within a healthy grove.

Man has introduced a new dimension into fungus dispersal by harnessing powerful sources of energy for transport at ever increasing speed. Because so much of transport is concerned with moving raw or manufactured plant materials, man must be considered, from a mold's-eye point of view, as one of the most significant of the accidental vectors. Plant pathologists may even sometimes be concerned with fungi which have become specifically adapted to man—a condition perhaps exemplified in the proliferation of species of *Botrytis* on *Allium* and other monocotyledonous bulbs, which we dig, transport, and subject to various cultural regimes.

The work of man as a vector is seen in its most spectacular form when a readily dispersed fungus is carried to a new area which it had been unable to reach by its normal dispersal processes. Examples of this are given below (Section III, D), but much of the activity of man in transporting organisms within their existing range goes on inconspicuously, as it did in the relatively slow spread of *Synchytrium endobioticum* in Europe and America.

E. Raindrop Splash

Many fungi produce sticky spores embedded in mucilage and not easily removed by wind (Stepanov, 1935). The first rain swells the mucilage and allows the spores to float free in films of water (Nisikado *et al.,* 1955). In experiments on splash dispersal of conidia of *Fusarium solani,* Gregory *et al.* (1959) found that most spores were carried in the larger splash droplets with a median diameter of 140 µ and with median horizontal and vertical travel of approximately 20 cm. Few droplets traveled beyond 70 cm in still air, but clearly wind must greatly extend this range, though the subject has been little studied. Faulwetter (1917a,b) suggested that bacterial crop pathogens might be dispersed by windblown rain, and fungi were splashed in rain experimentally by Weston and Taylor (1948).

The smallest splash droplets must evaporate rapidly, leaving their contained solids suspended in air as droplet nuclei, and the few spores so carried must be regarded as truly airborne. Apart from the dispersal of droplet nuclei, splash dispersal seems most efficient in bringing about a very local vertical and horizontal spread within a tree, bush, or crop. Drip from leaves can produce large drops (often falling at less than their terminal velocity) from fine rain or mist consisting of drops which are too small themselves to splash efficiently. One feature of splash dispersal is that a spore can be splashed and resplashed, whereas in dispersal by dry air a spore once deposited is usually out of range of further eddies.

Recent studies show that raindrops falling on a *dry* surface can put many spores into the air by a quite different mechanism (Hirst, 1961; Hirst and Stedman, 1962). The rapid puff of air, moving ahead of the radially spreading splash of a raindrop during the millisecond after collision with a dry surface, probably accounts for the great increase in the dry-spore types sometimes found in the atmosphere after start of rain.

F. Wind Transport

Many fungi exploit the properties of moving air for dispersal, a habit they share with seeds and pollen of many flowering plants, with pteridophytes, bryophytes, myxomycetes, and with the Streptomycetaceae (Actinomycetes). Wind dispersal seems particularly favorable for colonization and perhaps for transfer of genetic material, but more often diploidization seems to be by insects (which home more accurately on the target) or by rain splash.

1. Physical Requirements

Basically wind dispersal depends on air movement caused by pressure and temperature differences in different parts of the atmosphere. Properties making the atmosphere suitable for dispersal include: movement of wind, turbulence, viscosity, layering, and convection. As subsidiary factors we must consider the wind gradient near the ground, the pattern of atmospheric circulation, and solar radiation.

It can be assumed that the properties of spores have arisen as adaptations toward liberation, dispersal, and deposition. Properties of dry airborne spores affecting dispersal are: their shape, size, surface roughness, density, pigmentation, and possibly electrostatic charge.

Wind speed varies with position. Movement may be slight in shelter among vegetation, and the speed usually increases with increasing height above ground. Friction with obstacles on the ground slows the wind and generates mechanical turbulence. Heating of the ground by solar radiation produces thermal turbulence and convection. Air is viscous, and in still air spores fall under gravity at constant terminal velocities (Gregory, 1961) depending on surface drag through the viscous air (Table I). With-

TABLE I
REPRESENTATIVE TERMINAL VELOCITIES DETERMINED EXPERIMENTALLY AND CALCULATED TRAJECTORY TO GROUND ASSUMING NONTURBULENT WIND MOVING AT 1 M SEC

Fungus	Approx. spore size (μ)	Observed terminal velocity (cm/sec)	Estimated trajectory	
			Assumed liberation height	Distance (m)
Helminthosporium sativum	75 × 20	2.0	1 m	50
Puccinia recondita (uredospores)	25 × 20	1.26	1 m	80
Agaricus campestris	8 × 5	0.13	5 cm	40
Lycoperdon pyriforme	4	0.05	5 cm	100

out atmospheric turbulence the dispersal distance would be restricted to spore trajectories resultant from wind speed and terminal velocity (examples in Table I), whereas it is an observed fact that many spores occur in the atmosphere much higher than the point of liberation.

For a model of dispersal we turn to the familiar smoke plume from a chimney, widening as it is diluted with smoke-free eddies while it travels downwind. Variations in the vertical temperature gradient and stability of the atmosphere can greatly modify the amount of vertical diffusion possible to such a plume. With industrial effluent from chimney stacks, five types of plume are recognized (U.S. Weather Bureau, 1955) which, on a smaller scale, are relevant to spore dispersal in wind. (1) *Looping:* in strong lapse conditions (i.e., when the ground is heated by solar radiation, and temperature decreases rapidly with increasing height) the plume shows loops as parts of it are carried up in ascending thermal eddies, and other parts carried down to ground by compensatory air movements. (2) *Coning:* under weak lapse conditions, common in overcast weather, the plume is shaped like a cone with a horizontal axis. (3) *Fanning:* with temperature inversion (e.g., air cooled by ground radiation to a clear night sky), the plume may fan out in the horizontal plane but fail to diffuse vertically. (4) *Lofting:* when the plume forms a cone in air with a normal temperature lapse *above* a temperature inversion, such as may develop at ground level at sunset, particles may be unable to penetrate down into the inversion, at the top of which a large concentration may accumulate. (5) *Fumigation:* with a temperature inversion aloft, a large concentration may accumulate as the cone forms in a layer of air near the ground which is beginning to warm under solar radiation at sunrise.

Under lofting conditions bubbles of heated air may rise intermittently from areas of vegetation where the ground layer is being heated by the sun. These bubbles may rise more or less vertically to considerable heights, carrying their spore load to the level at which cumulus clouds are being formed. Meanwhile cooler air is drawn horizontally to replace the bubble, and the usual eddy-diffusion processes continue until the next bubble forms. Buoyancy thus forms an additional mechanism by which spores can be carried upward, supplementing the normal upward diffusion due to the turbulence created by friction where wind flows over rough ground.

Conditions for fanning are comparatively unusual out of doors. Because wind is usually turbulent some spores will reach the ground nearer and some much farther than their trajectories in streamline wind (Table I) indicate. Streamline air may occur over smooth surfaces, or within a few centimeters of the ground, though here surface irregularities may set up stationary eddies. This streamline or laminar layer of flowing air is thicker at slower than at greater wind speeds, and it gets thinner as the wind speed increases. Spore liberation mechanisms serve to take spores across this nonturbulent layer of air (in which they would sink under gravity) into the turbulent circulation of the atmosphere where there is opportunity for distant dispersal, both vertically to the top of the convective layer of the atmosphere and horizontally to an indefinite distance until the spores are removed from suspension by being deposited on surfaces or washed out of the air by rain. Before this happens, however, a spore may be damaged by desiccation or radiation and be unable to infect or even to germinate. Pigmented spores seem more resistant than hyaline ones to ultraviolet and visible radiation (Ward, 1893; Weston, 1931; English and Gerhardt, 1946). It is unlikely that loss of viability of spores in air modifies local dispersal processes, but dryness and radiation may well set a limit to long-distance dispersal, and although little is yet known about viability in air, fungi probably differ widely in their tolerance of these factors.

2. *Diffusion Theories*

Theoretical studies on the limits of wind dispersal began with Schmidt (1918) on the basis of his theory of turbulent diffusion in the atmosphere. Following this lead, Schrödter (1954, 1960) estimated the "probable flight range," defined as the distance from the source at which 50% of the particles liberated will have been deposited. Schrödter put the flight range for medium-sized spores ($14 \times 6\ \mu$) at 800 km in a moderately turbulent wind of 2 m/sec.

Meanwhile Sutton (1932, 1953) had put forward a different theory of eddy diffusion to predict the concentration of suspended matter at points in a diffusing cloud as it travels downwind from the source. Sutton's equations were modified by Gregory (1945) to allow for the fact that a cloud of fungus spores, emitted at ground level, is depleted by deposition on the ground over which it travels, and it was evident that a rapid decrease in concentration is to be expected within short distances of the source. For example when large spores are liberated at ground level over 90% should be deposited within 100 m of the source [not 99.9% as I stated in error (Gregory, 1952, 1958)]. This formula was modified by Chamberlain (1956; and see U.S. Weather Bureau, 1955) to allow for liberation at different heights above ground level. Later work, largely unpublished (see Gregory, 1962) using Chamberlain's modification of our 1945 formula, gives much shorter distances for the probable flight range than those predicted by Schrödter.

Other formulations of atmospheric diffusion now being developed (Pasquill, 1961; F. B. Smith, 1962) may prove valuable for predicting dispersal over longer distances, but meanwhile the modifications of Sutton's theory have proved satisfactory for distance of tens of meters (Gregory et al., 1961; Sreeramulu and Ramalingam, 1961). Such theories apply best to conditions favorable for coning of the plume, they apply only in simple conditions of dispersal over ground with uniform topography, and at best can be expected to hold for travel of only a few kilometers. Little is yet known about deviations introduced by topographical features and meteorological incidents, and the justification for computing expected values for greater distances will lie mainly in detecting causes of deviation from expectation.

3. Diffusion Experiments

The problem of flight range can also be studied experimentally by liberating spores artificially and trapping them at various points downwind. Spores of the club moss *Lycopodium clavatum* are often used for this purpose, and they have dimensions comparable with uredospores of rusts. The few experiments reported yield some rather surprising results. Sreeramulu and Ramalingam (1961) liberated known numbers of spores over level ground in India at a height of 0.5 m and trapped them on sticky slides placed horizontally on the ground along various radii from the mean wind direction and up to 30–40 m downwind of the source. Figure 1 shows the numbers of spores trapped per square centimeter at each sampling point in one daytime experiment in which they liberated 9.39×10^8 spores. By making the assumption that numbers trapped change linearly between sampling points the total number deposited within the sampling area can be estimated. In this experiment with wind averaging 4.3 m/sec, it seems that 8.1% of spores liberated were deposited within 30 m. In

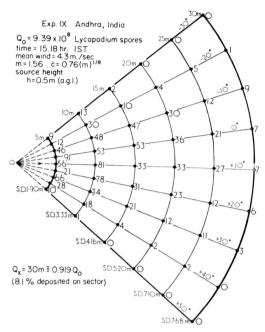

FIG. 1. Plan of sampling area in experimental liberation of *Lycopodium* spores (Sreeramulu and Ramalingam, 1961), showing numbers of spores trapped (and standard deviations) at various positions downwind from a point source. Abbreviation: a.g.l. = above ground level; Q_o = number of particles liberated; Q_x = total number of particles remaining in cloud after it has moved a distance x; c = coefficient of diffusion.

another experiment under less turbulent conditions at night, 91.6% were deposited within the sampling area. The smaller spores of *Podaxis* used in a few tests gave a smaller percentage recovery. Table II summarizes the results from all similar published experiments known to me from which percentage recovery can be calculated.

Figure 1 also exemplifies the rapid decrease in the numbers of spores deposited at distances of tens of meters from the source. Incidence of plant disease in the field also shows this effect when spread is from a point source. Spores of *Peronospora tabacina* from tobacco blue mold lesions, for example, produce leaf spots on plants for several meters downwind, but beyond this lesions are few (Waggoner and Taylor, 1955). Information on this point is necessarily incomplete, however, as the total number of lesions produced from a source cannot be estimated, so the percentage beyond the area surveyed, possibly at great distances, cannot be estimated either. Results from experiments on percentage recovery (Table II) in-

TABLE II
PERCENTAGE RECOVERY OF EXPERIMENTALLY LIBERATED SPORES WITHIN THE SAMPLING AREA

Experiment	Liberation height (m)	Maximum distance sampled (m)	Recovery in sector %
Stepanov (1935) *Tilletia caries* spores (diameter 17 µ)	1.0–1.5	40	8.6–11.2
Gregory et al. (1961) *Lycopodium* spores (diameter 32 µ)	0.25–0.5	10	13.5–24.4
Sreeramulu and Ramalingam (1961) *Lycopodium* spores (diameter 32 µ)	0.5	day: 30 night: 40	5.4–12.1 9.5–91.6
Podaxis pistillaris spores (diameter 14 × 11 µ)	0.5	day: 35 night: 35	0.23–0.48 1.6

dicate, as do theoretical considerations, that Schrödter's estimates of probable flight distance may be too large, but more experiments of this kind are needed.

4. Dispersal Gradients

The decrease in numbers of spores deposited (or in suspension) with increase in distance from the source is called the dispersal gradient. There is always a spore-deposition gradient, but there may not always be a resulting infection gradient. Infection gradients are common in agriculture where large areas of susceptible tissue are exposed to infection. But in natural vegetation, approximating to equilibrium conditions, there may be countless spore-deposition gradients over ground where all available sites for fungal growth are already fully occupied, and a fresh mycelium will be established only occasionally when a new site arises (we know nothing yet about possible gene gradients in such communities). Spore-concentration gradients can be measured in relation to a *Ganoderma* fruit body in a woodland, but this does not evoke a corresponding gradient of new *Ganoderma* pilei; neither do new agarics arise in a gradient around a "fairy-ring." The territory is ecologically closed to new mycelia until some unspecified event happens.

Published records of gradients have been compiled by Gregory (1945) and Wolfenbarger (1946, 1959).

5. Termination of Dispersal

a. Sedimentation. Wind dispersal of a spore can terminate in one of several ways. In still air or at very low wind speeds the spore may sediment under gravity—an effect seen under the pilei of agarics in closed vegetation. Normally outdoor air is too mobile for such effects to be noticed, and in wind tunnel tests the effect of sedimentation was slight at wind speeds of 2 m/sec and upward.

b. Boundary-Layer Exchange. This is a process which replenishes the laminar layer and thus allows even minute spores to sediment. The demarcation between the laminar surface layer and the turbulent wind stream is not constant. From time to time spore-bearing eddies break into the laminar layer, remove spore-free air and leave in exchange small volumes of air laden with spores. These spores will sediment under gravity and pass out of the range of further eddies (see Chamberlain, 1962). Turbulence is more efficient than sedimentation in bringing down spores to the boundary layer where this exchange can occur.

c. Impaction. When a small surface like a leaf or twig projects into the wind spores may be deposited by impaction on the windward side. The oncoming air stream has to flow around the obstruction but airborne spores will be carried toward the surface by their own momentum before they can in turn be deflected by the laterally deflected wind flowing around the obstacle (Gregory, 1951; Gregory and Stedman, 1953). Deposition by impaction is inefficient when small spores are blown slowly toward large obstructions; conversely it is more efficient when large spores are blown fast toward small objects. So it seems that large spores, in addition to carrying a bigger food reserve, have the advantage of being a favorable size for impaction on surfaces. Dry-spored, air-dispersed leaf pathogens usually have comparatively large spores (*Phytophthora, Helminthosporium,* uredospores, aeciospores, etc.).

In contrast, dry-spored soil inhabitants are characterized by small spores, unsuitable for impaction (*Penicillium, Aspergillus*). Among vegetation where the wind speed normally reaches an upper limit of about 2 m/sec, spores of *Lycoperdon perlatum* (4–5 µ diameter) would not be impacted at all, even on objects as narrow as 1 mm in diameter. Evidently we must look to processes other than impaction to deposit the minute spores of puffballs, earthstars, and the common molds. The loose smuts of cereals (*Ustilago* spp.) with spores in the 8–9 µ range, would not be impacted efficiently on leaves and stems, but on surfaces as narrow as the glumes and stigmas of a grass impaction might reach an efficiency of 50–75%. *Agaricus campestris* spores (7 × 6 μ) should be near the lower limit for impaction on grass leaves and stems at 2 m/sec. Uredospores of *Puccinia graminis* and conidia of *Erysiphe graminis* would impact on a wheat leaf with efficiencies near 40–60%. *Botrytis polyblastis*, with spores up to 90 μ in diameter, would also be relatively efficiently impacted on *Narcissus* leaves.

Although a high impaction efficiency may be necessary to fungi attacking leaves and stems, it may be disadvantageous for spores produced among dense vegetation. Johnstone *et al.* (1949) point out that the ability of a particle to penetrate among close vegetation is the inverse of its impaction efficiency. In close vegetation a high impaction efficiency would lessen the chance of a spore getting very far from its point of liberation. The large-spored leaf and stem fungi appear as specialized *impactors*, whereas the minute-spored puffballs and molds are specialized *penetrators*, perhaps normally deposited by processes other than impaction.

d. *Turbulent Deposition.* Spore-laden air flowing over horizontal surfaces will deposit spores much faster than expected for sedimentation under gravity. In wind-tunnel tests, turbulent deposition increases with wind speed, and at 5–9 m/sec deposition may be as great on the under side of a horizontal surface as it is on the upper, an effect clearly not due either to impaction or sedimentation under gravity.

e. *Rain Wash.* This process appears effective with small spores, which are deposited only inefficiently by other processes. In nature rain is probably the most important factor in removing from the air the remnant of a spore cloud which has escaped deposition near the source (May, 1958; McDonald, 1962).

Natural raindrops range in size up to about 5 mm in diameter (larger drops become unstable and break up into smaller drops during their fall); they have terminal velocities of 2–9 m/sec. The pick-up of small spheres in the path of falling raindrops has been studied theoretically. To judge from published data (see Gregory, 1961) the minute spores of *Lycoperdon* and the soil-inhabiting penicillia would fail to be collected at all by drops smaller than 1 mm in diameter, but efficiency of collection would rise to a maximum of about 15% with drops 2 mm in diameter, decreasing again with still larger drops. Basidiospores of *Agaricus campestris* should begin to be collected by raindrops over 0.2 mm in diameter, reach a maximum of 30% efficiency with 2.0 mm, and decrease slightly with larger diameters. Collection of *Tilletia caries* spores, of *Puccinia* uredospores and of conidia of *Erysiphe graminis* would occur with any possible raindrop, reaching a maximum of about 80% efficiency with drops 2.8 mm in diameter.

22. *Dispersal* 723

The spores of *Ustilago* are not easily wetted, but are nevertheless readily collected by rain. In one test, 2 mm of rain falling during 2 hours brought down 200 times as many spores as were deposited during the whole day on a similar area exposed to wind but screened from rain (Hirst, 1959). The transport of *Ustilago* in falling raindrops may indeed play a role in infecting the developing ear of a cereal plant (Malik and Batts, 1960). Little is known of the pick-up by raindrops of anisometric spores, and how properties other than terminal velocity affect pick-up. Davies (1961) showed that wettable spores of *Cephalosporium, Fusarium, Verticillium,* and *Pullularia (Aureobasidium)* are carried *within* raindrops, but the "nonwettable" spores of *Aspergillus, Cladosporium,* and *Penicillium* adhere to the surface of the drop. He also observed that when the drop rolls over a nonwettable leaf surface, nonwettable spores will tend to be deposited in the rear of the drop, but wettable spores will be carried onward with the drop until it comes to rest.

III. RESULTS OF WIND-DISPERSAL PROCESSES

A. Vertical Distribution

As a result of the spore-liberation mechanisms, wind, atmospheric turbulence, and convection, the atmosphere is populated with fungus spores (Stakman *et al.*, 1923). In general over land the concentration decreases logarithmically with increasing height above ground level, but many deviations from the ideal pattern have been recorded (Gregory, 1961, p. 134). Below rain clouds, the air may be washed free from spores; concentrations may be greater below a temperature inversion; convection may bring bubbles of spore-laden air among relatively spore-free air.

1. Over Land

Records of *Puccinia graminis* uredospores trapped by aircraft flying over southern Manitoba in 1930–1931 are particularly instructive (Craigie, 1945). A selection of these is shown in Fig. 2, where curves *A* and *D* during rust outbreaks approach the ideal pattern of a logarithmic decrease with height. Here the spores were presumably of local origin, carried up from below by thermal and frictional turbulence. On the other hand curve *B* is interpreted as exemplifying the vertical distribution pattern when rust spores are being transported from a distant source to an area which itself is not producing spores, but which instead is acting as a "sink," removing spores from the lower part of the air mass. In this case the lower part of the spore cloud was depleted by various processes (ground deposition, rain wash), and the uredospore concentration, although small, was four times as large at 14,000 feet as it was at 1000–5000 feet. Pattern *C*, during the height of a moderate rust outbreak in 1931, shows very uniform concentration from 1000 to 5000 feet, but very few spores at 7000 feet and over. In Fig. 2, assuming an air speed for the plane of about 150 mph and a sampling efficiency of 100% for the apparatus used, the concentration at 1000 feet would be approximately 1000 spores/m³ for A, and 0.1 spores/m³ for B.

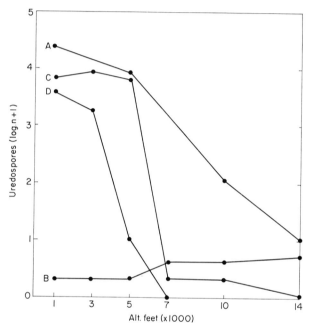

FIG. 2. Numbers of uredospores of *Puccinia graminis* (plotted as: $\log_{10} n + 1$) trapped per square centimeter of sticky slide per 10 minutes of flight at various altitudes over southern Manitoba during rust epidemics (Craigie, 1945). A, August 5, 1930; B, June 22, 1931; C, July 27, 1931; D, August 5, 1931.

2. Over Oceans

Trapping from aircraft reveals a by no means negligible spore concentration over oceans; for example at 9000 feet over the North Atlantic, Pady and Kelly (1954) recorded up to 137 fungus spores/m³ in an air mass of polar origin and 530/m³ in a tropical air mass. Newman (1948) also found considerable numbers of fungi at 4000 feet over the Tasman Sea. Records suggest that in mid-ocean there are fewer spores near the surface of the sea than at greater altitudes; perhaps spores are removed from the wind near the surface during travel over water by various processes including rain and spray wash. However the sampling methods used in aircraft and ships have not been comparable, so that the reality of the inverted concentration gradient over the ocean is still unconfirmed.

B. The Air Spora near the Ground

Air near the ground contains a constantly changing population of spores of fungi, as well as of other organisms and pollen. This constitutes the air spore flora or "air spora," and a great impetus was given to its study when Hirst (1952) developed the automatic volumetric spore trap. Changes in composition of the air spora with season in a temperate climate are illustrated by Gregory and Hirst (1957) and Lacey (1962). In temperate countries, as would be expected, different components of the air spora reach their maximum concentration at different seasons. A dry summer day has a characteristic air spora, usually dominated by *Cladosporium* spp., smuts, rusts, etc. This spora is soon removed by rain (often after a transient increase at the onset of the rain) and replaced by a damp-air spora (Hirst, 1953), which is characterized by ascospores and by many hyaline undistinguished-looking spores. At night the spora again changes, the daytime *Cladosporium* cloud disappears and is replaced by basidiospores of Sporobolomyces, polypores, boleti, and agarics, and by ascospores.

Most of the fungi of the air spora are saprophytes, but a substantial percentage are plant pathogens, a few are pathogens of animals (among which spores of Entomophthoraceae probably predominate), and some are potentially allergens. In certain localities such human pathogens as *Histoplasma capsulatum* and *Coccidioides immitis* evidently occur in the air (Furcolow, 1961; C. E. Smith *et al.,* 1961).

The air spora varies according to weather, locality, season, and time of day. A study by Lacey (1962) illustrating its main variations is based on visual identification of the catch in Hirst spore traps. At 0.5 m above ground level near a small stream in southern England, air was sampled continuously from May 14 to September 25, 1958. The mean concentration of fungus spores in the air over this period was nearly 30,000 spores/m^3. Of these 57% were classified as spores of basidiomycetes (including 35% of Sporobolomycetaceae). Another 14% were classified as ascospores, and 17% as fungi imperfecti (including 15% *Cladosporium*). Spores not classifiable in any of the groups cited totaled 11.8%, while phycomycetes (mainly *Peronospora* type) and mycelial fragments each made up 0.1%. The combination of visual (microscopic) with cultural trapping methods has given comparable but more precise results in studies of the aeromycology of Kansas (e.g., Pady and Kramer, 1960).

C. Spread over Long Distances

Controversy has raged over the significance of wind dispersal; some consider that its effectiveness is extremely local, pointing out for example that although *Endothia parasitica* discharges ascospores freely into the air it has spread relatively slowly on chestnuts in the United States, and was arrested for 10 years by a tract 30–40 miles wide free of chestnut trees. Parker-Rhodes (1950) suggests that 2 miles of open water may be sufficient for the genetical isolation of a population of *Panaeolus papilionaceus*. In contrast, Stover (1962) considers that ascospores of *Mycosphaerella musicola* must have been carried at high altitudes by winds from eastern Australia to the Caribbean in 1933. The rapid decrease in number of lesions of plant pathogens within quite short distances of a source of infection, which on extrapolation rapidly approaches zero, is sometimes quoted as evidence of poor distribution of spores in air, but this is fallacious because the total number of lesions *outside* the area surveyed is unknown. Others point to the records of spores trapped at high altitudes over land, and on flights over oceans and polar regions (Section III, B, 2). There is good evidence on both sides of the controversy, and clearly a dilemma has to be resolved.

Meanwhile the phenomenon of long-distance spread has been demonstrated for the cereal rusts by the concerted efforts of a generation of scientists in laboratories scattered over North America (for summaries see Craigie, 1940, 1945; Stakman and Harrar, 1957). To simplify a complex story, *Puccinia graminis* and *P. recondita* for various reasons do not survive the cold winters of the northern part of that continent or the hot dry summers of the southern part. Spring-sown wheat in the northern United States and Canada receives spore showers of these fungi annually from rusted autumn-sown wheat in Mexico and Texas. In some years it moves by a succession of short jumps with intervening pauses for local multiplication, but in other years spores travel for hundreds of miles when atmospheric pressure distribution produces southerly winds. Similarly, winter wheat in the south becomes infected during the autumn by spore showers from the north. Long-distance transport of cereal rusts occurs also in India (Mehta, 1952), in the U.S.S.R. (see Chester, 1946), and in Western Europe (Ogilvie and Thorpe, 1961). There is no reason to suppose that these cereal rusts are peculiar in the way they behave—they are simpler to study because their migration is obligate, but many other fungi which are less well studied may also migrate long distances annually. Much of this long distance migration probably goes on undetected, and although quantitatively less successful than local transport, it must be accepted as normal in airborne fungi, except for the most fragile organisms.

Eddy diffusion theory and spore liberation experiments agree in principle that a substantial proportion of spores liberated near ground level are deposited close to the source. But a proportion still escape deposition near the source and are likely to be carried high into the atmosphere where they can be widely dispersed. Such may be the explanation of the dilemma outlined earlier.

D. Extension of Geographical Range

There is no theoretical reason why windborne spores should not be carried in small quantities between any two parts of the globe. The fact that some fungi are more limited in distribution than their growth requirements indicate, suggests that their viability limits their distribution, and that they may be unable to cross oceans and deserts on the winds. Extension of geographical range then has to wait on transport by some other route, commonly human activity. Far-reaching results may ensure when a plant pathogen is introduced into an area previously uninfested (Woodham-Smith, 1962).

Puccinia polysora is one of the rust fungi attacking maize (*Zea mays*). There is evidence that it has been in the southeastern United States at least since 1879; probably for longer, because American host varieties sustain little damage, as though a balance had been established by selection. In 1949 the fungus suddenly appeared causing a severe disease of maize in Sierra Leone where, unlike American maize varieties, the African ones were highly susceptible and the attack was crippling. Once established in Sierra Leone it spread, evidently by wind, reaching all other parts of West Africa by 1951, Congo and East Africa by 1952, Rhodesia and Madagascar by 1953, and the remote islands of the Indian Ocean by 1955 (Fig. 3). Simultaneously another focus was developing, apparently starting in the Philippines in 1948, and spreading successively to Malaya and Siam, reaching Queensland in 1959 and Fiji in 1961.

Cammack (1959) has considered possible modes of immigration of *P. polysora* into Africa and rejected the possibility of wind transport in favor of introduction by aircraft with seed corn or corn-on-the-cob. Evidently until about 1949 the fungus lived inconspicuously in America on tolerant varieties, separated from vast areas of highly susceptible maize by the Atlantic Ocean which formed an impassable barrier to natural spread by wind. Once established in Africa natural barriers were insufficient to prevent its spread by wind east and south over the rest of the continent, doubtless in a series of hops, at the average rate of about 750 miles per year.

The spread of tobacco blue mold (*Peronospora tabacina*) is also well documented. This fungus was first described in Australia in 1890. It did not succeed in crossing the drier areas of that continent to reach Western Australia until 1950. It appeared in North America in 1921 and in South America in 1938. Its invasion of Europe has been spectacular. It first occurred in England and Holland in 1958, probably introduced by aircraft

(Klinkowski, 1962). By the following year it was well-established in Germany, and by 1960 it had invaded nearly all Europe including Eastern Russia; France, Belgium, and Germany lost 60–65% of their tobacco crop. By 1961 it had reached Tunisia, Algeria, and Greece; and in 1962 it reached Turkey, Morocco, Syria, Lebanon, and Persia, averaging approximately 700 miles per year since its first discovery in Europe.

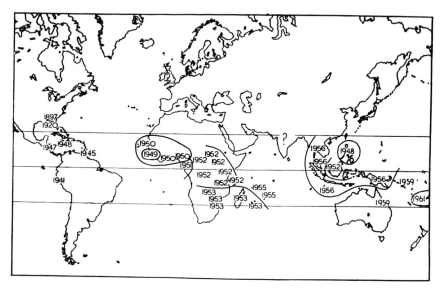

FIG. 3. Occurrence of *Puccinia polysora* in America, and spread from new foci in West Africa and the Philippine Islands (with acknowledgments to R. H. Cammack).

IV. CONCLUSIONS

Assuming that it is advantageous to a species to occupy the maximum amount of habitat, and to distribute and store material for genetic variation, we can now contrast the effectiveness of various dispersal methods. Autonomous dispersal (including mycelial extension) is extremely limited in range. Splash dispersal is less restricted and occurs in weather often favorable for spore germination. Dispersal by insect vectors has a precision other methods lack, and can cover long distances, although comparatively slowly. Wind transport can cover long distances rapidly, but landing is hazardous and must often occur under conditions unfavorable for further growth; for success spores must be produced in vast numbers. The most spectacular extensions of geographical range occur when an efficiently wind-dispersed fungus is carried across its natural barriers by man's power-driven transport.

22. Dispersal

REFERENCES

A small proportion of the relevant literature is cited here, but in the following list works marked with an asterisk (*) include extensive bibliographies.

Austwick, P. K. C. (1958). Insects and the spread of fungal disease. In "Biological Aspects of the Transmission of Disease" (C. Horton-Smith, ed.), pp. 73-79. Oliver & Boyd, Edinburgh and London.

Bakshi, B. K. (1950). Fungi associated with ambrosia beetles in Great Britain. *Brit. Mycol. Soc. Trans.* 33:111-120.

Brodie, H. J. (1931). The oidia of *Coprinus lagopus* and their relation with insects. *Ann. Botany (London)* 45:315-344.

Brues, C. T. (1946). "Insect Dietary," 466 pp. Harvard Univ. Press, Cambridge, Massachusetts.

Buller, A. H. R. (1933). "Researches on Fungi," Vol. V, pp. 1-167. Longmans, Green, New York.

Cammack, R. H. (1959). Studies on *Puccinia polysora* Underw. II. A consideration of the method of introduction of *P. polysora* into Africa. *Brit. Mycol. Soc. Trans.* 42:27-32.

*Carter, W. (1962). "Insects in Relation to Plant Disease," 705 pp. Wiley (Interscience), New York.

Chamberlain, A. C. (1956). Aspects of travel and deposition of aerosol and vapour clouds. *At. Energy Res. Estab. (Gt. Brit.), Rept.* HP/R1261:1-35.

Chamberlain, A. C. (1962). Transport of particles across boundary layers. *U.K. At. Energy Authority, Res. Group, Memo.* M1122:1-13.

Chester, K. S. (1946). "The Nature and Prevention of the Cereal Rusts as Exemplified in the Leaf Rust of Wheat," 269 pp. Chronica Botanica, Waltham, Massachusetts.

Clinton, G. P., and F. A. McCormick. (1936). Dutch elm disease—*Graphium ulmi. Conn. Agr. Expt. Sta., New Haven, Bull.* 389:701-752.

Craigie, J. H. (1931). An experimental investigation of sex in the rust fungi. *Phytopathology* 21:1001-1040.

*Craigie, J. H. (1940). Aerial dissemination of plant pathogens. *Proc. 6th Pacific Sci. Congr. 1939* Vol. 4, pp. 753-767. California Univ. Press, Berkeley and Los Angeles.

Craigie, J. H. (1945). Epidemiology of stem rust in Western Canada. *Sci. Agr.* 25:285-401.

Crowe, T. J. (1963). Possible insect vectors of the uredospores of *Hemileia vastatrix* in Kenya. *Brit. Mycol. Soc. Trans.* 46:24-26.

Davies, R. R. (1961). Wettability and the capture, carriage and deposition of particles by raindrops. *Nature* 191:616-617.

Dobbs, C. G. (1942). On the primary dispersal and isolation of fungal spores. *New Phytologist* 41:63-69.

English, H., and F. Gerhardt. (1946). The effect of ultra-violet radiation on the viability of fungus spores and on the development of decay in sweet cherries. *Phytopathology* 36:100-111.

Faulwetter, R. C. (1917a). Dissemination of the angular leafspot of cotton. *J. Agr. Res.* 8:457-475.

Faulwetter, R. C. (1917b). Wind-blown rain, a factor in disease dissemination. *J. Agr. Res.* 10:639-648.

Ferguson, M. C. (1902). A preliminary study of the germination of the spores of *Agaricus campestris* and other Basidiomycetous fungi. *Bull. Bur. Plant Ind. U.S. Dept. Agri.* No. 16, 40 pp.

Fowler, M. E. (1952). Oak wilt surveys in 1951. *Plant Disease Reptr.* 36:162-165.

Fracker, S. B. (1936). Progressive intensification of uncontrolled plant disease outbreaks. *J. Econ. Entomol.* 29:923-940.

Furcolow, M. L. (1961). Airborne histoplasmosis. *Bacteriol. Rev.* 25:301-309.

Garrett, S. D. (1953). Rhizomorph behaviour in *Armillaria mellea* (Vahl) Quél. 1. Factors controlling rhizomorph initiation by *A. mellea* in pure culture. *Ann. Botany (London)* [N.S.] 17:63-79.

Gäumann, E. A. (1950). "Principles of Plant Infection" (Transl. by W. B. Brierley), 543 pp. Crosby, Lockwood, London.

*Gregory, P. H. (1945). The dispersion of air-borne spores. *Brit. Mycol. Soc. Trans.* 28:26-72.

Gregory, P. H. (1951). Deposition of air-borne *Lycopodium* spores on cylinders. *Ann. Appl. Biol.* 38:357-376.

Gregory, P. H. (1952). Fungus spores. *Brit. Mycol. Soc. Trans.* 35:1-18.

Gregory, P. H. (1958). A correction. *Brit. Mycol. Soc. Trans.* 41:202.

*Gregory, P. H. (1961). "The Microbiology of the Atmosphere," 251 pp. Wiley (Interscience), New York and Leonard Hill, London.

Gregory, P. H. (1962). The dispersal distance problem. *Pollen Spores* 4:348-349.

Gregory, P. H., and J. M. Hirst. (1957). The summer air-spora at Rothamsted in 1952. *J. Gen. Microbiol.* 17:135-152.

Gregory, P. H., and O. J. Stedman. (1953). Deposition of air-borne *Lycopodium* spores on plane surfaces. *Ann. Appl. Biol.* 40:651-674.

Gregory, P. H., E. J. Guthrie, and M. E. Bunce. (1959). Experiments on splash dispersal of fungus spores. *J. Gen. Microbiol.* 20:328-354.

Gregory, P. H., T. J. Longhurst, and T. Sreeramulu. (1961). Dispersion and deposition of Airborne *Lycopodium* and *Ganoderma* spores. *Ann. Appl. Biol.* 49:645-658.

Heald, F. D., and R. A. Studhalter. (1914). Birds as carriers of the chestnut-blight fungus. *J. Agr. Res.* 2:405-422.

Heim, R. (1942). Les champignons des termitières. Nouveaux aspects d'un problème de biologie et de systématique générales. *Rev. Sci.* 80:69-86.

Hirst, J. M. (1952). An automatic volumetric spore trap. *Ann. Appl. Biol.* 39:257-265.

Hirst, J. M. (1953). Changes in atmospheric spore content: diurnal periodicity and the effects of weather. *Brit. Mycol. Soc. Trans.* 36:375-393.

*Hirst, J. M. (1959). Spore liberation and dispersal. *In* "Plant Pathology Problems and Progress, 1908–1958" (C. S. Holton, ed.), pp. 529-538. University of Wisconsin Press, Madison, Wisconsin.

Hirst, J. M. (1961). The aerobiology of *Puccinia graminis* uredospores. *Brit. Mycol. Soc. Trans.* 44:138-139.

Hirst, J. M., and O. J. Stedman. (1962). Raindrop collision with plant surfaces as a cause of dry spore liberation. *Rept. Rothamsted Exptl. Sta. 1961* pp. 114-115.

Holmes, F. W. (1958). Recorded Dutch elm disease in North America as of 1957. *Plant Disease Reptr.* 42:1299-1300.

*Ingold, C. T. (1953). "Dispersal in Fungi," 197 pp. Oxford Univ. Press (Clarendon), London and New York.

Jinks, J. L. (1952). Heterocaryosis in wild *Penicillium*. *Heredity* 6:77-87.

Johnstone, H. F., W. E. Winsche, and L. W. Smith. (1949). The dispersion and deposition of aerosols. *Chem. Rev.* 44:353-371.
Klinkowski, M. (1962). Die europäische Pandemie von *Peronospora tabacina* Adam, dem Erreger des Blauschimmels des Tabaks. *Biol. Zentr.* 81:75-89.
Kouyeas, V., and B. Anastassiadis. (1962). Dissemination of *Deuterophoma tracheiphila* Petri by the common magpie (*Pica pica* L.). *Ann. Inst. Phytopathol. Benaki* [N.S.] 4:52-55.
Lacey, M. E. (1962). The summer air-spora of two contrasting adjacent rural sites. *J. Gen. Microbiol.* 29:485-501.
Leach, J. G. (1940). "Insect Transmission of Plant Diseases," 615 pp. McGraw-Hill, New York.
Lodder, J., and N. J. W. Kreger-van Rij. (1952). "The Yeasts: A Taxonomic Study," 713 pp. North-Holland Publ., Amsterdam, and Interscience, New York.
McDonald, J. E. (1962). Collection and washout of airborne pollen and spores by raindrops. *Science* 135:435-437.
Malik, M. M. S., and C. C. V. Batts. (1960). The determination of the reaction of barley varieties to loose smut. *Ann. Appl. Biol.* 48:39-50.
Mason, E. W. (1937). Annotated account of fungi received at the Imperial Mycological Institute. *Mycological Papers, Commonwealth Mycological Inst.*, No. 14, 31 pp.
May, F. G. (1958). The washout of *Lycopodium* spores by rain. *Quart. J. Roy. Meterol. Soc.* 84:451-458.
Mehta, K. C. (1952). Further studies on cereal rusts in India. Part II. *Indian Council Agr. Res. Sci. Monogr.* No. 18, 368 pp.
Newman, I. V. (1948). Aerobiology on commercial air routes. *Nature* 161:275-276.
Nisikado, Y., T. Inouye, and Y. Okamoto. (1955). Conditions of the spores of the scabbed wheat ear suspended in rain drops. *Ber. Ohara Inst. Landwirtsch. Biol., Okayama Univ.* 10:125-134.
Nutman, F. J., F. M. Roberts, and K. R. Bock. (1960). Method of uredospore dispersal of the coffee leaf rust fungus, *Hemileia vastatrix*. *Brit. Mycol. Soc. Trans.* 43:509-515.
Ogilvie, L., and I. G. Thorpe. (1961). New light on epidemics of black stem rust of wheat. *Sci. Progr. (London)* 49:209-227.
Pady, S. M., and C. D. Kelly. (1954). Aerobiological studies of fungi and bacteria over the Atlantic Ocean. *Can. J. Botany* 32:202-212.
Pady, S. M., and C. L. Kramer. (1960). Kansas Aeromycology. X: Basidiomycetes. *Trans. Kansas Acad. Sci.* 63:125-134.
Parker-Rhodes, A. F. (1950). The basidiomycetes of Skokholm Island. III. Genetic isolation of *Panaeolus papilionaceus*. *New Phytologist* 49:328-334.
Parkin, E. A. (1942). Symbiosis and Siricid wasps. *Ann. Appl. Biol.* 29:268-274.
Pasquill, F. (1961). "Atmospheric Diffusion: The Dispersion of Windborne Material from Industrial and Other Sources," 300 pp. Van Nostrand, Princeton, New Jersey.
Schmidt, W. (1918). Die Verbreitung von Samen und Blütenstaub durch die Luftbewegung. *Oesterr. Botan. Z.* 67:313-328.
Schrödter, H. (1954). Die Bedeutung von Massenaustausch und Wind für die Verbreitung von Pflanzenkrankheiten. Ein Beitrag zur Epidemiologie. *Nachr. Deut. Pflanzenschutzdienst (Berlin)* [N.F.] 8:166-172.
*Schrödter, H. (1960). Dispersal by air and water—the flight and landing. *In* "Plant Pathology" (J. G. Horsfall and A. E. Dimond, eds.), Vol. III, pp. 169-227. Academic Press, New York.

Shantz, H. L., and R. L. Piemiesel. (1917). Fungus fairy rings in Eastern Colorado and their effect on vegetation. *J. Agr. Res.* 11:191-246.
Smith, C. E., D. Pappagianis, H. B. Levine, and M. Saito. (1961). Human coccidioidomycosis. *Bacteriol Rev.* 25:310-320.
Smith, F. B. (1962). The problem of deposition in atmospheric diffusion of particulate matter. *J. Atmospheric Sci.* 19:429-434.
Sreeramulu, T., and A. Ramalingam. (1961). Experiments on the dispersion of *Lycopodium* and *Podaxis* spores in the air. *Ann. Appl. Biol.* 49:659-670.
Stakman, E. C., and J. G. Harrar. (1957). "Principles of Plant Pathology," 581 pp. Ronald Press, New York.
Stakman, E. C., A. W. Henry, G. C. Curran, and W. N. Christopher. (1923). Spores in the upper air. *J. Agr. Res.* 24:599-606.
Steinhaus, E. A. (1946). "Insect Microbiology," 763 pp. Cornell Univ. Press (Comstock), Ithaca, New York.
*Stepanov, K. M. (1935). Dissemination of infective diseases of plants by air currents. (Russian, English title). *Bull. Plant Protection (USSR)* [2] *Phytopathol.* 8:1-68.
Stover, R. H. (1962). Intercontinental spread of banana leaf spot (*Mycosphaerella musicola* Leach). *Tropical Agr. (London)* 39:327-338.
Sturgis, W. C. (1898). On some aspects of vegetable pathology and the conditions which influence the dissemination of plant diseases. *Botan. Gaz.* 25:187-194.
Sutton, O. G. (1932). A theory of eddy diffusion in the atmosphere. *Proc. Roy. Soc.* A135:143-165.
Sutton, O. G. (1953). "Micrometeorology," 333 pp. McGraw-Hill, New York.
Talbot, P. H. B. (1952). Dispersal of fungus spores by small animals inhabiting wood and bark. *Brit. Mycol. Soc. Trans.* 35:123-128.
U.S. Weather Bureau. (1955). "Meteorology and Atomic Energy," 169 pp. U.S. At. Energy Comm., Washington, D.C.
van der Plank, J. E. (1963). "Plant Diseases: Epidemics and Control," 349 pp. Academic Press, New York.
Waggoner, P. E., and G. S. Taylor. (1955). Tobacco blue mold epiphytotics in the field. *Plant Disease Reptr.* 39:79-85.
Ward, H. M. (1893). Further experiments on the action of light on *Bacillus anthracis*. *Proc. Roy. Soc.* 53:23-44.
Webster, J. (1959). Experiments with spores of aquatic hyphomycetes. I. Sedimentation, and impaction on smooth surfaces. *Ann. Botany (London)* [N.S.] 23:595-611.
Weston, W. A. R. D. (1931). The effect of ultra-violet radiation on the urediniospores of some physiological forms of *Puccinia graminis*. *Sci. Agr.* 12:81-87.
Weston, W. A. R. D., and R. E. Taylor. (1948). "The Plant in Health and Disease," 173 pp. Crosby, Lockwood, London.
*Wolfenbarger, D. O. (1946). Dispersion of small organisms. Distance dispersion rates of bacteria, spores, seeds, pollen and insects, incidence rates of disease and injuries. *Am. Midland Naturalist* 35:1-152.
*Wolfenbarger, D. O. (1959). Dispersion of small organisms. Incidence of viruses and pollens; dispersion of fungus spores and insects. *Lloydia* 22:1-106.
Woodham-Smith, C. (1962). "The Great Hunger: Ireland 1845-49," 510 pp. Hamish Hamilton, London.
Zentmeyer, G. A., P. P. Wallace, and J. G. Horsfall. (1944). Distance as a dosage factor in the spread of Dutch elm disease. *Phytopathology* 34:1025-1033.

CHAPTER 23

Dormancy and Spore Germination

ALFRED S. SUSSMAN[1]

Department of Botany
University of Michigan
Ann Arbor, Michigan

I. INTRODUCTION

Spores are both the end and the beginning of the development of fungi. As the climax of the life history they are found frequently to have a specialized and complex morphology, which differs from that of vegetative cells. Moreover, spores may be associated with sexual reproduction and the morphological and metabolic controls with which this process is associated. At the same time, spores are embryonic in function to the extent that they retain the capacity for rapid and sustained growth and mitotic activity. Therefore, they are embryonic in function and resemble the totipotent cells of higher organisms in this respect. Such developmental versatility, and the important role that spores play in nature, make them a favored object of research in basic and applied biology.

The classic book by de Bary (1887) summarizes the knowledge of spore germination up to that time and defines many of the problems in this field. Reviews of work performed at the beginning of this century and before include those of Duggar (1901), Ferguson (1902), Dodge (1912), and Doran (1922). Germination has been reviewed for the slime molds (Smart, 1937), phycomycetes (R. Emerson, 1950), yeasts (Tites, 1926), smuts (Davis, 1924; Fischer, 1951), rusts (Arthur, 1929), and other basidiomycetes (Fries, 1943; Kneebone, 1950) and *Aspergillus niger* (Yanagita, 1964). Recent general reviews include those of Wolf and Wolf (1947), Hawker (1950), Gottlieb (1950), Lilly and Barnett (1951), V. W. Cochrane (1958), and Sussman (1965a).

---

[1] The author would like to acknowledge the financial support provided by the National Science Foundation during the writing of this paper.

II. TERMINOLOGY OF DORMANCY AND GERMINATION

A variety of states, based upon metabolic intensity, have been described for organisms. These range from the *active,* or vegetative, condition of most organisms, to the *cryptobiotic* state which is imposed by temperatures low enough to vitrify the contents of cells. The latter state also has been referred to as ametabolism, anabiosis, abiosis, anhydrobiosis, and latent life (Keilin, 1959). Dormant metabolism lies somewhere between these extremes.

"Internal" and "external" factors influencing dormancy were identified by Doran (1922). He included among the internal ones the maturity of the spore, its longevity and "animation," and "a poorly understood factor which may be called vitality. . . ." On the other hand, temperature, light, water, oxygen, nutrients, and toxic substances are included among the external factors. Such a dichotomy also was recognized by Mandels and Norton (1948) and is discussed by Sussman (1965a), from which the following definitions are taken:

Dormancy—any rest period or reversible interruption of the phenotypic development of an organism.

Constitutional dormancy—a condition wherein development is delayed due to an innate property of the dormant stage such as a barrier to the penetration of nutrients, a metabolic block or the production of a self-inhibitor.

Exogenous dormancy—a condition wherein development is delayed because of unfavorable chemical or physical conditions of the environment.

Maturation—the complex of changes associated with the development of the resting stage of dormant organisms or of the germinable stage in those without a dormant period.

Activation—the application of environmental stimuli which induce germination.

Afterripening—the treatments undergone in nature which lead to germination; activation under natural circumstances.

Germination—a process which leads to the first irreversible stage which is recognizably different from the dormant organism, as judged by physiological or morphological criteria.

The distinction between these terms may become clearer by using the example of the oospores of *Phytophthora cactorum* (Blackwell, 1943) that require a 3- to 4-week delay or "maturation" period until nuclear fusion is accomplished. An "afterripening" period of 6–7 months follows which can be reduced by freezing the spores. Thus, "maturation" precedes "afterripening," which, in turn, can be abbreviated through "activation" by low temperatures. In contrast to oospores of *P. cactorum,* maturation occurs before the spores are shed in the case of many other spores. Furthermore, the afterripening period may be very short, or extended over several years, as in *Peronospora schleideniana* [*P. destructor*] (McKay, 1935, 1939).

A prerequisite for dormant cells is the ability to survive environmental upsets that would be lethal to the organism at other stages of its development. Moreover, a corollary of these definitions is that constitutional dormancy will not exist in ephemeral organisms, for selection favors, among organisms lacking resistance, those which germinate rapidly (Garrett, 1956; Sussman, 1965b).

Resistance is not restricted to spores, for the vegetative mycelium of fungi can often survive drastic environmental conditions (Zimmerman, 1925; Hawker, 1957). Survivability of the vegetative organism may be effected without changes in its structure, or morphological alterations may occur in response to environmental pressures (Hawker, 1957). Usually, however, fungi persist through the formation of special resistant stages such as modifications of the mycelium like "dauerzellen" of yeasts, or the chlamydospores of other fungi. Aggregates of hyphae, including sclerotia, rhizomorphs, and parts of fruiting bodies also may serve to perpetuate the fungi. However, spores usually are the most resistant of the stages in the fungus life history (Sussman, 1965b; cf. chapter by Sussman in Volume III of this treatise).

III. MEANS OF ACTIVATION

Return to the conditions which permit vegetative development breaks environmentally induced dormancy. On the other hand, according to the definition given previously, constitutive dormacy can be overcome only by a treatment that is *not* required by the organism during vegetative development. Thus, organisms which are constitutively dormant will fail to develop even when provided conditions under which vegetative development will proceed, unless an activation treatment (trigger) is applied.

Various physical and chemical factors serve as activators including temperature, light, moisture, and various chemicals (Sussman, 1965a). Frequently, a combination of treatments is required whereby more than one environmental variable must be manipulated before activation is accomplished. In any case, it is often possible to relate the treatment required to the distribution of the organism in nature, thereby defining the selective advantage which accrues to a particular trigger. However, this is not invariably the case and the biological role of some activators remains undefined.

A. Temperature Extremes

The requirement for a heat shock appears to be most characteristic of ascomycetes although spores of *Phycomyces blakesleeanus* require treatment at 50°C to germinate (Sommer and Halbsguth, 1957). Many of these are coprophilous, and it is possible that the requirement for heat is associated with their passage through the digestive tracts of animals and subsequent incubation in an environment in which high temperatures are generated by microbial action.

Dodge (1912) appears to have been the first to have used temperatures in excess of body temperature when he treated spores of *Ascobolus carbonarius* at 70°C. Previously, however, Welsford (1907) had shown that 37°C would activate spores of *A. furfuraceus*. Temperatures in the range of 40°C also have been reported to activate spores of *Reticularia* sp. (Jahn, 1905) and *Ustilago striiformis* (Kreitlow, 1943), and conidia of *Neurospora sitophila* (Ishii and Miyamoto, 1954).

Wide differences exist in the time needed to break dormancy at low temperatures. There is a range of 3 hours in the case of aeciospores of *Puccinia graminis* to 5 or 6 months in the resting spores of *Physoderma* and spores of *Tilletia caries*. However, factors like maturity and the source of the spores influence the duration of the treatment, as in the case of *T. caries*, which can germinate in 16 days at 3°C (Gassner and Niemann, 1954) but are said by C. S. Holton (1943) to require 5 months at 4°C.

Often a distinction has to be made beween the temperature that is optimal for afterripening and that for germination. Thus, frequently it is necessary to transfer the organism from the low temperature at which it is afterripened to its optimum for germination, which is usually between 15° and 30°C. The basidiomycetes listed by Kneebone (1950), as well as several others noted in the review by Sussman (1965a), fall in this category.

An interesting correlation exists in that those fungi for which high temperature serves as an activator are mainly saprophytes. By contrast, the large majority of fungi which respond to cold-treatment are pathogens or mycorrhizal fungi, including a large number of basidiomycetes.

B. Light

As in the case of the organisms which respond to cold-treatment, those that are activated by light are mostly parasites and, of these, the basidiomycetes are in the majority. This generalization holds except for a few saprophytic phycomycetes which appear in the list assembled by Sussman (1965a). It is reasonable to suppose that, as might be the case for the cold temperature requirement, light is a means through which an environmental signal helps to synchronize the activities of the host and pathogen.

23. *Dormancy and Spore Germination* 737

Different spore types of a single organism may respond differently to light. For example, whereas the teliospores of *Puccinia graminis* germinate better in light (Sibilia, 1930), its uredospores do not require light to germinate.

A variable that must be considered is the age of the spore, for Hahne (1925) mentions that only older spores of *Tilletia tritici* [*T. caries*] and *T. levis* [*T. foetida*] require light whereas those that are younger than two years old germinate in the dark. Furthermore, Meiners and Waldher (1959) note that two collections of *T. cerebrina* were inhibited by light but the germination of a third was stimulated.

Interaction between light and temperature is demonstrated in the work of Gassner and Niemann (1954) which shows that the proper combination of these factors is required for the germination of several rusts.

Unfortunately, little detailed information is available as to the action spectra and exact quantities of light needed to break dormancy in fungus spores. Hebert and Kelman (1958) have shown that as little as 0.1–0.2 foot-candles of illumination for 8 hours daily effected significant increases in the germination of resting sporangia of *Physoderma maydis*. Blue light was most effective, as in the case of conidia of *Oidium monilioides* (Sempio and Castori, 1950) and the other fungi studied.

C. Chemicals

Various complex media have been used to activate fungus spores including extracts from seedlings, oils, leaf distillates and wood products, diffusates from yeasts and other microorganisms, self-activators, paraffins, and soil extracts.

A variety of substances has been found to serve as triggers within the different groups of fungi, except for the Myxomycetes, for which Elliott (1949) has found sodium glycocholate and sodium taurocholate to be effective with spores of over 50 species. Solvents like alcohols and acetone, which also function as wetting agents, activate ascospores of *Neurospora tetrasperma* (Sussman *et al.*, 1959), uredospores of *Puccinia graminis* f. sp. *tritici* (French *et al.*, 1957), spores of *Urocystis tritici* [*U. agropyri*] (Noble, 1924), and conidia of *Penicillium frequentans* (Dobbs and Hinson, 1953). Other solvents, like chloroform and ethyl ether, have similar effects, as does furfural, which activates ascospores of several pyrenomycetes (Sussman, 1965a) and the several aldehydes used by French *et al.* (1957) with uredospores of *Puccinia graminis* f. sp. *tritici*.

Many naturally occurring compounds induce germination including esters (Brown, 1922), indoleacetic acid (Van Sumere *et al.*, 1957), lactones (Allen, 1955; French, 1961), organic acids (Duggar, 1901), amino acids (Yanagita, 1955), and vitamins (von Güttenberg and Strutz, 1952). Inorganic materials and drugs of several types also have been used.

However, the role of some of these substances must be interpreted with caution because it is not clear whether they are required as activators, or for subsequent development. Moreover, many of the older experiments were performed without adequate control of pH so that the specificity of the data can be questioned along with the purity of the chemicals (von Güttenberg and Strutz, 1952).

Endogenous stimulators of germination have been found in spores of myxomycetes (Smart, 1937), uredospores of *Puccinia graminis* f. sp. *tritici* (Ezekiel, 1930; French *et al.*, 1957), and a factor from *Agaricus campestris*, which may be 2,3-dimethyl-1-pentene (McTeague *et al.*, 1959), enhances the germination of its own basidiospores. Considerable effort has gone into identifying the stimulator from wheat rust uredospores, and French and Weintraub (1957) have suggested that it might be *n*-nonanal (pelargonaldehyde). But there is reason to believe that the natural factor is very labile so that this conclusion may be questioned.

D. Miscellaneous Activators

Alternate wetting and drying has been suggested to be the equivalent of freezing (Arthur, 1929), and is especially effective with rust spores (Maneval, 1922). High and low temperature fluctuations also may serve to disrupt dormancy in spores, including teliospores of *Puccinia glumarum* [*P. striiformis*] (Raeder and Bever, 1931) and resistant sporangia of *Blastocladia pringsheimii* (Blackwell, 1940). This kind of fluctuating environment, along with wetting and drying, may describe the "overwintering" treatment received by many spores in nature.

Floating or soaking of spores have been described as effecting the germination of rusts (Arthur, 1929) and Noble (1924), C. S. Holton (1943), and Lowther (1948) specify that smut spores must be presoaked before maximal germination is possible. The self-inhibitors of rusts (Allen, 1955) and of *Erysiphe graminis* (Domsch, 1954) probably are dissipated by this means.

The transfer of spores to distilled water, or to a dilute medium, is sometimes a means of activation as in the case of *Blastocladiella* (Cantino, 1951). In this case the "cracking" of the pitted wall of the resting sporangium is inhibited by even trace amounts of anions like $\overline{NO_3}$ and $\overline{CO_3}$ so that the old medium must be replaced by one containing low levels of these substances.

IV. MECHANISMS OF DORMANCY

A. Constitutive Dormancy

Innate properties of the cell determine this type of dormancy. Therefore, all restraints upon development which originate within the spores themselves are included in this category. These restraints include permeability, anhydrobiosis, and self-inhibitors and will be discussed below.

1. Permeability

A classic explanation of dormancy has been that a permeability barrier must be breached before germination can be induced. Some of the observations that lent credence to this suggestion established that dormant periods were markedly curtailed when resting stages were formed under conditions that resulted in the formation of abnormally thin cell walls (Brierley, 1917; Gwynne-Vaughan and Williamson, 1933; Stüben, 1939). Moreover, Blackwell (1935) and McKay (1939) have drawn attention to the fact that the oospores of *Peronospora destructor* seem to germinate only after much of the thick outer wall has been autodigested, and others have shown that cracking of the outer wall of sporangia of *Allomyces* (Machlis and Ossia, 1953) and *Blastocladiella* (Cantino, 1951) must precede germination. But in none of these cases has permeability been studied, so the correlation is incomplete.

This question was studied in some detail in ascospores of *Neurospora tetrasperma* which can germinate in conductivity-grade water (Sussman, 1954), so it is unlikely that changes in permeability to dissolved substances is involved in their dormancy. Nevertheless, experiments did indicate that distinct changes do occur at about 150 minutes after activation. Permeability to water has been tested by suspending ascospores in concentrated glycerol. Under these conditions, even dormant cells quickly become shrunken and an air bubble appears suggesting that water can leave the cell freely (unpublished observations of the author). Dehydrated cells regain their turgor in water and retain their viability as well so that ingress of water is not blocked either.

Conidiospores of *Phycomyces blakesleeanus* which have been activated by acetate have been shown by Borchert (1962) to undergo a drastic change in permeability to heavy metals. However, heat-activated ones change only after an hour after treatment so that the relation of permeability to dormancy in this case is not clear. Enzymatic treatments which may affect the wall appear to enhance germinability (Brierley, 1917) and the response to activating chemicals (Lowry *et al.*, 1956). However, as in the cases discussed above, no definitive evidence exists to link the breaking of dormancy to a change in permeability.

2. Anhydrobiosis

Although this mechanism frequently has been invoked to explain bacterial spore dormancy (Lewis et al., 1960), it has not been applied very often to fungus spores. The data which reveal ascospores of *Neurospora* to be permeable to water would tend to rule out anhydrobiosis as a mechanism in this case. Moreover, hydration may *prevent* germination in the powdery mildews (Brodie and Neufeld, 1942), instead of inducing development. Therefore, there is little evidence to support the concept that anhydrobiosis is a determinant of dormancy in the fungi.

3. Self-Inhibitors

The fact that high concentrations of certain spores germinate less well than lower ones has led to the suggestion that self-inhibitors are present in these organisms. For example, Boyd (1952) has shown with *Fusarium caeruleum* that when a concentration of 2000 conidia per field is used, only 1% germinate. Self-inhibitors may be present in a variety of organisms, including conidia of *Glomerella cingulata* (B. T. Lingappa, 1963), *Erysiphe graminis* (Domsch, 1954), and *Peronospora manshurica* (Dunleavy and Snyder, 1963), uredospores of *Puccinia graminis* f. sp. *tritici* (Allen, 1955), and uredospores and aeciospores of *P. sorghi* and *P. purpureum* (Le Roux and Dickson, 1957).

Another source of self-inhibitors may be those sporangia in which germination does not occur. For example, von Stosch (1935) showed that spores of *Didymium* did not germinate within the sporangia, even under high humidities. Therefore, control is probably exerted this way in other cases, although instances are known where spores do germinate within sporangia (Chamberlain and Allison, 1945; Schnathorst, 1959; Benjamin, 1963).

Allen (1955) was the first to study the properties of the inhibitory materials and he was able to demonstrate that the germination of uredospores of *P. graminis* f. sp. *tritici* was inhibited across an air gap by emanations from actively metabolizing spores. Carbon dioxide was ruled out in this case but must be considered a possibility in other instances where this gas in low concentrations prevents germination (Stock, 1931; Magie, 1935).

The chemical nature of the inhibitor from uredospores of *P. graminis* f. sp. *tritici* was investigated by Forsyth (1955) who found a parallel between the inhibitory activity of trimethylethylene and that of the natural inhibitor, and similar means of counteracting their inhibitory effects were noted. Similar absorption spectra in acetone were found thereby strengthening the possibility that trimethylethylene is the inhibitor. Trimethylamine has been isolated from spores of *Tilletia caries* and shown to inhibit germination in low concentrations (Ettel and Halbsguth, 1963), and these workers suggest that this substance is the endogenous inhibitor of smut spores.

Nonvolatile inhibitors that are isolable from uredospores of *P. graminis* f. sp. *tritici* have been described by Van Sumere et al. (1957). Of these, only ferulic acid inhibited at all concentrations down to 1 µg/ml so that it may have a physiological role of significance *in vivo*. Glutamic and aspartic acids were reported to be self-inhibitors of germination of uredospores of *Uromyces phaseoli* [*U. appendiculatus*] (Wilson, 1958), but this has been disputed by Bell (1960).

4. Metabolic

The striking increases in respiratory rates that ensue upon the activation of many types of dormant cells suggests that important metabolic changes occur at this time. This is borne out by the fact that different physiological stages are distinguishable during germination even though no morphological changes are discernible. Furthermore, abundant instances have been presented by Sussman (1965a) to illustrate the fact that the optimum temperature for growth often differs from that for germination. Therefore, it is reasonable to expect that the induction of dormancy in some cases is associated with a metabolic block or with a nutritional deficiency that must be removed before germination can occur. As a matter of fact, Fries (1948) has provided experimental evidence to suggest that there might be some selective advantages in heterotrophy, under certain conditions, inasmuch as mutant conidia of *Ophiostoma multiannulatum* survive longer than do those of the wild type.

An instance where a nutritional requirement is unique for spores, as compared with vegetative mycelium, has been studied by Schopfer (1942) with *Rhizopus suinus*. In this case, *meso*-inositol is required only for zygospore germination, not for the subsequent development of the hyphae. Although other spores have been shown to germinate in response to niacinamide (von Güttenberg and Strutz, 1952), thiamine (Hawker, 1950), and *l*-alanine (Yanagita, 1955), it is not clear whether mycelial growth is enhanced by these substances as well. If this were the case, then the metabolic block inducing dormancy is probably not associated with these requirements.

The discussion above underlines the fact that nutritional data can only be suggestive of the basic mechanisms underlying dormancy and that definitive evidence must come from studies of the enzyme systems which are present in the organism during its separate stages. The difficulties involved in this approach are many, for not only must large quantities of spores be obtained for such experiments but one is always confronted with the question of the nature of the primary reaction that triggers germination. It is to be expected in a process involving several enzymatic steps that the activity of many enzymes may change during germination. Which step, then, is the one that is affected by the activating treatment, thereby setting in motion the biochemical and physiological changes that are described later? Moreover, the above analysis has assumed that a single key reaction in a catenary sequence is responsible for the activation process, but it is also possible that models based upon multiple loci would also furnish a satisfactory explanation of this process.

The first attempt to analyze the effect of metabolic triggers upon activation was that of Goddard and Smith (1938) who showed that the anaerobic CO_2 production of ascospores of *Neurospora tetrasperma* increased in proportion to the number of germinating cells. The presence of the enzyme pyruvic carboxylase was inferred from experiments wherein pyruvic acid reversed the toxicity of fluoride for anaerobic carbon dioxide production. On the other hand, dormant cells were considered to lack this enzyme because exogenously added pyruvate failed to stimulate the fermentative release of carbon dioxide. On this basis it was suggested that the metabolic block that imposed dormancy upon these ascospores was due to the lack of pyruvic carboxylase whose presence in activated cells permitted germination to proceed. This suggestion was examined by Sussman *et al.* (1956) who determined the pyruvic carboxylase activity of dormant, activated, and germinating spores and showed that extracts prepared from all these sources contained the enzyme. Although the activity of the dormant cell extracts was lower than those in the other cases, it was sufficient to account for observed rates of carbon dioxide evolution in activated spores. In addition, it was shown that the coenzyme, diphosphothiamine, was present in almost equivalent amounts in dormant as well as germinating spores.

Therefore, another mechanism has been proposed, based upon the observation that trehalose occurs in large amounts in dormant ascospores of *Neurospora* (B. T. Lingappa and Sussman, 1959; Sussman and Lingappa, 1959) but is used only after activation is accomplished (Fig. 1). On the basis of the latest work on this subject (Hill and Sussman, 1964), "de novo" synthesis of trehalase is ruled out and one of the following mechanisms of activation is suggested: (a) An inhibitor of an enzyme responsible for trehalose degradation (trehalase ?) is destroyed. (b) A precursor is converted into the enzyme by activation in a manner analagous to the trypsinogen-trypsin transformation. (c) The enzyme and its substrate are separated spatially inside the cell and activation brings them together. (d) A series of interlocking enzyme reactions are shifted from one steady-state level to another, as suggested by Delbrück (1949). This approach needs to be extended to other organisms before its generality can be assessed.

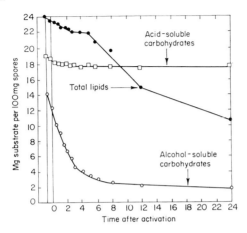

FIG. 1. Effect of activation upon the amount of lipids and carbohydrates in ascospores of *Neurospora tetrasperma*. From B. T. Lingappa and Sussman (1959).

B. Exogenous Dormancy

Unfavorable physical or chemical conditions of the environment can delay the development of organisms in a seasonal, as well as irregular, manner. An example of seasonal dormancy is the response of higher plants to temperature variations in temperate regions. However, non-seasonal fluctuations in humidity, inhibitory principles, and other environmental variables also may affect development. This form of dormancy often is called "quiescence" and occurs in many organisms. It is most important for spores and vegetative stages that are not constitutively dormant. Moreover, even spores that have an endogenously imposed dormant period may have dormancy reimposed by environmental factors under certain conditions (Goddard, 1939; Sun and Sussman, 1960; Doguet, 1959; Bromfield, 1964).

1. Inhibitors

a. Soil Fungistasis. That fungistatic principles exist in soils has been abundantly confirmed. Many of these data are reviewed by Garrett (1956) and in the proceedings of a recent symposium (Baker and Snyder, 1965). Very different types of soils, of wide geographical distribution, have inhibitory effects upon spores. However, Dobbs *et al.* (1960) have found that soils fluctuate in their ability to inhibit, and B. T. Lingappa and Lockwood (1963) suggest that the techniques used often influence the results of such studies.

As Garrett (1956) pointed out, the ecological significance of the "widespread fungistasis" may be in the survival value that accrues to an organism if it is restrained from germinating until substrate is available. In fact, it has been shown by Dobbs and Hinson (1953) and others that a substrate itself (glucose) may serve to overcome the inhibition in unsterilized soil. Other means of reversal include, heat-treatment (autoclaving), or prolonged drying, extraction with organic solvents, treatment with citrate-phosphate buffer, addition of nutrients to soil, growth in the vicinity of roots, and addition of charcoal to soil (Dobbs and Hinson, 1953; Brian, 1960; Jackson, 1960; B. T. Lingappa and Lockwood, 1961).

The nature of the fungistatic principle is not clear for it has proved difficult to distinguish between the lack of an essential metabolite(s) and the presence of an inhibitor (Brian, 1960). Although the latter possibility generally is favored, preexisting inhibitory materials have not been unambiguously demonstrated. Accordingly, B. T. Lingappa and Lockwood (1961) have proposed that fungus spores provide nutrients to soil in their immediate vicinity, thereby permitting the growth of other microbes which liberate antibiotics. However, the data are not conclusive and the question remains.

b. *Inhibitors in Marine Environments.* The existence of fungistatic principles in estuarine sediments has been reported by Borut and Johnson (1962). Thus, spores of *Aspergillus wentii, Penicillium janthinellum,* and *Zygorhynchus moelleri* germinated to an insignificant extent in untreated or filtered sea water, as compared to that in a 3.5% NaCl solution. Moreover, vegetative stages are able to grow in the sea waters in which spores failed to germinate. All the fungi whose spores germinated in distilled water showed such a response, and small amounts of nutrients helped to overcome the toxic effect. Almost nothing is known of the chemical identity or source of the inhibitors in sea water, and it is to be hoped that such data will soon be available.

c. *Plant Inhibitors.* Inhibitory principles that contribute to the resistance of plants to pathogens are reviewed by Gäumann (1950) and may be found in soil (Melin, 1946; Winter, 1955). Phenols, mustard oils, and other plant products serve in this way.

2. *Environmental Factors*

Often the cardinal temperatures for the development of spores is narrow. This fact is especially relevant to the role of temperature as an inducer of exogenous dormancy in the lower ranges. Thus, even vegetative stages of fungi survive very well at cold temperatures (cf. Volume III) so that the cessation of development in the cold usually is reversible. Therefore, dormancy is induced in a manner analagous to that by which many higher plants and some animals become quiescent in winter. Such dormancy is less likely to be induced at temperatures above the maximum for growth because of limited survival, except under dry conditions, or with highly resistant stages.

Relative humidity probably can determine whether or not germination will occur. High humidities usually are required for the development of most fungus spores (Sussman, 1965a) so, if spores can withstand desiccation, low humidities can be a means of enforcing a quiescent period. A mechanism whereby such resistance can be engendered is suggested by the data of Terui and Mochizuki (1955) which disclose that the Q_{O_2} of conidia of *Aspergillus niger* is greater than 5 at 100% relative humidity but falls to 1 at 60%. The exhaustion of endogenous reserves is thereby delayed, and the chances for the survival of this organism are correspondingly improved under conditions of low humidity.

Altered levels of CO_2 and O_2 might be expected to occur in soils that undergo seasonal changes in water level, certain strata of aquatic environments, etc., so that reversible restraints upon the development of certain organisms could occur in these environments.

V. CRITERIA OF GERMINATION

The usual method for following the germination of fungus spores is the protrusion of the germ tube, but other markers have been used as well. Thus, changes in the diameter, weight, and volume of germinating spores of *Aspergillus niger* have been used by Yanagita (1957). The swelling of certain spores during germination, such as conidia of *A. oryzae,* has been followed by the decrease in the transmittance of light (Terui and Mochizuki, 1955), and Mandels and Darby (1953) have used this technique with conidia of *Myrothecium verrucaria, Curvularia brachyspora,* and others.

As will be shown later, metabolic changes occur during germination and some of these have been used to follow this process. One example is that of dormant spores of *M. verrucaria,* which have little or no ability to metabolize glucose (Mandels *et al.,* 1956). Respiratory increases during germination have been observed for a number of other fungus spores as well (Sussman, 1965a). Other metabolic parameters have been followed during germination including total nitrogen, protein nitrogen and nucleic acid synthesis (Yanagita, 1957). Early stages in the germination process may be followed in certain spores by loss of heat resistance (Y. Lingappa and Sussman, 1959).

VI. CHANGES DURING GERMINATION

A. Morphological and Cytological

There is one nucleus per ascospore in *Saccharomyces cerevisiae,* and its structure is similar to those in the vegetative cells (Hashimoto et al., 1958). During germination the ascospores swell and vacuoles form near the nucleus. No alteration in the structure of the nucleus occurs during germination, and the nuclear membrane appears to persist throughout the process. As swelling progresses the outer spore coat breaks, usually at more than one point, but the inner one remains intact and forms the new vegetative cell wall. No mitochondria were found in resting ascospores although small granules of varying size can be found scattered through the periphery of the ascospore. Mitochondria appear as soon as swelling begins and they seem to be functionally and structurally similar to those of other organisms. However, it is likely that these spores were poorly fixed before germination so that the mitochondria were destroyed (Hawker and Abbott, 1963). Therefore, the "de novo" origin of mitochondria in this system cannot be accepted at this time.

The germination of sporangiospores of *Rhizopus* (Hawker and Abbott, 1963) and of conidia of *Botrytis cinerea* (Hawker and Hendy, 1963) has been studied and, although mitochondria are present in the ungerminated spores, these organelles increase greatly in number during germination. Moreover, the endoplasmic reticulum is reported to be sparse before germination but to increase during this process. A difference between the above spores involves the wall which forms the germ tube. In the case of *Rhizopus,* a new elastic inner wall forms as one of the first stages of germination and becomes the wall of the germ tube. By contrast, the inner wall of the conidium of *Botrytis* surrounds the emergent germ tube.

Detailed studies of the germination of ascospores of *Neurospora tetrasperma* (Lowry and Sussman, 1965) and of basidiospores of *Schizophyllum commune* (Voelz and Niederpreum, 1964) reveal that the endoplasmic reticulum is sparse in dormant spores and increases greatly during germination. Furthermore, there seems to be a change in the size and shape of the mitochondria of both spores during the germination process. Moreover, the wall of the germ tube in both these cases is continuous with the inner wall of the spore, thereby resembling conidia of *Botrytis* in this respect.

The impermeability of certain spores, and the destructive effects of certain fixatives used in electron microscopy, have led to difficulties that have restricted studies of the ultrastructure of germinating spores. Although there is too little work on this subject to warrant many generalizations, it appears that the endoplasmic reticulum is sparse in several of the ungerminated cells that have been examined. Furthermore, changes in the form, size, and numbers of mitochondria have been recorded so that these organelles may be intimately concerned in the transition from the dormant to the vegetative condition.

B. Biochemical Events

1. Respiratory Changes

Fungus spores usually show a marked increase in respiratory activity during germination. Such data were first reported for the fungi by Goddard (1935) and Goddard and Smith (1938) with ascospores of *Neurospora*

TABLE I
RESPIRATORY CHANGES IN GERMINATING FUNGAL SPORES

Organism	Resting			Germinating		
	$Q_{O_2}{}^a$	$Q_{CO_2}{}^b$	R.Q.	$Q_{O_2}{}^a$	$Q_{CO_2}{}^b$	R.Q.
Phycomyces blakesleeanus incubated 100 minutes (Rudolph, 1961)	1.9	—	1.0	11.4	—	1.0
Neurospora tetrasperma, ascospores, incubated 4 hours (R. W. Holton, 1960)	0.4	—	0.6	15–25	—	0.65
Puccinia graminis f. sp. *tritici*, uredospores, incubated 72 hours (Shu et al., 1954)	1.6	1.0	0.65	1.4	1.0	0.70
Aspergillus oryzae, conidia, incubated 3 hours (Terui and Mochizuki, 1955)	1.26	—	1.4–2.2	2.17	—	0.6–1.0
A. niger, conidia, incubated 6 hours (Yanagita, 1957)	0.4	—	—	1.8	—	—
Myrothecium verrucaria, conidia, incubated 2 hours (Mandels, 1963)	1.0	—	—	75	—	—

^{a} Q_{O_2} = mm^3 O$_2$/hr mg dry wt.
^{b} Q_{CO_2} = mm^3 CO$_2$/hr mg dry wt.

tetrasperma. These cells remain dormant unless a heat shock, or chemical treatment, is applied, after which they will germinate, utilizing endogenous substrates for energy (Sussman, 1961). Almost immediately upon being activated by heat, ascospores of this organism respire at an increased rate that may be 20–30 times that of the dormant organism, as the data in Tables I and II reveal. Such increases in respiratory rate also have been reported when chemicals like furfural are used to break the dormancy of ascospores of *N. tetrasperma* (Sussman, 1953) and *N. crassa* (M. R. Emerson, 1954). Moreover, as the data in Table II reveal, there are changes in the fermentative capacity of these cells as expressed in terms of the carbon dioxide released under anaerobic conditions.

Interesting parallels to these events are to be found during the germination of spores of *Phycomyces blakesleeanus,* as demonstrated in the work of Halbsguth and Rudolph (1959) and Rudolph (1960, 1961). Thus, a

TABLE II

COMPARISON OF RESPIRATORY RATES OF DORMANT, ACTIVATED, AND GERMINATING ASCOSPORES OF *Neurospora tetrasperma* AT 26°C

		Respiratory rates	
Parameter	Dormant	Activated, 1–2 hours after activation	Germinating, 3–5 hours after activation
$Q_{O_2}{}^a$ (mm³ O_2/hr mg dry wt.)	0.21–0.59	4.5–10.9	16.4–24.2
$Q_{CO_2}{}^b$ (mm³ CO_2/hr mg dry wt.)	0.13–0.36	—	10.0–13.8
R.Q.^{b}	0.57	—	0.59
Anaerobic CO_2 as $Q_{CO_2}^{N\ a}$	0.03	5.0–10.9	1.0–2.0

^{a} Data of R. W. Holton (1960).
^{b} Data of Goddard (1935).

heat activation is required in order to ensure maximum germination of these spores, and both increased oxygen uptake and carbon dioxide production result.

Similar respiratory changes have been described for the germination of conidia of *Myrothecium verrucaria* (Mandels and Norton, 1948; Mandels and Darby, 1953), *Aspergillus oryzae* (Terui and Mochizuki, 1955), and *A. niger* (Yanagita, 1957). In these spores, as with those of *Phycomyces,* exogenous substrates are required, in contrast to the ascospores of *Neurospora* which germinate even in distilled water. Moreover, the kinetics of oxygen uptake during germination were similar enough in several of these cases to permit a mathematical description in the form of $y = b + (k\ t^2)/2$, which can be fitted to parabolic curves (Mandels *et al.,* 1956).

Uredospores of *Puccinia graminis* f. sp. *tritici* have appeared to be an exception to the rule that respiratory increases are expected during germination (Table I). In this case, Shu *et al.* (1954) observed that both the amount of respiratory activity, and the respiratory quotient (R.Q.) of ungerminated and germinating spores were equivalent. Inasmuch as the respiration of the germinating spores was measured 3 days after incubation was begun, transitory increases in rate may have been missed. As a matter of fact, recent data suggest that when these spores are activated with pelargonaldehyde, there is a rapid increase in respiratory metabolism which is succeeded by a period during which the rate diminishes to approximately that of the resting spore (Allen, 1963).

A second exception occurs in the case of macroconidia of *Fusarium solani* f. *phaseoli* (V. W. Cochrane *et al.*, 1963c). Dormant spores of this organism oxidize acetate, malonate, and ethanol by way of the tricarboxylic acid and glycollic acid cycles. During germination, the respiratory rate of cells provided ethanol (V. W. Cochrane *et al.*, 1963c) or mannose (V. W. Cochrane *et al.*, 1963b) is not increased, whereas that of cells given glucose rises more than twofold. Slight increases are obtained when cells are germinated on fructose or trehalose (V. W. Cochrane *et al.*, 1963b).

These differences in the response to substrates during germination may relate to the role that spores play in nature. Thus, the thick wall, relative impermeability, and great longevity of *Neurospora* ascospores (Sussman, 1961) suggest that it functions as a resting spore. As such, there is obvious selective advantage in the low rate of metabolism of the dormant spore, and in its reliance upon endogenous substrates. This is to be contrasted to the macroconidia of *Fusarium*, which do not need to be activated, depend upon external substrates, and respire at a relatively rapid rate soon after harvest (V. W. Cochrane *et al.*, 1963a).

2. Substrates for Germination

The fact that spores of many fungi contain fatlike droplets which appear to coalesce when germination occurs suggested to Kordes (1923) that lipids serve as an important storage material during germination. However, the qualitative nature of these observations, and recent data to be discussed below, suggest that this question must be reexamined.

First of all, it is necessary to distinguish between those spores that require an exogenous source of energy before germination can proceed, and those that do not. Among the former are conidia of *Fusarium* which, despite containing 20% lipid, still require a carbohydrate before they will germinate (J. C. Cochrane *et al.*, 1963). Similarly, conidia of *Myrothecium verrucaria*, which have sufficient endogenous reserves to germinate (about 20% of their dry weight), still require exogenous substrates (Mandels, 1963). The R.Q. of conidia of *Aspergillus oryzae* during germination was markedly affected by the substrate in which the spores were germinated. Similarly, starved conidia of *Cochliobolus miyabeanus* utilize a variety of exogenously added sugars during germination, along with an endogenous glucan (Oku, 1960).

Spores that do not require exogenous substrates for germination include uredospores of rusts. For example, Shu *et al.* (1954) showed that only endogenous fats and proteins furnish the substrates for germinating uredospores of *Puccinia graminis* f. sp. *tritici*. In fact, sugars and sugar alcohols accumulate in these spores at this time (Reisener *et al.*, 1962) although it is not yet certain that some of these are not used during germination. Flax-rust uredospores (*Melampsora lini*) also metabolize fats during germination but a shift in the R.Q. suggests that a carbohydrate also may be used as a substrate (Frear, 1960). When conidia of *Cochliobolus miyabeanus* germinate in distilled water, carbohydrate reserves are the primary substrate for germination (Oku, 1960). These results may be explicable in terms of the data obtained with ascospores of *Neurospora tetrasperma* by B. T. Lingappa and Sussman (1959). In these spores, lipids are utilized by dormant cells but trehalose is the major substrate of germinating ones. However, lipids continue to be used, even while the sugar is still present, and become the sole source of energy when trehalose is exhausted (Fig. 1). Therefore, it may be that many, if not most, spores require the simultaneous utilization of lipids and carbohydrates for germination to proceed.

3. Respiratory Enzymes

Quantitative and qualitative differences exist in the enzyme complements of resting spores and other stages, and the data in Tables III and IV reveal that enzymes may be enriched in spores, as well as reduced in activity.

TABLE III
RESPIRATORY ENZYMES IN WHICH ACTIVITY IS ENHANCED IN SPORES

Organism and stage	Enzyme (relative activity, %)	Reference
Neurospora tetrasperma	Cytochrome oxidase	R. W. Holton
Ascospores, resting	100	(1960)
Mycelium, 43 hour	20	
Mycelium, 68 hour	39	
Mycelium, 89 hour	31	
Neurospora crassa	Trehalase	Hill and Sussman
Macroconidia, resting	100	(1964)
Macroconidia, germinating, 10 hour	14	
Mycelium, 3 day	3.7	
Mycelium, 16 day	70	
Mycelium, 27 day	94	
Glomerella cingulata	Cytochrome oxidase	Sussman and Markert
Conidia, resting	100	(1953)
Mycelium, 2 day	53	
Mycelium, 4 day	48	
Mycelium, 9 day	50	

That the rate at which cytochrome c is reduced may limit the respiration of uredospores of *Puccinia graminis* f. sp. *tritici* was suggested by White and Ledingham (1961). Also, R. W. Holton (1960) has shown that,

TABLE IV
Respiratory Enzymes in Which Activity is Diminished in Spores

Organism and stage	Enzyme (relative activity, %)			Reference
	Trehalase	Invertase		
Neurospora crassa and *N. tetrasperma*				Hill and Sussman (1964)
Ascospores, resting	0.74	3.1		
Ascospores, germinating, 2 hour	3.	3.6		
Macroconidia, resting	100.	100.		
Macroconidia, germinating, 10 hour	14.	14.		
Mycelium, 3 day	3.7	43		
Mycelium, 16 day	70	480		
Mycelium, 27 day	94	393		
	Succinic dehydrogenase	Aldolase		
Neurospora crassa				Zalokar (1959)
Conidia, resting	11	31		
Mycelium, 8 hour	105	59		
Mycelium, 4 day	100	100		

TABLE IV (Continued)

Organism and stage	Enzyme (relative activity, %)				Reference
Puccinia graminis f. sp. *tritici*	Cytochrome oxidase		DPNH-cyt. -c reductase	Succinic cyt. -c reductase	White and Ledingham (1961)
Uredospores, resting	56		38	31	
Uredospores, germinated	100		100	100	
Ustilago maydis	Triose PO$_4$ dehydrogenase		Isocitric dehydrogenase	Malic dehydrogenase	Gottlieb and Caltrider (1963)
Teliospores, resting	15		43	19	
Teliospores, germinating, 6 hour	30		64	21	
Teliospores, germinating, 12 hour	100		100	100	
Aspergillus niger	Aldolase	Phosphoglucomutase		phosphohexoisomerase	Bhatnager and Krishnan (1960)
Conidia, resting	0	0		0	
Conidia, germ. (12 hour) (no germ tube)	0	0		0	
Conidia, germ. (18 hour) (germ tubes)	13	26		100	
Conidia and hyphae, germ. 24 hour	100	100		—	

although cell-free extracts of dormant ascospores of *Neurospora tetrasperma* required the addition of exogenous cytochrome c for cytochrome oxidase activity to be manifested, extracts of other stages possessed an endogenous supply of this enzyme. However, cytochrome oxidase itself is not limiting the metabolism of ascospores of *Neurospora* (Cheng, 1954; R. W. Holton, 1960), conidia of *Glomerella cingulata* (Sussman and Markert, 1953), uredospores of *Puccinia graminis* f. sp. *tritici* (White and Ledingham, 1961), or basidiospores of *Schizophyllum commune* (Niederpruem, 1964).

Glycolytic enzymes vary markedly in titer when resting spores and vegetative stages are compared (Table IV). For example, Kornfeld and Knight (1962) found that xylose reductase could not be induced in dormant spores of *Penicillium chrysogenum* whereas abundant enzyme was formed by germinating ones. Moreover, Zalokar (1959) has shown that aldolase activity is low in conidia compared to the mycelium of *Neurospora crassa*. Also, β-galactosidase activity is lower in these conidia than in mycelium that is 96 hours old, but young mycelium has even less enzyme than the spores. In *Ustilago maydis*, germination of teliospores is characterized by the appearance of key enzymes of both the hexose monophosphate shunt and the tricarboxylic acid cycle (Gottlieb and Caltrider, 1963).

As noted previously, the respiration of germinating ascospores of *Neurospora tetrasperma* increases steeply and the R.Q. rises from 0.6 to about 1.0 (Sussman, 1961). During the first 2 hours after activation, evidence for a fermentative type of metabolism is found in the release of acetaldehyde, ethanol, lactate, and pyruvate (Sussman *et al.*, 1956). However, after this time, these fermentation products no longer accumulate in such large amounts and the R.Q. decreases to about 0.6 again, signalizing a changeover to lipid metabolism again, unless an exogenous source of sugar is provided. Concomitantly, the full complement of tricarboxylic acid cycle products appears, suggesting that a strongly oxidative type of metabolism is evolved, in contrast to the fermentative system of the newly activated spore. Some of the metabolic steps involved in the transformation of ascospores from primarily fermentative organisms to strongly aerobic ones are outlined in Fig. 2. As Rudolph (1961) points out, it is still not certain whether enzymatic changes, or merely a change in substrates, explain these observations.

Striking parallels exist between the metabolic events described above for *Neurospora* ascospores and those reported for sporangiospores of *Phycomyces blakesleeanus* by Halbsguth and Rudolph (1959) and Rudolph (1960, 1961). Thus, after a heat shock of a few minutes at 54°C, carbon dioxide evolution is increased markedly over that of resting cells. In addition, oxygen uptake is enhanced, but less so than in the case of carbon dioxide. Data obtained through the use of inhibitors, and the accumulation of metabolic products like acetaldehyde and pyruvate, suggest a transition from a fermentative type of metabolism to terminal oxidations based upon oxygen, as in the case of *Neurospora*. Another instance

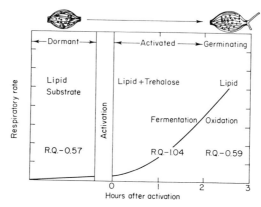

FIG. 2. Summary outline of metabolic events during the germination of ascospores of *Neurospora*. From Sussman (1961).

where a glycolytic metabolism is followed by a more aerobic type may be that of germinating spores of *Fusarium solani* (V. W. Cochrane et al., 1963b) so that there may be some generality in this mechanism.

It has been claimed by Newburgh and Cheldelin (1958) that spores of the smut *Tilletia caries* differ from the vegetative mycelium in the way that glucose-1-C^{14} and glucose-3,4-C^{14} are metabolized. On the other hand, Turel and Ledingham (1959) could show no such difference with uredospores of *Melampsora lini*. However, labeling patterns alone lead to difficulties of interpretation (Blumenthal, 1965) so that these data must still be considered to be tentative.

Changes in the contribution of the hexose monophosphate shunt and the Embden-Meyerhof-Parnas pathways have been described for germinating conidia of *Aspergillus niger* (Yanagita, 1964).

4. Synthesis of Macromolecules

Germinating uredospores of *Puccinia graminis* f. sp. *tritici* have been shown to synthesize chitin (Shu et al., 1954), trehalose and other sugars and sugar alcohols (Reisener et al., 1962), and amino acids (Kastings et al., 1959). Although such spores can incorporate amino acids into proteins, they cannot effect a net synthesis of proteins (Shu et al., 1954). Other uredospores for which no net synthesis of proteins could be found include those of *Puccinia helianthi, P. sorghi,* and *Uromyces appendiculatus* (Staples *et al.*, 1962).

On the other hand, spores of saprophytes, including conidia of *Glomerella cingulata, Aspergillus niger,* and *Neurospora sitophila* have been shown to incorporate C^{14}-labeled acetate into amino acids and proteins (Staples *et al.*, 1962). Moreover, experiments with S^{35} have revealed that germinating spores of *A. niger* form sulfur-containing amino acids from choline sulfate (Takebe and Yanagita, 1959; Takebe, 1960). According to Yanagita (1957, 1964) synthesis begins about 3 hours after the start of the incubation of conidia of *Aspergillus niger,* whereas DNA and protein synthesis begin somewhat later. These activities are accompanied by considerable uptake of inorganic phosphate and by increases in dry weight, volume, and total nitrogen. These data have been corroborated by Nishi (1961) who found, in addition, that although the turnover of RNA increases during the germination of these spores, that of DNA remains unchanged, even though it duplicated a few hours after incubation was begun. Takebe (1960) has found that choline sulfate accumulates in sizable amounts in conidia of *A. niger* and is one of the sources of sulfur in the synthesis of proteins during germination. Most of the newly synthesized protein is soluble (Hoshino, 1961) although the wall of dormant spores has the highest incorporating activity for amino acids in cell-free systems.

Whether mRNA synthesis occurs initially upon the germination of spores of *A. niger* is not yet clear. That such might occur is suggested by the fact that during germination the nucleotide ratio of RNA changes: the purine/pyrimidine ratio drops from 1.2 to nearly 1.0 (Table V).

In *Aspergillus nidulans* Shepherd (1957) found that protein nitrogen rose from 26% in the conidium to 36% in the mycelium. Early in the germination period the RNA content of the conidia actually fell and that of DNA and lipid nitrogen did not change. However, immediately before the protrusion of the germ pore, a slow increase in RNA and protein occurred. Rapid synthesis of nucleic acids and protein did not occur until the vegetative phase of growth began.

There is evidence that mRNA is not stored in ascospores of *Neurospora crassa.* Growing hyphae, resting conidia, and dormant ascospores contain the same population of ribosomes (Henney and Storck, 1963a) and of total ribosomal and soluble RNA (Henney and Storck, 1963b). However, dormant spores do not contain polyribosomes, which appear first in the early stages of germination (Henney and Storck, 1964). Presumably, germination is accompanied by mRNA synthesis and subsequent banding of ribosomes (polysomes).

The nuclear cap of zoospores of aquatic fungi has been found by Lovett (1963) to be a "package" of ribosomes. Inasmuch as the cap breaks

TABLE V

Nucleotide Composition of RNA's Extracted from Germinating Spores of *Aspergillus niger* of Different Ages[a]

Duration of cultivation (hours)	Adenylic acid	Guanylic acid	Uridylic acid	Cytidylic acid	Ratio: Purine/pyrimidine	Ratio: 6-Amino/6-keto
0	1.00[b]	1.22	0.94	0.91	1.20	0.88
2	1.00	1.14	1.10	0.94	1.05	0.87
4	1.00	1.28	1.21	1.18	0.96	0.88
6	1.00	1.17	1.12	0.97	1.02	0.87

[a] Data from Hoshino et al. (1962).
[b] Numbers indicate relative values of amounts of nucleotides, taking those of adenylic acid as unity.

down very soon after the start of germination it is tempting to assign it a role. Thus, the cap might serve as a reservoir of RNA and protein or, alternatively, as a preformed source of programmed ribosomes that could initiate protein synthesis soon after germination begins. However, these possibilities have not been tested and further work is needed.

5. *Isozymes in Spores and Vegetative Cells*

Are the enzymes of similar function in spores and vegetative cells identical in structure, that is, are they determined by the same cistron? Some scattered observations suggest that there are cases where isozymes, or enzymes of similar function but different properties otherwise, exist in spores and vegetative cells. This is the case for ascorbic acid oxidase in *Myrothecium verrucaria* wherein conidia have a different form of the enzyme than do hyphae (White and Smith, 1961). More recently, Solomon *et al.* (1964) have studied the acid and alkaline phosphatases and nonspecific esterases of *Dictyostelium discoideum*. Only three different acid phosphatases and esterases were found in the spores compared with 5 and 7–10, respectively, that appeared from the migrating pseudoplasmodia and culminating stages. As for alkaline phosphatase, two bands appeared in spores, migrating pseudoplasmodia, and culminating stages, but only one wider band was formed by extracts of myxamoebae. It is important to note the possibility that cases may be found where qualitative differences between enzymes of similar function may be found to exist in spores and vegetative stages *in the absence of significant quantitative ones*. The relevance of such changes to dormancy and germination remains to be assessed.

VII. STAGES IN THE GERMINATION PROCESS

A summary of the stages that ensue between the activation and germination of *Neurospora* ascospores is provided in Table VI. Alterations in each of four physiological markers are used as a means of defining these stages. It will be noted that, counting the dormant stage, at least five recognizably different stages exist. Undoubtedly, overlap between these exists in that certain biochemical processes are common to several stages. Nevertheless, these serve to define the minimum number of steps in the germination process whose origin and basis must be understood.

The definition of stages is possible in the germination of spores of other fungi as well. In the case of conidia of *Aspergillus niger,* Yanagita (1957) and Yanagita *et al.* (1962) distinguished between the stages of "endogenous" and "exogenous" swelling on the basis that carbon dioxide was necessary for the latter but not for the former. Furthermore, the "exogenous" phase was temperature-sensitive, whereas the "endogenous" was not.

A similar suggestion was made for spores of *Mucor rouxii* and *M. hiemalis* by Wood-Baker (1955), except that oxygen was required for the second phase but not for the first. Differing metabolic requirements served to distinguish the early stages in the germination of conidia of *Myrothecium verrucaria* which could swell in yeast extract alone, but needed further supplements in order to progress further (Mandels and Darby, 1953).

TABLE VI

SUMMARY OF THE STAGES BETWEEN ACTIVATION AND GERMINATION AND THE PHYSIOLOGICAL MARKERS WHICH CHARACTERIZE THEM IN *Neurospora tetrasperma*[a]

Condition of spores	Minutes after activation	Physiological marker			
		Q_{O_2}	R.Q.	Thermal resistance	Deactivability at 4°C or in N_2
Dormant	—	0.3	0.6	+	—
Activated					
Stage 1	0–20	0.5–4	1.2	+	+
Stage 2	30–60	4–10	1.0	—	+
Stage 3-n	60–150	15–30	1.0	—	—
Germinating	150	30	0.6	—	—

[a] Data from Sussman (1961).

VIII. ROLE OF SPORES IN NATURE

Three roles have been ascribed to spores in nature including the enhancement of survivability and disseminability, and timing of growth to ensure that active growth occurs when conditions are most favorable (Sussman and Halvorson, 1966).

A. Enhancement of Survivability

This subject will be reviewed in detail by Sussman in Volume III so only a brief summary of the subject will be provided here. Evidence for the survival of microbes has been conflicting as far as the relative numbers of spore-formers and non-spore-formers to be found in soil (Warcup, 1960; Durbin, 1961). Therefore, these difficulties must be considered in evaluating the data.

The data suggest that fungus spores are more resistant to extremes of temperature and deleterious radiations and chemicals than are their vegetative counterparts. However, vegetative stages of some organisms also may be very resistant and enjoy great longevity (Warcup, 1957; Barton, 1965).

B. Enhancement of Disseminability

Stoke's Law has been used by Lamanna (1952) and Gregory (1961) to calculate the terminal velocity of bacterial and fungus spores. Although, theoretically, vegetative cells can be airborne as readily as spores, in some cases the probability of their survival is less because of radiation, desiccation, etc. (Sussman and Halvorson, 1966).

The fact of the spread of fungus spores over long distances is well established. For example, Stakman and Hamilton (1939) have shown that uredospores of wheat rust can travel at least 600 miles in a viable condition. Other studies, such as those of Kramer *et al.* (1959) and Sreeramulu (1958), establish that fungus spores predominate over vegetative cells as components of the atmospheric flora. This conclusion is strengthened by data from different parts of the world which reveal the presence of hyphae in only small amounts in air samples (Gregory, 1961). Yeasts are distributed widely in the atmosphere, frequently as vegetative cells, but are usually only a small proportion of the flora. By reason of the varied mechanisms for making large numbers of them airborne, and their ability to float and to survive in air, spores are the most effective means of dispersal available to fungi by this means.

C. Spores as Timing Devices

This type of adaptation confers selective advantage upon organisms whose environments undergo fluctuations in moisture, temperature, light and in other factors which affect survivability. Lees (1961) has proposed that diapause serves such a function in some insects and an analogous one may be played by spore dormancy. In the latter, timing can be considered to occur at two stages of development, including spore formation and germination.

1. Timing in Sporulation

Reduction in the supply of certain nutrients often induces sporulation, whereas the provision of glucose and related hexoses suppresses this process. Thus, the sporulation of yeasts (Miller, 1959) and other fungi (Hawker, 1957) is favored by dilution of the medium, or deprivation of nutrients, after growth has ceased. Even media upon which depauperate growth has been made from the start will enhance the fertility of interallelic crosses in *Neurospora* (Ishikawa, 1962).

Therefore, it is possible that there has been selection for strains of fungi which respond to unfavorable environmental situations by the production of spores. To the extent that this generalization holds, the induction of spore formation represents a timing device which introduces a phase of the life cycle which usually is suited to tide the organism over the unfavorable period.

2. Timing and Germination

It can be considered that dormant spores represent a simple timing system in which an arresting device must be overcome by an activator. Arrest may be accomplished by the types of dormant mechanisms described before. A few instances in nature where spores appear to abet survival by acting as timing devices will be mentioned below.

The prevention of the germination of spores at the place of their production (self-inhibitors) assures their dissemination to new environments and subsequent mixing of gene pools by the formation of heterokaryons and sexual reproduction. The work of Macfarlane (1952) suggests that any of several means of suppressing the germination of resting spores of *Plasmodiophora brassicae,* including the presence of exogenous inhibitors, enhanced their survival.

A possible advantage of the need for extreme temperatures for activation is that they may serve as cues which anticipate seasonal changes in weather. Thus, basidiospores of *Flammula alnicola,* a fungus causing decay of conifers in Canada, are activated by a temperature that occurs in that latitude coincidentally with the start of growth of the host (Denyer, 1960).

Chemical activators of spores of plant pathogens often are produced by host plants, according to Garrett (1956). Other aspects of the function of spores as timing devices are covered by Sussman and Halvorson (1966).

REFERENCES

Allen, P. J. (1955). *Phytopathology* **45**:259-266.
Allen, P. J. (1963). Personal communication.
Arthur, J. C. (1929). "The Plant Rusts. The Uredinales," Chapter VI, 446 pp. Wiley, New York.
Baker, K., and W. C. Snyder. (1965). "Ecology of soil-borne plant pathogens-prelude to biological control," 571 p. Univ. of California Press, Berkeley, California.
Barton, L. V. (1965). *In* "Encyclopedia of Plant Physiology (A. Lang, ed.), Vol. 15, Part 2, pp. 1058-1085. Springer, Berlin.
Bell, A. A. (1960). *Phytopathology* **50**:629 (Abstract).
Benjamin, R. (1963). Personal communication.
Bhatnagar, G. M., and P. S. Krishnan. (1960). *Arch. Mikrobiol.* **37**:211-214.
Blackwell, E. M. (1935). *Nature* **135**:546.
Blackwell, E. M. (1940). *Brit. Mycol. Soc. Trans.* **24**:68-86.
Blackwell, E. M. (1943). *Brit. Mycol. Soc. Trans.* **26**:93-103.
Blumenthal, H. J. (1965). *In* "The Fungi" (G. C. Ainsworth and A. S. Sussman, eds.), Chapter 10, pp. 229-268. Academic Press, New York.
Borchert, R. (1962). *Beitr. Biol. Pflanz.* **38**:31-61.
Borut, S., and T. W. Johnson. (1962). *Mycologia* **54**:181-193.
Boyd, A. E. W. (1952). *Ann. Appl. Biol.* **39**:322-329.

23. Dormancy and Spore Germination

Brian, P. W. (1960). In "The Ecology of Soil Fungi" (D. Parkinson and J. S. Waid, eds.), pp. 115-129. Univ. of Liverpool Press, Liverpool.
Brierley, W. B. (1917). Ann. Botany (London) 31:127-132.
Brodie, H. J., and C. C. Neufeld. (1942). Can. J. Res. C20:41-61.
Bromfield, K. R. (1964). Phytopathology 54:68-74.
Brown, W. (1922). Ann. Botany (London) 36:285-300.
Cantino, E. C. (1951). Antonie van Leeuwenhoek, J. Microbiol. Serol. 17:59-96.
Chamberlain, D. W., and J. L. Allison. (1945). Phytopathology 35:241-248.
Cheng, S. C. (1954). Plant Physiol. 29:458-467.
Cochrane, J. C., V. W. Cochrane, F. G. Simon, and J. Spaeth. (1963). Phytopathology 53:1155-1160.
Cochrane, V. W. (1958). "Physiology of Fungi," 524 pp. Wiley, New York.
Cochrane, V. W., J. C. Cochrane, C. B. Collins, and F. G. Serafin. (1963a). Am. J. Botany 50:806-814.
Cochrane, V. W., S. J. Berry, F. G. Simon, J. C. Cochrane, C. B. Collins, J. A. Levy, and P. K. Holmes. (1963b). Plant Physiol. 38:533-541.
Cochrane, V. W., J. C. Cochrane, J. M. Vogel, and R. S. Coles, Jr. (1963c). J. Bacteriol. 86:312-319.
Davis, W. H. (1924). Phytopathology 14:251-267.
de Bary, A. (1887). "Comparative Morphology, and Biology of the Fungi, Mycetozoa, and Bacteria," 525 pp. Oxford Univ. Press (Clarendon), London and New York.
Delbrück, M. (1949). Unités biologiques douées de continuité genetique. Colloq. Intern. Centre Natl. Rech. Sci. (Paris) 8:33-34.
Denyer, W. B. G. (1960). Can. J. Botany 38:909-920.
Dobbs, C. G., and W. H. Hinson. (1953). Nature 172:197-199.
Dobbs, C. G., W. H. Hinson, and J. Bywater. (1960). In "The Ecology of Soil Fungi" (D. Parkinson and J. S. Waid, eds.), pp. 130-147. Univ. of Liverpool Press, Liverpool.
Dodge, B. O. (1912). Bull. Torrey Botan. 39:139-197.
Doguet, G. (1959). Bull. Soc. Botan. France 106:177-186.
Domsch, K. H. (1954). Arch. Mikrobiol. 20:163-175.
Doran, W. L. (1922). Bull. Torrey Botan. Club 49:313-340.
Duggar, B. M. (1901). Botan. Gaz. 31:38-66.
Dunleavy, J., and G. Snyder. (1963). Proc. 74th Ann. Meeting Iowa Acad. Sci. 69:118-121.
Durbin R. D. (1961). Botan. Rev. 27:522-560.
Elliott, E. W. (1949). Mycologia 41:141-170.
Emerson, M. R. (1954). Plant Physiol. 29:418-428.
Emerson, R. (1950). Ann. Rev. Microbiol. 4:169-200.
Ettel, G. E., and W. Halbsguth. (1963). Beitr. Biol. Pflanz. 39:451-488.
Ezekiel, W. N. (1930). Univ. Minn., Agr. Expt. Sta., Tech. Bull. 67:1-62.
Ferguson, M. C. (1902). U. S. Dept. Agr., Bur. Plant Industry Bull. 16:1-40.
Fischer, G. W. (1951). "The Smut Fungi," 387 pp. Ronald Press, New York.
Forsyth, F. R. (1955). Can. J. Botany 33:363-373.
Frear, D. S. (1960). N. Dakota Farm Res. 21:18-20.
French, R. C. (1961). Botan. Gaz. 122:194-198.
French, R. C., and R. L. Weintraub. (1957). Arch. Biochem. Biophys. 72:235-237.
French, R. C., L. M. Massey, Jr., and R L. Weintraub. (1957). Plant Physiol. 32:389-393.

Fries, N. (1943). *Symbolae Botan. Upsalienses* **6**:1-81.
Fries, N. (1948). *Physiol. Plantarum* **1**:330-341.
Garrett, S. D. (1956). "Biology of Root Infecting Fungi," 292 pp. Cambridge Univ. Press, London and New York.
Gassner, G., and E. Niemann. (1954). *Phytopathol. Z.* **21**:367-394.
Gäumann, E. A. (1950). "Principles of Plant Infection," 543 pp. Crosby, Lockwood, London.
Goddard, D. R. (1935). *J. Gen. Physiol.* **19**:45-60.
Goddard, D. R. (1939). *Cold Spring Harbor Symp. Quant. Biol.* **7**:362-376.
Goddard D. R., and P. E. Smith. (1938). *Plant Physiol.* **24**:241-264.
Gottlieb, D. (1950). *Botan. Rev.* **16**:229-257.
Gottlieb, D., and P. G. Caltrider. (1963). *Nature* **197**:916-917.
Gregory, P. H. (1961). "The Microbiology of the Atmosphere," 251 pp. Wiley (Interscience), New York.
Gwynne-Vaughan, H. C. I., and H. S. Williamson. (1933). *Brit. Mycol. Soc. Trans.* **18**:127-134.
Hahne, J. (1925). *Kuehn-Arch.* **9**:157-163.
Halbsguth, W., and H. Rudolph. (1959). *Arch. Mikrobiol.* **32**:296-308.
Hashimoto, T., S. F. Conti, and H. B. Naylor. (1958). *J. Bacteriol.* **76**:406-416.
Hawker, L. E. (1950). "Physiology of Fungi," 360 pp. Oxford Univ. Press (Univ. London), London and New York.
Hawker, L. E. (1957). *Symp. Soc. Gen. Microbiol.* **7**:238-258.
Hawker, L. E., and P. M. Abbott. (1963). *J. Gen. Microbiol.* **32**:295-298.
Hawker, L. E., and R. J. Hendy. (1963). *J. Gen. Microbiol.* **33**:43-46.
Hebert, T. T., and A. Kelman. (1958). *Phytopathology* **48**:102-106.
Henney, H., and R. Storck. (1963a). *Science* **142**:1675-1676.
Henney, H., and R. Storck. (1963b). *J. Bacteriol.* **85**:822-826.
Henney, H., and R. Storck. (1964). *Proc. Natl. Acad. Sci. U.S.* **51**:1050-1055.
Hill, E. P., and A. S. Sussman. (1964). *J. Bacteriol.* **88**:1556-1566.
Holton, C. S. (1943). *Phytopathology* **33**:732-735.
Holton, R. W. (1960). *Plant Physiol.* **35**:757-766.
Hoshino, J. (1961). *Ann. Rept. Inst. Food Microbiol., Chiba Univ.* **14**:53-58.
Hoshino, J., A. Nishi, and T. Yanagita. (1962). *J. Gen. Appl. Microbiol.* **8**:233-245.
Ishii, R., and T. Miyamoto. (1954). *J. Ferment. Technol.* **22**:276-278.
Ishikawa, T. (1962). *Neurospora Newsletter* **2**:19.
Jackson, R. M. (1960). *In* "The Ecology of Soil Fungi" (D. Parkinson and J. S. Waid, eds.), pp. 168-176. Univ. of Liverpool Press, Liverpool.
Jahn, E. (1905). *Ber. Deut. Botan. Ges.* **23**:489-497.
Kastings, R., A. J. McGinnis, and W. C. Broadfoot. (1959). *Nature* **184**:1943.
Keilin, D. (1959). *Proc. Roy. Soc.* **B150**:149-192.
Kneebone, L. R. (1950). Dissertation, Pennsylvania State College, State College, Pennsylvania.
Kordes, H. (1923). *Botan. Arch.* **3**:282-311.
Kornfeld, J. M., and S. G. Knight. (1962). *Mycologia* **54**:407-414.
Kramer, C. L., S. M. Pady, C. T. Rogerson, and L. G. Ouye. (1959). *Trans. Kansas Acad. Sci.* **62**:184-199.
Kreitlow, K. W. (1943). *Phytopathology* **33**:1055-1063.
Lamanna, C. (1952). *Bacteriol. Rev.* **16**:90-93.
Lees, A. D. (1961). Discussion, *in* "Cryptobiotic Stages in Biological Systems" (N. Grossowicz, S. Hestrin, and A. Keynan, eds.), pp. 132-143. Elsevier, Amsterdam.

Le Roux, P. M., and J. G. Dickson. (1957). *Phytopathology* **47**:101-108.
Lewis, J. C., N. S. Snell, and H. K. Burr. (1960). *Science* **132**:544-545.
Lilly, V. G., and H. L. Barnett. (1951). "Physiology of the Fungi," 464 pp. McGraw-Hill, New York.
Lingappa, B. T. (1963). Unpublished data.
Lingappa, B. T., and J. L. Lockwood. (1961). *J. Gen. Microbiol.* **26**:473-485.
Lingappa, B. T., and J. L. Lockwood. (1963). *Phytopathology* **53**:529-531.
Lingappa, B. T., and A. S. Sussman. (1959). *Plant Physiol.* **34**:466-472.
Lingappa, Y., and A. S. Sussman. (1959). *Am. J. Botany* **46**:671-678.
Lovett, J. S. (1963). *J. Bacteriol.* **85**:1235-1246.
Lowry, R. J., and A. S. Sussman. (1965). In press.
Lowry, R. J., A. S. Sussman, and B. von Böventer-Heidenhain. (1956). *Mycologia* **48**:241-252.
Lowther, C. V. (1948). *Phytopathology* **38**:309-310.
Macfarlane, I. (1952). *Ann. Appl. Biol.* **39**:239-256.
Machlis, L., and E. Ossia. (1953). *Am. J. Botany* **40**:358-365 and 465-468.
McKay, R. (1935). *Nature* **135**:306-307.
McKay, R. (1939). *J. Roy. Hort. Soc.* **64**:272-285.
McTeague, D. M., S. A. Hutchinson, and R. I. Reed. (1959). *Nature* **183**:1736.
Magie, R. O. (1935). *Phytopathology* **25**:131-159.
Mandels, G. R. (1963). *Ann. N.Y. Acad. Sci.* **102**:724-739.
Mandels, G. R., and R. T. Darby. (1953). *J. Bacteriol.* **65**:16-26.
Mandels, G. R., and A. B. Norton. (1948). *Quartermaster Gen. Lab. Res. Rept., Microbiol. Ser.* **11**:1-50.
Mandels, G. R., H. S. Levinson, and M. T. Hyatt. (1956). *J. Gen. Physiol.* **39**:301-309.
Maneval, W. E. (1922). *Phytopathology* **12**:471-488.
Meiners, J. P., and J. T. Waldher. (1959). *Phytopathology* **49**:724-728.
Melin, E. (1946). *Symbolae Botan. Upsalienses* **8**:1-16.
Miller, J. J. (1959). *Wallerstein Lab. Commun.* **22**:267-328.
Newburgh, R. W., and V. H. Cheldelin. (1958). *J. Bacteriol.* **76**:308-311.
Niederpruem, D. J. (1964). *J. Bacteriol.* **88**:210-215.
Nishi, A. (1961). *J. Bacteriol.* **81**:10-19.
Noble, R. J. (1924). *J. Agr. Res.* **27**:451-489.
Oku, H. (1960). *Plant Cell Biol.* **1**:231-239.
Raeder, J. M., and W. M. Bever. (1931). *Phytopathology* **21**:767-789.
Reisener, H. J., H. R. Goldschmid, G. A. Ledingham, and A. S. Perlin. (1962). *Can. J. Biochem. Physiol.* **40**:1248-1251.
Rudolph, H. (1960). *Planta* **55**:424-437.
Rudolph, H. (1961). *Planta* **57**:284-312.
Schnathorst, W. C. (1959). *Phytopathology* **49**:464-468.
Schopfer, W. H. (1942). *Verhandl. Schweiz. Naturforsch. Ges.* pp. 122-123.
Sempio, C., and M. Castori. (1950). *Riv. Biol.* (Perugia) **42**:287-294.
Shepherd, C. J. (1957). *J. Gen. Microbiol.* **16**:i.
Shu, P., K. G. Tanner, and G. A. Ledingham. (1954). *Can. J. Botany* **32**:16-23.
Sibilia, C. (1930). *Boll. Staz. Regia. Patol. Veg.* **10**:164-190.
Smart, R. F. (1937). *Am. J. Botany* **24**:145-159.
Solomon, E. P., E. M. Johnson, and J. H. Gregg. (1964). *Develop. Biol.* **9**:314-326.
Sommer, L., and W. Halbsguth. (1957). *Forschungsber. Wirtsch. Verkehrsministeriums Nordrhein-Westfalen* No. 411 90 pp. Westdeutscher, Köln.

Sreeramulu, T. (1958). *J. Indian Botan. Soc.* 37:220-228.
Stakman, E. C., and L. M. Hamilton. (1939). *Plant Disease Reptr.* Suppl. 117:69-83.
Staples, R. C., R. Syamananda, V. Kao, and R. J. Block. (1962). *Contrib. Boyce Thompson Inst.* 21:345-362.
Stock, T. (1931). *Phytopathol. Z.* 3:231-239.
Stüben, H. (1939). *Planta* 30:353-383.
Sun, C. Y., and A. S. Sussman. (1960). *Am. J. Botany* 47:589-593.
Sussman, A. S. (1953). *Am. J. Botany* 40:401-404.
Sussman, A. S. (1954). *J. Gen. Physiol.* 38:59-77.
Sussman, A. S. (1961). *Quart. Rev. Biol.* 36:109-116.
Sussman, A. S. (1965a). *In* "Encyclopedia of Plant Physiology" (A. Lang, ed.), Vol. 15, Part 2, pp. 933-1025. Springer, Berlin.
Sussman, A. S. (1965b). *In* "Ecology of Soil-borne Plant Pathogens—Prelude to Biological Control" (K. F. Baker, and W. C. Snyder, eds.), pp. 99-109. Univ. of California Press, Berkeley, California.
Sussman, A. S., and H. O. Halvorson. (1966). "Spores: Their Dormancy and Germination." Harper & Row, New York. In press.
Sussman, A. S., J. R. Distler, and J. S. Krakow. (1956). *Plant Physiol.* 31:126-135.
Sussman, A. S., and B. T. Lingappa. (1959). *Science* 130:1343.
Sussman, A. S., R. J. Lowry, and E. Tyrrell. (1959). *Mycologia* 51:237-247.
Sussman, A. S., and C. L. Markert. (1953). *Arch. Biochem. Biophys.* 45:31-40.
Takebe, I. (1960). *J. Gen. Appl. Microbiol.* 6:83-89.
Takebe, I., and T. Yanagita. (1959). *Plant Cell Physiol. (Tokyo)* 1:17-28.
Terui, G., and T. Mochizuki. (1955). *Technol. Rept. Osaka Univ.* 5:219-227.
Tites, D. (1926). *Bull. Sci. Acad. Royal Belg. Ser. V* 12:545-553.
Turel, F. L. M., and G. A. Ledingham. (1959). *Can. J. Microbiol.* 5:537-545.
Van Sumere, C. F., C. Van Sumere-de Preter, L. C. Vining, and G. A. Ledingham. (1957). *Can. J. Microbiol.* 3:847-862.
Voelz, H., and D. J. Niederpreum. (1964). *J. Bacteriol.* 88:1497-1502.
von Güttenberg, H. V., and I. Strutz. (1952). *Arch. Mikrobiol.* 17:189-198.
von Stosch, H. A. (1935). *Planta* 23:623-656.
Warcup, J. H. (1957). *Soils Fertilizers* 20:1-5.
Warcup, H. H. (1960). *In* "The Ecology of Soil Fungi" (D. Parkinson and J. S. Waid, eds.), pp. 3-21. Univ. of Liverpool Press, Liverpool.
Welsford, E. (1907). *New Phytologist* 6:156-161.
White, G. A., and G. A. Ledingham. (1961). *Can. J. Botany* 39:1131-1148.
White, G. A., and F. G. Smith. (1961). *Nature* 190:187-189.
Wilson, E. M. (1958). *Phytopathology* 48:595-600.
Winter, A. G. (1955). *Z. Pflanzenernaehr. Dueng. Bodenk.* 69:224-237.
Wolf, F. A., and F. T. Wolf. (1947). "The Fungi," Vol. II, 538 pp. Wiley, New York.
Wood-Baker, A. (1955). *Brit. Mycol. Soc. Trans.* 38:291-297.
Yanagita, T. (1955). *Ann. Rept. Inst. Food Microbiol., Chiba Univ.* 8:79.
Yanagita, T. (1957). *Arch. Mikrobiol.* 26:329-344.
Yanagita, T. (1964). *In* "Synchrony in Cell Division and Growth" (E. Zeuthen, ed.), Chapter 14, pp. 391-420. Wiley, New York.
Yanagita, T., I. Takebe, A. Nishi, and N. Shimizu. (1962). *Ann. Rept. Inst. Food Microbiol., Chiba Univ.* 14:47-48.
Zalokar, M. (1959). *Am. J. Botany* 46:555-559.
Zimmerman, A. (1925). *Centr. Bakteriol., Parasitenk. Abt. II.* 65:311-418.

Author Index

Numbers in italics refer to pages on which the complete references are listed.

A

Abbott, McV. P., 437, *467*
Abbott, P. M., 746, *762*
Abe, S., 214, *229*
Adams, A. M., 366, *369*
Adams, M. S., 256, *272*
Agar, H. D., 57, 195, *206*
Ahmad, M., 474, 491, 496, *504*
Ainsworth, G. C., 181, 182, 201, 202, *206*, 391, *408*
Ajello, L., 300, 301, *330*
Alasoadura, S. O., 390, 391, *408*
Aldrich, H., 213, 214, *230*
Alexander, M., 6, 7, 8, 12, 14, *60*, *61*, 350, *378*
Alexopoulos, C. J., 127, *128*, 212, 214, 217, 219, 220, 222, 224, 225, *230*, *233*, 285, *330*, 340, *369*, 479, *504*
Algranati, I. D., 57, *57*
Allen, J. R., 238, *272*
Allen, P. J., 341, *369*, 737, 738, 740, 748, *760*
Allison, J. L., 740, *761*
Almad, F., 9, 16, *58*
Altman, P. L., 415, *431*
Ames, L. M., 355, *370*, 490, *504*, 556, 557, *559*
Anastassiadis, B., 714, *731*
Andersen, A. L., 455, *467*
Anderson, F. B., 11, 12, 16, *57*
Anderson, J. D., 220, *230*
Anderson, M. L., 260, 263, 264, 267, *281*
Anderson, N. A., 351, *379*
Andes, J. O., 494, *504*
Andrus, C. F., 361, *370*
Antikajian, G., 300, 301, *330*
Arditti-Muchnik, R., 609, *614*
Arima, K., 14, *57*
Arlett, C. F., 621, 636, 652, *657*, *658*
Armstrong, J. J., 348, *370*
Arnow, P. M., 39, 42, 46, 47, 48, *59*, *60*
Aronescu, A., 357, 358, *370*
Aronson, J. M., 267, *272*, 289, 301, *330*
Arthur, J. C., 733, 738, *760*

Aschan, K., *see* Aschan-Aberg, K.
Aschan-Aberg, K., 396, 397, *408*, 448, 465, 638, *658*
Asthana, R. P., 462, *465*
Atkinson, G. F., 154, *176*, 284, *330*
Atwood, K. C., 571, 572, 579, 580, 582, 586, *587*
Austwick, P. K. C., 711, *729*

B

Bachmann, B. J., 5, 15, 19, 20, 21, 34, 36, 37, 45, 54, 55, *57*
Backus, E. J., 556, *559*
Backus, M. P., 356, 363, *370*, 428, *431*, 489, 500, *504*, 528, *559*
Bacon, E. L., 47, *58*
Bacon, J. S. D., 8, 11, *57*
Bacon, S. S., 47, *58*
Badcock, E. C., 388, *408*
Bainbridge, B. W., 609, *614*
Bajaj, V., 348, *370*
Baker, E. E., 202, *206*
Baker, G. E., 342, *370*
Baker, K., 743, *760*
Baker, R., 354, *370*
Baker, R. D., 182, *206*
Baker, R. E. D., 446, 452, *465*
Bakerspigel, A., 555, 558, *559*, 565, 668, 675, *705*, *705*
Bakshi, B. K., 361, *370*, 713, *729*
Bakshi, K., 454, *465*
Baldwin, H. H., 220, 223, *230*, 368
Balle, S., 558, *564*
Banbury, G. H., 422, *431*, 456, *465*
Bang, Y. N., 14, *60*
Bannerjee, S. N., 454, *465*
Barber, R., 364, *378*
Barbesgaard, P., 358, *370*
Bard, S., 263, *281*
Barksdale, A. W., 289, 299, *330*, 417, 418, 419, *431*, 488, 489, 493, *504*
Barnes, B., 351, *370*

Barnett, H. L., 341, 346, 349, 350, 354, 361, 362, 366, 367, *370, 377, 378*, 394, 402, *408, 410*, 436, 443, 445, 448, 452, 455, 458, 462, *465, 467, 468*, 487, *504*, 733, *763*
Barratt, R. W., 357, *370, 383*, 515, 524, *559*
Barrett, J. T., 301, *330*
Barron, G. L., 125, *128*, 571, *586*, 592, 608, *614*
Barry, E. G., 524, *559*
Bartnicki-Garcia, S., 8, *57*, 196, 198, 199, 200, 201, *206, 368*
Barton, A. A., 194, *206*
Barton, L. V., 758, *760*
Bass, C., 167, *176*
Bassler, L. M., 456, *468*
Basu, S. N., 349, 353, 354, 366, *370, 371*, 441, *465*
Batts, C. C. V., 723, *731*
Bauch, R., 67, *80*, 492, 500, *504*, 665, *675*
Baumann-Grace, J. B., *57*
Baxter, M. G., 492, 493, *509*, 558, *564*, 665, 666, *676*
Bayliss-Elliott, J. S., 681, *705*
Beadle, G. W., 85, 92, *112*, 357, *370*, 569, 570, 572, 579, 580, 584, *586, 588*
Bean, W. J., 368, *370*
Beaufield, V., 364, *378*
Behal, F. J., 350, *370*
Bell, A. A., 741, *760*
Belozerskii, A. N., 348, *377*, 406, *410*
Belozersky, A. N., *see* Belozerskii, A. N.
Benedict, W. G., 215, *230*
Benjamin, R., 740, *760*
Benjamin, R. K., 135, *149*, 487, *504*
Bensaude, M., 167, *176*, 663, *675*
Bent, K. J., 20, *57*
Berg, C. M., 608, *614*
Berliner, M. D., *369*
Bernet, J., 673, *675*
Berry, S. J., 749, 754, *761*
Bessey, E. A., 135, *149*, 340, *370*, 476, *504*
Bevan, E. A., 644, *659*
Bever, W. M., 738, *763*
Bhatnagar, G. M., 341, 342, *371*, 752, *760*
Bhattacharyya, J. P., 349, 353, *370, 371*
Bianchi, D. E., 79, *80*, *369*
Bille-Hansen, E., 396, *408*

Birch, L. C., 293, *330*
Bisby, G. R., 225, *230*, 391, *408*
Bishop, H., 300, *330*, 416, *431*, 488, *504*
Bistis, G. N., 355, 356, 363, 365, *371*, 428, 429, *431*, 483, 490, 493, *504*, 584, *586*, 669, *675*
Blackwell, E. M., 308, *330*, 734, 738, 739, *760*
Blakeslee, A. F., 420, *431*, 480, 481, 501, *505, 510*
Blaskovics, J. C., 246, *272*
Bleul, J., 351, 353, *371*
Block, R. J., 755, *764*
Blodgett, E. C., 452, *465*
Blodgett, E. W., 356, *371*
Blondel, B., 288, 289, 306, *330*
Bloom, B. A., 261, *281*, 521, 524, *563*
Blumenthal, H. J., 68, *81*, 754, *760*
Blumer, S., 392, *411*, 479, *510*, 558, 565
Bock, K. R., 700, *705, 707*, 712, *731*
Boam, T. B., 607, *614*
Bohn, W., 558, *559*
Boidin, J., 491, *505*
Bole-Gowda, B. N., 520, *559*
Bommer, C., 84, 98, 107, *109*
Bonar, L., 452, *468*
Bonner, D. M., 5, 15, 19, 20, 21, 34, 36, 37, 45, 54, 55, *57*
Bonner, J. T., 220, *232, 236*, 238, 239, 240, 241, 243, 244, 245, 246, 247, 248, 250, 252, 254, 256, 262, *272, 273, 278*, 391, 393, *409*
Boone, D. M., 365, *371*, 556, *562*
Borchert, R., 739, *760*
Borges, W., 77, *82*
Borodulina, U. C., 14, *57*
Borowska, Z., 39, 48, *59*
Borriss, H., 395, *409*
Borrow, A., 91, 92, 93, *109*
Borut, S., 744, *760*
Bossert, W. H., 415, *433*
Boulton, A. A., 41, *57*
Bowers, W. D., Jr., 195, *207*
Bowman, D. H., 452, *465*
Boyd, A. E. W., 740, *760*
Boyd, D. H., 494, *509*
Boyer, G., 119, *130*
Brachet, J., 205, *206*
Brack, A., 394, *410*

Bradley, S. G., 236, *273*, *279*
Brandt, W. H., 346, *369*, *371*
Braude, A. I., 204, *207*
Braunitzer, G., 422, *432*
Brawner, T. C., 575, 580, *587*
Brefeld, O., 97, 100, 102, 106, 107, 108, *109*, 352, *371*, 430, *431*
Brenner, S., *57*
Bretzloff, C. W., 344, 362, 367, *371*, 556, *559*
Brian, P. W., 20, *57*, 343, *371*, 744, *761*
Brierley, W. B., 122, *128*, 343, *371*, 739, *761*
Bright, I. B., 455, *465*
Broadfoot, W. C., 754, *762*
Brock, T. D., 5, 49, *58*, 65, *80*, 364, *369*, *371*
Brodie, A. F., 190, *206*
Brodie, H. J., 403, *409*, 478, *505*, 701, 705, 712, 729, 740, *761*
Bromfield, K. R., 743, *761*
Bronsweig, R. D., 247, 260, 265, *275*
Brooks, F. T., 368, *370*
Brooks, W. E., 365, *374*
Brown, A. H. S., 94, *109*
Brown, D. H., 316, *330*
Brown, S., 91, *109*
Brown, W., 85, 88, 90, *109*, 441, 455, *465*, *466*, 737, *761*
Brühmüller, M., 263, 265, *273*, *281*
Brues, C. T., 711, *729*
Brunswik, H., 491, 492, *505*, 558, *559*
Bryan, G. W., 595, *614*
Buchwald, N. F., 698, *705*
Budd, K., 344, *371*
Bufton, A. W. J., 590, *616*
Bullen, J. J., 185, *206*
Buller, A. H. R., 86, 89, 90, 99, 108, *109*, 170, *176*, 240, *273*, 388, 393, 394, 398, 400, 404, 407, 408, *409*, 422, *431*, 459, *466*, 489, 490, 491, 500, *505*, *506*, 556, 557, *559*, 560, 568, *586*, 680, 682, 689, 690, *705*, 709, *729*
Bunce, M. E., 700, *706*, 714, *730*
Burgeff, H., 420, *431*, 501, *505*, 554, *559*, 569, 572, 584, *586*
Burger, M., 47, *58*
Burgert, I. A., 341, *371*
Burkholder, P. R., 91, 92, *109*, 188, *206*
Burnett, J. H., 474, 496, *505*, 662, *675*

Burns, J. A., 72, 73, *80*
Burr, H. K., 740, *763*
Buston, H. W., 354, *371*, *372*
Butler, E. E., 344, *372*
Butler, E. J., 301, 308, *330*
Butler, G. M., 85, 86, 87, 88, 93, 96, 97, *109*, 388, 389, *409*
Buxton, E. W., 585, *586*, 608, 613, *614*
Bywater, J., 743, *761*

C

Cabid, E., 57, *57*
Cadman, E., 214, 215, *230*, *233*
Cailleux, R., 394, *410*
Cain, R. F., 119, 122, *128*, 135, *149*
Callaway, J. L., 182, *206*
Callow, D. S., 91, *111*
Calpouzos, L., 354, *372*
Caltrider, P. G., 108, *109*, 752, 753, *762*
Calvet, J., 15, 19, *59*
Camici, L., 91, *110*
Cammack, R. H., 727, *729*
Campbell, A. H., 102, 105, *110*
Campbell, A. M., 548, *559*
Campbell, C. C., 186, *206*
Campbell, R. N., 361, *372*
Canter, H. M., 293, *330*
Cantino, E. C., 286, 288, 289, 290, 292, 293, 301, 303, 304, 305, 306, 310, 311, 313, 314, 315, 316, 317, 318, 319, 320, 321, 322, 324, 325, 326, 327, 328, 329, *330*, *331*, *332*, *333*, *334*, *335*, *336*, 359, *372*, 436, 454, *466*, 486, *505*, 738, 739, *761*
Capon, B., 595, *614*
Caretta, G., 125, *128*
Carilli, A., 91, *110*
Carlile, M. J., 93, 94, *110*, 345, 346, 347, 351, 368, *368*, *372*, 436, 441, *466*, *467*
Carminatti, H., 57, *57*
Carpenter, J. B., 697, *705*
Carr, A. J. H., 362, 365, *372*, 495, *505*, 556, *559*
Carroll, G., 227, 228, *230*
Carter, H. P., 10, 14, *58*
Carter, W., 711, *729*
Case, M. E., 530, 532, 533, 535, 536, 537, 545, 546, 547, *560*, 607, *614*
Caspari, E., 656, *658*
Castori, M., 737, *763*

Catcheside, D. G., 491, *505*
Chadefaud, M., 137, 146, *149*, 340, 365, 367, *372*
Chain, E. B., 91, *110*
Chaix, P., 42, *59*
Chamberlain, A. C., 718, 721, *729*
Chamberlain, D. W., 740, *761*
Chaudhuri, S. D., 439, 441, 442, *467*
Cheal, W. F., 445, *466*
Cheldelin, V. H., 754, *763*
Cheng, S. C., 753, *761*
Chester, K. S., 726, *729*
Chester, V. E., 75, 76, *80*
Chesters, C. G. C., 141, *149*
Chevaugeon, J., 85, *110*, 342, *372*, 638, *658*
Chèvremont, M., 641, *658*
Chilton, S. J. P., 494, *506*, 556, *560*, *563*
Chimènes, A. M., 78, *81*
Chin, B., 350, *372*
Chinn, S. H. F., 33, *58*
Chiquoine, A. D., 244, 245, 247, 248, 252, 254, *273*
Chodat, F., 307, *332*
Christenberry, G. A., 459, *466*
Christensen, J. J., 479, *505*, 558, *566*
Christie, T., 293, *332*
Christopher, W. N., 723, *732*
Chung, C. W., 190, *208*
Chung, K. L., 195, *206*
Cienkowski, L., 214, *230*
Cihlar, C., 226, *230*
Cirillo, V. P., 47, 48, *58*
Clark, D. S., 91, 92, *110*
Claussen, P., 487, 501, *505*
Clegg, J. S., 265, *273*
Clinton, G. P., 554, *560*, 713, *729*
Clutterbuck, A. J., 591, 594, 610, *614*
Cochrane, J. C., 749, 754, *761*
Cochrane, V. W., 91, *110*, 289, *332*, 340, 341, 343, 367, *372*, *385*, 436, *466*, 733, 749, 754, *761*
Cocking, E. C., 16, 17, 29, 38, *58*
Coker, W. C., 298, *332*, 483, 484, *505*
Coles, R. S., Jr., 749, *761*
Collins, A. E., 352, *373*
Collins, C. B., 749, 754, *761*
Collins, O. R., 212, 214, *230*
Colson, B., 356, *372*, 557, *560*
Coman, D. R., 240, 255, *273*

Combépine, G., 359, *384*
Conant, N. F., 182, 186, *206*
Connell, C. H., 67, *80*
Conti, S. F., 49, *58*, 365, *369*, *372*, 746, *762*
Converse, J. L., 352, *372*
Cooke, W. B., 118, 119, *128*
Coonradt, V. L., 569, 570, 572, 580, 584, *586*
Coons, G. H., 454, 459, *466*
Cooper, A. H., 48, *58*
Corner, E. J. H., 101, 104, 107, *110*, 134, 147, *149*, 152, 154, 175, *176*, 367, *372*, 387, 391, 403, *409*
Couch, J. N., 298, 301, 308, *332*, 416, *431*, 479, 480, 486, 488, 500, *505*
Cox, B. S., 651, *658*
Cox, V. J., 121, *129*, 697, *706*
Coy, C. E., 342, *381*
Coy, D. O., 582, 583, *588*, 608, *617*
Coyle, M. B., 527, *560*
Craigie, J. H., 489, 500, *505*, 557, *560*, 662, *675*, 712, 723, 724, 726, *729*
Crasemann, J. M., 286, 305, 311, *332*, *335*, 553, *563*
Croft, J. H., 621, 653, 654, 655, *658*
Crook, E. M., 6, 8, *58*
Crosier, W., 554, *560*, *564*
Crowe, T. J., 712, *729*
Cummins, G. B., 557, *561*
Curran, G. C., 723, *732*
Curtis, C. R., 368
Curtis, N. S., 72, 75, *80*
Curtis, P. J., 343, *371*
Cutter, V. M., Jr., 357, *383*, 553, 554, 557, *560*, *566*

D

Dacosta, E. W. B., 388, *412*
Dainko, J. L., 5, 15, 25, 36, 37, 39, 43, 47, *61*
Dale, E., 353, *372*
Damle, S. P., 348, *370*
Dangeard, P. A., 353, 362, 367, *372*
Daniel, J. W., 220, 222, *230*
Daniel, L. E., 349, *374*
Darby, R. T., 340, 342, *378*, 745, 748, 758, *763*
Dark, F. A., 57
DasGupta, A., 353, *372*

Davey, C. B., 289, 292, 299, *335*
Davidoff, F., 268, *273*
Davies, M. E., 293, *332*
Davies, R., 11, *58*
Davies, R. R., 723, *729*
Davis, B. D., 387, 407, *409*
Davis, R. H., 549, *560*, 572, 579, 580, 581, *586*, *586*
Davis, W. H., 733, *761*
Dawid, W., 422, *432*
Day, P. R., 352, *374*, 492, 493, *505*, 514, 558, *560*, *561*, 568, 577, 583, *587*, *588*, 628, *658*
Dayal, R., 292, *332*
de Bary, A., 83, 94, 95, 97, 100, 102, 104, 105, 107, 108, *110*, 196, *207*, 225, *230*, 416, *431*, 733, *761*
de Bruyn, H. L. G., 488, *505*, *506*
Dee, J., 214, 215, *230*
De Haan, R. L., 258, *273*
Deighton, F. C., 121, *128*
Dekker, J., 20, *58*
De Kloet, S. R., 48, *58*
de la Fuente, G., 47, *59*
Delbrück, M., 592, *615*, 743, *761*
Delp, C. J., 341, *372*
Denny, F. E., 360, 367, *373*, 454, 455, *466*
Denyer, W. B. G., 388, *409*, 760, *761*
Derx, H. G., 689, *705*
Desmazières, J. B. H. J., 126, *128*
de Terra, N., 19, *58*
De Vries, G. H., 116, 117, *128*
Dhillon, T. S., 570, *587*
Dick, E. A., 173, *177*
Dick, S., 584, *586*
Dickens, J. S. W., 94, *110*
Dickerson, A. G. F., 342, 348, *379*
Dickson, H., 638, *658*
Dickson, J. G., 740, *763*
Diddens, H. A., 66, *80*
Dillon Weston, W. A. R., 445, *466*
Dion, W. M., 91, *110*
Distler, J. R., 345, *382*, 742, 753, *764*
Dittmer, D. S., 415, *431*
Dixon, P. A., 454, 465, 479, *506*, 701, *705*
Dobbs, C. G., 711, *729*, 737, 743, 744, *761*
Dobzhansky, T., 586, *586*

Dodd, M. R., 239, 240, *272*
Dodge, B. O., 225, *231*, 343, 353, 355, 356, 357, 358, 359, 363, 365, *373*, *381*, 428, *431*, 489, 490, 500, 501, *506*, *510*, 557, *560*, 569, *586*, 663, 667, 668, *675*, 689, *705*, 733, 736, *761*
Dodge, C. W., 473, *507*
Doguet, G., 743, *761*
d'Oliviera, B., 628, *658*
Domnas, A., 318, *332*
Domsch, K. H., 738, 740, *761*
Donk, M. A., 165, 167, 168, 169, 175, *176*
Doran, W. L., 341, *373*, 733, 734, *761*
Douglas, H. C., 57, 195, *206*
Douglas, H. W., 352, *373*
Dowding, E. S., 356, 365, *373*, 489, 490, *506*, 557, *560*, 568, *586*, 607, *617*, 668, *675*, 705, *705*
Doyle, W. T., 219, *230*
Drayton, F. D., 487, 489, *506*
Drayton, F. L., 355, *373*, 375
Dring, V. J., 697, *706*
Driver, C. H., 362, 363, *373*
Drouhet, E., 185, *207*
Duckworth, R. B., 92, *110*
Duell, E. A., 38, 42, *58*
Duggar, B. M., 733, 737, *761*
Dukmo, H., 49, *61*
Dunleavy, J., 740, *761*
Dunwell, J. L., 9, 16, *58*
Durbin, R. D., 758, *761*
Durkee, Th., *369*
Dutta, S. K., 243, *277*, 607, *614*
Dykstra, R., 227, 228, *230*

E

Eakin, R. E., 350, *370*
Eberhardt, B. M., *369*
Ebert, J. D., 269, *273*
Eddy, A. A., 3, 15, 16, 19, 36, 37, 41, 43, 45, 50, 51, *57*, *58*, 71, 72, 73, 74, 75, *80*, *81*
Edgerton, C. W., 364, *384*, 494, *506*, 556, *560*, *563*, *566*
Edwards, G. A., 182, 184, 202, *208*
Eger, G., 393, *409*
Eggins, H. O. W., *368*
Eggman, L., 220, *232*, 233
Ehrlich, H. G., 558, *560*

Eichenmuller, J. J., 554, *565*
Eilers, F. I., 344, *371*
Eisenberg, G. M., 352, *380*
Eisman, P. C., 203, *207*
El-Ani, A. S., 366, *373*, 484, 487, 495, *506*, 530, 531, 535, 536, 537, 540, 541, 547, 550, 555, 556, *560*, 562, *563*
Elbers, P. F., 32, *58*
Eldredge, D., Jr., 262, *272*
Ellingboe, A. H., 477, 492, 493, *506*, *509*, 666, *676*
Elliott, C. G., 595, *614*
Elliott, E. W., 212, *231*, 737, *761*
Ellis, M. B., 121, 124, 126, *128*
Elorza, M. V., 53, *58*
Elvin, P. A., 11, *58*
Emberger, L., 146, *149*
Emerson, M. R., 15, 19, 21, 36, 43, 45, 53, *58*, 343, 344, *373*, 747, *761*
Emerson, R., 85, *110*, 286, 298, 303, 304, 309, 310, 311, *332*, *333*, 426, *431*, 454, *466*, 479, 483, 484, 486, 495, 500, *506*, 550, 553, *561*, 733, *761*
Emerson, S., 15, 19, 21, 36, 43, 45, 53, *58*, 91, *110*, 522, 527, 535, 548, 555, *561*
Emmons, C. W., 136, *149*, 352, 353, *373*
Engelmann, C., 355, 365, *380*, 490, *510*, 557, *564*, 582, *588*, 667, *676*
England, D. J. F., 342, 348, 349, *370*, *379*
English, H., 717, *729*
Ennis, H. L., 240, 251, 257, *273*
Ephrussi, B., 78, *81*, 555, *561*, 620, 621, 630, 631, 632, 640, 648, *658*, *660*
Ernest, C. T., 364, *384*, 556, *566*
Erwin, D. C., 293, *333*
Eschenbecker, F., 77, 78, *81*, *82*
Esser, K., 355, 362, 364, 365, *373*, *374*, 474, 484, 487, 493, 495, 496, *506*, *507*, 662, 663, 664, 666, 668, 669, 670, 671, 673, 674, *675*, *676*
Ettel, G. E., 741, *761*
Etzhold, H., 350, *374*
Evans, M. M., 342, *374*
Ezekiel, W. N., 738, *761*

F

Falck, R., 98, 100, 101, *110*, 389, *409*, 683, *705*

Falcone, G., 11, *60*, 67, *81*, *82*, 192, 193, 194, 200, 203, *207*, *208*
Fantini, A. A., 362, *380*, 608, 612, *614*
Faulkner, B. M., 621, 655, *658*
Faull, J. H., 365, *374*
Faulwetter, R. C., 715, *729*
Faust, R. G., 264, *273*
Fayod, V., 154, *176*
Fennell, D. I., 239, 265, 277, 570, 571, *588*
Ferguson, M. C., 710, *730*, 733, *761*
Fikry, A., 350, *374*
Filosa, M. F., 241, 251, 264, 265, *273*, *274*, *280*
Fincham, J. R. S., 352, *374*, 514, *561*, 577, *587*
Fischer, G. W., 733, *761*
Fisher, H. W., 246, *277*
Fitzgerald, P. H., *369*
Fitz-James, P. C., *58*
Flason, E. H., 73, *82*
Fleetwood-Walker, P. M., 293, *333*
Flentje, N. T., 88, *110*
Fling, M., 358, *376*
Foley, J. M., 305, *333*
Folkes, B. F., 436, 451, *467*
Forbes, E., 594, 600, 603, 606, 607, *614*, *616*
Forster, C. L., 366, *374*
Forsyth, F. R., 740, *761*
Foster, J. W., 14, *58*, 93, *110*, 196, *207*, 349, 367, *374*, *375*
Fothergill, P. G., 293, *333*
Fowell, R. R., 366, *374*
Fowler, M. E., 712, *730*
Fox, D. L., 303, *333*
Fracker, S. B., 710, *730*
Francis, D. W., 239, *274*
Franke, G., 490, *507*, 667, *675*
Frascella, E. B., 243, 244, 248, *272*
Fraser, H. C. I., 365, *374*
Fratello, B., 607, *614*
Frauenstein, K., 354, *374*
Frear, D. S., 750, *761*
Freese, E., 534, *561*
Freifelder, D., 194, *207*
French, R. C., 737, 738, *761*
Frey, R., 6, *58*
Friend, J., 368, *372*

Author Index

Fries, N., 350, 357, *374*, 492, *507*, 733, 741, *762*
Friis, J., 47, *58*
Fu, F. L., 241, *280*
Fujumoto, J., 10, 13, 19, *61*
Fuller, M. S., 289, 291, 301, *333*, *335*
Funk, A., 143, *149*
Furcolow, M. L., 725, *730*
Furuya, A., 7, 17, *58*

G

Gabriel, O., 367, *379*
Gaertner, A., 289, 290, *333*
Gäumann, E. A., 135, 149, *149*, 340, 362, *374*, 387, *409*, 473, *507*, 711, *730*, 744, *762*
Gale, E. F., 185, *207*
Gale, G. R., 42, *58*
Galindo, J. A., 554, *561*
Gallegly, M. E., 554, *561*, *565*
Galleymore, H. B., 393, 398, *409*
Gandy, D. G., 644, *658*
Gans, M., 665, *676*
Garay, A. S., 346, *374*
Garber, E. D., 570, 582, *587*, *588*, 595, 607, 608, 609, *614*, *617*
Garcia Acha, I., 5, 8, 10, 15, 16, 17, 18, 19, 21, 28, 29, 33, 35, 37, 39, 45, 46, 49, *58*, *59*, *60*, *61*
Garcia Mendoza, C., 4, 5, 10, 15, 16, 18, 20, 25, 31, 33, 40, 51, *59*, *62*
Garner, H. R., 7, *59*
Garnjobst, L., 357, *370*, 515, 524, *559*, 575, *587*, *588*, 611, *614*
Garrett, S. D., 94, 95, 96, 97, 101, *110*, 389, *409*, 711, *730*, 735, 743, 744, 760, *762*
Garzuly-Janke, R., 200, *207*
Gascón, S., 9, 10, 11, 12, 14, 17, 21, 27, 28, 30, 37, 45, *59*, *60*
Gasic, G., 258, *274*
Gasic, T., 258, *274*
Gasperini, G., 14, *59*
Gassner, G., 736, 737, *762*
Gattani, M. L., 33, *59*
Gebhardt, L. P., 204, *207*
Geftic, S. G., 203, *207*
Gehenio, P. M., 214, *231*
Gehrig, R. F., 350, *374*
Gerhardt, F., 717, *729*

Gerhardt, P., *57*
Gerisch, G., 240, 244, 251, 256, 258, 259, *274*
Geys, K., 73, *81*
Gezelius, K., 236, 252, 254, 263, 265, *274*
Giaja, J., 3, 16, *59*
Gibor, A., 641, *658*
Gibson, A., 633, 636, *658*
Gilbert, H. C., 211, 212, 215, *231*
Giles, N. H., 530, 532, 533, 535, 545, 546, 547, *560*, 607, *614*
Gillett, W. A., 613, *615*
Gilliland, R. B., 71, 72, 73, 74, 76, *81*
Gillmor, R. G., 240, 241, *273*
Girbardt, M., 5, *59*, 366, *374*
Glassey, M., 521, 524, *563*
Glen-Bott, J. I., 454, *466*
Glynne, M. D., 702, *705*
Goddard, D. R., 343, 344, *374*, 742, 743, 747, *748*
Goldschmid, H. R., 749, 754, *763*
Goldstein, A., 288, 314, 315, 317, 318, 322, 324, 325, 326, *331*, *333*
Goldstein, S., 290, 291, *333*
Goldstone, E., 238, *272*
Goodwin, D. C., 225, 226, *231*
Goos, R. D., 97, 100, *110*, 116, 118, 119, 120, 121, 128, *128*, 355, *375*
Gordee, R. S., 106, 108, *110*
Gots, J. S., 190, *206*
Gottlieb, D., 341, *375*, 733, 752, 753, *762*
Gough, F. J., 554, *565*
Gräntz, F., 450, *466*
Granick, S., 641, *658*
Grant, H., 528, 529, *561*
Gray, W. D., 223, *231*
Green, E., 454, *466*
Gregg, J. H., 236, 245, 247, 248, 250, 252, 257, 258, 260, 261, 262, 263, 264, 265, 268, 269, 270, *274*, *275*, *279*, 757, *763*
Gregory, P. H., 446, *466*, 693, 700, 701, 702, *705*, *706*, 710, 714, 716, 718, 720, 721, 722, 723, 725, *730*, 759, *762*
Greis, H., 354, 362, *375*, 487, *507*
Gresham, G. A., 204, *207*
Griffin, D. M., 633, 636, *658*
Griffith, F., 589, *614*
Grigg, G. W., 357, *375*, 592, *614*
Grigorakis, L., 120, *128*

Grimstone, A. V., 287, *333*
Grindle, M., 570, 576, 585, *587*, 611, *614*, 620, 621, 632, 633, 636, 652, *657*, *658*
Grobstein, C., 246, *275*
Gross, S. R., 574, *587*
Grove, W. B., 126, *128*
Grover, S., 86, 87, *110*
Groves, J. W., 355, *375*, 487, *506*
Gruen, H. E., 406, *409*
Gueguen, F., 124, *128*
Guerra, P., 65, *81*
Guilliermond, A., 365, *375*, 478, 479, 500, *507*
Gunness, M., 348, *382*
Guthrie, E. J., 700, *706*, 714, *730*
Gutowsky, H. S., 236, *278*
Gutter, Y., 351, *375*
Guttes, E., 215, 221, 224, *231*
Guttes, S., 215, 221, 224, *231*, *232*
Gwynne-Vaughan, H. C. I., 343, 344, 355, *375*, 739, *762*

H

Haagen Smit, A. J., 417, 418, *433*
Hackney, A. L., 263, 264, 268, *275*
Haddad, S. A., 69, *81*
Hadland, S. A., 683, 685, 686, *706*
Hadley, G., 92, 93, *111*, 349, *375*, 441, *466*
Hagen, U., 68, *81*
Hagimoto, H., 406, *410*
Haglund, W. A., 292, *333*
Hahne, J., 737, *762*
Halbsguth, W., 736, 741, 748, 753, *761*, *762*, *763*
Haldane, J. B. S., 589, *614*
Hale, G. W. F., 66, *81*
Hall, J. F., 78, *81*
Hall, M. P., 458, *466*
Halpin, J. E., 351, *377*
Halvorson, H. O., 758, 759, 760, *764*
Hamilton, E., 79, 80, *81*
Hamilton, J. G., 15, 19, *59*
Hamilton, L. M., 759, *764*
Hammarlund, C., 689, *706*
Hanlin, R. T., 145, *149*
Hanna, W. F., 492, *507*, 558, *561*
Hansen, E., 450, *466*
Hansen, E. C., 67, *81*
Hansen, H. N., 351, 352, 367, *375*, *382*, 487, *507*, 569, 572, 584, 585, *587*, 656, *658*
Hanson, A. M., 300, 301, *333*
Harder, R. B., 303, *333*, 479, 486, 500, *507*, 638, *658*
Hardwick, W. A., 367, *375*
Harmsen, L., 101, *111*
Harper, R. A., 225, *231*
Harrar, G., 342, *374*
Harrar, J. G., 712, 726, *732*
Harris, G. C. M., 92, *110*
Harris, M., 621, *658*
Harrison, K. A., 159, *176*
Harrold, C. E., 92, 93, *111*, 349, *375*, 441, *466*
Harsch, M., 48, *58*
Harter, L. L., 351, 361, *370*, *375*
Hartmann, M., 473, 487, *507*
Hashimoto, T., 746, *762*
Haskins, N. A., 119, *128*
Haskins, R. H., 33, *59*, 118, *128*
Hastie, A. C., 608, *614*
Hatch, M. D., 206, *207*
Hatch, W. R., 302, 305, *333*, 553, *561*
Havir, E. A., 223, *233*
Hawirko, R. Z., 195, *206*
Hawker, L. E., 289, *333*, 340, 344, 345, 349, 354, 362, 363, 366, 367, *375*, 392, *410*, 436, 437, 438, 439, 440, 441, 442, 443, 444, 447, 450, 453, 456, 462, 464, 465, *466*, *467*, 733, 735, 741, 746, 759, *762*
Hawn, E. J., 88, *110*
Hawthorne, D. C., 555, *561*
Haxo, F. T., 304, *336*, 361, *375*
Hayduck, F., 72, *81*
Hayes, W., 610, *614*
Heagy, F. C., 593, 594, *615*
Heald, F. D., 714, *730*
Heath, L. A. F., 368
Hebert, T. T., 737, *762*
Hecker, E., 427, *431*
Heftmann, E., 242, *275*
Heick, H. M. C., 42, *59*
Heim, R., 394, *410*, 713, *730*
Hein, I., 83, 99, 100, *111*, 389, *410*
Heineman, H. S., 204, *207*
Heinemann, P., 160, *176*
Hejmánek, M., 347, *376*
Hejmánková-Uhrová, N., 347, *376*

Hemmings, H. G., 343, *371*
Hemmons, L. M., 590, *616*
Henderson, R. M., 368, *376*
Hendy, R. J., 746, *762*
Henney, H., 361, *376*, 755, *762*
Henney, M., 214, *230, 231*
Henriksson, L. E., 367, *376*
Henry, A. W., 723, *732*
Henry, B. W., 455, *467*
Hepden, P. M., 450, 451, 456, 464, *467*
Heredia, C., 47, *59*
Hering, T. F., 94, *111*
Herman, A., 65, *81*
Hertzenberg, L. A., 648, *659*
Hervey, A., 402, *411*
Heslot, H., 362, 365, 366, *376*, 556, *561*
Heway, B. S. A., 28, *60*
Heyman-Blanchet, T., 42, *59*
Hickman, C. J., 29, *59*
Hide, D., 293, *333*
Hiesey, W. M., 288, *333*
Higgins, B. B., 355, *376*
Hill, D. W., 204, *207*
Hill, E. P., 369, 742, 750, 751, *762*
Hillegas, A. B., 300, *334*
Hino, S., 621, *659*
Hinson, W. H., 737, 743, 744, *761*
Hinton, A., 186, *207*
Hiratsuka, Y., 557, *561*
Hirsch, H. E., 487, *507*
Hirsch, H. M., 357, 358, 359, 360, *376, 384*, 451, *467*
Hirschberg, E., 260, 263, 264, *275*
Hirst, J. M., 715, 723, 725, *730*
Hodapp, E. L., 214, 221, *231*
Hoffman, M. E., 241, *272*
Hoffmann-Ostenhof, O., 367, 369, *379*
Hofmann, A., 394, *410*
Hohl, H. R., 236, 238, 246, *275*
Holden, M., 16, *59*
Holliday, R., 537, 544, 549, 558, *561, 562*, 607, 608, *615*
Holling, M., 644, *658*
Holloway, B. W., 575, *587*, 611, *615*
Holmes, F. W., 713, *730*
Holmes, P. K., 749, 754, *761*
Holter, H., 5, 15, 25, 28, 36, 45, 46, 48, 49, 51, *59*
Holton, C. S., 736, 738, *762*

Holton, R. W., 343, 344, *376, 382*, 747, 748, 750, 753, *762*
Hopp, H., 447, *467*
Hopwood, D. A., 610, *615*
Horecker, B. L., *60*
Horenstein, E. A., 289, 304, 305, 314, 316, 317, 318, 322, 327, 328, *331, 332, 334*, 359, *372*
Horikoshi, K., 6, 7, 10, 12, 13, *59*
Horne, A. S., 441, *466, 467*
Horne, R. W., *61*, 200, *208*
Horowitz, N. H., 358, 359, *376*, 537, *562*
Horsfall, J. G., 349, *380*, 713, *732*
Hoshino, J., 342, *376*, 755, 756, *762*
Hostak, M. B., 242, *275*
Hotson, J. W., 103, 105, *111*
Hottinguer, H., 78, *81*, 621, 630, 632, *658*
Hough, J. S., 69, 76, 79, *81*, 82
Houston, B. S., 459, *467*
Howard, F. L., 214, 215, 224, 226, *231*, 250, *275*
Howe, H. B., Jr., 523, 557, *562*
Hrushovetz, S. B., 342, *376*
Hsu, T. C., 517, *565*
Hudson, H. J., 121, *128*
Huebschman, C., 515, *562*, 571, *587*
Hüttig, W., 558, *562*
Huffman, D. M., 243, *275*
Hughes, S. J., 115, 116, 119, 120, 121, 122, 123, 124, 125, 126, *128, 129*, 347, *376*
Humphrey, J. E., 484, *507*
Humphreys, T., 255, *275*
Hungate, M. V. G., 361, *376*
Hutchinson, F., 294, *334*
Hutchinson, J. M., 607, 613, *615*
Hutchinson, S. A., 693, *707*, 738, *763*
Hutner, S. H., 238, *272*
Hutton, K. E., 366, *376*
Hyatt, M. T., 286, 301, 303, 304, 305, 311, 314, 316, 318, 325, *331*, 486, *505*, 745, 748, *763*

I

Ida, S., 10, 12, *59*
Ikeda, Y., 7, 17, *58*, 592, 594, 608, 612, 613, *615, 617*
Imai, T., 10, 17, 37, 43, 46, *61*
Imler, L., 159, *176*
Ingold, C. T., 120, 121, *129*, 351, 365,

376, 393, 407, *410*, 446, 456, *467*, 680, 683, 684, 685, 686, 688, 690, 695, 697, 698, 699, 703, *706*, 711, *730*
Ingram, M., 65, *81*
Inoue, S., 38, 42, *58*
Inouye, T., 714, *731*
Isaac, I., 103, 107, *111*, 345, *376*
Isaac, P. K., 195, *206*
Ishii, R., 736, *762*
Ishikawa, T., 759, *762*
Ishitani, C., 592, 594, 608, 612, 613, *615*, *617*
Islam, M. F., 47, *59*
Ito, T., 358, 366, *376*, 669, *675*

J

Jackson, R. M., 744, *762*
Jacob, F., 404, *410*, 548, *562*
Jacques, J. E., 119, *129*
Jahn, E., 214, 225, *231*, 736, *762*
Jansen, H. F., 72, 73, 74, *81*
Jarvis, W. R., 695, 701, *706*
Jefferys, E. G., 91, 92, 93, *109*
Jerebzoff, S., 351, *377*
Jeunehomme, C., 75, *82*
Jeynes, M. H., *57*
Jinks, J. L., 354, *377*, *378*, 528, 550, *562*, 569, 578, 579, 582, 584, 585, *587*, *588*, 610, *615*, 620, 621, 624, 627, 631, 633, 636, 637, 638, 641, 645, 647, 648, 652, 653, 654, 655, 656, *657*, *659*, 709, *730*
Johnson, D. F., 242, *275*
Johnson, E. M., 264, *279*, 757, *763*
Johnson, T., 557, *562*, 628, *659*
Johnson, T. W., 351, *377*, 744, *760*
Johnston, I. R., 6, 8, *58*
Johnston, J. R., 6, 33, *59*
Johnstone, H. F., 722, *731*
Joly, P., 351, *377*
Jonasson, L., 492, *507*
Jones, F. R., 341, *377*
Jones, R. C., 553, *561*
Jump, J. A., 221, *231*

K

Käfer, E., 555, *564*, 590, 597, 600, 601, 603, 604, 605, 606, 607, 609, *615*, *616*, *617*
Kahn, A. J., 241, 243, 251, *275*, *276*
Kaiser, W. J., 346, *377*
Kandler, O., *57*
Kane, K. K., 391, 393, *409*
Kanouse, B. B., 308, *334*
Kao, V., 755, *764*
Karling, J. S., 300, 301, *334*, 500, *507*
Kastings, R., 754, *762*
Katznelson, H., 293, *333*
Kauffman, C. H., 416, *431*
Kavanaugh, F., 346, *381*, 554, *565*
Keck, K., 329, *334*
Keech, D. B., 42, *62*
Kehl, H., 421, *431*
Keilin, D., 734, *762*
Keitt, G. W., 354, 365, 367, *371*, *377*, 556, *559*, 562, *565*, *566*
Kellenberger, E., 57, 304, *336*
Kelly, C. D., 724, *731*
Kelman, A., 737, *762*
Kelso, A. P., 240, 241, *273*
Kempton, F. E., 127, *129*
Kendrick, W. B., 119, *129*
Kennedy, D., 687, *707*
Kerl, I., 354, 356, *377*
Kerr, N. S., 213, 214, *231*, 241, *280*
Kessell, R. H. J., 91, 92, 93, *109*
Kessler, G., 6, *59*, 192, 200, *207*, *208*
Kevorkian, A. G., 300, *334*
Keyworth, W. G., 447, 456, *467*
Khan, A. H., 354, *372*
Kihara, M., 342, *377*
Kijima, M., 74, *81*
Killian, C., 354, *377*
Killian, K., 556, *562*
Kimball, A. W., 580, *587*
King, T. H., 292, *333*
Kingsolver, C. H., 390, *411*
Kinsky, S. C., 20, 39, 42, 48, 49, 57, *59*, 360, *377*
Kiritani, K., 579, 582, *587*
Kitani, Y., 530, 531, 535, 536, 537, 540, 541, 547, 556, *560*, *562*, *563*
Klebs, G., 298, *334*, 353, 355, 367, *377*, 446, 450, 452, *467*
Klein, D. T., 571, *587*
Kleiner, I. S., 267, *276*
Klieneberger-Nobel, E., *57*
Klinkhammer, F., 305, *334*
Klinkowski, M., 728, *731*
Kneebone, L. R., 733, 736, *762*
Kniep, H., 167, *176*, 301, 302, *334*, 473,

Author Index

478, 479, 492, 497, 500, *507*, 558, *562*, *663*, *675*
Knight, S. G., 348, 350, *372, 374, 382, 753, 762*
Kobel, H., 394, *410*
Koch, R., 68, *81*
Koch, W., 393, 398, 402, *410*
Koch, W. J., 287, *334*
Kodo, S., 74, *81*
Köhler, E., 420, *432*
Köhler, F., 421, 422, *432*
Koevenig J. L., 211, 212, 214, 215, 217, *231*
Koffler, H., 6, 7, *59*
Kogané, F., 89, *112*, 349, *385*
Kolderie, M. Q., 244, 245, 247, 248, 252, 254, *273*
Konijn, T. M., 240, 241, *276*
Koningsberger, V. V., 48, *58, 62*
Konishi, M., 406, *410*
Koontz, P. G., Jr., 239, *273*
Kordes, H., 342, *377*, 749, *762*
Korf, R. P., 104, 107, *111*, 147, *149*
Korn, E. D., 6, *59*, 268, *273*
Kornfeld, J. M., 753, *762*
Kostellow, A. B., 263, 264, *276*
Kouyeas, V., 714, *731*
Kozinn, P. J., 204, *209*
Krafczyk, H., 421, 422, *432*, 501, *508*
Krakow, J. S., 345, *382*, 742, 753, *764*
Kramer, C. L., 725, *731*, 759, *762*
Krause, R., 289, 292, 299, *334*
Kreger, D. R., 6, *59*
Kreger-van Rij, N. J. W., 63, 65, 66, 67, 82, 189, *208*, 712, *731*
Kreitlow, K. W., 736, *762*
Krichevsky, M. I., 265, *276*
Krishnan, P. S., 341, 342, 348, *370, 371*, 753, *760*
Kritskii, M. S., *410*
Krivanek, J. O., 252, 254, 263, 264, 265, 266, 268, 269, *275, 276*
Krivanek, R. C., 252, 254, 266, 269, *276*
Krongelb, G. S., 392, *411*, 492, 494, *509*, 558, *564*, 665, *676*
Krumhaar, H., 72, *82*
Kuehn, H. H., 136, *149, 150*
Kühner, R., 154, 159, 167, *176*
Kuenen, R., 474, 496, *506*, 662, 664, 666, 673, *675*

Kulaev, I. S., 348, *377*, 406, *410*
Kulayev, I. S., *see* Kulaev, I. S.
Kurung, J. M., 186, *207*
Kusano, S., 420, *432*
Kusserow, R., 72, *81*
Kuwana, H., 669, *675*

L

Lacey, M. E., 725, *731*
Lacoste, L., 367, *377*
Laer, H., 73, *81*
Lafferty, H. A., 122, *129*
Lamanna, C., 759, *762*
Lambert, E. B., 456, *467*
Lamedica, G. M., 67, *81*
Lamey, H. A., 554, *565*
Lamoure, D., 668, *675*
Lampen, J. O., 20, 36, 39, 42, 45, 46, 47, 48, 49, 57, *58, 59, 60, 61*
Lander, C. A., 100, *111*
Lange, H., 72, *81*
Lange, M., 160, *176*, 491, *508*
Langeron, M., 86, 94, 96, *111*, 113, 120, *129*
Langeron, N., 65, *81*
Langford, M. H., 556, *562*
Larpent, J. P., 87, 93, *111*
Larsh, H. W., 186, *207*
Laskaris, T., 33, *60*
Laskin, A. I., 39, 48, *59*
Laskowski, W., 621, *659*
Last, F. T., 644, *658*
Lata, M., 360, *381*
Laustsen, O., 491, 500, *511*
Leach, C. M., 351, *369, 377*, 459, *467*
Leach, J. G., 702, *706*, 711, *731*
Leak, L. V., 288, 289, 305, 306, 310, 314, *332*
Leakey, C. L. A., 102, *111*
Leal, J. A., 10, 33, *58, 60*
Lechevalier, H., 189, *209*
Lederberg, J., 580, 581, *588*, 636, *660*
Ledingham, G. A., 737, 741, 747, 748, 749, 750, 754, *763, 764*
Lee, B. T. O., 365, *377*
Lee, F., 238, 241, 251, *279, 280*
Lee, J. J., 238, *272*
Lee, S., 32, *60*
Lees, A. D., 759, *762*
Lefort, C., 638, *658*

Lentz, P. L., 168, 172, 173, *177*
Leonian, L. H., 454, 459, *467,* 488, *508*
Le Roux, P. M., 740, *763*
Leupold, U., 491, *508*
Levenberg, B., 162, *177*
Levene, H., 571, *587*
Levey, R. H., 391, 393, *409*
Levi, J. D., 65, *81,* 364, *377,* 427, *432*
Levine, H. B., 725, *732*
Levine, L., 257, 259, 270, *279*
Levine, S., 67, *81,* 182, *207*
Levinson, H. S., 745, 748, *763*
Levy, J. A., 749, 754, *761*
Lewis, B. G., 347, *372*
Lewis, D., 662, 668, *675*
Lewis, J. C., 740, *763*
Lhoas, P., 607, *615*
Liddel, G. U., 242, 260, 261, *275, 276*
Liddle, L. B., 595, *614*
Lillehoj, E. B., 46, *61*
Lilly, V. G., 341, 346, 349, 350, 354, 361, 362, 366, 367, *370, 377, 378,* 394, 402, *408, 410,* 436, 443, 445, 448, 452, 455, 458, 462, *465, 467, 468,* 733, *763*
Lindeberg, G., 348, *378*
Lindegren, C. C., 14, *60,* 69, 79, 80, *81, 82,* 357, 358, 364, 365, *378,* 489, 491, *508,* 530, 535, 555, *562,* 621, *659*
Lindegren, G., 357, *378,* 491, *508*
Lindner, P., 73, *82*
Lindquist, W., 72, 73, *82*
Lingappa, B. T., 344, *382,* 740, 742, 743, 744, 750, *763, 764*
Lingappa, Y., 745, *763*
Link, G. K. K., 473, *508*
Linnane, A. W., *62*
Linskens, H., 415, *432*
Linton, A. H., 436, *467*
Lippe, T. Z., 402, *410*
Lissouba, P., 530, 531, 532, 533, 535, 537, 556, *562, 564*
Llanos, C. M., 298, *334*
Lloyd, A. G., 10, *60*
Lloyd, D., 308, *334*
Lloyd, E. C., 91, 92, 93, *109*
Lloyd, P. B., 91, 92, 93, *109*
Lockard, J. D., 394, *410*
Lockhart, W. R., 181, *207*
Lockwood, J. L., 10, 14, 33, *58, 60,* 298, *334,* 743, 744, *763*

Lockwood, L. B., 366, *378,* 448, *468*
Lodder, J., 63, 65, 66, *80, 82,* 712, *731*
Loegering, W. Q., 557, *562*
Lövlie, A., 250, *276*
Lohwag, H., 84, 98, 105, 107, 108, *111*
Lohwag, K., 388, *410*
Long, T. J., 397, 398, *410*
Longhurst, T. J., 718, 720, *730*
López-Belmonte, F., 8, 15, 19, 39, 45, 46, 47, 49, *58, 60, 61*
López-Rubira, F., *60*
Lopriore, G., 455, *468*
Loughheed, T. C., 96, *111,* 347, *378*
Lovett, J. S., 288, 289, 305, 306, 310, 311, 314, 315, 317, 318, 320, 321, 322, 324, 326, 327, 329, *331, 332, 334,* 755, *763*
Lovgren, N., 267, *279*
Lowry, R. J., 343, 365, *369, 378,* 737, 739, 746, *763, 764*
Lowther, C. V., 738, *763*
Lu, B. C., 403, *410*
Lucas, G. B., 494, *506,* 556, *560, 563*
Luck, D. J. L., 640, 641, *659*
Lukens, R. J., 368
Lund, J. W. G., 293, *330*
Luria, S. E., 592, *615*
Luttrell, E. S., 137, 141, *150*
Luyet, B. J., 214, *231*
Lwoff, A., 290, *334*
Lythgoe, J., 288, 289, 305, 306, 310, 314, *332,* 457, *468*

M

Ma, R., 361, *381*
Maaschelein, C. A., 75, *82*
McAlear, J. H., 365, *379*
McCallan, S. E. A., 341, *384*
McCarty, M., 14, *60*
McClary, D. O., 189, 195, *207,* 366, *378*
McClintock, B., 364, *378,* 517, 521, 522, 524, *563*
McCormack, H. W., 143, *150*
McCormick, F. A., 713, *729*
McCranie, J., 480, *508*
McCurdy, H. D., Jr., 288, 314, 315, 317, 318, 320, 322, 324, 326, *335*
McCutcheon, M., 240, *276*
Macdonald, J. A., 97, 100, 101, *111*
McDonald, J. E., 722, *731*

Macdonald, K. D., 590, 606, 613, *615*, *616*
McDonough, E. S., 558, *560*
McDonough, M. W., 354, *378*
Macfarlane, I., 453, *468*, 760, *763*
McGahen, J. W., 361, 362, 363, 365, *378*, *384*, 428, *432*, 495, *508*, *511*, 556, *563*, *566*
McGinnis, A. J., 754, *762*
Machlis, L., 91, *111*, 301, 305, 309, 310, *335*, 415, 420, 426, *432*, 495, *508*, 553, *563*, 739, *763*
McKay, R., 735, 739, *763*
McKeehan, M. S., 246, *276*
Mackinnon, J. E., 190, 203, *207*
McLellan, W. L., 48, *60*
Macleod, H., 358, *376*
McManus, S. M. A., 211, 214, 215, 220, *231, 232*
McQuillen, K., 16, 19, 28, 36, 43, 50, *57*, *60*
Macrae, R., 662, *675*
Macrae, R. M., 11, 12, 16, *60*
McTeague, D. M., 738, *763*
Madelin, M. F., 394, 395, *410*
Mader, E. O., 400, *410*
Magie, R. O., 740, *763*
Magrou, J., 347, *378*
Mahadevan, P. R., *369*
Mahoney, M., 620, 632, 633, 636, 651, 653, *659*
Makower, M., 644, *659*
Malamy, M., *60*
Malik, M. M. S., 723, *731*
Malmgren, H., 348, *378*
Mandels, G. R., 340, 341, 342, 343, *378*, 734, 745, 747, 748, 749, 758, *763*
Maneval, W. E., 738, *763*
Mangenot, M. F., 119, 121, 122, *129*
Mankowski, Z. J., 66, *82*, 189, *208*, 264, *276*, 345, *379*
Marcou, D., 628, 638, 654, *659, 660*
Marcovich, H., 621, *659*
Marczynski, R., 396, *410*
Mariat, F., 185, *207*, 347, *378*
Marini, F., 42, 46, 47, *60*
Markert, C. L., 244, *276*, 362, *378*, 382, 428, *432*, 750, 753, *764*
Marneffe, H., 347, *378*
Marsh, P. B., 456, *468*
Marshall, B., 697, 698, 699, *706*
Martin, D. S., 182, *206*
Martin, G. W., 212, 214, 226, *232*, 688, *706*
Martin, H. H., 43, *60*
Maruyama, Y., 350, *378*
Mason, E. W., 113, 117, 118, 119, 120, 121, 122, 127, *129*, 712, *731*
Masschelein, C. A., *60*
Massey, L. M., Jr., 737, 738, *761*
Mather, K., 354, *378*, 494, *508*, 653, 654, 655, *659*
Mathew, K. T., 96, *111*, 389, *410*
Mathieson, M. J., 366, *379*, 495, *508*
Matikian, N., *369*
Matthews, V. D., 303, 308, *335*
Maufang, E., 72, *82*
Maurizio, A., 484, *508*
May, F. G., 722, *731*
Mayer, R. L., 203, *207*
Mehta, K. C., 726, *731*
Meinecke, G., 15, 24, *60*
Meiners, J. P., 737, *763*
Melin, E., 744, *763*
Mendlik, E., 72, 73, 74, *81*
Mercer, E. H., *276*
Meredith, D. S., 121, *129*, 695, 696, *706*
Merson, G., 256, 263, 264, *275*
Metzenberg, R. L., 47, *60*, *62*, 537, *562*
Micheli, P. A., 681, *706*
Michels, M., 361, *380*
Middleton, R. B., 493, *509*, 558, *564*, 577, 583, *587*, 666, *676*
Miles, P. G., 487, 494, *509*, 583, *588*, 666, *676*
Millbank, J. W., 11, 12, 16, *60*
Miller, C. W., 351, *379*
Miller, G. R., 366, *378*
Miller, J. H., 138, 148, *150*
Miller, J. J., 366, 367, *369*, *379*, 380, 383, 759, *763*
Miller, M. W., 595, *614*
Miller, O. K., 159, 166, *177*
Millin, D. J., 48, *58*
Milne, B. D., 8, 11, *57*
Milner, H. W., 288, *333*
Minagawa, T., 361, *379*
Minoura, K., 117, 118, *129*
Mitchell, H. K., 357, 361, *384*, 528, *563*, 620, 628, 629, 648, 650, *659*

Mitchell, M. B., 365, *379*, 527, 528, 530, 532, 534, 548, *563*, 620, 628, 629, 650, *659*
Mitchell, P., 289, *335*
Mitchell, R., 6, 7, 14, *60*
Mitter, J. H., 441, *467*
Mittmann, G., 361, *379*
Miyamoto, T., 736, *762*
Mochizuki, T., 745, 747, 748, *764*
Moewus, F., 214, *232*, 486, *508*
Mohr, H., 329, *335*, 456, *468*
Moldavskaya, E. A., 73, *82*
Monod, J., 404, *410*
Moor, H., 57, *60*
Moore, E. J., 102, 107, 109, *111*, 146, *150*, 354, *379*
Moore, R. H., 20, *57*
Moore, R. T., 365, *379*
Mordue, E. M., 94, *110*, 347, *372*
Moreau, C., 362, *379*
Moreau, F., 113, *129*, 340, 356, 358, 361, *379*
Moreau, M., 353, *379*
Moreau, Mme. F., 340, 356, 361, *379*
Morgan-Jones, J. F., 367, *376*
Morpurgo, G., 607, *614*, *615*
Morris, E. O., 69, 79, *82*
Mortimer, R. K., 33, *59*, 555, *561*
Morton, A. G., 92, *111*, 342, 348, 349, 351, 352, *379*, 454, *468*
Morton, J. A., 348, *370*
Moruzi, C., 358, *379*
Moscona, A., 255, *276*
Mounce, I., 492, *508*
Mousseau, J., 530, 531, 532, 533, 537, 556, *562*, *564*
Moustacchi, E., 621, *659*
Mrak, E. M., 202, *206*, 452, *468*
Mühlethaler, K., 57, *60*, 265, *276*
Müller, D., 690, *706*
Müller, E., 138, 142, *150*, 354, *379*
Mukai, F., 571, *586*
Mukherjee, K. S., 214, *232*
Mulder, E. G., 349, *379*
Mullins, J. T., 486, 487, 489, *508*
Munk, A., 146, *150*
Munson, R. G., 102, 105, *110*
Murphy, P. A., 554, *563*
Murray, J. C., *369*
Murray, N. E., 534, *563*
Murray, T. J., 189, 204, *209*
Myers, F. L., 16, *60*
Myers, W. F., 187, *207*

N

Nakajima, H., 220, *232*
Nakamura, K., 613, *615*
Nakata, K., 346, *379*
Nandi, P. N., 353, *372*
Nannfeldt, J. A., 137, *150*
Nason, A., 360, *379*
Naylor, H. B., 365, *372*, 746, *762*
Necas, O., 15, 42, 46, 47, 50, 51, 53, *60*
Nelson, R. R., 493, *508*
Nesemann, G., 402, *410*
Neufeld, C. C., 740, *761*
Neurath, P. W., *369*
Neveroske, R. L., 10, *60*
Newburgh, R. W., 754, *763*
Newman, I. V., 724, *731*
Newmeyer, D., 524, *559*
Nicholas, D. J. D., 360, *379*, *384*
Nickerson, W. J., 5, 6, 8, 11, *57*, *59*, *60*, 66, 67, *81*, *82*, 182, 184, 189, 190, 191, 192, 193, 194, 195, 196, 198, 199, 200, 201, 202, 203, *206*, *207*, *208*, *209*, 264, 276, 277, 345, 368, 427, 432, 464, *468*
Nicolas, G., 10, *60*
Niederpreum, D. J., 392, 393, *410*, 746, 753, *763*, *764*
Niemann, E., 736, 737, *762*
Nikaido, H., 268, *276*
Nilsson, S., 120, *129*
Nishi, A., 341, 342, 348, *376*, *380*, 755, 757, *762*, *763*, *764*
Nisikado, Y., 714, *731*
Nitimargi, N. M., 441, *468*
Nixon, I. S., 92, 93, *109*
Noble, R. J., 737, 738, *763*
Nobles, M. K., 85, 88, 89, *111*, 478, *508*, 662, *675*
Nobs, M. A., 288, *333*
Norman, A., 515, *563*
North, R. J., *62*
Northcote, D. H., 6, 16, 56, *59*, *60*, 200, *208*
Northover, J., 347, *372*
Norton, A. B., 734, 748, *763*
Nossal, P. M., 42, *62*

Novaes, M., 6, 9, 11, 12, 14, 17, 37, *59*, *60*
Noviello, C., 104, 107, *111*
Novotny, H. M., 361, *380*
Nulty, W. L., 366, *378*
Nutman, F. J., 700, *707*, 712, *731*
Nutting, W. H., 426, *432*
Nygaard, O. F., 221, *232*

O

Ochoa, A. G., 9, 11, 12, 14, 17, 21, 27, 28, 30, 37, 45, *59*, *60*
Oettinger, M. T., 494, *509*, 665, *676*
Ogilvie, L., 445, *468*, 726, *731*
O'Hern, E. M., 28, *60*
Oikawa, K., 668, *675*
Okamoto, Y., 714, *731*
Oku, H., 749, 750, *763*
Olien, C. R., 390, *411*
Olive, E. W., 236, *277*
Olive, L. S., 243, *275*, *277*, 362, 364, 365, 366, *371*, *372*, *373*, *380*, *384*, 484, 495, *505*, *506*, *508*, 517, 530, 531, 535, 536, 537, 540, 541, 547, 550, 555, 556, *559*, *560*, *562*, *563*, *566*, 670, *675*, 690, *707*
Olson, E. O., 495, *508*
Ono, M., 10, 13, 19, *61*
Oort, A. J. P., 558, *563*
Ordal, Z. J., 67, *81*, 182, *207*
Orr, G. F., 136, *150*
Orten, J. M., 267, *276*
Orth, H., 445, *468*
Orton, P. D., 159, *177*
Osborn, M. J., 266, 267, 268, *279*
Ossia, E., 309, *335*, 739, *763*
Oswald, J. W., 459, *467*
Ottolenghi, P., 5, 15, 25, 28, 36, 38, 45, 46, 47, 49, 51, *58*, *59*, *61*
Ouye, L. G., 759, *762*
Owens, R. G., 341, 358, 359, 361, *380*

P

Pady, S. M., 724, 725, *731*, 759, *762*
Page, O. T., 346, *380*
Page, R. M., *368*, 687, *707*
Page, W. M., 355, 365, *380*
Palmiter, D. H., 354, 367, *377*, 556, *562*
Pantidou, M. E., 166, *177*, 387, 388, *411*
Pantin, C. F. A., 287, *335*

Papavizas, G. C., 289, 292, 299, *335*
Papazian, H. P., 392, *411*, 493, 494, *508*, 558, *563*, 638, *659*, 662, 666, *675*
Pappagianis, D., 725, *732*
Parag, Y., 577, *587*
Paravicini, R., 351, *383*
Park, D., 14, *61*, 86, 88, 90, 93, *111*, *112*
Park, J. T., *61*
Parker-Rhodes, A. F., 726, *731*
Parkin, E. A., 713, *731*
Parkinson, D., 352, *373*
Parmeter, J. R., 578, *588*
Pasquill, F., 718, *731*
Pasteur, L., 72, *82*
Pateman, J. A., 365, *377*
Paton, D., 239, *273*
Patouillard, N., 154, *177*
Paul, W. R. C., 346, *380*
Peacock, C. L., 186, 187, 188, *208*
Pease, D. C., 355, *382*
Peiris, J. W. L., 346, *380*, 441, *468*
Perkins, D. D., 520, 521, 524, 556, *559*, *563*
Perkins, H. R., 11, *61*
Perkins, S. M., 450, *467*
Perlin, A. S., 749, 754, *763*
Perrott, P. E., 300, *335*
Petersen, H. E., 284, 308, *335*
Petersen, R. H., 117, 120, 121, *129*
Pethybridge, G. H., 122, *129*, 554, *563*
Pfeffer, W., 240, *277*
Pfutzner-Eckert, R., 246, *277*
Phaff, H. J., 5, 10, 13, 16, 17, *61*
Phillips, W. D., 270, *277*
Piemiesel, R. L., 711, *732*
Pillai, N. C., 348, *380*
Pinckard, J. A., 695, *707*
Pine, L., 186, 187, 188, *208*
Pinto-Lopes, J., 662, *676*
Pirt, S. J., 91, *111*
Pittenger, T. H., 527, *560*, 571, 572, 575, 579, 580, 582, *586*, *587*, 620, 628, 636, 649, *660*
Pittman, D. D., 621, *660*
Plempel, M., 421, 422, *432*
Plomley, N. J. B., 85, 87, 88, 92, 93, *111*
Plunkett, B. E., 97, *112*, 396, 397, 398, 400, 401, 403, *411*, 438, 447, 448, 456, 457, 459, 462, *468*

Pontecorvo, G., 477, 484, 494, *509*, 555, *564*, 570, 571, 573, 579, 580, 581, *587*, 590, 591, 592, 594, 596, 600, 601, 603, 604, 605, 606, 607, 608, 610, 611, 612, *615*, *616*
Porter, C. L., 106, 108, *110*
Potgieter, H. J., 6, 8, 12, *61*
Powers, H. R., Jr., 557, *562*
Prakash, V., 520, 523, *564*
Prescott, D. M., 251, *277*
Preston, R. D., 289, *330*
Prévost, G., 492, 493, *509*
Pritchard, R. H., 599, 605, *616*
Prout, T., 571, *587*
Prud'Homme, N., 665, *676*
Puck, T. T., 246, *277*

Q

Quinlan, M. S., 252, *277*
Quintanilha, A., 558, *564*, 662, *676*

R

Racker, E., 284, *335*
Raeder, J. M., 738, *763*
Rafaeli, D. E., 243, *277*
Rakoczy, L., 223, *232*
Ramakrishnan, K., 126, *130*
Ramalingam, A., 718, 719, 720, *732*
Ramanis, Z., 650, *660*
Ramirez, C., 367, *380*
Ranby, B. G., 265, *274*
Rankin, W. H., 684, *707*
Ranzoni, F. V., 120, *130*
Raper, C. A., 494, *509*, 665, *676*
Raper, J. R., 89, 90, *112*, 355, 358, 363, *371*, *380*, 392, *411*, 415, 416, 417, 418, 428, 429, *431*, *432*, *433*, 443, 461, *468*, 474, 476, 477, 484, 485, 487, 488, 489, 491, 492, 493, 494, 498, 499, *504*, *506*, *508*, *509*, 558, *564*, 568, 570, 571, 576, 577, 583, 584, *586*, *587*, *588*, 662, 665, 666, 669, *675*, *676*
Raper, K. B., 84, *112*, 117, 124, *130*, 236, 238, 239, 240, 241, 242, 246, 247, 248, 252, 256, 258, 265, 268, *272*, *275*, *276*, *277*, *280*, 284, 295, 296, 298, 299, *335*, 353, *383*
Rapoport, H., 426, *432*
Raubitschek, F., 189, *209*

Raut, C., 621, 641, *660*
Rawitscher-Kunkel, E., 415, 420, *432*
Reddick, D., 554, *564*
Reed, R. I., 738, *763*
Rees, H., 578, 579, 582, *588*
Reese, E., 352, *380*
Reese, J. E., 346, *371*
Reich, E., 641, *659*
Reijenders, A. F. M., 152, *177*
Reinhardt, M. O., 342, *380*
Reinsch, P. F., 308, *335*
Reischer, H. S., 453, *468*
Reisener, H. J., 749, 754, *763*
Reisert, P. S., 291, *335*
Reiss, F., 204, *209*
Remsberg, R. E., 105, 106, *112*
Renner, O., 491, *509*
Rettger, L. J., 66, *82*
Revalier, E., 66, *82*
Reynolds, D. M., 10, 12, *61*
Rich, A., 270, *277*
Rich, S., 349, *380*
Rickard, B., 354, *378*
Rippon, J. W., 201, 202, *208*
Ritchie, D., 85, *112*, 362, *380*
Rizet, G., 355, 365, 366, *380*, 490, *510*, 530, 531, 532, 533, 537, 556, 557, *562*, *564*, 582, *588*, 620, 628, 638, *660*, 667, 671, *676*
Robak, H., 125, *130*
Robbins, W. J., 346, 361, *381*, 402, *411*, 448, 453, *468*, 554, *565*
Roberg, M., 349, *381*
Roberts, C. F., 612, *616*
Roberts, F. M., 700, *707*, 712, *731*
Robertson, N. F., 20, 30, *61*, 453, *468*
Robinow, C. F., 43, *61*, 66, *82*, 555, *565*
Robinson, P. M., 93, *112*
Robinson, W., 354, 368, *381*, 446, 458, *468*
Robson, J. E., 195, *208*
Rodenhiser, H. A., 479, *505*
Rodriguez Aguirre, M. J., 5, 8, 10, 15, 16, 17, 19, 21, 28, 29, 35, 37, 38, 39, *58*, *59*, *60*, *61*
Rogers, C. H., 100, *112*
Rogers, D. P., 169, *177*
Rogerson, C. T., 759, *762*
Rolnick, A., 365, *373*, 490, *506*
Romagnesi, H., 170, *177*

Roman, H., 78, *81*, 530, 535, 555, *565*, 630, 632, *658*
Romano, A. H., 8, *61*, 189, 191, 208, *209*, 264, *276*, *277*
Romero, S., 554, *565*
Ronsdorf, L., 421, 422, *433*
Roper, J. A., 484, *509*, *510*, 590, 591, 592, 593, 594, 596, 599, 600, 606, 607, 609, 610, 612, *614*, *615*, *616*, 621, 636, 650, *660*
Rorem, E. S., 309, 310, *335*
Rorke, J., 239, *277*
Rose, A. N., 9, 16, *58*
Rosenbaum, J., 554, *565*
Rosenthal, G., 239, *277*
Rosinski, M. A., 361, *381*
Ross, I. K., 213, 214, 215, 220, 224, 225, 226, 227, *232*, *233*, 243, *277*, *281*
Ross, R. G., 354, 366, *381*
Rossignol, J. L., 531, 532, 533, 537, 556, *562*, *564*
Rost, H., 5, 9, 15, 16, 28, 37, 38, 45, *61*
Rothwell, A., 91, *109*
Rothwell, B., 91, *109*
Rowell, J. B., 390, *411*, 558, *565*, 665, *676*
Rubio-Huertos, M., *57*
Rudin, A. D., 73, 74, 75, *80*, *81*
Rudolph, E. D., 103, 107, 108, *112*, 346, *381*
Rudolph, H., 747, 748, 753, *762*, *763*
Runyon, E. H., 240, *277*
Rusch, H. P., 215, 221, 222, 223, 224, *230*, *231*, *232*, 260, *275*, *368*
Russell, D. W., 8, *61*
Ryan, F. J., 85, 92, *112*, 341, 357, *381*, 571, 579, 580, 581, *587*, *588*

S

Saccas, A., 341, *381*
Sager, R., 628, 650, *660*
Sagromsky, H., 351, *381*
St. Johnston, J. H., 73, *82*
St. Lawrence, P., 524, *565*
Saito, M., 725, *732*
Sakaguchi, K., 13, *59*, 592, 608, 612, *615*, *617*
Salton, M. R. J., 9, 11, 14, *57*, *61*
Salvin, S. B., 184, 186, *208*, 298, *335*, 484, *510*

Samuel, E. W., 240, 245, 262, *278*
SanAntonio, J. P., 392, *411*, 558, *564*, 570, 576, 577, 583, *588*
Sanderson, R., 352, *380*
Sansome, E. R., 358, *381*, 480, 488, *510*, 528, 557, *565*, 574, *588*, 591, 609, *616*
Sanwal, B. D., 360, *381*
Sarachek, A., 390, *411*
Sartoris, G. B., 361, *381*
Sass, J. E., 491, *510*, 668, *676*
Satina, S., 480, *510*
Satomura, Y,. 10, 13, 19, *61*
Sauton, B., 349, *381*
Savage, E. J., 554, *565*
Sawyer, W. H., Jr., 154, *177*
Scaramella, P., 124, *130*
Schade, A. L., 300, *335*
Schaeffer, P., 548, *562*
Schecroun, J., 628, 638, *660*
Scheiber, E., 367, *379*
Scheller-Correns, E., 394, 395, *411*
Scherffel, A., 284, *335*
Scherr, G. H., 182, 186, 201, 202, 203, 208, *209*
Schipper, M. A. A., 94, *110*
Schlenk, F., 5, 15, 25, 36, 37, 39, 43, 47, *61*
Schmidt, C. G., 390, *411*
Schmidt, M. B., 448, 453, *468*
Schmidt, W., 717, *731*
Schmiedeknecht, M., 345, *381*
Schmilde, A., 698, *707*
Schnathorst, W. C., 740, *763*
Schneiderhohn, G., 395, *411*
Schönborn, W., 353, *381*
Schönfeld, E., 72, *82*
Scholes, P. M., 222, *232*
Schopfer, W. H., 392, *411*, 479, *510*, 558, *565*, 741, *763*
Schrödter, H., 717, *731*
Schuckling, K., 72, *81*
Schünemann, E., 215, *232*
Schuster, R., 225, 227, *232*
Schutte, K. H., 398, *411*
Schwartz, M. N., 68, *81*
Schwartz, W., 554, *565*
Scott, M. A., 365, *378*
Seaver, B., 557, *565*
Sellin, M. A., 93, *110*
Sempio, C., 737, *763*

Sentandreu, R., 4, 25, 31, 33, 47, 51, *61*
Serafin, F. G., 749, *761*
Sermonti, G., 91, *110*, 607, 608, 610, 613, *614*, *615*, *617*
Seydal, S., 66, *82*
Seydoux, J., 350, 359, 366, *384*
Seyffert, H., 72, *82*
Shaffer, B. M., 239, 240, 241, 243, 245, 255, 256, *276*, *278*
Shanor, L., 367, *381*, 487, *504*
Shanta, P., 350, *381*
Shantz, H. L., 711, *732*
Sharp, E. L., 390, *411*
Sharpe, H. S., 620, 632, 633, 638, 653, *660*
Shatkin, A. J., 42, *61*, 87, *112*, 357, *381*
Shaw, M. J., 239, *272*
Shay, J. R., 556, *562*, *565*, *566*
Shear, C. L., 343, 356, *381*, 489, 500, *510*
Sheng, G., 357, 361, *381*
Sheng, T. C., 361, *381*
Shepherd, C. J., 755, *763*
Sherman, F., 79, *82*, 648, *660*
Sherwood, N. P., 187, *207*
Shimizu, N., 342, *383*, 757, *764*
Shockman, G. D., 20, 36, 45, 49, *61*
Shu, P., 747, 748, 749, 754, *763*
Sibilia, C., 737, *763*
Siemienski, J., 204, *207*
Silagi, S., 651, *660*
Silbereisen, K., 73, *82*
Silberg, S. L., 186, *207*
Simon, F. G., 749, 754, *761*
Simpson, W. C., 621, 641, *660*
Sinden, J. W., 394, *412*
Singer, R., 157, 165, 167, 170, *177*
Singleton, J. R., 364, 365, *373*, *381*, 490, *506*, 517, 522, 523, *565*
Sinnott, E. W., 91, 92, *109*, 387, *411*
Sisler, H. D., 342, *381*
Sjöwall, M., 554, *565*
Skinner, C. E., 188, *209*
Skinner, S. E., 67, *80*
Skolko, A. J., 491, 492, *510*, 668, *676*
Skujins, J. J., 8, 12, *61*
Skupienski, F. X., 214, 215, *232*, 243, *278*
Slavenburg, J. H., 48, *62*
Sleumer, H. O., 558, *565*
Slifkin, M. K., 236, 239, *278*
Sloan, B. J., 355, *381*

Slobodkin, L. B., 294, *335*
Slonimski, P. P., 640, *658*
Slooff, W. C., 63, *82*
Smart, R. F., 211, 212, *232*, 733, 738, *763*
Smith, A. H., 151, 152, 153, 157, 159, 160, 165, 166, 167, 168, 172, *177*, 494, *510*
Smith, C. E., 202, *206*, 725, *732*
Smith, D. T., 182, *206*
Smith, E. C., 212, *232*, 456, *468*
Smith, F. B., 718, *732*
Smith, F. G., 757, *764*
Smith, G., 94, *109*, 120, *130*
Smith, J. H., 87, *112*, 342, *381*
Smith, L. W., 722, *731*
Smith, P. E., 343, *374*, 742, 747, *762*
Smith, R. E., 569, 572, 584, *587*
Smith, S. B., 390, *411*
Smithies, W. R., 15, *61*
Smoot, J. J., 554, *565*
Snell, N. S., 740, *763*
Snell, W. H., 173, *177*
Snider, P. J., 90, 96, *112*, 390, *411*, 568, 572, 576, *588*
Snyder, G., 740, *761*
Snyder, W. C., 351, 367, *375*, *382*, 487, *507*, 584, *587*, 743, *760*
Sörgel, G., 303, *333*, 479, 486, 448, *469*, 500, *507*, 553, *565*
Sohler, A., 8, *61*
Solomon, E. P., 264, *279*, 757, *763*
Sols, A., 47, *59*
Somers, C. E., 517, *565*
Sommer, L., 736, *763*
Sonneborn, D. R., 251, 257, 259, 268, 270, *279*
Sonneborn, J. M., 296, *336*
Spaeth, J., 749, 754, *761*
Spalla, C., 554, *566*
Sparrow, F. K., Jr., 283, 286, 288, 298, 300, 308, *336*, 486, *510*
Spencer, J. F. T., 33, *59*
Spiegel, M., 255, *279*
Spiltoir, C. F., 487, *510*
Spoerl, E., 390, *411*, *412*
Sproston, T., 355, *382*
Srb, A. M., *369*, 621, 628, 651, *660*
Sreeramulu, T., 718, 719, 720, *730*, *732*, 759, *764*
Srinivasan, K. S., 348, *380*

Author Index

Stadler, D. R., 93, *112*, 517, 530, 532, 533, 535, 537, *566*
Stakman, E. C., *558*, *566*, 712, 723, 726, *732*, 759, *764*
Staley, J. M., 390, *411*
Stantial, H., 366, *382*
Staples, R. C., 755, *764*
Staples, S. O., 268, *279*
Stedman, O. J., 715, 721, *730*
Steinberg, R. A., 352, *382*
Steinhaus, E. A., 711, 713, *732*
Stepanov, K. M., 714, 720, *732*
Stern, C., 596, *617*
Stevens, F. L., 351, *382*, 460, *469*
Stevenson, J. L., 33, *61*
Steward, F. C., 329, *336*
Stewart, H. B., 42, *59*
Steyn-Parvé, E. P., 48, *62*
Stiefel, S., 395, *412*
Still, C. C., 223, *232*
Stock, T., 740, *764*
Stockley, H. M., 195, *208*
Stoiamovitch, C., 243, *277*
Stokes, J. L., 348, 349, *374*, *382*
Stoller, B. B., 394, *412*
Stoneman, B., 556, *566*
Storck, R., 361, *376*, 755, *762*
Stover, R. H., 726, *732*
Strange, R. E., *57*
Strasburger, F., 225, *232*
Stratton, H. M., 88, *110*
Straub, J., 362, 364, 365, *374*, 484, 495, *506*, *507*
Strauss, B. S., 359, 361, *379*, *382*
Strickland, W. N., 520, *559*
Strømnaes, O., 608, 609, *617*
Struble, F. B., 556, *566*
Strunk, Ch., 4, 5, 21, 24, 27, 29, 30, 31, 33, 45, 49, 54, 56, *59*, *61*
Strutz, I., 738, 741, *764*
Stuben, H., 739, *764*
Studhalter, R. A., 714, *730*
Stüben, H., 487, *510*
Sturgeon, R. J., 8, *61*
Sturgis, W. C., 712, *732*
Sturtevant, A. H., 524, *566*
Subramanian, C. V., 116, 120, 121, 122, 124, 125, 126, *130*
Suminae, K., 49, *61*
Sun, C. Y., 743, *764*

Sussman, A. S., 341, 343, 344, 362, 365, 369, *371*, *378*, *382*, 733, 734, 735, 736, 737, 739, 741, 742, 743, 745, 746, 747, 749, 750, 751, 752, 753, 754, 758, 759, 760, *762*, *763*, *764*
Sussman, M. 236, 238, 240, 241, 243, 247, 251, 257, 259, 260, 264, 265, 266, 267, 268, 269, 270, *272*, *273*, *279*, *280*
Sussman, R. R., 241, 243, 247, 251, 257, 267, 268, 270, *277*, *279*, *280*
Sutton, D. D., 47, *61*
Sutton, O. G., 718, *732*
Svihla, G., 5, 15, 25, 36, 37, 39, 43, *61*
Swait, J. C., 91, *109*
Swart, H. J., 122, *130*
Swartz, D., 101, *112*
Swiezynski, K. M., 568, 577, 583, *588*
Swinbank, P., 683, *707*
Syamananda, R., 755, *764*
Szilvinyi, A., 68, *82*

T

Tabata, S., 10, 17, 37, 43, 46, *61*
Taber, W. A., 67, *82*, 94, 97, *112*, 203, *208*, 346, 347, *382*, 391, 392, 397, 398, *412*
Taggart, J., 693, *707*
Taha, E. E., 348, *382*
Takada, M., 51, *61*
Takahashi, M., 14, *57*
Takebe, I., 342, *383*, 755, 757, *764*
Takemaru, T., 493, *510*
Takeuchi, I., 238, 244, 245, 252, 257, 260, 262, 263, 270, *280*
Talbot, P. H. B., 155, 169, *177*, 711, *732*
Talice, R. U., 65, 66, *81*, *82*
Tamblyn, N., 388, *412*
Tanner, K. G., 747, 748, 749, 754, *763*
Tanaka, H., 13, *61*
Tanaka, K., 123, 124, *130*
Tarn, T. R., 88, *112*
Tarr-Gloor, E., 594, 600, *616*
Tarurenko, E., 346, *383*
Taschdjian, C. L., 204, *209*
Tatum, E. L., 19, 42, 58, *61*, 85, 87, 92, *112*, 357, *369*, *370*, *381*, *383*, 575, *579*, *588*
Taylor, E. E., 456, *468*
Taylor, G. S., 720, *732*

Taylor, I. F., 8, 11, *57*
Taylor, J. J., 184, 185, *209*
Taylor, R. E., 715, *732*
Tazawa, M., 260, 262, *280*
Tector, M. A., 607, *617*
Terakawa, H., 493, *510*
Termi, G., 10, 17, 37, 43, 46, *61*
Terui, G., 745, 747, 748, *764*
Tewari, V. P., 105, *112*
Thaxter, R., 308, *336*, 487, *510*
Therrien, C. D., 215, 216, 227, *232*
Thielke, C., 351, *383*
Thiers, H. D., 159, 172, *177*
Thimann, K. V., 300, *335*, 427, *432*
Thind, K. S., 101, *110*
Thirumalachar, M. S., 351, *383*
Thom, C., 84, 89, *112*, 117, 124, *130*, 256, 277, 352, 353, *382*, *383*
Thompson, D'Arcy W., 408, *412*
Thorne, R. S. W., 74, *82*
Thornsson, K. G., 32, *61*
Thorpe, I. G., 726, *731*
Threlkeld, S. F. H., 548, *566*
Thung, T. H., 452, *469*
Tinline, R. E., 608, 611, *617*
Tissières, A., 620, 628, *659*
Tites, D., 733, *764*
Tomcsik, J., *57*
Tomkins, R. G., 341, *383*
Tomlin, B. P., 662, *675*
Tonino, G. J. M., 48, *62*
Towe, A. M., 530, 532, 533, 537, *566*
Towler, D. A., 348, 349, *379*
Townsend, B. B., 99, 100, 102, 103, 105, 106, 107, *112*, 345, 346, *383*, 389, *412*
Townsend, G. F., 69, *82*
Tracey, M. V., 16, *59*
Tremaine, J. H., 366, *383*
Trevithick, J. R., 47, *62*
Trione, E. J., *369*
Trygstad, C. W., 257, *275*
Tschierpe, H. J., 394, *412*
Ts'O, P.O.P., 220, *232*, *233*
Tubaki, K., 116, 119, 120, 121, *130*
Tuppy, H., 643, *660*
Turel, F. L. M., 754, *764*
Turian, G. 286, 288, 289, 290, 292, 301, 304, 305, 306, 307, 310, 311, 314, 315, 316, 317, 318, *330*, *332*, *336*, 350, 358, 359, 360, 361, 362, 366, *369*, *383*, *384*, 464, *469*
Turner, J. F., 206, *207*
Tuveson, R. W., 582, 583, *588*, 608, *617*
Tyler, A., 255, 263, 269, *280*
Tyrrell, E., 737, *764*

U

Uchida, K., 594, 612, 613, *615*, *617*
Uebelmesser, E. R., 698, *707*
Uozumi, T., 14, *57*
Upshall, A., 621, *660*
Utter, M. F., 38, 42, *58*, *62*

V

Vakili, N. G., 666, *676*
Valder, P. G., 98, *112*
van Beverwijk, A. L., 118, *130*, 454, *469*
Van Beyma, T. K., 122, *130*
Vanbreuseghem, R., 113, 120, *129*
van Dam, G. J. W., 48, *58*, *62*
Vandendries, R., 491, *510*
van der Plank, J. E., 710, *732*
van Rij, N. J. W., *see* Kreger-van Rij, N. J. W.
Van Sumere, C. F., 737, 741, *764*
Van Sumere-de Preter, C., 737, 741, *764*
van Wermeskerken, R. K. A., 48, *58*
Varitchak, B., 367, *384*
Venkat Ram, C. S., 345, *384*
Venner, H., 5, 9, 15, 16, 28, 37, 38, 45, *61*
Verkaik, C., 421, *433*
Viala, P., 119, *130*
Villanueva, J. R., 4, 5, 6, 8, 9, 10, 11, 12, 14, 15, 16, 17, 18, 19, 20, 21, 25, 27, 28, 29, 30, 31, 33, 35, 37, 39, 40, 45, 47, 49, 51, *58*, *59*, *60*, *61*
Vining, L. C., 94, 97, *112*, 737, 741, *764*
Vinograd, J., 220, *232*, *233*
Vishniac, H. S., 292, *337*
Vitols, E. R., *62*
Voderberg, K., 395, *412*
Voelz, H., 746, *764*
Vogel, J. M., 749, *761*
Volkmann, D., 359, 366, *384*
von Arx, J. A., 138, 142, *150*
von Böventer-Heidenhain, B., 343, *378*, *382*, 739, *763*

von Güttenberg, H. V., 738, 741, *764*
von Hofsten, A., 351, *384*
von Hofsten, B., 351, *384*
von Hofsten, V., 350, *384*
von Minden, M., 308, *337*
Von Schuckmann, W., 256, *280*
von Stosch, H. A., 214, 226, 227, *233*, 740, *764*
von Wettstein, F., 226, *233*
von Witsch, H., 351, *384*
Vuillemin, P., 113, 120, *131*, 348, *384*

W

Wachter, J. P., 390, *412*
Wager, H., 500, *510*
Waggoner, P. E., 720, *732*
Wagner, B., 361, *379*
Wagner, F., 351, *384*
Wagner, R. P., 357, 361, *384*, 517, *565*
Wagner, S., 358, *370*
Waksman, S. A., 13, *62*, 189, *209*
Waldher, J. T., 737, *763*
Walker, C. G., 360, *384*
Walker, L. B., 154, *177*
Wallace, P. P., 713, *732*
Warcup, H. H., 758, *764*
Warcup, J. H., 758, *764*
Ward, C., 263, *281*
Ward, H. M., 717, *732*
Ward, J. M., 191, *209*, 223, *232*, *233*
Ward, V., 8, *61*
Wardlaw, C. W., 121, *131*, 408, *412*
Ware, B., 354, *370*
Warren, G. H., 388, *412*
Watanabe, Y., 358, *376*
Waterhouse, G. M., 287, 298, *337*
Watkins, G. M., 100, *112*
Watling, R., 168, *177*
Weaver, R. H., 182, 201, 203, *209*
Webb, M., 182, *209*
Webley, D. M., 8, 11, *57*
Webster, J., 688, *707*, 711, *732*
Wehmeyer, L. E., 142, *150*
Weibull, C., 8, 32, *57, 62*
Weijer, J., 607, *617*
Weinfurtner, F., 77, *82*
Weinkauff, A. M., 241, *280*
Weintraub, R. L., 737, 738, *761*

Weiss, B., 5, 32, 33, 34, 42, *62*, *369*
Weiss, P., 255, *280*
Welden, A. L., 224, 225, *233*
Wellman, R. H., 341, *384*
Welsch, M., 14, *62*
Welsford, E., 736, *764*
Wenham, S., 72, 75, *80*
Went, F. A. F. C., 360, *384*
Westergaard, M., 357, 358, *384*, 527, 537, *566*
Weston, W. A. R. D., 715, 717, *732*
Weston, W. H., Jr., 342, *384*, 688, *707*
Wheeler, H. E., 361, 362, 363, 364, 365, *373*, *378*, *384*, 428, 432, 495, *508*, *510*, *511*, 556, *563*, *566*
Whiffen, A. J., 303, 308, *332*, *337*, 479, 480, 486, 500, *505*
White, G. A., 750, 752, 753, 757, *764*
White, G. J., 251, 260, 263, 265, 266, 268, 269, *279*, *280*
Whitehouse, H. L. K., 474, 481, 487, 491, 492, *511*, 537, *566*, 574, *588*, *662*, *676*
Whiteside, W. C., 143, 144, *150*, 354, *384*
Whitfield, F. E., 239, 258, *273*, *280*
Whitney, H. S., 578, *588*
Whittingham, W. F., 236, 268, *280*
Whittle, C. H., 204, *207*
Whymper, J. W. T., 455, *465*
Wickerham, L. J., 66, *82*
Wiesner, J., 450, *466*
Wilcox, M. S., 489, *511*
Wilcoxian, R. D., 390, *411*
Wilde, C. E., 246, *280*
Wildner, G., 643, *660*
Wiles, H. E., 73, *82*
Wilkie, D., 620, 621, 632, 633, 636, 641, 651, 653, *659, 660*
Willetts, H. J., 102, 103, 105, 106, 107, *112*, 345, *383*
Williams, E. B., 556, *566*
Williams, W., 426, *432*
Williamson, D. H., 3, 15, 36, 37, 43, 45, 50, 51, *58*
Williamson, H. S., 343, 344, 355, *375*, 739, *762*
Willoughby, L. G., 289, 290, 301, *337*
Wilson, C. M., 226, 227, *233*, 243, *280*,

281, 303, 309, *333, 337,* 426, *431,* 480, 484, 495, 499, *506, 511,* 553, *561, 566*
Wilson, E. E., 354, *384*
Wilson, E. M., 741, *764*
Wilson, E. O., 415, *433*
Wilson, G. B., 355, *381*
Wilson, H. V., 255, *281*
Wilson, J. F., 575, *588*
Wilson, M., 214, 215, *233*
Winge, Ö., 427, *433,* 479, 491, 500, *511*
Winsche, W. E., 722, 731
Winslow, C. E. A., 73, *82*
Winsten, S., 189, 204, *209*
Winter, A. G., 744, *764*
Wolf, F. A., 733, *764*
Wolf, F. T., 223, *233,* 558, *566,* 733, *764*
Wolfenbarger, D. O., 710, 721, *732*
Wollman, C., 214, 215, 220, 222, *233*
Wollman, E. L., 548, *562*
Wood-Baker, A., 758, *764*
Woodham-Smith, C., 727, *732*
Woodruff, H. B., 349, *374*
Woodward, R., 352, *380*
Woodward, R. C., 685, *707*
Wright, B. E., 242, 252, 254, 260, 261, 263, 264, 265, 267, 273, *274, 275, 276, 281*
Wright, J. E., 158, 174, *177*
Wright, R. E., 636, *660*
Wright, S., 296, 297, *337*
Wyttenbach, E. G., 570, *587*

Y

Yamagishi, S., 342, *385*
Yamamoto, B. T., 51, *61*
Yanagita, T., 89, *112,* 123, 124, *130,* 341, 342, 349, *376, 385,* 733, 738, 741, 745, 747, 748, 754, 755, 756, 757, *762, 764*
Yarwood, C. E., 342, *385,* 445, *469*
Yaw, K. E., 553, *566*
Ycas, M., 621, *660*
Yegian, D., 186, *207*
Yotsuzanagi, Y., 79, *82*
Yu, C. C., *see* Yu-Sun, C. C. C.
Yuill, E., 117, *131*
Yuill, J. L., 117, *131*
Yunis, E. J., 204, *207*
Yurchenco, J. A., 388, *412*
Yu-Sun, C. C. C., 343, 368, 369, *385,* 556, *566*

Z

Zabka, G. G., 214, *230, 232*
Zaczynski, E. J., 256, *281*
Zajdela, F., 42, *59*
Zalokar, M., 40, *62,* 85, 88, *112,* 358, 360, 361, *385,* 751, 753, *764*
Zeldin, M. H., 223, *233*
Zeller, S. M., 152, 153, 159, 166, *177*
Zentmeyer, G. A., 713, *732*
Zickler, H., 355, 363, 365, *385,* 428, *433,* 487, 490, *511,* 522, *566,* 669, *676*
Ziegler, A. W., 480, *511*
Zimmerman, A., 735, *764*
Zoberi, M. H., 697, 699, 700, *707*

Subject Index

An asterisk (*) after a page number indicates an illustration.

A

Acanthophyses, 175, 176
Acervulus, 127
Acrasin, 240, 241, 257
Actidione, 48, 268
Aeration affecting reproduction, 453-456
Agaricine, 162
Aleuriospore, 113, 115*, 120-121
Ammonia, growth inhibition by, 455
Amphotericin B, 48
Amyloid reaction, 159
Aneuploids in *Aspergillus nidulans*, 601
Annellophore, 115, 120
Antibiotics, action of, on fungi, 48
Aphanoplasmodium, 219
Apothecium, 147*
Arthrospores, 64*, 113, 115*, 116, 124-125, 352
Asci, 364
Ascocarp, 133-135
Ascogenous hyphae, 364
Ascogonia, morphogenesis of, 355-363
Ascospores, 365
Auxotrophs, selection for, 606

B

Ballistospore discharge, 689, 711
Barrage formation, 557, 628, 638, 656, 671
Basauxic conidiophore, 125
Basidiole, 167, 169-170
Basidium, 167, 168-169
Bicarbonate affecting *Blastocladiella*, 318, 319
Biotin for perithecial development, 444
Biphialide, 122
Bipolar incompatibility, 663
Blackfellow's bread, 107
Blastospore, 64*, 113, 115*, 116
  types of, 117
Brachybasidiole, 169
Bulbils, 102, 108

C

Capillitium of myxomycetes, 225-226
Carbon compounds affecting reproduction, 439
Carbon dioxide affecting
  Blastocladiella reproduction, 311
  dimorphism, 185, 196-201
  fruit body development in basidiomycetes, 394, 397, 405
  reproduction, 454
Caulocystidia, 170, 175
Cell
  adhesion in Acrasiales, 255
  shape in basidiomycetes, 162-163
  wall, nature of, 5
Cellular slime molds, organization and synthesis in, 235-281
Cheilocystidia, 170, 175
Chemotropism of zygophores, 420-426
Chitin, 6, 20, 325
Chitinase, 6, 7, 8
Chlamydospores, 113, 345
Chromospheres, 309
Clamp connections, 157, 166-167
Colonies, 84-93
  corporate, 90
  development of, 92
  submerged, 90
  surface, 85
Conidia, 113, 123*, 348
Conidiophore, 113, 115*
Conidium verum, 113, 122
Contact stimuli for reproduction, 461
Conversion ratios, 530-531
Coremium, 127
Crossing over, 524-527, 596-600
Cysteine determining dimorphism, 67, 186
Cystidia, 168, 170-176
  types of, 170, 175
Cystine determining dimorphism, 186
Cytochrome oxidase in spores, 750, 752

787

Cytoplasmic membranes, composition and isolation of, 40-42

D

Dendrophyses, 175, 176
Dermatocystidia, 170, 175
Dermatophytes, yeast-like form of, 202-203
Dextrinoid reaction, 159
Dichophyses, 175, 176
Dictyospore, 113, 115*
Digitoxin disrupting protoplasts, 38
Dimitic construction, 101
Dimorphism, 90, 181-209
   in *Candida*, 188-195
   in *Mucor*, 196-201
   nutrition-dependent, 185-201
   pathogenicity and, 201-205
   temperature-dependent, 182-188
Dioecism, 661
Dispersal by
   animals, 711-724
   ballistics, 711
   rain, 714, 722
   water, 711
   wind, 715-728
DNA, 184, 227, 264-265, 267, 306-307, 310, 311, 316, 317, 322, 342, 451, 593, 755
DNA:RNA ratio in *Blastocladiella*, 306
Dormancy of spores, 734-745
Dual phenomenon, 656

E

Electron microscopy of
   Acrasiales, 256
   Blastocladiella, 288
   Physarum, 234
   protoplasts, 30
   spores, 117, 124, 437
   yeast cells, 195
Endocystidia, 170, 175
Episomic inheritance, 545
Excipulum, terminology of, 147
Extranuclear inheritance, 619-660
   chromosomal control of, 651
   determinants of
      interaction between, 647
      location of, 640
      properties of, 644
   heterokaryon test for, 637
   nature of, 639-652
   origin of, 619
   role of, 652

F

Fairy rings, 84, 710-711
Falciphore, 122
Falx, 122
Filipin, 48
Flocculation in yeasts, 71
Fradicin inducing filamentation in *Candida*, 189
Fungi, aquatic
   morphogenesis in, 283-337
   phylogeny of, 285, 291, 295
   synthetic capacities of, 291
Fungicides inhibiting reproduction, 456, 460

G

Gangliospore, 116
Geotropism, 460
   of basidiomycete fruit bodies, 400, 405
Germination of spores, 745-748
Gloeocystidia, 174, 176
Gravity, see Geotropism
Griseofulvin, 20, 48

H

Haploidization, 600-601
Helix pomatia digestive juice, lysis of fungal cells by, 3, 11, 16, 18, 27, 34
Hermaphroditism, 550
Heterobasidium, nomenclature of, 169
Heterokaryosis, 567-588
   as a mechanism of natural variation, 584-586
   criteria for, 568
   dominance in, 572
   heterokaryon formation, 573
   nuclear ratios in, 570
Heteromerous tissue, 165
Heteroplasmons, origin of, 645
Heterothallism, 480, 484-493, 550
Homothallism, 480, 483-484
   relative, 494
Hormones, sex, in fungi, 415-433
Humidity affecting
   basidiomycete fruit body development, 399, 405
   reproduction, 444-447

Hydrogen-ion concentration affecting
  ascospore maturation, 366
  Blastocladiella reproduction, 311
  flocculation in yeasts, 73
  reproduction, 447-449
Hymenium of basidiomycetes, 167
Hyphae
  binding, 155
  branching of, 388
    in basidiomycetes, 164
  differentiation of, 98
  generative and skeletal, 155
  walls of, in basidiomycetes, 155-158
Hyphoids, 175, 176

I

Incompatibility, 489-493, 661-675
  definitions, 661
  evolution and, 674
  heterogenic, 670-673
  homogenic, 663-669
  systems of, 662
Inheritance, mechanisms of
  episomic, 545-548
  extranuclear, 619-660
  heterokaryosis, 567-588
  Mendelian, 513-566
  parasexual cycle, 589-617
Initiator cells, 240
Inositol for perithecial development, 444
Insects
  spore dispersion by, 713
  spore liberation by, 702
Intragenic recombination, 531-534
Iron salts as test reagent for basidiomycetes, 161
Isozymes in spores, 757
Isthmospores, 126

L

Laminarin in fungal cell wall, 7, 8
Lamprocystidia, 173, 176
Leptocystidia, 172, 175
Life cycles in fungi, 474-480, 549-558
Light affecting
  basidiomycete carpophore development, 393, 394, 396, 397, 398, 400, 401, 403, 405
  perithecial development, 353
  reproduction, 457
  spore discharge, 697
  spore germination, 736-737
Linkage, meiotic and mitotic compared, 604
Lysozyme, 7-9
Lytic enzymes
  production of, by actinomycetes, 9

M

Macroconidia, 356
Meiosporangium in Blastocladiales, 308
Meiospore, 550, 551, 552*
Melzer's solution, 158
Mendelian inheritance, 513-566
Meristem aleuriospore, 116
Meristem arthrospore, 116
Meristem spore, 113
Microconidia, 355
Microsclerotia, 102
Mimics, chromosomal-extrachromosomal, 650
Mirror yeasts, 694
Mitic system, 154-155
Mitochondria, 42, 88
Mitotic
  analysis, techniques for, 605-607
  crossing over, 596
  segregation, 595
Monoecism, 661
Morphogenesis in
  aquatic fungi, 283-337
  ascomycetes, 339-385
  basidiomycetes, 387-412
  cellular slime molds, 235-281
  myxomycetes, 211-233
Mycelium
  filamentous, 83
  membranous, 83
  of yeasts, 64*
  strands of, 388
Mycosclerids, 156*, 158, 174, 176
Myxamoebae of myxomycetes, 213-216, 234

N

Nitrogen nutrition
  affecting reproduction, 440
  of aquatic phycomycetes, 291-293
Nonreciprocal recombination, 530-535
Nuclear ratios in heterokaryons, 578-584
Nystatin, 38, 47, 48

O

Oidia, 345
Oxygen
  consumption by *Dictyostelium*, 261-262
  requirements for reproduction, 454

P

Paramutation, 624
Parasexual cycle, 477, 589-617
  applications of, 609
  compared to sexual cycle, 603
  in *Aspergillus nidulans*, 590-607
  in nature, 610-612
  in other fungi, 607-609
  phytopathology and, 613
Pellicles, types of yeast, 70
Perithecial development in ascomycetes, 367
Petite mutants, 75, 78, 625, 630-632, 636, 640, 642, 643, 650
Phaneroplasmodium, 219
Phase contrast microscopy of
  protoplasts, 29
  sporophores, 120
Phialospore, 113, 115*, 116, 121-124
Phototropism of basidiomycete fruit bodies, 401, 403, 405
Pileocystidia, 170, 175
Pimacrin, 48
Plectenchyma, 108
Pleurocystidia, 170, 175
Pleuroradulaspore, 116, 119
Polaron, 532, 544
Polyphialide, 122
Porospore, 116, 124
Potassium hydroxide, as a test reagent for hyphal walls, 160, 173
Prosenchyma, 108
Protoperithecia, 360
Protoplasmodium, 219
Protoplasts of fungi, 3-62
  composition of, 39-43
  conjugation between, 49
  definition of, 3
  fixation of, 32
  morphology of, 20-33
  number per cell, 28-29
  osmotic sensitivity of, 37-39
  permeability of, 46
  physiology of, 43-49

  preparation of, 15-20
  properties of, 36-39
  respiration of, 46
  reversion of, 50-57
Pseudocompatibility, 667-668
Pseudomycelium, 64*, 67
Pseudoparaphyses, 141
Pseudoparenchyma, 108
Pseudoplasmodium formation in Acrasiales, 242-254
Pseudorhizae, 108
Pycnidium, 127*
Pycnosclerotia, 108

R

Radiation affecting reproduction, 456
  see also Light; UV radiation
Radula spore, 113, 118, 122
  types of, 119
Rain, spore dissemination by, 700, 711
Recombination models, 535-545
Reproduction, environmental influences on, 435-469
Respiratory enzymes in spores, 750
Rhizomorphs, 95, 389
RNA, 184, 254, 264-265, 267, 306-307, 310-312, 316, 323, 326, 327, 342, 451, 755-756
RNA:DNA ratio, in hyphal tips, 464

S

Sclerotia, 83, 101-108, 221-222, 345-346
Serology of *Dictyostelium*, 256-259, 269-271
Setae, 127
Sex hormones, 415-433
Sexuality
  anomalies in, 493-496
  mechanisms of, 496-501
  patterns of, 480-493
Shaffer reaction, 161
Sirenin, 426
Skeletal hyphae, 155, 156*, 158
Sodium dodecyl sulfate, disrupting protoplasts, 38
Soil, lysis of fungal cells by, 13-15
Soil fungistasis, 743-744
Somatic segregation, 644-647
Sonic vibration affecting fungal protoplasts, 39

Sorocarp, 236, 237*, 238*
Speciation, 656
Spore groups, Saccardo's, 114
Spores
  dormancy of, 734-745
    mechanisms, 739
    terminology, 734
  formation of, by protoplasts, 45
  germination of, 745-758
    activators for, 738
    terminology, 734
  isozymes in, 757
  lysis of, 33
  morphogenesis of, sexual, 352
  protoplasts from, 33-36
  release of, by
    active discharge, 679-699
    animals, 702-705
    passive methods, 699-702
  role of, 758-760
Sporodochium, 127
Sporogenous cells, 126
Sporophore, 113, 126
Staling, 88, 93, 455
Strands, mycelial, 83, 84, 94-101
Strepzyme, 8, 11, 13, 26, 27
Subhymenium in basidiomycetes, 163
Sulfhydryl compounds affecting dimorphism, 67-68, 187-189
Sulfovanillin test for *Russula*, 161
Sulfur nutrition of aquatic phycomycetes, 291-293
Swarm cells of myxomycetes, 213-216
Sympodioconidia, 119
Syngen, 296
Synnemata, 94, 96, 126, 346

T

Tellurite media affecting dimorphism, 67
Temperature affecting
  basidiomycete stipe development, 395, 405
  dimorphism, 182-188
  reproduction, 449-453
  spore germination, 736

Terminoradulaspore, 116, 119
Terminus spore, 113
Tetrad ratios, 534
Tetrapolar incompatibility, 663
Thallospore, 113, 115*
Thiamine requirements, 443
  of basidiomycetes, 396, 398
  for perithecial development, 444
Treberine and yeast flocculence, 74
Trehalase in spores, 750-751
Tuckahoe, 107

U

UV radiation affecting
  cytoplasmic membrane, 39
  perithecial development, 368
  protoplasts of *Candida utilis*, 43

V

Viridin, 48
Vitamins affecting
  ascospore formation, 366
  reproduction, 442

W

Water, see Humidity
Wounding affecting conidial production, 461

Y

Yeasts
  aggregation of cells of, 63-82
  asexual conjugation in, 66
  bottom, 71
  cell wall of
    digestion, vitamins affecting, 9
    lysis by *Cytophaga*, 8, 11
  flocculence in, 71-76
  giant colonies of, 77*, 79*
  petite forms of, 75
  sexual aggregation in, 65
  top, 71

Z

Zygophores, chemotropism of, 420-426

Index
to Fungi, Lichens, and Actinomycetes

An asterisk (*) after a page number indicates an illustration.

A

Absidia, 86*, 87
Acanthocystis, 173
Achlya, 289, 292, 298, 299, 416-419, 430, 443, 461, 480, 483
Achlya ambisexualis, 299, 417, 418, 488, 489
Achlya bisexualis, 299, 417, 418, 489
Achlya colorata, 453
Acrasiales
  organization and synthesis in, 235-281
  metabolism of, 260-270
Acrasis rosea, 243
Acrospermum compressum, 148
Actinomyces
  lytic enzymes from, 9
Actinomycetes
  lytic enzymes from, 9
Acyrostelium leptosomum, 242, 252, 265
Agaricus, 160, 161, 162
Agaricus arvensis, 99*
Agaricus augustus, 171*
Agaricus bisporus, 96, 389, 393, 394, 667
Agaricus campestris, 96, 100, 389, 393*, 398, 405, 407, 408, 716, 722, 738
Agaricus tabularis, 711
Akanthomyces, 116
Aleuria repanda, 681
Allescheriella, 120
Allomyces
  gamete differentiation in, 464
  hyphal branching in, 85
  life cycle of, 479, 483, 495, 499, 500, 502
  meiospore of, 550
  morphogenesis of, 287, 296, 301*-310
  sex hormones of, 426, 430
  sporangium germination in, 739
Allomyces arbuscula, 498*, 550, 553

Allomyces macrogynus, 288
Alternaria, 17, 124, 349, 351, 461
Alternaria dianthi, 351
Alternaria solani, 368
Amanita, 154
Amauroascus aureus, 136
Anguillospora, 121
Annellophora, 120
Anthasthoopa, 126
Anthomyces, 712
Anthostoma, 145
Anthostomella, 145
Aphanomyces, 289, 292, 299, 416
Apodachlya, 300
Apostemidium guernisaci, 148
Arachniotus flavoluteus, 136
Arcyria cinerea, 221*, 228, 229*
Armillaria mellea, 89, 94, 95*, 97, 98, 99*, 100, 101, 398, 711
Arnaudiella, 142
Arthrinium, 125
Arthrobotrys, 115, 119
Ascobolus
  apothecial development of, 454
  dormancy in, 343
  heterothallism in, 490, 493, 501
  phenocopies in, 535
  phototrophism in, 681
  sex hormones, 428, 430
  sexuality in, 502
Ascobolus carbonarius, 428, 736
Ascobolus furfuraceus, 736
Ascobolus immersus, 85, 368, 369, 530, 533, 552*, 556
Ascobolus magnificus, 355, 552*
Ascobolus stercorarius, 147, 356, 363, 365, 429, 483, 663, 669
Ascochyta pisi, 459
Ascocybe grovesii, 479

Ascomycetes
  embryogenesis in, 364
  fertilization in, 363
  heterokaryosis in, 574-576
  incompatibility in, 662
  perithecial development in, 367
  sex hormones in, 427
Ascophaera, 487
Ascophanus granuliformis, 147
Aseroe rubra, 702
Aspergillus, 438, 452, 642, 654, 656, 699, 721, 723
Aspergillus alliaceus, 103, 107
Aspergillus amstelodami, 351, 353
Aspergillus echinulatus, 351
Aspergillus flavus, 7, 348
Aspergillus fumigatus, 18, 608
Aspergillus glaucus, 353, 354, 635, 638
  extrachromosomal inheritance in, 620, 621, 622*, 624, 625
  variants of, 631-633, 636, 638
Aspergillus japonicus, 368
Aspergillus manginii, 353
Aspergillus nidulans
  conidia of, 555, 572, 585, 755
  extrachromosomal inheritance in, 620, 621, 622*, 625
  heterokaryons of, 576, 611
  lysis of, 13
  meiospore of, 552*, 555
  nonsexual variant of, 631
  nuclear ratios in, 570
  parasexual cycle in, 590-607
  perithecial density in, 626, 634
  protoplasts of, 17
  relative homothallism in, 494
  variants of, 632, 633, 635-637, 650, 651
Aspergillus niger
  cell wall of, 6
  colony of, 89, 92
  dormancy in, 341, 342
  parasexual cycle in, 607
  spore germination in, 733, 745, 747, 748, 752, 754-757
  sporulating structure of, 117, 124
  sporulation in, 348-352, 442
Aspergillus oryzae
  diploids of, 592, 612
  lysis of, 8, 10, 12, 13
  nuclear ratios in, 570, 582
  protease production by, 613
  spore germination in, 745, 747-749
Aspergillus repens, 351
Aspergillus rugulosus
  parasexual cycle in, 607
Aspergillus sojae, 592, 594, 608
Aspergillus wentii, 744
Asterodon, 174
Asterophlyctis, 300
Asterophora lycoperdoides, 699
Atichia glomerulosa, 140
Aureobasidium, 116, 723
Aureobasidium pullulans, 119
Auricularia, 446, 460

B

Bactridium, 115, 120, 121
Badhamia utriculosa, 446
Bagnisiella mirabilis, 140
Bahusakala olivacea-nigra, 125
Balladyna, 140
Basidiobolus, 713
Basidiobolus ranarum, 687
Basidiomycetes
  basidiocarp structure of, 151-177
  heterokaryosis in, 576-578
  incompatibility in, 662
  morphogenesis in, 387-412
Battarraea, 699
Beauveria, 116, 119
Bispora, 116
Bisporomyces lignicola, 122
Bitunicatae, 137, 138-142
Blastocladia, 308, 309, 310, 455
Blastocladia pringsheimii, 454, 738
Blastocladiales, 285, 290, 291, 302
  sex hormones in, 426
Blastocladiella, 487, 500, 502
  morphogenesis in, 302*-310
  spore germination in, 738-739
Blastocladiella britannica, 327, 328
Blastocladiella emersonii
  morphogenesis in, 288, 303-305, 307, 311-313*, 315*, 317, 318, 321*, 324, 327*-329, 464
Blastomyces dermatitidis, 182*, 184, 202
Boletus, 166
Boletus calopus, 159
Boletus rubellus, 160

Index to Fungi, Lichens and Actinomycetes

Bombardia, 145, 355, 363, 428, 490, 522, 552*, 669
Botrytis, 104, 108, 115, 119, 456, 701, 714
Botrytis allii, 102, 103*
Botrytis anthophila, 703, 712
Botrytis cinerea, 102, 105, 106*, 346, 441, 457, 572, 584, 695, 746
Botrytis polyblastis, 722, see also *Stromatinia narcissi*
Bremia lactucae, 445
Buellia disciformis, 140
Bulgaria inquinans, 366, 681, 698
Bulleria, 63

C

Cacumisporium tenebrosum, 122
Caliciopsis pinea, 143
Calonectria, 145
Calvatia, 699
Calvatia gigantea, 710
Campylospora chaetocladia, 121
Candida, 64*, 78, 181
Candida albicans
   chlamydospores of, 345, 464
   dimorphism in, 188, 192, 195, 200-205
   divisionless strains of, 193
   petite colonies of, 79
   pseudomycelium of, 67
Candida pulcherrima, 78
Candida reukaufii, 712
Candida utilis, 4
   protoplasts of, 12, 15, 18, 20, 22, 25, 26*, 28, 30, 33, 37, 39, 41*-43, 47, 52*
Cantharellus floccosus, 156*
Catenaria, 289
Catenularia, 116
Catenularia cuneiformis, 122
Cephaloascus fragrans, 704
Cephalosporium, 723
Cephalosporium mycophilum, 582-583, 608
Cephalotheca, 136
Cephalotheca savoryi, 137*
Ceratiomyxa fruticulosa, 211, 215, 226, 227
Ceratobasidium, 168
Ceratocystis, 684, 704, 713
Ceratocystis adiposa, 361, 441, 704
Ceratocystis fagi, 712
Ceratocystis ips, 703
Ceratocystis moniliformis, 361
Ceratocystis picea, 361
Ceratocystis ulmi, 361, 703, 712
Ceratostomella adiposa, see *Ceratocystis adiposa*
Ceratostomella ampullacea, 684
Ceratostomella fimbriata, 361, 452, 495
Ceratostomella pluriannulata, 361
Ceratostomella variospora, 361
Cercospora musae, see *Mycosphaerella musae*
Cercospora personata, see *Mycosphaerella berkleyii*
Cercosporella herpotrichoides, 702
Chaetomella atra, 127
Chaetomidium, 144
Chaetomium, 142, 143, 144, 684, 701
Chaetomium brasiliense, 143, 354
Chaetomium cochlioides, 354, 441
Chaetomium convolutum, 354, 366
Chaetomium fimeti, 144
Chaetomium globosum, 87, 88, 92, 143, 354, 366, 441, 448
Chaetosphaeria innumera, 144*
Chalara, 122
Cheilymenia stercorea, 147
Chlorociboria aeruginascens, 147
Choanephora cucurbitarum, 445, 452, 455, 457, 458, 462
Chromocrea spinulosa, 366, 495
Chroogomphus, 159, 166
Chroogomphus vinicolor, 171*
Chrysosporium, 120
Chytidiomycetes, 285
Chytridiales, 285, 290, 291, 300
   sex hormones in, 420
Chytriomyces, 291
Cladochytridium, 289, 290, 300, 301
Cladosarum olivaceum, 117
Cladosporium, 17, 116, 117, 699, 702*, 723, 725
Cladosporium herbarum, 117, 118*
Cladosporium mansonii, 203
Cladosporium sphaerospermum, 117
Clathrosphaerina, 454
Clathrus ruber, 712
Clavariadelphus pistillaris, 152, 694
Claviceps, 102, 105, 107, 108, 345, 346, 703

Claviceps purpurea, 105, 107, 346, 703
Coccidioides immitis, 28, 725
Coccomyces hiemalis, 355
Cochliobolus, 493
Cochliobolus miyabeanus, 749, 750
Cochliobolus sativus, 608, 610
Colletotrichum atramentarium, 345
Colletotrichum lagenarium, 607
Collybia fusipes, 108
Collybia setulosa, 171*
Collybia velutipes, 392, 397, 398, 400, 405, 448, 456, 457, 666
Comatricha, 215, 225
Comatricha laxa, 214, 215, 226
Comatricha nodulifera, 219
Comatricha typhoides, 213
Conocybe tenera, 171*
Coprinus, 168, 169, 457, 460, 692
Coprinus atramentarius, 690
Coprinus cinereus, 396
Coprinus comatus, 405, 407
Coprinus congregatus, 396
Coprinus disseminatus, 86*, 388
Coprinus ephemerus, 447
Coprinus fimetarius, 552*, 558, 663
Coprinus heptemerus, 396
Coprinus lagopus, 86, 394, 406, 576, 577, 628, 666, 690
Coprinus macrorhizus, 638
Coprinus sassii, 396
Coprinus stercorarius, 102-108
Coprinus sterquilinus, 404, 405, 459
Coprotrichum purpurascens, 125
Cordana musae, 696
Cordyceps, 105, 145, 438
Cordyceps militaris, 367, 685
Coremiella ulmariae, 125
Coronophorales, 143
Corticium filamentosa, 697
Corticium solani, 8, 103-106*, 108, 578
Cortinarius, 160, 161, 166
Cortinarius orichalceus, 161
Cortinarius sanguineus, 161
Cortinarius semisanguineus, 161
Coryneliales, 143
Costantiella, 119
Crinipellis zonata, 171*
Crucibulum, 701
Cryptococcus, 78
Cryptospora longispora, 146

Ctenomyces reflexa, 136
Culicidospora, 121
Cunninghamella elegans, 87
Curvularia, 124
Curvularia brachyspora, 745
Cystoderma, 156*, 163
Cytidia salicina, 552*
Cytosporina, 441
Cyathus, 701
Cyathus stercoreus, 403, 552*

D

Dacrymyces, 168
Dactuliophora, 102
Daldinia, 145
Daldinia concentrica, 446, 684, 697, 698
Dasyobolus immersus, 680, 681, 685, 686
Dasyscyphus, 365
Dasyscyphus protractus, 681
Debaryomyces, 452
Debaryomyces kloeckeri, 80
Deightoniella, 121, 699
Deightoniella indica, 126
Deightoniella torulosa, 695, 696*
Dendriphiopsis, 124
Dendrophoma obscurans, 127*
Dendrosphaera eberhardtii, 137
Dendryphion, 124
Deuteromycetes, sporulating structures of, 113-131
Deuterophoma tracheiphila, 714
Diaporthe, 441
Diatrype, 146
Diatrype stigma, 684
Dictyoarthrinium, 125
Dictyomorpha dioica, 486
Dictyostelium discoideum, 236-245, 247, 248, 251, 253*, 254, 256-270, 704, 757
Dictylostelium mucoroides, 241, 244, 245, 247, 249*-251, 263-266, 270
Dictyostelium purpureum, 236, 243, 268
Dictyuchus, 416
Dictyuchus monosporus, 488
Didymium, 215, 740
Didymium difforme, 214
Didymium iridis, 212, 213, 214, 216, 225, 227, 228*
Didymium nigripes, 213, 216, 225, 227
Dilophospora alopecuri, 711

Index to Fungi, Lichens and Actinomycetes

Diplocladium, 17
Diplodia zeae, 127*
Diplophosphora, 126
Dipodascus uninucleatus, 704
Discomycetes, 133, 134, 146-149
  Inoperculatae, 148
  Operculatae, 149
Discosia, 115
Dothidea, 140
Dothidea sambuci, 139*, 140
Dothideales, 138-140
Dothiora, 140
Dwayabeeja sundra, 126

E

Echinostelium minutum, 219
Eidamiella deflexa, 136
Elaphomyces, 461, 703
Ellisiodothis inquinans, 141
Emericellopsis salmosynnemata, 608, 610
Endochytrium, 300
Endogone, 462, 703, 705
Endomyces, 63
Endophyllum euphorbiae-sylvaticae, 712
Endophragmia, 121
Endosporostilbe, 122
Endothia parasitica, 127, 684, 714, 726
Englerula macarangae, 140
Entomophthora coronata, 688
Entomophthora muscae, 687
Epichloë typhina, 685, 698
Eremascus, 502
Eremascus fertilis, 446
Eremothecium ashbyii, 195
Erysiphales, 143
Erysiphe, 116, 125, 143
Erysiphe graminis, 722, 738, 740
Euascomycetes, 134
Eurotiales, 136-137
Eurotium herbariorum, 351, 366, 448
Eurotium repens, 450
Eurotium rugulosum, 448
Exosporium, 124

F

Fenestella, 142
Flammula alnicola, 760
Fomes fomentarius, 693, 698
Fomes vegetus, 408
Fuligo septica, 211, 212, 222

Fungi,
  dissemination of, 677-764
  life cycles in, 474-480, 501
  morphogenesis in, 179-412
  physiology of reproduction in, 413-469
  reproduction and inheritance in, 471-676
  sexual mechanisms in, 496-503
  sexual patterns in, 480-496
  sporulating structures of, 113-177
  vegetative structures of, 413-512
Fungi Imperfecti, see Deuteromycetes
Fusariella, 123
Fusarium, 8, 88, 441, 453, 455, 457, 461, 723
Fusarium caeruleum, 740
Fusarium culmorum
  protoplast, 5, 13, 16, 17, 21, 23*, 25*, 27-29, 34*, 35*, 39-41, 45, 46, 53*-55*
Fusarium moniliforme, 341
  see also *Gibberella fujikuroi*
Fusarium moniliforme f.sp. fici, 712
Fusarium oxysporum, 7, 14, 93, 346, 351, 570, 608
Fusarium oxysporum f.sp. cubense, 350
Fusarium oxysporum f.sp. gladioli, 345
Fusarium oxysporum f. sp. pisi, 582
Fusarium solani, 8, 12, 345, 700, 714, 754
Fusarium solani f. sp. phaseoli, 749

G

Galerina, 166, 173
Galerina allospora, 157
Galerina thujina, 171*
Galerina umbrinipes, 171*
Galerina vittaeformis var. albescens f. tetraspora, 171*
Ganoderma, 720
Ganoderma applanatum, 447, 693, 694, 698
Ganoderma lucidum, 402
Geastrum, 701
Gelasinospora, 145
Gelasinospora calospora, 355
Gelasinospora tetrasperma, 667
Geoglossum, 147, 460, 685
Geotrichum, 116
Geotrichum candidum, 124
Gibberella, 145

Index to Fungi, Lichens and Actinomycetes

Gibberella fujikuroi, 93, 348
  see also *Fusarium moniliforme*
Gliocladium roseum, 17, 704
Gloeotinia temulenta, 148
Glomerella, 340, 355, 364, 365, 428
Glomerella cingulata, 361-363, 494, 495, 556, 740, 750, 753, 755
  meiospore of, 552*
Gnomonia erythrostoma, 438
Gnomonia intermedia, 450
Gnomonia vulgaris, 367, 450
Gonatobotryum, 115
Gonytrichum, 122
Graphium, 346
Graphium cuneiferum, 704
Graphium ulmi, 347
Gymnascales, 135-136
Gymnoascus, 135*
Gymnoascus reesii, 136
Gymnopilus spectabilis, 156*
Gyromitra esculenta, 147

H

Hansenula wingei, 49, 65, 363, 369
Hansfordiella, 121
Haplaria, 119
Helicobasidium purpureum, 94, 96, 98
Helicodendron, 454
Helminthosporium, 17, 116, 124, 721
Helminthosporium gramineum, 459
Helminthosporium oryzae, 351
Helminthosporium sativum, 342, 716
Helvella, 148, 460
Helvella crispa, 147, 149
Hemiascomycetes, 134
Hemileia vastatrix, 33, 700, 712
Heterosporium, 115, 119
Hirsutella, 116
Hirsutella gigantea, 96, 347
Histoplasma capsulatum, 185, 188, 205, 725
Histoplasma farciminosum, 185, 206
Hormodendrum, 116
Hydnum, 460, 694
Hygrophorus, 154
Hymenogaster, 703
Hymenogaster tener, 100
Hypholoma fasciculare, 94
Hypochytridiomycetes, 285
Hypocopra, 145
Hypocrea, 145
Hypocrella, 145
Hypomyces, 368
Hypomyces solani, 354
Hypomyces solani f. sp. cucurbitae, 487
Hyponectria, 145
Hypoxylon, 145
Hypoxylon cohaerens, 146
Hypoxylon fuscum, 697
Hypoxylon multiforme, 146
Hypoxylon serpens, 146
Hysterium, 125

I

Isaria cretacea, 94, 97, 346, 347, 399
Isoachlya, 292

K

Koorchalomella, 126
Kusanobotrys bambusae, 140

L

Lacellina, 126
Lacellinopsis, 121, 126
Lactarius, 164
Lactarius vellereus, 171*
Lagenidales, 285, 292
Lambertella copticola, 105
Lamproderma, 225, 226
Lasiobotrys lonicerae, 142
Leccinum, 156, 163
Lembosia, 140
Lentinus, 107
Lentinus edodes, 666
Lentinus lepideus, 391, 392*, 398, 405
Lentinus tuber-regium, 398
Lenzites trabea, 402
Lepiota, 163
Leptographium, 120, 713
Leptomitales, 285, 291, 292, 300
Leptosphaeria acuta, 142, 685
Leptosphaeria doliolum, 142
Leptosphaeria rusci, 367
Licea biforis, 220
Lipomyces lipofer, 42
Lomachashaska, 126
Lopadostoma, 146
Lophophacidium, 146
Lophotrichus, 143
Lycogala epidendrum, 701

Index to Fungi, Lichens and Actinomycetes

Lycoperdon, 701
Lycoperdon gemmatum, 100
Lycoperdon gigantea, see Calvatia gigantea
Lycoperdon perlatum, 721
Lycoperdon pyriforme, 716
Lycophyllum palustre, 151

M

Marasmius, 446
Marasmius androsaceus, 97, 100, 101
Marasmius cohaerans, 173
Margarinomyces heteromorpha, 119
Mortierella, 160, 164
Melampsora lini, 750, 754
Melanomma, 142
Melanomma pulvis-pyrius, 141
Melanospora destruens, see Sordaria destruens
Melanospora zamiae, 441, 444
Merulius, 101
Merulius lacrymans, see Serpula lacrimans
Microascus, 144
Micromonospora AS, 8, 9, 18
Micromonospora challea, 11, 12, 16
Microsphaera alphitoides, 453
Microsphaera quercina, see M. alphitoides
Microsporum, 121
Microsporum audouinii, 203
Monilia, 351, 458
Monilia fructigena, 458
Monoblepharidales, 285, 291, 300
Monoblepharis, 502
Morchella, 148, 460, 681
Morchella esculenta, 149
Mucor, 430, 501, 502
Mucor hiemalis, 421, 446, 758
Mucor mucedo, 420, 421, 422, 423, 425, 455
Mucor racemosus, 345, 450, 455
Mucor ramannianus, 704
Mucor rouxiana, see M. rouxii
Mucor rouxii, 196, 197, 198*, 199, 200, 201, 758
Mucor sphaerosporus, 17
Mucor subtilissimus, 196, 197, 199
Mucorales, sex hormones of, 420
Mycena, 151, 158, 159, 165, 169, 172
Mycena borealis, 171

Mycena corticola, 171*
Mycena gypsea, 171*
Mycena iodiolens, 156*
Mycena latifolia, 171*
Mycena pelianthina, 171*
Mycena pura, 171*
Mycena rosella, 171*
Mycena subcaerulea, 151
Mycolevis, 160
Mycosphaerella berkeleyii, 350
Mycosphaerella musae, 354
Mycosphaerella musicola, 726
Mycosphaerella pinodes, 448
Mycosphaerella tulipiferae, 355
Myiocopron smilacis, 141
Myriangiales, 138
Myriangium duriaei, 138
Myriostigmella quatteriae, 140
Myrothecium verrucaria, 17, 342, 745, 747-749, 757, 758
Myxomycetes
  capillitium in, 225
  morphogenesis in, 211-233
  myxamoebae of, 213-216, 234
  plasmodium of, 217-222
    types of, 219*
  spore germination in, 211-213
  sporulation of, 222-229

N

Naematoloma, 171*
Nectaromyces, 712
Nectria cinnabarina, 700
Nectria mammoidea, 145
Nectria stenospora, 633, 636
Nematogonium, 115
Neottiospora carinum, 126
Neuronectria peziza, 145
Neurospora
  cell membrane of, 42
  dormancy in, 740, 742
  extrachromosomal inheritance, 640, 641, 649, 651, 656
  incompatibility in, 663
  mendelian inheritance in, 535, 545, 548
  morphogenesis of, 340, 341, 342, 352, 354, 355
  mutant *pan* of, 583
  mutant *poly* of, 360
  nuclear ratios of, 573

perithecial development in, 428
protoplasts of, 36
sexual mechanism in, 477, 489, 500, 502
spore germination in, 749, 754
Neurospora crassa
  cell wall degradation of, 12
  colony, 88
  copulation in, 498*
  dormancy, 343
  extrachromosomal inheritance, 620, 621, 622, 656
  female sterility in, 369
  heterokaryosis in, 569, 570, 572, 574, 575, 580, 581, 586, 611
  hyphal tips of, 579
  incompatibility in, 669
  lysis resistance in, 8
  mating type locus of, 490
  meiospore of, 552*
  mendelian inheritance in, 515-529, 555
  microconidia of, 627
  mutant *mi* of, 635, 636, 640
  mutant *os* of, 19
  mutant *poky* of, 625, 628, 629, 650, 651
  osmotic mutant *M16* of, 19
  parasexual cycle not detected in, 607, 608
  perithecial development in, 451
  protoperithecia of, 627
  protoplasts of, 5, 21, 28, 33, 34, 42, 43, 47
  spore germination in, 747, 750, 751, 753, 755
  sporulation in, 356-361, 364-366
Neurospora sitophila
  ascogonium of, 528
  fertilization in, 428
  perithecial development in, 454, 455
  sclerotia of, 108
  sex organs of, 490
  spore dormancy in, 736
  spore germination in, 755
  sporulation in, 356, 357, 358, 359, 363, 367
  suppression of chromosomal gene action in, 651
Neurospora tetrasperma
  heterokaryosis in, 568, 569, 574

meiospore of, 552*
mendelian inheritance in, 557
morphogenesis in, 343, 344, 356, 357, 365, 366
pseudocompatibility in, 667
sex organs of, 490
spore germination in, 737, 739, 742, 743, 746-748, 750, 751, 753
Nigrospora, 120
Nigrospora sphaerica, 688*
Nocardia
  lysozyme lysis resistant, 8
Nowokowskiella, 291

O

Oedocephalum, 713
Oidiodendron, 125
Oidium monilioides, 737
Oncopodium, 121
Onygena equina, 136, 148, 343
Oomycetes, 285, 286
Oospora suaveolens, 21, 22*, 27, 30
Ophiobolus, 142
Ophiostoma, 340, 357
Ophiostoma adiposum, see *Ceratocystis adiposa*
Ophiostoma fimbriatum, see *Ceratostomella fimbriata*
Ophiostoma multiannulatum, 350, 351, 552*, 741
Orbilia curvatispora, 147
Orbilia luteorubella, 147
Ostropa barbara, 148
Otthia spireae, 141*
Oudemansiella radicata, 690, 691*

P

Pachyma, 107
Paecilomyces, 94
Panaeolus papilionaceus, 726
Panus strigosus, 156
Papularia, 125
Papulospora, 103, 105
Paracoccidioides brasiliensis, 184
Patellaria atrata, 140
Penicillium, 89, 438, 446, 450, 454, 633, 636, 656, 699, 709, 721, 723
Penicillium brefeldianum, 353
Penicillium chrysogenum, 7, 91, 351, 608, 612, 613, 753

Index to Fungi, Lichens and Actinomycetes

Penicillium claviforme, 347
Penicillium cyclopium, 352, 579, 582, 585
Penicillium digitatum, 124, 607
Penicillium egyptiacum, 136
Penicillium expansum, 592, 608
  diploids of, 592
Penicillium frequentans, 737
Penicillium glaucum, 24, 352
Penicillium griseofulvum, 15, 342, 348, 349, 351, 352
Penicillium isariiforme, 94
Penicillium italicum, 17, 608
Penicillium janthinellum, 744
Penicillium javanicum, 366
Penicillium lilaceum, 18
Penicillium luteum, 136, 352
Penicillium notatum, 93, 349, 441, 477, 570, 591
Penicillium ochrochloron, 18
Penicillium roquefortii, 348, 350
Penicillium spiculisporum, 136
Penicillium spinulosum, 352
Penicillium urticae, 89
Penicillium vermiculatum, 353
Penicillium wortmanii, 136, 353
Peroneutypa, 146
Peronospora, 416, 699
Peronospora destructor, 445, 735, 739
Peronospora manshurica, 740
Peronospora parasitica, 452
Peronospora schleideniana, see *P. destructor*
Peronospora tabacina, 695, 719, 727
Peronosporales, 285, 291, 292
Pestalotia, 115, 342, 437
Pestalotia annulata
  variant, 638
Peziza, 147
Phallus impudicus, 95*, 97, 100, 101, 702, 712
Phialophora, 116, 122
Phlyctochytrium, 290
Pholiota, 713
Pholiota lubrica, 156*
Phomopsis, 441
Phycomyces, 457, 572
Phycomyces blakesleeanus, 421, 423, 446, 449, 453, 498*, 554*, 736, 739, 747-748, 753
Phycomyces nitens, 421

Phylloporus, 161
Phyllosticta, 458
Phymatotrichum omnivorum, 94, 96, 100, 101, 103, 104, 108
Physarales, 224
Physarella oblonga, 213
Physarum flavicomum, 213, 214, 216
Physarum gyrosum, 212, 214, 215, 217, 219*
Physarum nudum, 223
Physarum polycephalum, 214, 215, 219, 220-224, 251, 258
Physarum pusillum, 214, 216
Physoderma, 736
Physoderma maydis, 737
Phytophthora, 10, 18, 416, 445, 446, 550, 699, 721
Phytophthora cactorum, 446, 480, 734
Phytophthora infestans, 445, 553
Phytophthora phaseoli, 712
Pichia, 64, 70, 78
Pilobolus, 457, 687, 711
Pilobolus crystallinus, 421
Pilobolus microsporus, 450
Pilobolus sphaerosporus, 697
Pityrosporum, 63
Plasmodiophora brassicae, 760
Plasmodiophoromycetes, 285, 286
Plectascales, 137
Plectomycetes, 133, 134, 135-137
Plenodomus fuscomaculans, 454, 459
Pleosphaeria, 142
Pleospora, 142
Pleospora bromi, 354
Pleospora gaeumanii, 354
Pleospora herbarum, 459
Pleospora scirpicola, 685
Pleosporales, 141
Pleurotus ostreatus, 398, 666
Pleurotus spodoleucus, 666
Pluteus, 166
Pluteus cervinus, 156*
Pluteus salicinus, 173
Podaxis, 699, 719
Podaxis pistillaris, 720
Podosphaeria, 143
Podosphaeria leucotricha, 684
Podospora, 340, 441, 493, 502
Podospora anserina
  ascospores of, 365

barrage reaction in, 557, 628, 638, 656, 671*
extrachromosomal inheritance in, 620, 624
heterokaryosis in, 568
mating type lows of, 490
meiospore of, 552*, 556, 557
mutants of, 355
nuclear ratio in, 582
pseudocompatibility in, 667, 668*, 670, 671*, 673, 674
tetrad analysis in, 557
variants of, 638, 654
Podospora fimicola
spore discharge, 680, 686
Podospora minuta, 355
Polychytrium, 300
Polyozellus multiplex, 161
Polyphagus, 300
Polyporus betulinus, 692, 693
Polyporus brumalis, 94, 97, 397, 398, 400, 405, 447, 454, 459, 462, 699
Polyporus conchifer, 701
Polyporus glomeratus, 156
Polyporus mylittae, 107
Polyporus rhinoceros, 107
Polyporus sacer, 107
Polyporus squamosus, 105
Polyporus tomentosus var. *circinatus*, 171*
Polyporus tuberaster, 105, 107
Polyporus umbellatus, 105
Polyporus versicolor, 402
Polysphondylium pallidum, 238, 241, 270
Polyspondylium violaceum, 238*, 240, 241, 243, 256, 257
Polystictus versicolor protoplasts, 4, 5, 17, 21, 23*, 24*, 27*, 31*, 32, 44*, 45, 49, 54*, 56*
Polystigma, 145
Poria ambigua, 402
Poria cocos, 107
Preussia, 139, 140
Pringsheimia, 140
Psathyrella, 160, 173
Psathyrella camptopoda, 171*
Psathyrella disseminata, 99
Psathyrella subatrata, 173
Pseudeurotium, 136, 144
Pseudopeziza ribis, 356, 452

Pseudotorula heterospora, 126
Psilocybe mexicana, 394
Puccinia, 656
Puccinia anomala, see *P. hordei*
Puccinia antirrhini, 453
Puccinia glumarum, see *P. striiformis*
Puccinia graminis
appressorium of, 390
dispersal of, 722-724, 726
dormancy in, 736
life cycle of, 557
meiospore of, 552*
physiologic races of, 628, 655
seasonal sporulation in, 438
spore germination in, 737
Puccinia graminis f.sp. *tritici*, 737, 738, 740, 747-749, 750, 752, 753, 754
Puccinia helianthi, 755
Puccinia hordei, 628, 655
Puccinia obtegens, see *P. punctiformis*
Puccinia polysora, 727, 728
Puccinia punctiformis, 712
Puccinia purpureum, 740
Puccinia recondita, 716, 726
Puccinia sorghi, 740, 755
Puccinia striiformis, 738
Pyrenomycetes, 133, 134, 137-146
Pyricularia oryzae, 455
Pyridularia musae, 119
Pyronema, 356, 501, 502
Pyronema confluens, see *P. omphalodes*
Pyronema domesticum, 102, 104, 105, 107, 146, 147
Pyronema omphalodes, 354, 355, 368, 441, 457, 458
Pythium 10, 18, 416, 445
Pythium debaryanum, 480

Q

Quaternaria, 146

R

Ramularia, 101, 115, 119
Ramularia alospora, 119
Ramularia urticae, 119
Ramularia vallisumbrosae, 446
Rehmiodothis, 146
Resupinatus, 158
Reticularia, 215, 736
Rhinocladiella, 119

Rhizidiomyces, 301
Rhizoctonia solani, see *Corticium solani*
Rhizophlyctis, 301
Rhizophydium, 290, 291, 300, 301
Rhizopogon, 157, 159-166, 168, 703
Rhizopogon pseudoaffinis, 152, 153
Rhizopus, 196, 437, 487, 501, 746
Rhizopus arrhizus, 18
Rhizopus microsporus, 17
Rhizopus nigricans, see *R. stolonifer*
Rhizopus sexualis, 446, 449, 450, 452-454, 456, 464
Rhizopus stolonifer, 420, 421, 480
Rhizopus suinus, 741
Rhodotorula, 78
Roesleria pallida, 148
Russula, 161, 164, 407
Russula aeruginosa, 156*
Russula citrina, 408

S

Saccharomyces, 63, 64*, 78, 196, 369, 502
Saccharomyces carlsbergensis, 45, 46, 48, 50, 57, 78
Saccharomyces cerevisiae
  ascospore of, 746
  budding in, 194
  cell wall of,
    composition, 200
    digestion, 12
  conjugation in, 364, 427
  extrachromosomal inheritance in, 620, 621
  flocculence in, 71
  genetics of, 530, 534, 551, 552*, 554
  giant colonies of, 77*, 78
  microcolonies of, 65, 69*, 80
  petite strains of, 78, 630, 631, 632, 636
  protoplasts of, 15-17, 19, 37, 42, 46-48, 50
  sporulation in, 367, 450
Saccharomyces fragilis, 37
Saccharomycodes, 63, 502
Saccobolus, 681, 685
Sadasivania girisa, 125
Sakireeta, 126
Samukuta, 126
Saprolegnia, 289, 292, 299, 416

Saprolegnia hypogyna, 416
Saprolegnia mixta, 450
Saprolegniales, 285, 291, 297, 415
Sapromyces reinschii, 416
Sarcoscypha, 147
Sarcoscypha protracta, 108, 681, 682*
Savulescua, 144
Schiffnerula pulchra, 140
Schizophyllum commune
  fruit body development in, 392, 405, 446
  genetics of, 558
  heterokaryosis in, 572, 576, 583
  meiospore of, 552*
  sexual mechanism of, 492-494, 498*, 663, 666, 669
  spore germination in, 746, 753
  spore liberation, 697, 699
Schizosaccharomyces, 63, 64*
Schizosaccharomyces pombe, 27*, 28, 46, 491, 552*
Schizothyrium perexiguum, 140
Schizoxylon berkelyanum, 148
Scleroplea, 142
Sclerospora phillipinensis, 688
Sclerotinia, 102, 105, 107, 345, 445, 712
Sclerotinia fructicola, 341, 349, 459
Sclerotinia fructigena, 459, 703
Sclerotinia gladioli, 103*, 355
Sclerotinia libertiana, 10
Sclerotinia sclerotiorum, 104, 105, 368
Sclerotinia trifoliorum, 355
Sclerotinia tuberosa, 147
Sclerotium, 102, 108
Sclerotium cepivorum, 102, 108
Sclerotium rolfsii, 103, 104, 105, 346
Scopulariopsis, 116, 120
Scopulariopsis brevicaulis, 348
Septonema, 116
Serpula lacrimans, 95*, 96, 98, 99*, 100, 101, 389, 402, 693, 711
Siphonaria, 500, 502
Siridium, 115
Sirodesmium, 125
Sistotrema, 156*
Solenia anomala, 487
Sordaria, 145, 340, 355, 437
Sordaria destruens, 349, 361
Sordaria fimicola
  genetics of, 495, 530, 540, 555, 670

hyphal branching in, 86*, 87
morphogenesis in, 344, 362, 365-367
perithecial development in, 438, 440-444, 447, 448, 453, 457, 462
spores discharge in, 683, 685, 686, 697-699
Sordaria macrospora, 361, 364, 365, 366, 495
Sordaria verruculosa, 697
Sparassis, 460
Spegazzinia, 125
Sphacelotheca sorghi, 33
Sphaerobolus, 391, 689, 697, 711
Sphaerobolus stellatus, 390
Sphaerocybe concentrica, 347
Sphaerospora minuta, 119
Sphaerotheca, 143
Sphaerotheca mors-uvae, 684
Sphaerostilbe repens, 89, 94, 97, 100
Spondylocladium, 124
Sporidesmium, 120
Sporobolomyces, 63, 690, 694
Sporobolomyces roseus, 699
Sporoschima, 122
Sporothrix schenckii, 185, 206
Sporotrichum, 119
Starkeyomyces, 126
Stemonitales, 224
Stemonitis, 226
Stemonitis fusca, 215, 225, 226
Stemonitis nigrescens, 213
Stemphylium, 124
Stereum, 460, 694
Stereum sanguinolentum, 713
Stictis stellata, 148
Stomiopeltis, 142
Streptomyces, 18
 lysozyme lysis of, 8
 lytic activity of, 9
Streptomyces albidoflavus, 10, 16, 46
Streptomyces coelicolor, 610
Streptomyces GM, 10, 16
Streptomyces RA, 17, 21
Stromatinia narcissi, 487
 see also *Botrytis polyblastis*
Stysanus, 120, 346
Suillus, 166, 170, 172
Synchytrium, 420, 502
Synchytrium endobioticum, 420, 711, 714

Synchytrium fulgens, 420
Syzgitus megalocarpa, 446, 450, 452

T

Taphrina, 202
Teichospora, 142
Termitomyces, 713
Tetrachaetum, 121
Thamnidium elegans, 452, 457
Thielavia, 136
Thielaviopsis basicola, 122
Thyridaria, 142
Tilletia, 689, 690
Tilletia caries, 720, 722, 736, 737, 741, 754
Tilletia cerebrina, 737
Tilletia foetida, 737
Tilletia levis, see *T. foetida*
Tilletiopsis, 694
Torula herbarum, 126
Tremella, 446
Tricellula inaequalis, 117
Trichia, 695
Trichocladium, 120
Trichoderma viride, 10, 18, 457
Trichodothis, 142
Trichophyton mentagrophytes, 347, 350
Trichophyton rubrum, 203
Trichosporium, 121
Trichosporon, 63, 64*
Trichothecium, 699
Trichothecium roseum, 13, 17, 18, 116, 121, 700
Tripospermum myrti, 121
Tuber, 437, 703
Tuberales, 135, 149
Typhula, 102, 104, 105, 107, 108
Typhula gyrans, 106*
Typhula intermedia, 106*
Typhula phacorrhiza, 106*

U

Uncinula necator, 341
Unitunicatae, 142-146
Urocystis agropyri, 737
Urocystis tritici, see *U. agropyri*
Uromyces appendiculatus, 741, 755
Uromyces phaseoli, see *U. appendiculatus*

Index to Fungi, Lichens and Actinomycetes

Ustilaginales
  incompatibility in, 665
Ustilago, 699, 721, 723
Ustilago maydis, 33, 452, 549, 551, 552*, 610, 752, 753
Ustilago sphaerogena, 390
Ustilago striiformis, 736
Ustilago violacea, 703
Ustilago zeae, see U. maydis

V

Venturia, 340
Venturia inaequalis, 354, 552, 556
Venturia pyrina, 445
Verpa conica, 147
Verticillium, 17, 33, 369, 723
Verticillium alboatrum, 106, 108, 346, 365-367, 608
Verticillium dahliae, 103
Verticillium hemileiae, 10
Vibrissea truncorum, 148
Volucrispora, 117, 118
Volvariella, 154

W

Wettsteinina gigaspora, 141

X

Xylaria, 145, 446, 713
Xylaria hypoxylon, 94, 700
Xylosphaera, see Xylaria

Z

Zygorhynchus moelleri, 744
Zygosaccharomyces, 502
Zygosporium, 122, 699
Zygosporium oscheoides, 695
Zythia fragariae, 127*